10th UPDATED EDITION

NTA CSIR UGC NET/JRF

MATHEMATICAL SCIENCE

PART-2

APPLIED MATHEMATICS & STATISTICS

IfAS | IFAS Publications

Design & Published by:
IFAS Publications

Address:
Shivranjan Complex,
Someshwar Wadi, Near
Rajwada Hotel, Baner Road,
Pune 411 008.

Contact No.: +91-960 489 7388

Website: https://ifasonline.com

Price: ₹895.00

ISBN: 978-81-972252-6-0

PREFACE

This book "**Mathematical Science-Part 2**" presents solutions of the previous year questions of CSIR NET Mathematics exam from year June 2011 to Dec 2025. Part 2 is for the Applied Mathematics section and Statistics. Applied section includes topics Ordinary Differential Equations, Partial Differential Equations, Calculus of Variation, Integral Equations, Numerical Analysis and Classical Mechanics. Each of this topic(chapter) is further subdivided into units. This fine sorting of questions will help the students to prepare for each subtopic effectively.

The book will help the reader to understand and solve all the previous year questions. Regular practice is the key to success in any competitive exam, and this book allows you to hone your problem-solving skills. We have tried to keep the material as simple as possible with easy explanations. The practice of these questions will help the students not only for CSIR exam but also for other competitive exams like TIFR, GATE, PhD entrances, etc.

We have attempted to maintain the same unified organization of the content that has been useful to students in the past. A word or suggestion from your side may add another feather to the cap in the compilation of questions in this book. The author looks forward to the comments, suggestions, and criticism from the students. Constructive suggestions and user feedback would be highly appreciated, gratefully acknowledged, and suitably incorporated. We wish all the best to all aspirants who are preparing for these exams.

AIM AND SCHEME OF EXAMINATION

The Council of Scientific and Industrial Research (CSIR) has entrusted the responsibility of conducting CSIR-UGC NET in **CBT mode** to **NTA**. **CSIR-UGC NET** is a test being conducted to determine the eligibility 'for Junior Research Fellowship (JRF) and for Lectureship/Assistant Professor' in Indian universities and colleges subject to fulfilling the eligibility criteria laid down by UGC. Online applications for JRF/NET are invited twice a year on all India basis through Press Notification of CSIR-UGC NET for JRF and LS/APCSIR and UGC provide Research Fellowships for training in methods of research under expert guidance of faculty members/scientists working in University Department/ National Laboratories and Institutions in various fields of Science. CSIR-UGC NET Fellowships are tenable in Universities/IITs/Post Graduate Colleges/Govt.

Research Establishments including those of the CSIR, Research & Development establishments of recognized public or private sector industrial firms and other recognized institutions. Only bonafide Indian Citizens are eligible for the test. CSIR-UGC NET Fellowship is tenable in India. The programme is aimed at National Science & Technology Human Resource Development.

The pattern for the Single Paper **MCQ** test shall be as given below:-

1. The MCQ test paper of each subject shall carry a maximum of **200** marks.
2. The exam shall be for duration of three hours
3. The question paper shall be divided in three parts

Part 'A' shall be common to all subjects. This part shall be a test containing a maximum of **20 MCQ** questions of General Aptitude. The candidates shall be required to answer any **15** questions of **2** marks each. The total marks allocated to this section shall be **30** out of **200**

Part 'B' shall contain subject-related **40** conventional **MCQs**, each of **3 marks**. The candidates shall be required to answer any **25** questions of **3** marks each. The total marks allocated to this section shall be **75** out of **200**.

Part 'C' shall contain **60** higher value **MSQ** questions that may test the candidate's knowledge of scientific concepts and/or application of the scientific concepts. The candidates shall be required to answer any **20** questions of **4.75** marks each. The total marks allocated to this section shall be **95** out of 200.

Negative marking in Part A & B is @ 25%; no negative marking in Part C)

ANALYSIS OF CUT OFF FOR CSIR NET EXAMINATION

Cut Off for Junior Research Fellowships (JRF)						
YEAR	**UR (%)**	**EWS (%)**	**OBC (%)**	**SC (%)**	**ST (%)**	**PH/VH (%)**
JUN 2018	56.25 %	-	47.38 %	37.00 %	27.75 %	25.00 %
DEC 2018	48.63 %	-	41.00 %	31.88 %	25.25 %	25.00 %
JUN 2019	55.75 %	46.63 %	48.88 %	37.75 %	30.50 %	28.50 %
DEC 2019	53.63 %	48.13 %	46.25 %	35.13 %	27.50 %	25.00 %
NOV 2020	57.00 %	51.38 %	50.75 %	40.25 %	30.88 %	28.75 %
FEB 2022	49.25 %	44.87 %	42.75 %	34.37 %	27.00 %	25.00 %
SEP 2022	48.38 %	42.75 %	40.50 %	32.38 %	27.13 %	25.00 %
JUN 2023	54.13 %	47.50 %	46.00 %	35.88 %	28.25 %	25.38 %
DEC 2023	54.87 %	47.62 %	47.12 %	36.00 %	29.62 %	26.12 %
JUN 2024	58.875 %	50.750 %	49.750 %	37.000 %	30.625 %	25.375 %
DEC 2024	50.25 %	43.50 %	43.625 %	34.375 %	29.375 %	25.375 %
JUN 2025	53.375 %	46.00 %	43.375 %	35.375 %	30.75 %	25.125 %
DEC 2025	42.000 %	36.500 %	36.250 %	29.500 %	26.375 %	25.000 %

Cut Off for Lectureship (LS)						
YEAR	**UR (%)**	**EWS (%)**	**OBC (%)**	**SC (%)**	**ST (%)**	**PH/VH (%)**
JUN 2018	50.63 %	50.63 %	42.64 %	33.30 %	25.00 %	25.00 %
DEC 2018	43.77 %	43.77 %	36.90 %	28.69 %	25.25 %	25.00 %
JUN 2019	50.18 %	41.97 %	43.99 %	33.98 %	25.00 %	25.00 %
DEC 2019	48.27 %	43.32 %	41.63 %	31.62 %	25.00 %	25.00 %
NOV 2020	51.30 %	46.23 %	45.67 %	36.25 %	27.79 %	25.87 %
JUN 2021	44.32 %	40.38 %	38.47 %	30.93 %	30.93 %	25.00 %
SEP 2022	43.54 %	38.47 %	36.45 %	29.14 %	25.00 %	25.00 %
JUN 2023	48.71 %	42.75 %	41.40 %	32.29 %	25.42 %	25.00 %
DEC 2023	49.38 %	42.86 %	42.41 %	32.40 %	26.66 %	25.00 %
JUN 2024	52.9875 %	45.675 %	44.775 %	33.300 %	27.5625%	25.000 %
DEC 2024	45.225 %	39.15 %	39.2625 %	30.9375 %	26.4375%	25.00 %
JUN 2025	48.038 %	41.40 %	39.038 %	31.838 %	27.675 %	25.000 %
DEC 2025	37.800 %	33.000 %	33.00 %	26.550 %	25.000 %	25.000 %

INDEX

APPLIED MATHEMATICS

SECTION-I

SECTION – II

SECTION - I

ORDINARY DIFFERENTIAL EQUATIONS

No. of questions asked from year 2011-2025

Units		2011		2012		2013		2014		2015		2016		2017		2018		2019		2020	2022		2023		2024	2025		
		Jun	Dec	Jun	Dec	Jun	Dec	Jun	Dec	Jun	Dec	Jun	Dec	Jun	Dec	Jun	Dec	Jun	Dec	Nov	Feb	Sep	Jun	Dec	Jul	Feb	Jun	Dec
1.1	Differential Equation First order	-	-	-	1	-	1	-	-	2	1	-	-	1	1	2	-	-	1	1	1	-	-	1	-	1	3	-
1.2	Questions on Variation of Parameters Method, Cauchy–Euler L.D.E.	-	-	2	-	2	-	-	-	-	-	1	-	-	1	-	-	1	-	1	-	-	-	1	1	2	-	1
1.3	Wronskian	2	2	-	-	-	2	2	2	1	-	1	2	-	-	1	3	2	-	-	1	-	-	-	-	-	-	2
1.4	Questions on Existence and Uniqueness of First Order Initial value Problems.	1	1	1	1	2	-	1	2	2	-	1	1	-	1	-	-	1	1	1	-	2	4	2	2	1	1	2
1.5	Questions Based on Strum Liouville's Boundary Value Problems	1	-	1	-	1	-	1	1	-	1	1	-	-	1	1	1	1	2	1	1	-	-	-	-	-	1	-
1.6	Methods of Solving First Order System of Ordinary Differential Equations	-	1	1	2	-	-	1	1	2	-	1	2	-	1	1	1	-	4	7	1	2	1	-	1	1	-	-
1.7	Questions Based on Green's Functions	1	1	-	1	1	1	-	-	1	-	-	-	-	-	-	-	-	-	-	-	-	-	-	1	-	-	-

ORDINARY DIFFERENTIAL EQUATIONS

CHAPTER 1

Unit 1.1: Differential Equations of First and Higher orders

MCQ (Multiple Choice Questions)

1. Let $y_1(x)$ and $y_2(x)$ be the solution of the differential equation $\frac{dy}{dx} = y + 17$ with initial conditions $y_1(0) = 0$, $y_2(0) = 1$. Then
(a) y_1 and y_2 will never intersect
(b) y_1 and y_2 will intersect at $x = 17$
(c) y_1 and y_2 will intersect at $x = e$
(d) y_1 and y_2 will intersect at $x = 1$

[Dec 2012]

2. Let $y(x)$ be a continuous solution of initial value problem $y' + 2y = f(x), y(0) = 0$,
Where $f(x) = \begin{cases} 1, & 0 \le x \le 1 \\ 0, & x > 1 \end{cases}$
Then $y\left(\frac{3}{2}\right)$ is equal to
(a) $\frac{\sinh(1)}{e^3}$ (b) $\frac{\cosh(1)}{e^3}$
(c) $\frac{\sin h(1)}{e^2}$ (d) $\frac{\cosh(1)}{e^2}$

[June 2015]

3. The singular integral of the ODE $(xy' - y)^2 = x^2(x^2 - y^2)$ *is*
(a) $y = x \sin x$ (b) $y = x \sin\left(x + \frac{\pi}{4}\right)$
(c) $y = x$ (d) $y = x + \frac{\pi}{4}$

[June 2015]

4. Consider the ODE on $\mathbb{R}, y'(x) = f(y(x))$. If f is an even function and y is an odd function, then
(a) $-y(-x)$ is also a solution
(b) $y(-x)$ is also a solution
(c) $-y(x)$ is also a solution
(d) $y(x)y(-x)$ is also a solution

[Dec 2015]

5. Consider the differential equation
$$(x-1)y'' + xy' + \frac{1}{x}y = 0$$
Then
(a) $x = 1$ is the only singular point
(b) $x = 0$ is the only singular point
(c) Both $x = 0$ and $x = 1$ are singular points
(d) Neither $x = 0$ not $x = 1$ are singular points

[Dec 2017]

6. Consider the ordinary differential equation $y' = y(y-1)(y-2)$
Which of the following statements is true?
(a) If $y(0) = 0.5$ then y is decreasing
(b) If $y(0) = 1.2$ then y is increasing
(c) If $y(0) = 2.5$ then y is unbounded
(d) If $y(0) < 0$ then y is bounded below

[June 2018]

7. Let $|f(x)| \le 4|x|$ for $x \in \mathbb{R}$. The largest possible value of $|x(1)|$where $x'(t) = f(x(t)), t > 0, x(0) = 3$ is
(a) $3e^4$ (b) $4e^3$
(c) $12e^3$ (d) $12e^4$

[Dec 2019]

8. Consider the ODE $ty' - 3y = t^2y^{\frac{1}{2}}$, $y(1) = 1$ Find the value of $y(2)$
(a) 14 (b) 16
(c) 0 (d) 8

[Nov 2020]

9. The smallest real number λ for which the problem $-y'' + 3y = \lambda y$, $y(0) = 0, y(\pi) = 0$ has a non-trivial solution is
(a) 3 (b) 2
(c) 1 (d) 4

[Dec-2023]

10. If $\phi(x) = x$ is a solution of the ordinary differential equation (ODE)
$$\frac{d^2y}{dx^2} - \left(\frac{2}{x^2} + \frac{1}{x}\right)\left(x\frac{dy}{dx} - y\right) = 0, 0 < x < \infty,$$
then the general solution of the ODE is given by
(a) $(a + be^{-2x})\,x, a, b \in \mathbb{R}$ (b) $(a + be^{2x})x, a, b \in \mathbb{R}$
(c) $ae^x + bx, a, b \in \mathbb{R}$ (d) $(a + be^x)x, a, b \in \mathbb{R}$

[June 2025]

Answer Key

1	2	3	4	5	6	7	8	9	10
a	c	c	a	c	c	a	b	d	d

EXPLANATION

1. **Explanation (a)**
We have
$\frac{dy}{dx} = y + 17$
To solve this, apply separation of variable method
We get,
$\frac{dy}{y+17} = dx$
Now,
Integrating both side
$\log(y + 17) = x + c$
$\Rightarrow (y + 17) = e^{x+c}$
$\Rightarrow (y + 17) = Ae^x$ $(\because A = e^c)$
$\Rightarrow y(x) = Ae^x - 17$
Now, use the initial condition

$y_1(0) = 0$ and $y_2(0) = 1$
$\Rightarrow y_1(0) = A - 17 = 0$
$\Rightarrow A = 17$
$\Rightarrow y_1(x) = 17(e^x - 1)$ (1)
And
$y_2(0) = A - 17 = 1$
$\Rightarrow A = 18$
$y_2(x) = 18e^x - 17$ (2)
Let us assume that,
y_1 and y_2 intersect at x_0
$\Rightarrow y_1(x_0) = y_2(x_0)$
$\Rightarrow 17(e^{x_0} - 1) = 18e^{x_0} - 17$
$\Rightarrow e^{x_0} = 0$
Which is never possible
So, we got contradiction
$\Rightarrow$Initial assumption y_1 and y_2 intersect at x_0 is wrong.
$\Rightarrow y_1$ and y_2 will never intersect
$\Rightarrow$ option (a) is correct answer and option (b), (c) and (d) are incorrect.

2. **Explanation (c)**
Given initial value problem is,
$y' + 2y = f(x)$ and $y(0) = 0$
Where $f(x) = \begin{cases}1, & 0 \le x \le 1\\ 0, & x > 1\end{cases}$
Case 1) when $0 \le x \le 1$
$\Rightarrow y' + 2y = 1$
$\Rightarrow \frac{dy}{1-2y} = dx$
Now, integrating both side
We get,
$\frac{\log(1-2y)}{-2} = x + c$
$\Rightarrow \log(1-2y) = -2x - 2c$
$\Rightarrow y(x) = -Ae^{-2x} + \frac{1}{2}$
Now use the initial condition
y(0)=0 $\Rightarrow y(0) = -A + \frac{1}{2} = 0$
$\Rightarrow A = \frac{1}{2}$
Y(x) become,
$\Rightarrow y(x) = -\frac{1}{2}e^{-2x} + \frac{1}{2}$ (1)
Case 2) when x>1
$\Rightarrow y' + 2y = 0$
$y(x) = c_1e^{-2x}$ (2)
From eq^n (1) and eq^n (2)
y(x) become
$$y(x) = \begin{cases}-\frac{1}{2}e^{-2x} + \frac{1}{2}, & 0 \le x \le 1\\ c_1e^{-2x}, & x > 1\end{cases}$$
Since y(x) is continuous, so y(x) is continuous at x=1
$\Rightarrow -\frac{1}{2}e^{-2} + \frac{1}{2} = c_1e^{-2}$
$c_1 = -\frac{1}{2} + \frac{1}{2}e^2$
When x>1
$\Rightarrow y(x) = -\frac{1}{2}e^{-2x} + \frac{1}{2}e^{2-2x}$
$\Rightarrow y\left(\frac{3}{2}\right) = -\frac{1}{2} \Rightarrow e^{-3} + \frac{1}{2}e^{-1}$
$\Rightarrow y\left(\frac{3}{2}\right) = \frac{e - e^{-1}}{2e^2}$
$\Rightarrow y\left(\frac{3}{2}\right) = \frac{\sinh(1)}{e^2}$
$\Rightarrow$option (c)is the correct answer and option (a),(b) and (d) are incorrect.

3. **Explanation (c)**
Given differential equation is
$(xy' - y)^2 = x^2(x^2 - y^2)$
From above option onlyy = x satisfied the given differential equation.
$\Rightarrow$option c) is correct answer and option a),b),d) is incorrect.

4. **Explanation (a)**
We have
$y'(x) = f(y(x))$ (1)
If f is even
$\Rightarrow f(-x) = f(x)$
If y is odd
$\Rightarrow y(-x) = -y(x)$
For option (a)
$-y(-x)$is a solution of equation (1)
$(-y(-x))' = y(x)'$
$f(-y(-x)) = f(y(x))$
From above option a) is correct.
For option b)
Let us assume that $y(-x)$ is also a solution of equation
$\Rightarrow (y(-x))' = -y'(x)$
$\Rightarrow f(y(-x)) = f(y(x))$
$-y'(x) = f(y(x))$
Which is not possible
So we got contradiction here.
$\Rightarrow y(-x)$ is not solution of equation (1)
For option C)
Let us assume that -y(x) is solution of equation (1)
$\Rightarrow (-y(x))' = -y'(x)$
$\Rightarrow f(-y(x)) = f(y(x))$
$f(y(x)) = -y'(x)$
Which is not possible
$\Rightarrow -y(x)$ is not a solution of equation (1)
For option d)
Let us assume that $y(x)y(-x)$ is also a solution of equation (1)
$(y(x)y(-x))' = -(y'(x))^2$
$= -2y(x)y'(x)$
$f(y(x)y(-x)) = f(y^2(x))$
$\Rightarrow (y(x)y(-x))' = f(y(x)y(-x))$
Which is not possible
$\Rightarrow y(x)y(-x)$ is not a solution of equation (1)
$\Rightarrow$option a) is the correct answer and option b),c) and d) are incorrect.

5. **Explanation (c)**

Given differential equation is

$(x-1)y'' + xy' + \frac{y}{x}=0$

$\Rightarrow y''+\frac{x}{(x-1)}y' + \frac{y}{(x-1)x}=0$ (1)

$y'' + a(x)y' + b(x)y = 0$ (2)

Comparing the above two equation and we get the value of a(x) and b(x)

$\Rightarrow a(x) = \frac{x}{x-1}$ and $b(x) = \frac{y}{x(x-1)}$

For x=0

$\lim_{x\to 0}(x-0)a(x) = \lim_{x\to 0} x\frac{x}{x-1} = 0$ (3)

And

$\lim_{x\to 0}(x-0)^2 c = \lim_{x\to 0} x^2\frac{1}{x(x-1)} = 0$ (4)

For x=1

$\lim_{x\to 1}(x-1)a(x)$

$\Rightarrow \lim_{x\to 1}(x-1)\frac{x}{x-1} = 1$ (5)

$\lim_{x\to 1}(x-1)^2 b(x) = \lim_{x\to 1}(x-1)^2\frac{1}{x(x-1)}=0$ (6)

From equation 3),4),5) and 6) x=0,1 are the regular singular point.

$\Rightarrow$ option c) is the correct answer and a),b) and d) are incorrect.

6. **Explanation: (c)**

We have

$y' = y(y-1)(y-2)$

By using wavy curve method

if $y\epsilon(-\infty,0)\cup(1,2)$ then

$y' < 0 \Rightarrow y$ is decreasing

If $y\epsilon(0,1)\cup(2,\infty)$ then

$y'>0 \Rightarrow y$ is increasing

$\Rightarrow$Option c) is the correct answer and option a),b) and d) are incorrect.

7. **Explanation (a)**

$x'(t) = f(x(t)), \quad t>0, \quad x(0)=3$

And $|f(x)| \le 4|x|$

So $x'(t) \le 4(x(t))$

$\Rightarrow \frac{x'(t)}{x(t)} \le 4$

Integrating both sides, we get

$\Rightarrow \log(x(t)) \le 4t + \log c$; c an arbitary constant

$\Rightarrow x(t) \le ce^{4t}$

As $x(0)=3 \Rightarrow 3 \le ce^{\circ} \quad \Rightarrow c=3$

$\therefore x(t) \le 3e^{4t} \quad \Rightarrow x(1) \le 3e^4$

So $|x(1)|$ is $3e^4$

$\Rightarrow$ Option a) is correct answer and option b), c) and d) are incorrect.

8. **Explanation (b)**

$ty' - 3y = t^2 y^{\frac{1}{2}} - - - (*)$

Dividing both sides by $ty^{\frac{1}{2}}$, we get

$\Rightarrow y^{-1/2}y' - 3\frac{y^{\frac{1}{2}}}{t} = t$

$\Rightarrow \frac{1}{y^{\frac{1}{2}}}y' - \frac{3}{t}y^{\frac{1}{2}} = t$ .... (i)

Let $y^{\frac{1}{2}} = u$ .... (ii)

Differentiating both sides w.r.t t, we get

$\Rightarrow y^{-1/2}\frac{dy}{dt} = 2\frac{du}{dt}$

$\Rightarrow \frac{1}{y^{\frac{1}{2}}}\frac{dy}{dt} = 2\frac{du}{dt}$ .... (iii)

Putting (ii) and (iii) in equation (i),

$2\frac{du}{dt} - \frac{3}{t}u = t$

$\Rightarrow \frac{du}{dt} - \frac{3}{2t}u = \frac{1}{2}t$ .... (iv)

Equation (iv) 1st order linear differential equation

So the integrating factor for (iv) is

$= e^{\int -\frac{3}{2t}dt} = e^{-\frac{3}{2}\log t} = e^{-\log t^{\frac{3}{2}}}$

$= \frac{1}{t^{\frac{3}{2}}}$

So $u.\frac{1}{t^{\frac{3}{2}}} = \int \frac{1}{2}t.\frac{1}{t^{\frac{3}{2}}}dt + c$

$\Rightarrow \frac{u}{t^{\frac{3}{2}}} = \int \frac{1}{2}t^{-\frac{1}{2}}dt + c$

$= \left(\frac{1}{2}\right)\frac{t^{-\frac{1}{2}+1}}{-\frac{1}{2}+1} + c = \left(\frac{1}{2}\right)\frac{t^{\frac{1}{2}}}{\frac{1}{2}} + c$

$= t^{\frac{1}{2}} + c$

$\Rightarrow u = t^{\frac{1}{2}}t^{\frac{3}{2}} + ct^{\frac{3}{2}}$

$\Rightarrow y^{\frac{1}{2}} = t^2 + ct^{\frac{3}{2}}$

$\Rightarrow y = \left(t^2 + ct^{\frac{3}{2}}\right)^2$ .... (v)

Now using $y(1)=1$ in (v), we get

$1 = (1+c.1)^2 = 1 = 1+c$

$\Rightarrow c = 1-1 = 0$

$\therefore y(t) = (t^2)^2 = t^4$

$\Rightarrow y(2) = 2^4 = 16$

$\Rightarrow$Option b) is correct answer and option a), c) and d) are incorrect.

9. **Explanation: (d)**

Given: $-y'' + 3y = \lambda y$

$y'' + (\lambda - 3)y = 0.$

Let $\lambda - 3 = \mu^2, \mu > 0$

$\Rightarrow y'' + \mu^2 y = 0$

$\Rightarrow y(x) = c_1\cos ux + c_2\sin ux$

Now, $y(0) = 0$

$\Rightarrow c_1 = 0$

$\therefore y(x) = c_2 \sin \mu x$

$y(\pi) = 0 \Rightarrow c_2 \sin \mu\pi = 0$

Now, if we take $c_2 = 0 \Rightarrow$ trivial solution.

So, to get non-trivial solution take $\sin \mu\pi = 0$

$\Rightarrow \sin \mu\pi = 0 = \sin n\pi$

$\Rightarrow \mu\pi = n\pi, n\in\mathbb{N}$

$\Rightarrow \mu = n, n\in\mathbb{N}$

$\therefore$ Now, we have $\lambda - 3 = n^2, n\in\mathbb{N}$

$\Rightarrow \lambda = 3 + n^2, n\in\mathbb{N}$

For $n=1$, we have $\lambda = 4 \Rightarrow$ option (4) is correct.

10. Explanation: (d)

Let $y = xu(x)$. Then $y' = u + xu'$, $y'' = 2u' + xu''$, and
$xy' - y = x(u + xu') - xu = x^2u'$.
Substitute into the ODE:
$(2u' + xu'') - (\frac{2}{x^2} + \frac{1}{x})(x^2u') = 0; \Rightarrow; 2u' + xu'' - (2 + x)u' = x(u'' - u') = 0.$
For $x > 0$: $u'' - u' = 0 \Rightarrow u = Ae^x + B$. Hence
$y = xu = x(Ae^x + B) = (a + be^x)x,$
Correct Answer: 4

MSQ - Multiple Select Questions

1. Let $y: \mathbb{R} \to \mathbb{R}$ satisfy the initial value problem $y'(t) = 1 - y^2(t)$, $t \in \mathbb{R}$, $y(0) = 0$. Then
(a) $y(t_1) = 1$ for some $t_1 \in \mathbb{R}$
(b) $y(t) > -1$ for all $t \in \mathbb{R}$
(c) y is strictly increasing in $\mathbb{R}$
(d) y is increasing in $(0, 1)$ and decreasing in $(1, \infty)$
[Dec 2013]

2. Consider the solution of the ordinary differential equation $y'(t) = -y^3 + y^2 + 2y$ subject to $y(0) = y_0 \in (0, 2)$. Then $\lim_{t \to \infty} y(t)$ belongs to
(a) $\{-1, 0\}$ (b) $\{-1, 2\}$
(c) $\{0, 2\}$ (d) $\{0, +\infty\}$
[June 2017]

3. Assume that $a: [0, \infty) \to \mathbb{R}$ is a continuous function. Consider the ordinary differential equation $y'(x) = a(x)y(x), x > 0, y(0) = y_0 \neq 0$.
Which of the following statements are true?
(a) If $\int_0^\infty |a(x)|\,dx < \infty$, then y is bounded
(b) If $\int_0^\infty |a(x)|\,dx < \infty$, then $\lim_{x \to \infty} y(x)$ exists
(c) If $\lim_{x \to \infty} a(x) = 1$, then $\lim_{x \to \infty} |y(x)| = \infty$
(d) If $\lim_{x \to \infty} a(x) = 1$, then y is monotone
[June 2018]

4. If $y(x)$ is a solution of the equation $4xy'' + 2y' + y = 0$. Satisfying $y(0) = 1$. Then $y''(0)$ is equal to
(a) 1/24 (b) 1/12
(c) 1/6 (d) 1/2
[Feb 2022]

5. Consider the non-homogeneous ordinary differential equation (ODE)
$$\frac{d^2y}{dx^2} + 5\frac{dy}{dx} + 6y = \sin(e^{-5x}), x > 0.$$
Then which of the following statements are true?
(a) Every solution of the ODE is bounded on $(0, \infty)$
(b) There exists a solution of the ODE which is unbounded on $(0, \infty)$
(c) Every solution of the ODE is unbounded on $(0, \infty)$
(d) Every solution of the ODE tends to zero as $x \to \infty$
[Feb. 2025]

6. Consider the ordinary differential equation (ODE)
$$\frac{d^2y}{dx^2} + (\cos(x))\frac{dy}{dx} + (\sin(x))y = 0.$$
Let $\varphi_1(x), \varphi_2(x)$ be solutions of the ODE, satisfying
$\varphi_1(0) = 1, \frac{d\varphi_1}{dx}(0) = 0$, and $\varphi_2(0) = 0, \frac{d\varphi_2}{dx}(0) = 1$.
Then which of the following statements are true?
(a) $\varphi_1(x + 2\pi)$ is also a solution of ODE
(b) $\varphi_2(x + 4\pi)$ is also a solution of ODE
(c) There are NO constants a, b such that $\varphi_2(x + 4\pi) = a\varphi_1(x) + b\varphi_2(x)$
(d) There exist $a, b \in \mathbb{R}$ such that $\varphi_1(x + 2\pi) = a\varphi_1(x) + b\varphi_2(x)$.
[June 2025]

7. For a continuous function q defined on $\mathbb{R}$, consider the ordinary differential equation (ODE)
$$\frac{d^2y}{dx^2} + q(x)y = 0, x \in \mathbb{R}.$$
Then which of the following statements are FALSE?
(a) There exists a q such that $\cos(x)$ and $e^x \cos(x)$ are solutions of ODE
(b) There exists a q such that $\sin(x)$ and $\cos(x)$ are solutions of ODE
(c) There exists a q such that $e^x \sin(x)$ and $e^x \cos(2x)$ are solutions of ODE
(d) There exists a q such that xe^x and $x(x-1)e^x$ are solutions of ODE
[June 2025]

Answer Key

1	2	3	4	5	6	7
b, c	b, c	a, b, c	b	a,d	a,b,d	a,c,d

Explanation

1. **Explanation (b), (c)**
Given initial problem is
$y'(t) = 1 - y^2(t)$
Now, apply the separation of variable method
$$\Rightarrow \frac{dy}{1 - y^2(t)} = dt$$
Integrating both sides, we get
$$\frac{1}{2}\log\frac{1 + y}{1 - y} = t + c$$
Using the initial condition, $y(0) = 0$
$\Rightarrow c = 0$
$$\Rightarrow \frac{1 + y}{1 - y} = e^{2t}$$
$\Rightarrow 1 + y = (1 - y)e^{2t}$
$$\Rightarrow y(t) = \frac{e^{2t}-1}{e^{2t}+1} \quad (1)$$
$\Rightarrow$for option a)
$$y(t_1) = \frac{e^{2t_1} - 1}{e^{2t_1} + 1} = 1$$
$\Rightarrow e^{2t_1} - 1 = e^{2t_1} + 1$
$\Rightarrow -1 = 1$
Which is never possible.
For option b)
$$y(t) = 1 - \frac{2}{e^{2t} + 1} > 1 - 2 > -1$$
$\Rightarrow y(t) > -1$ for all $t \in \mathbb{R}$
For option c)

differentiating equation (1)
we get

$$y'(t) = \frac{2e^{2t}(1+e^{2t}) - 2e^{2t}(e^{2t}-1)}{(1+e^{2t})^2}$$

$\Rightarrow y'(t) = \frac{4e^{2t}}{(1+e^{2t})^2} > 0$

$\Rightarrow y(t)$ is strictly increasing for all t$\in \mathbb{R}$

For option d)

From option c)$y(t)$ never decreasing in$(1,\infty)$

$\Rightarrow$option b) and c) are correct answer and option a) and d) are incorrect.

2. Explanation (b), (c)

Given ordinary differential equation is

$y'(t) = -y^3 + y^2 + 2y$

$\Rightarrow y' = -y(y^2 - y + 2)$

$\Rightarrow y' = -y(y+1)(y-2)$

By using wavy curve method

If $y \in (-\infty,-1) \cup (0,2)$

$\Rightarrow y' > 0$

$\Rightarrow$ y is increasing

And

If $y \in (-1,0) \cup (2,\infty)$

$\Rightarrow y' < 0$

$\Rightarrow$ y is decreasing

Now use the initial condition

$y(0) = y_0 \in (0,2)$

$\Rightarrow \lim_{t\to\infty} y(t) = 2$

$\Rightarrow$ option b) and c) are correct answer and option a) and d) are incorrect.

3. Explanation (a), (b), (c)

Given differential equation is

$y'(x) = a(x)y(x)$

$\Rightarrow \frac{y'(x)}{y(x)} = a(x)$

Now integrating both sides,

$$\int_{x_0}^{x} \frac{y'(x)}{y(x)} dy = \int_{x_0}^{x} a(x)dx$$

$\log\left(\frac{y(x)}{y(x_0)}\right) = \int_{x_0}^{x} a(x)dx$

$$\frac{y(x)}{y(x_0)} = e^{\int_{x_0}^{x} a(x)dx}$$

$y(x) = y(x_0)e^{\int_{x_0}^{x} a(x)dx}$

Now using initial condition, $y(0) = y_0$

$\Rightarrow y(x) = y_0 e^{\int_0^x a(x)dx}$

If $\lim_{x\to\infty} \int_0^x |a(x)|dx < \infty$

$\Rightarrow \lim_{x\to\infty} y(x)$ exist

$\Rightarrow y(x)$ is bounded.

If $\lim_{x\to\infty} a(x) = 1$, then $\lim_{x\to\infty} y(x) = \infty$

Now take $a(x) = 1 + \frac{6x}{3x^2+1}$

$\Rightarrow y(x) = y_0 e^{\int_0^x \left(1+\frac{6x}{3x^2+1}\right)dx}$

$\Rightarrow y(x) = y_0 e^{(x+\log(3x^2+1))_0^x}$

$\Rightarrow y(x) = y_0(3x^2+1)e^x$

$\Rightarrow y(x)$ is not monotone.

From above explanation,

$\Rightarrow$ option a), b) and c) are correct and option d) is incorrect.

4. Explanation: (b)

Consider the given ODE

$4xy'' + 2y' + y = 0$ (1)

$\Rightarrow y'' + \frac{1}{2x}y' + \frac{1}{4x}y = 0$

Comparing with $y'' + P(x)y' + Q(x)y = 0$

$\Rightarrow P(x) = \frac{1}{2x}, Q(x) = \frac{1}{4x}$

$\Rightarrow x = 0$ is the singular point

Now

$P = \lim_{x\to 0}(x-0)\frac{1}{2x} = \frac{1}{2}$

$q = \lim_{x\to 0}(x-0)^2\frac{1}{4x} = 0$

Now indicial equation is

$m(m-1) + pm + q = 0$ (2)

Put the value of p and q in above equation, we get

$m^2 - m + \frac{m}{2} = 0$

$\Rightarrow m\left(m - 1 + \frac{1}{2}\right) = 0$

$\Rightarrow m\left(m - \frac{1}{2}\right) = 0$

$\Rightarrow m = 0, m = \frac{1}{2}$

Now $y = \sum_{n=0}^{\infty} a_n x^{m+n}$

$y' = \sum_{n=0}^{\infty} m + n\, a_n x^{m+n-1}$

$y'' = \sum_{n=0}^{\infty}(m+n)(m+n-1)a_n x^{m+n-2}$

$\Rightarrow$ equation (1) become

$4x\left[\sum_{n=0}^{\infty}(m+n)(m+n-1)a_n x^{m+n-2}\right] + 2\sum_{n=0}^{\infty}(m+n)a_n x^{m+n-1} + \sum_{n=0}^{\infty} a_n x^{m+n} = 0$

$\Rightarrow 4x(m)(m-1)a_0 x^{m-2} + \sum_{n=0}^{\infty}(m+n)(m+n-1)a_n x^{m+n-2} + 2m a_0 x^{m-1} + 2\sum_{n=1}^{\infty}(m+n)a_n x^{m+n-1} + \sum_{n=0}^{\infty} a_n x^{m+n}$

$\Rightarrow (4m^2 - 4m)a_0 x^{m-1} + 2m a_0 x^{m-1} + 4x\sum_{n=0}^{\infty}(m+n+1)(m+n)a_{n+1} x^{m+n-1} + 2\sum_{n=0}^{\infty}(m+n+1) a_{n+1} x^{m+n} + \sum_{n=0}^{\infty} a_n x^{m+n}$

$\Rightarrow [4(m+n+1)(m+n) + 2(m+n+1)]a_{n+1} + a_n = 0$

$\Rightarrow a_{n+1} = \frac{-a_n}{4(m+n+1)(m+n)+2(m+n+1)}$

For $m = 0$,

$\Rightarrow a_{n+1} = \frac{-a_n}{4(n+1)(n)+2(n+1)}$

Now, $n = 0$

$\Rightarrow a_1 = \frac{-a_0}{2}$

$n = 1$,

$\Rightarrow a_2 = \frac{-a_1}{12} = \frac{a_0}{24}$ $\quad (\because a_1 = \frac{-a_0}{2})$

Now,

$y(x) = a_0 + a_1 x + a_2 x^2 + \cdots$

$\Rightarrow y(x) = a_0 - \frac{a_0 x}{2} + \frac{a_0 x^2}{24} + \cdots$

$y(0) = 1$ *(Given)*

$\Rightarrow a_0 = 1$

$\Rightarrow y(x) = 1 - \frac{x}{2} + \frac{x^2}{24} + \cdots$

$\Rightarrow y(x) = \frac{-1}{2} + \frac{x}{12} + \cdots$

$\Rightarrow y''(x) = \frac{1}{12} + \cdots$

$y''(0) = \frac{1}{12}$

$\Rightarrow$ option (b) is correct answer.

5. Explanation: (a), (d)

Given $\frac{d^2y}{dx^2} + 5\frac{dy}{dx} + 6y = \sin(e^{-5x})$, for $x > 0$.

The homogeneous equation is $\frac{d^2y}{dx^2} + 5\frac{dy}{dx} + 6y = 0$.

It's characteristic equation is $r^2 + 5r + 6 = 0$.

Factoring the characteristic equation gives $(r+2)(r+3) = 0$ and the roots are $r_1 = -2$ and $r_2 = -3$.

The general solution to the homogeneous equation is $y_h(x) = c_1e^{-2x} + c_2e^{-3x}$, where c_1 and c_2 are arbitrary constants.

Since the non-homogeneous term is $\sin(e^{-5x})$, we can guess a particular solution of the form $y_p(x) = A\sin(e^{-5x}) + B\cos(e^{-5x})$.

Calculate the first and second derivatives of $y_p(x)$:

$$\frac{dy_p}{dx} = -5e^{-5x}(A\cos(e^{-5x}) - B\sin(e^{-5x}))$$

$$\frac{d^2y_p}{dx^2} = 25e^{-10x}(-A\sin(e^{-5x}) - B\cos(e^{-5x})) + (-5)^2e^{-10x}(-A\sin(e^{-5x}) + B\cos(e^{-5x}))$$

We can observe that the particular solution will be bounded because $\sin(e^{-5x})$ and $\cos(e^{-5x})$ are bounded between -1 and 1, and their derivatives are also bounded.

The general solution is $y(x) = y_h(x) + y_p(x) = c_1e^{-2x} + c_2e^{-3x} + A\sin(e^{-5x}) + B\cos(e^{-5x})$.

As $x \to \infty$, $e^{-2x} \to 0$ and $e^{-3x} \to 0$.

Also, as $x \to \infty$, $e^{-5x} \to 0$, so $\sin(e^{-5x}) \to 0$ and $\cos(e^{-5x}) \to 1$.

Therefore, as $x \to \infty$, $y(x) \to 0$.

Since both the homogeneous and particular solutions are bounded, every solution of the ODE is bounded on $(0, \infty)$.

Therefore, every solution of the ODE is bounded on $(0, \infty)$ and tends to zero as $x \to \infty$.

Thus, options (a) and (d) are correct.

6. Explanation: (a), (b), (d)

- The ODE is linear with coefficients $\cos x, \sin x$ which are 2π-periodic. Hence if $\phi(x)$ is a solution then $\phi(x + 2\pi)$ (and any integer multiple shift) is also a solution. So (1) and (2) are true.
- ϕ_1, ϕ_2 is a fundamental set of solutions (initial conditions at (0) give the identity fundamental matrix). Any solution can be written uniquely as a linear combination $a\phi_1(x) + b\phi_2(x)$. Since $\phi_1(x + 2\pi)$ is a solution, there exist real (a,b) with $\phi_1(x + 2\pi) = a\phi_1(x) + b\phi_2(x)$. Thus (4) is true.
- (3) is false because $\phi_2(x + 4\pi)$ is a solution and so can be expressed as a linear combination of ϕ_1, ϕ_2.

7. Explanation: (a), (c), (d)

If two nontrivial functions y_1, y_2 solve $y'' + q(x)y = 0$ on an interval where they do not vanish, then necessarily

$$\frac{y_1''(x)}{y_1(x)} = \frac{y_2''(x)}{y_2(x)} \text{ for all } x$$

(where equalities extend by continuity if possible). Check each pair.

(a) $y_1 = \cos x, ; y_1'' = -\cos x \Rightarrow y_1''/y_1 = -1$ (where defined).
$y_2 = e^x\cos x, ; y_2'' = -2e^x\sin x \Rightarrow y_2''/y_2 = -2\tan x$.
These are not equal for all x (would force $\tan x = 1/2$), so no continuous q exists. (a is false.)

(b) $y_1 = \sin x, ; y_1'' = -\sin x$ and $y_2 = \cos x, ; y_2'' = -\cos x$.
Both give $y''/y = -1$ where defined, so $q \equiv -1$ works. (b is true.)

(c) $y_1 = e^x\sin x$ gives $y_1''/y_1 = 2\cot x$.
$y_2 = e^x\cos 2x$ gives $y_2''/y_2 = -3 - 4\tan 2x$. These are not identically equal, so no continuous q works. (c is false.)

(d) $y_1 = xe^x \Rightarrow y_1''/y_1 = (x+2)/x = 1 + 2/x$.
$y_2 = x(x-1)e^x \Rightarrow y_2''/y_2 = (x+3)/(x-1) = 1 + 2/(x-1)$. These are different functions (equal only at $x = -1$), so no single continuous q on $\mathbb{R}$ can serve. (d is false.)

Hence the false statements are a, c and d.

Unit 1.2: Questions on Variation of Parameters Method, Cauchy–Euler L.D.E.

MCQ - Multiple Choice Questions

1. Let V be the set of all bounded solutions of the ODE $u''(t) - 4u'(t) + 3u(t) = 0, t \in \mathbb{R}$. Then V
(a) Is a real vector space of dimension 2
(b) Is a real vector space of dimension 1
(c) Contains only the trivial function $u \equiv 0$
(d) Contains exactly two functions

[June 2012]

2. Consider the equation of an ideal planar pendulum given by $\frac{d^2x}{dt^2} = -\sin x$, where x denotes the angle of displacement. For sufficiently small angles of displacement, the solution is given by (where a, b are constant)
(a) $x(t) = a\cosh t + b\sinh t$
(b) $x(t) = a + bt$
(c) $x(t) = ae^t + .be^{2t}$
(d) $x(t) = a\cos t + b\sin t$

[June 2013]

3. The general solution of the differential equation $\frac{d^2y}{dx^2} + y = f(x), x \in (-\infty, \infty)$, where f is a continuous, real-valued function on $(-\infty, \infty)$, is (Where A, B, C and k are arbitrary constants)
(a) $y(x) = A\cos x + B\sin x + \int_0^x f(t)\sin(x-t)dt$
(b) $y(x) = \cos(x+k) + C\int_0^x f(t)\sin(x-t)dt$
(c) $y(x) = A\cos x + B\sin x + \int_0^x f(x-t)\sin t\, dt$
(d) $y(x) = A\cos x + B\sin x + \int_0^x f(x+t)\cos t\, dt$

[June 2013]

4. Let $y(x)$ be the solution of $x^2y''(x) - 2y(x) = 0, y(1) = 1, y(2) = 1$. Then the value of $y(3)$is
(a) $\frac{11}{21}$ (b) 1
(c) $\frac{17}{21}$ (d) $\frac{11}{7}$

[June 2019]

5. Consider the differential equation $x^2y'' - 2x(x+1)y' + 2(x+1)y = 0$. If a polynomial is a solution, then the degree of the polynomial is equal to
(a) 1 (b) 2
(c) 3 (d) 4

[Nov 2020]

6. Let φ denote the solution to the boundary value problem (BVP)
$$\begin{cases} (xy')' - 2y' + \frac{y}{x} = 1, & 1 < x < e^4 \\ y(1) = 0, y(e^4) = 4e^4. \end{cases}$$
Then the value of $\varphi(e)$ is
(a) $-\frac{e}{2}$ (b) $-\frac{e}{3}$
(c) $\frac{e}{3}$ (d) e

[July 2024]

7. Given that $y_1(x) = e^{2x}$ is a solution of the ordinary differential equation (ODE)
$$x\frac{d^2y}{dx^2} - (3+4x)\frac{dy}{dx} + (4x+6)y = 0, x > 0.$$
Let $y_2 = y_2(x)$ be the solution of the ODE satisfying the conditions $y_2(1) = \frac{e^2}{4}, \frac{dy_2}{dx}(1) = \frac{3e^2}{2}$.
Then which of the following statements is true?
(a) y_2 is a strictly increasing function on $(0, \infty)$
(b) $e^{-2x}y_2(x) \to 1$ as $x \to \infty$
(c) y_2 is a strictly decreasing function on $(0, \infty)$
(d) $e^{-2x}y_2(x) \to 0$ as $x \to \infty$

[Feb. 2025]

8. Suppose that the differential equation
$$\frac{d^2y}{dx^2} + P(x)\frac{dy}{dx} + e^{2x}y = 0, x \in \mathbb{R}$$
transforms into a second order differential equation with constant coefficients under the change of independent variable given by $s = s(x)$ satisfying $\frac{ds}{dx}(0) = 1$. Then which of the following statements is true?
(a) $e^{-x}(P(x)+1)$ is a constant function on $\mathbb{R}$
(b) $e^{-2x}P(x)$ is a constant function on $\mathbb{R}$
(c) $s(x) = \frac{e^{2x}}{2}, x \in \mathbb{R}$
(d) $P(x) \to 1$ as $x \to \infty$

[Feb. 2025]

Answer Key

1	2	3	4	5	6	7	8
c	d	a	d	a	a	a	a

EXPLANATION

1. **Explanation (c)**
Given ODE is
$u''(t) - 4u'(t) + 3u(t) = 0 \ t \in R$ ... (1)
Auxiliary equation is
$m^2 - 4m + 3 = 0$
$\Rightarrow m^2 - 3m - m + 3 = 0$
$\Rightarrow m(m-3) - (m-3) = 0$
$\Rightarrow m = 1,3$
Complementary function is
$u(t) = c_1e^t + c_2e^{3t}$
$u(t)$ is bounded if $c_1 = c_2 = 0$
$u(t)$ is bounded is given
$\Rightarrow u(t) = 0e^t + 0e^{3t} = 0$
$\Rightarrow$ Equation (1) contain the trivial function $u \equiv 0$
From above explanation
$\Rightarrow$ Only option (c) is the correct answer and (a),b) and d) incorrect.

2. **Explanation (d)**
Given ODE
$\frac{d^2x}{dt^2} = -\sin x$
Where x is the angel of displacement, for small angle
$\sin x \cong x$
$\Rightarrow \frac{d^2x}{dt^2} = -x$
$\Rightarrow \frac{d^2x}{dt^2} + x = 0$

⇒ Auxiliary equation of above equation is

$m^2 + 1 = 0$

$\Rightarrow m = \pm 1$

$\Rightarrow x = c_1 \cos t + c_2 \sin t$

Option (d) is the correct answer and option a), b) and c) are incorrect.

3. Explanation (a)

Given Differential Equation is

$\frac{d^2y}{dx^2} + y = f(x)$ .... (1)

Auxiliary equation of equation (1) is $m^2 + 1 = 0$

$\Rightarrow m \neq 1$

C.F. is

$y(x) = A\cos x + B \sin x$

Now find the PI

To find the general solution of equation (1)

Use the variation of parameter method

$a(x) = \cos x,\ b(x) = \sin x$

$w = \begin{vmatrix} \cos x & \sin x \\ -\sin x & \cos x \end{vmatrix} = cos^2 x + sin^2 x = 1$

$w(x) = 1$

$g(x) = -\int_0^x \frac{b(t)R}{w} dt$

$= \int_0^x \frac{\sin t\, f(t)dt}{1}$

$h(x) = \int_0^x \frac{a(t)R\, dt}{w}$

$= \int_0^x \frac{\cos t\, f(t)}{1} dt$

General solution is

$y(x) = A\cos x + B\sin x - a(x)\int_0^x \sin t f(t)dt + \int_0^x \cos t f(t)dt$

$y(x) = A\cos x + B \sin x - \int_0^x \sin t\, cosx f(t)dt + \int_0^x \cos t\, sinx\, f(t)dt$

$y(x) = A\cos x + B\sin x + \int_0^x f(t)\sin(x-t)\, dt$

Option (a) is the correct answer and Option (b), (c), (d) are incorrect.

4. Explanation (d)

Given ODE is

$x^2 y''(x) - 2y(x) = 0$ .... (1)

This is the second order differential equation with constant coefficient,

To solve this,

Put $\log x = z$

$\Rightarrow x = e^z$

Equation (1) become

$(D(D-1) - 2)y = 0$

Auxiliary equation is

$\Rightarrow m^2 - m - 2 = 0$

$m = \frac{1 \pm \sqrt{9}}{2} = \frac{1 \pm 3}{2}$

$m = 2, -1$

Complementary function is

$y = \frac{1}{x} c_1 + c_2 x^2$

Now use the given condition

$y(1) = 1$

$y(2) = 1$

$y(1) = \frac{c_1}{1} + c_2 = 1$

$c_1 + c_2 = 1$ .... (2)

$y(2) = \frac{c_1}{2} + 4c_2 = 1$

$c_1 + 8c_2 = 2$ .... (3)

From equation (2) and (3)

$c_1 = 1 - c_2$ equation (3)

$\Rightarrow 1 - c_2 + 8c_2 = 2$

$1 + 7c_2 = 2$

$c_2 = \frac{1}{7}$

Put $c_2 = \frac{6}{7}$

Equation becomes

$y(x) = \frac{6}{7x} + \frac{1}{7}x^2$

$y(3) = \frac{6}{21} + \frac{9}{7} = \frac{33}{21}$

$y(3) = \frac{11}{7}$

⇒ Option (d) is the correct answer and option a),b) and c) are incorrect.

5. Explanation (a)

$x^2y'' - 2x(x+1)y' + 2(x+1)y = 0$ ... (i)

$\Rightarrow y'' - \frac{2x(x+1)}{x^2}y' + \frac{2(x+1)}{x^2}y = 0$

$\Rightarrow y'' - \frac{2(x+1)}{x}y' + \frac{2(x+1)}{x^2}y = 0$ ... (*)

Comparing (*) with $y'' + P(x)y' + Q(x)y = 0$

We get $P = \frac{-2(x+1)}{x}$ and $Q = \frac{2(x+1)}{x^2}$

Now $P + Qx = \frac{-2(x+1)}{x} + x.\frac{2(x+1)}{x^2}$

$= \frac{-2(x+1)}{x} + \frac{2(x+1)}{x^2} = 0$

$\Rightarrow P + Qx = 0$

So $y = x$ is a solution of (i) and $y = x$ is a polynomial of degree 1

So option (a) correct.

6. Explanation: (a)

Given

$\begin{cases} (xy')' - 2y' + \frac{y}{x} = 1, & 1 < x < e^4 \\ y(1) = 0, y(e^4) = 4e^4. \end{cases}$

$xy'' + y' - 2y' + \frac{y}{x} = 1$

$xy'' - y' + \frac{y}{x} = 1$

$x^2y'' - xy' + y = x$

Put $x = e^z$

$\frac{d^2y}{dz^2} - \frac{dy}{dz} + y = e^z$

$\Rightarrow \frac{d^2y}{dz^2} - \frac{dy}{dz} + y = 0$

A.E: $m^2 - 2m + 1 = 0$

$\Rightarrow m = 1,1$

C.F = $(C_1 + C_1 \log x)x$

Now $y_p = \frac{1}{(D_1 - 1)^2} e^z = \frac{z^2}{2!} e^z$

$= \frac{(\log x)^2 x}{2}$

$$y(x) = (C_1 + C_2 \log x)x + \frac{(\log x)^2 x}{2}$$

Now use given condition: $y(1) = 0$ & $y(e^4) = 4e^4$

$\Rightarrow 0 = C_1$

$y(e^4) = 4e^4$

$$\Rightarrow 4e^4 = (4C_2)e^4 + \frac{e^4(16)}{2}$$

$4 = 4C_2 + 8$

$4C_2 = -4$

$C_2 = -1$

$$\therefore y(x) = (-\log x)x + \frac{(\log x)^2 x}{2}$$

$$\phi(e) = (-\log e)e + \frac{e(\log e)^2}{2} = -\frac{e}{2}$$

Hence option (a) is correct.

7. **Explanation: (a)**

Using reduction of order formula,

$$y_2(x) = y_1(x) \int \frac{e^{-\int P(x)dx}}{y_1(x)^2} dx,$$

where $P(x) = -\frac{3+4x}{x}$

(coefficient of $\frac{dy}{dx}$ after dividing ODE by x).

Simplifying, we get,

$$y_2(x) = \frac{1}{4}x^4 e^{2x}$$

Clearly, y_2 is strictly increasing function on $(0, \infty)$ and thus option (a) is correct.

All other options are incorrect as $e^{-2x}y_2(x) = \frac{x^4}{4} \to \infty$ as $x \to \infty$.

8. **Explanation: (a)**

Given the differential equation:

$$\frac{d^2y}{dx^2} + P(x)\frac{dy}{dx} + e^{2x}y = 0$$

Using the chain rule:

$$\frac{dy}{dx} = \frac{dy}{ds}\frac{ds}{dx}$$

$$\frac{d^2y}{dx^2} = \left(\frac{ds}{dx}\right)^2 \frac{d^2y}{ds^2} + \frac{d^2s}{dx^2}\frac{dy}{ds}$$

Substituting these into the original equation gives:

$$\left(\frac{ds}{dx}\right)^2 \frac{d^2y}{ds^2} + \left(\frac{d^2s}{dx^2} + P(x)\frac{ds}{dx}\right)\frac{dy}{ds} + e^{2x}y = 0$$

For constant coefficients, we need:

1. The coefficient of $\frac{dy}{ds}$ to be constant: $\frac{d^2s}{dx^2} + P(x)\frac{ds}{dx} =$ constant
2. The coefficient of y to be constant: $e^{2x}\left(\frac{ds}{dx}\right)^{-2} =$ constant

From the second condition:

$$e^{2x}\left(\frac{ds}{dx}\right)^{-2} = C$$

Taking square root

$$\frac{ds}{dx} = e^x\sqrt{C}$$

Given $\frac{ds}{dx}(0) = 1$, we find $\sqrt{C} = 1$, so:

$$\frac{ds}{dx} = e^x$$

$$s(x) = e^x$$

Option (a): $e^{-x}(P(x) + 1)$ is a constant function.

- From $\frac{d^2s}{dx^2} + P(x)\frac{ds}{dx} =$ constant, with $\frac{d^2s}{dx^2} = e^x$ and $\frac{ds}{dx} = e^x$,

we get: $e^x + P(x)e^x =$ constant

Thus, $e^{-x}(P(x) + 1)$ is indeed a constant function.

Option (b): $e^{2x}P(x)$ is a constant function.

- This is not generally true unless $P(x) = 0$, which is not specified.

Option (c): $s(x) = \frac{e^{2x}}{2}$.

- We derived $s(x) = e^x$, not $\frac{e^{2x}}{2}$.

Option (d): $P(x) \to 1$ as $x \to \infty$.

- Since $P(x)$ is constant, it does not tend to 1 unless it was already 1.

Thus, option (a) is correct.

MSQ (Multiple Select Question)

1. The Solution of the boundary value problem $\frac{d^2y}{dx^2} + y = \text{cosec}x$; $0 < x < \frac{\pi}{2}$ $y(0) = 0, y\left(\frac{\pi}{2}\right) = 0$ is

(a) Convex (b) Concave

(c) Negative (d) Positive

[June 2012]

2. Let $y: \mathbb{R} \to \mathbb{R}$ be solution of the ordinary differential equation, $2y'' + 3y' + y = e^{-3x}, x \in \mathbb{R}$ satisfying $\lim_{x\to\infty} e^x y(x) = 0$. Then

(a) $\lim_{x\to\infty} e^{2x}y(x) = 0$

(b) $y(0) = \frac{1}{10}$

(c) y is a bounded function on $\mathbb{R}$

(d) $y(1) = 0$

[June 2016]

3. Consider the differential equation $\frac{d^2y}{dx^2} - 2\tan x\frac{dy}{dx} - y = 0$ defined on $\left(-\frac{\pi}{2}, \frac{\pi}{2}\right)$. Which among the following are true?

(a) There is exactly one solution $y = y(x)$ with $y(0) = y'(0) = 1$ and $\left(\frac{\pi}{3}\right) = 2\left(1 + \frac{\pi}{3}\right)$

(b) There is exactly one solution $y = y(x)$ with $y(0) = 1, y'(0) = -1$ and $y''\left(\frac{\pi}{3}\right) = 2\left(1 + \frac{\pi}{3}\right)$

(c) Any solution $y = y(x)$ satisfies $y''(0) = y(0)$

(d) If $y_1 and\ y_2$ are any two solutions then $(ax + b)y_1 = (cx + d)y_2$ for some $a, b, c, d \in \mathbb{R}$

[Dec 2017]

4. Consider the initial value problem $x^2y'' - 2x^2y' + (4x - 2)y = 0, y(0) = 0$.

Suppose $y = \varphi(x)$ is a polynomial solution satisfying $\varphi(1) = 1$. Which of the following statements are true?

(a) $\varphi(4) = 16$ (b) $\varphi(2) = 2$

(c) $\varphi(5) = 25$ (d) $\varphi(3) = 3$

[DEC-2023]

5. Suppose $y_1(x)$ and $y_2(x)$ are two linearly independent solutions of the differential equation
$x^2y'' + \frac{(1+\sin x)x}{2}y' - \frac{3}{2}(\cos x)y = 0, x > 0$
satisfying $y_2(0) = 0$.
Then which of the following statements are true?
(a) $\lim_{x\to0^+} \frac{y_2(x)}{x^2y_1(x)}$ exists.
(b) $\lim_{x\to0^+} \frac{y_2(x)}{xy_1(x)}$ exists.
(c) $\lim_{x\to0^+} \frac{xy_1(x)}{y_2(x)}$ does NOT exist.
(d) $\lim_{x\to0^+} \frac{x^2y_1(x)}{y_2(x)}$ exists.

[Dec 2025]

ANSWER KEY				
1	2	3	4	5
a, c	a, b	a, b, c, d	a, c	a,b,c

Explanation

1. Explanation (a), (c)

Given BVP is
$\frac{d^2y}{dx^2} + y = \csc x$ ... (1)
Auxiliary equation of equation (1) is
$m^2 + 1 = 0$
$m = \pm 1$
$y(x) = c_1 \cos x + c_2 \sin x$
Now apply the method of variation of parameter $a(x) = \cos x$, $b(x) = \sin x$
$w = \begin{vmatrix} \cos x & \sin x \\ -\sin x & \cos x \end{vmatrix} = 1$
$g(x) \int = -\int \frac{b(x)R}{w} dx$
$= -\int \frac{\sin x \; cosec\, x}{1} dx$
$g(x) = -x$
$h(x) = \int \frac{a(x)R}{w} dx$
$= \int \frac{\cos x \; cosec\, x}{1} dx$
$= \int \cot x \, dx$
$h(x) = \log \sin x$
General solution of equation (1)
$y = c_1 \cos x + c_2 \sin x + (-x \cos x) + \sin x \log \sin x$ ... . (2)
Now use the given condition
$y\left(\frac{\pi}{2}\right) = y(0) = 0$
$y(0) = c_1 = 0$
$\Rightarrow c_1 = 0$
$y\left(\frac{\pi}{2}\right) = c_2 = 0$
$c_2 = 0$
∴ Equation (2) become
$y = -x\cos x + \sin x \log \sin x$
For option (a)
$y = -x\cos x + \sin x \log \sin x$
$y' = -(-x\sin x + \cos x) + \frac{\sin x}{\sin x}\cos x + \cos x \log \sin x$
$y' = x \sin x - \cos x + \cos x + \cos x \log \sin x$
$y' = x \sin x + \cos x \log \sin x$
$y'' = x \cos x + \sin x + \frac{\cos x}{\sin x}\cos x + \log \sin x\,(-\sin x)$
$y'' = x \cos x + \sin x + \cot x \, . \cos x - \sin x \log \sin x$
$y'' > 0$ for $x \in \left(0, \frac{\pi}{2}\right)$
$\Rightarrow y(x)$ is convex
⇒ option (a) is correct.
For option (b)
from option (a),
option (b) is wrong.
For option (c)
$y = -x \cos x + \sin x \log \sin x$
$x \cos x > 0$ for $x \in \left(0, \frac{\pi}{2}\right)$
$\Rightarrow -x \cos x < 0$ for $x \in \left(0, \frac{\pi}{2}\right)$
And
$\log \sin x < 0$ for $x \in \left(0, \frac{\pi}{2}\right)$
$\Rightarrow \sin x \log \sin x < 0$ for $x \in \left(0, \frac{\pi}{2}\right)$
$\Rightarrow -x \cos x + \sin x \log \sin x < 0$
$\Rightarrow y = -x \cos x + \sin x \log \sin x$ is negative in $\left(0, \frac{\pi}{2}\right)$
For option (d) is wrong
Only option (a) and (c) are correct and (b) and (d) are incorrect.

2. Explanation (a), (b)

Given ODE is
$2y'' + 3y' + y = e^{-3x}$ ..... (1)
Auxiliary equation of equation (1) is
$2m^2 + 3m + 1 = 0$
$2m^2 + 2m + m + 1 = 0$
$2m(m+1) + (m+1) = 0$
$\Rightarrow (2m+1)(m+1) = 0$
$m = -\frac{1}{2}, -1$
Complementary function is
$y(x) = c_1 e^{-\frac{1}{2}x} + c_2 e^{-x}$
Now Find PI
PI $= \frac{1}{2D^2+3D+1} e^{-3x}$
$= \frac{e^{-3x}}{18-9+1}$
$= \frac{e^{-3x}}{10}$
$PI = \frac{1}{10}e^{-3x}$
General solution is
$y = CF + PI$
$y(x) = c_1 e^{-\frac{1}{2}x} + c_2 e^{-x} + \frac{1}{10}e^{-3x}$ ... (2)
Now
$\lim_{x\to\infty} e^x y(x) = \lim_{x\to\infty} \left[c_1 e^{-\frac{1}{2}x} + c_2 e^{-x} + \frac{1}{10}e^{-3x}\right]$
$\lim_{x\to\infty} e^x y(x) = \lim_{x\to\infty} \left[c_1 e^{\frac{1}{2}x} + c_2 + \frac{1}{10}e^{-2x}\right]$ ..... (3)
$\lim_{x\to\infty} e^x y(x) = 0$ (given)
$\Rightarrow c_1 = c_2 = 0$
⇒equation (3) become
$y(x) = \frac{1}{10}e^{-3x}$

Now check the option

For option (a)

$\lim_{x\to\infty} e^{2x}y(x) = \lim_{x\to\infty} e^{2x}\frac{1}{10}e^{-3x}$

$\lim_{x\to\infty} e^{2x}y(x) = 0$

⇒ option a) is correct.

For Option (b)

put $x = 0$ is equation (2)

$y(0) = \frac{1}{10}$

⇒ Option (b) is the correct

For option (c)

$\lim_{x\to\infty} y(x) = \infty$

⇒ $y(x)$ is not bounded

For option (d)

put $x = 1$ in equation (2)

$y(1) = \frac{1}{10}e^{-3} \neq 0$

⇒ Option (d) is wrong

⇒ Option (a) and (b) are the correct answer and option c) and d) are wrong.

3. Explanation (a), (b), (c), (d)

Given differential equation is

$\frac{d^2y}{dx^2} - 2\tan x\frac{dy}{dx} - y = 0$ ... (1)

Comparing $\frac{d^2y}{dx^2} + P\frac{dy}{dx} + Qy = R$

With equation (1)

$P = -2\tan x, \qquad Q = -1$ and $R = 0$

Now to solve equation (1)

By the change of dependent variable method

$I = Q - \frac{1}{2}\frac{dp}{dx} - \frac{p^2}{4}$

$I = = -1 + \frac{1}{2}(2\sec^2 x) - \frac{4\tan^2 x}{4}$

$I = -1 - \tan^2 x + \sec^2 x$

$I = 0$

Part of $c.f.$

$u = e^{\frac{1}{2}}\int Pdx$

$u = e^{-1/2}\int -2\tan x\, dx$

$u = e^{-\log\cos x}$

$u = \frac{1}{\cos x} = \sec x$

Now complementary solution of equation is

$y = uv$

$y = \sec x\, v$

$y = uv$

$\frac{d^2v}{dx^2} + Iv = \frac{R}{u}$

$\frac{d^2v}{dx^2} + 0 = 0$

$v = c_1x + c_2 \neq 0$

$\Rightarrow y = \sec x(c_1x + c_2)$

$y = c_1 x\sec x\,(c_1x + c_2)$

$y = c_1 x\sec x + c_2\sec x$ .... (2)

Now check the option

For option (a)

$y(0) = y'(0) - 1$

$c_2 = 1$

$y' = c_1(x\sec x\tan x + \sec x) + c_2\sec x\tan x$

$y'(0) = c_1 = 1$

$\Rightarrow c_1 = 1$

Equation (2) become

$y = x\sec x + \sec x$

Now $y\left(\frac{\pi}{3}\right) = \frac{\pi}{3}(2) + 2$

$= \frac{2\pi}{3} + 2$

$y\left(\frac{\pi}{3}\right) = 2\left(1 + \frac{\pi}{3}\right)$

There is exactly one solution $y = y(x)$ *with* $y(0) = y'(0) = 1$ *and* $y\left(\frac{\pi}{3}\right) = 2\left(1 + \frac{\pi}{3}\right)$

⇒ Option (a) is the correct.

For option (b)

$y(0) = 1, \quad y'(0) = -1$

$\Rightarrow y(0) = c_2 = 1$

$y'(0) = c_1 = -1$

$y(x) = -x\sec x + \sec x$

$y\left(-\frac{\pi}{3}\right) = \frac{\pi}{3}\sec\left(-\frac{\pi}{3}\right) + \sec\left(-\frac{\pi}{3}\right) = \frac{\pi}{3}2 + 2$

There is exactly one solution

$y = y(x)$ with $y(0) = 1, y'(0) = -1$ and $y\left(-\frac{\pi}{3}\right) = 2\left(1 + \frac{\pi}{3}\right)$

For option (c)

$y(x) = c_1x\sec x + c_2\sec x$

$y(x) = c_1x\sec x + c_2\sec x$

$y(0) = c_2$

$y'(x) = c_1(x\sec x\tan x + \sec x) + c_2\sec x\tan x$

$y(x) = c_1\sec x(x\tan x + 1) + c_2\sec x\tan x$

$y''(x) = c_1\sec x\tan x(x\tan x + 1) +$
$c_2\sec x\tan x\tan x + c_1\sec x\,(x\sec^2 x + \tan x) +$
$c_2\sec^3 x$

$y''(0) = c_2$

$y''(0) = y(0)$

⇒ Any solution $y = y(x)$ satisfies $y''(0) = y(0)$

⇒option c) is correct.

For option (d)

y_1 and y_2 are the solution of given equation so,

$y_1(x) = (c_1x + c_2)\sec x$

$y_2(x) = (c_3x + c_4)\sec x$

Above equation written as

$y_1(x) = (ax + b)\sec x$

$y_2(x) = (cx + d)\sec x$

$\Rightarrow \frac{y_1(x)}{ax+b} = \sec x$ and

$\frac{y_1(x)}{cx+d} = \sec x$

$\frac{y_1(x)}{ax+b} = \frac{y_2(x)}{cx+d}$

$(ax + b)y_1(x) = y_2(x)(x + d)$

⇒ if y_1 and y_2 are any two solutions then $(ax + b)y_1 = (cx + d)y_2$ for some $a, b, c, d \in R$

⇒ option (d) is also correct.

⇒ Option $a), b), c)$, and $d)$ are correct answer.

4. Explanation: (a), (c)

The initial value problem is

$\Rightarrow x^2y'' - 2x^2y' + (4x - 2)y = 0$

$\Rightarrow y'' - 2y' + \frac{(4x-2)}{x^2} y = 0$

Comparing with the standard form

$\Rightarrow y'' + p(x)y' + Q(x)y = 0$, we get

$\Rightarrow p(x) = -2$ and $Q(x) = \frac{4x-2}{x^2}$ ... (1)

$\therefore$ By reduction of order method

$\Rightarrow y = x^2$ is a solution if

$\Rightarrow 2 + 2xp + x^2Q = 0$

$\Rightarrow 2 + 2x(-2) + x^2 \frac{(4x-2)}{x^2} = 0$ from (1)

$\therefore y = x^2$ is a solution.

And we have $y = \phi(x)$

$\Rightarrow \phi(4) = 16$ and $\phi(5) = 25$ Solution.

$\Rightarrow$ Option (a) and (c) are correct.

5. **Explanation: (a), (b), (c)**

Analysis of the ODE using Frobenius Method

Standard Form

Divide by x^2: $y'' + \frac{(1+\sin x)}{2x} y' - \frac{3\cos x}{2x^2} y = 0$

This has a regular singular point at $x = 0$.

Write $p(x) = x \cdot \frac{(1+\sin x)}{2x}$, $q(x) = x^2 \cdot \frac{-3\cos x}{2x^2}$

At $x = 0$:

$p_0 = \lim_{x\to 0} x \cdot \frac{(1+\sin x)}{2x} = \frac{1+0}{2} = \frac{1}{2}$

$q_0 = \lim_{x\to 0} x^2 \cdot \frac{-3\cos x}{2x^2} = \frac{-3}{2}$

Indicial equation:

$r(r-1) + p_0 r + q_0 = 0$

$r(r-1) + \frac{1}{2}r - \frac{3}{2} = 0$

$r^2 - \frac{r}{2} - \frac{3}{2} = 0$

$2r^2 - r - 3 = 0$

$(2r-3)(r+1) = 0$

$r_1 = \frac{3}{2}, r_2 = -1$

The two Frobenius solutions behave near $x = 0$ as:

$y_1(x) \sim c_1 x^{3/2}$ ($r_1 = 3/2$, larger root)

$y_2(x) \sim c_2 x^{-1}$ ($r_2 = -1$, smaller root)

But $y_2(0) = 0$ is given — so the solution corresponding to $r_2 = -1$ is ruled out (it blows up).

Therefore:

$y_1(x)$

$\sim x^{-1}$ (larger in magnitude near 0, does NOT vanish)

$y_2(x) \sim x^{3/2}$ (satisfies $y_2(0) = 0$)

With $y_1(x) \sim x^{-1}$ and $y_2(x) \sim x^{3/2}$ as $x \to 0^+$:

Statement 1: $\lim_{x\to 0^+} \frac{y_2(x)}{x^2 y_1(x)}$

$\frac{y_2}{x^2 y_1} \sim \frac{x^{3/2}}{x^2 \cdot x^{-1}} = \frac{x^{3/2}}{x} = x^{1/2} \to 0$

Limit exists $(= 0) \to$ TRUE

Statement 2: $\lim_{x\to 0^+} \frac{y_2(x)}{x\, y_1(x)}$

$\frac{y_2}{x\, y_1} \sim \frac{x^{3/2}}{x \cdot x^{-1}} = \frac{x^{3/2}}{1} = x^{3/2} \to 0$

Limit exists $(= 0)$ $\to$ TRUE

Statement 3: $\lim_{x\to 0^+} \frac{x\, y_1(x)}{y_2(x)}$ does NOT exist

$\frac{x\, y_1}{y_2} \sim \frac{x \cdot x^{-1}}{x^{3/2}} = \frac{1}{x^{3/2}} \to \infty$

Limit does NOT exist $(\to \infty) \to$ TRUE

Statement 4: $\lim_{x\to 0^+} \frac{x^2 y_1(x)}{y_2(x)}$

$\frac{x^2\, y_1}{y_2} \sim \frac{x^2 \cdot x^{-1}}{x^{3/2}} = \frac{x}{x^{3/2}} = x^{-1/2} \to \infty$

Limit does NOT exist → FALSE

Correct answer: 1, 2 and 3

Unit 1.3: Wronskian

MCQ - Multiple Choice Questions

1. Consider the ODE
$u''(t) + P(t)u'(t) + Q(t)u(t) = R(t), t \in [0,1]$
There exist continuous function P, Q and R defined on $[0,1]$ and two solutions u_1 and u_2 of the ODE such that the Wronskian W of u_1 and u_2 is
(a) $W(t) = 2t - 1, \quad 0 \le t \le 1$
(b) $W(t) = \sin 2\pi t, \quad 0 \le t \le 1$
(c) $W(t) = \cos 2\pi t, \quad 0 \le t \le 1$
(d) $W(t) = 1, \quad 0 \le t \le 1$
[June 2011]

2. Let $y_1(x)$ and $y_2(x)$ from a fundamental set of solution of $\frac{d^2y}{dx^2} + p(x)\frac{dy}{dx} + q(x)y = 0,\ a \le x \le b$, where $p(x)$ and $q(x)$ are real values continuous function on $[a,b]$. If x_0 and x_1, with $x_0 < x_1$, are consecutive zeros of $y_1(x)$ in (a,b), then
(a) $y_1(x) = (x - x_0)q_0(x)$, where $q_0(x)$ is continuous on $[a,b]$ with $q_0(x) \neq 0$
(b) $y_1(x) = (x - x_0)^2 p_0(x)$, where $q_0(x)$ is continuous on $[a,b]$ with $p_0(x_0) \neq 0$
(c) $y_2(x)$ has no zeros in (x_0, x_1)
(d) $y_2(x_0) = 0$ but $y'_2(x_0) \neq 0$
[Dec 2011]

3. Let W be the Wronskian of two linearly independent solution of ODE
$$2y'' + y' + t^2y = 0;\quad t \in \mathbb{R}$$
Then, for all t, there exists a constant $C \in \mathbb{R}$ such that $W(t)$ is
(a) Ce^{-t}
(b) $Ce^{-t/2}$
(c) Ce^{2t}
(d) Ce^{-2t}
[Dec 2013]

4. Let $Y_1(x)$ and $Y_2(x)$ defined on $[0,1]$ be twice continuously differentiable functions satisfying $Y''(x) + Y'(x) + Y(x) = 0$. Let $W(x)$ be the Wronskin of y_1 and y_2 and satisfy $W\left(\frac{1}{2}\right) = 0$. Then
(a) $W(x) = 0$ for $x \in [0,1]$
(b) $W(x) \neq 0$ for $x \in [0,1/2) \cup (1/2,1]$
(c) $W(x) > 0$ for $x \in (1/2,1]$
(d) $W(x) < 0$ for $x \in [0,1/2)$
[June 2014]

5. Let y_1 and y_2 be two solutions of the problem
$$\left.\begin{matrix} y''(t) + ay'(t) + by(t) = 0, t \in \mathbb{R} \\ y(0) = 0 \end{matrix}\right\}$$
Where a and b are real constant. Let ω be the Wronskian of y_1 and y_2. Then
(a) $\omega(t) = 0, \forall t \in \mathbb{R}$
(b) $\omega(t) = c, \forall t \in \mathbb{R}$ for some positive constant c
(c) ω is a non-constant positive function
(d) There exists $t_1, t_2 \in \mathbb{R}$ such that $\omega(t_1) < 0 < \omega(t_2)$
[June 2016]

6. The boundary value problem
$$x^2y'' - 2xy' + 2y = 0$$
Subject to the boundary conditions
$$y(1) + \alpha y'(1) = 1$$
$$y(2) + \beta y'(2) = 2$$
Has a unique solution if
(a) $\alpha = -1, \beta = 2$ (b) $\alpha = -1, \beta = -2$
(c) $\alpha = -2, \beta = 2$ (d) $\alpha = -3, \beta = \frac{2}{3}$
[Dec 2016]

7. Consider the ordinary differential equation $y'' + P(x)y' + Q(x)y = 0$ where P and Q are smooth functions. Let y_1 and y_2 be any two solutions of the ODE. Let $W(x)$ be the corresponding Wronskian. Then which of the following is always true?
(a) If y_1 and y_2 are linearly dependent then $\exists\, x_1, x_2$ such that $W(x_1) = 0$ and $W(x_2) \neq 0$
(b) If y_1 and y_2 are linearly independent $W(x) = 0\ \forall x$
(c) If y_1 and y_2 are linearly dependent $W(x) \neq 0\ \forall x$
(d) If y_1 and y_2 are linearly independent then $W(x) \neq 0\ \forall x$
[June 2018]

8. If $y_1(x)$ and $y_2(x)$ are two solutions of the differential equation
$$(\cos x)y'' + (\sin x)y' - \left(1 + e^{-x^2}\right)y = 0\ \forall x \in \left(\frac{-\pi}{2}, \frac{\pi}{2}\right)$$
With $y_1(0) = \sqrt{2}$, $y'_1(0) = 1$, $y_2(0) = -\sqrt{2}$, $y'_2(0) = 2$ then the Wronskian of $y_1(x)$ and $y_2(x)$ at $x = \frac{\pi}{4}$ is
(a) $3\sqrt{2}$ (b) 6
(c) 3 (d) $-3\sqrt{2}$
[Dec 2018]

9. Consider the 2nd order ODE $\ddot{x} + p(t)\ddot{x} + p(\dot{x}) + q(t)x = 0$ and let x_1, x_2 be two solutions of this ODE in $[a,b]$. Which of the following statements are true for the Wronskian w of x_1, x_2 ?
(a) $W = 0$ in (a,b) implies that x_1, x_2 are independent
(b) W can change sign in (a,b)
(c) $W(t_0) = 0$ for some $t_0 \in (a,b)$ implies that $W = 0$ in (a,b)
(d) $W(t_0) = 1$ for some $t_0 \in (a,b)$ implies that $W = 1$ in (a,b)
[Feb 2022]

10. For $a \in \mathbb{R}$, let $y_1(x)$ and $y_2(x)$ be solutions of the differential equation
$$y'' + (e^{x^2} + \cos x)\,y = 0$$
such that
$$y_1(0) = 3, y'_1(0) = -1, y_2(0) = -5, y'_2(0) = a.$$
Suppose $W(y_1, y_2)(x)$ denotes the Wronskian of y_1 and y_2. If $W(y_1, y_2)\left(\frac{1}{2}\right) = 4$, then the value of a is
(a) 2 (b) 3
(c) 4 (d) -3
[Dec 2025]

ANSWER KEY									
1	2	3	4	5	6	7	8	9	10
d	a	b	a	a	a	d	c	c	b

EXPLANATION

1. Explanation (d)

Given differential equation is

$u''(t) + P(t)u'(t) + Q(t)u(t) = R(t)$, t∈ [0,1] (1)

u_1 and u_2 are the solution of above equation and W is the wronskian of the equation (1)

We know that,

The wronskian either identically zero or never zero.

⟹ option d) is the correct answer and option a), b) and c) are incorrect.

2. Explanation (a)

Given differential equation is

$\frac{d^2y}{dx^2}$+p(x)$\frac{dy}{dx}$ + q(x)y = 0 (1)

And y_1(x) and $y_2(x)$ form a fundamental set of solution

For option a)

Let x_0 is the zero of y_1(x) then $y_1(x)$ is satisfied

$y_1(x) = (x - x_0)q_0(x)$

where q_0(x) is continuous and q_0(x)≠ 0

⟹option a) is correct.

For option b)

from equation 1)

y_1 cannot have repeated root.

For option c)

Any two consecutive root of y_1 there exist exactly one root of y_2.

For option d)

from equation 1) $y_2(x)$ can not have common zero.

⟹ option a) is the correct answer and b), c) and d) are incorrect.

3. Explanation (b)

Given differential equation is

$2y'' + y' + t^2y = 0$ (1)

$a(t)y'' + b(t)y' + d(t)y = 0$ (2)

Comparing equation 1) and 2)

⟹ a(t) = 2, b(t) = 1 and d(t) = t²

Now use the Abel formula

W(t)=$Ce^{-\int\frac{b(t)dt}{a(t)}}$

W(t)=$Ce^{-\int\frac{dt}{2}}$

W(t)=$Ce^{-\frac{t}{2}}$

⟹ option b) is the correct answer and option a), c) and d) are incorrect.

4. Explanation (a)

Given differential equation is

$Y''(x) + Y'(x) + Y(x) = 0$ 1)

Y_1(x) and Y_2(x) are the solution of equation (1) and W is the Wronskian of $Y_1(x)$ and $Y_2(x)$.

We know that,

Wronskian either identically zero or never zero.

⟹ option a) is the correct answer and option b), c) and d) are the incorrect.

5. Explanation (a)

Given ODE is

$y''(t) + ay'(t) + by(t) = 0, t \in R$ (1)

y_1 and y_2 are the solution of equation (1)

and W is the wronskian of y_1 and y_2

$y(0) = 0$ (Given)

⇒ $y_1(0) = 0$ and $y_2(0) = 0$ (2)

Now

$w(t) = \begin{vmatrix} y_1(t) & y_2(t) \\ y_1'(t) & y_2'(t) \end{vmatrix}$

$\Rightarrow w(0) = \begin{vmatrix} y_1(0) & y_2(0) \\ y_1'(0) & y_2'(0) \end{vmatrix}$

$= y_1(0)y_2'(0) - y_2(0)y_2'(0)$

$\Rightarrow w(0) = 0$ From Equation (2)

Now using able formula

$w(t) = Ae^{-\int adt} = Ae^{-at}$

$w(t) = Ae^{-at}$

$w(0) = 0$

$\Rightarrow w(0) = A$

$\Rightarrow w(t) = w(0)e^{-at} = 0$

$\Rightarrow w(t) = 0\ \forall t \in R$

And option (a) is the correct.

We know that,

Wronskian either identically zero or never zero.

⇒ Option (a) is the correct answer and option b), c) and d) are incorrect.

6. Explanation (a)

We have

$x^2y'' - 2xy' + 2y = 0$ ……………… ①

This is the Cauchy problem with constant coefficient.

To solve this

Put $\log(x) = z \Rightarrow x = e^z$ and $\frac{d}{dz} = D$

$\Rightarrow (D(D-1) - 2D + 2)y = 0$

$\Rightarrow (D^2 - D - 2D + 2)y = 0$

$\Rightarrow (D^2 - 3D + 2)y = 0$

Auxillary equation of above equation is

$m^2 - 3m + 2 = 0$

$\Rightarrow m^2 - 2m - m + 2 = 0$

$\Rightarrow m = 1,2$

Complementary function is

$y = Ae^z + Be^{2z}$ (∵ A, B are constant)

$\Rightarrow y = Ax + Bx^2$ ……… ①

Now use the Boundary condition,

$\left.\begin{array}{l} y(1) + \alpha y'(1) = 1 \\ y(2) + \beta y'(2) = 2 \end{array}\right\}$ (Given)

From equation (2)

$\Rightarrow A + B + A\alpha + 2\beta\alpha = 1$ and

$2A + 4B + A\beta + 4\beta B = 2$

$\Rightarrow A(1+\alpha)+B(1+2\alpha)=1$

$A(2+\beta)+B(4+4\beta)=2$ ....③

Equation ③ written in augmented matrix from

$[P:Q]=R$

$\begin{bmatrix}1+\alpha & 1+2\alpha & 1\\ 2+\beta & 4+4\beta & 2\end{bmatrix}=\begin{bmatrix}A\\B\end{bmatrix}$ ....④

Where $P=\begin{bmatrix}1+\alpha & 1+2\alpha\\ 2+\beta & 4+4\beta\end{bmatrix}$ $a=\begin{bmatrix}1\\2\end{bmatrix}$ $R=\begin{bmatrix}A\\B\end{bmatrix}$

Equation ④ has unique solution if rank $(P)=rank\,[P:Q]$

$\Rightarrow P=\begin{vmatrix}1+\alpha & 1+2\alpha\\ 2+\beta & 4+4\beta\end{vmatrix}\neq 0$ then it has unique solution: Now check the option.

Option (A)

$\alpha=-1,\beta=2$

$\Rightarrow P=\begin{vmatrix}0 & -1\\ 4 & 12\end{vmatrix}=4\neq 0$

$\Rightarrow$ It has unique solution

Option (B)

$\alpha=-1,\beta=-2$

$\Rightarrow P=\begin{vmatrix}0 & -3\\ 0 & -4\end{vmatrix}=0$

It has no unique solution

Option (C)

$\alpha=-2,\beta=2$

$\Rightarrow P=\begin{vmatrix}-1 & -3\\ 4 & 12\end{vmatrix}=-12+12=0$

$\Rightarrow$ it has no unique solution

Option (D)

$\alpha=-3,\beta=\frac{2}{3}$

$\Rightarrow P=\begin{vmatrix}-2 & -5\\ \frac{8}{3} & \frac{20}{3}\end{vmatrix}=0$

$\Rightarrow$ It has no unique solution

$\Rightarrow$ Option (a) is the correct answer and option (b),(c),(d) are incorrect.

7. Explanation (d)

Given ODE is

$y''+p(x)y'+Q(x)y=0$ ....(1)

y_1 and y_2 are the solution of equation (1) and W is the wronskian of y_1 and y_2

We know that

Wronskian is either identically zero or never zero and

If $w(y_1,y_2)\neq 0$ then y_1 and y_2 are linearly independent and vice versa.

If $w(y_1,y_2)=0$ then y_1 and y_2 Linearly dependent and vice versa.

From above explanation

Only option (d) is the correct answer and Option (a), (b), (c) are incorrect.

8. Explanation (c)

Given ODE is

$\cos xy''+\sin xy'-(1+e^{-x^2})y=0 \quad \forall\ x\in\left(\frac{-\pi}{2},\frac{\pi}{2}\right)$

y_1 and y_2 are the solution of equation (1) and w is the wronskian of y_1 and y_2

$\left.\begin{matrix}y_1(0)=\sqrt{2} & y_1'(0)=1\\ y_2(0)=-\sqrt{2} & y_2'(0)=2\end{matrix}\right\}$ Given

$w(x)=\begin{vmatrix}y_1(x) & y_2(x)\\ y_1'(x) & y_2'(x)\end{vmatrix}$

$=\begin{vmatrix}\sqrt{2} & -\sqrt{2}\\ 1 & 2\end{vmatrix}$

$w(0)=2\sqrt{2}+\sqrt{2}=3\sqrt{2}$

By Abel's formula

$w(x)=Ae^{-\int\frac{\sin x}{\cos x}dx}$

$=Ae^{\log(\cos x)}$

$w(x)=A\cos x$

$w(0)=3\sqrt{2}$

$\Rightarrow 3\sqrt{2}=A$

$A=3\sqrt{2}$

$\Rightarrow w(x)=3\sqrt{2}\cos x$

Now check the wronskian at

$x=\frac{\pi}{4}$

$\Rightarrow w\left(\frac{\pi}{4}\right)=3\sqrt{2}\cos\frac{\pi}{4}$

$\Rightarrow w\left(\frac{\pi}{4}\right)=3$

Option c) is the correct answer and (a), (b), (d) are incorrect.

9. Explanation: (c)

Consider the given second order ODE

$\ddot{x}+p(t)\dot{x}+q(t)x=0$

x_1 and x_2 are two solutions of given ODE in [a, b]

We know that Wronskian is either identically zero or never zero.

$\Rightarrow$ Option (c) is the correct answer.

10. Explanation: (b)

The given differential equation is $y''+(e^{x^2}+\cos x)y=0$

Compare with the standard form

$$y''+p(x)y'+q(x)y=0$$

Here,

$$p(x)=0$$

Property of the Wronskian:

For two solutions y_1,y_2,

$$W'(x)=-p(x)W(x)$$

Since $p(x)=0$,

$$W'(x)=0$$

So the Wronskian is constant.

Therefore

$$W\left(\frac{1}{2}\right)=W(0)$$

Given $W\left(\frac{1}{2}\right)=4$

Hence

$$W(0)=4$$

Compute W(0)

$$W(x)=\begin{vmatrix}y_1 & y_2\\ y_1' & y_2'\end{vmatrix}=y_1y_2'-y_1'y_2$$

Using the given values:
$y_1(0) = 3, y_1'(0) = -1, y_2(0) = -5, y_2'(0) = a$

$$W(0) = 3a - (-1)(-5)$$

$\Rightarrow W(0) = 3a - 5$
Using $W(0) = 4$
$3a - 5 = 4$
$\Rightarrow 3a = 9$
$\Rightarrow a = 3$

MSQ - Multiple Select Questions

1. Let $y_1(x)$ and $y_2(x)$ form a fundamental set of solutions to the differential equation
$$\frac{d^2y}{dx^2} + p(x)\frac{dy}{dx} + q(x)y = 0, a \le x \le b$$
Where $p(x)$ and $q(x)$ are continuous in $[a, b]$, and x_0 is a point in (a, b). Then
(a) Both $y_1(x)$ and $y_2(x)$ cannot have a local maximum at x_0
(b) Both $y_1(x)$ and $y_2(x)$ cannot have a local minimum at x_0
(c) $y_1(x)$ cannot have a local maximum at x_0 and $y_2(x)$ cannot have local minimum at x_0 and $y_2(x)$ cannot have local minimum at x_0 simultaneously
(d) Both $y_1(x)$ and $y_2(x)$ cannot vanish at x_0 simultaneously

[June 2011]

2. Let $\frac{d^2y}{dx^2} - q(x)\, y = 0, 0 \le x < \infty$,
$$y(0) = 1, \frac{dy}{dx}(0) = 1$$
Where $q(x)$ is a positive monotonically increasing continuous function. Then
(a) $y(x) \to \infty \; as \; x \to \infty$
(b) $\frac{dy}{dx} \to \infty \; as \; x \to \infty$
(c) $y(x)$ has finitely many zeros in $[0, \infty)$
(d) $y(x)$ has infinitely many zeros in $[0, \infty)$

[Dec 2011]

3. Let y be a non-trivial solution of the boundary value problem $y'' + xy = 0, x \in [a, b], y(a) = y(b) = 0$, then
(a) $b > 0$
(b) y is monotone in $(a, 0)$ if $a < 0 < b$
(c) $y'(a) = 0$
(d) y has infinitely many zeros in $[a, b]$

[Dec 2013]

4. Let $y_1(x)$ and $y_2(x)$ from a complete set of solutions to the differential equation
$$y'' - 2xy' + \sin(e^{2x^2})\, y = 0, x \in [0, 1]$$
With $y_1(0) = 0, y'_1 = 1, y_2(0) = 1, y'_2(0) = 1$.
Then the Wronskian $W(x)$ of $y_1(x)$ and $y_2(x)$ at $x = 1$ is
(a) e^2
(b) $-e$
(c) $-e^2$
(d) e

[June 2014]

5. Let P, Q be continuous real valued functions defined on [-1,1] and $u_i: [-1,1] \to R, i = 1,2$ be solutions of the ODE:
$$\frac{d^2u}{dx^2} + P(x)\frac{du}{dx} + Q(x)u = 0, x \in [-1,1]$$
Satisfying $u_1 \ge 0, u_2 \le 0$ and $u_1(0) = u_2(0) = 0$. Let w denote Wronskian of u_1 and u_2, then
(a) u_1 and u_2 are linearly independent.
(b) u_1 and u_2 are linearly dependent.
(c) $w(x) = 0 \; for \; all \; x \in [-1,1]$
(d) $w(x) \ne 0 \; for \; all \; x \in [-1,1]$

[Dec 2014]

6. Let $y: R \to R$ be a solution of the ODE
$$\left.\begin{aligned} \frac{d^2y}{dx^2} - y = e^{-x}, x \in R \\ y(0) = \frac{dy}{dx}(0) = 0 \end{aligned}\right\}$$
Then
(a) y attains its minimum on R.
(b) y is bounded on R
(c) $\lim_{x\to\infty} e^{-x}y(x) = \frac{1}{4}$
(d) $\lim_{x\to\infty} e^{x}y(x) = \frac{1}{4}$

[Dec 2014]

7. Let P be a continuous function on R and W the Wronskian of two linearly independent solutions $y_1 \; and \; y_2$ of the ODE:
$$\frac{d^2y}{dx^2} + (x^2 + 1)\frac{dy}{dx} + P(x)y = 0, x \in R.$$
Let $W(1) = a, W(2) = b \; and \; W(3) = c$, then
(a) $a < 0 \; and \; b > 0$
(b) $a < b < c \; or \; a > b > c$
(c) $\frac{a}{|a|} = \frac{b}{|b|} = \frac{c}{|c|}$
(d) $0 < a < b \; and \; b > c > 0$

[June 2015]

8. Let $x: [0,3\pi] \to R$ be a nonzero solution of the ODE
$$x''(t) + e^{t^2}x(t) = 0 \; for \; t \in [0,3\pi]$$
Then the Cardinality of the Set
$\{t \in [0,3\pi]: x(t) = 0\}$ is
(a) Equal to 1
(b) Greater than or equal to 2
(c) Equal to 2
(d) Greater than or equal to 3

[Dec 2016]

9. The method of Variation Parameters to solve the differential equation
$y'' + p(x)y' + q(x)y = r(x), wher \; x \in I$ and $p(x), q(x), r(x)$
Are non-zero continuous functions on an interval I, seeks a particular solution of the form $y_p(x) = v_1(x)y_1(x) + v_2(x)y_2(x)$, where y_1, y_2 are linearly independent solutions of $y'' + p(x)y' + q(x)y = 0$, and $v_1(x) and \; v_2(x)$ are functions to be determined. Which of the following statements are necessarily true?
(a) The Wronskian of $y_1 \; and \; y_2$ is never zero in I.
(b) v_1, v_2 and $v_1y_1 + v_2y_2$ are twice differentiable
(c) $v_1 \; and \; v_2$ may not be twice differentiable but $v_1y_1 + v_2y_2$ is twice differentiable.
(d) The solution set of $y'' + p(x)y' + q(x)y = r(x)$ consists of functions of the form $ay_1 + by_2 + y_p$ where $a, b \in R$ are arbitrary constants.

[Dec 2018]

10. Three Solutions of a certain second order non-homogeneous linear differential equation are $y_1(x) = 1 + xe^{x^2}, y_2(x) = (1 + x)e^{x^2} - 1, y_3(x) = 1 + e^{x^2}$.
Which of the following is (are) general solution(s) of the differential equation?
(a) $(C_1 + 1)y_1 + (C_2 - C_1)y_2 - C_2y_3$, where C_1 and C_2 are arbitrary constants.
(b) $C_1(y_1 - y_2) + C_2(y_2 - y_3)$, where C_1 and C_2 are arbitrary constants.
(c) $C_1(y_1 - y_2) + C_2(y_2 - y_3) + C_3(y_3 - y_1)$ where C_1, C_2 and C_3 are arbitrary constants.
(d) $C_1(y_1 - y_3) + C_2(y_3 - y_2) + y_1$, where C_1 and C_2 are arbitrary constant.

[Dec 2018]

11. Consider the equation $y''(x) + a(x)y(x) = 0, a(x)$ is continuous function with period T.
Let $\phi_1(x)$ and $\phi_2(x)$ be the basis for the solution satisfying $\phi_1(0) = 1, \phi'_1(0) = 0, \phi_2(0) = 0, \phi_2'(0) = 1$. Let $W(\phi_1, \phi_2)$ denote the Wronskian of ϕ_1 and ϕ_2. Then
(a) $W(\phi_1, \phi_2) = 1$
(b) $W(\phi_1, \phi_2) = e^x$
(c) $\phi_1(T) + \phi_2'(T) = 2$ if the given differential equation has a nontrivial periodic solution with period T.
(d) $\phi_1(T) + \phi_2'(T) = 1$ if the given differential equation has a nontrivial periodic solution with period T.

[June 2019]

12. Let $y_1(x)$ be any non-trivial real valued solution of $y''(x) + xy(x) = 0, 0 < x < \infty$.
Let $y_2(x)$ be the solution of $y''(x) + y(x) = x^2 + 2, y(0) = y'(0) = 0$. Then
(a) $y_1(x)$ has infinitely many zeros.
(b) $y_2(x)$ has infinitely many zeros.
(c) $y_1(x)$ has finitely many zeros.
(d) $y_2(x)$ has finitely many zeros.

[June 2019]

13. Consider the ordinary differential equation (ODE)
$$y'' + r(x)y = 0,$$
Where
$$r(x) = \begin{cases} x^3 \sin\left(\frac{1}{x}\right), & x \neq 0 \\ 0, & x = 0 \end{cases}$$
Then which of the following statements are true?
(a) There exists a non-trivial solution ϕ of ODE, and $\alpha, \beta \in \mathbb{R}, \alpha < \beta$ such that ϕ has infinitely many zeros in $[\alpha < \beta]$.
(b) There exists a non-trivial solution ϕ of ODE, and a sequence $\{x_n\}$ such that $x_n \to \infty$ and $\phi(x_n) = 0$ for all $n \in \mathbb{N}$.
(c) If ϕ_1, ϕ_2 are two linearly independent solutions of ODE, then their Wronskian is a constant function on $\mathbb{R}$.
(d) There exists a non-trivial solution of ODE which vanishes at most at one point in $(0, \infty)$.

[Dec 2025]

Answer Key

1	2	3	4	5	6	7	8	9
a,b,c,d	a,b	a,b	b	b,c	a,c	b,c	b,d	a,c,d
10	**11**	**12**	**13**					
a,d	a,c	a,d	b,c					

Explanations

1. **Explanation (a), (b), (c), (d)**
Given ODE is
$$\frac{d^2y}{dx^2} + p(x)\frac{dy}{dx} + q(x)y = 0 \quad (1)$$
$y_1(x)$ and $y_2(x)$ fundamental set of solution.
$\Rightarrow y_1(x)$ and $y_2(x)$ cannot vanish at x_0 simultaneously
Here y_1 and y_2 are linearly independent solution of equation (1)
$w = (y_1, y_2) \neq 0$
$\Rightarrow y_1(x)$ and $y_2(x)$ cannot have a maxima or minima at x_0
From above explanation
$\Rightarrow$ Option (a), (b), (c), (d) are correct answer.

2. **Explanation (a), (b)**
Given ODE is
$$\frac{d^2y}{dx^2} - q(x)y = 0 \qquad 0 \leq x < \infty \text{ ....(1)}$$
And $y(0) = 1, \frac{dy}{dx}(0) = 1$ {given}
Comparing equation (1) with
$$\frac{d^2y}{dx^2} + a(x)y = 0 \text{ ....(2)}$$
$\Rightarrow a(x) = -q(x)$
From equation (2)
If $a(x) < 0 \Rightarrow -q(x) < 0$ (q(x) is positive)
$\Rightarrow y(x)$ monotonically decreasing function
$\Rightarrow y(x)$ has atmost one zero
$\Rightarrow$ equation 1) has atmost one zero
From given condition $y'(x) > 1$
$y(x)$ is increasing
$\Rightarrow y(x) \to \infty$ as $x \to \infty$ and
$\frac{dy}{dx} \to \infty$ as $x \to \infty$
From above explanation option (a), (b) are correct and Option (c) and (d) are incorrect.

3. **Explanation (a), (b)**
Given BVP is
$$y'' + xy = 0 \qquad x \in [a, b] \qquad (1)$$
$y(a) = y(b) = 0$
Comparing equation (1) with $y'' + p(x)y = 0$
$\Rightarrow p(x) = x$
Let us assume that $p(x) = x < 0$
$\Rightarrow y(x)$ has at most one zero but from given $y(x)$ has two zero
$\Rightarrow$ Our initial assumption is wrong
$\Rightarrow p(x) = x > 0$
$\Rightarrow b > 0$
$\Rightarrow$ Option (a) is the correct answer and option b),c) and d) are incorrect.

4. Explanation (b)

Given ODE is

$y'' - 2xy' + \sin(e^{2x^2})y = 0 \qquad x \in [0,1]$

y_1 and y_2 are the solution of equation (1) and w is the wronskian of y_1 and y_2

$y_1(0) = 0, \qquad y_1'(0) = 1$

$y_2(0) = 1, \qquad y_1'(0) = 1$

Now,

$w(x) = \begin{vmatrix} y_1(x) & y_2(x) \\ y_1'(x) & y_2'(x) \end{vmatrix}$

$w(0) = \begin{vmatrix} 0 & 1 \\ 1 & 1 \end{vmatrix}$

$w(0) = -1$

Now use the Abel Formula

$w(x) = Ae^{-\int -2x\, dx}$

$w(x) = Ae^{x^2}$

$w(0) = A = -1$

$\Rightarrow w(x) = -e^{x^2}$

Now check the wronskian at $x = 1$

$\Rightarrow w(1) = -e$

$\Rightarrow$ Option (b) is the correct answer and (a) ,(c), (d) are incorrect.

5. Explanation (b), (c)

Given ODE is

$\frac{d^2y}{dx^2} + p(x)\frac{dy}{dx} + q(x)y = 0, x \in [-1,1]$.....................(1)

$y_1(x)$ and $y_2(x)$ are the solution of equation (1) and w is the wronskian of u_1 and u_2

$w = \begin{vmatrix} u_1(x) & u_2(x) \\ u_1'(x) & u_2'(x) \end{vmatrix} = u_1(x)u_2'(x) - u_1'(x)u_2(x)$

$u_1(0) = u_2(0) = 0 \qquad$ (Given)

$w(0) = 0$

$\Rightarrow u_1$ and u_2 are linearly independent and We know that wronskian either identically zero or never zero.

$\Rightarrow w(x) = 0\ \forall x \in [-1,1]$

u_1 and u_2 are linearly dependent

$\Rightarrow$ Option (b) and (c) are the correct answer and option (a) and (d) are incorrect.

6. Explanation (a), (c)

Given ODE is

$\frac{d^2y}{dx^2} - y = e^{-x}, x \in R$...........................(1)

$\Rightarrow (D^2 - 1)y = e^{-x}$

Auxiliary equation of above equation is

$m^2 - 1 = 0$

$m = \pm 1$

Complementary function is

$y = c_1e^x + c_2e^{-x}$

Now find the PI

$PI = \frac{1}{D^2-1}e^{-x}$

$PI = \frac{xe^{-x}}{-2}$

$\Rightarrow$ General solution of Equation (1) is

$y(x)$ =C.F+P.I.

$y(x) = c_1e^x + c_2e^{-x} + \left(-\frac{1}{2}\right)xe^{-x}$ ....(2)

Now use the initial condition

$y(0) = y'(0) = 0$......................(given)

$y(0) = c_1 + c_2 = 0$

$\Rightarrow c_1 = -c_2$

$y'(0) = c_1 - c_2 - \frac{1}{2} = 0$

$\Rightarrow c_1 - c_2 = \frac{1}{2}$

$c_1 - c_2 = \frac{1}{2}$

$c_1 + c_1 = \frac{1}{2}$

$c_1 = \frac{1}{4}$

$\Rightarrow c_2 = -\frac{1}{4}$

Equation (2) become

$\Rightarrow y(x) = \frac{1}{4}e^x - \frac{1}{4}e^{-x} - \frac{1}{2}xe^{-x}$

To check option

For option (a)

$y'(0) = 0 \qquad$ (Given)

$y''(x) = \frac{1}{4}e^x - \frac{1}{4}e^{-x} + \frac{1}{2}xe^{-x} + e^{-x}$

$y''(0) = 1 > 0$

$\Rightarrow y$ attain its minima at $x = 0$

$\Rightarrow$ Option (a) is the correct.

For Option (b)

As $x \to \infty, y(x)$ also tends to ∞ So $y(x)$ is not bounded on $\mathbb{R}$

For Option c)

$\lim_{x\to\infty} e^{-x}y(x) = \lim_{x\to\infty} e^{-x}\left(\frac{1}{4}e^x - \frac{1}{4}e^{-x} - \frac{1}{2}xe^{-x}\right)$

$= \lim_{x\to\infty}\left(\frac{1}{4} - \frac{1}{4}e^{-2x} - \frac{1}{2}xe^{-2x}\right)$

$= \frac{1}{4}$

$\Rightarrow \lim_{x\to\infty} e^{-x}y(x) = \frac{1}{4}$

$\Rightarrow$ Option (c) is the correct.

For Option (d)

$\lim_{x\to\infty} e^xy(x) = \lim_{x\to\infty} e^x\left(\frac{1}{4}e^x - \frac{1}{4}e^{-x} - \frac{1}{2}xe^{-x}\right)$

$= \lim_{x\to\infty}\left(\frac{1}{4}e^x - \frac{1}{4}e^{-x} - \frac{1}{2}xe^{-x}\right)$

$\lim_{x\to\infty} e^xy(x) = \infty$

Option (a) and (c) are the correct answer and option (b) and (d) are incorrect.

7. Explanation (b), c)

Given ODE is

$\frac{d^2y}{dx^2} + (1 + x^2)\frac{dy}{dx} + p(x)y = 0\ \forall x \in R \qquad (1)$

y_1 and y_2 are the linearly independent solution of equation (1) and w is the wronskian of y_1 and y_2

$w(y_1, y_2) \neq 0$

$\left.\begin{array}{l} w(1) = a, w(2) = b \\ w(3) = c \end{array}\right\} (Given)$

Now using able formula

$w(x) = A_1e^{-\left(x+\frac{x^3}{3}\right)}$

$w(x) = A_1e^{-\frac{4}{3}} = a$

$\Rightarrow a = A_1e^{-4/3}$

$w(2) = A_1e^{\frac{-14}{3}} = b \Rightarrow b = A_1e^{-\frac{14}{3}}$

$w(3) = A_1e^{-12} = c \Rightarrow A_1e^{-12}$

$12 > \frac{14}{3} > \frac{4}{3}$

$\Rightarrow e^{12} > e^{\frac{14}{3}} > e^{\frac{4}{3}}$

$\Rightarrow e^{-12} < e^{-\frac{14}{3}} < e^{-\frac{4}{3}}$

For option B

If A_1 are positive than $A_1e^{-12} < A_1e^{-\frac{14}{3}} < A_1e^{-\frac{4}{3}}$

$\Rightarrow c < b < a$

If A_1 are negative then $A_1e^{-12} > A_1e^{-\frac{14}{3}} > A_1e^{-\frac{4}{3}}$

$\Rightarrow c > b > a$

⇒ Option B is the correct

For option C

$\frac{a}{|a|} = \frac{A_1e^{-\frac{4}{3}}}{\left|A_1e^{\frac{4}{3}}\right|} = 1$

$\frac{b}{|b|} = \frac{A_1e^{-\frac{14}{3}}}{\left|A_1e^{-\frac{14}{3}}\right|} = 1$

$\frac{c}{|c|} = \frac{A_1e^{-\frac{4}{3}}}{\left|A_1e^{-\frac{4}{3}}\right|} = 1$

$\frac{a}{|a|} = \frac{b}{|b|} = \frac{c}{|c|}$

Option (c) is the correct.

For option (d)

Exponential function always positive

From option (b)

Option (d) is incorrect

For option (a)

From option (d)

Option (a) is incorrect

⇒ Option (b) and (c) are correct answer and option (a) and (d) are incorrect.

8. Explanation (b), (d)

Given ODE is

$x''(t) + e^{t^2}x(t) = 0$ for $t \in [0, 3\pi]$

$\because e^{t^2}$ is continuous

$\Rightarrow a_m > \frac{k^2\pi^2}{(b-a)^2}$

$\Rightarrow a_m > \frac{k^2\pi^2}{9\pi^2} (\because b = 3\pi, a = 0)$

$\Rightarrow 1 > \frac{k^2}{9}$

$\Rightarrow 1 > \frac{9}{k^2}$

$\Rightarrow k^2 > 9$

$\Rightarrow k \geq 3$

⇒ The cardinality of given set is greater than or equal to 3

⇒ option (b), (d) are correct and (a) and (c) incorrect.

9. Explanation (a), (c), (d)

Given Differential Equation is

$y'' + p(x)y' + q(x)y = r(x)$ (1)

Where $p(x).q(x)$ and $r(x)$ are continuous function on an interval I and particular solution of equation (1) is

$y_p(x) = v_1(x)y_1(x) + v_2(x)y_2(x)$

y_1 and y_2 are LI solution of equation (1)

Now check the option

Option (A)

y_1 and y_2 are LI solution of equation (1)

$\Rightarrow w(y_1, y_2) \neq 0 \; \forall \; x \in I$

⇒ Option (a) is the correct answer

Option (B)

As v_1, v_2 are not solution of the given differential equation

We can't say that v_1 and v_2 are twice differentiable but we have a guaranty that $v_1y_1 + v_2y_2$ is twice differentiable because this is the solution given Differential equation.

From above explanation

Option (a), (c) and (d) are correct answer and option b) is incorrect.

10. Explanation (a), (d)

Given second order non homogeneous Linear Differential equation is

$y_1(x) = 1 + xe^{x^2}$

$y_2(x) = (1 + x)e^{x^2} - 1$

$y_3(x) = 1 + e^{x^2}$

Now check option

For Option (a)

$(c_1 + 1)y_1 + (c_2 - c_1)y_2 - c_2y_3$

$(c_1 + 1)y_1 + (c_2 - c_1)y_2 - c_2y_3$

$c_1y_1 + y_1 + c_2y_2 - c_1y_1 - c_2y_3$..........................(1)

We know that,

Let $y_1, y_2 \ldots\ldots, y_n$ are the solution of second order non homogeneous linear Differential Equation then

$c_1y_1 + c_2y_2 + c_3y_3 + \cdots + c_ny_n \neq 0$ is a solution of second order non homogeneous linear differential equation iff $c_1 + c_2 + c_3 + \ldots + c_n = 1$ (2)

From equation (1)

$c_1 + c_2 + c_1 - c_2 + 1 = 1$

⇒Option (a) is the correct.

For option (b)

Similarly

$c_1(y_1 - y_2) + c_2(y_2 - y_3)$

$c_1 + c_2 - c_1 - c_2 = 0 \neq 1$

From option (a)

Option (b) is incorrect

Option (c)

$c_1(y_1 - y_2) + c_2(y_2 - y_3) + c_3(y_3 - y_1)$

Adding all coefficient

$c_1 - c_1 + c_2 - c_2 + c_3 - c_3 = 0 \neq 1$

Option (c) is incorrect by (a)

For option (d)

$c_1(y_1 - y_3) + c_2(y_3 - y_2) + y_1$

Adding all coefficient

$c_1 - c_1 + c_2 - c_2 + 1 = 1$

⇒Option (d) is correct

⇒ options a) and d) correct and options b) and c) are incorrect

11. Explanation (a), (c)

Given ODE is

$y''(x) + a(x)y(x) = 0 \dots\dots\dots\dots\dots (1)$

For option (A)

Now use the Abel Formula

$w = Ae^{-\int 0dx} = A$

$\Phi_1(x), \Phi_2(x)$ are the solution of equation (1)

and w is the wronskian of Φ_1 and Φ_2

$w(\Phi_1(x), \Phi_2(x) = \begin{vmatrix} \Phi_1(x) & \Phi_2(x) \\ \Phi_1'(x) & \Phi_2'(x) \end{vmatrix}$

$w(\Phi_1(0), \Phi_2(0) = \begin{vmatrix} 1 & 0 \\ 0 & 1 \end{vmatrix} = 1$

$\Rightarrow w(0) = 1$

$\Rightarrow c = 1$

$w(x) = 1 \; \forall \; x$

$\Rightarrow$ Option (a) is the correct.

For Option (B)

From option (A),

option (B) is incorrect

For option (3)

Φ_1 and Φ_2 are the periodic solution of equation (1)

$\Rightarrow \Phi_1(x+T) = \Phi_1(x) \dots\dots\dots (2)$

$\Rightarrow \Phi_2(x+T) = \Phi_2(x) \dots\dots\dots. (3)$

$\Rightarrow \Phi_2'(x+T) = \Phi_2'(x)$

Put $x = 0$ in equation (2) and (3)

$\Phi_1(T) = \Phi_1(0)$

$\Phi_2'(T_2) = \Phi_2'(0)$

$\Phi_1(T) + \Phi_2'(T_2) = \Phi_1(0) + \Phi_2'(0)$

$\Phi_1(0) = 1$ and $\Phi_2'(0) = 1$

$\Phi_1(T) + \Phi_2'(T_2) = 1 + 1 = 2$

Option (3) is incorrect

For option (d)

from option (c), Option (d) is the incorrect answer

$\Rightarrow$option a) and c) is correct answer and option b) and d) incorrect.

12. Explanation (a), (d)

Given ODE

$y''(x) + xy(x) = 0 \; \forall \; x \in (0, \infty) \dots\dots\dots\dots\dots (1)$

And $y_1(x)$ is the non trival solution of equation (1)

And $y''(x) + y(x) = x^2 + 2$ (2)

$y_2(x)$ is the solution of equation (2)

$y''(x) + p(x)y(x) = 0$ Comparing with equation (1)

$\Rightarrow p(x) = x \; \forall \; x \in (0, \infty)$

We know that If $p(x) = x > 0 \; \forall (x \in (0, \infty)$

$y_1(x)$ has infinitely many zero

$\Rightarrow$ Option (a) is the correct.

Consider

$y'' + y = x^2 + 2$

Auxillary equation is

$m^2 + 1 = 0 \Rightarrow m = \pm 1$

$y(x) = c_1 \cos x + c_2 \sin x$

Now find PI

$PI = \frac{1}{D^2+1} x^2 + 2$

$= (1 + D^2)^{-1} x^2 + 2$

$= \left(1 - D^2 + \frac{D^4}{4}\right)(x^2 + 2)$

$= x^2 + 2 - 2$

$PI = x^2$

General solution is

$\Rightarrow y(x) = c_1 \cos x + c_2 \sin x + x^2$

Now use the initial condition $y_2(0) = y_2'(0) = 0$

$\Rightarrow c_1 = 0$

$y_2'(x) = -c_1 \sin x + c_2 \cos x + 2x$

$\Rightarrow c_2 = 0$

$y(x) = x^2$

$y(x)$ has only one zero

$\Rightarrow y_2(x)$ has finitely many zero

$\Rightarrow$ Option (d) is correct.

$\Rightarrow$ Option a) and d) are correct answer and option b) and c) incorrect

13. Explanation: (b), (c)

We have the ODE $y'' + r(x)y = 0$

This is a second-order linear homogeneous ODE.

For an equation $y'' + p(x)y' + q(x)y = 0$, the Wronskian satisfies Abel's identity,

$W(x) = Ce^{-\int p(x)dx}$

Here our equation has no y' term, so $p(x) = 0$

Thus, $W(x) = Ce^{-\int 0dx} = C$

So, the Wronskian is constant on $\mathbb{R}$.

Statement 3 is TRUE

Behaviour of $r(x)$

For large x: $r(x) = x^3 \sin(1/x)$

Use expansion: $\sin(1/x) \approx 1/x$

Thus $r(x) \approx x^2$

So asymptotically the equation behaves like $y'' + x^2 y = 0$

Solutions of such equations are oscillatory, producing infinitely many zeros as $x \to \infty$.

Hence there exists a solution with zeros $x_n \to \infty$.

Statement 2 TRUE.

Statement 1

It claims: There is a solution having infinitely many zeros in a finite interval.

Since $r(x)$ is continuous on $\mathbb{R}$, Sturm theory says: Zeros of nontrivial solutions are isolated.

So, infinitely many zeros cannot accumulate inside a finite interval.

Statement 1 FALSE

Statement 4

It claims: There exists a solution that vanishes at most once on $(0, \infty)$.

But the equation is oscillatory for large x, so every nontrivial solution has infinitely many zeros eventually.

Statement 4 FALSE

Final Answer Correct statements: 2 and 3

Unit 1.4: Questions on Existence and Uniqueness of First Order Initial Value Problems

MCQ (Multiple Choice Questions)

1. Let P be a polynomial of degree N, with $N \geq 2$. Then the initial value problem $u'(t) = P(u(t)), u(0) = 1$ has always
   (a) A unique solution in $\mathbb{R}$
   (b) N number of distinct solution in $\mathbb{R}$
   (c) No solution in any interval containing 0 for some P
   (d) A unique solution in an interval containing 0

[June 2011]

2. Consider the equation
$$\frac{dy}{dx} = (1 + f^2(t))y(t), y(0) = 10 : t \geq 0$$
where f is a bounded continuous function on $[0, \infty)$. Then
   (a) This equation admits a unique solution $y(t)$ and further $\lim_{t\to\infty} y(t)$ exists and is finite
   (b) This equation admits two linearly independent solutions
   (c) This equation admits a bounded solution for which $\lim_{t\to\infty} y(t)$ does not exist
   (d) This equation admits a unique solution $y(t)$ and further $\lim_{t\to\infty} y(t) = \infty$

[Dec 2011]

3. Consider the initial value problem
$$y'(t) - f(t)y(t), y(0) = 1$$
where $f: \mathbb{R} \to \mathbb{R}$ is continuous.
Then this initial value problem has
   (a) Infinitely many solutions for some f
   (b) A unique solution in $\mathbb{R}$
   (c) No solution in R for some f
   (d) A solution in an interval containing 0, but not on $\mathbb{R}$ for some f

[June 2012]

4. Consider the initial value problem (IVP)
$$\frac{dy}{dx} = y^2, y(0) = 1, (x, y) \in \mathbb{R} \times \mathbb{R}$$
Then there exists a unique solution of the IVP on
   (a) $(-\infty, \infty)$
   (b) $(-\infty, 1)$
   (c) $(-2, 2)$
   (d) $(-1, \infty)$

[June 2013]

5. Let $y: \mathbb{R} \to \mathbb{R}$ be differentiable and satisfy the ODE
$$\left.\begin{aligned}\frac{dy}{dx} &= f(y), x \in \mathbb{R}\\ y(0) &= y(1) = 0\end{aligned}\right\}$$
where $y: \mathbb{R} \to \mathbb{R}$ is a Lipschitz continuous function.
Then
   (a) $y(x) = 0$ if and only if $x \in \{0,1\}$
   (b) y is bounded
   (c) y is strictly increasing
   (d) $\frac{dy}{dx}$ is unbounded

[Dec. 2014]

6. The initial value problem $y' = 2\sqrt{y},\ y(0) = a$, has
   (a) A unique solution if $a < 0$
   (b) No solution if $a > 0$
   (c) Infinitely many solutions if $a = 0$
   (d) A unique solution if $a \geq 0$

[June 2015]

7. Let k be a positive integer. Consider the differential equation $\begin{cases}\frac{dy}{dt} = y^{\frac{5k}{5k+2}} & \text{for } t > 0\\ y(0) = 0\end{cases}$
Which of the following statements are true?
   (a) It has a unique solution which is continuously differentiable on $(0, \infty)$
   (b) It has at most two solution which are continuously differentiable on $(0, \infty)$.
   (c) It has infinitely many solutions which are continuously differentiable on $(0, \infty)$.
   (d) It has no continuously differentiable solution on $(0, \infty)$

[Nov 2020]

8. Let $f: \mathbb{R}^2 \to \mathbb{R}$ be continuous and $f(t, x) < 0$ if $tx > 0$, $f(t, x) > 0$ if $tx < 0$. Consider the problem of solving the following: $\dot{x} = f(t, x), x(0) = 0$. Which of the following is true?
   (a) There exists a unique local solution
   (b) There exists a local solution but may not be unique
   (c) There may not exist any solution
   (d) If local solution exists then it is unique

[SEP 2022]

9. Let $f: \mathbb{R}^2 \to \mathbb{R}$ be a locally Lipschitz function. Consider the initial value problem
$\dot{x} = f(t, x), x(t_0) = x_0$
for $(t_0, x_0) \in \mathbb{R}^2$. Suppose that $J(t_0, x_0)$ represents the maximal interval of existence for the initial value problem. Which of the following statements is true?
   (a) $J(t_0, x_0) = \mathbb{R}$
   (b) $J(t_0, x_0)$ is an open set.
   (c) $J(t_0, x_0)$ is a closed set.
   (d) $J(t_0, x_0)$ could be an empty set.

[JUNE 2023]

10. Consider the initial value problem (IVP)
$$\begin{cases} y'(x) = \sqrt{|y(x) + \epsilon|}, x \in \mathbb{R}\\ y(0) = y_0\end{cases}$$
Consider the following statements:
S1: There is an $\epsilon > 0$ such that for all $y_0 \in \mathbb{R}$, the IVP has more than one solution.
S2: There is a $y_0 \in \mathbb{R}$ such that for all $\epsilon > 0$, the IVP has more than one solution.
Then
   (a) both S_1 and S_2 are true
   (b) S_1 is true but S_2 is false
   (c) S_1 is false but S_2 is true
   (d) both S_1 and S_2 are false

[July 2024]

. **Consider the following statements:**
(P) The initial value problem

$$y' = f(y), \text{ where } f(y) = \begin{cases} y\cos\frac{1}{y}, & y \neq 0 \\ 0, & y = 0 \end{cases}$$
$$y(0) = 0$$

has at most one solution.
(Q) If $z(x)$ is the solution of the initial value problem

$$z' = \frac{(1-z^4)^{100}}{1+z^2},$$
$$z(0) = 0,$$

then for each $\alpha \in (0,2)$, there exists $x_\alpha \in \mathbb{R}$ such that $z(x_\alpha) = 1 - \alpha$.
Then which of the following statements is true?
(a) Both (P) and (Q) are true.
(b) (P) is true, (Q) is FALSE.
(c) (P) is FALSE, (Q) is true.
(d) Both (P) and (Q) are FALSE.

[Dec 2025]

Answer Key

1	2	3	4	5	6	7	8	9	10
c	d	b	b	b	c	c	a	b	d
11									
a									

EXPLANATION

1. **Explanation (c)**
Given initial value problem is $u'(t) = p(u(t))$
Here $p(u(t))$ is a polynomial and we know that polynomial function always continuous by existence and uniqueness then of IVP the given problem has unique solution in an interval containing zero
⇒ Only option (d) is correct and other (a), (b), (c) are incorrect.

2. **Explanation (d)**
Given ODE is
$\frac{dy}{dt} = (1 + f^2(t))y(t), \quad y(0) = 1 \quad t \geq 0$
$f(t)$ is any bounded function
$f(t) = c$ (c any positive constant)
$f^2(t) = k \quad (\because c^2 = k)$
$\frac{dy}{dt} = (1+k)y(t)$
$\frac{dy}{y} = (1+k)dt$
$\log y = t + kt + c$
$\log y = (1+k)t + c$
$y = e^{(1+k)t} \quad (\because e^c = c_1)$
$y(0) = 1$ (Given)
$y(0) = c_1 = 1$
$\Rightarrow c_1 = 1$
$y = e^{(1+k)t}$
$\lim_{x\to\infty} y(t) = \infty$
⇒ equation (1) admits unique solution $y(t)$ and further $\lim_{t\to\infty} (t) = \infty$
⇒ Option (d) is the correct answer and option (a), (b), (c) are incorrect.
Alternatively
Let f (t) = 0 then f (t) is continuous and bounded on $[0,\infty)$,
Then $y'(t) = y(t)$
$\Rightarrow \frac{dy}{y} = dt$
Integrating both sides we get, $\Rightarrow y(t) = ce^t$ and using the initial condition $y(0) = 1$
We get $y(t) = e^t$ and for $t \to \infty, y(t) \to \infty$, so using this it discards option (a) as $t \to \infty, y(t) \to \infty$ again option (b), (c) discarded as we get unique solution which is unbounded. Hence option (d) is correct.

3. **Explanation (b)**
Given IVP is
$y'(t) = f(t)y(t)$.........(1)
f is continuous function
To solve this,
apply the separation of variable method.
$\frac{y'(t)}{y(t)} = f(t)$
Integrating
$y(t) = e^{\int f(t)dt} \Rightarrow y(t) = e^{\int f(t)dt}c_1$
$\because f(t)$ is continuous
So take $f(t) = c$
$\Rightarrow y(t) = c_1 e^{\int c\,dt}$
$y(t) = e^{ct}c_1$
$y(0) = 1$ (given)
$\Rightarrow y(0) = c_1 = 1$
$y(t) = e^{ct}$
Now take $c = 1$
$\Rightarrow y(t) = e^t$
Here we got unique solution
⇒ option (b) is correct answer and option (a),(c),(d) are incorrect.

4. **Explanation (b)**
Given ODE is
$\frac{dy}{dx} = f(y), x \in R$
Take $f(y) = 0$
$\Rightarrow \frac{dy}{dx} = 0$
$y = A$ (A is constant)
And $y(0) = y(1) = 0$(Given)
$\Rightarrow y(x) = 0$
$\Rightarrow y$ is bounded
$\Rightarrow y$ is not strictly increasing
⇒ option (b) is the correct answer and option (a), (c), (d) are incorrect.

5. **Explanation (b)**

6. Explanation (c)

Consider the given IVP

$y' = 2\sqrt{y}, y(0) = a$

$\Rightarrow \dfrac{dy}{2\sqrt{y}} = dx$

Integrating both sides, we get $y^{1/2} = x + a$

Then for $a = 0$, the given IVP has infinitely many solutions of the form

$y(x) = \begin{cases}(x-c)^2 & If\ x \geq c \\ 0 & If\ x < c\end{cases}$ Provided $c \geq 0$.

Hence, option (c) is correct.

7. Explanation (c)

$f(x,y) = y^{\frac{5k}{5k+2}}$

Since k is a positive integer we have

$0 < 5k < 5k + 2$

$\Rightarrow 0 < \dfrac{5k}{5k+2} < 1$

$\Rightarrow 0 < \alpha < 1$

Let $\alpha = \frac{5k}{5k+2}$

So $f(x,y) = y^{\alpha}\ ; 0 < \alpha < 1$

Since y^{α} is continuous in the rectangle

R:$|x| \leq a, |y| \leq b$ about the origin.

Thus there exist at least one solution of

$\frac{dy}{dx} = y^{\alpha}$ on $|x| \leq h$ such that $y(0) = 0$

Now

$\left|\frac{f(x_1y_1) - f(x_1y_2)}{y_1 - y_2}\right| = \left|\frac{y_1^{\alpha} - y_2^{\alpha}}{y_1 - y_2}\right|$

Let $y_1 = \epsilon > 0$ and $y_2 = -\epsilon$, then

$\left|\frac{\epsilon^{\alpha} + \epsilon^{\alpha}}{\epsilon + \epsilon}\right| = \left|\frac{2\epsilon^{\alpha}}{2\epsilon}\right| = \frac{1}{\epsilon^{1-\alpha}}$

Since this becomes unbounded as $\epsilon \to 0$, so f does not satisfy the Lipschitz condition.

So we cannot say anything about unique-ness.

Now $\frac{dy}{dx} = y^{\alpha} \Rightarrow y^{-\alpha}dy = dx$

Integrating, we set

$\Rightarrow \dfrac{y^{-\alpha+1}}{1-\alpha} = x + c_1$

$\Rightarrow y^{1-\alpha} = (1-\alpha)(x-c)$

$\Rightarrow y = \{(1-\alpha)(x-c)\}^{\frac{1}{1-\alpha}}$ .... (i)

And $y = 0$ also satisfy the given

Equation with the ivp

So $y = \begin{cases} 0 & ;\ 0 \leq x < c \\ \{(1-\alpha)(x-c)\}^{\frac{1}{1-\alpha}} & ;\ x \geq c\end{cases}$

At $x = c, y$ is continuous

And for different values of c we set different solutions.

Hence we concluded, infinitely many solution continuously differentiable on $(0, \infty)$.

So option (a), (b) and (d) are wrong and option (c) correct.

8. Explanation: (a)

$\frac{dy}{dx} = f(x,y), x(0) = 0$

Given that $f(x,y) > 0$ if $xy < 0$

$f(x,y) < 0$ if $xy > 0$

i.e. $\frac{dx}{dt} > 0$ if $xy < 0$

& $\frac{dx}{dt} < 0$ if $xy > 0$

Case i) Suppose $x > 0$ & $y > 0$

$\Rightarrow xy > 0$

$\Rightarrow \frac{dy}{dx} < 0 \Rightarrow x$ is decreasing

But $x(0) = 0$ which is not possible

Case ii) Suppose $x > 0$ & $y < 0$

$\Rightarrow xy < 0$

$\Rightarrow \frac{dy}{dx} > 0 \Rightarrow x$ is increasing

But $x(0) = 0$ which is not possible

Case iii) suppose $x < 0$ & $y < 0$

$\Rightarrow xy > 0$

$\Rightarrow \frac{dy}{dx} < 0 \Rightarrow x$ is decreasing.

But $x(0) = 0$ which is not possible

Case iv) $x < 0$ & $y > 0$

$\Rightarrow xy < 0$

$\Rightarrow \frac{dy}{dx} > 0 \Rightarrow y$ is increasing

But $y(0) = 0$ which is not possible

∴ From case (i), (ii), (iii) & (iv)

Only $y(x) = 0\ \forall x$ is possible solution

⇒ Unique solution

⇒ Option (a) is correct

9. Explanation: (b) By the statement of existence and uniqueness theorem $J(t_0, x_0)$ is an open set so option (b) is correct.

10. Explanation: (d)

Given : $\epsilon > 0$

$\frac{dy}{dx} = \sqrt{|y+\varepsilon|}$

Take $y_0 = 1$

Let D = $\{(x,y) \in \mathbb{R}^2 | x \in \mathbb{R}, y > 0\}$

$f(x,y) = \sqrt{|y+\varepsilon|}$ → which is continuous

∴ solution exists.

$\left|\frac{\partial f}{\partial y}\right| = \left|\frac{1}{2\sqrt{|y+\varepsilon|}}\right|$ → which is bounded.

∴ By existence and uniqueness theorem, solution is unique.

∴ S_1 is incorrect.

Now, take $y_0 = 0$

$\frac{dy}{dx} = \sqrt{|y+\varepsilon|}$

If $\varepsilon = 1$ and $y(0) = 0$

$\frac{dy}{dx} = \sqrt{|y+\varepsilon|}$ which continuous.

Let D = $\{(x,y) \epsilon \mathbb{R}^2 | x \in \mathbb{R}, y > -1\}$

$\frac{\partial f}{\partial y} = \frac{1}{2\sqrt{|y+1|}}$ which is continuous and bounded.

∴ By uniqueness theorem, It has a unique solution.

Therefore S_2 is incorrect.

Hence option (d) is correct.

11. Explanation: (a)

(P)

$$f(y) = \begin{cases} y\cos\left(\frac{1}{y}\right), & y \neq 0 \\ 0, & y = 0 \end{cases}$$

Since $|\cos(1/y)| \leq 1$, we have

$$|f(y)| = |y\cos(1/y)| \leq |y|.$$

Thus f(y) satisfies a local Lipschitz condition near $y = 0$. Hence by the uniqueness theorem for first-order ODEs, the IVP $y' = f(y)$, $y(0) = 0$has at most one solution. Therefore, (P) is true.

(Q)

$$z' = \frac{(1-z^4)^{100}}{1+z^2}, z(0) = 0$$

Since $(1-z^4)^{100} \geq 0$and $1 + z^2 > 0$, we get

$$z'(x) \geq 0,$$

so z(x)is monotonically increasing.

Equilibrium points occur at $z = \pm 1$, and the solution starting from $z(0) = 0$ remains in $(-1,1)$.

For $\alpha \in (0,2)$, we have $1 - \alpha \in (-1,1)$. Hence there exists $x_\alpha$such that

$$z(x_\alpha) = 1 - \alpha.$$

Thus (Q) is true.

MSQ - Multiple Select Questions

1. The differential equation

$$\frac{dy}{dx} - 60(y^2)^{1/5}; x > 0$$

$y(0) = 0$ has

(a) A unique solution
(b) Two solutions
(c) No solution
(d) Infinite number of solutions

[Dec. 2012]

2. Consider the initial value problem (IVP)

$$\frac{dy}{dx} = xy^{1/3}, y(0) = 0, (x,y) \in \mathbb{R} \times \mathbb{R}$$

Then, which of the following are correct?

(a) The function $f(x,y) = xy^{1/3}$ does notsatisfy a Lipschitz condition withrespect to y in any neighbourhood of $y = 0$
(b) There exists a unique solution for the IVP
(c) There exists no solution for the IVP
(d) There exist more than one solution for the IVP

[June 2013]

3. Let $u(t)$ be a continuously differentiable function taking non-negative values for $t > 0$ satisfying $u'(t) = 3u(t)^{2/3}$ and $u(O) = 0$. Which of the following are possible solutions of the above equation?

(a) $u(t) = 0$
(b) $y(t) = t^3$
(c) $u(t) = \begin{cases} 0 & \text{for } 0 < t < 1 \\ (t-1)^3 & \text{for } t \geq 1 \end{cases}$
(d) $u(t) = \begin{cases} 0 & \text{for } 0 < t < 3 \\ (t-3)^3 & \text{for } t \geq 3 \end{cases}$

[June 2014]

4. For the initial value problem

$$\frac{dy}{dx} = y^2 + \cos^2 x, x > 0$$
$$y(0) = 0$$

The largest interval of existence of the solution predicted by Picard's theorem is:

(a) $[0,1]$ (b) $\left[0,\frac{1}{2}\right]$
(c) $\left[0,\frac{1}{3}\right]$ (d) $\left[0,\frac{1}{4}\right]$

[June 2015]

5. Let $u(t)$ be a continuously differentiable function taking non-negative values for $t > 0$ and satisfying $u'(t) = 4u^{3/4}(t); u(0) = 0$. Then

(a) $u(t) = 0$
(b) $u(t) = t^4$
(c) $u(t) = \begin{cases} 0 & \text{for } 0 < t < 1 \\ (t-1)^4 & \text{for } t \geq 1 \end{cases}$
(d) $u(t) = \begin{cases} 0 & \text{for } 0 < t < 10 \\ (t-10)^4 & \text{for } t \geq 10 \end{cases}$

[Dec 2014]

6. For $\lambda \in \mathbb{R}$, consider the differential equation

$$y'(x) = \lambda \sin(x + y(x)), y(0) = 1,$$

Then this initial value problem has:

(a) No solution in any neighborhood of 0
(b) A solution in $\mathbb{R}$ if$|\lambda| < 1$
(c) A solution in a neighborhood of 0
(d) A solution in $\mathbb{R}$ only if $|\lambda| < 1$

[June 2016]

7. Consider the initial value problem

$y'(t) = f(y(t)), y(0) = a \in \mathbb{R}$, where $f: \mathbb{R} \to \mathbb{R}$ which of the following statements are necessarily true?

(a) There exists a continuous function $f: \mathbb{R} \to \mathbb{R}$ and $a \in \mathbb{R}$ such that above problem does not have a solution in any neighborhood of 0
(b) The problem has unique solution for every $a \in \mathbb{R}$ when f is Lipschitz continuous
(c) When f is twice continuously differentiable, the maximal interval of existence for the above initial value problem is $\mathbb{R}$
(d) The maximal interval of existence for the above problem is $\mathbb{R}$ when f is bounded and continuously differentiable

[Dec. 2016]

8. If the solution to

$$\begin{cases} \frac{du}{dx} = y^2 + x^2, x > 0 \\ y(0) = 2 \end{cases}$$

exists in the interval $[0, L_0)$ and the maximal interval of existence of

$$\begin{cases} \frac{dz}{dx} = z^2, x > 0 \\ z(0) = 1 \end{cases}$$

Is $[0, L_1)$, then which of the following statement are correct?

(a) $L_1 = 1, L_0 > 1$ (b) $L_1 = 1, L_0 \leq 1$
(c) $L_1 = 2, L_0 \leq 1$ (d) $L_1 = 2, L_0 < 1$

[Dec 2017]

9. Let $f: \mathbb{R} \to \mathbb{R}$ be Lipschitz function such that $f(x) = 0$ if and only if $x = \pm n^2$ where $n \in \mathbb{N}$. Consider the initial value problem: $y'(t) = f(y(t)), y(0) = y_0$.
Then which of the following are true?
(a) y is a monotone function for all $y_0 \in \mathbb{R}$
(b) For any $y_0 \in \mathbb{R}$, there exists $M_{y_0} > 0$ such that $|y(t)| \le M_{y_0}$ for all $t \in \mathbb{R}$
(c) There exists $y_0 \in \mathbb{R}$, such that the corresponding solution y is unbounded
(d) $\sup_{t,x \in R} |y(t) - y(s)| = 2n + 1$ if $y_0 \in (n^2, (n+1)^2), n \ge 1$

[June 2019]

10. Let $g: \mathbb{R} \to \mathbb{R}$ be locally Lipschitz and $xg(x) \le 0\ \forall x \in \mathbb{R}$. Then which of the following statements are true for the initial value problem
$$x'(t) = g(x(t)), x(0) = x_0 \in \mathbb{R}$$
(a) There exists a local solution.
(b) For any $x_0 \in \mathbb{R}$, the solution exists on $[0, \infty]$.
(c) There is a finite time blow-up for some x_0
(d) All the solutions are bounded on $[0, \infty]$

[Dec 2019]

11. Consider the two following initial value problems:
(I) $y'(x) = y^{\frac{1}{2}}$,
$y(0) = 0$.
(II) $y'(x) = -y^{\frac{1}{2}}$,
$y(0) = 0$
Which of the following statements are true?
(a) I is uniquely solvable
(b) II is uniquely solvable
(c) I has multiple solutions
(d) II has multiple solutions

[SEP 2022]

12. Consider the problem
$$y' = (1 - y^2)^{10} \cos y, \quad y(0) = 0$$
Let J be the maximal interval of existence and K be the range of the solution of the above problem. Then which of the following statements are true?
(a) $J = \mathbb{R}$ (b) $K = (-1,1)$
(c) $J = (-1,1)$ (d) $K = [-1,1]$

[DEC-2023]

13. Let $f \in C^1(\mathbb{R})$ be bounded. Let us consider the initial-value problem
$$(P) \begin{cases} x(t) = f(x(t)), t > 0, \\ x(0) = 0. \end{cases}$$
Which of the following statements are true?
(a) (P) has solution(s) defined for all $t > 0$.
(b) (P) has a unique solution.
(c) (P) has infinitely many solutions.
(d) The solution(s) of (P) is/are Lipschitz.

[JUNE 2023]

14. Consider the following initial value problem (IVP),
$$\frac{du}{dt} = t^2u^3, \quad u(0) = 0.$$
Which of the following statements are correct?
(a) The function $g(t,u) = t^2u^{\frac{1}{5}}$ does not satisfy the Lipschitz's condition with respect to u in any neighborhood of $u = 0$.
(b) There is no solution for the IVP.
(c) There exists more than one solution for the IVP.
(d) The function $g(t,u) = t^2u^{\frac{1}{5}}$ satisfies the Lipschitz's condition with respect to u in some neighborhood of $u = 0$ and hence there exists a unique solution for the IVP.

[JUNE 2023]

15. Let us consider the following two initial value problems
$$(P) \begin{cases} x'(t) = \sqrt{x(t)}, t > 0 \\ x(0) = 0, \end{cases}$$
And
$$(P) \begin{cases} y'(t) = -\sqrt{y(t)}, t > 0 \\ y(0) = 0, \end{cases}$$
Which of the following statements are true?
(a) (P) has a unique solution in $[0, \infty)$.
(b) (Q) has a unique solution in $[0, \infty)$.
(c) (P) has infinitely many solutions in $[0, \infty)$.
(d) (Q) has infinitely many solutions in $[0, \infty)$.

[JUNE 2023]

16. Consider the following initial value problem
$$y' = y + \frac{1}{2}|sin\,(y^2)|, \quad x > 0, \quad y(0) = -1$$
Which of the following statements are true?
(a) there exists an $\alpha \in (0, \infty)$ such that $\lim_{x \to \alpha^-} |y(x)| = \infty$
(b) $y(x)$ exists on $(0, \infty)$ and it is monotone
(c) $y(x)$ exists on $(0, \infty)$, but not bounded below
(d) $y(x)$ exists on $(0, \infty)$, but not bounded above

[DEC-2023]

17. Consider the initial value problem (IVP)
$$y'(x) = \frac{\sin(y(x))}{1 + y^4(x)}, x \in \mathbb{R},$$
$$y(0) = y_0$$
Then which of the following statements are true?
(a) There is a positive y_0 such that the solution of the IVP is unbounded
(b) There is a negative y_0 such that the solution of the IVP is bounded
(c) For every $y_0 \in \mathbb{R}$, every solution of the IVP is bounded
(d) For every $y_0 \in \mathbb{R}$, there is a solution to the IVP for all $x \in \mathbb{R}$

[JULY 2024]

18. For $b \in \mathbb{R}$, let $y_b = y_b(x)$ be the unique solution of the initial value problem $\frac{dy}{dx} = y^5 + y^4 + y^3 + y^2 + y + 1$, $y(0) = b$ defined on its maximal interval of existence I_b.
Then which of the following statements are true?
(a) There exists an $\alpha \in (0, \infty)$ such that for every $b \in \mathbb{R}$ with $b > \alpha$, the solution y_b is bounded above on I_b
(b) There exists an $\alpha \in (0, \infty)$ such that for every $b \in \mathbb{R}$ with $b > \alpha$, the solution y_b is bounded below on I_b

(c) There exists an $\alpha \in (-\infty, 0)$ such that for every $b \in \mathbb{R}$ with $b < \alpha$, the solution y_b is bounded above on I_b

(d) There exists an $\alpha \in (-\infty, 0)$ such that for every $b \in \mathbb{R}$ with $b < \alpha$, the solution y_b is bounded below on I_b

[Feb. 2025]

19. Let $D = \{(x, y) \in \mathbb{R}^2 : -1 \le a \le 1, -1 \le y \le 1\}$, and $f: D \to \mathbb{R}$ be the function defined by $f(x, y) = 1 + \sqrt{y_+}$, where $y_+ = max\{y, 0\}$. Consider the initial value problem (IVP)
$\frac{dy}{dx} = f(x, y), y(0) = 0.$
Then which of the following statements are true?
(a) f is a Lipschitz continuous function on D
(b) f is NOT a Lipschitz continuous function on D
(c) IVP has at least one solution
(d) IVP has NO solution

[June 2025]

20. Consider the following statements:
(P) The initial value problem
$y' + y = e^{-x^2}, y(0) = 0$
has a Taylor series solution about the point $x = 0$.
(Q) The initial value problem
$y' + y = r(x), y(0) = 0$, where $r(x) = \begin{cases} e^{-\frac{1}{x^2}}, & x \ne 0 \\ 0, & x = 0 \end{cases}$
has a Taylor series solution about the point $x = 0$.
Then which of the following statements are true?
(a) (P) is true. (b) (P) is FALSE.
(c) (Q) is true. (d) (Q) is FALSE.

[Dec 2025]

Answer Key				
1	2	3	4	5
d	a, d	a, b, c, d	b	a, b, c, d
6	7	8	9	10
b, c	b, d	*	a, b, d	a, b, d
11	12	13	14	15
b, c	a, b	a, b, d	a, c	b, c
16	17	18	19	20
b, c	b, c, d	b,c	b,c	a,d

EXPLANATION

1. **Explanation (d)**
Result: The differential equation
$\frac{dy}{dx} = y^\alpha ; y(b) = 0 ; b \in \mathbb{R}$
And $\alpha \in (0,1)$ has infinite number of linearly independent solutions.
In this case $\alpha = \frac{2}{5} \in (0,1)$.
Hence, option (d) is correct.

2. **Explanation (a), (d)**
$\frac{dy}{dx} = xy^{1/2} ; y(0) = 0$
For unique solution
$f(x, y)$ must satisfy lipschitz condition
so $\frac{|f(x, y_1) - f(x, y_2)|}{|y_1 - y_2|} = \frac{|xy_1^{1/3} - xy_2^{1/3}|}{|y_1 - y_2|}$
which is unbounded in any neighborhood of $y = 0$.
Hence, f does not satisfy Lipschitz's condition w.r.t. y in any neighbourhood of $y = 0$, So we can not say anything about the Uniqueness but we can solve the IVP
Solving $\frac{dy}{dx} = xy^{1/3} ; y(0) = 0$
$\Rightarrow \frac{dy}{y^{\frac{1}{3}}} = xdx$, integrating we get $\Rightarrow \frac{y^{2/3}}{2/3} = \frac{x^2}{2} + c$
$y(0) = 0 \Rightarrow c = 0$
$\Rightarrow y(x) = \left(\frac{x^2}{3}\right)^{3/2}$ is a solution.
Also $y(x) = 0$ is a solution of this Differential equation.
Hence, options (a) and (d) are correct.

3. **Explanation (a), (b), (c), (d)**
$u'(t) = 3u(t)^{2/3}$; $u(0) = 0$ -- (1)
By method of separation of variables,
$\Rightarrow \frac{du}{u^{\frac{2}{3}}} = 3dt$ and integrating , we get
$\Rightarrow 3u^{\frac{1}{3}} = 3t + 3c \Rightarrow u(t) = (t + c)^3$
c is arbitrary constant using $u(0) = 0 \Rightarrow c = 0$
$\Rightarrow u(t) = t^3$ is a solution of (1),
$u(t) = 0$ is also solution of (1)
By shifting the curve $u(t) = t^3$ on the x- axis
We know that
$u(t) = \begin{cases} 0 ; & 0 < t < k \\ (t - k)^3; & t \ge k \end{cases}$
Is also a solution of (1) $\forall k \in \mathbb{R}^+$
Hence, option (a), (b), (c) and (d) is correct.

4. **Explanation (b)**
The largest interval of existence of the solution predicted by Picard's theorem is given by $|x - x_0| < h$
Where $h = \min\left\{\frac{b}{M}, a\right\}, |y - y_0| < b$ and $|x - x_0| < a$
here $x_0 = 0, y_0 = 0$ and $M = \sup_R |f(x, y)|$
Here, $f(x, y) = y^2 + \cos^2 x$
$R = \{(x, y) | |x| \le a ; |y| \le b\}$
So, $M = \sup_R\{f(x, y)\} = |y^2 + \cos^2 x| \le |y^2| + |\cos^2 x| = 1 + b^2$
($\because |\cos^2 x| \le 1$)
$$h = \min\left\{\frac{b}{1 + b^2}, a\right\}$$
Let, $h(b) = \frac{b}{1+b^2}$
$$h'(b) = \frac{1 + b^2 - 2b^2}{(1 + b^2)^2}$$
$$h'(b) = 0$$
$\Rightarrow 1 - b^2 = 0 \Rightarrow b = 1, -1$
$$h = \min\left\{\frac{1}{2}, a\right\}$$
Since, we have to maximize h

$\therefore h = \frac{1}{2}$

Hence the largest interval in which, there always exists a solution is $\left[0, \frac{1}{2}\right]$

So, option (b) is correct.

5. **Explanation (a), (b), (c), (d)**

$u'(t) = 4u^{3/4}(t)\,; u(0) = 0 \quad - - - (1)$

By using method of separation of variables,

$\frac{du}{u^{3/4}} = 4dt$

Integrating both sides we get

$=> \frac{u^{-\frac{3}{4}+1}}{-\frac{3}{4}+1} = 4t + 4c$

$=> 4u^{1/4} = 4t + 4c$

$=> u^{\frac{1}{4}} = t + c$

$\Rightarrow u(t) = \ (t + c)^4,$

where c is an arbitrary constant.

Using $u(0) = 0$, we get $c = 0$

$\Rightarrow u(t) = \ t^4$is a solution of (1) so option (b) is correct.

$u(t) = 0$ satisfy (1) and the initial condition. So, a) solution of (1), option (a) is correct.

By shifting the curve

$u(t) = t^4$ on the x-axis we can construct infinitely many solutions such as

$$u(t) = \begin{cases} 0\ ;\ \ 0 < t < d \\ (t-d)^4\ ; t \geq d \end{cases}$$

$\forall\, d \in \mathbb{R}^+$

Now for d = 1, d = 10 respectively option (c), (d) are correct.

Hence, option (a), (b), (c), (d) are correct.

6. **Explanation (b), (c)**

$y'(x) = \lambda Sin\ (x + y)\,, y(0) = 1$

$f(x, y) = \lambda Sin\ (x + y)$

$\frac{\partial f}{\partial y} = \lambda Cos\ (x + y)$

Which is bounded so f is Lipchitz function on whole R.

Then given ODE has a unique solution in nbd of 0.

For $\lambda = 0, y = 1$ is a solution of ODE on R.

Therefore for $|\lambda| < 1$ there is a solution on R. So option (b) and (c) correct.

7. **Explanation (b), (d)**

$y'(t) = f\big(y(t)\big), y(0) = \ a \in \mathbb{R}$, where $f\colon \mathbb{R} \to \mathbb{R}$

(a) From Existence and Uniqueness Theorem if f is continuous then there exists at least one solution in any neighborhood of 0. So, option (a) wrong.

(b) If f is Lipschitz continuous function then by Picard's Theorem we get always unique solution. Hence option (b) is correct.

Now if f is bounded and continuously differentiable in R, then it is Lipschitz Continuous on R, so by Picard's theorem we get the maximal interval of existence is R so option (c) incorrect and option (d) correct.

8. **Explanation (*)**

$$\frac{du}{dx} = y^2 + x^2\,, x > 0$$

Incorrect because meaning of u is not defined.

9. **Explanation (a), (b), (d)**

$f$is a Lipschitz function

$f(x) = 0$ if and only if $x = \pm n^2$

$f$is continuous and bounded

$y' = f(y)$

$\Rightarrow \frac{dy}{dx} = f(y)$

$\left|\frac{dy}{f(y)}\right| = dx$

Now, $f(y) \neq 0 \Rightarrow y \neq \pm n^2$

y is continuous

$\Rightarrow y \in (-n^2, n^2)$

a) If y is not monotonic $\Rightarrow y'(t) = 0$ for some

$\Rightarrow f(y) = 0$

$\Rightarrow y = \pm n^2$

A contradiction

$\Rightarrow y$is monotonic

b) As $y \in (-n^2, n^2) y$ is bounded $\therefore$ for any $y_0 \ldots . My_0 > 0$

that$|y(t)| \leq My_0\ \forall\, t$

c) $y \in (-n^2, n^2) \Rightarrow y$is bounded

d) If $y_0 \in (n^2, (n + 1)^2)$

Now y is monotonic

$\Rightarrow \sup|y(t) - y(s)| = (n + 1)^2 - n^2 = 2n + 1$

10. **Explanation (a), (b), (d)**

$g\colon \mathbb{R} \to \mathbb{R}$

$xg(x) \leq 0 \quad \forall x \in \mathbb{R}.$

Let $g(x) = -x \quad \forall x \in \mathbb{R}$

$x'(t) = g(x(t))$

$\Rightarrow \frac{dx}{dt} = -x \Rightarrow \frac{dx}{x} = -dt$, integrating

$\Rightarrow \log x = -t \quad t(\log c)$

$\Rightarrow x = ce^{-t}$

$\because x(0) = x_0 \Rightarrow c = x_0$

$\Rightarrow \quad x = x_0 e^{-t} \quad \ldots\ldots (*)$

Since for any$x_0 \in \mathbb{R}$ there exist a solution and also given as g is Locally Lipschitz

So the solution $(*)$is local solution.

Since $x = x_0 e^{-t}$ is infinitely continuous.

So option(c) wrong.

And $|x(t)| = |x_0 e^{-t}| \leq |x_0|$, so it is bounded. So option (a), (b) and (d) are correct.

11. **Explanation: (b), (c)**

$\frac{dy}{dx} = y^{\frac{1}{2}}$

$y^{-\frac{1}{2}}$dy = dx

$2y^{\frac{1}{2}} = x + c$

$y(0) = 0 \Rightarrow c = 0$

$\Rightarrow 2y^{\frac{1}{2}} = x$

$\Rightarrow y^{\frac{1}{2}} = \frac{x}{2}$

$\Rightarrow y(x) = \frac{x^2}{4}$

Also, $y(x) \equiv 0$ is a solution.

So I has multiple solutions.

Now, consider,

$\frac{dy}{dx} = -y^{\frac{1}{2}}$

$y^{-\frac{1}{2}}dy = -dx$

$2y^{\frac{1}{2}} = -x + c$

$y(0) = 0 \Rightarrow c = 0$

$\Rightarrow 2y^{\frac{1}{2}} = -x$

$\Rightarrow y^{\frac{1}{2}} = \frac{-x}{2}$

which is NOT possible because square root cannot be negative

12. Explanation: (a), (b)

Consider the ODE

$\frac{dy}{dx} = (1-y^2)^{10}\cos y, y(0) = 0$

Observe that $y(x) \equiv 1, \forall x$ and $y(x) \equiv -1\ \forall x$ are solutions of this DE

Using direction field and existence and uniqueness theorem,

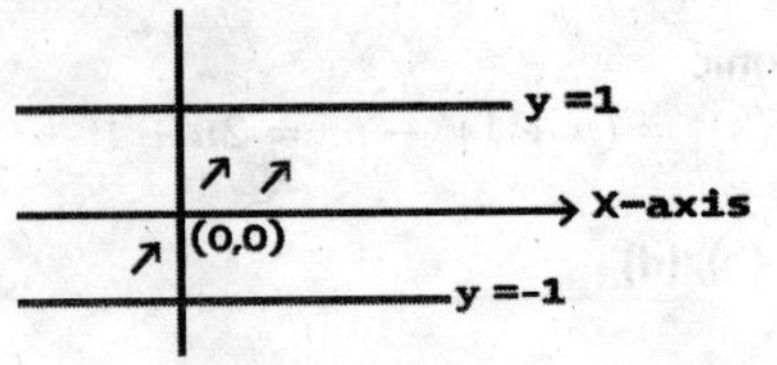

$y(x)$ is bounded and values of $y(x) \in (-1,1)$ and also,

$\frac{\partial f}{\partial y} = -(1-y^2)^{10}\sin y + 10(1-y^2)^9(-2y)\cos y$

is bounded for all $x \in (-\infty,\infty) \times y \in (-1,1)$

$\Rightarrow f(x,y) = (1-y^2)^{10}\cos y$ satisfies

Lipchitz condition on $(-\infty,\infty) \times (-1,1)$

$\therefore y(x)$ is defined on $\mathbb{R}$.

So options (a) & (b) are correct.

13. Explanation: (a), (b), (d)

Consider the given I.V.P

$x'(t) = f(x(t)), t > 0, x(0) = 0$

Given that the function $f \in C^1(\mathbb{R})$

→ By existence and uniqueness theorem, there is unique solution to this IVP in some neighborhood of $x_0 = 0$.

$x'(t) = f(x(t))$ implies $x'(t)$ exists, $\forall t > 0$ and it is continuous also.

So, $x(t)$ is differentiable and its derivative $f(x(t))$ is bounded.

So, $x(t)$ is Lipschitz.

So, options (a), (b) and (d) are correct options.

14. Explanation: (a), (c)

Consider the IVP

Also, $\frac{du}{dt} = t^2u^{\frac{1}{5}}$

$\Rightarrow \int u^{-\frac{1}{5}}du = \int t^2\,dt$

$\frac{5}{4}u^{4/5} = \frac{t^3}{3} + c$

$u(0) = 0 \Rightarrow c = 0$

$\frac{5}{4}u^{4/5} = \frac{t^3}{3}$

$u^{4/5} = \frac{4}{15}t^3$ is also a solution to this IVP.

So, the function $f(t,u) = t^2u^{\frac{1}{5}}$ cannot be Lipschitz.

So, options (a) and (c) are correct.

15. Explanation: (b), (c)

(P) Consider the IVP: $x'(t) = \sqrt{x(t)}$

$x(0) = 0$

we know that the IVP of the form $\frac{dx}{dt} = x^\alpha, x(0) = 0, \alpha \in (0,1)$

always has infinite solutions

$\therefore$ (p) has infinite solutions,

Q. $\frac{dy}{dt} = -y^{\frac{1}{2}}$

$\Rightarrow y^{-\frac{1}{2}}dy = -dt$

Integration use get,

$2y^{\frac{1}{2}} = -t + c$

$\Rightarrow y^{\frac{1}{2}} = \frac{-t}{2} + c_1$

Now $y(0) = 0 \Rightarrow c_1 = 0$

$\Rightarrow y^{\frac{1}{2}} = \frac{-t}{2}, t > 0$

which is not possible.

Also observe that

$y(t) \equiv 0, \forall t$ is also a solution to this IVP.

(Q) has unique solution.

So, option (b) and (c) are correct.

16. Explanation: (b), (c)

$\frac{dy}{dx} = y + \frac{1}{2}|\sin y^2|,\ y(0) = -1$

using existence and uniqueness theorem, and direction field

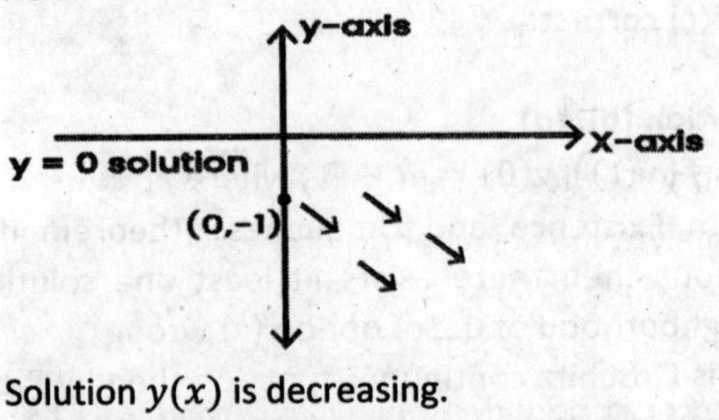

Solution $y(x)$ is decreasing.

$y(x)$ is bounded above by 0 but not bounded below.

So, $y(x)$ exist on $(0,\infty)$

$\therefore$ options (b) & (c) are correct.

17. Explanation: (b), (c), (d)

$y'(x) = \frac{\sin(y(x))}{1+y^4(x)}, x \in \mathbb{R}$

Here

(1) The function $\sin(y(x))$ is bounded with values between -1 and 1.

(2) The denominator $1 + y^4(x)$ is always positive and grows as $y(x)$ increases, making the overall expression for $y'(x)$ relatively small for large values of $y(x)$.

We know that the function $\frac{\sin(y)}{1+y^4}$ is continuous and satisfies the conditions for the existence and uniqueness of solutions for all $x \in \mathbb{R}$ for any initial condition y_0.

For option (a):

There is no initial value y_0 that leads to an unbounded solution because the derivative $y'(x)$ is always small enough to prevent $y(x)$ from becoming unbounded. So, option (a) is incorrect.

For option (b):

The solution for a negative y_0 is also bounded, so option (b) is correct.

For option (c):

Every solution is bounded for all y_0 due to the behavior of $y'(x)$, therefore option (c) is correct.

For option (d):

For every y_0, there is a solution to the IVP for all $x \in \mathbb{R}$ because the IVP has a unique solution globally. So, option (d) is correct.

Hence options (b), (c) and (d) are correct.

18. Explanation: (b), (c)

Given $\frac{dy}{dx} = y^5 + y^4 + y^3 + y^2 + y + 1$ and $y(0) = b$

Note that $y^5 + y^4 + y^3 + y^2 + y + 1 = \frac{y^6-1}{y-1}$ for $y \neq 1$.

• For $y > -1, \frac{dy}{dx} > 0$, so y is increasing.

• For $y < -1, \frac{dy}{dx} < 0$, so y is decreasing.

We analyze the sign of $\frac{dy}{dx}$ to determine the behavior of $y(x)$ for different values of b.

Step 1: Analyze the sign of $\frac{dy}{dx}$

• $\frac{dy}{dx} = y^5 + y^4 + y^3 + y^2 + y + 1.$

• $\frac{dy}{dx} = \frac{y^6-1}{y-1}$ for $y \neq 1.$

• $\frac{dy}{dx} > 0$ if $y > -1.$

• $\frac{dy}{dx} < 0$ if $y < -1.$

Step 2: Analyze the behavior of $y(x)$ for $b > -1$

• If $b > -1$, then $y(0) = b > -1.$

• Since $\frac{dy}{dx} > 0$ for $y > -1$, $y(x)$ is increasing.

• Thus, $y(x)$ is bounded below by b and -1, but not bounded above.

Step 3: Analyze the behavior of $y(x)$ for $b < -1$

• If $b < -1$, then $y(0) = b < -1.$

• Since $\frac{dy}{dx} < 0$ for $y < -1$, $y(x)$ is decreasing.

• Thus, $y(x)$ is bounded above by b and -1, but not bounded below.

Step 4: Determine the correct statements

- Statement (a): False, because for $b > 0$, $y(x)$ is increasing and not bounded above.
- Statement (b): True, because for $b > 0$, $y(x)$ is increasing and bounded below by -1. We can choose $\alpha = 0$.
- Statement (c): True, because for $b < -1$, $y(x)$ is decreasing and bounded above by -1. We can choose $\alpha = -2$.
- Statement (d): False, because for $b < -1$, $y(x)$ is decreasing and not bounded below.

Thus, options (b) and (c) are correct.

19. Explanation: (b), (c)

1. $f(x,y) = 1 + \sqrt{y_+} = 1 + \sqrt{\max(y,0)}$. The derivative with respect to (y) is

$$\frac{\partial f}{\partial y} = \begin{cases} \frac{1}{2\sqrt{y}}, & y > 0[2mm]0, \quad y < 0 \end{cases}$$

At (y=0), the derivative blows up from the right ($\frac{1}{2\sqrt{y}} \to \infty$), so (f) is **not Lipschitz continuous** on (D). Hence (2) true, (1) false.

2. Existence of solution: (f) is continuous on (D), and the IVP is defined at ((0,0)). By **Peano's existence theorem**, the IVP has **at least one solution**. So (3) true, (4) false.

Final answer: **(2) and (3).**

20. Explanation: (a), (d)

(P):

$$e^{-x^2} = \sum_{n=0}^{\infty} \frac{(-x^2)^n}{n!} = \sum_{n=0}^{\infty} \frac{(-1)^n x^{2n}}{n!}$$

$$= 1 - x^2 + \frac{x^4}{2!} - \ldots$$

This series converges for all $x \in \mathbb{R}$ (entire function).

Since $r(x) = e^{-x^2}$ is analytic at $x = 0$, the solution $y(x)$ is also analytic at $x = 0$, and can be written as: $y(x) = \sum_{n=0}^{\infty} a_n x^n$ with coefficients determined recursively from the ODE.

(P) is TRUE.

(Q):

$$\lim_{x \to 0} \frac{e^{-1/x^2}}{x^n} = 0 \text{ for all } n$$

So, all derivatives of $r(x)$ at $x = 0$ are zero:

$r^{(n)}(0) = 0, \forall\, n \geq 0$

The Taylor series of $r(x)$ about $x = 0$ is:

$\sum_{n=0}^{\infty} \frac{r^{(n)}(0)}{n!} x^n = 0$

But $r(x) \neq 0$ for $x \neq 0$, so $r(x)$ is smooth but NOT analytic at $x = 0$.

The Taylor series $\equiv 0$ does not represent $r(x)$, so no Taylor series solution exists for the ODE.

(Q) is FALSE.

Correct answer: Statements 1 and 4

Unit 1.5: Questions Based on Sturm Liouville Boundary Value Problems

MCQ: Multiple Choice Questions

1. For $\lambda \in \mathbb{R}$, consider the boundary value problem

$$\left.\begin{aligned} x^2\frac{d^2y}{dx^2} + 2x\frac{dy}{dx} + \lambda y = 0, \quad x \in [1,2] \\ y(1) = y(2) = 0 \end{aligned}\right\} - (P_\lambda)$$

Which of the following statements is true?

(a) There exists a $\lambda_0 \in \mathbb{R}$ such that (P_λ) has a non-trivial solution for any $\lambda > \lambda_0$

(b) $\{\lambda \in \mathbb{R}: (P_\lambda)$ has a non – trivial solution$\}$ is a dense subset of $\mathbb{R}$

(c) For any continuous function $f:[1,2] \to \mathbb{R}$ with $f(x) \neq 0$ for some $x \in [1,2]$, there exists a solution u of (P_λ) for some $\lambda \in \mathbb{R}$ such that $\int_1^2 fu \neq 0$

(d) There exists a $\lambda \in \mathbb{R}$ such that (P_λ) has two linearly independent solutions

[Dec 2014]

2. The set of real numbers λ for which the boundary value problem $\frac{d^2y}{dx^2} + \lambda y = 0,\ y(0) = 0,\ y(\pi) = 0$ has non-trivial solution is

(a) $(-\infty,\ 0)$

(b) $\{\sqrt{n} | n \text{ is a positive integer}\}$

(c) $\{n^2 | \text{n is a positive integer}\}$

(d) $\mathbb{R}$

[Dec 2017]

3. The positive values of λ for which the equation $y''(x) + \lambda^2 y(x) = 0$ has non-trivial solution satisfying $y(0) = y(\pi)$ and $y'(0) = y'(\pi)$ are

(a) $\lambda = \frac{2n+1}{2}, n = 1,2, \ldots$ (b) $\lambda = 2n, n = 1,2, \ldots$

(c) $\lambda = n,\ n = 1,2, \ldots$ (d) $\lambda = 2n - 1,\ n = 1,2, ..$

[June 2019]

4. Let $(\lambda_n)_{n\in\mathbb{N}}$ be the sequence of eigenvalues of the Sturm-Liouville problem

$$\frac{d}{dx}\left(x\frac{dy}{dx}\right) + \frac{\lambda}{x}y = 0, 1 < x < e^{2\pi}.$$

$y(1) = 0, y(e^{2\pi}) = 0.$

Then $\sum_{n=1}^{\infty}\frac{1}{\lambda_n}$ is equal to

(a) $\frac{\pi^2}{12}$ (b) $\frac{2\pi^2}{3}$

(c) $\frac{\pi^2}{4}$ (d) $\frac{\pi^2}{16}$

[June 2025]

Answer Key

1	2	3	4
c	c	b	b

EXPLANATION

1. **Explanation (c)** Consider the given BVP

$x^2\frac{d^2y}{dx^2} + 2x\frac{dy}{dx} + \lambda y = 0$.....(1)

$y(1) = y(2)$

This is the strum liouville Boundary value problem

We know that the eigenvalue of BVP are always countable and there exist exactly one eigenvector function corresponding to each eigenvalue λ u is a eigen function corresponding to eigenvalue λ

$\Rightarrow \int_1^2 fu \neq 0$ ($\because$ f(x) and u are non zero) from above explanation

Option (c) is correct and (a), (b) and (d) are incorrect.

2. **Explanation (c)** Consider the given BVP

$\frac{d^2y}{dx^2} + \lambda y = 0 \ldots.. (1)$

To solve this, we discuss the three cases

Case (1) if $\lambda = 0$

$\frac{d^2y}{dx^2} = 0$

$y = Ax + B$

$y(0) = 0 \quad y(\pi) = 0$ .....(Given)

$\Rightarrow B = 0$ and $A = 0$

$\Rightarrow y(x) = 0$

We get trivial solution

Case (2) $\lambda > 0, \quad \Rightarrow \lambda = \mu^2, \mu \neq 0$

Equation (1)

$\Rightarrow \quad \frac{d^2y}{dx^2} + \mu^2 y = 0$

Auxiliary equation is

$\Rightarrow m^2 + \mu^2 = 0$

$\Rightarrow m = \pm\, \mu i$

C.F. is

$y(x) = c_1 \cos \mu x + c_2 \sin \mu x$

Now use the given Boundary condition

$y(0) = 0, y(\pi) = 0$

$c_1 = 0$

$y(\pi) = c_2 \sin \mu\pi = 0$

$c_2 \neq 0$

$\sin \mu\pi = 0$

$\mu\pi = n\pi$

$= \mu = n, n \in \mathbb{N}$

$\mu = \sqrt{\lambda}$

$\Rightarrow \lambda = n^2$

$\lambda = \{n^2 | \text{n is positive integer}\}$ has non trival solution

Case 3: $\lambda < 0$, $\quad \Rightarrow \lambda = -\mu^2$

$\frac{d^2y}{dx^2} - \mu^2 y = 0\ m^2 - \mu^2 = 0$

$m = \pm\mu$

$y = c_1 e^{\mu x} + c_2 e^{-\mu x},\ y(0) = 0$

$\Rightarrow c_1 = -c_2$

$y(\pi) = c_1 e^{\mu\pi} + c_1 e^{-\mu\pi} = 0$

$\Rightarrow c_1 e^{\mu\pi} = -c_1 e^{-\mu\pi}$

$c_1 e^{\mu\pi} = c_1 e^{-\mu\pi}$

$e^{\mu\pi} = e^{-\mu\pi}$

This is never possible

$\Rightarrow c_1 = c_2 = 0$

$y(x) = 0$

We get again trivial solution

From above explanation

Only option (c) is correct and option (a), (b) and (d) are incorrect.

3. **Explanation (b)**

Consider the given BVP

$y''(x) + \lambda^2 y(x) = 0$..................(1)

λ is positive

$y(0) = y(\pi)$

$y(0) = y'(\pi)$

Now auxiliary equation of equation (1) is

$m^2 + \lambda^2 = 0$

$\Rightarrow m = \pm\lambda i$

$\rightarrow y(x) = c_1 \cos\lambda x + c_2 \sin\lambda x$

Now use the Boundary condition

$y(0) = c_1$

$y(\pi) = c_1 \cos\lambda\pi + c_2 \sin\lambda\pi$

$= (1 - \cos\lambda\pi)c_1 - c_2 \sin\lambda\pi = 0$..........(2)

Now

$y'(x) = -c_1\lambda \sin\lambda x + c_2\lambda \cos\lambda x$

$y'(0) = c_2\lambda$..................(3)

$\Rightarrow c_2\lambda(1 - cos\lambda\pi) + c_1 - c_2 \sin\lambda\pi = 0$

From equation (2) and (3)

$$\begin{vmatrix} 1 - cos\lambda\pi & -\sin\lambda\pi \\ \lambda\sin\lambda\pi & \lambda(1-\cos\lambda\pi) \end{vmatrix} = 0$$

$(1 - \cos\lambda\pi) + \sin^2\lambda\pi = 0 \quad (\because \lambda > 0)$

$1 + \cos^2\lambda\pi + \sin^2\lambda\pi - 2\,cos\lambda\pi = 0$

$2 - 2\cos\lambda\pi = 0$

$2\cos\lambda\pi = 2$

$\cos\lambda\pi = 1$

$\Rightarrow \cos\lambda\pi = \cos 2n\pi.$

$\lambda\pi = 2n\pi$

$\lambda = 2n, \ \forall n \in \mathbb{N}$

From above explanation

Only option (b) is the correct and a), c) and d) are incorrect.

4. **Explanation: (b)**

Use the change of variable $t = \ln x$ (so $t \in (0, 2\pi)$). Then $xy_x = y_t$ and $(xy_x)_x = \frac{1}{x}y_{tt}$, so the equation becomes $y_{tt} + \lambda y = 0$ with $y(0) = y(2\pi) = 0$. Hence $\lambda_n = (n\pi/(2\pi))^2 = n^2/4$, so

$$\sum_{n=1}^{\infty} \frac{1}{\lambda_n} = 4\sum_{n=1}^{\infty} \frac{1}{n^2} = 4\cdot\frac{\pi^2}{6} = \frac{2\pi^2}{3}$$

MSQ (Multiple Select Questions)

1. For the boundary value problem,

$$y'' + \lambda y = 0$$
$$y(-\pi) = y(\pi)$$
$$y'(-\pi) = y'(\pi)$$

To some eigen value λ, there corresponds

(a) Only one eigen function

(b) Two eigen functions

(c) Two linearly independent eigen functions

(d) Two orthogonal eigen functions

[June 2011]

2. For the boundary value problem

$$y'' + \lambda y = 0; \ y(0) = 0, y(1) = 0$$

There exists an eigen value λ for which there corresponds an eigen function in (0, 1) that

(a) Does not change sign (b) Changes sign

(c) Is positive (d) Is negative

[June 2012]

3. Consider the boundary value problem (BVP)

$$u'' + \lambda u = 0, u(0) = u'(\pi) = 0$$
$$u' \equiv \frac{du}{dx}, u'' \equiv \frac{d^2u}{dx^2}, \lambda \in \mathbb{C}$$

Let K denote a non-negative integer.

Then, which of the following are correct?

(a) There exist eigen value of the BVP and the corresponding eigen functions constitute an orthogonal set.

(b) The eigen values of the BVP are $\left(k + \frac{1}{2}\right)^2$ with the corresponding eigen functions $\left\{\sin\left(k + \frac{1}{2}\right)x\right\}$

(c) The eigen values of the BVP are $(k+1)^2$ with the corresponding eigen functions $\{\sin(k+1)x\}$

(d) There exists no non-real eigen values for the BVP.

[June 2013]

4. Consider the boundary value problem

$$-u''(x) = \pi^2 u(x), x \in (0,1), u(0) = u(1) = 0$$

If u and u' are continuous on [0, 1] then

(a) $\int_0^1 u^3(x)dx = 0$

(b) $u'^2(x) + \pi^2 u^2(x) = u'^2(0)$

(c) $u'^2(x) + \pi^2 u^2(x) = u'^2(1)$

(d) $\int_0^1 u^2(x)dx = \frac{1}{\pi^2}\int_0^1 u'^2(x)dx$

[June 2014]

5. Consider the boundary value problem

$$-u''(x) = \pi^2 u(x); \ x \in (0,1)$$
$$u(0) = u(1) = 0$$

If u and u' are continuous on [0, 1], then

(a) $u'^2(x) + \pi^2 u^2(x) = u'^2(0)$

(b) $\int_0^1 u'^2(x)dx - \pi^2\int_0^1 u^2(x)dx = 0$

(c) $u'^2(x) + \pi^2 u^2(x) = 0$

(d) $\int_0^1 u'^2(x)dx - \pi^2\int_0^1 u^2(x)dx = u'^2(0)$

[Dec 2015]

6. The problem

$$\left.\begin{array}{l} -y'' + (1+x)y = \lambda y, \ x \in (0,1) \\ y(0) = y(1) = 0 \end{array}\right\}$$

Has a non-zero solutions

(a) For all $\lambda < 0$

(b) For all $\lambda \in [0, 1]$

(c) For some $\lambda \in (2, \infty)$

(d) For a countable number of λ's

[June 2016]

7. Consider the Strum-Liouville problem

$y'' + \lambda y = 0, y(0) = 0$ and $y(\pi) = 0$

Which of the following statements are true?

(a) There exists only countably many characteristic value

(b) There exist uncountable many characteristic value

(c) Each characteristic function corresponding to the characteristic value λ has exactly $[\sqrt{\lambda}]-1$ zeros in $(0,\pi)$

(d) Each characteristic function corresponding to the characteristic value λ has exactly $[\sqrt{\lambda}]$ zeros in $(0,\pi)$

[June 2018]

8. Consider the eigen value problem
$y''+\lambda y=0$ for $x\in(-1,1)$
$$y(-1)=y(1)$$
$$y'(-1)=y'(1)$$
Which of the following statements are true?
(a) All eigen values are strictly positive
(b) All eigen values are non-negative
(c) Distinct eigen functions are orthogonal in $L^2[-1,1]$
(d) The sequence of eigen values is bounded above.

[Dec 2018]

9. Consider the Eigen value problem
$((1+x^4)y')'+dy=0,\quad x\in(0,1)$
$y(0)=0,\ y(1)+2y'(1)=0$
Then which of the following statements are true?
(a) All the eigen values are negative
(b) All the eigen values are positive
(c) There exist some negative eigen values & some positive eigen values
(d) There are no eigen values

[Dec 2019]

10. Let y be a solution of
$(1+x^2)y''+(1+4x^2)y=0,\quad x>0$
$y(0)=0$. Then y has
(a) Infinitely many zeros in $[0,1]$
(b) Infinitely many zeros in $[1,\infty)$
(c) At least n zeros in $[0,n\pi],\forall n\in\mathbb{N}$.
(d) At most 3n zeros in $[0,n\pi],\forall n\in\mathbb{N}$.

[Dec 2019]

11. The following two-point boundary value problem
$$\begin{cases} y''(x)+\lambda y(x)=0 \text{ for } x\in(0,\pi)\\ y(0)=0\\ y(\pi)=0\end{cases}$$
Has a trivial solution $y=0$. It has a non-trivial solution for
(a) no values of $\lambda\in\mathbb{R}$ (b) $\lambda=1$
(c) $\lambda=n^2:\forall n\in\mathbb{N},n>1$ (d) $\lambda\le 0$

[Nov 2020]

12. Let u be a positive eigenfunctions with eigenvalue λ for the boundary value problem $\ddot{u}+2\dot{u}+a(t)u=\lambda u,\dot{u}(0)=0=\dot{u}(1)$ where $a:[0,1]\to(1.\infty)$ is a continuous function.
Which of the following statements are possibly true?
(a) $\lambda>0$
(b) $\lambda<0$
(c) $\int_0^1(\dot{u})^2\,dt=2\int_0^1 u\dot{u}dt+\int_0^1(a(t)-\lambda)\,u^2dt$
(d) $\lambda=0$

[Feb 2022]

ANSWER KEY					
1	2	3	4	5	6
c, d	a, b, c, d	a, b, d	b, c, d	a, b	c, d
7	8	9	10	11	12
a, c	a, c	b	b, c, d	b, c	a,c

EXPLANATION

1. **Explanation (c), (d)**
$y''+\lambda y=0$ – – – (i)
$y(-\pi)=y(\pi),y'(-\pi)=y'(\pi)$ – – – (ii)
Case-I: Take $\lambda=0$
$\Rightarrow y''=0$
$\Rightarrow y(x)=c_1+c_2x$
$\Rightarrow y'(x)=c_2$
Since $y(-\pi)=y(\pi),\ y'(-\pi)=y'(\pi)$
$c_1-c_2\pi=c_1+c_2\pi, c_2=-c_2$
$\Rightarrow 2c_2=0$
$\Rightarrow c_2=0$
$\Rightarrow y(x)=c_1$ (arbitrary constant)
$\Rightarrow \lambda=0$ is a eigen value and the corresponding eigenfunction is $y(x)=c_1$
Case-II:
If <0, Take $\lambda=-\mu^2,\mu\neq0$
$\Rightarrow y''-\mu^2y=0$
$\Rightarrow m^2-\mu^2=0$
$\Rightarrow m=\pm\mu$
$\Rightarrow y(x)=c_1e^{\mu x}+c_2e^{-\mu x}$
$\Rightarrow y'(x)=\mu c_1e^{\mu x}-\mu c_2e^{-\mu x}$
Since $y(-\pi)=y(\pi)$
$c_1e^{-\mu\pi}+c_2e^{\mu\pi}=c_1e^{\mu\pi}+c_2e^{-\mu\pi}$
$c_1+c_2e^{2\mu x}+c_1e^{2\mu x}+c_2$
$\Rightarrow c_1(1-e^{2\mu\pi})+c_2(e^{2\mu\pi}-1)=0$ ... (1)
Since $y'(-\pi)=y'(\pi)$
$\mu c_1e^{-\mu\pi}-\mu c_2e^{\mu\pi}=\mu c_1e^{\mu\pi}-\mu c_2e^{-\mu\pi}$
$\Rightarrow c_1-c_2e^{2\mu\pi}=c_1e^{2\mu\pi}-c_2$
$\Rightarrow c_1(1-e^{2\mu\pi})+c_2(1-e^{2\mu\pi})=0$ ... (2)
(1) and (2) represents the following system
$$\begin{bmatrix}1-e^{2\mu\pi} & e^{2\mu\pi}-1\\ 1-e^{2\mu\pi} & 1-e^{2\mu\pi}\end{bmatrix}\begin{bmatrix}c_1\\c_2\end{bmatrix}=\begin{bmatrix}0\\0\end{bmatrix}$$
Since, determinant of coefficient matrix is
$(1-e^{2\mu\pi})^2+(1-e^{2\mu\pi})^2\neq0$
$(\because \mu\neq0)$
$\Rightarrow c_1=c_2=0$
(If $\det(A)\neq0$ in $AX=0$ then $X=0$)
$\Rightarrow y(x)=0$
$\Rightarrow$ There exists no negative eigenvalue.
Case III: If $\lambda>0$ Take $\lambda=\mu^2,\mu\neq0$
$\Rightarrow y''+\mu^2y=0$
$\Rightarrow m^2+\mu^2=0$
$\Rightarrow m=\pm i\mu$
$\Rightarrow y(x)=c_1\cos\mu x+c_2\sin\mu x$
$\Rightarrow y'(x)=-\mu c_1\sin\mu x+\mu c_2\cos\mu x$
Since $y(-\pi)=y(\pi)$
$\Rightarrow c_1\cos\mu\pi-c_2\sin\mu\pi$
$=c_1\cos\mu\pi+c_2\sin\mu\pi$
$\Rightarrow 2c_2\sin\mu\pi=0$

$\Rightarrow c_2 = 0 \text{ or } \sin\mu\pi = 0$
$\Rightarrow \mu\pi = n\pi, n \in \mathbb{Z}\backslash\{0\}$
$\Rightarrow \mu = n, n \in \mathbb{Z}\backslash\{0\}$
$\Rightarrow \lambda = \mu^2 = n^2, n \in \mathbb{N}$
Also, $y'(-\pi) = y'(\pi)$
$\Rightarrow \mu c_1 \sin\mu\pi + \mu c_2 \cos\mu\pi$
$= -\mu c_1 \sin\mu\pi + \mu c_2 \cos\mu\pi$
$\Rightarrow 2\mu c_1 \sin\mu\pi = 0$
$\Rightarrow \mu\pi = n\pi, n \in \mathbb{Z} \Rightarrow \mu = n$
(same again)
$\Rightarrow \lambda = n^2, n \in \mathbb{Z}$
$\Rightarrow y(x) = c_1 \cos nx + c_2 \sin nx, n \in \mathbb{N}$
Take $y(x) = y_n(x), c_1 = A_n, c_2 = B_n$
$\Rightarrow y_n(x) = A_n \cos(nx) + B_n \sin(nx), n \in \mathbb{N}$
Now, linearly independent eigen functions are $\cos(nx), \sin(nx)$ and

$$\int_{-\pi}^{\pi} \cos(nx)\sin(nx)\,dx$$

$$= 2\int_{0}^{\pi} \cos(nx)\sin(nx)\,dx$$

$$= \int_{0}^{\pi} \sin(2nx)\,dx$$

$$= -\left[\frac{\cos(2nx)}{2n}\right]_0^{\pi}$$

$$= -\frac{1}{2n}[0]$$

$= 0$
$\Rightarrow \cos(nx)$ *and* $\sin(nx)$ are orthogonal.
Hence, options (c) and (d) are correct.

2 Explanation (a), (b), (c), (d) Given BVP is
$y'' + \lambda y = 0 \ldots\ldots (1)$
$y(0) = y(1) = 0$
This is the sturm liouville Boundary Value problem to solve this
Discuss the three cases
Case (1)
If $\lambda = 0$
Equation (1)
$\Rightarrow y'' = 0$
$y(x) = Ax + B$
Now use the boundary condition
$y(0) = B = 0$
$y(1) = A = 0$
$y(x) = 0$
This is the trivial solution of equation (1)
Case (2)
If $\lambda < 0 \Rightarrow \lambda = -\mu^2$
Equation (1)
$\Rightarrow y'' - \mu^2 y = 0$
Auxillary equation is
$m^2 - \mu^2 = 0$
$m = \pm\mu$
$C.F.$ is
$y(x) = c_1 e^{\mu x} + c_2 e^{-\mu x}$
$y(0) = (c_1 + c_2) = 0$
$\Rightarrow c_1 = -c_2$
$y(1) = c_1 e^{\mu} + c_2 e^{-\mu} = 0$
$c_1 e^{\mu} - c_1 e^{-\mu} = 0$
$c_1(e^{\mu} - e^{-\mu}) = 0$
$(\because e^{\mu} \neq e^{-\mu})$
$\Rightarrow c_1 = 0$
$\Rightarrow c_2 = 0$
$\Rightarrow y(x) = 0$
is the trivial solution of equation (1)
Case (3): If $\lambda > 0 \Rightarrow \lambda = \mu^2$
$y'' + \mu^2 y = 0$
Auxillary equation is
$m^2 + \mu^2 = 0$
$m = \pm\mu i$
$y(x) = c_1 \cos\mu x + c_2 \sin\mu x$
$y(0) = c_1 = 0$
$y(1) = c_1 \cos\mu + c_2 \sin\mu$
$c_2 \sin\mu = 0$
$\Rightarrow \sin\mu = 0, c_2 \neq 0$
$\mu = n\pi \quad n \in z - \{0\}$
$y = c_2 \sin n\pi x \quad \forall n \in z - \{0\}$
Is the non trivial solution of equation (1)
c_2 is arbitrary so, $y = c_n \sin n\pi x \quad \forall n \in Z$
If $0 < x < 1$
$0 < n\pi x < n\pi$
$y_n = c_n \sin n\pi x \quad \forall n \in z - \{0\}$
We get non trivial solution and when we put $n = 1,2,3,4,$.then we get all option are correct
$\Rightarrow$ option $(a), (b), (c)$ and (d) are correct

3. Explanation (a), (b), (d)
Given BVP is
$u'' + \lambda u = 0$
$u = (0) = u'(\pi) = 0$
This is the strum Liouville Boundary value problem
To solve this, consider the three cases
Case (1):
If $\lambda = 0$
Equation (1) become
$u'' = 0$
$\Rightarrow u(x) = Ax + B$
Given boundary condition
$u(0) = u'(\pi) = 0$
$u(0) = B = 0$
$u'(\pi) = A = 0$
$u(x) = 0$
This is the trivial solution of equation (1)
Case (2) $\lambda < 0$
$\Rightarrow \lambda = -\mu^2$
Equation (1) become
$u'' - \mu^2 u = 0$
Auxillary equation is
$m^2 - \mu^2 = 0$
$m = \pm\mu$
$u(x) = c_1(x) = c_1 e^{-\mu x}$
$u(x) = c_1 e^{\mu x} + c_2 e^{-\mu x}$
$u(0) = u'(\pi) = 0$

$u(0) = c_1 + c_2 = 0$
$c_1 = -c_2$
$u'(x) = \mu c_1 e^{\mu x} - c_2\mu\, e^{-\mu x}$
$u'(\pi) = \mu c_1 e^{\mu\pi} - c_1\mu e^{-\mu\pi} = 0$
$\mu c_1(e^{\mu\pi} + e^{-\mu\pi}) = 0$
$c_1 = 0$
$c_2 = 0$
$y(x) = 0$
We get again trivial solution of equation (1)
Case (3):
$\lambda > 0$
$\Rightarrow \lambda = \mu^2$
Equation (1) become
Auxillary equation is
$m^2 + \mu^2 = 0$
$m = \pm\alpha i$
C.F. is
$u(x) = c_1\cos\mu x + c_2\sin\mu x$
$u(0) = c_1 = 0$
$u'(\pi) = -c_1\sin\mu\pi + c_2\mu\cos\alpha\pi \quad \cos\frac{(2k+1)}{2}\pi$
$\Rightarrow c_2\mu\cos\mu\pi = 0\ , c_2 \neq 0$
$\cos\mu\pi = \cos\frac{(2k+1)}{2}\pi$
$\mu = \frac{2k+1}{2} = k + \frac{1}{2}$
$= \lambda = \mu^2 = \left(k + \frac{1}{2}\right)^2$
$y(x) = \sin\left(k + \frac{1}{2}\right)x$
We know that the eigen functions corresponding to distinct eigen values are orthogonal
Here all eigenvalues are imaginary
Option (a), (b) and (d) are correct and c) is incorrect.

4. **Explanation (b), (c), (d)** Given BVP is
$-u''(x) = \pi^2\mu(x) \qquad x \in (0,1)$
$u(0) = u(1) = 0$
$u''(x) = \pi^2\mu(x) = 0$
auxillary equation is
$m^2 + \pi^2 = 0$
$m = \pm\pi i$
Complementary function is
$u(x) = c_1\cos\pi x + c_2\sin\pi x$
Now using boundary condition,
$\Rightarrow u(0) = c_1 = 0$
$u(1) = c_1\cos\pi + c_2\sin\pi = 0$
$\Rightarrow c_2\sin\pi = 0$
$\Rightarrow \sin\pi = 0 \ (\because c_2 \neq 0)$
$\Rightarrow u(x) = c_2\sin\pi x$
$\Rightarrow u'(x) = \pi c_2\cos\pi x$
Now check the option for option (a)
$\int_0^1 u^3(x)dx = \int_0^1 (c_2)^3\sin^3\pi x$
$= \int_0^1 c_2\frac{(3\sin x - \sin 3x)}{4}dx$
$\frac{c_2}{4}\int_0^1 (3\sin x - \sin 3x)\,dx$
$\frac{c_2}{4}\left[-3\cos x + \cos\frac{3x}{3}\right]_0^1$
$\frac{c_2}{4}\left[\left[-\cos 1 + \frac{\cos 3}{3}\right] - \left[-3 + \frac{1}{3}\right]\right]$

$\int_0^1 u^3(x)dx \neq 0$
Option a) is not correct
For option (b)
$u(x) + \pi^2u^2(x) = (c_2\pi\cos\pi x)^2 + \pi^2c_2^2\sin^2\pi x$
$= c_2^2\pi^2$
$u'^2(x) + \pi^2u^2(x) = u'^2(0)$
Option (b) is correct
For option (c)
$u^2(x) + \pi^2u^2(x) = u'^2(0)$
Option (b) is correct
For option c)
$u^2(x) + \pi^2u^2(x) = (c_2\pi\cos\pi x)^2 + \pi^2c_2^2\sin^2\pi x$
$= c_2\pi^2$
$u'^2(x) + x^2u^2(x) = u'^2(1)$
$(\because u'^2(1) = c_2^2\pi^2 cos^2\pi = c_2\pi^2)$
Option c) is correct.
For option (d)
$\int_0^1 u^2(x)dx = \int_0^1 c_2^2\sin^2\pi x\,dx$
$= c_2^2\int_0^1\frac{1-\cos 2\pi x}{2}dx$
$c_2^2\left[\frac{1}{2}x - \frac{\sin 2\pi x}{4\pi}\right]_0^1$
$\int_0^1 u^2(x)dx = c_2[\frac{1}{2} - 0] = \frac{c_2^2}{2}$
Now $\frac{1}{\pi^2}\int_0^1 u_1^2(x)dx$
$\frac{1}{\pi^2}\int_0^1(c_2\pi cos\pi x)^2dx$
$= c_2^2\int_0^1\left[\frac{1+\cos 2\pi x}{2}\right]dx.$
$= c_2^2\left[\frac{1}{2}x - \frac{\sin 2\pi x}{4\pi}\right] = c^2.\frac{1}{2}$
$\frac{1}{\pi^2}\int_0^1 u'^2(x)dx = \frac{c_2^2}{2}$
$\int_0^1 u^2(x) = \frac{1}{\pi^2}\int_0^1 u'^2(x)dx$
From above explanation
Option (b), (c) and (d) are correct and option a) is incorrect.

5. **Explanation (a), (b)**
Consider the given boundary value problem
$-u''(x) = \pi^2u(x);\ x \in (0,1)$
$u(0) = u(1) = 0$
$u''(x) + \pi^2u(x) = 0$
Auxiliary equation is
$m^2 + \pi^2 = 0$
$m = \pm\pi i$
Complementary function is
$u(x) = c_1\cos\pi x + c_2\sin\pi x$
Now use the boundary condition
$u(0) = c_1 = 0$
$u(1) = \sin\pi = 0, c_2 \neq 0$
$u(x) = c_2\sin\pi x$
Now check the option
For option (a)
$u'^2(x) + \pi^2u^2(x) = (c_2\,\pi\,cos\,\pi x)^2 + \pi^2\ (c_2\sin\pi x)^2$
$= (c_2\pi\cos\pi x)^2 + \pi^2(c_2\sin\pi x)^2$
$u'^2(0) = c_2^2\pi^2(\cos 0) = c_2^2\pi^2$
$u'^2(x) + \pi^2u^2(x) = u'^2(0)$

$\Rightarrow$Option a) is correct.

For option (b)

$\int_0^1 u'^2(x)dx - \pi^2 \int_0^1 u^2(x)dx =$

$\int_0^1 c^2\pi^2 \cos^2 \pi x - \pi^2 \int_0^1 c_2^2 \sin^2 \pi x \, dx =$

$c_2^2\pi^2 \int_0^1 \frac{1+\cos 2\pi x}{2} - \left(\frac{1-\cos 2\pi x}{2}\right) dx$

$= c_2^2\pi^2 \int_0^1 \cos 2\pi x$

$= c_2^2\pi^2 \left[\frac{\sin 2\pi x}{2}\right]_0^1 = 0$

$\Rightarrow \int_0^1 u'^2(x)dx - \pi^2 \int_0^1 u^2(x)dx = 0$

$\Rightarrow$ Option (b) is correct

For option c)

$u'^2(x) + \pi^2 u^2(x) = c_2^2(\pi^2 \cos^2 \pi x + \pi^2 \sin^2 \pi x)$

$= c^2\pi^2$

Option(c) is incorrect

For option (d)

$$\int_0^1 u'^2(x)dx - \pi^2 \int_0^1 u^2(x)dx =$$

$$= \int_0^1 c_2^2\pi^2 \cos^2 \pi x \, dx - \pi^2 \int_0^1 c_2^2 \sin^2 \pi x$$

$$= c^2\pi^2 \int_0^1 \cos^2 \pi x - sin^2\pi x \, dx = c^2\pi^2 \int_0^1 cos2\pi x \, dx$$

$$c^2\pi^2 \left[\frac{\sin 2\pi x}{2}\right]_0^1 = 0$$

And $u'^2(0) = c^2\pi^2$

$$\Rightarrow \int_0^1 u'^2(x)\,dx - \pi^2 \int_0^1 u^2(x)dx \neq u'^2(0)$$

Option d is incorrect.

Only option (a) and (b) are correct and Option (c) and (d) are incorrect.

6. Explanation (c), (d) Consider the given problem

$-y'' + (1+x)y = \lambda y, x \in (0,1)$

$y(0) = y(1) = 0$......equation (1)

$\Rightarrow -y'' + ((1+x) - \lambda)y = 0$

$y'' + (\lambda - 1 - x)y = 0 \ldots\ldots (2)$

$y'' + py = 0$ comparing with equation (2)

$p = \lambda - (1+x)$

Now discuss the three cases

Case 1: If $p = 0$

$\Rightarrow \lambda - (1+x) = 0$

Then, $y'' = 0 \Rightarrow y(x) = Ax + B$

Now apply boundary condition

$= y(0) = B = 0$

$y(1) = A = 0$

$y(x) = 0$

This is trivial solution of equation (1)

Case 2: If $p < 0$

$\Rightarrow \lambda - (1+x) < 0$

Put $\lambda - (1+x) = -t^2$

Equation (2) become

$y^2 - t^2 y = 0$

Auxiliary equation is

$m^2 - t^2 = 0$

$m = \pm t$

$\Rightarrow y(x) = c_1 e^t + c_2 e^{-t}$

$y(0) = c_1 + c_2 = 0$

$c_1 = -c_2$

$y(1) = c_1 e + c_2 e^{-1} = 0$

$c_1(e - e^{-1}) = 0$

$\Rightarrow c_1 = 0 \qquad (\because e \neq e^{-1})$

$\Rightarrow c_1 = c_2 = 0 \Rightarrow y(x) = 0$

Again get trivial solution

Now case 3: $p > 0$

$\lambda - (1+x) > 0$

Put $\lambda - (1+x) = t^2$

Equation (1) become

$\Rightarrow y'' + t^2 y = 0$

Auxiliary equation is

$m^2 + t^2 = 0 \Rightarrow m = \pm ti$

Complementary function is

$y(x) = c_1 \cos tx + c_2 \sin tx$

$y(0) = c_1 = 0$

$y(1) = c_2 \sin t = 0$

$\Rightarrow \sin t = 0, c_2 \neq 0$

$t = n\pi$

$\Rightarrow y(x) = c_2 \sin n\pi x$

$\lambda = n^2\pi^2 \quad \forall n \in \mathbb{N}$

Countable number of $\lambda's$ solution exist

Now $\lambda - (1+x) > 0$ and $x \in (0,1)$

$\lambda > 1 + x$

$\lambda > 2$

$\lambda \in (2, \infty)$

If $\lambda \in (2, \infty)$ then $y(x)$ has non zero solution

From above explanation option (c) and (d) are correct and option (a) and (b) are incorrect.

7. Explanation (a), (c)

Consider the given strum Liouville problem

$y'' + \lambda y = 0,\ y(0) = 0$ and $y(\pi) = 0$

We know that

The eigen value of strum Liouville problem are countable and each eigen function corresponding to the characteristic value

λ_n has

$\sqrt{\lambda} - 1$ zeros in $(0, \pi)$

From above explanation only option (a) and (c) correct and option (b) and (d) incorrect

8. Explanation (a), (c) Consider the given BVP

$y'' + \lambda y = 0$

$y(-1) = y(1)$

$y'(-1) = y'(1)$

Given problem is the periodic boundary value problem.

By the properties of periodic BVP

1) All eigen value are strictly positive

2) Distinct eigen function are orthogonal

From above explanation

Option (a) and (c) are correct and (b) and (d) are incorrect

9. Explanation (b)

$((1+x^4)y')' + dy = 0$

$y(0) = 0, \quad y(1) + 2y'(1) = 0$

It $\lambda = 0$, then

$((1+x^4)y')' = 0$

Integrating, $(1+x^4)\frac{dy}{dx} = c_1$,

where c_1 is a constant.

$\frac{dy}{dx} = \frac{c_1}{(1+x^4)}$ ... (1)

Solving (1) we have

$y(x) = c_1\left[\frac{1}{4\sqrt{2}}\log\left[\frac{x^2+1+\sqrt{2}x}{x^2+1-\sqrt{2}x}\right] + \frac{1}{2\sqrt{2}}tan^{-1}(\sqrt{2}x-1) + tan^{-1}(\sqrt{2}x+1)\right] + c_2$

$y(0) = 0 \quad \Rightarrow 2 = 0$

$y(1) + 2y'(1) = 0 \Rightarrow c_1 = 0$

$\Rightarrow c_1 = c_2 = 0$

Hence, for $\lambda = 0$ the solution becomes trivial.

Now compare the given eq^n with

$\frac{d}{dx}\left[P(x)\frac{dy}{dx}\right] - q(x)y + \lambda r(x)y = 0, \quad a < x < b$

$\alpha_1 y(a) - \alpha_2 y'(a) = 0$

$\beta_1 y(b) + \beta_2 y'(b) = 0$

For the given problem, we have

$p(x) = 1 + x^4$ & $a = 0, b = 1$

$q(x) = 0$ $\quad \alpha_1 = 1, \alpha_2 = 0$

$r(x) = 1$ $\quad \beta_1 = 1, \beta_2 = 2$

Thus, $p(x), q(x) \& r(x)$ are continuous function $\& p(x) > 0 \& r(x) > 0 \forall x \in [a,b]$

$\therefore$ By theorem, $\exists\, \lambda_1 < \lambda_2 < \cdots$

Now, $q(x) = 0 \& \alpha_1, \alpha_2, \beta_1, \beta_2 \geq 0$

Hence, $\lambda_n \geq 0$ for all n

Thus, since $\lambda = 0$ corresponds to trivial solution therefore we have eigenvalues λ_n such that $\lambda_n > 0$ for all n.

Hence, all the eigen values of this S.L problem are positive.

10. Explanation (b), (c), (d)

$(1+x^2)y'' + (1+4x^2)y = 0,$

$x > 0, y(0) = 0$

$y''(0) = 0$

$$y'' + \frac{(1+4x^2)}{(1+x^2)}y = 0$$

$y'' + q(x)y = 0$

$q(x) = \frac{1+4x^2}{1+x^2}y > 0 \quad \forall x > 0$

$\int_1^\infty g(x)dx = \int_1^\infty \frac{1+4x^2 dx}{(1+x^2)}$

$= 4[x]_1^\infty - [tan^{-1}x]_1^\infty = \infty$

By strum- comparison theorem a non-trivial solution has at least one –two between $k\pi, S(k+1)\pi$ or has at least one two in $[0, n\pi] \forall n \in N$

So, option (b) correct and (b) → (a) has at least n- zeros.

(d) $y = \sin 3x$ which non-monotonic solution

$Sin\ 3x = 0, 3x = n\pi, x = \pi n/3$

→ has at most $3n$ zeros in $[0, n\pi]$

11. Explanation (b), (c)

$y''(x) + \lambda y(x) = 0$ ... (1) ; $x \in (0,\pi)$

$\left.\begin{array}{l} y(0) = 0 \\ y(\pi) = 0 \end{array}\right\}$ ... (2)

Case-1: Let for $\lambda = 0$,

$y''(x) = 0 \Rightarrow y(x) = A + Bx$ .... (3)

$y(0) = A + B.0 = 0$

$\Rightarrow 0 = A$

And $y(\pi) = A + B\pi$

$\Rightarrow 0 = 0 + B\pi\ (\because A = 0) \Rightarrow B = 0$

$\therefore y(x) = 0$ trivial solution

So for $\lambda = 0$, we have no eigen values

Case-II

Let for $\lambda < 0$; $\lambda = -\alpha^2$; $\alpha > 0$

So equation (i) becomes,

$y''(x) - \alpha^2 y(x) = 0$

Auxiliary equation is $m^2 - \alpha^2 = 0 \Rightarrow m = \pm\alpha$

$\therefore y(x) = c_1 e^{\alpha x} + c_2 e^{-\alpha x}$ .... (4)

Now $y(0) = 0 \Rightarrow c_1 + c_2 = 0$............. (i)

$y(\pi) = 0 \Rightarrow c_1 e^{2\pi} + c_2 e^{-\alpha\pi} = 0$............ (ii)

Solving (i) and (ii), we get

$c_1 = c_2 = 0$

$\therefore y(x) = 0$ so we get trivial solution for $\lambda < 0$

Hence from case-I and case-II we get $\lambda \leq 0$ is not an eigenvalue i.e. option (d) correct.

Case-III

Let $\lambda > 0$; $\lambda = \alpha^2$; $\alpha > 0$

The given equation becomes, $y'' + \alpha^2 y = 0$

$\Rightarrow m^2 + \alpha^2 = 0 \Rightarrow m = \pm\alpha i$

$\therefore y(x) c_3 \cos\alpha x + c_4 \sin\alpha x$.......... (5)

$y(0) = c_3 \cos 0 + c_4 \sin 0 \Rightarrow 0 = c_3$

$y(x) = c_4 \sin\alpha x$

$\Rightarrow y(\pi) = c_4 \sin\alpha\pi \Rightarrow 0 = c_4 \sin\alpha\pi \Rightarrow \sin\alpha\pi = 0\ (\because c_4 \neq 0)$

$\Rightarrow \sin\alpha\pi = \sin n\pi$; $n \in \mathbb{Z}^+$

$\Rightarrow \alpha\pi = n\pi$; $n \in \mathbb{Z}^+ \Rightarrow \alpha = n$; $n \in \mathbb{Z}^+$

$\therefore \lambda = n^2$; $\forall n \in \mathbb{N}$ and $n > 1$

And for $n = 1, \lambda = 1$ so option (b) and (c) are correct and option (a) wrong.

System of differential equation.

12. Explanation: (a) $\lambda > 0$

(c) $\int_0^1 (\dot{u})^2\, dt = 2\int_0^1 u\,\dot{u}dt + \int_0^1 (a(t) - \lambda)\, u^2 dt$

Unit 1.6: Methods of Solving First Order System of Ordinary Differential Equations

MCQ - Multiple Choice Questions

1. Let $y(t) = \begin{pmatrix} y_1(t) \\ y_2(t) \end{pmatrix}$ satisfy $\frac{dy}{dt} = Ay\,; t > 0$
$y(0) = \begin{pmatrix} 0 \\ 1 \end{pmatrix}$ where A is a 2×2 constant matrix with real entries satisfying trace $A = 0$ and $det\, A > 0$. Then $y_1(t)$ and $y_2(t)$ both are
(a) Monotonically decreasing functions of t
(b) Monotonically increasing functions of t
(c) Oscillating function of t
(d) Constant function of t

[Dec. 2012]

2. Consider the initial value problem in $\mathbb{R}^2$,
$$Y' = AY + BY\,; Y(0) = Y_0$$
where $A = \begin{bmatrix} 1 & 0 \\ -1 & 1 \end{bmatrix}, B = \begin{bmatrix} 1 & -1 \\ 0 & 1 \end{bmatrix}$. Then $Y(t)$ is given by
(a) $e^{tA}e^{tB}Y_0$ (b) $e^{tB}e^{tA}Y_0$
(c) $e^{t(A+B)}Y_0$ (d) $e^{-t(A+B)}Y_0$

[June 2014]

3. Consider the system of ODE in $\mathbb{R}^2$.
$$\frac{dY}{dt} = AY, \quad Y(0) = \begin{pmatrix} 0 \\ 1 \end{pmatrix}, t > 0$$
where $A = \begin{bmatrix} -1 & 1 \\ 0 & -1 \end{bmatrix}$ *and* $Y(t) = \begin{pmatrix} y_1(t) \\ y_2(t) \end{pmatrix}$. Then
(a) $y(t)$ and $y_2(t)$ are monotonically increasing for $t > 0$
(b) $y(t)$ and $y_2(t)$ are monotonically increasing for $t > 1$
(c) $y(t)$ and $y_2(t)$ are monotonically decreasing for $t > 0$
(d) $y(t)$ and $y_2(t)$ are monotonically decreasing for $t > 1$

[June 2015]

4. Let $A = \begin{bmatrix} -2 & 1 & 0 \\ 0 & -2 & 1 \\ 0 & 0 & -2 \end{bmatrix}, x(t) = \begin{bmatrix} x_1(t) \\ x_2(t) \\ x_3(t) \end{bmatrix}$ and $|x(t)| = (x_1^2(t) + x_2^2(t) + x_3^2(t))^{1/2}$. Then any solution of the first order system of the ordinary differential equation $\left.\begin{matrix} x'(t) = Ax(t) \\ x(0) = x_0 \end{matrix}\right\}$ satisfies
(a) $\lim\limits_{t\to\infty}|x(t)| = 0$ (b) $\lim\limits_{t\to\infty}|x(t)| = \infty$
(c) $\lim\limits_{t\to\infty}|x(t)| = 2$ (d) $\lim\limits_{t\to\infty}|x(t)| = 12$

[June 2016]

5. Let $(x(t), y(t))$ satisfy the system of ODE
$$\frac{dx}{dt} = -x + ty$$
$$\frac{dy}{dt} = tx - y$$
If $(x_1(t), y_1(t))$ and $(x_2(t), y_2(t))$ are two solution and $\Phi(t) = x_1(t)y_2(t) - x_2(t)y_1(t)$ then $\frac{d\Phi}{dt}$ is equal to
(a) -2Φ (b) 2Φ
(c) $-\Phi$ (d) Φ

[Dec. 2016]

6. The critical point (0,0) for the system
$$x'(t) = x - 2y + y^2 \sin x$$
$$y'(t) = 2x - 2y - 3y\cos(y^2)$$ is a
(a) Stable spiral point (b) Unstable spiral point
(c) Saddle point (d) Stable node

[Dec. 2018]

7. For the following system of ordinary differential equations
$$\frac{dx}{dt} = x(3 - 2x - 2y)$$
$$\frac{dy}{dt} = y(2 - 2x - y)$$
The critical point $(0, 2)$ is
(a) A Stable spiral (b) An unstable spiral
(c) A stable node (d) An unstable node

[Dec 2019]

8. Consider the system of ordinary differential equation
$$\frac{dx}{dt} = 4x^3y^2 - x^5y^4$$
$$\frac{dy}{dt} = x^4y^5 + 2x^2y^3$$
Then for this system there exists
(a) A closed path in $\{(x, y) \in R^2 | x^2 + y^2 \le 5\}$
(b) A closed path in $\{(x, y) \in R^2 | 5 < x^2 + y^2 \le 10\}$
(c) A closed path in $\{(x, y) \in R^2 | x^2 + y^2 > 10\}$
(d) No closed path in R^2

[Dec 2019]

9. The critical point $(0, 1)$ of the system of equations
$$x'(t) = x^2 + y^2 - 2x$$
$$y'(t) = 3x^2 - x + 3y$$ is a
(a) Stable point (b) Source point
(c) Saddle point (d) Spiral stable point

[Dec 2019]

10. Let $y_0 > 0, z_0 > 0$ and $\alpha > 1$.
Consider the following two differential equations:
$$(*)\begin{cases} \dfrac{dy}{dx} = y^\alpha \; for\; t > 0 \\ y(0) = y_0 \end{cases}$$
$$(**)\begin{cases} \dfrac{dz}{dt} = -z^\alpha \; for\; t > 0 \\ z(0) = z_0 \end{cases}$$
We say that the solution to a differential equation exists globally if it exists for all $t > 0$. Which of the following statements are true?
(a) Both $(*)$ and $(**)$ have global solution.
(b) None of $(*)$ and $(**)$ have global solution.
(c) There exists a global solution for $(*)$ and there exists a $T < \infty$ such that $\lim\limits_{t\to T}|z(t)| = +\infty$
(d) There exists a global solution for $(**)$ and there exists a $T < \infty$ such that $\lim\limits_{t\to T}|y(t)| = +\infty$

[Nov 2020]

11. For $\lambda \in \mathbb{R}$, consider the system of differential equations

$$x_1' = x_1 + 2x_2 + 2x_3$$
$$x_2' = 2x_2 + x_3$$
$$x_3' = -x_1 + 2x_2 + \lambda x_3. \text{ If } \vec{x}(t) = \vec{\alpha} t e^{2t}$$

(for some $\vec{\alpha}$) is a solution of the system then the value of λ is

(a) 2 (b) 4
(c) 6 (d) 1

[Nov 2020]

12. Consider the linear system $y' = Ay + h$, where $A = \begin{pmatrix} 1 & 1 \\ 4 & -2 \end{pmatrix}$ and $h = \begin{pmatrix} 3t+1 \\ 2t+5 \end{pmatrix}$

Suppose $y(t)$ is a solution such that

$$\lim_{t\to\infty} \frac{y(t)}{t} = d \in \mathbb{R}^2$$

What is the value of d?

(a) $\begin{pmatrix} -\frac{4}{3} \\ -\frac{5}{3} \end{pmatrix}$ (b) $\begin{pmatrix} \frac{4}{3} \\ \frac{5}{3} \end{pmatrix}$

(c) $\begin{pmatrix} \frac{2}{3} \\ -\frac{5}{3} \end{pmatrix}$ (d) $\begin{pmatrix} -\frac{2}{3} \\ -\frac{5}{3} \end{pmatrix}$

[SEP 2022]

13. Suppose $x(t)$ is the solution of the following initial value problem in $\mathbb{R}^2$

$\dot{x} = Ax, x(0) = x_0$ where $A = \begin{bmatrix} 5 & 4 \\ 1 & 2 \end{bmatrix}$

Which of the following statements is true?

(a) $x(t)$ is a bounded solution for some $x_0 \neq 0$.
(b) $e^{-6t}|x(t)| \to 0$ as $t \to \infty$, for all $x_0 \neq 0$.
(c) $e^{-t}|x(t)| \to \infty$ as $t \to \infty$, for all $x_0 \neq 0$.
(d) $e^{-10t}|x(t)| \to 0$ as $t \to \infty$, for all $x_0 \neq 0$.

[JUNE 2023]

Answer Key									
1	2	3	4	5	6	7	8	9	10
c	c	d	a	a	c	c	d	c	d
11	12	13							
*	a	d							

EXPLANATION

1. **Explanation (c)**

Given $\frac{dy}{dt} = Ay$, $t >= 0$

Now $y(0) = \begin{pmatrix} 0 \\ 1 \end{pmatrix}$

Characteristic equation of 2 × 2 matrix (A) is

$\lambda^2 - (trace\ A) + \det(A) = 0$

$\lambda^2 + det(A) = 0$ {$\because$ trace $A = 0$}

$\lambda^2 = -\det(A)${$\because \det(A) > 0$}

$\lambda^2 = \pm ci$, $(\det(A) = c,$ cis any number)

λ_1, λ_2 are purely imaginary

$\Rightarrow y_1$ and y_2 are oscillating function of t

From above explanation

Option (c) is the correct answer and option (a), (b) and (d) are incorrect.

2. **Explanation (c)**

Given IVP is

$Y'(t) = AY + BY$

$Y'(t) = (A + B)Y$

To solve this,

By method of separation of variable

$\frac{Y'(t)}{Y(t)} = (A + B)$

$\log Y(t) = (A + B)t + C_1$

$Y(t) = e^{(A+B)t}c$

$Y(0) = Y_0$ (given)

$Y(0) = ce^0$

$y(0) = Y_0$

$\Rightarrow Y(t) = Y_0$

$\Rightarrow Y(t) = Y_0 e^{(A+B)t}$

From above equation

$\Rightarrow$ Option (c) is the correct and option a) ,b),c) are incorrect.

3. **Explanation (d)**

Given system of ODE is

$\frac{dY}{dt} = AY$ $Y(0) = \begin{pmatrix} 0 \\ 1 \end{pmatrix}$ $t > 0$ ……. (1)

$A = \begin{bmatrix} -1 & 1 \\ 0 & -1 \end{bmatrix}$

$\frac{dY}{dt} = \begin{bmatrix} -1 & 1 \\ 0 & -1 \end{bmatrix} \begin{bmatrix} Y_1 \\ Y_2 \end{bmatrix}$

$Y_1' = -Y_1 + Y_2$………….(2)

$Y_2' = -Y_2$ … …. . (3)

From equation (3)

$\frac{Y_2'}{-Y_2} = dt$

$\log Y_2 = -t + c_1$

$Y_2 = e^{-t}c \because e^{c_1} = c$

$Y_2(0) = 1$………. (given)

$Y_2 = e^{-t}$

$Y_1' + Y_1 = e^{-t}$

This is the linear Differential Equation

$Y_1 e^t = \int 1\, dt + c$

$Y_1 e^t = t + c$

$Y_1 = +e^{-t}ce^{-t}$

$Y_1(0) = 0$

$\Rightarrow Y_1 = te^{-t}$

Now $Y_1 = te^{-t}$

$Y_1' = -te + e^{-t}(1 - t)$

Case 1 $Y_1' > 0$ if $t < 1$

Case 2 $Y_1' < 0$ if $t > 1$

$\Rightarrow Y_1$ is decreasing if $t > 1$

$Y_2 = e^{-t}$

$Y_2' = -e^t$

$Y_2' < 0$ if $t > 1$

$\Rightarrow Y_2$ is decreasing

$\Rightarrow Y_1(t)$ and $Y_2(t)$ are monotonically decreasing for $t > 1$

From above explanation

Only Option (d) is the correct answer and option (a), (b) and (c) are incorrect

4. **Explanation (a)**

Consider

$$A = \begin{bmatrix} -2 & 1 & 0 \\ 0 & -2 & 1 \\ 0 & 0 & -2 \end{bmatrix} x(t) = \begin{bmatrix} x_1(t) \\ x_2(t) \\ x_3(t) \end{bmatrix}$$

And $|x(t) = [x_1^2(t) + x_2^2(t) + x_3^2(t)]^{1/2}$

Now

$x'(t) = Ax(t)$

$$x'(t) = \begin{bmatrix} -2 & 1 & 0 \\ 0 & -2 & 1 \\ 0 & 0 & -2 \end{bmatrix}\begin{bmatrix} x_1(t) \\ x_2(t) \\ x_3(t) \end{bmatrix}$$

$$\begin{bmatrix} x_1'(t) \\ x_2'(t) \\ x_3'(t) \end{bmatrix} = \begin{bmatrix} -2 & 1 & 0 \\ 0 & -2 & 1 \\ 0 & 0 & -2 \end{bmatrix}\begin{bmatrix} x_1(t) \\ x_2(t) \\ x_3(t) \end{bmatrix}$$

$x_1'(t) = -2x_1 + x_2$

$x_2' = -2x_2 + x_3$

$x_3' = -2x_3$

$\frac{x_3'}{x_3} = -2dt$

$\log x_3 = -2t + c_1$

$x_3 = e^{-2t}c \qquad (e^{c_1} = c)$

And $x_3(0) = x_0 \qquad (\because x(0) = x_0)$

$\Rightarrow c = x_0$

$x_3 = e^{-2t}x_0$

$x_2' = -2x_2 + x_3$

$x_2' + 2x_2 = x_3$

$x_2' + 2x_2 = e^{-2t}x_0$

$x_2e^{2t} = x_0t + c_3$

$x_2 = te^{-2t}x_0 + c_3e^{-2t}$

$x_2(0) = x_0$

$\Rightarrow x_2 = te^{-2t}x_0 + x_0e^{-2t}$

$x_2 = x_0e^{-2t}(1+t)$

Now

$x_1'(t) = -2x_1 + x_2$

$x_1'(t) = -2x_1 + x_0e^{-2t}(1+t)$

$x_1'(t) + 2x_1 = x_0e^{-2t}(1+t)$

$x_1e^{2t} = x_0\left(t + \frac{t^2}{2}\right) + c_2$

$x_0 = c_2$

$x_1 = x_0e^{-2t}\left(1 + t + \frac{t^2}{2}\right)$

now

$|x(t)| = \left(x_1^2(t) + x_2^2(t) + x_3^2(t)\right)^{\frac{1}{2}}$

$= |x_0^2e^{-4t}\left(1 + 1 + \frac{t^2}{2}\right)^2 + x_0^2e^{-4t}(1+t)^2 + x_0^2e^{-4t}|$

$|x(t)| = x_0^2e^{-4t}\left(\left(1 + 1 + \frac{t^2}{2}\right)^2 + (1+t)^2 + 1\right)$

$$\lim_{t\to\infty} |(x(t)| = \lim_{t\to\infty} x_0^2e^{-4t}\left(\left(1 + 1 + \frac{t^2}{2}\right)^2 + (1+t)^2 + 1\right)$$

$\lim_{t\to\infty} |(x(t)| = 0$

$\Rightarrow$option (a) is correct from option (a) option (b) , (c) and (d) are wrong.

5. **Explanation (a)**

Consider $\frac{dx}{dt} = -x + ty \Rightarrow x' = -x + ty$ ....(1)

$\frac{dy}{dt} = tx - y \Rightarrow y' = tx - y$ ....(2)

and $\varphi(t) = x_1(t)y_2(t) - x_2(t)y_1(t)$

$\Rightarrow \varphi'(t) = x_1(t)y_2'(t) + y_2(t)x_1'(t) - x_2'(t)y_1(t) - y_1'(t)x_2(t)$

from equation (1) and (2)

$\varphi'(t) = x_1(t)(tx_2 - y_2) + y_2(t)(-x_1 + ty_1) - y_1(t)(-x_2' + ty_2) - x_2(t)(tx_1 - y_1)$

$\varphi'(t) = -2\left(x_1(t)y_2(t) - 2x_2(t)y_1(t)\right)$

$= -2\varphi(t)$

$\Rightarrow$option (a) is correct and from above all the three option (b), (c) and (d) are incorrect.

6. **Explanation (c)**

Consider given system of equation

$x'(t) = f = x - 2y + y^2 \sin x$

$y'(t) = g = 2x - 2 = 3y\cos(y^2)$

now

$\frac{\partial(fg)}{\partial(x,y)} = \begin{vmatrix} fx & fy \\ gx & gy \end{vmatrix}$

$\frac{\partial(fg)}{\partial(x,y)} =$

now check at (0,0)

$A = \begin{vmatrix} 1 & -2 \\ 2 & -5 \end{vmatrix}$

characteristic equation is

$C(A) = \lambda^2 + 4\lambda - 1 = 0$

$\lambda = \frac{-4 \pm \sqrt{(16+4)}}{2}$

$\lambda = \frac{-4 \pm 2\sqrt{5}}{2}, -2 \pm \sqrt{5}$

$\lambda = -2 + \sqrt{5}, -2 - \sqrt{5}$

One eigen value is negative and one eigen value is positive

$\Rightarrow$ (0,0) is saddle point.

7. **Explanation (c)**

$\frac{dx}{dt} = x(3 - 2x - 2y) = 3x - 2x^2 - 2xy = f(x,y)$

$\frac{dy}{dt} = y(2 - 2x - y) = 2y - 2xy - y^2 = g(x,y)$

The Jacobian matrix of this system

$$J = \begin{bmatrix} f_x(x,y) & f_y(x,y) \\ g_x(x,y) & g_y(x,y) \end{bmatrix}$$

Then find eigen value of J at (a,b) gives behavior of critical points & for critical point

$f_x = 0, \qquad f_y = 0$

$g_x = 0, \qquad g_y = 0$

Here we have given (0, 2)

$f(x,y) = 3x - 2x^2 - 2xy$

$f_x(x,y) = 3 - 4x - 2y$

$f_y(x,y) = -2x$

$g(x,y) = 2y - 2xy - y^2$

$g_x(x,y) = -2y$

$g_y(x,y) = 2 - 2x - 2y$

$$J(0,2) = \begin{bmatrix} 3 - 4x - 2y & -2x \\ -2y & 2 - 2x - 2y \end{bmatrix}_{(0,2)}$$

$$J(0,2) = \begin{bmatrix} -1 & 0 \\ -4 & -2 \end{bmatrix}$$

Eigen value of $J(0,2) = -1, -2$

$\lambda_1 = -1, \lambda_2 = -2, \lambda_1, \lambda_2 < 0$

$\Rightarrow (0,2)$ Stable Node

8. Explanation (d)

System of ordinary differential equation

$$\frac{dx}{dt} = 4x^3y^2 - x^5y^4 = f(x,y)$$

$$\frac{dy}{dt} = x^4y^5 + 2x^2y^3 = g(x,y)$$

$x' = f(x,y), y' = g(x,y)$

$$\frac{\partial f}{\partial x} = 12x^2y^2 - 5x^4y^4$$

$g(x,y) = x^4y^5 + 2x^2y^3$

$$\frac{\partial g}{\partial y} = 5x^4y^4 + 6x^2y^2$$

Now, $\frac{\partial f}{\partial x} + \frac{\partial g}{\partial y} = 18x^2y^2 \neq 0$

Has same sign in whole R^2

By Bendixson's criteria

System of ordinary diff ^{n}Eq^n has NO trajectory or closed path in R^2.

9. Explanation (c)

$x'(t) = x^2 + y^2 - 2x = f(x,y)$;

$f_x = 2x - 2, \quad g_x = 6x - 1$

$y'(t) = 3x^2 - x + 3y = g(x,y) \quad f_y = 2y \; g_y = 3$

$$J(0,0) = \begin{bmatrix} f_x(0,0) & f_y(1,0) \\ g_x(0,0) & g_y(0,0) \end{bmatrix} = \begin{bmatrix} -2 & 0 \\ -1 & 3 \end{bmatrix}$$

Now eigen values $J(0,0)$ are -2 and 3 as $-2 < 0$ and $3 > 0$

So the critical point is a saddle point.

10. Explanation (d)

Given $\alpha > 1; y_0 > 0$ and $z_0 > 0$

Let $\alpha = 2, y_0 = 1 = z_0$

Then $(*)$ becomes; $\frac{dy}{dt} = y^2 \quad ; for\ t > 0$, $y(0) = 1$

Then $\frac{dy}{y^2} = dt$

Integrating, we get

$$\Rightarrow \frac{y^{-2+1}}{-2+1} = t + c$$

$$\Rightarrow y^{-1} = -(t+c) \Rightarrow y = \frac{-1}{t+c}$$

Now $y(0) = 1; \Rightarrow 1 = \frac{-1}{c}$

$\Rightarrow c = -1$

$$\therefore y = \frac{-1}{t-1} = \frac{1}{1-t}$$

$$i.e. y(t) = \frac{1}{1-t}$$

$\lim_{t\to 1}|y(t)| = +\infty$ i.e. not

Defined so $(*)$ has not

Global solution. Hence option (a) not correct.

Now from $(*)(*)$; $\frac{dz}{dt} = -z^2$

$z(0) = 1$

$$\frac{dz}{dt} = -z^2 \Rightarrow \frac{dz}{z^2} = -dt$$

Integrating, we get

$$\Rightarrow \frac{z^{-2+1}}{-2+1} = -t + c \Rightarrow \frac{1}{z} = -c + t$$

$$\Rightarrow z = \frac{1}{t-c}$$

$z(0) = 1$

$$\Rightarrow 1 = \frac{1}{0-c} \Rightarrow -c = 1$$

$\Rightarrow c = -1$

$$\therefore z(t) = \frac{1}{t+1}$$

Since $t > 0$; $\lim_{t\to T}|z(t)|$ is finite value for any $T < \infty$.

So we get $(**)$ has a global solution.

Hence option (b) and (c) are incorrect.

As $z(t)$ has global solution and $\lim_{t\to T}|z(t)|$ is finite.

Hence option (d) correct.

11. Explanation (*)

Since the solution of the system is of the form $x(t) = ce^{\lambda t}\vec{\beta} \to \vec{\beta}$ is any vector and λ is the eigenvalue of the coefficient matrix of the system.

Given $\vec{x}(t) = \vec{\alpha}\, te^{2t}$ is a solution of the system, so $\lambda = 2$ must be an eigen value of the coefficient matrix, so for this we go through all the options to obtain 2 as eigen value of A.

$$A = \begin{bmatrix} 1 & 2 & 2 \\ 0 & 2 & 1 \\ 0 & 2 & \lambda - 1 \end{bmatrix}$$

(a) If $\lambda = 2$

$$\Rightarrow A = \begin{bmatrix} 1 & 2 & 2 \\ 0 & 2 & 1 \\ 0 & 2 & 1 \end{bmatrix}$$

Since $R_2 = R_3 \Rightarrow 0$ is an eigen value of A and clearly 1 is an eigen value of A (as$|A - I| = 0$). Trace (A) = 4

Let the 3rd eigen value is λ_3 then

$0 + 1 + \lambda_3 = 4 \Rightarrow \lambda_3 = 4 - 1 = 3$

So for $\lambda = 2$, we not get 2 is an eigen value of A. So option (a) not correct.

(b) If $\lambda = 4$, then

$$\Rightarrow A = \begin{bmatrix} 1 & 2 & 2 \\ 0 & 2 & 1 \\ 0 & 2 & 3 \end{bmatrix}$$

Now to evaluating eigen value of A, we need to solve $|A - xI| = 0$

$$\Rightarrow \begin{vmatrix} 1-x & 2 & 2 \\ 0 & 2-x & 1 \\ 0 & 2 & 3-x \end{vmatrix} = 0$$

$\Rightarrow (1-x)[(2-x)(3-x) - 2] = 0$

$\Rightarrow (1-x)(x^2 - 5x + 6 - 2) = 0$

$\Rightarrow (1-x)(x^2 - 5x + 4) = 0$

$\Rightarrow (1-x)(x^2 - 4x - x + 4) = 0$

$\Rightarrow (1-x)(4-x)(1-x) = 0$

So eigen value of A are 1, 4, 1,

i.e. option (b) is correct.

(c) If $\lambda = 6$, then

$$\Rightarrow A = \begin{bmatrix} 1 & 2 & 2 \\ 0 & 2 & 1 \\ 0 & 2 & 5 \end{bmatrix}$$

For eigen values of A, we need to solve |A – xI| = 0

$$\Rightarrow \begin{vmatrix} 1-x & 2 & 2 \\ 0 & 2-x & 1 \\ 0 & 2 & 5-x \end{vmatrix} = 0$$

$\Rightarrow (1-x)\{(2-x)(5-x)-2\} = 0$

$\Rightarrow (1-x)\{10+x^2-7x-2\} = 0$

$\Rightarrow (1-x)(x^2-7x+8) = 0$

$x = 1$ and $x = \frac{7\pm\sqrt{49-32}}{2} = \frac{7\pm\sqrt{17}}{2}$

So option (c) is also incorrect as A has eigen values 1, $\frac{7+\sqrt{17}}{2}$ and $\frac{7-\sqrt{17}}{2}$

(d) If $\lambda = 1$,

$$\Rightarrow A = \begin{bmatrix} 1 & 2 & 2 \\ 0 & 2 & 1 \\ 0 & 2 & 0 \end{bmatrix}$$

For eigen values of A, we need to solve |A – xI| = 0

$$\Rightarrow \begin{vmatrix} (1-x) & 2 & 2 \\ 0 & 2-x & 1 \\ 0 & 2 & -x \end{vmatrix} = 0$$

$\Rightarrow (1-x)\{-x(2-x)-2\} = 0$

$\Rightarrow (1-x)(x^2-2x-2) = 0$

$\Rightarrow x = 1$ and $x = \frac{1\pm\sqrt{4-8}}{2} = 1\pm i$

So, A has Eigen values 1, $1+i$ and $1-i$. Hence option (d) not correct.

So, none of the options are correct.

12. Explanation: (a)

$y' = Ay + h$

$$\begin{bmatrix} y_1'(t) \\ y_2'(t) \end{bmatrix} = \begin{bmatrix} 1 & 1 \\ 4 & -2 \end{bmatrix}\begin{bmatrix} y_1 \\ y_2 \end{bmatrix} + \begin{bmatrix} 3t+1 \\ 2t+5 \end{bmatrix}$$

$\frac{dy_1}{dt} = y_1 + y_2 + (3t+1)$ ------- (1)

$\frac{dy_2}{dt} = 4y_1 + 2y_2 + (2t+5)$ ------- (2)

From (1)

$(D-1)y_1 - y_2 = 3t+1$ ------- (3)

From (2)

$-4y_1 + (D+2)y_2 = (2t+5)$ -------(4)

Operate $(D+2)$ on (3)

$(D+2)(D-1)y_1 - (D+2)y_2 = (D+2)(3t+1)$ -- (5)

Adding (4) and (5), we get,

$[(D+2)(D-1)-4]y_1 = (2t+5)+(5+6t)$

$(D^2+D-6)y_1 = 8t+10$ ---------- (6)

Now we obtain complementary function,

Consider, $(D^2+D-6)y_1 = 0$

A.E. $m^2+m-6 = 0$

$\Rightarrow m = -3, 2$

C.F. $= c_1e^{-3t} + c_2e^{2t}$

Now, to obtain P.I. consider,

$y_P = \frac{1}{D^2+D-6}(8t+10)$

$= \frac{1}{-6\left(1-\frac{(D^2+D)}{6}\right)}(8t+10)$

$= -\frac{1}{6}\left[1+\frac{D^2+D}{6}+\left(\frac{D^2+D}{6}\right)^2\right](8t+10)$

$= -\frac{1}{6}\left[(8t+10)+\frac{1}{6}(8)+\frac{1}{36}(0)\right]$

$= -\frac{1}{6}\left(8t+\frac{34}{3}\right)$

$y_1(t) = c_1e^{-3t} + c_2e^{2t} - \frac{1}{6}\left(8t+\frac{34}{3}\right)$

$\lim_{t\to\infty}\frac{y_1(t)}{t} = d$ Constant

$\Rightarrow c_2 = 0$

$\therefore$ constant $= -\frac{1}{6}(8) = -\frac{4}{3}$.

So, option (a) is correct.

13. Explanation: (d)

Consider the matrix $A = \begin{bmatrix} 5 & 4 \\ 1 & 2 \end{bmatrix}$

$Ch_A(x) = x^2-7x+6 = 0$

$\Rightarrow x = 6, 1$

$\therefore$ General solution for the given system is,

$x(t) = c_1v_1e^{6t} + c_2v_2e^t$

where v_1 and v_2 are eigenvectors corresponding to eigenvalues 6 & 1 respectively, and c_1, c_2 are arbitrary constants.

If $x_0 \neq 0$, then as $t\to\infty$ solution will be unbounded.

But $e^{-10t}|x(t)| \to 0$ as $t\to\infty$, $\forall x \neq 0$

As $e^{-10t}\cdot e^{6t} = e^{-4t} \to 0$

& $e^{-10t}\cdot e^{t} = e^{-9t} \to 0$ as $t\to\infty$

So, option (d) is correct option.

MSQ: Multiple Select Questions

1. Consider the first order system of linear equations

$$\frac{dX}{dt} = AX\,;\, A = \begin{bmatrix} 3 & 2 \\ -2 & -1 \end{bmatrix}; X = \begin{bmatrix} x_1(t) \\ x_2(t) \end{bmatrix}$$

Then

(a) The coefficient matrix A has a repeated eigenvalue $\lambda = 1$

(b) There is only one linearly independent eigenvector $X_1 = \begin{bmatrix} 1 \\ -1 \end{bmatrix}$

(c) The general solution of the ODE is $(aX_1 + bX_2)e^t$, where a, b are arbitrary constant

$$X_1 = \begin{bmatrix} 1 \\ -1 \end{bmatrix}, X_2 = \begin{bmatrix} 1 \\ -1 \end{bmatrix} = \begin{bmatrix} t \\ \frac{1}{2}-t \end{bmatrix}$$

(d) The vectors X_1 and X_2 in the option 3 given above are linearly independent.

[Dec. 2011]

2. Consider the system of ODE

$$\frac{d}{dx}Y = AY, Y(0) = \begin{bmatrix} 2 \\ -1 \end{bmatrix}$$

Where $A = \begin{pmatrix} 1 & 2 \\ 0 & -1 \end{pmatrix}$ and $Y = \begin{bmatrix} y_1(t) \\ y_2(t) \end{bmatrix}$. Then

(a) $y_1(x) \to \infty$ and $y_2(x) \to 0$ as $x \to \infty$

(b) $y_1(x) \to 0$ and $y_2(x) \to 0$ as $x \to \infty$

(c) $y_1(x) \to \infty$ and $y_2(x) \to -\infty$ as $x \to -\infty$

(d) $y_1(x), y_2(x) \to -\infty$ as $x \to -\infty$

[June. 2012]

3. Let $A = \begin{pmatrix} 0 & 1 & 0 \\ 0 & 0 & 1 \\ 0 & 0 & 0 \end{pmatrix}$ and $y = \begin{pmatrix} y_1(t) \\ y_2(t) \\ y_3(t) \end{pmatrix}$ satisfy $\frac{dy}{dt} = Ay; t > 0; y(0) = \begin{pmatrix} 1 \\ 1 \\ 1 \end{pmatrix}$. Then

(a) $y_1(t) = 1 + t + \frac{t^2}{2}, y_2(t) = 1 + t, y_3(t) = 1$
(b) $y_1(t) = 1 + t, y_2(t) = 1 + t + \frac{t^2}{2}, y_3(t) = 1$
(c) $y_1(t) = 1, y_2(t) = 1 + t, y_3(t) = 1 + t + \frac{t^2}{2}$
(d) $y_1(t) = e^{tA}y(0)$

[Dec. 2012]

4. The system of ODE

$$\left.\begin{aligned} \frac{dx}{dt} &= (1+x^2)y, t \in \mathbb{R} \\ \frac{dy}{dt} &= -(1+x^2)x, t \in \mathbb{R} \\ (x(0), y(0)) &= (a,b) \end{aligned}\right\}$$

has a solution:
(a) Only if $(a,b) = (0,0)$
(b) For any $(a,b) \in \mathbb{R} \times \mathbb{R}$
(c) Such that $x^2(t) + y^2(t) = a^2 + b^2$ for all $t \in \mathbb{R}$
(d) Such that $x^2(t) + y^2(t) \to \infty$ for all $t \to \infty$ if $a > 0$ and $b > 0$

[Dec. 2014]

5. The critical point of the system

$$\frac{dx}{dt} = -4x - y, \frac{dy}{dt} = x - 2y \text{ is an}$$

(a) Asymptotically stable node
(b) Unstable node
(c) Asymptotically stable spiral
(d) Unstable spiral

[June 2015]

6. Let $(x(t), y(t))$ satisfy for $t > 0$

$$\frac{dx}{dt} = -x + y, \frac{dy}{dt} = -y, x(0) = y(0) = 1$$

(a) $e^{-t} + t\,y(t)$ (b) $y(t)$
(c) $e^{-t}(1+t)$ (d) $-y(t)$

[Dec. 2016]

7. Consider a system of first order differential equations $\frac{d}{dt}\begin{bmatrix} x(t) \\ y(t) \end{bmatrix} = \begin{bmatrix} x(t) + y(t) \\ -y(t) \end{bmatrix}$. The solution space is spanned by

(a) $\begin{bmatrix} 0 \\ e^{-t} \end{bmatrix}$ and $\begin{bmatrix} e^t \\ 0 \end{bmatrix}$ (b) $\begin{bmatrix} e^{-t} \\ 0 \end{bmatrix}$ and $\begin{bmatrix} \cosh t \\ e^{-t} \end{bmatrix}$
(c) $\begin{bmatrix} e^{-t} \\ -2e^{-t} \end{bmatrix}$ and $\begin{bmatrix} \sinh t \\ e^{-t} \end{bmatrix}$ (d) $\begin{bmatrix} e^{-t} \\ 0 \end{bmatrix}$ and $\begin{bmatrix} e^t - \frac{1}{2}e^{-t} \\ e^{-t} \end{bmatrix}$

[Dec. 2017]

8. Consider the system of differential equations

$$\frac{dx}{dt} = 2x - 7y$$
$$\frac{dy}{dt} = 3x - 8y$$

Then the critical point $(0,0)$ of the system is an
(a) Asymptotically stable node
(b) Unstable node
(c) Asymptotically stable spiral
(d) Unstable spiral

[June 2018]

9. Let $f: \mathbb{R}^2 \to (-\infty, 0]$ be such that $f(0,0) = 0$. Consider the following systems of ODES

$$x'(t) = f(x(t), y(t)), y'(t) = y^2(t), t > 0$$

A set $S \subseteq \mathbb{R}^2$ is said to be positively invariant set if the following holds.
Assume that $(x(0), y(0)) \in S$. Then for $t \geq 0$, if the solution $(x(t), y(t))$ exists, then $(x(t), y(t)) \in S$. Then which of the following sets are positively invariant.
(a) $\{(x,y) \in \mathbb{R}^2 : x \leq 0, y \leq 0\}$
(b) $\{(x,y) \in \mathbb{R}^2 : y \geq 0\}$
(c) $\{(x,y) \in \mathbb{R}^2 : x \leq 0, y \leq -1\}$
(d) $\{(x,y) \in \mathbb{R}^2 : x \leq 0, y \geq 0\}$

[Dec 2019]

10. Let A be an $n \times n$ matrix with distinct eigen values $\{\lambda_1, \lambda_2, \dots \lambda_n\}$ with corresponding linearly independent eigenvectors $\{v_1, v_2, \dots v_n\}$
Then the non-homogeneous differential equation

$$x'(t) = Ax(t) + e^{\lambda_1 t} v_1$$

(a) Does not have a solution of the form $e^{\lambda_1 t}$ a for any vector $a \in \mathbb{R}^n$.
(b) Has a solution of the form $e^{\lambda_1 t}$ for any vector $a \in \mathbb{R}^n$.
(c) Has a solution of the form $e^{\lambda_1 t}a + te^{\lambda_1 t}b$ for some $a, b \in \mathbb{R}^n$.
(d) Does not have a solution of the form $e^{\lambda_1 t}a + te^{\lambda_1 t}b$ for any vectors $a, b \in \mathbb{R}^n$.

[Nov 2020]

11. Consider the solution

$$y_1 := \begin{pmatrix} e^{-3t} \\ e^{-3t} \\ 0 \end{pmatrix} \text{ and } y_2 := \begin{pmatrix} 0 \\ e^{-5t} \\ e^{-5t} \end{pmatrix} \text{ to the}$$

Homogeneous linear system of differential equation
$(*) y'(t) = \begin{pmatrix} -5 & 2 & -2 \\ 1 & -4 & -1 \\ -1 & 1 & -6 \end{pmatrix} y(t)$. Which of the following statements are true?
(a) y_1 and y_2 form a basis for the set of all solution to $(*)$
(b) y_1 and y_2 are linearly independent but do not form a basis for the set of all solutions to $(*)$.
(c) There exists another solution y_3 such that $\{y_1, y_2, y_3\}$ form a basis for the set of all solution to $(*)$.
(d) y_1 and y_2 are linearly dependent.

[Nov 2020]

12. Let x and y be continuously differentiable function on $[0, \infty)$ that satisfy the respectively initial value problem (ODES).

$$\frac{dx}{dt} + (\sin t - 1)x = \log(1+t), x(0) = 1;$$
$$\frac{dy}{dt} + (\sin t - 1)y - t, y(0) = 2$$

Define $z(t) = y(t) - x(t)$ for $t \geq 0$. Which of the following statements are true?
(a) $z(1) \leq 1$ (b) $z(2) \geq z(1)$
(c) $z(1) > 1$ (d) $z(2) \leq z(1)$

[Nov 2020]

13. Let $F: \mathbb{R}^2 \to \mathbb{R}$ be a locally Lipschitz function consider the system of ODES given by $\dot{x}_1 = \sin(e^{x_2})$, $\dot{x}_2 = f(x_1, x_2)$ with initial condition $(x_1(0), x_2(0) = (1,1)$ which of the following statements are true.
(a) There exist at most one local solution at time 0
(b) There exist always a global solution defined in $[0, \infty)$

(c) There might not be solution around the time $t = 0$
(d) There is at least one solution around time 0

[Nov 2020]

14. $F(x,y) = \left(y + x(1-x^2-y^2), -x + y(1-x^2-y^2)\right)$ and consider the ODE $(\dot{x},\dot{y})$ with initial condition $(x(0),y(0)) = \left(0,\frac{1}{2}\right)$. Which of the following statements are true?
(a) $x^2(t) + y^2(t) \to \infty$ as $t \to \infty$
(b) $x^2(t) + y^2(t) \to 0$ as $t \to \infty$
(c) $x^2(t) + y^2(t)$ remains bounded as $t \to \infty$
(d) $x^2(t) + y^2(t) \to 1$ as $t \to \infty$

[Nov 2020]

15. Consider the following two initial value ODEs
(A) $\frac{dx}{dt} = x^3, x(0) = 1;$
(B) $\frac{dx}{dt} = x\sin x^2, x(0) = 2.$
Related to these ODEs, we make the following assertions.
I. The solution to (A) blows up in finite time.
II. The solution to (B) blows up in finite time.
Which of the following statements is true?
(a) Both (I) and (II) are true
(b) (I) is true but (II) is false
(c) Both (I) and (II) are false
(d) (I) is false but (II) is true

[Feb 2022]

16. Let $A \in M_3(\mathbb{R})$ be skew-symmetric and let $x: [0,\infty) \to \mathbb{R}^3$ be a solution of $x'(t) = Ax(t)$, for all $t \in (0,\infty)$.
Which of the following statements are true?
(a) $\|x(t)\| = \|x(0)\|$, for all $t \in (0,\infty)$
(b) For some $a \in \mathbb{R}^3\backslash\{0\}, \|x(t) - a\| = \|x(0) - a\|, for\ all\ t \in (0,\infty)$
(c) $x(t) - x(0) \in im\ A, for\ all\ t \in (0,\infty)$
(d) $\lim_{t\to\infty} x(t)$ exists

[Sep 2022]

17. If $x_1 = x_1(t), x_2 = x_2(t)$ is the solution of the initial value problem
$$e^{-t}\frac{dx_1}{dt} = -x_1 + x_2,$$
$$e^{-t}\frac{dx_2}{dt} = -x_1 - x_2,$$
$x_1(0) = 1, x_2(0) = 0.$
and $r(t) = \sqrt{x_1^2(t) + x_1^2(t)}$, then which of the following statements are true?
(a) $r(t) \to 0$ as $t \to +\infty$
(b) $r(\ln 2) = e^{-1}$
(c) $r(\ln 2) = 2e^{-1}$
(d) $r(t)e^t \to 0$ as $t \to +\infty$

[July 2024]

18. If $x = x(t), y = y(t)$ is the solution of the initial value problem
$$\frac{dx}{dt} = x - 4e^{-2t}y,$$
$$\frac{dy}{dt} = e^{2t}x - y,$$
$$x(0) = 1, y(0) = 1,$$
then which of the following statements are true?
(a) $\lim_{t\to\infty} t^{-2}x(t)y(t) = 0$ (b) $x(1) = 0, y\left(\frac{1}{2}\right) = 0$
(c) $x\left(\frac{1}{2}\right) = 0, y(1) = 0$ (d) $\lim_{t\to\infty} t^{-2}x(t)y(t) = 2$

[Feb. 2025]

Answer Key				
1	2	3	4	5
a, b, c, d	a, c	a, d	b, c	a
6	7	8	9	10
a, c	c, d	A	a, b, d	a, c
11	12	13	14	15
b, c	b, c	a, d	c, d	B
16	17	18		
a, b, c	a, b, d	c,d		

EXPLANATION

1. **Explanation (a), (b), (c), (d)**
Consider the given system of Linear equation $\frac{dx}{dt} = Ax$
Where $A = \begin{bmatrix} 3 & 2 \\ -2 & -1 \end{bmatrix}$ $X = \begin{bmatrix} x_1 \\ x_2 \end{bmatrix}$
$A = \begin{bmatrix} 3 & 2 \\ -2 & -1 \end{bmatrix}$
Characteristic equation is $(A - \lambda I) = 0$
$\Rightarrow \lambda^2 - 2\lambda + 1 = 0 \Rightarrow \lambda = +1,1$
$\Rightarrow$ coefficient matrix A has a repeated Eigen value
For $\lambda = 1$
$A - \lambda I = \begin{bmatrix} 2 & 2 \\ -2 & -2 \end{bmatrix}$
$\Rightarrow \rho(A - \lambda I) = 1$
$\Rightarrow GM =$ nullity of $(A - \lambda I)$
$\Rightarrow GM = 1$
$\Rightarrow$ only one LI eigen vector
Now find the eigenvector corresponding eigenvalue $\lambda = 1$
$(A - \lambda I)\begin{bmatrix} x_1 \\ x_2 \end{bmatrix} = \begin{bmatrix} 2 & 2 \\ -2 & -2 \end{bmatrix}\begin{bmatrix} x_1 \\ x_2 \end{bmatrix} = \begin{bmatrix} 0 \\ 0 \end{bmatrix}$
$\Rightarrow 2x_1 = -2x_2$
$x_1 = -x_2 \Rightarrow \begin{bmatrix} x_1 \\ x_2 \end{bmatrix} = \begin{bmatrix} 1 \\ -1 \end{bmatrix}$
Now,
$x_1' = 3x_1 + 2x_2$
$x_2' = -2x_1 - x_2$
$x_1'' = 3x_1' + 2x_2'$
$x_1'' = 3xy' + e(-2xy - x_2)$
$x_1'' = 3xy' - 4xy - 2x_2$
$3xy' - 4xy - xi + 3x_1$
$x_1'' = 2x_1' - -x_1$
$x_1'' - 2x_1' + x_1 = 0$
Auxiliary equation is
$m^2 - 2m + 1 = 0$
$\Rightarrow m = 1,1$
C.F. is
$x = c_1e^t + c_2 + e^t \ldots\ldots (2)$
Now
$2x_2 = x_1' - 3x_1$
$2x_2 = c_1e^t + c_2(te^t + e^t) - 3(c_1e^t + c_2 + e^t)$

$$x_2 = \frac{1}{2}[c_1e^t + c_2(te^t + e^t) - 3c_1e^t - 3c_2te^t)$$
$$x_2 = \frac{1}{2}[c_1e^t + c_2 + e^t + c_2e^t - 3c_1e^t - 3c_2 + e^t]$$
$$x_2 = \frac{1}{2}[-2c_1e^t - 2c_2 + e^t + c_2e^t]$$
$$x_2 = -c_1e^t - c_2 + e^t + \frac{1}{2}c_2e^t$$
$$\rightarrow \begin{bmatrix} x_1 \\ x_2 \end{bmatrix} = c_1\begin{bmatrix} e^t \\ -e^t \end{bmatrix} = c_2\begin{bmatrix} +e^t \\ -te^t + \frac{1}{2}e^t \end{bmatrix}$$
$$\begin{bmatrix} x_1 \\ x_2 \end{bmatrix} = c_1e^t\begin{bmatrix} 1 \\ -1 \end{bmatrix} + c_2e^t\begin{bmatrix} t \\ \frac{1}{2} - t \end{bmatrix}$$
$$(ax_1 + bx_2)e^t$$
$$x_1 = \begin{bmatrix} 1 \\ -1 \end{bmatrix} x_2 = \begin{bmatrix} t \\ \frac{1}{2} - t \end{bmatrix}$$

From above x_1 and x_2 are LI

From above explanation

⇒All the options a),b),c) and d) are correct.

2. **Explanation (a), (c)** Consider the given system of ODE

$\frac{dY}{dx} = AY, \quad Y = \begin{bmatrix} y_1(x) \\ y_2(x) \end{bmatrix}$

Where $A = \begin{bmatrix} 1 & 2 \\ 0 & -1 \end{bmatrix}$, $Y(0) = \begin{bmatrix} 2 \\ -1 \end{bmatrix}$

$y_1' = y_1 + 2y_2$ (1)

$y_2' = -y_2$ (2)

$\Rightarrow \frac{y_2'}{y_2} = \text{DX}$

$\Rightarrow \text{LOG}y_2 = -\text{X} + \text{C}_1$

$\Rightarrow y_2 = \text{CE}^{-\text{X}} \quad (e^{c_1} = c)$

NOW USE THE GIVEN CONDITION

$y_2(0) = -1$

$\Rightarrow \text{C} = -1$

$\Rightarrow y_2 = -e^{-x}$

NOW, $y_1' = y_1 + 2y_2$

$y_1' = y_1 + 2(-e^{-x})$

$y_1' = y_1 - 2e^{-x}$

$y_1' - y_1 = -2e^{-x}$

This is the Linear differential equation

$$y_1e^{-x} = \int -2e^{-x}e^{-x}dx + c$$
$$= \frac{-2e^{-2x}}{-2} + c$$

$y_1e^{-x} = e^{-2x} + c$

$y_1 = e^{-x} + ce^x$

Now use the given conditions

$y_1(0) = 2$

$y_1(0) = 1 + c = 2$

$c = 1$

$y_1 = e^{-x} + e^x$

$y_1 = e^{-x} + e^x$ and $y_2 = -e^{-x}$

Now check the option

For option (a)

$\lim_{x\to\infty} y_1(x) = \lim_{x\to\infty} e^{-x} + e^x = \infty$

$\lim_{x\to\infty} y_2(x) = \lim_{x\to\infty} -e^{-x} = 0$

⇒ Option (a) is the correct.

for option (b)

From above option (a), option (b) is incorrect

For option (c)

$\lim_{x\to\infty} y_1(x) \quad = \lim_{x\to-\infty} e^{-x} + e^x$

$= \infty$

$\lim_{x\to\infty} y_2(x) \quad = \lim_{x\to-\infty} - e^{-x}$

$= -\infty$

⇒ Option c) is the correct

Now option (d)

From above option c),

option (d) is incorrect

⇒option a) and c) are correct and option b) and d) incorrect.

3. **Explanation (a), (d)**

Consider the given system of ODE $\frac{dy}{dt} = Ay$

Where $A = \begin{bmatrix} 0 & 1 & 0 \\ 0 & 0 & 1 \\ 0 & 0 & 0 \end{bmatrix}$ and $y(0) = \begin{pmatrix} 1 \\ 1 \\ 1 \end{pmatrix}$

Now

$y_1' = y_2$ (1)

$y_2' = y_3$ (2)

$y_3' = 0$ (3)

$y_3 = c$

$y_2' = c$

$y_2 = ct + c_1$

$y_2(0) = 1$ (Given)

$c_1 = 1$

Equation (1) become

$y_1' = ct + 1$

$$y_1 = \frac{ct^2}{2} + t + c_2$$

$y_1(0) = 1$ (given)

$c_2 = 1$

$$\Rightarrow y_1 = \frac{ct^2}{2} + t + 1$$

Now check the option

for option (a)

Take $y_3 = c = 1$

$y_3 = 1$

$\Rightarrow y_2 = t + 1$

$$\Rightarrow y_1 = \frac{t^2}{2} + t + 1$$
$$y_1 = 1 + t + \frac{t^2}{2}$$

Option (a) is correct

For optioin (b) from above option (a) option, (b) is incorrect

For option (c)

Form option (a) option, (c) is incorrect

for option (d)

Now

$$e^x = 1 + x + \frac{x^2}{x} + \frac{x^3}{3i} + \cdots$$
$$e^{tA} = 1 + tA + \frac{t^2A^2}{2} + \frac{(1+A)^3}{3!} + \ldots$$

$$e^{tA}y(0) = \left(1 + tA + \frac{(tA)^2}{2} + \frac{(tA)^3}{3!} + \cdots\right)y(0)$$

$$= \left(1 + tA + \frac{(tA)^2}{2} + \frac{(tA)^3}{3!} + \cdots\right)\begin{bmatrix}1\\1\\1\end{bmatrix}$$

$$= \begin{bmatrix}1 & t & \frac{t^2}{2}\\0 & 1 & t\\0 & 0 & 1\end{bmatrix}\begin{bmatrix}1\\1\\1\end{bmatrix}$$

$$e^{tA}y(0) = \begin{bmatrix}1 + t + \frac{t^2}{2}\\1 + t\\1\end{bmatrix} = \begin{bmatrix}y_1\\y_2\\y_3\end{bmatrix}$$

From above explanation,

⇒ option a) and d) are correct and option b) and c) incorrect.

4. Explanation (b), (c) Given system of ODE is

$\frac{dx}{dt} = (1 + x^2)y, t \in \mathbb{R}$

$\frac{dy}{dt} = -(1 + x^2)x, t \in \mathbb{R}$

Now use chain rule

$$\frac{dy}{dx} = \frac{\frac{dy}{dt}}{\frac{dx}{dt}} = \frac{-(1 + x^2)x}{(1 + x^2)y} = \frac{-x}{y}$$

$\frac{dy}{dx} = \frac{-x}{y}$

Integrating

$ydy + xdx = 0$

$y^3 + x^2 = c$

Now $(x(0), y(0)) = (a, b)$

$a^2 + b^2 = c$

$\Rightarrow x^2(t) + y^2(t) = a^2 + b^2\ \forall t \in \mathbb{R}$

For any $(a,b) \in \mathbb{R} \times \mathbb{R}$

We have a solution

⇒ form above explanation only option (b) and (c) are correct and Option (a) and (d) are incorrect.

5. Explanation (a) Consider the given system of ODE.

$\frac{dx}{dt} = -4x - y$

$\frac{dy}{dt} = x - 2y$

$\Rightarrow A = \begin{bmatrix}-4 & -1\\1 & -2\end{bmatrix}$

characteristic equation is

$\lambda^2 + 6\lambda + 9 = 0$

$\Rightarrow \lambda = -3, -3$

Both eigenvalue are real and negative

⇒ asymptotically stable node

⇒ option a) is correct and option b) ,c) and d)are incorrect.

6. Explanation (a), (c) Given system of ODE is

$\frac{dx}{dt} = -x(t) + y(t), \frac{dy}{dt} = -y(t)$

$x'(t) = -x(t) + y(t)$.......(1)

$y'(t) = -y(t)$.....(2)

From equation (2)

$\frac{y_1'(t)}{-y(t)} = dt$

$logy(t) = -t + c$

$y = e^{-t}c$

Now $y(0) = 1$.....(given)

$y(0) = c = 1$

$\Rightarrow c = 1$

$\Rightarrow y(t) = e^{-t}$

equation (1) become

$x'(t) = -x(t) + e^{-t}$

$x'(t) + x(t) = e^{-t}$

$\Rightarrow x(t)e^t = t + c$

Now $x(0) = 1$.....(Given)

$x(0) = 1$

$c = 1$

$\Rightarrow x(t)e^t = t + 1$

$x(t) = te^{-t} + e^{-t}$

$\Rightarrow x(t) = ty(t) + y(t)$

$x(t) = e^{-t} + ty(t) \qquad (\because y(t) = e^{-t})$

$x(t) = (1 + t)e^{-t}$

⇒ from above explanation,

Option (a) and (c) are correct and option (b) and (d) are incorrect.

Alternatively:

The matrix corresponding to the given system is $A = \begin{bmatrix}-1 & 1\\0 & -1\end{bmatrix}$ and its eigenvalues are obtained by taking $|A - \lambda I| = 0 \Rightarrow \lambda^2 + 2\lambda + 1 = 0$

$\Rightarrow (\lambda + 1)^2 = 0 \Rightarrow \lambda = -1, -1$ are eigen values

Then, the general solution is $X(t) = \alpha Ce^{-t} + \beta(Ct + D)e^{-t}$ where $X(t) = \begin{bmatrix}x(t)\\y(t)\end{bmatrix}$ and C is obtained by $(A + I)C = 0$ where $C = \begin{bmatrix}x_1\\x_2\end{bmatrix}$ i.e. $\begin{bmatrix}0 & 1\\0 & 0\end{bmatrix}\begin{bmatrix}x_1\\x_2\end{bmatrix} = 0$

$\Rightarrow x_2 = 0$ and x_1 is arbitrary

i.e. $C = \begin{bmatrix}1\\0\end{bmatrix}$ (say $C_1 = 1$) and D is obtained by

$(A + I)D = C$

$\Rightarrow \begin{bmatrix}0 & 1\\0 & 0\end{bmatrix}\begin{bmatrix}x_1\\x_2\end{bmatrix} = \begin{bmatrix}1\\0\end{bmatrix}$

$\Rightarrow x_2 = 1$ and x_1 is arbitrary.

$\Rightarrow D = \begin{bmatrix}1\\1\end{bmatrix}$ (let taking $x_1 = 1$)

$\Rightarrow X(t) = \begin{bmatrix}x(t)\\y(t)\end{bmatrix} = \alpha\begin{bmatrix}1\\0\end{bmatrix}e^{-t} + \beta\begin{bmatrix}t + 1\\0\end{bmatrix}e^{-t}$

$= \begin{bmatrix}\alpha e^{-t} + \beta(1 + t)e^{-t}\\\beta e^{-t}\end{bmatrix}$

$\Rightarrow x(t) = \alpha e^{-t} + \beta(1 + t)e^{-t}$

and $y(t) = \beta e^{-t}$

$\because y(0) = 1 \Rightarrow \beta = 1$

and $x(0) = 1 \Rightarrow \alpha + 1 = 1, \alpha = 0$

$\Rightarrow x(t) = (1 + t)e^{-t}$

$y(t) = e^{-t}$

$\Rightarrow x(t) = e^{-t} + ty(t)$ (as $y(t) = e^{-t}$)

Hence, option (a) and (c) are correct.

7. Explanation (c), (d) Consider the given system of first order differential equation

$$\frac{d}{dt}\begin{bmatrix}x(t)\\y(t)\end{bmatrix}=\begin{bmatrix}x(t)+y(t)\\-y(t)\end{bmatrix}$$

$\Rightarrow x'(t)=x(t)+y(t)$ ……………(1)

$y'(t)=-y(t)$ ………….(2)

From equation (1) and (2)

$y'(t)=-y(t)$

$\frac{y'(t)}{y(t)}=-dt$

Integrating both side

$\log y(t)=-t+c$

$y(t)=e^{-t}c$

Equation (1) become

$x'(t)=x(t)+e^{-t}c$

$x'(t)-x(t)=e^{-t}c$

$x'(t)-x(t)=ce^{-t}$

This is linear differential equation

$x(t)e^{-t}=\int ce^{-2t}\,dt+c_1$

$x(t)e^{-t}=\frac{ce^{-2t}}{-2}+c_1$

$x(t)=\frac{ce^{-t}}{-2}+c_1e^{t}$

$\Rightarrow y(t)=ce^{-t}$

$$\Rightarrow\begin{bmatrix}x(t)\\y(t)\end{bmatrix}=\begin{bmatrix}c_1e^{t}+\frac{ce^{-t}}{-2}\\ce^{-t}\end{bmatrix}$$

$$\begin{bmatrix}x(t)\\y(t)\end{bmatrix}=c_1\begin{bmatrix}e^{t}\\0\end{bmatrix}+c\begin{bmatrix}-\frac{e^{-t}}{2}\\e^{-t}\end{bmatrix}$$

$\Rightarrow$ solution space is spanned by

$\begin{bmatrix}e^{t}\\0\end{bmatrix}$ and $\begin{bmatrix}-\frac{e^{-t}}{2}\\e^{-t}\end{bmatrix}$

Now check the option

for option (a)

$\begin{bmatrix}0\\e^{-t}\end{bmatrix}$ and $\begin{bmatrix}e^{t}\\0\end{bmatrix}$ is never a linear combination of $\begin{bmatrix}e^{t}\\0\end{bmatrix}$ and $\begin{bmatrix}-\frac{e^{-t}}{2}\\e^{-t}\end{bmatrix}$

$\Rightarrow$ option (a) is incorrect

for option (b)

$$\begin{bmatrix}\cos ht\\e^{-t}\end{bmatrix}=\begin{bmatrix}\frac{e^{t}+e^{-t}}{2}\\e^{-t}\end{bmatrix}$$

$\begin{bmatrix}e^{t}\\0\end{bmatrix}$ and $\begin{bmatrix}\cos ht\\e^{-t}\end{bmatrix}$ is never a linear combination of $\begin{bmatrix}e^{t}\\0\end{bmatrix}$ and $\begin{bmatrix}-\frac{e^{-t}}{2}\\e^{-t}\end{bmatrix}$

For option (c)

$$\begin{bmatrix}\sin ht\\e^{-t}\end{bmatrix}=\begin{bmatrix}\frac{e^{t}-e^{-t}}{2}\\e^{-t}\end{bmatrix}$$

$\begin{bmatrix}\sin h(t)\\e^{-t}\end{bmatrix}$ and $\begin{bmatrix}e^{-t}\\2e^{-t}\end{bmatrix}$ is linear combination of $\begin{bmatrix}e^{t}\\0\end{bmatrix}$ and $\begin{bmatrix}-\frac{e^{-t}}{2}\\e^{-t}\end{bmatrix}$

$\Rightarrow$ solution space is spanned by

$\begin{bmatrix}\sin ht\\e^{-t}\end{bmatrix}$ and $\begin{bmatrix}e^{-t}\\2e^{-t}\end{bmatrix}$

For option (4)

$\begin{bmatrix}e^{t}\\0\end{bmatrix}$ and $\begin{bmatrix}e^{t}-\frac{1}{2}e^{-t}\\e^{-t}\end{bmatrix}$ is the linear combination of $\begin{bmatrix}e^{t}\\0\end{bmatrix}$ and $\begin{bmatrix}-\frac{e^{-t}}{2}\\e^{-t}\end{bmatrix}$

So solution space is spanned by $\begin{bmatrix}e^{t}\\0\end{bmatrix}$ and $\begin{bmatrix}e^{t}-\frac{1}{2}e^{-t}\\e^{-t}\end{bmatrix}$

$\Rightarrow$ option (c) and (d) are correct and option a) and b) are incorrect.

8. Explanation (a)

Consider the given system of differential equation

$\frac{dx}{dt}=2x-7y$

$\frac{dy}{dt}=3x-8y$

Critical point at (0,0)

$\Rightarrow A=\begin{bmatrix}2&-7\\3&-8\end{bmatrix}$

Now characteristics equation is

$\lambda^2+6\lambda+5=0$

$\Rightarrow(\lambda+2)(\lambda+3)=0$

$\lambda=-2,-3$

Both the eigen value are real and negative

$\Rightarrow$ critical point at (0,0) of the system is asymptotically stable node

Option (a) is correct and option b), c), d) are incorrect.

9. Explanation (a), (b), (d)

Let $f:\mathbb{R}^2\to(-\infty,0]$ be such that $f(0,0)=0$

$x'(t)=f(x(t),y(t)),y'(t)=y^2(t),t>0$

According positive invariant we must need$(0,0)\in S$

$x'(t)=f(x(0),y(0))=0$

i.e. $0\in S wrx(t)and y'(t)=y^2(t)$

$\Rightarrow\frac{dy}{y^2}=dt\Rightarrow\frac{-1}{y}=t+c$

$\Rightarrow y=\frac{-1}{t+c}$

as $t\to\infty\quad\to y=0$

so we get(0, 0) containing options are correct.

Now for option (a)$\{(x,y)\in\mathbb{R}^2:x\le0,y\le0\}(0,0)$ present so option (a) correct.

(b) $\{(x,y)\in\mathbb{R}^2:y\ge0\}$

Since x is arbitrary $\Rightarrow$ 0also in x

i.e. (0, 0) present so option (b) correct.

(c)$\{(x,y)\in\mathbb{R}^2:x\le0,y\le-1\}$

$y\le-1\Rightarrow(0,0)$ not present in the set

So, option (c) incorrect.

(d) $\{(x,y)\in\mathbb{R}^2:x\le0,y\ge0\}$

(0, 0) is present in the set.

So, option (d) correct.

10. Explanation (a), (c)

Let $A=[a_{11}]_{1\times1}$ and let $a_{11}=1$

Then A has eigen value $\lambda_1 = 1$

And the given system reduces to

$x'(t) = x(t) + e^{\lambda_1 t}v_1 = x(t) + e^t v_1$

$\Rightarrow x'(t) - x(t) = e^t v_1$............. (i)

Thus is a linear first order differential equation.

Integrating factor is $= e^{-\int dt} = e^{-t}$

$\therefore x(t).e^{-t} = \int e^t v_1.e^{-t}dt + c$

$\Rightarrow x(t)e^{-t} = v_1 t + c$

$\Rightarrow x(t) = v_1 t\,e^t + ce^t$

i.e. $x(t) = ce^{\lambda_1 t} + te^{\lambda_1 t}v$

So option (a) and (c) are correct and option (b) and (d) are wrong.

11. Explanation (b), (c)

$$A = \begin{bmatrix} -5 & 2 & -2 \\ 1 & -4 & -1 \\ -1 & 1 & -6 \end{bmatrix}_{3\times 3}$$

We have 3 linearly independent Solutions.

Hence we need three linearly independent solutions to span the solution of (*)

Hence option (a) incorrect and (c) correct.

As e^{-3t} can never be expressed as a linear combination of e^{-5t}, y_1 and y_2 are linearly independent but not form a basis.

So option (b) correct and (d) incorrect. (Ans)

12. Explanation (b), (c)

$\frac{dx}{dt} + (\sin t - 1)x = \log(1+t), x(0) =$ .... (i)

$\frac{dy}{dt} + (\sin t - 1)x = t, y(0) = 2$ .... (ii)

From (i), we get the integrating factor is

$= e^{\int(\sin t - 1)dt} = e^{-(\cos t + t)}$

$\therefore x(t).e^{-(\cos t+t)} = \int \log(1+t)e^{-(\cos t+t)}\,dt + c$

$\Rightarrow x(t) = e^{\cos t+t}\int e^{-\cos t - t}\log(1+t) + ce^{\cos t+t}$,

$\Rightarrow x(0) = e^{\cos 0+0}\int e^{-\cos 0-0}\log(1+0) + ce^{\cos 0+0}$

$\Rightarrow 1 = e.0 + ce \Rightarrow c = \frac{1}{e}$

$\therefore x(t) = e^{\cos t+t}\int e^{-(\cos t+t)}\log(1+t) + \frac{1}{e}e^{\cos t+t}$

Now from (ii), integrating factor is,

$e = e^{\int(\sin t-1)dt} = e^{-(\cos t+t)}$

$\therefore y(t)e^{-(\cos t+t)} = \int t.e^{(\cos t+t)}\,dt + d$

$\Rightarrow y(t) = e^{\cos t+t}\int t.e^{-\cos t-t}\,dt + de^{\cos t+t}$

$\Rightarrow y(0) = e^{\cos 0+0}\int 0.e^{-\cos 0-0}\,dt + de^{\cos 0+}$

$\Rightarrow 2 = 0 + de \Rightarrow d = \frac{2}{e}$

$\therefore y(t) = e^{\cos t+t}\int te^{-\cos t-t}\,dt + \frac{2}{e}e^{\cos t+t}$

Now

$z(t) = y(t) - x(t)$

$= e^{\cos t+t}[\int te^{-\cos t-t}dt - \int \log(t+1)e^{-\cos t-t}dt] + e^{\cos t+t}\left[\frac{2}{e} - \frac{1}{e}\right]$

$= e^{\cos t+t}\int e^{-\cos t-t}(t - \log(1+t))dt + \frac{1}{e}e^{\cos t+t}$

Since $t - \log(1+t) > 0 \forall t \in (0,\infty)$

We have $e^{\cos t+t} > 0 \forall t \in \mathbb{R}$

Hence $e^{\cos t+t}\int e^{-\cos t-t}[t - \log(1+t)]dt > 0 \forall t \in \mathbb{R}$

$\Rightarrow z(t) =$ positive number$+\frac{1}{e}e^{\cos t}.e^t$

$z(1) = +\text{ve value} + \frac{1}{e}.e.e^{\cos 1}$

$= (+\text{ve value}) + e^{\cos 1} > 1\,(\because e^{\cos 1} > 1)$

$\Rightarrow z(1) > 1$

So option (c) correct and option (a) wrong.

$z(2) = (+\text{ve value}) + \frac{1}{e}.e^{\cos 2}$

$= (+\text{ve value}) + e.e^{\cos 2}$

Since $e^{\cos 2+2} > e^{\cos 1+1}$

$\Rightarrow z(2) > z(1)$

So, option (b) and (c) are correct.

13. Explanation (a), (d)

$\dot{x}_1 = \sin(e^{x_2})$ .... (i)

$\dot{x}_2 = F(x_1, x_2)$ .... (ii)

$(x_1(0), x_2(0) = (1,1)$

$|\dot{x}_1| = |\sin(e^{x_2})| < 1$

i.e x_1 is also satisfy the Lipscitz condition.

Now $\dot{x}_2 = F(x_1,x_2)$ and $F(x_1,x_2)$ is Locally Lipscitz function.

So, both x_1 and x_2 satisfy Locally Lipshcitz function so by existence and uniqueness theorem, we get unique solution

$\Rightarrow$ Option (a) and (d) are correct.

Since the function Locally Lipchitz, so we cannot say about its solution existence Globally i.e. option (b) in correct.

Since we have unique solution around 0, so option (c) incorrect.

14. Explanation (b, c) (by CSIR): but Right answer (c, d)

$$\left.\begin{aligned} \frac{dx}{dt} &= \dot{x} = y + x(1 - x^2 - y^2) \\ \frac{dy}{dt} &= \dot{y} = -x + y(1 - x^2 - y^2) \end{aligned}\right\} \quad \text{.... (i)}$$

$(x(0), y(0)) = \left(0, \frac{1}{2}\right)$

$x\frac{dx}{dt} + y\frac{dy}{dt} = xy + x^2(1 - x^2 - y^2) - xy + y^2(1 - x^2 - y^2)$

$= (x^2 + y^2)(1 - x^2 - y^2)$

Let $x^2 + y^2 = z$

$\Rightarrow 2x\,dx + 2y\,dy = dz \Rightarrow xdx + ydy = \frac{dz}{2}$

$\therefore \frac{1}{2}\frac{dz}{dt} = z(1 - z)$

$\Rightarrow \frac{dz}{z(1-z)} = 2dt \Rightarrow \left(\frac{1}{z} + \frac{1}{1-z}\right)dz = 2dt$

Integrating both sides we get

$\Rightarrow \log z - \log(1-z) - 2t + c$

$\Rightarrow \log(x^2+y^2) - \log(1-x^2-y^2)$
$= 2t + c$

$$\log\frac{x^2+y^2}{1-x^2-y^2} = 2t + c$$

Putting $x(0) = 0, y(0) = \frac{1}{2}$

$$\Rightarrow \log\frac{0+{}^1/_4}{1-{}^1/_4} = 2.0 + c \Rightarrow \log\frac{{}^1/_4}{{}^3/_4} = c$$

$$\Rightarrow \log\frac{1}{3} = c$$

$$\therefore \frac{x^2+y^2}{1-x^2-y^2} = e^{2t+\log\frac{1}{3}}$$

$$\Rightarrow x^2+y^2 = (1-(x^2-y^2))e^{2t}.{}^1/_3$$

$$\Rightarrow (x^2+y^2) = \frac{1}{3}e^{2t} - \frac{1}{3}(x^2-y^2)e^{2t}$$

$$\Rightarrow (x^2+y^2)\left(1+\frac{1}{3}e^{2t}\right) = \frac{1}{3}e^{2t}$$

$$\Rightarrow (x^2+y^2) = \frac{{}^1/_3 e^{2t}}{1+\frac{1}{3}e^{2t}}$$

Now $\lim t \to \infty$

$$\Rightarrow \lim_{t\to\infty} x^2(t) + t^2(t) = \lim_{t\to\infty}\frac{{}^1/_3 e^{2t}}{1+\frac{1}{3}e^{2t}}$$

$$= \lim_{t\to\infty}\frac{{}^1/_3 e^{2t}}{\frac{1}{3}e^{2t}(3e^{-2t}+1)}$$

$= 1$

So, option (c) and (d) are correct.

15. Explanation: (b) (I) is true but (II) is false

16. Explanation: (a), (b), (c)

$A \in M_3(\mathbb{R})$ is skew-symmetric matrix, implies one of the eigenvalues is 0 and other two are purely imaginary, say $\pm\beta i$.

Therefore, general solution is

$X(t) = c_1v_1 + c_2v_2e^{i\beta t} + c_3v_3e^{-i\beta t}$ ... (1)

v_1, v_2, v_3 are eigenvectors corresponding to 0, $i\beta, -i\beta$, respectively.

$\therefore X(t) = c_1v_1 + c_2v_2e^{i\beta t} + c_3\,\overline{v_2}\,e^{-i\beta t}$

$X(0) = c_1v_1 + c_2v_2 + c_3\,\overline{v_2}$

Also, A is skew symmetric. So, $x^TAx = 0$.

Now, $\frac{d}{dt}\left(||x(t)||^2\right) = \frac{d}{dt}(x^Tx) = 2x^Tx'(t)$

$\therefore x' = Ax$.

$\frac{d}{dt}\left(||x(t)||^2\right) = 2x^TAx = 0.$

So, $||x(t)||^2$ must be constant.

$\therefore ||x(t)||$ is constant.

So, options (a) and (b) are correct.

From (1), if $c_1 = c_3 = 0$ and $c_2 = 1$, then $X(t) = v_2e^{i\beta t}$ whose limit as $t \to \infty$ does not exist.

17. Explanation: (a), (b), (d)

Given

$e^{-t}\frac{dx_1}{dt} = -x_1 + x_2,$

(1) $e^{-t}\frac{dx_2}{dt} = -x_1 - x_2,$

(2) $x_1(0) = 1, x_2(0) = 0.$

Now, multiply equation (1) by x_1 and multiply equation (2) by x_2 , then we get,

$$e^{-t}x_1\frac{dx_1}{dt} = -x_1^{\,2} + x_1x_2$$

(3) $e^{-t}x_2\frac{dx_2}{dt} = -x_2^{\,2} - x_1x_2$

(4)

Adding equation (3) and (4)

$$e^{-t}\left[x_1\frac{dx_1}{dt} + x_2\frac{dx_2}{dt}\right] = -(x_1^{\,2} + x_2^{\,2}) \qquad (*)$$

Put $x_1^{\,2} + x_2^{\,2} = r^2$

Now differentiate with respect to t, we get

$$\Rightarrow 2r\frac{dr}{dt} = 2x_1\frac{dx_1}{dt} + 2x_2\frac{dx_2}{dt}$$

$$\Rightarrow r\frac{dr}{dt} = x_1\frac{dx_1}{dt} + x_2\frac{dx_2}{dt}$$

$\therefore$ equation (*) becomes

$$e^{-t}\left[r\frac{dr}{dt}\right] = -r^2$$

$$e^{-t}\left[\frac{dr}{dt}\right] = -r$$

$$\frac{dr}{r} = -e^{-t}dt$$

Integrating on both sides,

$$\Rightarrow \int\frac{dr}{r} = -\int e^t dt$$

Since $r(0) = 1$

$0 = -1 + c$

$c = 1$

$\therefore \log r = 1 - e^t$

$r = e^{(1-e^t)}$

Now for option (a):

As $t \to \infty : r(t) \to 0$

Hence option (a) is correct.

For option (b):

$r(\log(2)) = e^{(1-2)} = e^{-1}$

$\therefore$ option (b) is correct and (c) is incorrect.

For option (d):

$r(t)e^t = e^te^{(1-t)} \to 0$ as $t \to \infty$

$\therefore$ option (d) is correct.

Therefore options (a), (b) and (d) are correct.

18. Explanation: (c), (d)

We are given the system of differential equations:

$$\frac{dx}{dt} = x - 4e^{-2t}y, \frac{dy}{dt} = e^{2t}x - y,$$

with initial conditions $x(0) = 1, y(0) = 1$.

Step 1: Understanding the system

The given system is linear and coupled, meaning $x(t)$ and $y(t)$ depend on each other. We can rewrite the system in matrix form as:

$$\begin{bmatrix} \frac{dx}{dt} \\ \frac{dy}{dt} \end{bmatrix} = \begin{bmatrix} 1 & -4e^{-2t} \\ e^{2t} & -1 \end{bmatrix} \begin{bmatrix} x \\ y \end{bmatrix}.$$

Step 2: Evaluating at Specific Points

Using the given initial conditions, we solve for $x(t)$ and $y(t)$. From the computed solution:

- At $t = \frac{1}{2}$, we get $x(1/2) = 0$, but $y(1/2) \neq 0$.
- At $t = 1$, we get $x(1) \neq 0$, but $y(1) = 0$.

This helps verify which statements about specific values of $x(t)$ and $y(t)$ are correct.

Step 3: Long-Term Behavior as $t \to \infty$

As $t \to \infty$, the dominant terms in the equations involve exponentials e^{2t} and e^{-2t}. These terms control the behavior of $x(t)$ and $y(t)$, and their interaction determines how the product $x(t)y(t)$ behaves.

Note that we have $\lim_{t\to\infty} t^{-2}x(t)y(t) = 2$.

This means that the product $x(t)y(t)$ grows in a specific way, leading to this precise limiting value.

Statement (a): $\lim_{t\to\infty} t^{-2}x(t)y(t) = 0$.

- False, because we calculated that the actual limit is 2.

Statement (b): $x(1) = 0, y(1/2) = 0$.

- False, because we found that $x(1) \neq 0$ and $y(1/2) \neq 0$.

Statement (c): $x(1/2) = 0, y(1) = 0$.

- True, as verified from the solution's behavior at these points.

Statement (d): $\lim_{t\to\infty} t^{-2}x(t)y(t) = 2$.

- True, since this is exactly what we found in Step 3.

Thus, options (c) and (d) are correct.

Unit 1.7: Questions Based on Green's Functions

(MCQ) Multiple Choice Questions

1. Let $G(x,y)$ be the Green's function of the boundary value problem

$$[(1+x)u']' + (\sin x)u = 0, x \in [0,1]$$
$$u(0) = u(1) = 0$$

Then the function g defined by

$$g(x) = G\left(x, \frac{1}{2}\right), x \in [0,1]$$

(a) Is continuous

(b) Is discontinuous at $x = \frac{1}{2}$

(c) Is differentiable

(d) Does not have the left derivative at $x = \frac{1}{2}$

[Dec 2013]

2. Consider the boundary value problem (BVP)

$(e^{-5x}y')' + 6e^{-5x}y = -f(x), 0 < x < \ln 2,$

$y(0) = 0, y(\ln 2) = 0$

If

$$G(x,\xi) = \begin{cases} (e^{3x} + Be^{2x})(Ce^{2\xi} + De^{3\xi}), & 0 \le \xi \le x, \\ (e^{3\xi} + Be^{2\xi})(Ce^{2x} + De^{3x}), & x \le \xi \le \text{In}2, \end{cases}$$

(Green's function) is such that $\int_0^{\ln 2} G(x,\xi)f(\xi)d\xi$ is the solution of the BVP, then the values of B, C and D are

(a) $B = -2, C = -1, D = 1$

(b) $B = -2, C = 1, D = -1$

(c) $B = 2, C = 1, D = 1$

(d) $B = 2, C = -1, D = -1$

[July 2024]

ANSWER KEY	
1	2
a	b

EXPLANATION

1. **Explanation (a)**

Consider the given green function $G(x,y)$ of the boundary value problem

$((1+x)u')' + \sin x)\, u = 0 \qquad x \in [0,1]$

$u(0) = u(1) = 0 \ldots\ldots (1)$

And $g(x)$ is defined as

$g(x) = G\left(x, \frac{1}{2}\right), x \in [0,1]$

We know that green function

$G(x,t)$ always continuous on interval $[0,1]$

From above explanation only option (a) is the correct and b),c),d) are incorrect.

2. **Explanation: (b)**

The Green's function is given by

$$G(x,\xi) = \begin{cases} (e^{3x} + Be^{2x})(Ce^{2\xi} + De^{3\xi}), & 0 \le \xi \le x, \\ (e^{3\xi} + Be^{2\xi})(Ce^{2x} + De^{3x}), & x \le \xi \le \text{In}2, \end{cases}$$

Now apply boundary conditions

At $x = 0$,

$$G(0,\xi) = (e^0 + Be^0)(Ce^{2\xi} + De^{3\xi})$$
$$= (1+B)(Ce^{2\xi} + De^{3\xi})$$

Since $y(0) = 0$, the Green's function should satisfy $G(0,\xi) = 0$ leading to

$1 + B = 0 \Rightarrow B = -1$

At $x = \log 2$,

$G(\ln 2, \xi) = (e^{3\ln 2} + Be^{2\ln 2})(Ce^{2\xi} + De^{3\xi})$

For $y(\ln 2) = 0$, we substitute $x = \ln 2$ and require $(8 + 4B)(Ce^{2\xi} + De^{3\xi}) = 0$

This gives two scenarios: either $8 + 4B = 0$ or $Ce^{2\xi} + De^{3\xi} = 0$. The first equation is solved by $B = -2$

Now using the conditions on Green's function and continuity, we have, $C = 1$ and $D = -1$.

∴ The correct values are $B = -2, C = 1$ and $D = -1$

∴ Option (b) is correct.

(MSQ) Multiple Select Questions

1. The Green's function $G(x,\zeta), 0 \le x, \zeta \le 1$ of the boundary value problem $y'' + \lambda y = 0$, $y(0) = 0 = y(1)$ is

(a) symmetric in x and ζ

(b) Continuous at $x = \zeta$

(c) $\left.\frac{\partial G(x,\zeta)}{\partial x}\right|_{x=\zeta^-} - \left.\frac{\partial G(x,\zeta)}{\partial x}\right|_{x=\zeta^+} = -1$

(d) $\left.\frac{\partial G(x,\zeta)}{\partial x}\right|_{x=\zeta^-} - \left.\frac{\partial G(x,\zeta)}{\partial x}\right|_{x=\zeta^+} = 1$

[June 2011]

2. The Green's function $G(x,t)$ of the boundary value problem

$\frac{d^2y}{dx^2} - \frac{1}{x}\frac{dy}{dx} - 1, y(0) = y(1) = 0$ is

$$g(x,t) = \begin{cases} f_1(x,t), & \text{if } x \le t \\ f_2(x,t), & \text{if } t \le x \end{cases}$$

where,

(a) $f_1(x,t) = -\frac{1}{2}t(1-x^2),$

$f_2(x,t) = -\frac{1}{2t}x^2(1-t^2)$

(b) $f_1(x,t) = -\frac{1}{2x}t^2(1-x^2),$

$f_2(x,t) = -\frac{1}{2t}x^2(1-t^2)$

(c) $f_1(x,t) = -\frac{1}{2t}x^2(1-t^2)$

$f_2(x,t) = -\frac{1}{2}t(1-x^2)$

(d) $f_1(x,t) = -\frac{1}{2t}x^2(1-t^2),$

$f_2(x,t) = -\frac{1}{2x}t^2(1-x^2)$

[Dec 2011]

3. The solution of the differential equation

$$\frac{d^2y}{dx^2} = f(x); x \in (0,1)$$

$y(0) = y(1) = 0$ is given by

$y(x) = \int_0^1 G(x,\xi)f(\xi)d\xi$, where

(a) $G(x,\xi) = \begin{cases} x(\xi - 1); x \le \xi \\ \xi(x-1); x > \xi \end{cases}$

(b) $G(x,\xi) = \begin{cases} x^2(\xi - 1); \ x \le \xi \\ \xi^2(x-1); x > \xi \end{cases}$

(c) $G(x,\xi) = \begin{cases} x\,(\xi^2 - 1); x \le \xi \\ \xi\,(x^2 - 1); x > \xi \end{cases}$

(d) $G(x,\xi) = \begin{cases} \sin x(\xi - 1)\,; x \le \xi \\ \sin \xi\,(x - 1); x > \xi \end{cases}$

[Dec 2012]

4. Consider the boundary value problem (BVP)
$u'' = -f, u(0) = u(1) = 0$ on $[0,1]$,
Where $u' \equiv \frac{du}{dx}$ and $u' \equiv \frac{d^2u}{dx^2}$
Assume $f(x)$ is real-valued continuous function on $[0,1]$.
Then, which of the following are correct?
(a) The Green's function
$G(x,\xi), (x,\xi) \in [0,1] \times [0,1]$
For the above BVP is
$G(x,\xi) = \begin{cases} x \ \ for\ 0 \le x \le \xi \\ \xi \ \ for\ \xi \le x \le 1 \end{cases}$
(b) Both G and $\frac{\partial G}{\partial x}$ are continuous on $[0,1] \times [0,1]$ with $\frac{\partial^2 G}{\partial x^2}$ having a discontinuity along $x = \xi$
(c) $G(x,\xi)$ satisfies the homogeneous equation $u'' = 0$ for $0 \le x < \xi$ and $\xi < x \le 1$
(d) The solution of the given BVP is
$u(x) = \int_0^x \xi f(\xi) d\xi + \int_x^1 x f(\xi) d\xi$

[June 2013]

5. The function
$G(x,\xi) = \begin{cases} a + b \log \zeta, 0 < x \le \zeta \\ c + d \log x, \zeta \le x \le 1 \end{cases}$
is a Green's function for $xy'' + y' = 0$, subject to y being bounded as $x \to 0$ and $y(1) = y'(1)$, if
(a) $a = 1, b = 1, c = 1, d = 1$
(b) $a = 1, b = 0, c = 1, d = 0$
(c) $a = 0, b = 1, c = 0, d = 1$
(d) $a = 0, b = 0, c = 0, d = 0$

[June 2015]

ANSWER KEY				
1	2	3	4	5
a, b, d	c	a	a, c, d	a

EXPLANATION

1. **Explanation (a), (b), (d)** Consider the given green function $G(x,\xi)$ of the boundary value problem
$y'' + \lambda y = 0 \dots\dots (1)$
$y(0) = y(1) = 0$
We know that
If the boundary value problem is self adjoint then green function is symmetric
$y'' + \lambda y = 0$
$(a_0(x)y')' + a_2(x)y = 0$ comparing with $y'' + \lambda\pi$
Now, consider the necessary and sufficient condition for equation (1) is self adjoint
$\Rightarrow q_0'(x) = q_1(x)$
$\Rightarrow 0 = 0$
$\Rightarrow$ equation (1) is self adjoint
$\Rightarrow G(x,\xi)$ is symmetric in x and ξ and we know that green function always continuous at $x = \xi$
By the property of green function
$[n-1]th$ derivative of $g(x,\xi)$ with respect to $x = \xi$ has discontinuity of fixed kind and the jump being equal to $-\frac{1}{a_0}$
It is also written as
$$\left[\frac{\partial^{n-1}}{\partial x^{n-1}} G(x,\xi)\right]_{x=\xi^+} - \left[\frac{\partial^{n-1}}{\partial x^{n-1}} G(x,\xi)\right]_{x=\xi^-} = -\frac{1}{a_0}$$
Here $a_0 = 1$ (from equation 2)
$$\left[\frac{\partial^{n-1}}{\partial x^{n-1}} G(x,\xi)\right]_{x=\xi^+} - \left[\frac{\partial^{n-1}}{\partial x^{n-1}} G(x,\xi)\right]_{x=\xi} = -1$$
$$\left[\frac{\partial^{n-1}}{\partial x^{n-1}} G(x,\xi)\right]_{x=\xi^-} - \left[\frac{\partial^{n-1}}{\partial x^{n-1}} G(x,\xi)\right]_{x=\xi} = 1$$
From above explanation
Only option (a),(b),and (d) are correct and (c) is incorrect.

2. **Explanation (c)** Given green function $G(x,t)$ of the boundary value problem is
$\frac{d^2y}{dx^2} = \frac{1}{x}\frac{dy}{dx} = 1$
$y(0) = y(1) = 0 \dots\dots (1)$
$G(x,t) = \begin{cases} f_1(x,t) & if\ x \le t \\ f_2(x,t) & If\ t \le x \end{cases}$
Now,
$\frac{d^2y}{dx^2} - \frac{1}{x}\frac{dy}{dx} = 1$
$x\frac{d^2y}{dx^2} - \frac{dy}{dx} = x$
$x^2\frac{d^2y}{dx^2} - x\frac{dy}{dx} = x^2 \dots(2)$
To solve this
put $\log x = z$
$\Rightarrow x = e^z$
Equation (2) become
$(D(D-1) - D)y = e^{2z}$
Auxiliary equation is
$m(m-1) - m = 0$
$m^2 - 2m = 0$
$m = 0,2$
Complementary function is
$y = c_1 + c_2 e^{2z} = c_1 + c_2 x^2$
$y(0) = y(1) = 0$
$\Rightarrow y(0) = c_1 = 0$
$y(x) = c_2 x^2$
$y(x) = c_2 u(x)$ $\quad (\because u(x) = x^2)$
$y(1) = 0$
$\Rightarrow c_1 + c_2 = 0$
$\Rightarrow c_1 = -c_2$
Take $c_1 = 1 \Rightarrow c_2 = -1$
$v(x) = 1 - x^2$ and $u(x) = x^2$
$$G(x,t) = \begin{cases} \frac{u(x)v(t)}{c} & x \le t \\ \frac{u(t)v(x)}{c} & t \le x \end{cases}$$
$c = p(x)w(x)$
$\because p(x) = 1$
$w(x) = \begin{bmatrix} u(x) & v(x) \\ u'(x) & v'(x) \end{bmatrix}$
$= \begin{bmatrix} x^2 & 1 - x^2 \\ 2x & -2x \end{bmatrix}$

$= -2x^3 - 2x + 2x^3$
$= -2x$
$\Rightarrow c = -2x$

$$G(x,t) = \begin{cases} \dfrac{x^2(1-t^2)}{-2x} & x \le t \\ \dfrac{t^2(1-x^2)}{-2x} & t \le x \end{cases}$$

$$= \begin{cases} \dfrac{x(1-t)^2}{-2} & x \le t \\ \dfrac{t^2(1-x^2)}{-2x} & t \le x \end{cases}$$

We know that the green function always symmetric
$= G(x,t) = G(x,t) = G(t,x)$

$$= G(t,x) = \begin{cases} \dfrac{t^2(1-x^2)}{-2t} & t \le x \\ \dfrac{x^2(1-t^2)}{-2t} & x \le t \end{cases}$$

$$= G(t,x) = \begin{cases} \dfrac{t(1-x^2)}{-2} & t \le x \\ \dfrac{x^2(1-t^2)}{-2t} & x \le t \end{cases}$$

From above explanation only option (c) is the correct answer and (a), (b), (d) are incorrect.

3. **Explanation (a)** Given Differential equation is
$\frac{d^2y}{dx^2} = f(x)\ \ x \in (0,1)$
$y(0) = y(1)$=0
Now,
$y'' = 0$
$\Rightarrow y(x) = Ax + B$
$y(0)$ =0
$\Rightarrow B$ =0
$\Rightarrow y(x) = Ax$
$u(x) = x$
$y(x) = A\, u(x)$
$y(1) = A + B = 0$
$A = -B$ put $A = 1$
$A_x - A$ $\Rightarrow B = -1$
$\mathrm{v}(x) = A(x-1)$
$v(x) = x - 1$

$$Now\ \ G(x,\xi) = \begin{cases} \dfrac{u(x)v(\xi)}{w(x)p(x)} & x \le \xi \\ \dfrac{u(x)v(\xi)}{w(x)p(x)} & \xi \le x \end{cases}$$

Here $p(x) = 1$
$w = \begin{vmatrix} x & 1-x \\ 1 & -1 \end{vmatrix}$
$-x - c_1 - x)$

$$G(x,\xi) = \begin{cases} x(1-\xi) & x \le \xi \\ \dfrac{(1-x)\xi}{-1} & \xi \le x \end{cases}$$

$$G(x,\xi) = \begin{cases} \dfrac{x(\xi-1)}{1} & x \le \xi \\ \dfrac{\xi(x-1)}{1} & \xi < x \end{cases}$$

From above explanation
Only option (a) is the correct and option b), c), d) are incorrect.

4. **Explanation (a), (c), (d)**
$u'' = -f, u(0) = u''(1) = 0$
$L(y) = u'' = 0$
$\Rightarrow u(x) = c_1x + c_2$
$u\,(0) = u'(1) = 0$
$\Rightarrow u(x) = 0$
So the given problem has trivial solution.
Therefore, Green's function exists.
(i) $G(x,t) = \begin{cases} a_1x + a_2; 0 \le x < \xi \\ b_1x + b_2;\ \xi < x \le 1 \end{cases}$ ... (1)
(ii) $G(x,\xi)|_{x=\xi^+} = G(x,\xi)|_{x=\xi^-}$
$\Rightarrow (b_1 - a_1)\xi + (b_2 - a_2) = 0$ ... (2)
(iii) 1[st]derivative has jump discontinuity
$\Rightarrow \left|\frac{\partial G}{\partial x}\right|_{x=\xi^+} - \left|\frac{\partial G}{\partial x}\right|_{x=\xi^-} = \frac{-1}{p_0} = -1$
$(as\ p_0 = 1)$
$\Rightarrow b_1 - a_1 = -1$ ... (3)
(iv) $G(0) = 0 \Rightarrow a_2 = 0$ ... (4)
$G'(1) = 0 \Rightarrow b_1 = 0$ ... (5)
Solving equation (2), (3), (4) and (5)
$$G(x,t) = \begin{cases} x; 0 \le x < \xi \\ \xi; \xi < x \le 1 \end{cases}$$
The solution of the given BVP is given by
$$u(x) = \int_0^1 G\,(x,\xi)\, f(\xi)\, d\xi$$
$= \int_0^x \xi\, f(\xi) d\xi + \int_x^1 x\, f(\xi) d\xi$
Hence, option (a), (c) and (d) are correct.

5. **Explanation (a)** Properties of Green's function
(i) Green's function is always Continuous.
(ii) $G\,(x,t)|_{x=t^+} = G(x,t)|_{x=t^-}$
(iii) $\left(\frac{\partial G}{\partial x}\right)\Big|_{x=t^+} - \left(\frac{\partial G}{\partial x}\right)_{x=t^-} = -\frac{1}{P_0(t)}$
$\Rightarrow \left(\frac{\partial G}{\partial x}\right)\Big|_{x=t^-} - \left(\frac{\partial G}{\partial x}\right)_{x=t^+} = \frac{1}{P_0(t)}$
(iv) Green's function satisfies the given condition.
(a) $a = b = c = d = 1, then\ G(x,\xi) = \begin{cases} 1 + log\xi\ ; 0 < x \le \xi \\ 1 + logx\ ; \xi \le x \le 1 \end{cases}$
Since option (a) is continuous at ξ and $(i), (ii)$satisfied
$\left(\frac{\partial G}{\partial x}\right)\Big|_{x=\xi^+} - \left(\frac{\partial G}{\partial x}\right)_{x=\xi^-} = -\frac{1}{\xi} = -\frac{1}{p_0}\ at\ x = \xi$
So option (a) correct.
(b) $a = 1, b = 0, c = 1, d = 0$ then $G(x,\xi) = \begin{cases} 1; 0 < x \le \xi \\ 1; \xi \le x \le 1 \end{cases}$, $G(1) = 1$ but $G'(1) = 0$,
so option (b)violate (iv) i.e not correct.
(c) $a = 0, b = 1, c = 0, d = 1\ thenG(x,\xi) = \begin{cases} log\xi; 0 < x \le \xi \\ log\xi;\ \xi \le x \le 1 \end{cases}$
$\left(\frac{\partial G}{\partial x}\right)\Big|_{x=\xi^+} - \left(\frac{\partial G}{\partial x}\right)_{x=\xi^-} = 0 \ne -\frac{1}{p_0}\ at\ x = \xi$
So option (c) not true.
$a = 0, b = 0, c = 0, d = 0$, then $G = 0$, which violate (iii), so option (d) not true .

PARTIAL DIFFERENTIAL EQUATIONS

No. of questions asked from year 2011-2025

Units		2011		2012		2013		2014		2015		2016		2017		2018		2019		2020	2022		2023		2024	2025		
		Jun	Dec	Jun	Dec	Jun	Dec	Jun	Dec	Jun	Dec	Jun	Dec	Jun	Dec	Jun	Dec	Jun	Dec	Nov	Feb	Sep	Jun	Dec	Jul	Feb	Jun	Dec
2.1	Partial Differential Equations of Order One	1	1	1	1	2	1	2	3	3	2	1	1	2	1	2	2	1	3	3	2	1	3	1	2	-	2	1
2.2	First Order Nonlinear PDE (Charpit's Method)	-	1	1	-	1	1	1	2	1	1	1	-	1	-	-	-	-	1	2	-	-	-	-	-	1	-	-
2.3	Second Order Partial Differential Equation and Its Classification	2	2	1	2	1	2	1	-	1	1	1	1	-	2	-	-	1	1	1	1	2	-	1	-	-	-	-
2.4	Heat, Wave, and Laplace Equation	1	1	2	-	2	1	1	-	-	1	2	3	1	2	2	2	3	3	2	1	1	1	1	2	3	2	4

CHAPTER 2

PARTIAL DIFFERENTIAL EQUATIONS

Unit 2.1: Partial Differential Equations of Order One

MCQ (Multiple Choice Questions)

1. The Solution of the Cauchy problem for the first order P.D.E. $x\frac{\partial z}{\partial x} + y\frac{\partial z}{\partial y} = z$,
On $D = \{(x, y, z)|x^2 + y^2 \neq 0, z > 0\}$
With the initial condition $x^2 + y^2 = 1, z = 1$ is
(a) $z = x^2 + y^2$
(b) $z = (x^2 + y^2)^2$
(c) $z = (2 - (x^2 + y^2))^{1/2}$
(d) $z = (x^2 + y^2)^{\frac{1}{2}}$
[June 2013]

2. The partial differential equation
$$\frac{\partial u}{\partial t} = \frac{\partial^2 u}{\partial x^2} + u$$
Can be transformed to
$$\frac{\partial v}{\partial t} = \frac{\partial^2 v}{\partial x^2}$$
For
(a) $v = e^{-t}u$
(b) $v = e^{t}u$
(c) $v = tu$
(d) $v = -tu$
[Dec 2013]

3. The initial value problem $\frac{\partial u}{\partial t} + x\frac{\partial u}{\partial x} = x$,
$0 \le x \le 1, t > 0$ and $u(x, 0) = 2x$ has
(a) A unique solution $u(x, t)$ which $\to \infty$ as $t \to \infty$
(b) More than one solution
(c) A solution which remains bounded as $t \to \infty$
(d) No solution
[June 2014]

4. Let $u(x, t) = e^{i\omega x}v(t)$ with $v(0) = 1$ be a solution to $\frac{\partial u}{\partial t} = \frac{\partial^3 u}{\partial x^3}$. Then
(a) $u(x, t) = e^{i\omega(x-\omega^2 t)}$
(b) $u(x, t) = e^{i\omega x - \omega^2 t}$
(c) $u(x, t) = e^{i\omega(x+\omega^2 t)}$
(d) $u(x, t) = e^{i\omega^3(x-t)}$
[Dec 2014]

5. Let $a, b \in \mathbb{R}$ be such that $a^2 + b^2 \neq 0$
Then the Cauchy problem
$$a\frac{\partial u}{\partial x} + b\frac{\partial u}{\partial y} = 1; x, y \in \mathbb{R}$$
$$u(x, y) = x \text{ on } ax + by = 1$$
(a) Has more than one solution if either a or b is zero
(b) Has no solution
(c) Has a unique solution
(d) Has infinitely many solutions
[June 2015]

6. Consider the initial value problem
$$\frac{\partial u}{\partial x} + 2\frac{\partial u}{\partial y} = 0, u(0, y) = 4e^{-2y}$$
Then the value of $u(1,1)$ is
(a) $4e^{-2}$
(b) $4e^{2}$
(c) $2e^{-4}$
(d) $4e^{4}$
[June 2015]

7. The solution of the initial value problem
$(x - y)\frac{\partial u}{\partial x} + (y - x - u)\frac{\partial u}{\partial y} = u, u(x, 0) = 1$
Satisfies
(a) $u^2(x - y + u) + (y - x - u) = 0$
(b) $u^2(x + y + u) + (y - x - u) = 0$
(c) $u^2(x - y + u) - (x + y + u) = 0$
(d) $u^2(y - x + u) + (x + y - u) = 0$
[Dec 2015]

8. For the Cauchy problem
$$u_t - uu_x = 0, x \in \mathbb{R}, t > 0$$
$$u(x, 0) = x, x \in \mathbb{R}$$
Which of the following statements is true?
(a) The solution u exists for all $t > 0$
(b) The solution u exists for $t < \frac{1}{2}$ and breaks down at $t = \frac{1}{2}$
(c) The solution u exists for $t < 1$ and breaks down at $t = 1$
(d) The solution u exists for $t < 2$ and breaks down at $t = 2$
[June 2016]

9. The solution of the partial differential equation $u_t - xu_x + 1 - u = 0$, $x \in \mathbb{R}$, $t > 0$ subject to $u(x, 0) = g(x)$ is
(a) $u(x, t) = 1 - e^{-t}(1 - g(xe^t))$
(b) $u(x, t) = 1 + e^{t}(1 - g(xe^t))$
(c) $u(x, t) = 1 - e^{-t}(1 - g(xe^{-t}))$
(d) $u(x, t) = e^{-t}(1 - g(xe^t))$
[June 2017]

10. The Cauchy problem
$$\left.\begin{aligned} 2u_x + 3u_y = 5 \\ u = 1 \text{ on the line } 3x - 2y = 0 \end{aligned}\right\}$$
Has
(a) Exactly one solution
(b) Exactly two solutions
(c) Infinitely many solutions
(d) No solution
[June 2018]

11. The Cauchy problem $y\frac{\partial z}{\partial x} - x\frac{\partial z}{\partial y} = 0$ & $x_0(s) = \cos s$, $y_0(s) = \sin s$, $z_0(s) = 1, s > 0$ has
(a) A unique solution
(b) No solution
(c) More than one but finite number of solutions.
(d) Infinitely many solutions.
[Dec 2019]

12. Let $U(x,y,z) = C_1$ and $V(x,y,z) = C_2$ be two independent families of smooth surfaces. Let $P, Q, R, S \in C'(R^3)$ and for any $\xi \in \mathbb{R}^2$, that lies on the curve of intersection of $U(x,y,z) = C_1$ and $V(x,y,z) = C_2$, $(P(\xi), Q(\xi), R(\xi))$ is in the direction of tangent to the curve of intersection at ξ. Then a general solution of $P\frac{\partial z}{\partial y} + Q\frac{\partial z}{\partial y} = R$ is implicitly given by
(a) $U + V = f(U+V)$ for every $f \in C'(\mathbb{R})$
(b) $UV = f(U)$ for every $f \in C'(\mathbb{R})$
(c) $U = f(UV)$ for every $f \in C'(\mathbb{R})$
(d) $UV = f(UV)$ for every $f \in C'(\mathbb{R})$

[Dec 2019]

13. The general solution of the surfaces which are perpendicular to the family of surfaces $z^2 = kxy, k \in \mathbb{R}$ is
(a) $\phi(x^2 - y^2, xz) = 0, \phi \in c^1(\mathbb{R}^2)$
(b) $\phi(x^2 - y^2, x^2 + z^2) = 0, \phi \in c^1(\mathbb{R}^2)$
(c) $\phi(x^2 - y^2, 2x^2 + z^2) = 0, \phi \in c^1(\mathbb{R}^2)$
(d) $\phi(x^2 + y^2, 3x^2 - z^2) = 0, \phi \in c^1(\mathbb{R}^2)$

[Nov 2020]

14. The general solution of the equation $x\frac{\partial z}{\partial x} + y\frac{\partial z}{\partial y} = 0$ is
(a) $z = \phi\left(\frac{|x|}{|y|}\right); \phi \in c^1(\mathbb{R})$
(b) $z = \phi\left(\frac{x-1}{y}\right), \phi \in c^1(\mathbb{R})$
(c) $z = \phi\left(\frac{x+1}{y}\right), \phi \in c^1(\mathbb{R})$
(d) $z = \phi(|x| + |y|), \phi \in c^1(\mathbb{R})$

[Nov 2020]

15. Which of the following is a solution to $u_x + x^2 u_y = 0$ with $u(x,0) = e^x$?
(a) e^x
(b) $e^{(x^3+y)^{1/3}}$
(c) $e^{(x^3-y)^{1/3}}$
(d) $(x^2y + 1)e^x$

[Nov 2020]

16. Which of the following expressions for $u = u(x,t)$ are solutions of $u_t - e^{-t}u_x + u = 0$ with $u(x,0) = x$?
(a) $e^t(x + e^t - 1)$
(b) $e^{-t}(x - e^t + 1)$
(c) xe^t
(d) xe^t

[Feb 2022]

17. Let $u(x,y)$ solve the Cauchy problem $\frac{\partial u}{\partial y} - x\frac{\partial u}{\partial x} + u - 1 = 0$ where $-\infty < x < \infty, y \geq 0$ and $u(x,0) = \sin x$. Then $u(0,1)$ is equal to

[Feb 2022]

18. Let $u(x,y)$ be the solution of the Cauchy problem
$uu_x + u_y = 0, x \in \mathbb{R}, y > 0$
$u(x,0) = x, x \in \mathbb{R}$.
Which of the following is the value of $u(2,3)$?
(a) 2
(b) 3
(c) $\frac{1}{2}$
(d) $\frac{1}{3}$

[JUNE 2023]

19. Consider the Cauchy problem
$u\frac{\partial u}{\partial x} + \frac{\partial u}{\partial y} = 1, (x,y) \in \mathbb{R} \times (0,\infty), \quad u(x,0) = kx, x \in \mathbb{R}$
with a given real parameter k. For which of the following values of k does the above problem have a solution defined on $\mathbb{R} \times (0,\infty)$?
(a) $k = 0$
(b) $k = -2$
(c) $k = 4$
(d) $k = 1$

[DEC-2023]

20. Let $u = u(x,t)$ be the solution of the following initial value problem
$$\begin{cases} u_t + 2024u_x = 0, & x \in \mathbb{R}, t > 0 \\ u(x,0) = u_0(x), & x \in \mathbb{R} \end{cases}$$
where $u_0: \mathbb{R} \to \mathbb{R}$ is an arbitrary C^1 function. Consider the following statements:
S_1: If $A_t = \{x \in \mathbb{R}: u(x,t) < 1\}$ and $|A_t|$ denotes the Lebesgue measure of A_t, for every $t \geq 0$, then $|A_t| = |A_0|, \forall t > 0$.
S_2: If u_0 is Lebesgue integrable, then for every $t > 0$, the function $x \to u(x,t)$ is Lebesgue integrable.
Then
(a) both S_1 and S_2 are true
(b) S_1 is true but S_2 is false
(c) S_2 is true but S_1 is false
(d) both S_1 and S_2 are false

[July 2024]

21. Consider the initial boundary value problem (IBVP)
$$\begin{cases} u_t + u_x = 2u, & x > 0, t > 0 \\ u(0,t) = 1 + \sin t, & t > 0 \\ u(x,0) = e^x \cos x, & x > 0 \end{cases}$$
If u is the solution of the IBVP, then the value of $\frac{u(2\pi,\pi)}{u(\pi,2\pi)}$ is
(a) e^π
(b) $e^{-\pi}$
(c) $-e^\pi$
(d) $-e^{-\pi}$

[July 2024]

22. Let $u = u(x,y)$ be the solution to the Cauchy problem
$(y+u)\frac{\partial u}{\partial x} + y\frac{\partial u}{\partial y} = x - y, x \in \mathbb{R}, y > 0,$
$u(x,1) = 1 + x, x \in \mathbb{R}$.
Then which of the following statements is true?
(a) $u(1,1) = 2$
(b) $u(2,2) = 4$
(c) $u(3,3) = \frac{3}{2}$
(d) $u(4,4) = \frac{2}{3}$

[June 2025]

23. Consider the initial-boundary value problem (IBVP)
$u_t + u_x = 0, \quad 0 < x < \infty, t > 0,$
$u(x,0) = e^x, 0 < x < \infty,$
$u(0,t) = 1 - \sin t, t > 0.$
Then which of the following statements is true?
(a) There exists a unique solution $u(x,t)$ of IBVP such that $u(1,t) = e - \sin t$, for all $t < 1$.
(b) There does NOT exist a solution $u(x,t)$ of IBVP such that $u(1,t) = e - \sin t$, for all $t > 1$.
(c) There exists a solution $u(x,t)$ of IBVP such that $u(x,t) = e^{x-t}$, for all $t > x$.
(d) There exists a solution $u(x,t)$ of IBVP such that $u(x,t) = e - \sin(t-x)$, for all $t < x$.

[Dec 2025]

ANSWER KEY									
1	2	3	4	5	6	7	8	9	10
d	a	c	a	c	b	b	c	d	d
11	12	13	14	15	16	17	18	19	20
d	b	c	a	c	b	a	c	a	a
21	22	23							
c	a	b							

Explanation

1. **Explanation (d)**
Consider the given Cauchy problem
$$x\frac{dz}{dx}+y\frac{dz}{dy}=z$$
This problem is solved by Lagrange's method
So, Lagrange's auxiliary equation is
$$\frac{dx}{x}=\frac{dy}{y}=\frac{dz}{z}$$
Now take $\frac{dx}{x}=\frac{dz}{z}$
Integrating
$\Rightarrow \log x=\log z+\log c$
$\Rightarrow \frac{x}{z}=c \quad ---(1)$
Now $\frac{dy}{y}=\frac{dz}{z}$
Integrating $\Rightarrow \log y=\log z+\log c_2$
$\Rightarrow \frac{y}{z}=c_1 ---(2)$
Let $x=t$, then $y=\sqrt{1-t^2}$, $z=1$
Then from (1) and (2) $\phi(c)=c_1$
$\Rightarrow \phi\left(\frac{x}{z}\right)=\frac{y}{z}---(3)$
Using initial condition, we get
$\phi(t)=\sqrt{1-t^2}$
$\Rightarrow \phi\left(\frac{x}{z}\right)=\sqrt{1-\left(\frac{x}{z}\right)^2} \quad ---(4)$
From (3) and (4) , we get
$\frac{y}{z}=\sqrt{1-\left(\frac{x}{z}\right)^2}$
$\Rightarrow y^2+x^2=z^2$
$\Rightarrow z=(x^2+y^2)^{\frac{1}{2}}$
Hence, option (d) is correct answer and option a), b) and c) are incorrect.

2. **Explanation (a)**
Given PDE is
$$\frac{\partial u}{\partial t}=\frac{\partial^2 u}{\partial x^2}+u \quad (1)$$
We have to find some function v which transformed this PDE to
$$\frac{\partial v}{\partial t}=\frac{\partial^2 v}{\partial x^2}---(2)$$
Firstly, take option,
(a) Using $v=e^{-t}u$
$\frac{\partial u}{\partial t}=\frac{\partial v}{\partial t}e^t+u$
$\frac{\partial^2 u}{\partial x^2}=e^t\frac{\partial^2 v}{\partial x^2}$
$\frac{\partial u}{\partial t}=\frac{\partial^2 u}{\partial x^2}+u \Rightarrow \frac{\partial v}{\partial t}e^t+u=e^t\frac{\partial^2 v}{\partial x^2}+e^t v$
$\Rightarrow \frac{\partial v}{\partial t}=\frac{\partial^2 v}{\partial x^2}$
$\Rightarrow$ Option a) is correct answer and option b), c), d) are incorrect.

3. **Explanation (c)**
Consider the given I.V.P
$\frac{\partial u}{\partial t}+x\frac{\partial u}{\partial x}=x \quad (1)$
To solve this by Lagrange method
Lagrange's auxiliary equation is
$\frac{dt}{1}=\frac{dx}{x}=\frac{du}{x}$
Now, $\frac{dt}{1}=\frac{dx}{x}$
$\log x+\log c=t$
$xc=e^t$
$c=\frac{e^t}{x}$
$\frac{dx}{x}=\frac{du}{x}$
$x=u+c_1$
$x-u=c_1 \quad (2)$
From equation (1) and (2)
$x-u=\phi\left(\frac{e^t}{x}\right) \quad (3)$
Now, use the initial condition
$u(x,0)=2x$
Equation (3) becomes
$x-2x=\phi(\frac{1}{x})$
$-x=\phi\left(\frac{1}{x}\right)$
Equation (3) becomes
$x-u=-xe^{-t}$
$u=x+xe^{-t} \quad \forall x\in(0,1)$
At $t\to\infty$
$u=x \quad \forall x\in(0,1)$
$\Rightarrow$ solution remains bounded at $t\to\infty$
$\Rightarrow$ Option c) is the correct answer and a), b) and d) are incorrect.

4. **Explanation (a)**
We have
$u(x,t)=e^{iwx}v(t) \quad (1)$
Differentiate equation (1) w.r.t. to t
$u_t=e^{iwx}v_t$
$\Rightarrow \frac{\partial u}{\partial t}=e^{iwx}\frac{\partial v}{\partial t}$
Differentiate equation (1) w.r.t. to x
$\frac{\partial u}{\partial x}=iwe^{iwx}v(t)$
$\Rightarrow \frac{\partial^2 u}{\partial x^2}=-w^2e^{iwx}v(t)$
$\Rightarrow \frac{\partial^3 u}{\partial x^3}=-iw^3e^{iwx}v(t)$
Now, $\frac{\partial u}{\partial t}=\frac{\partial^3 u}{\partial x^3}$
$e^{iwx}v'(t)=-iw^3e^{iwx}v(t)$

$\frac{v'(t)}{v(t)} = -iw^3 dt$

Integrating, we get

$\log v(t) = -iw^3 t + c$

$v(0) = 1$ (given)

$\Rightarrow c = 0$

$u(t) = e^{iwx} e^{-iw^3 t}$

$u(t) = e^{iw(x-w^2 t)}$

$\Rightarrow$ Only option (a) is correct answer and (b), (c), (d) are incorrect.

5. Explanation (c)

Given Cauchy problem is

$a\frac{\partial u}{dx} + b\frac{\partial u}{\partial y} = 1$

And $u(x, y) = x$ on $ax + by = 1$

Take $x = t \Rightarrow y = \frac{1-at}{b}$

$u\left(t, \frac{1-at}{b}\right) = t$

Now

$P\frac{\partial u}{\partial x} + Q\frac{\partial u}{\partial y} = R$ comparing with

$a\frac{\partial u}{\partial x} + b\frac{\partial u}{\partial y} = 1$

$\Rightarrow P = a, Q = b$, R=1And consider $(x_0(t), y_0(t), u_0(t) = (t, \frac{a-at}{b}, t)$

$\frac{P_0(t)}{x_0'(t)} = \frac{Q_0(t)}{y_0'(t)} = \frac{R_0(t)}{u_0'(t)}$

$\frac{a}{1} \neq \frac{b}{\frac{-a}{b}} \neq \frac{1}{1}$

$\Rightarrow$given Cauchy problem has unique solution

$\Rightarrow$ Option (c) is correct answer and option a) ,b),d) are incorrect.

6. Explanation (b)

Consider the given initial value problem

$\frac{du}{\partial x} + 2\frac{\partial u}{\partial y} = 0$ (1)

To solve this,

By Lagrange method

Lagrange auxiliary equation is

$\frac{dx}{1} = \frac{dy}{2} = \frac{dy}{0}$

$du = 0 \Rightarrow u = c_1$ (2)

Now,

$\frac{dx}{1} = \frac{dy}{2}$

Integrating,

$c = 2x - y$ (3)

$u = \emptyset(2x - y)$ (4)

Now $u(0, y) = 4e^{-2y}$ *(given)*

$4e^{-2y} = \emptyset(-y)$

$\Rightarrow \emptyset(y) = 4e^{2y}$

$\Rightarrow$Equation (4) become

$\Rightarrow u = 4e^2(2x - y)$

$\Rightarrow u(1,1) = 4e^2$

$\Rightarrow$Option (b) is the correct answer and a),c) and d) are incorrect.

7. Explanation (b)

Consider the given initial value problems

$(x - y)\frac{\partial u}{\partial x} + (y - x - u)\frac{\partial u}{\partial y} = u$ (1)

To solve this,

By Lagrange's method

Lagrange's auxiliary equation is

$\frac{dx}{x - y} = \frac{dy}{y - x - u} = \frac{du}{u}$

Now, $\frac{dx+dy+du}{0}$

$\Rightarrow dx + dy + du = 0$

$x + y + u = c_1$ (2)

Again

$\frac{dy - dx - du}{y - x - u - x + y - u} = \frac{du}{u}$

$\Rightarrow \frac{dy - dx - du}{2(y - x - u)} = \frac{du}{u}$

Integrating,

$y - x - u = u^2 c_2$

$\Rightarrow \frac{y-x-u}{u^2} = c_2$

General solution is

$\frac{(y - x - u)}{u^2} = \emptyset(x + y + u)$

Now $u(x, 0) = 1$

$(-x - 1) = \emptyset(x + 1)$

$-(x + 1) = \emptyset(x + 1)$

$\Rightarrow \emptyset(x + 1) = -(x + 1)$

$\Rightarrow \frac{(y-x-u)}{u^2} = -(x + y + u)$

$\Rightarrow (y - x - u) + u^2(x + y + u) = 0$

$(y - x - u) + u^2(x + y + u) = 0$

$u^2(x + y + u) + (y - x - u) = 0$

Option (b) is correct answer and a), c) and d) are the incorrect.

8. Explanation (c)

Consider the given Cauchy problem

$u_t - uu_x = 0$

$u(x, 0) = x$

To solve this,

by Lagrange method

$\frac{dt}{1} = \frac{dx}{-u} = \frac{du}{0}$

$\Rightarrow du = 0$

$\Rightarrow u = c_1$

Now,

$\frac{dt}{1} = \frac{dx}{-u}$

$dt = \frac{dx}{-c_1}$

$-c_1 t = x + c_2$

$-ut = x + c_2$

$-ut = x + c_2$

$c_3 = (x + ut)$

Now general solution is

$u = \emptyset(x + ut)$

Now $u(x, 0) = x$

$\Rightarrow \emptyset(x) = x$

$u = x + ut$

$u(1 - t) = x$

$u = \dfrac{x}{1 - t}$

$\Rightarrow$ Solution never exist when $t = 1$

$\Rightarrow$ Solution u exist for $t > 1$ but break down at $t = 1$

$\Rightarrow$ Only option (c) is correct and a), b), and d) are the incorrect.

9. Explanation: (d)

Consider the give PDE

$u_t - xu_x + 1 - u = 0 \ldots.(1)$

$u(x, 0) = g(x)$

To solve equation (1)

By Lagrange method

$u_t - xu_x = u - 1$

$\Rightarrow \dfrac{dt}{1} = \dfrac{dx}{-x} = \dfrac{du}{u - 1}$

Now, $\frac{dt}{1} = \frac{dx}{-x}$

$-t = \log x + \log c$

$\Rightarrow xe^t = c_1$

Now $\frac{dt}{1} = \frac{du}{u-1}$

$\log c + \log(u - 1)$=t

$c(u - 1) = e^t$

$c = \dfrac{e^t}{u - 1}$

general solution is

$\frac{e^t}{u-1} = \emptyset(xe^t)$

Now use initial condition

$u(x, 0) = g(x)$

$\frac{1}{g(x)-1} = \emptyset(x) \Rightarrow \emptyset(xe^t) = \frac{1}{g(xe^t)-1}$

$\dfrac{e^t}{u - 1} = \dfrac{1}{g(xe^t - 1)}$

$\Rightarrow u = 1 + e^t(g(xe^t - 1)$

No any option is correct.

10. Explanation (d)

Consider the given Cauchy problem,

$2u_x + 3u_y = 5$ (1)

$u = 1$ on the line $3x - 2y = 0$

$Pu_x + Qu_y = R$ compare with $2u_x + 3u_y = 5$

$\Rightarrow P = 2, Q = 3, R = 5$

$\dfrac{P}{x_0'(t)} = \dfrac{Q}{y_0'(t)} = \dfrac{R}{u_0'(t)}$

$(x_0(t), y_0(t), u_0(t)) = \left(t, \frac{3t}{2}, 1\right)$

$\frac{2}{1} = \frac{3}{\frac{3}{2}} = \frac{5}{0}$

$\frac{2}{1} = \frac{2}{1} \neq \frac{5}{0}$ (2)

We know that

If $\frac{P}{p_0'(t)} = \frac{Q}{q_0'(t)} \neq \frac{R}{r_0'(t)}$ then it has no solution

From equation (2)

Given Cauchy problem has no solution.

Hence, option (d) is correct answer and a),b),c) are incorrect.

11. Explanation (d)

$y\dfrac{\partial z}{\partial x} - x\dfrac{\partial z}{\partial y} = 0$

$(\cos s, \sin s, 1)$

$x_0 = \cos s, y_0 = \sin s, z_0 = 1$

$$J = \begin{vmatrix} P(x_0, y_0, \tau_0) & \dfrac{dx_0}{ds} \\ Q(x_0, y_0, \tau_0) & \dfrac{dy_0}{ds} \end{vmatrix} = \begin{vmatrix} \sin s & -\sin s \\ -\cos s & \cos s \end{vmatrix}$$

$= 0$

$\dfrac{dx}{y} = \dfrac{dy}{-x} = \dfrac{dz}{0}$

$x^2 + y^2 = c_1$ $\quad c_1 = 1$

$z = c_2$

Therefore, the general solution is $z = \emptyset(x^3 + y^2)$, now putting $x = \cos s, y = \sin s$ and $z = 1$ we get $\emptyset(1) = 1$. Now there are such infinite functions which satisfies such condition.

Hence, it has infinitely many solutions.

12. Explanation (b)

$P\dfrac{\partial z}{\partial y} + Q\dfrac{\partial z}{\partial y} = R$

Langrage's auxiliary equations are

$\dfrac{dx}{P} = \dfrac{dy}{Q} = \dfrac{dz}{R}$

$U(x, y, z) = C_1$ …… (1)

$V(x, y, z) = C_2$ …… (2)

Then the general solution is,

$C_1 = \phi(C_2)$ or $C_2 = \phi(C_1)$

Or, $U = \phi(V)$ or $V = \phi\,(U)$

So, if $\phi\,(U) = \frac{f(U)}{U} \Rightarrow V = \frac{f(U)}{U} \Rightarrow UV$

i.e. option (b) correct.

As form option (a), (c) and (d) we cannot express $u = \phi(V)\ or\ V = \phi(U)$.

So, the options are wrong.

13. Explanation (c)

$z^2 = kxy, k \in \mathbb{R}$

The given system of surface is

$\frac{z^2}{xy} = k$…………… (i)

Now $\frac{\partial f}{\partial x} = \frac{z^2}{y}.\left(-\frac{1}{y^2}\right) = \frac{-z^2}{xy^2}$

$\dfrac{\partial f}{\partial y} = \dfrac{z^2}{x}.\left(-\dfrac{1}{y^2}\right) = \dfrac{-z^2}{xy^2}$

$\dfrac{\partial f}{\partial z} = \dfrac{2z}{xy}$

The required orthogonal surface is the solution of,

$p\dfrac{\partial f}{\partial x} + q\dfrac{\partial f}{\partial y} = \dfrac{\partial f}{\partial z}$

$$\Rightarrow \frac{-z^2}{x^2y}p - \frac{z^2}{xy^2}q = \frac{2z}{xy}$$

$$\Rightarrow \frac{-pz}{x} - \frac{qz}{y} = 2 \Rightarrow \frac{p}{x} + \frac{q}{y} = \frac{-2}{z} \quad \text{............. (2)}$$

Lagrange's auxiliary equations for (2) is

$$\frac{dx}{1/x} = \frac{dy}{1/y} = \frac{dz}{-2/z} \quad \text{............. (3)}$$

Taking first two fractions,

$$\frac{dx}{1/x} = \frac{dy}{1/y} \Rightarrow xdx = ydy, \text{ now integrating}$$

$$\Rightarrow \frac{x^2}{2} = \frac{y^2}{2} + \frac{c_1^2}{2}$$

$$\Rightarrow x^2 - y^2 = c_1^2 \quad \text{............. (4)}$$

Taking first and 3rd fractions, we set

$$\frac{dx}{1/x} = \frac{dz}{-2/z} \Rightarrow xdx + \frac{z}{2}dz = 0$$

Integrating, we get

$$\Rightarrow \frac{x^2}{2} + \frac{z^2}{2}\cdot\frac{1}{2} = \frac{c_2^2}{2}$$

$$\Rightarrow 2x^2 + z^2 = 2c_2^2 \quad \text{............. (5)}$$

So from (4) and (5),

$\phi(x^2 - y^2, 2x^2 + z^2) = 0$ (Ans)

14. Explanation (a)

The Lagrange's auxiliary equation is

$$\frac{dx}{x} = \frac{dy}{y} = \frac{dz}{0} \quad \text{................. (1)}$$

From last ratio, $\frac{dz}{0}$ we set $z = c$.............(2)

And from first and second ratio

$\frac{dx}{x} = \frac{dy}{y}$, integrating we get

$\Rightarrow \log x = \log y + \log c_2$

$\Rightarrow \log|x| - \log|y| = \log c_2$ [$\because \log x$ not defined for $x > 0$]

$$\Rightarrow \log\frac{|x|}{|y|} = \log c_2$$

$$\Rightarrow \frac{|x|}{|y|} = c_2 \text{................ (3)}$$

So from (2) and (3)

$z = \phi\left(\frac{|x|}{|y|}\right); \phi \in c^1(\mathbb{R})$ (Ans)

15. Explanation (c)

The Lagrange's auxiliary equation is

$$\frac{dx}{1} = \frac{dy}{x^2} = \frac{du}{0} \text{------- (*)}$$

From $\frac{du}{0} \Rightarrow u = c_1$ ------ (i)

$\frac{dx}{1} = \frac{dy}{x^2} = x^2dx = dy \Rightarrow \frac{1}{3}x^3 = y + c_2$ ---- (ii)

Given $u(x,0) = e^x$

Let $x = t, y = 0, u = e^t$ ------ (**)

Using (**) in (i), we set $c_1 = e^t$---- (iii)

Using (**) in (ii), we get

$\frac{1}{3}t^3 = 0 + c_2 \Rightarrow c_2 = \frac{1}{3}t^3$ ---- (iv)

$\Rightarrow 3c_2 = t^3$

$\Rightarrow t = (3c_2)^{\frac{1}{3}}$

i.e. $u(x,y) = e^x$ so option (a) correct.

From (ii)

$$c_2 = \frac{1}{3}x^3 - y$$

Now

$$c_1 = e^{(3c_2)^{\frac{1}{3}}}$$

$$\Rightarrow u(x,y) = e^{\left(3\left(\frac{1}{3}x^3 - y\right)\right)^{\frac{1}{3}}}$$

$$= e^{(x^3-3y)^{\frac{1}{3}}}$$

So option (c) is correct.

16. Explanation: (b)

Consider the given PDE

$u_t - e^{-t}u_x + u = 0$-------(1)

To solve this,

by Lagrange method

Lagrange auxiliary equations is

$$\frac{dx}{-e^{-t}} = \frac{dt}{1} = \frac{du}{-u}$$

Consider $\frac{dt}{1} = \frac{du}{-u}$

$-t = \log u + \log c$

$uc_1 = e^{-t}$

$\Rightarrow ue^t = c_2$ ------- (2) ($\because \frac{1}{c_1} = c_2$)

now,

$$\frac{dx}{-e^{-t}} = dt$$

$dx = -e^{-t}dt$

Integrating, we get

$x = e^{-t} + c_3$

$x - e^{-t} = c_3$------- (3)

From equation (2) and (3)

$\phi(ue^t) = x - e^{-t}$------ (4)

Now, using given condition

$u(x,0) = x$

Let $x = p \quad u(p,0) = p$

Equation (4) become

$\phi(p) = p - 1$

$\Rightarrow \phi(ue^t) = ue^t - 1$

Equation (4) become

$ue^t - 1 = x - e^{-t}$

$u = e^{-t}(x - e^{-t} + 1)$

Option (b) is the correct answer.

17. Explanation (a) Consider the given PDE

$$\frac{\partial u}{\partial y} - x\frac{\partial u}{\partial x} + u - 1 = 0 \quad (1)$$

To solve this,

by Lagrange's method

Lagrange's auxiliary equation is

$$\frac{dy}{1} = \frac{dx}{-x} = \frac{du}{1-u}$$

Consider $\frac{du}{1} = \frac{dx}{-x}$

Integrating, we get

$e^{-y} = xc$

$\Rightarrow \frac{e^{-y}}{x} = c_1 \quad (2)$

Now, $\frac{dy}{1} = \frac{du}{1-u}$

Integrating, we get

$e^{-y} = (u-1)\,c_2$

$\Rightarrow c_2 = \frac{e^{-y}}{(u-1)}$ (3)

From equation (2) and (3)

$\Rightarrow \phi(c_1) = c_2$

$\phi\left(\frac{e^{-y}}{x}\right) = \frac{e^{-y}}{u-1}$ (4)

Now using given condition

$u(x,0) = \sin x$

$\Rightarrow$ equation (4) become

$\phi\left(\frac{1}{x}\right) = \frac{1}{\sin x - 1}$

Put above value in equation (4)

We get

$\frac{1}{\sin x e^{y} - 1} = \frac{e^{-y}}{u-1}$

$u - 1 = \frac{e^{-y}(\sin x e^{y} - 1)}{1}$

$u = 1 + e^{-y}(\sin x\, e^{y} - 1)$

Now

$u(0,1) = 1 - e^{-1} = 1 - \frac{1}{e}$

$\Rightarrow$ option (a) is the correct answer.

18. Explanation: (c)

Consider the given problem

$uu_x + u_y = 0; x \in \mathbb{R}, y > 0.$

Lagrange's A.E: $\frac{dx}{u} = \frac{dy}{1} = \frac{du}{0}$

$du = 0 \Rightarrow u = c_1$ ... (1)

Consider $\frac{dx}{u} = \frac{dy}{1}$

$\therefore \frac{dx}{c_1} = dy$

$\Rightarrow dx - c_1 dy = 0$

$\Rightarrow x - c_1 y = c_2$

i.e. $x - uy = c_2$ ... (2)

Now given initial data curve is

$u(x,0) = x$

Let $x = s, y = 0, u = s$

Put this curve in 1 and 2, we get

$s = c_1$ ... (3)

$s = c_2$ .... (4)

From (3) and (4)

$C_1 = C_2$

$\Rightarrow u = x - uy$

$\Rightarrow u + uy = x$

$\Rightarrow u(x,y) = \frac{x}{1+y}$

$u(2,3) = \frac{2}{4} = \frac{1}{2}$

So, option (c) is correct

19. Explanation: (a)

The Lagrange auxiliary equation is

$\frac{dx}{u} = \frac{dy}{1} = \frac{du}{1}$

$\Rightarrow dy = du$

$\Rightarrow y - u = c_1$ ... (1)

or $u - y = c_1$

and $\frac{dx}{u} = du$

$\Rightarrow dx = u\,du$

$\Rightarrow x + c_2 = \frac{u^2}{2}$

$\Rightarrow u^2 - 2x = c_2$ ... (2)

Now, we have, $u(x,0) = kx$

$\therefore$ curve in parametric form is $(s, 0, ks)$. Put in (1) and (2), we get,

$ks = c_1$ ... (3) and $k^2 s^2 - 2s = c_2$ ... (4)

Put (3) and (4)

$c_2 = c_1^2 - 2\frac{c_1}{k}$ ... $(k \neq 0)$

From (1) and (2), we have,

$u^2 - 2x = (u-y)^2 - \frac{2(u-y)}{k}$

$\Rightarrow u^2 - 2x = u^2 - 2uy + y^2 - \frac{2u - 2y}{k}$

$\Rightarrow -2x = -2u\left(y + \frac{1}{k}\right) + \left(y^2 + \frac{2}{k}y\right)$

$\Rightarrow 2u\left(y + \frac{1}{k}\right) = 2x + \left(y^2 + \frac{2}{k}y\right)$

$u = \frac{2x + \left(y^2 + \frac{2}{k}y\right)}{2\left(y + \frac{1}{k}\right)}, y \in (0,\infty)$

Now, if $k = -2$, then

$\frac{2x + (y^2 - y)}{2\left(y - \frac{1}{2}\right)}, y \in (0,\infty)$

$\Rightarrow$ The solution will not exist for $y = \frac{1}{2}$

$\Rightarrow$ option (b) is incorrect.

If $k = 4$, then $\left(y + \frac{1}{k}\right) = \left(y + \frac{1}{4}\right), y \in (0,\infty)$

$\Rightarrow$ The solution will exist

$\Rightarrow$ option (c) is correct.

and if $k = 1$, then $\left(y + \frac{1}{k}\right) = (y+1), y \in (0,\infty)$ has solution.

$\Rightarrow$ option (d) is correct.

Now, for $k = 0$, we have, from (3) and (4),

$c_1 = 0$ and $c_2 = -2s$

$\Rightarrow c_1 c_2 = 0$

$\Rightarrow (u-y)(u^2 - 2x) = 0$

$\Rightarrow u = y$ or $u^2 = 2x$

If $u = y$, then it satisfies the given condition.

Option (a) is correct.

20. Explanation: (a)

Given: $u_t + 2024u_z = 0, \quad x \in R, t > 0$
$u(x,0) = u_0(x), \quad x \in R$

Using Lagrange's method

$\frac{dt}{1} = \frac{dx}{2024} = \frac{du}{0}$

$du = 0 \Rightarrow u = C_1$ (1)

$2024t = x + C_2$

$x - 2024t = C_2$ (2)

From (1) and (2) $u = \phi(x - 2024t)$

$\therefore u(x,0) = u_0(x)$

$u_0(x) = \phi(x)$

$u = u_0(x - 2024t)$

Let $= T : u(x,t) = u_0(x - 2024T)$
$A_T = \{x \in \mathbb{R}|\ u_0(x - 2024T) < 1\}$
$|A_T| \longleftarrow$ Lebesgue measure of A_T
$A_0 = \{x \in \mathbb{R}|u_0(x) < 1\}$
$A_t = \{x \in \mathbb{R}|u_0(x - 2024)T < 1\}$
$\therefore A_0 = A_T$
Therefore option (a) is correct.

21. Explanation: (c)

$$\frac{dx}{1} = \frac{dt}{1} = \frac{du}{2u}$$

$\Rightarrow x - t = C_1$
$\Rightarrow \log u = 2t + C_2$
$\Rightarrow ue^{-2t} = C_2$
$\therefore \phi(x - t) = ue^{-2t}$ ... (1)
Using $u(0,t) = 1 + \sin t,\ \ t > 0$, we have,
$\phi(0 - t) = \phi(-t) = (1 + \sin t)e^{-2t}$ ... (2)
Put $t = -a$
$\phi(a) = (1 - \sin a)e^{2a}$
$(1 - \sin(x - t))e^{2(x-t)} = ue^{-2t}$ ... using (1)
$\therefore u(x,t) = e^{2x}[1 - \sin(x - t)]$
$\therefore u(\pi, 2\pi) = e^{2\pi}[1 - \sin(\pi - 2\pi)] = e^{2\pi}$
Now using $u(x,0) = e^x \cos x, x > 0$, we have,
$\phi(x) = e^x \cos x$
$\therefore e^{x-t}\cos(x - t) = ue^{-2t}$
$\therefore u(x,t) = e^{x+t}\cos(x - t)$
$\therefore u(2\pi,\pi) = e^{2\pi+\pi}[\cos(2\pi - \pi)] = -e^{3\pi}$
$\therefore \frac{u(2\pi,\pi)}{u(\pi,2\pi)} = \frac{-e^{3\pi}}{e^{2\pi}} = -e^{\pi}$
$\therefore$ Option (a) is correct.

22. Explanation: (a)

Method of characteristics for
$(y + u)u_x + yu_y = x - y, ; u(x,1) = 1 + x$.
Set $dy/ds = y \Rightarrow y = e^s$. Then
$\frac{dx}{ds} = y + u, \frac{du}{ds} = x - y.$
Compute for $S = x + u$ and $D = x - u$:
$S' = S \Rightarrow S = C_1e^s, D' + D = 2e^s \Rightarrow D = e^s + C_2e^{-s}$.
With $y = e^s$, solve
$x = \frac{1}{2}(S + D), u = \frac{1}{2}(S - D)$.
Impose $(x,1) = 1 + x$ *i.e.*, $at(s = 0), (y = 1)$: this gives $C_2 = -2$ and $C_1 = 2a + 1$ where $a = x(0)$. Eliminating (a), one finds
$u(x,y) = x - y + \frac{2}{y}$.
Check options:
$u(1,1) = 2, u(2,2) = 1, u(3,3) = \frac{2}{3}, u(4,4) = \frac{1}{2}$.
Only statement (1) is true.
Correct Answer: 1

23. Explanation: (b)

Given IBVP: $u_t + u_x = 0, x > 0,\ t > 0$
Initial condition

$$u(x,0) = e^x$$

Boundary condition

$$u(0,t) = 1 - \sin t$$

Characteristic curves:
For $u_t + u_x = 0$
characteristic equation is

$$\frac{dx}{dt} = 1$$

so

$$x - t = C$$

Thus the general solution is

$$u(x,t) = F(x - t)$$

Apply initial condition:

$$u(x,0) = e^x$$
$$F(x) = e^x$$

Hence

$$u(x,t) = e^{x-t}$$

This is valid for points whose characteristics intersect the initial line $t = 0$.
Characteristic from (x, t) meets $t = 0$ at

$$(x - t, 0)$$

This point must satisfy $x - t > 0$.
Thus $t < x$
So, $u(x,t) = e^{x-t}, t < x$
Check boundary condition compatibility:
At (0,0):
From initial condition

$$u(0,0) = e^0 = 1$$

From boundary condition

$$u(0,0) = 1 - \sin 0 = 1$$

So they are compatible only at the corner point.
But for $t > 1$, the characteristic through $(1, t)$ intersects the initial line instead of the boundary line.
Therefore the value along that characteristic is determined only by the initial condition, not the boundary condition.
Hence

$$u(1,t) = e^{1-t}$$

But the statement requires

$$u(1,t) = e - \sin t$$

which cannot be satisfied by any solution of the IBVP.
Thus such a solution does NOT exist.
Chec statements:

1. $u(1,t) = e - \sin t$for $t < 1$
   $\Rightarrow$ Not satisfied.
2. No solution exists with $u(1,t) = e - \sin t$for $t > 1$.
   $\Rightarrow$ Correct.
3. $u(x,t) = e^{x-t}$for $t > x$
   $\Rightarrow$ Wrong region.
4. $u(x,t) = e - \sin(t - x)$for $t < x$
   $\Rightarrow$ Does not satisfy PDE/conditions.

So, the correct option is (2).

MSQ: Multiple Select Questions

1. A general solution of the PDE
   $uu_x + yu_y = x$ is of the form
   (a) $f\left(u^2 - x^2, \frac{y}{x+u}\right) = 0$ where $f: \mathbb{R}^2 \to \mathbb{R}$ is C^1 and $\nabla f \neq (0,0)$ at every point

(b) $u^2 = g\left(\frac{y}{x+u}\right) + x^2, g \in C^1(\mathbb{R})$
(c) $f(u^2 + x^2) = 0, f \in C^1(\mathbb{R})$
(d) $f(x + y) = 0, f \in C^1(\mathbb{R})$

[June 2011]

2. The differential equation $x\frac{\partial u}{\partial x} + y\frac{\partial u}{\partial y} = 2u$ satisfying the initial condition $y = xg(x), x = f(x)$ with
(a) $f(x) = 2x, g(x) = 1$, has no solution
(b) $f(x) = 2x^2, \; g(x) = 1$, has infinite number of solutions
(c) $f(x) = x^3, g(x) = x$, has a unique solution
(d) $f(x) = x^4, g(x) = 4$, has a unique solution

[Dec 2011]

3. The Cauchy problem
$xu_x + yu_y = 0 \; u(x, y) = x$ on $x^2 + y^2 = 1$ has
(a) A solution for all $x \in \mathbb{R}, y \in \mathbb{R}$
(b) An unique solution in $\{(x, y) \in \mathbb{R}^2 : (x, y) \neq (0,0)\}$
(c) A bounded solution in $\{(x, y) \in \mathbb{R}^2 : (x, y) \neq (0,0)\}$
(d) An unique solution in $\{(x, y) \in \mathbb{R}^2 : (x, y) \neq (0,0)\}$ but the solution is unbounded.

[June 2012]

4. A bounded solution to the partial differential equation $\frac{\partial u}{\partial t} = \frac{\partial^2 u}{\partial x^2} + e^{-t}$ is
(a) $u(x, t) = -e^{-t}$ (b) $u(x, t) = e^{-x}e^{-t}$
(c) $u(x, t) = e^{-x} + e^{-t}$ (d) $u(x, t) = x - e^{-t}$

[Dec 2012]

5. Let f be a function of $\mathbb{R}^2$ such that $\frac{\partial f}{\partial x}(x, y) = \frac{\partial f}{\partial y}(x, y)$ for all $(x, y) \in \mathbb{R}^2$
(a) $f(x, y) - f(y, x) = (x - y)\frac{\partial f}{\partial x}(x^*, y^*) + (y - x)\frac{\partial f}{\partial y}(x^*, y^*)$ for some point $(x^*, y^*) \in \mathbb{R}^2$
(b) f is a constant on all lines parallel to the line $x = -y$
(c) $f(x, y) = 0$ for all $(x, y) \in \mathbb{R}^2$
(d) $f(x, y) = f(-y, x)$ for all $(x, y) \in \mathbb{R}^2$

[June 2013]

6. Let $xyu = c_1$ and $x^2 + y^2 - 2u = c_2$, where c_1 and c_2 are arbitrary constant, be the first integrals of the PDE
$$x(u + y^2)\frac{\partial u}{\partial x} - y(u + x^2)\frac{\partial u}{\partial y} = (x^2 - y^2)u$$
Then the solution of the PDE with $x + y = 0, \; u = 1$ is given by
(a) $x^3 + y^3 + 2xyu^2 + 2x^2u = 0$
(b) $x^3 + yx^2 + (x^2 + xy)u = 0$
(c) $x^2 + y^2 + 2(xy - 1)u + 2 = 0$
(d) $x^2 - y^2 - u(x + y - 2) - 2 = 0$

[June 2014]

7. Let $u(x, t)$ satisfy for $x \in \mathbb{R}, t > 0$
$$\frac{\partial^2 u}{\partial t^2} + \frac{\partial u}{\partial t} + 2\,\frac{\partial^2 u}{\partial x^2} = 0$$
A solution of the form $u = e^{ix}v(t)$ with $v(0) = 0$ and $v'(0) = 1$
(a) Is necessarily bounded (b) Satisfies $|u(x, t)| < e^t$
(c) Is necessarily unbounded (d) Is oscillatory in x

[Dec 2014]

8. Consider the Cauchy problem of finding $u = u(x, t)$ such that
$$\frac{\partial u}{\partial t} + u\frac{\partial u}{\partial x} = 0 \; for \; x \in \mathbb{R}, t > 0$$
$$u(x, 0) = u_0(x), \qquad x \in \mathbb{R}$$
Which choices(s) of the following functions for u_0 yields a C^1 solution $u(x, t)$ for all $x \in \mathbb{R}$ and $t > 0$.
(a) $u_0(x) = \frac{1}{1+x^2}$ (b) $u_0(x) = x$
(c) $u_0(x) = 1 + x^2$ (d) $u_0(x) = 1 + 2x$

[Dec 2014]

9. For an arbitrary continuously differentiable function f, which of the following is a general solution of $z(px - qy) = y^2 - x^2$
(a) $x^2 + y^2 + z^2 = f\,(xy)$
(b) $(x + y)^2 + z^2 = f\,(xy)$
(c) $x^2 + y^2 + z^2 = f\,(y - x)$
(d) $x^2 + y^2 + z^2 = f\,((x + y)^2 + z^2)$

[June 2015]

10. Let $u(x, t)$ satisfy the wave equation
$$\frac{\partial^2 u}{\partial t^2} = \frac{\partial^2 u}{\partial x^2}; x \in (0, 2\pi), t > 0$$
$u(x, 0) = e^{i\omega x}$ for some $\omega \in \mathbb{R}$. Then
(a) $u(x, t) = e^{i\omega x}e^{i\omega t}$
(b) $u(x, t) = e^{i\omega x}e^{-i\omega t}$
(c) $u(x, t) = e^{i\omega x}\left(\frac{e^{i\omega t} + e^{-i\omega t}}{2}\right)$
(d) $u(x, t) = t + \frac{x^2}{2}$

[Dec 2015]

11. The Cauchy problem
$$y\frac{\partial u}{\partial x} - x\frac{\partial u}{\partial y} = 0$$
$$u = g \; on \, \Gamma$$
Has a unique solution in a neighborhood of Γ for every differentiable Function $g : \Gamma \to \mathbb{R}$ if
(a) $\Gamma = \{(x, 0) : x > 0\}$
(b) $\Gamma = \{(x, y) : x^2 + y^2 = 1\}$
(c) $\Gamma = \{(x, y) : x + y = 1, x > 1\}$
(d) $\Gamma = \{(x, y) : y = x^2, x > 0\}$

[Dec.2016]

12. Consider the partial differential equation
$x\frac{\partial u}{\partial x} + yu\frac{\partial u}{\partial y} = -xy \;\; for \;\; x > 0$ subject to $u = 5$ $on \;\; xy = 1. \; Then$
(a) $u(x, y)$ exists when $xy \leq 19$ and $u(x, y) = u(y, x) \; for \; x > 0, y > 0$
(b) $u(x, y)$ exists when $xy \geq 19$ and $u(x, y) = u(y, x)$ for $x > 0, y > 0$
(c) $u(1, 11) = 3, \; u(13, -1) = 7$
(d) $u(1, -1) = 5, u(11, 1) = -5$

[June 2017]

13. Consider the Lagrange equation
$$x^2\frac{\partial z}{\partial x} + y^2\frac{\partial z}{\partial y} = (x + y)z$$
Then the general solution of the given equation is
(a) $F\left(\frac{xy}{z}, \frac{x-y}{z}\right) = 0$ for an arbitrary differentiable function F

(b) $F\left(\frac{x-y}{z}, \frac{1}{x}-\frac{1}{y}\right)=0$ for an arbitrary differentiable function F

(c) $z=f\left(\frac{1}{x}-\frac{1}{y}\right)$ for an arbitrary differentiable function f

(d) $z=xy\,f\left(\frac{1}{x}-\frac{1}{y}\right)$ for an arbitrary differentiable function f

[Dec. 2017]

14. Let a be a fixed real constant. Consider the first order partial differential Equation $\frac{\partial u}{\partial t}+a\frac{\partial u}{\partial x}=0$, $x \in \mathbb{R}$, $t>0$ with the initial data $u(x,0)=u_0(x), x \in \mathbb{R}$ where u_0 is a continuously differentiable function. Consider the following two statements.
S_1 : There exists a bounded function u_0 for which the solution u is unbounded.
S_2 : If u_0 vanishes outside a compact set then for each fixed $T>0$ there exists a compact set $K_T \subset \mathbb{R}$ such that $u(x,T)$ vanishes for $x \notin K_T$.
Which of the following are true?
(a) S_1 is true and S_2 is false
(b) S_1 is true and S_2 is also true
(c) S_1 is false and S_2 is true
(d) S_1 is false and S_2 is also false

[June 2018]

15. Let $u(x,t)$ be a function that satisfies the PDE: $u_t+uu_x=1$, $x \in \mathbb{R}$, $t>0$ and the initial condition $u\left(\frac{t^2}{4}, t\right)=\frac{t}{2}$. Then the IVP has
(a) Only one solution
(b) Two solutions
(c) An infinite number of solutions
(d) Solutions none of which differentiable on the characteristic base curve

[Dec. 2018]

16. Consider the IVP:
$$xu_x+tu_t=u+1, \quad x \in \mathbb{R}, t \geq 0$$
$$u(x,t)=x^2 \;, t^2=x^2$$
Then
(a) The solution is singular at (0, 0)
(b) The given space curve $(x,t,u)=(\xi,\xi^2,\xi^2)$ is not a characteristic Curve at (0, 0)
(c) There is no base characteristic curve in the (x,t) plane passing through (0,0)
(d) A necessary condition for the IVP to have a unique C^1 solution (0, 0) does not hold

[Dec. 2018]

17. The general solution $z=z(x,y)$ of
$$(x+y)z\,z_x+(x-y)z\,z_y=x^2+y^2 \text{ is}$$
(a) $F(x^2+y^2+z^2, z^2-xy)=0$ for arbitrary C^1 function F
(b) $F(x^2-y^2-z^2, z^2-2xy)=0$ for arbitrary C^1 function F
(c) $F(x^2+y^2+z^2, z-2xy)=0$ for arbitrary C^1 function F
(d) $F(x^3-y^3-z^3, z-2x^2y^2)=0$ for arbitrary C^1 function F

[June 2019]

18. If $u(x,y)$ is the solution of the following problem $u\frac{\partial u}{\partial x}+\frac{\partial u}{\partial y}=1$, such that $u(x_0(s),y_0(s))=u_0$, where $x_0(s)=s, y_0(s)=s, u_0(s)=\frac{1}{2}$ then $u(2,1)$ is equal to
(a) $\frac{1}{2}$ (b) $-\frac{1}{2}$
(c) 1 (d) -1

[Dec 2019]

19. Let $u:\mathbb{R}^2 \to \mathbb{R}$ be the solution to the Cauchy problem:
$$\begin{cases} \partial_x u+2\partial_y u = 0 & \text{for } (x,y) \in \mathbb{R} \\ u(x,y) = \sin(x) & \text{for } y=3x+1, x \in \mathbb{R} \end{cases}$$
Let $v:\mathbb{R}^2 \to \mathbb{R}$ be the solution to the Cauchy problem:
$$\begin{cases} \partial_x v+2\partial_y v = 0 & \text{for } (x,y) \in \mathbb{R}^2, \\ v(x,y) = \sin(x) & \text{for } x \in \mathbb{R} \end{cases}$$
Which of the following statements are true?
(a) u changes sign in the interior of S
(b) $u(x,y)=v(x,y)$ along a line in S
(c) v changes sign in the interior of S
(d) v vanishes along a line in S

[JUNE 2023]

20. Let u be a solution of the following PDE:
$u_x+xy_u=0,$
$u(x,0)=e^x.$
Which of the following statements are true?
(a) $u(2,1)=e^2$ (b) $u\left(1,\frac{1}{2}\right)=1$
(c) $u(-2,1)=e^{-\sqrt{2}}$ (d) $u(-2,1)=e^{\sqrt{2}}$

[SEP 2022]

21. Let $u=u(x,y)$ be the solution to the following Cauchy problem
$u_x+u_y=e^u$ for $(x,y) \in \mathbb{R} \times \left(0,\frac{1}{e}\right)$ and $u(x,0)=1$, for $x \in \mathbb{R}$.
Which of the following statements are true?
(a) $u\left(\frac{1}{2e},\frac{1}{2e}\right)=1$ (b) $u_x\left(\frac{1}{2e},\frac{1}{2e}\right)=0$
(c) $u_y\left(\frac{1}{4e},\frac{1}{4e}\right)=\log 4$ (d) $u_y\left(0,\frac{1}{4e}\right)=\frac{4e}{3}$

[JUNE 2023]

22. Consider the Cauchy problem (CP)
$x\frac{\partial u}{\partial x}+\frac{\partial u}{\partial y}=1.$
$u(0,y)=e^y, y \in R.$
Then which of the following statements are true?
(a) There is NO neighbourhood of the origin on which (CP) has a solution
(b) (CP) has a unique solution defined on some neighbourhood of the origin
(c) (CP) has a unique solution defined on some neighbourhood of the point (0, 1) in the xy-plane
(d) (CP) has an infinite number of solutions, each of which is defined on some neigh- bourhood of the origin

[June 2025]

ANSWER KEY					
1	2	3	4	5	6
a, b	a, b, c, d	b, c	a	a, b	c
7	8	9	10	11	12
b, c, d	b, d	a, b, d	a, b, c	a, c, d	a, c
13	14	15	16	17	18
a, b, d	c	b, d	a, b, c, d	b	b
19	20	21	22		
b, c, d	b, c	b, d	a		

Explanation

1. Explanation (a), (b)

Consider the given PDE

$uu_x + yu_y = x$

To solve this by Lagrange method,

Lagrange's auxiliary equation is

$$\frac{dx}{u} = \frac{dy}{y} = \frac{du}{x}$$

Consider

$$\frac{dx}{u} = \frac{du}{x}$$

Integrating, we get

$\Rightarrow u^2 - x^2 = c_1 --- (2)$

Now, consider

$$\frac{du+dx}{u+x} = \frac{dy}{y}$$

Integrating $\Rightarrow \frac{y}{u+x} = c_2 --- (3)$

Therefore, from (2), (3) the general solution is

$f\left(u^2 - x^2, \frac{y}{u+x}\right) = 0$ where $f: \mathbb{R}^2 \to \mathbb{R}$ is C^1 and $\nabla f \neq (0,0)$ at every point

Or $\quad u^2 - x^2 = g\left(\frac{y}{u+x}\right) \Rightarrow u^2 = g\left(\frac{y}{u+x}\right) + x^2 \quad g \in C^1(\mathbb{R})$

Hence, option (a) and (b) are correct are correct answer and option c) and d) are incorrect.

2. Explanation (a), (b), (c), (d)

Consider the given PDE

$$x\frac{\partial u}{\partial x} + y\frac{\partial u}{\partial y} = 2u --- (1)$$

Comparing with (1) $P\frac{\partial u}{\partial x} + Q\frac{\partial u}{\partial y} = R$, we get $P = x, Q = y, R = 2u, y = x\,g(x), u = f(x)$

$$(x_0(t), y_0(t), u_0(t)) = (x, xg(x), f(x))$$

Now discuss three cases:

Case 1: If $\frac{P}{\frac{dx_0}{dt}} = \frac{Q}{\frac{dy_0}{dt}} = \frac{R}{\frac{dz_0}{dt}}$ then given problem has infinite solution.

Case 2: If $\frac{P}{\frac{dx_0}{dt}} \neq \frac{Q}{\frac{dy_0}{dt}} \neq \frac{R}{\frac{dz_0}{dt}}$ then given problem has unique solution.

Case 3: If $\frac{P}{\frac{dx_0}{dt}} = \frac{Q}{\frac{dy_0}{dt}} \neq \frac{R}{\frac{dz_0}{dt}}$ then given problem has no solution.

Now check the option,

For option (a) $f(x) = 2x$ and $g(x) = 1$

$x = t, y = t, u = 2t$

$$\frac{x}{1} = \frac{x}{1} \neq \frac{4x}{2}$$

$\Rightarrow$ No solution

Option (b)

$f(x) = 2x^2$ and $g(x) = 1$

$x = t, y = t, u = 2t^2$

$$\frac{x}{1} = \frac{x}{1} = \frac{4x^2}{4x}$$

$\Rightarrow$ Infinite solution

Option (c):

$f(x) = x^3$ and $g(x) = x$

$x = t, y = t^2, u = t^3$

$$\frac{x}{1} \neq \frac{x^2}{2x} \neq \frac{2x^3}{3x^2}$$

$\Rightarrow$ Unique solution

Option (d):

$f(x) = x^4, g(x) = x$

$$\Rightarrow \frac{x}{1} \neq \frac{x^2}{2x} \neq \frac{x}{4}$$

$\Rightarrow$ Unique solution

Hence, option (a), (b), (c) and (d) are correct answer.

3 Explanation (b), (c)

The given Cauchy problem is

$xu_x + yu_y = 0$

$u(x, y) = x$ on $x^2 + y^2 = 0$

To solve this, By Lagrange's method

Lagrange's auxiliary equation is

$$\frac{dx}{x} = \frac{dy}{y} = \frac{du}{0} \qquad (1)$$

$du = 0 \Rightarrow u = c_1 \qquad (2)$

Consider $\quad \frac{dx}{x} = \frac{dy}{y}$

$$\Rightarrow \log x = \log y + \log c \Rightarrow \frac{x}{y} = c_2 \qquad (3)$$

So, the general solution obtained from (2) and (3) is

$$\phi(u) = \frac{x}{y} \qquad (4)$$

The initial condition $u(x, y) = x$ on $x^2 + y^2 = 1$

Here put x=t $\quad \Rightarrow \phi(t) = \frac{t}{\sqrt{1-t^2}}$

$$\Rightarrow \frac{x}{y} = \frac{u}{\sqrt{1-u^2}}$$

$$\Rightarrow \left(\frac{x}{y}\right)^2 = \frac{u^2}{1-u^2}$$

$$\Rightarrow u = \frac{x}{\sqrt{x^2+y^2}}$$

Which is unique in $\{(x, y) \in \mathbb{R}^2 : (x, y) \neq (0, 0)\}$ and

$u(x, y) = \frac{x}{\sqrt{x^2+y^2}} \leq 1$

$\Rightarrow u(x, y)$ is bounded in $\{(x, y) \in \mathbb{R}^2 : (x, y) \neq (0, 0)\}$ from above explanation.

Hence, option (b) and (c) are correct answer and option a) and d) are incorrect.

4. Explanation (a)

Consider the given PDE

$$\frac{\partial u}{\partial t} = \frac{\partial^2 u}{\partial x^2} + e^{-t}$$

Now check the option which satisfy the given PDE

For option a)

$u(x,t) = -e^{-t}$

$\frac{\partial u}{\partial t} = e^{-t}$

$\frac{\partial^2 u}{\partial x^2} = 0$

$\frac{\partial u}{\partial t} = \frac{\partial^2 u}{\partial x^2} + e^{-t}$

$e^{-t} = e^{-t}$

$\Rightarrow u(x,t) = -e^{-t}$ satisfied the given PDE

Similarly for option b), c) and d) is not satisfied the given PDE.

$\Rightarrow$ Option a) is the correct answer and option b),c) and d) are incorrect

5. **Explanation (a) (b)**

Consider the given partial differential equation

$\frac{\partial f}{\partial x}(x,y) = \frac{\partial f}{\partial y}(x,y)$ – – – (1)

$\frac{\partial f}{\partial x} = \frac{\partial f}{\partial y} = \alpha$ (say)

Consider $\frac{\partial f}{\partial x} = \alpha$

Integrating, we get

$f(x,y) = \alpha x + g(y)$

Also $\frac{\partial f}{\partial y} = \alpha$

Integrating, we get

$f(x,y) = \alpha y + h(x)$

Comparing, we get

$f(x,y) = \alpha x + \alpha y = \alpha(x+y)$

So, $f(x,y) - f(y,x) = 0$

For option a)

$f(x,y) - f(y,x) = (x-y)\frac{\partial f}{\partial x}(x^*,y^*) + (y-x)\frac{\partial f}{\partial y}(x^*,y^*)$

$\frac{\partial f}{\partial x}(x-y+y-x) = 0$

Option a) is correct.

For Option (b)

Any line parallel to $x = -y$ is of the form

$x = -y + k$, then

$f(x,y)|_{x=-y+k} = c(-y+k+y) = ck$

Which is constant

Option b) is correct.

From above explanation option

Hence, options a), b) are correct and c) and d) are incorrect.

6. **Explanation (c)**

Consider the given PDE

$x(u+y^2)\frac{\partial u}{\partial x} - y(u+x^2)\frac{\partial u}{\partial y} = (x^2-y^2)u$ (1)

$xyu = c_1$ and $x^2+y^2-2u = c_2$ (2)

Now $x+y=0, u=1$ (given)

From equation (2)

$x^2+y^2-2u = \Phi(xyu)$ (3)

$x^2+x^2-2 = \Phi(-x^2)$

$-2(1-x^2) = \Phi(-x^2)$

Equation 3) become

$x^2+y^2-2u = -2(1+xyu)$

$x^2+y^2-2u+2+2xyu = 0$

$\Rightarrow x^2+y^2+2(xy-1)u+2 = 0$

$\Rightarrow$ c) is the correct answer and option a), b) and d) are incorrect.

7. **Explanation (b), (c), (d)**

Consider the given PDE

$\frac{\partial^2 u}{\partial t^2} + \frac{\partial u}{\partial t} + 2\frac{\partial^2 u}{\partial x^2} = 0$ – – – (1)

$u = e^{ix}v(t)$ is the solution of equation (1), we get

$e^{ix}v''(t) + e^{ix}v'(t) - 2e^{ix}v(t) = 0$

$\Rightarrow v''(t) + v'(t) - 2v(t) = 0$ – – – (2)

The auxiliary equation of (2) is

$m^2 + m - 2 = 0$

$\Rightarrow m = 1, -2$

Complementary function is

$\Rightarrow v(t) = c_1e^t + c_2e^{-2t}$ – –(3)

And $v'^{(t)} = c_1e^t - 2c_2e^{-2t}$ – – – (4)

$v'(0) = 1$ *and* $v(0) = 0$ (Given)

$\Rightarrow c_1 = \frac{1}{3}, c_2 = -\frac{1}{3}$

$\Rightarrow v(t) = \frac{1}{3}e^t - \frac{1}{3}e^{-2t}$

$\therefore u(x,t) = e^{ix}\,v(t) = e^{ix}\left(\frac{1}{3}e^t - \frac{1}{3}e^{-2t}\right),$

$\Rightarrow u(x,t)$ is unbounded.

$|u(x,t)| = \left|\frac{1}{3}e^t - \frac{1}{3}e^{-2t}\right||e^{ix}| < e^t$

Also, $u(x,t) = e^{ix}v(t) = (cosx + isinx)v(t)$

$\because$ *sinx and cosx* are oscillatory functions.

$\Rightarrow$ *u(x,t) is oscillatory in x.*

From above explanation,

$\Rightarrow$ options (b), (c) and (d) are correct answer and a) are incorrect.

8. **Explanation (b), (d)** Consider the given Cauchy problem

$\frac{\partial u}{\partial t} + u\frac{\partial u}{\partial x} = 0$ *for* $x \in \mathbb{R}, t > 0$

$u(x,0) = u_0(x)$, $x \in \mathbb{R}$

To solve this,

By Lagrange's method

Lagrange's auxiliary equation is

$\frac{dx}{u} = \frac{dt}{1} = \frac{du}{0}$

$\Rightarrow du = 0$

$\Rightarrow u = c_1$ – – – (1)

Now consider, $\frac{dx}{u} = \frac{dt}{1}$

We get $c_2 = x - ut$ – (2)

So from (1) and (2) general solution is

$u = \phi(x-ut)$ – – – (3)

Using $u(x,0) = u_0(x)$

$\Rightarrow u_0(x) = \Phi(x)$

Now discuss the option

For option a) $u_0(x) = \frac{1}{1+x^2}$

$$u = \frac{1}{1+(x-ut)^2}$$

Here we cannot write u in term of x and t

For option b)

$u_0(x) = x$

$\Rightarrow u = x - ut$

$\Rightarrow u = \dfrac{x}{1+t}$

$\Rightarrow$ u can be written in the term of x and t

For option c) $u_0(x) = 1 + x^2$

$u = 1 + (x-ut)^2$

$u(1+2t) = 1 + x^2 = u^2t^2$

u cannot be written in terms of x and t.

For Option (d)

$u_0(x) = 1 + 2x$

$u = 1 + 2(x - ut)$

$u = \frac{1+2x}{1+2t}$ can be written in term of x and t.

Hence, options (b) and (d) are correct answer and option a) and c) are incorrect.

9. Explanation (a), (b), (d)

Consider the given PDE

$z(px - qy) = y^2 - x^2$

To solve this,

By Lagrange's method

Lagrange's auxiliary equation is

$$\frac{dx}{zx} = \frac{dy}{-zy} = \frac{dz}{y^2-x^2}$$

Consider, $\frac{x\,dx+y\,dy+z\,dz}{zx^2-zy^2+zy^2-zx^2} = \frac{x\,dx+y\,dy+z\,dz}{0}$

Integrating, we get

$x^2 + y^2 + z^2 = c_1$ ---(1)

$$\frac{dx}{zx} = \frac{dy}{-zy}$$

$\Rightarrow logx = -logy + \log c_1$

$\Rightarrow xy = c_2$ --- (2)

For option a)

$x^2 + y^2 + z^2 = f(xy)\, f(xy)$

For option b)

$(x+y)^2 + z^2 = f(xy)$

$x^2 + y^2 + z^2 + 2xy = f(xy)$

$x^2 + y^2 + z^2 = f(xy)$

For option c)

$x^2 + y^2 + z^2 = f(y - x)$ is never possible.

For option d)

$x^2 + y^2 + z^2 = f((x+y)^2 + z^2)$. i.e option (d) correct

From above explanation options (a), (b) and (d) are correct answer and option (c) is incorrect.

10. Explanation (a), (b), (c)

Consider the given wave equation

$$\frac{\partial^2 u}{\partial t^2} = \frac{\partial^2 u}{\partial x^2}; x \in (0, 2\pi), t > 0$$

$u(x, 0) = e^{i\omega x}$ for some $\omega \in \mathbb{R}$

Now to find the solution of equation 1)

To solve this, check the option

For option (a)

$u(x,t) = e^{i\omega x}e^{i\omega t}$

$\Rightarrow u(x,0) = e^{i\omega x}$

Also, $u_{tt} = (i\omega)^2 e^{i\omega x}e^{i\omega t}$ --- (1)

$u_{xx} = (i\omega)^2 e^{i\omega x}e^{i\omega t}$ --- (2)

From (1) and (2)

We get $\frac{\partial^2 u}{\partial t^2} = \frac{\partial^2 u}{\partial x^2}$,

$u(x,t) = e^{i\omega x}e^{i\omega t}$ satisfied the given equation.

so option (a) correct.

For option (b)

$u(x,t) = e^{i\omega x}e^{-i\omega t}$

$\Rightarrow u(x,0) = e^{i\omega x}$

And $u_{tt} = (-i\omega)^2 e^{i\omega x}e^{i\omega t}$ --- (3)

$u_{xx} = (i\omega)^2 e^{i\omega x}e^{i\omega t}$ --- (4)

From (3) and (4) we get $\Rightarrow \frac{\partial^2 u}{\partial t^2} = \frac{\partial^2 u}{\partial x^2}$,

$u(x,t) = e^{i\omega x}e^{-i\omega t}$ satisfied the given wave equation so option (b) correct.

For option c)

Solution of wave equation is

Consider the given wave equation is

$$\frac{\partial^2 u}{\partial t^2} = \frac{\partial^2 u}{\partial x^2}; x \in (0, 2\pi), t > 0$$

$u(x,0) = e^{i\omega x}$ for some $\omega \in \mathbb{R}$

Here c = 1 and $f(x) = e^{i\omega x}$

$$u(x,t) = \frac{1}{2}(f(x+ct) + f(x-ct)) + \frac{1}{2c}\int_{x-ct}^{x+ct} g(s)ds$$

$$u(x,t) = \frac{1}{2}\left(e^{i\omega(x+t)} + e^{i\omega(x-t)}\right)$$

$$u(x,t) = e^{i\omega x}\left(\frac{e^{i\omega t} + e^{-i\omega t}}{2}\right)$$

$\Rightarrow u(x,0) = e^{i\omega x}$

Option (c) also correct.

Option (d)

$$u(x,t) = t + \frac{x^2}{2}$$

$\Rightarrow u(x,0) = \frac{x^2}{2}$

$\Rightarrow u(x,t) = t + \frac{x^2}{2}$ not satisfied the given wave equation.

$\Rightarrow$ Option (d) incorrect.

Hence, options (a), (b) and (c) are correct answer and option d) is incorrect.

11. Explanation (a), (c), (d)

Consider the given Cauchy problem

$$y\frac{\partial u}{\partial x} - x\frac{\partial u}{\partial y} = 0$$

$u = g$ on Γ

To check the unique solution in the neighbourhood of Γ discuss all the option

For option a) $\Gamma = \{(x, 0): x > 0\}$

$P\frac{\partial u}{\partial x} + Q\frac{\partial u}{\partial y} = R$ comparing with equation (1)

$\Rightarrow P = y, Q = -x, R = 0$

Where $\Delta = \begin{vmatrix} P(x_0, y_0, z_0) & Q(x_0, y_0, z_0) \\ \frac{dx_0}{dt} & \frac{dy_0}{dt} \end{vmatrix}$

The given curve is $\Gamma : (t,0) for\ x = t , y = 0$

$\Delta = \begin{vmatrix} 0 & -t \\ 1 & 0 \end{vmatrix} = t \neq (as\ x > 0)$

$\Rightarrow$ unique solution

For option (b) $\Gamma = \{(x,y): x^2 + y^2 = 1\}$

$\Gamma: \left(t, \sqrt{(1-t^2}\right)$: for $x = t, y = \sqrt{(1-t^2}$

$\Delta = \begin{vmatrix} \sqrt{(1-t^2} & -t \\ 1 & \frac{-t}{\sqrt{(1-t^2}} \end{vmatrix} = 0$,

$\Rightarrow$ Not unique solution.

Option b) is incorrect.

For option (c) $\Gamma = \{(x,y): x + y = 1 , x > 1\}$

The parametric form of the given curve is

$\Gamma: (t , 1 - t);\ t > 1$

$\Delta = \begin{vmatrix} 1-t & -t \\ 1 & -1 \end{vmatrix} = 2t - 1 \neq 0 ;\ \forall t > 1$

$\Rightarrow$ unique solution

For option (d) $\Gamma = \{(x,y): y = x^2 , x > 0\}$

The given curve is $\Gamma: (t , t^2); x = t, y = t^2, t > 0$

$\Delta = \begin{vmatrix} t^{12} & -t \\ 1 & 2t \end{vmatrix} = 2t^3 + t \neq 0 ;\ \forall t > 0$

$\Rightarrow$ unique solution

$\Rightarrow$ options (a), (c) and (d) are correct and option b) is incorrect.

12. Explanation (a), (c)

Consider the given PDE

$x\frac{\partial u}{\partial x} + yu\frac{\partial u}{\partial y} = -xy$

$for\ \ x > 0\ ,\ u = 5\ \ on\ \ xy = 1$ (1)

To solve this,

By Lagrange's method

Lagrange's auxiliary equation is

$\frac{dx}{x} = \frac{dy}{yu} = \frac{du}{-xy}$

Consider $\frac{ydx + xdy + udu}{xy} = \frac{du}{-xy}$

$\Rightarrow ydx + xdy + udu + du = 0$

$\Rightarrow ydx + xdy + (1 + u)du = 0$

Integrating, we get

$xy + \frac{(u+1)^2}{2} = c$ (2)

Now, consider

$\frac{dx}{x} = \frac{du}{-xy}$

$ydx = -du$

Integrating, we get

$xy + u = c_1$ (3)

By the given conditions $xy = 1 , u = 5$

From equation (2)

$c = 1 + \frac{(5+1)^2}{2}$

$c = 19$

$19 = xy + \frac{(u+1)^2}{2}$

$u = -1 + \sqrt{2(19 - xy)}$

$u(x,y)$ is exist if $xy \leq 19$ and $u(x,y) = u(y,x)$ for $x > 0, y > 0$

From above explanation

Option a) is correct and option b) is incorrect.

For option c)

$u(1,11) = -1 + \sqrt{2(19 - 11)}$.

$u(1,11) = -1 + 4$

$u(1,11) = 3$

$u(13,-1) = -1 + \sqrt{2(19 + 13)}$

$u(13,-1) = 7$

$\Rightarrow$ option c) also correct.

For option d) $u(1,-1) = -1 + \sqrt{2(19 + 1)}$

$u(1,-1) = -1 + \sqrt{40}$

$u(1,-1) = -1 + 2\sqrt{10} \neq 5$

$u(11,1) = -1 + \sqrt{2(19 - 11}$

$u(11,1) = -1 + 4$

$u(11,1) = -5$

$\Rightarrow$option d) is incorrect.

$\Rightarrow$Option a) and c) is correct answer and b) and d) are incorrect.

13. Explanation (a), (b), (d)

Consider the given PDE

$x^2\frac{\partial z}{\partial x} + y^2\frac{\partial z}{\partial y} = (x + y)z$ (1)

To solve this,

By Lagrange's method

Lagrange's auxiliary equation is

$\frac{dx}{x^2} = \frac{dy}{y^2} = \frac{dz}{(x+y)z}$

Consider,

$\frac{dx - dy}{x^2 - y^2} = \frac{dz}{(x+y)z}$

$\frac{dx - dy}{(x-y)(x+y)} = \frac{dz}{(x+y)z}$

$\frac{dx - dy}{(x-y)} = \frac{dz}{z}$

Integrating,

$\log(x - y) = \log z + \log c$

$(x - y) = zc$

$c = \frac{(x-y)}{z}$ (2)

Now, consider

$\frac{dx}{x^2} = \frac{dy}{y^2}$

$\frac{-1}{x} = \frac{-1}{y} + c_1$

$\frac{-1}{x} + \frac{1}{y} = c_1$ (3)

$\frac{\frac{dx}{x} + \frac{dy}{y}}{x + y} = \frac{dz}{(x+y)z}$

Integrating $\Rightarrow logx + logy = logz + logc_2$

$\Rightarrow \log(xy) = \log(zc_2)$

$\Rightarrow xy = zc_2$

$\Rightarrow c_2 = \frac{xy}{z}$ - - - (4)

From equation (2), (3) and (4) one solution is

$F\left(\frac{xy}{z}, \frac{x-y}{z}\right) = 0$

Another solution is

$F\left(\frac{x-y}{z}, \frac{1}{x} - \frac{1}{y}\right) = 0$

Also, $\frac{z}{xy} = f\left(\frac{1}{x} - \frac{1}{y}\right)$

$\Rightarrow z = xy\, f\left(\frac{1}{x} - \frac{1}{y}\right)$ is also a solution.

$\Rightarrow$ option (a), (b) and (d) are correct answer and c) is incorrect.

14. Explanation (c) Consider the given PDE

$\frac{\partial u}{\partial t} + a\frac{\partial u}{\partial x} = 0$, $x \in \mathbb{R}$, $t > 0$ (1)

To solve this,

By Lagrange's method

Lagrange's auxiliary equation is

$$\frac{dx}{a} = \frac{dt}{1} = \frac{du}{0}$$

$du = 0 \Rightarrow u = c$ – – – (2)

Consider

$\frac{dx}{a} = \frac{dt}{1}$

integrating, we get

$x - at = c_1$ – – – (3)

So from (2) and (3) we get ,

$u = \phi(x - at)$

$\Rightarrow u(x,t) = \phi(x - at)$

Using initial condition

$u(x,0) = u_0(x)$ (given)

we get $u(x,0) = u_0(x) = \phi(x)$

$\Rightarrow u(x,t) = u_0(x - at)$

If $u_0(x - at)$ is a bounded function, then $u_0(x)$ is also a bounded function and vice versa.

$\Rightarrow S_1$ is false.

$\Rightarrow$ option a) and b) are incorrect.

Let u_0 vanish on $x \in [a_1, a_2]$, P > 0 be any fixed number

$u_0(x) = 0$ on $x \notin [a_1, a_2]$

Now, $u_0(x - aP) \neq 0$

$\Rightarrow x - aP \in [a_1, a_2]$

$\Rightarrow a_1 \le x - aP \le a_2$

$\Rightarrow a_1 + aP \le x \le a_2 + aP$

$\Rightarrow u_0(x,P) \neq 0$ in $[a_1 + \text{aP}, a_2 + \text{aP}]$ and $u_0(x,P) = 0$ on $x \notin [a_1 + \text{aP}, a_2 + \text{aP}]$

$\because E_p = [a_1 + \text{aP}, a_2 + \text{aP}]$

$\Rightarrow S_2$ is true. So, option c) is the correct answer and a), b) and d) are incorrect.

15. Explanation (b), (d)

Consider the given PDE

$u_t + uu_x = 1$, $x \in \mathbb{R}$, $t > 0$ (1)

To solve this,

By Lagrange's method

Lagrange's auxiliary equation is

$$\frac{dx}{u} = \frac{dt}{1} = \frac{du}{1}$$

Consider,

$$\frac{dt}{1} = \frac{du}{1}$$

$\Rightarrow t - u = c$ – – – (2)

Now, consider

$\frac{dx}{u} = \frac{du}{1}$

Integrating,

$\Rightarrow x - \frac{u^2}{2} = c_1$ – – – (3)

$\Rightarrow 2x - u^2 = c_2$

From equation (1) and (2), general solution is

$2x - u^2 = \phi(t - u)$

Now, $u\left(\frac{t^2}{4}, t\right) = \frac{t}{2}$ (given)

$$\phi\left(t - \frac{t}{2}\right) = \left(\frac{2t^2}{4} - \frac{t^2}{4}\right)$$

$$\Rightarrow \phi\left(\frac{t}{2}\right) = \left(\frac{t}{2}\right)^2$$

$2x - u^2 = (t - u)^2$

$2x - u^2 = t^2 + u^2 - 2xu$

$2u^2 - 2tu - 2x + t^2 = 0$

$\Rightarrow 2u^2 - 2ut + t^2 - 2x = 0$

This is the quadratic equation in u

$$u = \frac{2t \pm \sqrt{(-2t)^2 - 8(t^2 - 2x)}}{4}$$

$$u = \frac{t \pm \sqrt{t^2 - 2(t^2 - 2x)}}{2}$$

$\Rightarrow u = \frac{t \pm \sqrt{4x^2 - t^2}}{2}$ (4)

$$\Rightarrow u = \frac{t + \sqrt{4x^2 - t^2}}{2}, \frac{t - \sqrt{4x^2 - t^2}}{2}$$

$\Rightarrow$ given initial value problem has two solution.

$\Rightarrow$ option b) is correct and option a) and c) incorrect.

Now differentiate equation (4) w.r.t. to x

$$u_x = \frac{2x}{\sqrt{4x^2 - t^2}}$$

Differentiating equation (4) w.r.t. to t

$$u_t = \frac{1}{2} \pm \frac{\frac{t}{2}}{\sqrt{4x^2 - t^2}}$$

$\Rightarrow$Partial derivative of u w.r.to x and t are not continuous at x = $\frac{t^2}{4}$.

$\Rightarrow$ Solution does not exist on differentiable curve.

$\Rightarrow$Option d) is correct.

Hence, option (b) and (d) are correct answer and option a) and c) are incorrect.

16. Explanation (a), (b), (c), (d)

Consider the given PDE Lagrange's auxiliary equation is

$$\frac{dx}{x} = \frac{dt}{t} = \frac{du}{u+1}$$

Consider $\frac{dx}{x} = \frac{du}{u+1}$

Integrating,

$\log x = \log(u + 1) + c_1$

$\Rightarrow \frac{x}{u+1} = c_1$ – – – (1)

Consider, $\frac{dx}{x} = \frac{dt}{t}$

$\Rightarrow \log x = \log t + c_2 \Rightarrow \frac{x}{t} = c_2$ – –(2)

Also, the initial curve

$u(x, t) = x^2$, $t^2 = x^2$

takinng $x = s, t = s^2, u = s^2$ i.e (s, s^2, s^2),

So, from equation (1) and (2)

$\Rightarrow c_1 = \frac{s}{s^2+1}$ and $c_2 = \frac{s}{s^2} = \frac{1}{s}$

$c_1 = \frac{1}{s+\frac{1}{s}}$

$\Rightarrow c_1 = \frac{1}{\frac{1}{c_2}+c_2} = \frac{c_2}{1+c_2^2}$

$\Rightarrow \frac{x}{u+1} = \frac{\frac{x}{t}}{1+\frac{x^2}{t^2}} = \frac{\frac{x}{t}}{\frac{t^2+x^2}{t^2}} = \frac{xt}{x^2+t^2}$

$\Rightarrow \frac{1}{u+1} = \frac{t}{x^2+t^2}$

$=> \frac{x^2+t^2}{t} = u+1$

$u = \frac{x^2+t^2}{t} - 1$

At (0,0); $u = -1$, hence, singular.

At (0,0); $u = -1$, not the given initial curve.

The base characteristics is $\frac{x}{t} = c_2$ which does not Pass through (0, 0).

Condition for the IVP to have a unique solution is

$\begin{vmatrix} s & s \\ 1 & 2s \end{vmatrix} = 2s^2 - s \neq 0$

But if s is non zero.

Hence, option (a), (b), (c) and (d) are correct.

17. Explanation (b)

Consider the given partial differential equation is

$(x+y)z\, z_x + (x-y)z\, z_y = x^2 + y^2$ (1)

To solve this

By Lagrange's method

Lagrange's auxiliary equation is,

$$\frac{dx}{(x+y)z} = \frac{dy}{(x+y)z} = \frac{dz}{x^2+y^2}$$

Consider $\frac{xdx-ydy-zdz}{x^2z+xyz-xyz+zy^2-x^2z-y^2z}$

$xdx - ydy - zdz = 0$

Integrating, we get

$x^2 - y^2 - z^2 = c_1$ (1)

Now, consider $\frac{ydx+xdy}{xyz+y^2z+x^2z-xyz} = \frac{dz}{x^2+y^2}$

$\frac{ydx+xdy}{(y^2+x^2)z} = \frac{dz}{x^2+y^2}$

$ydx + xdy = zdz$

Integrating both side

$xy = \frac{z^2}{2} + c_2$

$z^2 - 2xy = c_3$ (3)

From equation (2) and (3)

$F(x^2-y^2-z^2, z^2-2xy) = 0$

for arbitrary C^1 function F

From above explanation

Option b) is correct and option (a), (c) and (d) are incorrect.

18. Explanation (b)

Consider the given PDE

Lagrange's auxiliary equation is,

$\frac{dx}{u} = \frac{dy}{1} = \frac{du}{1}$ .....(*)

Consider

$\frac{dx}{u} = \frac{du}{1} \Rightarrow dx = udu$

Integrating we get

$\Rightarrow \frac{1}{2}u^2 = x + c$ ......(i)

$x_0(s) = s, y_0(s) = s, u_0(s) = s/2$

$\Rightarrow \frac{1}{2}\cdot\frac{s^2}{4} = s + c \Rightarrow c = \frac{s^2}{8} - s$ ....(ii)

Now consider,

$\frac{dy}{1} = \frac{du}{1}$

Integrating, we get

$\Rightarrow y + c_1 = u$

$\Rightarrow s + c_1 = \frac{s}{2} \Rightarrow c_1 = \frac{-s}{2}$

$\Rightarrow -2c_1 = s$ ......(iii)

$c = \frac{(-2c_1)^2}{8} - (-2c_1) = \frac{4c_1^2+16c_1}{8}$

$\Rightarrow c = \frac{c_1^2+4c_1}{2} = \frac{c_1(c_1+4)}{2}$

$\Rightarrow \frac{u^2}{2} - x = \frac{(u-y)(u-y+4)}{2}$

$\Rightarrow u^2 - 2x = (u-y)^2 + 4(u-y)$

$\Rightarrow \frac{u^2-2x}{2} = \frac{(u-y)^2+4(u-y)}{2}$

$\Rightarrow u^2 - 2x = u^2 - 2uy + y^2 + 4u + 4y$

$\Rightarrow 2uy - 4u = 2x + y^2 - 4y$

$\Rightarrow u(2y-4) = 2x + y^2 - 4y$

$\Rightarrow u(x,y) = \frac{2x+y^2-4y}{2y-4}$

$\Rightarrow u(2,1) = \frac{(2.2)+1-4}{2-4} = \frac{5-4}{-2} = \frac{-1}{2}$

$\Rightarrow$ option b) is the correct answer and a), c) and d) are incorrect.

19. Explanation: (b), (c), (d)

Consider,

$\frac{\partial u}{\partial x} + \frac{2\partial u}{\partial y} = 0$, (x,y) $\in R^2$

u(x, y) = sin x for y = 3x + 1

Lagrange's A.E = $\frac{dx}{1} = \frac{dy}{2} = \frac{du}{0}$

du = 0 $\Rightarrow$ u = c_1 (1)

also $\frac{dx}{1} = \frac{dy}{2}$ $\Rightarrow$ 2x – y = c_2 (2)

i.e, y – 2x = c_2

Now given initial data curve is:

take x = s $\Rightarrow$ y = 3s + 1 & u = sin(s). Put this curve in (1) and (2), we get,

sin(s) = c_1 (3)

2s – 3s – 1 = c_2 (4)

From (3) and (4)

c_1 = sin (c_2 - 1) (5)

u= sin (-2x + y - 1) (6)

Now consider,

$\frac{\partial v}{\partial x} + \frac{2\partial v}{\partial y} = 0$

v(x, 0) = sin x
Solution of Lagrange's A.E. are
v = c_3 (7)
& -4 + 2x = c_4 (8)
Initial data curve is:
Taking x = s, y = 0, v = sin (s)
Put this in (7) & (8), we get,
sin (s) = c_3 (9)
& 2s = r.c_4 (10)
From (9) & (10)
$c_3 = \sin\left(\frac{c_4}{2}\right)$ (11)
$v = \sin\left(\frac{2x-4}{2}\right)$ (12)
S = [0,1] ×[0,1]
U = sin(y − (2x + 1))
2x + 1 ≥ 1 ∀ x ∈ [0,1]
And y ≤ 1 ∀ y ∈ [0,1]
⟹ y − (2x + 1) ≤ 0
⟹ sin (y − (2x + 1)) ≤ 0 ∀ (x, y) ∈ [0,1] × [0,1]
So, u does not change its sign in the interior of S.

2. Consider,
$y - 2x - 1 = \frac{2x-4}{2}$
⇒ 2y − 4x − 2 = 2x − y
⇒ 3y − 2 = 6x
⇒ 3y = 6x + 2
$y = 2x + \frac{2}{3}$
So along this line in S, u(x ,y) = v(x, y).
3. $v(0, 1) = \sin\left(\frac{-1}{2}\right) < 0$
v(0, 1) = sin (1) < 0
So, v changes sign in the interior of S.
4. Along the line $y = 2x$, v vanishes.
So, options (b), (c) and (d) are correct.

20. Explanation: (b), (c)

Lagrange A.E: $\frac{dx}{1} = \frac{dy}{x} = \frac{du}{0}$
du = 0 ⇒ u=c_1 -------------(1)
consider, xdx-dy = 0
$\Rightarrow \frac{x^2}{2} - y = c_2$
$\Rightarrow x^2 - 2y = c_2$ ------(2)
Now, u(x,0) = e^x
In parametric form,
(s,o,e^s)
Put this in (a) & (b) we get,
$e^s = c_1$ -------(3)
$u = e^{-\sqrt{c_2}}$
$u = e^{-\sqrt{x^2-2y}}$
So, $u(1, \frac{1}{2}) = 1$
$u(-2,1) = e^{-\sqrt{2}}$
So, options (b) & (c) are correct.

21. Explanation: (b), (d) Consider the DE: $u_x + u_y = e^u$

Lagrange's AE:
$\frac{dx}{1} = \frac{dy}{1} = \frac{du}{e^u}$
Consider dx = dy
⇒ x-y=c_1 ... (1)
Consider
$dx = \frac{du}{e^u}$
$\Rightarrow x = -e^{-u} + c_2$
$\Rightarrow x + \frac{1}{e^u} = c_2$ --- (2)
Now u(x,0) = 1
Taking x=s, y=0, u=1
Put this curve in (1) & (2), we get,
s = c_1 ... (3)
$s + \frac{1}{e} = c_2$ --- (4)
from (3) & (4)
$c_2 = c_1 + \frac{1}{e}$
$x + \frac{1}{e^u} = x - y + \frac{1}{e}$
$y = \frac{1}{e} - \frac{1}{e^u}$ ... (5)
Put, $x = \frac{1}{2e}$, $y = \frac{1}{2e}$
$\frac{1}{2e} = \frac{1}{e} - \frac{1}{e^u}$
$\Rightarrow \frac{-1}{2e} = \frac{1}{e^u}$
$e^u = 2e$
u = log(2e)
So, $u_x = 0$
from (5)
$\frac{1}{e^u} = \frac{1}{e} - y$
$\Rightarrow \frac{1}{e^u} = \frac{1-ey}{e}$
$\Rightarrow e^u = \frac{e}{(1-ey)}$
$\Rightarrow u = \log\left(\frac{e}{1-ey}\right)$
$u_y = \frac{1}{\left(\frac{e}{1-ey}\right)} \times \frac{e^2}{(1-ey)^2}$
$u_y = \frac{e}{(1-ey)}$
$u_y\left(\frac{1}{4e}, \frac{1}{4e}\right) = \frac{e}{1-e\frac{1}{4e}} = \frac{4e}{3}$
So, options (b) and (d) are correct.

22. Explanation: (a) Characteristics solve

$$\frac{dx}{ds} = x, \frac{dy}{ds} = 1, \frac{du}{ds} = 1,$$

with initial points $(0, r)$ on the curve $x = 0$. Since $x(0) = 0$ the solution of $dx/ds = x$ with $x(0) = 0$ is $x(s) \equiv 0$. Thus, every characteristic through the initial curve stays on $x = 0$: the initial curve is characteristic.

Along these characteristics $\frac{du}{dy} = \frac{du/ds}{dy/ds} = 1$, so any solution must satisfy

$$u_y(0, y) = 1 \text{ for all } y.$$

But the prescribed data gives $u(0, y) = e^y$, so $u_y(0, y) = e^y$, which is not equal to 1 except at $y = 0$. Therefore, the Cauchy data are incompatible on any neighborhood of the origin (0,0) (compatibility holds only at the single point $y = 0$), so no solution exists on any neighborhood of the origin. Hence (1) is true and (2), (3), (4) are false.

Unit 2.2: First Order Nonlinear PDE (Charpit's Method)

MCQ - Multiple Choice Questions

1. Let $u = u(x,y)$ be the complete integral of the PDE $\frac{\partial u}{\partial x}\frac{\partial u}{\partial y} = xy$ passing through the points $(0,0,1)$ and $\left(0,1,\frac{1}{2}\right)$ in the $x - y - u$ space.
Then the value of $u(x,y)$ evaluated at $(-1,1)$ *is*
(a) 0 (b) 1
(c) 2 (d) 3
[Dec.2011]

2. Let u be of the boundary value problem
$$u'' + \frac{1}{t}u' = f(t), t \in (0,1)$$
$$u'(0) = a, u(1) = b$$
Define for $x^2 + y^2 \le 1$, $v(x,y) = u(\sqrt{x^2+y^2})$
And $g(x,y) = f(\sqrt{x^2+y^2})$, *then v is a solution*
Of the PDE
$$v_{xx} + v_{yy} = g \text{ in } \{(x,y) : x^2 + y^2 < 1\}$$
$$v(x,y) = 0 \text{ on } \{(x,y): x^2 + y^2 = 1\}$$
If
(a) $a > 0$ and $b > 0$ (b) $a > 0$ and $b = 0$
(c) $a = 0$ and $b = 0$ (d) $a < 0$ and $b = 0$
[June 2012]

3. Let $x = x(s), y = y(s), u = u(s), s \in \mathbb{R}$ be the characteristic Curve of the PDE
$$\left(\frac{\partial u}{\partial x}\right)\left(\frac{\partial u}{\partial y}\right) - u = 0$$
Passing through a given curve
$$x = 0, y = \tau, u = \tau^2, \tau \in \mathbb{R}$$
Then the characteristics are given by
(a) $x = 3\tau(e^s - 1), y = \frac{\tau}{2}(e^{-s} + 1), u = \tau^2 e^{-2s}$
(b) $x = 2\tau(e^{-s} - 1), y = \tau(2e^{2s} - 1), u = \frac{\tau^2}{2}(1 + e^{-2s})$
(c) $x = 2\tau(e^s - 1), y = \frac{\tau}{2}(e^s + 1), u = \tau^2 e^{2s}$
(d) $x = \tau(e^{-s} - 1), y = -2\tau\left(e^{-s} - \frac{3}{2}\right), u = \tau^2(2e^{-2s} - 1)$
[June 2014]

4. The Charpit's equation for the PDE
$up^2 + q^2 + x + y = 0$, $p = \frac{\partial u}{\partial x}, q = \frac{\partial u}{\partial y}$
Are given by
(a) $\frac{dx}{-1-p^3} = \frac{dy}{-1-qp^2} = \frac{du}{2p^2u+2q^2} = \frac{dp}{2pu} = \frac{dq}{2q}$
(b) $\frac{dx}{2pu} = \frac{dy}{2q} = \frac{du}{2p^2u+2q^2} = \frac{dp}{-1-p^3} = \frac{dq}{-1-qp^2}$
(c) $\frac{dx}{up^2} = \frac{dy}{q^2} = \frac{du}{0} = \frac{dp}{x} = \frac{dq}{y}$
(d) $\frac{dx}{2q} = \frac{dy}{2pu} = \frac{du}{x+y} = \frac{dp}{p^2} = \frac{dq}{qp^2}$
[Dec. 2014]

5. Let $u = u(x,y)$ be the solution of the Cauchy problem $x\frac{\partial u}{\partial x} + y\frac{\partial u}{\partial y} = u, (x,y) \ne (0,0), u(x,1) = \sqrt{1+x^2}, x \in \mathbb{R}$.
Then which of the following statements is true?
(a) $u(1,0) = 0$
(b) $u(x_1,y_1) = u(x_2,y_2)$ whenever $x_1^2 + y_1^2 = x_2^2 + y_2^2$
(c) $u(1,y) = \sqrt{2}$ for all $y \in \mathbb{R}$
(d) $u(x_1,y_1) = u(x_2,y_2)$ whenever $x_1 + y_1 = x_2 + y_2$
[Feb. 2025]

Answer Key

1	2	3	4	5
a	c	c	b	b

Explanation

1. **Explanation (a)**
Consider the given PDE
$$\frac{\partial u}{\partial x}\frac{\partial u}{\partial y} = xy \quad --- (1)$$
$\Rightarrow pq = xy$ where $p = \frac{\partial u}{\partial x}$ and $q = \frac{\partial u}{\partial y}$
Equation (1) is of the form $f(p,q) = 0$
$\frac{p}{x} = \frac{y}{q} = a$
$\Rightarrow p = ax$ and $q = \frac{y}{a}$
Solution is given by
$\Rightarrow du = pdx + qdy$
$\Rightarrow du = ax\,dx + \frac{y}{a}dy$
Integrating
$\Rightarrow u = a\frac{x^2}{2} + \frac{y^2}{2a} + c \quad --- (1)$
Where c is a constant
Putting (0,0,1) in equation (1), we get $c = 1$
Putting $\left(0,1,\frac{1}{2}\right)$ in equation (1), we get $a = -1$
$\Rightarrow u(x,y) = -\frac{x^2}{2} - \frac{y^2}{2} + 1$
$\Rightarrow u(-1,1) = -\frac{1}{2} - \frac{1}{2} + 1 = 0$
Hence, option (a) is correct and option b),c),and d) are incorrect.

2. **Explanation (c)**
Consider the given boundary value problem
$u'' + \frac{1}{t}u' = f(t), t \in (0,1)$
$u'(0) = a, u(1) = b$ (1)
Take $f(t) = 0$ (2)
Equation (1) become
$u'' + \frac{1}{t}u' = 0$ (3)
To solve this,
put $\log x = z \Rightarrow x = e^z$
Auxiliary equation of equation (2) is
$m(m-1) + m = 0$
$m^2 = 0$
Complementary function is
$u(x) = Az + B$
$u(x) = A\log t + B$

Now use the given boundary condition

$u' = 0, u(1) = b$

$\mathrm{u(1) = Alog1 + B = b}$

$\mathrm{B = b}$ and $u'(t) = \frac{A}{t}$ which is not defined at t = 0

$\mathrm{u(x) = 0}$

u(x) has only trivial solution.

$v(x,y) = 0 \; for \; x^2 + y^2 \leq 1$

$g(x,y) = f(\sqrt{x^2+y^2}) = 0$ from (1)

$\because$ v(x, y) is the solution of $v_{xx} + v_{yy} = 0$ Also $v(x,y) = 0$

$x^2 + y^2 = 1$ *and* $u'(x)$ also exist if a = 0

Only option (c) is correct and a), b) and d) are incorrect.

3. **Explanation (c)**

Consider the given PDE

$\left(\frac{\partial u}{\partial x}\right)\left(\frac{\partial u}{\partial y}\right) - u = 0$

This equation is of the form f(f(p, q, u) = 0

Solution of this equation is

$\mathrm{du} = \sqrt{a}\sqrt{u}\,\mathrm{dx} + \frac{\sqrt{a}}{\sqrt{u}}\mathrm{dy}$

$\Rightarrow \frac{du}{\sqrt{u}} = \sqrt{a}\,\mathrm{dx} + \frac{1}{\sqrt{a}}\mathrm{dy}$

Integrating, we get

$2\sqrt{u} = \sqrt{a}\,x + \frac{1}{\sqrt{a}}\,y + d$

From given condition

$x = 0, y = t, u = t^2$

$\Rightarrow 2t = \sqrt{a}.0 + \frac{1}{\sqrt{a}}t + d$

$\Rightarrow \frac{1}{\sqrt{a}} = 2, d = 0$

$a = \frac{1}{4}$

$2\sqrt{u} = \frac{x}{2} + 2y$

$4u = \left(\frac{1}{2}x + 2y\right)^2$

From above explanation only option c) is correct answer and a), b), d) are incorrect.

4. **Explanation (b)**

Consider the given PDE

$up^2 + q^2 + x + y = 0$

$\Rightarrow f = up^2 + q^2 + x + y$

Now to find the charpit equation

We know that Charpit's auxiliary equations are

$$\frac{dx}{f_p} = \frac{dy}{f_q} = \frac{du}{pf_p + qf_q} = \frac{dp}{-(f_x + pf_u)} = \frac{dq}{-(f_y + qf_u)}$$

$f_p = 2up \; ; f_q = 2q \; ; f_x = 1 \quad ; \; f_y = 1; f_u = p^2$

$$\Rightarrow \frac{dx}{2pu} = \frac{dy}{2q} = \frac{du}{2up^2+2q^2} = \frac{dp}{-(1+p^3)} = \frac{dq}{-(1+qp^2)}$$

From this,

Only option (b) is correct answer and a), c) and d) are incorrect.

5. **Explanation: (b)**

The PDE is:

$$x\frac{\partial u}{\partial x} + y\frac{\partial u}{\partial y} = u$$

This is a first-order linear PDE, and its characteristic equations are:

$$\frac{dx}{x} = \frac{dy}{y} = \frac{du}{u}.$$

From $\frac{dx}{x} = \frac{dy}{y}$,

$\ln|x| = \ln|y| + C_1 \Rightarrow \frac{x}{y} = C_1.$

From $\frac{dx}{x} = \frac{du}{u}$

$\ln|x| = \ln|u| + C_2 \Rightarrow \frac{u}{x} = C_2.$

Thus, the general solution is:

$$u(x,y) = x \cdot f\left(\frac{x}{y}\right),$$

where f is an arbitrary function.

The initial condition is $u(x,1) = \sqrt{1+x^2}$. Substituting $y = 1$ into the general solution:

$$u(x,1) = x \cdot f\left(\frac{x}{1}\right) = \sqrt{1+x^2}.$$

$$f(x) = \frac{\sqrt{1+x^2}}{x}.$$

Substituting back into the general solution:

$$u(x,y) = x \cdot \frac{\sqrt{1+\left(\frac{x}{y}\right)^2}}{\frac{x}{y}} = y \cdot \sqrt{1+\left(\frac{x}{y}\right)^2}$$

$$u(x,y) = \sqrt{y^2+x^2}$$

1. $u(1,0) = 0$: Substituting $x = 1, \; y = 0$: $u(1,0) = \sqrt{1^2+0^2} = 1 \neq 0$. **(False).**
2. $u(x_1,y_1) = u(x_2,y_2)$ **whenever** $x_1^2 + y_1^2 = x_2^2 + y_2^2$: Since $u(x,y) = \sqrt{x^2+y^2}$, this statement is **true**.
3. $u(1,y) = \sqrt{2}$ **for all** $y \in \mathbb{R}$: Substituting $x = 1$: $u(1,y) = \sqrt{1+y^2}$. This is not equal to $\sqrt{2}$ for all y. (False)
4. $u(x_1,y_1) = u(x_2,y_2)$ **whenever** $x_1 + y_1 = x_2 + y_2$: This is **false** because $u(x,y) = \sqrt{x^2+y^2}$ depends on $x^2 + y^2$, not $x + y$.

Thus, option (b) is correct.

MSQ - Multiple Select Questions

1. Consider the first order PDE

$$p + q = pq \text{ where } p \equiv \frac{\partial z}{\partial x}, q \equiv \frac{\partial z}{\partial y}.$$

Then which of the following are correct?

(a) The Charpit's equations for the above PDE reduce to

$$\frac{dx}{1-q} = \frac{dy}{1-p} = \frac{dz}{-pq} = \frac{dp}{p+q} = \frac{dq}{0}$$

(b) A solution of the Charpit's equation is

$q = b$, where b is a constant

(c) The corresponding value of p *is* $p = \frac{b}{b-1}$

(d) A solution of the equation is

$$z = \frac{b}{b-1}x + by + a$$

Where a and b are constants

[June 2013]

2. Let $z = z(x, y)$ be a solution of $\frac{\partial z}{\partial x}\frac{\partial z}{\partial y} = 1$
Passing through (0,0,0). Then $(z(0,1)$ *is*
(a) 0 (b) 1
(c) 2 (d) 4
[Dec 2013]

3. Let $u = u(x, t)$ be the solution of the Cauchy problem
$$\frac{\partial u}{\partial t} + \left(\frac{\partial u}{\partial x}\right)^2 = 1 \quad x \in \mathbb{R}, t > 0$$
$$u(x, 0) = -x^2 \quad x \in \mathbb{R}$$
Then
(a) $u(x, t)$ exists for all $x \in \mathbb{R}$ *and* $t > 0$
(b) $|u(x, t)| \to \infty$ as $t \to t^*$ for some $t^* > 0$ and $x \neq 0$
(c) $u(x, t) \leq 0$ for all $x \in \mathbb{R}$ and for all $t < 1/4$
(d) $u(x, t) > 0$ for some $x \in \mathbb{R}$ and $0 < t < 1/4$
[Dec. 2014]

4. Which of the following are complete integrals of the partial differential Equation $pqx + yq^2 = 1$?
(a) $z = \frac{x}{a} + \frac{ay}{x} + b$ (b) $z = \frac{x}{b} + \frac{ay}{x} + b$
(c) $z^2 = 4(ax + y) + b$ (d) $(z - b)^2 = 4(ax + y)$
[June 2015]

5. A solution of the PDE
$$x\frac{\partial u}{\partial x} + y\frac{\partial u}{\partial y} + \left(\frac{\partial u}{\partial x}\right)^2 + \left(\frac{\partial u}{\partial y}\right)^2 - u = 0$$
Represents
(a) An ellipse in the $x - y$ plane
(b) An ellipsoid in the xyu plane
(c) A parabola in the $u - x$ plane
(d) A hyperbola in the $u - y$ plane
[Dec. 2015]

6. Consider the Cauchy problem for the Eikonal equation
$$p^2 + q^2 = 1; \quad p \equiv \frac{\partial u}{\partial x}, q \equiv \frac{\partial u}{\partial y},$$
$u(x, y) = 0$ *on* $x + y = 1$, $(x, y) \in \mathbb{R}^2$. Then
(a) The Charpit's equation for the differential equation are $\frac{dx}{dt} = 2p; \frac{dy}{dt} = 2q; \frac{du}{dt} = 2; \frac{dp}{dt} = -p; \frac{dq}{dt} = -q$
(b) The Charpit's equations for the differential equation are $\frac{dx}{dt} = 2p; \frac{dy}{dt} = 2q; \frac{du}{dt} = 2; \frac{dp}{dt} = 0; \frac{dq}{dt} = 0$
(c) $u(1, \sqrt{2}) = \sqrt{2}$
(d) $u(1, \sqrt{2}) = 1$
[June 2016]

7. If a complete integral of the partial differential equation
$$x(p^2 + q^2) = zp; p = \frac{\partial z}{\partial x}, q = \frac{\partial z}{\partial y}$$
Passes through the curve $x = 0, z^2 = 4y$, then the envelope of this family Passing through $x = 1$ and $y = 1$ has
(a) $z = -2$ (b) $z = 2$
(c) $z = \sqrt{2 + 2\sqrt{2}}$ (d) $z = -\sqrt{2 + 2\sqrt{2}}$
[June 2017]

8. A possible initial strip $(x_0, y_0, z_0, p_0, q_0)$ for the Cauchy problem $pq = 1$ where $p = \frac{\partial z}{\partial x}$, $q = \frac{\partial z}{\partial y}$&$x_0(s) = s$, $y_0(s) = \frac{1}{s}$, $z_0(s) = 1$ for $s > 1$ is
(a) $\left(s, \frac{1}{s}, 1, \frac{1}{s}, s\right)$ (b) $\left(s, \frac{1}{s}, 1, \frac{-1}{s}, -s\right)$
(c) $\left(s, \frac{1}{s}, 1, \frac{1}{s}, -s\right)$ (d) $\left(s, \frac{1}{s}, 1, \frac{-1}{s}, s\right)$
[Dec 2019]

9. Consider the PDE
$$z = x\frac{\partial z}{\partial x} + y\frac{\partial z}{\partial y} + \frac{\partial z}{\partial x}\frac{\partial z}{\partial y}$$
Which of the following statements are true?
(a) The complete integral is $z = xa + yb + ab, a, b$ arbitary constants.
(b) The complete integral is $z = ax + by + \sqrt{a^2 + b^2}$ a, b arbitary constants.
(c) The particular solution passing through $x = 0$ and $z = y^2$ is $\left(\frac{x}{y} - y\right)^2$
(d) The particular solution passing through $x = 0$ and $z = y^2$ is $\left(\frac{x}{y} + y\right)^2$
[Nov 2020]

10. Consider the Partial differential equation.
$$x\left(\frac{\partial u}{\partial x}\right)^2 + y\left(\frac{\partial u}{\partial y}\right)^2 + (x + y)\frac{\partial u}{\partial x}\frac{\partial u}{\partial y} - u\left(\frac{\partial u}{\partial x} + \frac{\partial u}{\partial y}\right) + 1 = 0$$
Which of the following statements are correct?
(a) The general solution of the PDE can be expressed in the form $u(x, y) = ax + by + \frac{1}{a+b}$, where a and b arbitrary constants
(b) The general solution of the PDE can be expresses in the form $u(x, y) = f(ax + by) + \frac{1}{a+b}$, where a and b arbitrary constant and f is an arbitrary function.
(c) The Charpit's equation are
$$\frac{dx}{p^2+pq} = \frac{dy}{q^2+pq} = \frac{dU}{p(p^2+pa)+q(p^2+pq)} = \frac{dp}{0} = \frac{dq}{0}$$
(d) The Charpit's equation are
$$\frac{dx}{2px+(x+y)q-u} = \frac{dy}{2qy+(x+y)p-u} = \frac{dP}{0} = \frac{dq}{0} = \frac{du}{p(2px+(x+y)q-u)+q(2qy+(x+y)p-u)}$$
[Nov 2020]

Answer Key				
1	2	3	4	5
b, c, d	a	b, d	a, d	c
6	7	8	9	10
b, d	c, d	a, b	a, c	a, d

Explanation

1. **Explanation (b), (c), (d)**
Consider the given PDE
$p + q = pq$
$\Rightarrow f = p + q - pq = 0$
This is nonlinear PDE of form f(p, q) = 0
To solve this, put q = b
$$\Rightarrow p = \frac{b}{b - 1}$$
Now, solution is

$dz = pdx + qdy$

$\Rightarrow dz = \dfrac{b}{b-1}dx + bdy$

$\Rightarrow z = \frac{b}{b-1}x + by + c$ (c is constant)

Now,

Charpit's auxiliary equations are

$$\frac{dx}{f_p} = \frac{dy}{f_q} = \frac{dz}{pf_p + qf_q} = \frac{dp}{-(f_x + pf_z)} = \frac{dq}{-(f_y + qf_x)}$$

$$\Rightarrow \frac{dx}{1-q} = \frac{dy}{1-p} = \frac{dz}{p+q-2pq} = \frac{dp}{0} = \frac{dq}{0}$$

From above explanation,

Options (b), (c) and (d) are correct answer and option (a) is incorrect.

2. Explanation (a)

Consider the given PDE

$$\frac{\partial z}{\partial x}\frac{\partial z}{\partial y} = 1$$

$\Rightarrow pq - 1 = 0 - - - (1)$

This is nonlinear PDE of the form

$f(p, q) = 0$

Put $p = a$ in equation (1), we get

$\Rightarrow q = \dfrac{1}{a}$

Solution is

$dz = adx + \frac{1}{a}dy$

Hence, $z = ax + \frac{1}{a}y + c$

Passing through (0, 0, 0)

$\Rightarrow c = 0$

$z = ax + \frac{1}{a}y$ (2)

Now to to find the value of z(0,1)

Firstly to find the General integral

General integral is obtained by eliminating 'a' from (1)

And $\dfrac{\partial z}{\partial a} = 0$

i.e. $\dfrac{\partial z}{\partial a} = -x + \frac{1}{a^2}y = 0$

$\Rightarrow a = \pm\sqrt{\dfrac{y}{x}}$

Therefore, $z = \pm 2\sqrt{xy}$

$\Rightarrow z(0, 1) = 0$

From this option (a) is correct answer and option b), c) and d) are the incorrect.

3. Explanation (b), (d)

Consider the given PDE

$\dfrac{\partial u}{\partial t} + \left(\dfrac{\partial u}{\partial x}\right)^2 = 1$ $\quad x \in \mathbb{R}, t > 0$

$u(x, 0) = -x^2$ $\quad x \in \mathbb{R}$

$p^2 + q = 1$ (1)

This is nonlinear PDE of the form $f(p, q) = 0$

To solve this, put p = a in equation (1)

$\Rightarrow q = 1 - a^2$

Solution is

$du = p\,dx + q\,dt$

$\Rightarrow du = adx + (1 - a^2)dt$

Integrating, we get

$u = ax + (1 - a^2)t + b - - - - - - -(2)$

(Where b is an arbitrary constant.)

$\Rightarrow a^2\left(\frac{1}{4} - t\right) + ax + t - u$

This is quadratic in a to eliminate a take discriminant is equal to zero

$\Rightarrow x^2 - 4\left(\dfrac{1}{4} - t\right)(t - u) = 0$

$\Rightarrow u = t - \dfrac{x^2}{1 - 4t}$

Which is the required solution of given PDE and at $t = \frac{1}{4}$ does not exist

u(x, t) does not exist $\forall x \in \mathbb{R}$

From above explanation option a) is incorrect.

For option b)

When $t = \frac{1}{4}$ then $|u(x, t)| \to \infty$

$\Rightarrow t \to t^* = \frac{1}{4}$ for some $t^* > 0$ and $x \neq 0$

Then $|u(x, t)| \to \infty$

For option c)

Take $t = \frac{1}{9} < \frac{1}{4}$ and $x = 0$

$\Rightarrow u(x, t) = \frac{1}{9} > 0$

Option c) is incorrect

For option d),

From option c)

⇒Option d) is correct

⇒Option b) and d) are correct answer and option a) and c) are incorrect.

4. Explanation (a), (d)

Consider the given PDE

$pqx + yq^2 = 1$

Now check option

For option (a)

$z = \frac{x}{a} + \frac{ay}{x} + b$ then differentiating partially with respect to x and y,

We get $p = \frac{1}{a} - \frac{ay}{x^2}$ and $q = \frac{a}{x}$, where $p = \frac{\partial z}{\partial x}, q = \frac{\partial z}{\partial y}$

Now,

$$pqx + yq^2 = \left(\frac{1}{a} - \frac{ay}{x^2}\right)\frac{a}{x}.x + y\left(\frac{a}{x}\right)^2 = 1 - \frac{a^2y}{x^2} + \frac{a^2y}{x^2} = 1$$

⇒ Option a) is correct.

For option (b)

$z = \frac{x}{b} + \frac{ay}{x} + b$ then differentiating partially with respect to x and y, we get

$$p = \frac{1}{b} - \frac{ay}{x^2} \quad and \quad q = \frac{a}{x}, where\ p = \frac{\partial z}{\partial x}, q = \frac{\partial z}{\partial y}$$

$pqx + yq^2 = \left(\frac{1}{b} - \frac{ay}{x^2}\right).\frac{a}{x}.x + y\left(\frac{a}{x}\right)^2 = \frac{a}{b} - \frac{a^2y}{x^2} + \frac{a^2y}{x^2} \neq 1$ so option not satisfy the given PDE.

⇒Option b) is incorrect.

for option (c)

$z^2 = 4(ax + y) + b$ then differentiating partially with respect to x and y, we get $2zp = 4a \Rightarrow p = \frac{2a}{z}$

And $2zq = 4 \Rightarrow q = \frac{2}{z}$, where $p = \frac{\partial z}{\partial x}$, $q = \frac{\partial z}{\partial y}$

Now, $pqx + yq^2 = \frac{4ax+4y}{z^2} = \frac{(z)^2-b}{(z)^2} \neq 1$

so option (c) is incorrect.

For option (d)

$(z-b)^2 = 4(ax+y)$

$2(z-b)p = 4a$

$\Rightarrow p = \frac{a}{(z-b)}$

And $2(z-b)q = 4$

$\Rightarrow q = \frac{2}{(z-b)}$, where $p = \frac{\partial z}{\partial x}$, $q = \frac{\partial z}{\partial y}$

Now, $pqx + yq^2 = \frac{4ax+4y}{(z-b)^2} = \frac{(z-b)^2}{(z-b)^2} = 1$

$\Rightarrow$ Option d) is correct.

$\Rightarrow$ Option (a) and (d) are correct are correct answer and (b), (c) are incorrect.

5. **Explanation (c)**

Consider the given PDE

$$x\frac{\partial u}{\partial x} + y\frac{\partial u}{\partial y} + \left(\frac{\partial u}{\partial x}\right)^2 + \left(\frac{\partial u}{\partial y}\right)^2 - u = 0$$

$u = px + qy + p^2 + q^2$ – – – (1)

Solution of this PDE is

$u = ax + by + a^2 + b^2$ (2)

For elimination of a and b

put $\frac{\partial u}{\partial a} = 0$ and $\frac{\partial u}{\partial b} = 0$

$x + 2a = 0$ and $y + 2b = 0$

$\Rightarrow a = \frac{-x}{2}$ and $b = \frac{-y}{2}$

Put this value in equation (2)

We get,

$u = -\frac{1}{2}(x^2 + y^2)$

This the equation of parabola in the $u - x$ plane

Hence, option (c) is correct answer and a), b), d) are incorrect.

6. **Explanation (b), (d)**

Consider the given PDE

$p^2 + q^2 = 1$; $u(x,y) = 0$ on $x + y = 1$

Charpit's auxiliary equation are

$$\frac{dx}{f_p} = \frac{dy}{f_q} = \frac{dz}{pf_p + qf_q} = \frac{dp}{-(f_x + pf_z)} = \frac{dq}{-(f_y + qf_z)} = dt$$

$$\frac{dx}{dt} = 2p, \frac{dy}{dt} = 2q, \quad \frac{dz}{dt} = 2, \frac{dp}{dt} = 0, \frac{dq}{dt} = 0$$

Given PDE is of the form

$f(p,q) = 0$

To solve this, put $p = a$

$\Rightarrow q = \sqrt{1-a^2}$

General solution is

$du = pdx + qdy$

$\Rightarrow du = adx + \sqrt{1-a^2}dy$

Integrating, we get,

$u = ax + \sqrt{1-a^2}y + b$

Now using given condition

$0 = ax + \sqrt{1-a^2}(1-x) + b$

$\Rightarrow b = -ax - \sqrt{1-a^2}(1-x)$

$\Rightarrow u = ax + \sqrt{1-a^2}y - ax - \sqrt{1-a^2}(1-x)$

$\Rightarrow u = \sqrt{1-a^2}y - \sqrt{1-a^2}(1-x)$

$\Rightarrow u = \sqrt{1-a^2}(y - 1 + x)$

Now differentiating u w.r.to a

$\frac{du}{da} = 0$

$\frac{du}{da} = (y-1+x)\frac{-a}{\sqrt{1-a^2}} = 0$

$\Rightarrow a = 0$

$\Rightarrow u(x,y) = y - 1 + x$

$u(1,\sqrt{2}) = \sqrt{2} - 1 + 1$

$\Rightarrow u(1,\sqrt{2}) = \sqrt{2}$

$\Rightarrow$Option b), c) are correct answer and a), d) are incorrect.

7. **Explanation (c), (d)**

Consider the given PDE

$x(p^2 + q^2) = zp$ – – – (1)

Charpit's auxiliary equation are

$$\frac{dx}{f_p} = \frac{dy}{f_q} = \frac{dz}{pf_p+qf_q} = \frac{dp}{-(f_x+pf_z)} = \frac{dq}{-(f_y+qf_z)} = dt$$

$$\frac{dx}{2xp-z} = dt, \quad \frac{dy}{2xq} = dt, \quad \frac{dz}{p(2xp-z)+2xq^2} = dt, \frac{dp}{q^2} = dt,$$

$\frac{dq}{pq} = dt$

Now, consider $\frac{dq}{pq} = \frac{dp}{q^2}$

$\frac{dq}{p} = \frac{dp}{q}$

Integrating, we get

$p^2 + q^2 = a^2$

Equation 1) become

$xa^2 = zp$

$p = \frac{xa^2}{z}$

$q = \sqrt{a^2 - \left(\frac{xa^2}{z}\right)^2}$

Now general solution is ,

$du = pdx + qdy$

$du = \frac{xa^2}{z}dx + \sqrt{a^2 - \left(\frac{xa^2}{z}\right)^2}dy$

$Z^2 = a^2x^2 + (ay+b)^2$

Now use the given condition we get

$z^2 = a^4(x^2+y^2) + a^2(2y - z^2) + 1 = 0$

Which is quadratic equation in a

Now take discriminant

$(2y - z^2)^2 - 4(x^2 + y^2) = 0$

Now at (1, 1)

$z = \pm\sqrt{2 + 2\sqrt{2}}$

From above explanation

Option c), d) are correct answer and a),b) are incorrect.

8. **Explanation (a), (b)**

$(x_0, y_0, z_0, p_0, q_0)$

$pq = 1$

$x_0(s) = s, y_0(s) = \frac{1}{s}, z_0(s) = 1$

$x_0(s) = x(0, s) = s$

$y_0(s) = y(0, s) = \frac{1}{s}$

$z_0(s) = z(0, s) = 1$

$u = u(x, y)$

$p_0 q_0 = 1$

$u_0 = u_0(x, y)$

$\frac{du_0}{ds} = p_0 \frac{dx_0}{ds} + q_0 \frac{dy_0}{ds}$

$0 = p_0 + q_0 \times \frac{-1}{s^2}$

$p_0 s^2 = q_0$

$p_0 q_0 = 1$

$\Rightarrow s^2 = q_0^2$

$q_0 = \pm s$

$q_0 = s, -s$

9. **Explanation (a), (c)**

$z = px + qy + pq$ so it is a Clairaut's equation, so the complete integral is $z = ax + by + ab$, a, b arbitary constants.

So, option (a) is correct but not (b).

Now

$z = ax + by + ab$ passing through $x = 0$ and $z = y^2$

$z = ax + by + ab$............. (1)

$x = 0, z = y^2$ let $y = t, z = t^2$

So, equation (1) becomes,

$t^2 = a.0 + b.t + ab \Rightarrow t^2 = bt + ab$............... (2)

Differentiating (2) w.r.t t,

$\Rightarrow 2t = b \Rightarrow {}^b/_2 = t$

Now putting $t = {}^b/_2$ in equation (2), we get

${}^{b^2}/_4 = b.{}^b/_2 + ab \Rightarrow ab = \frac{b^2}{4} - \frac{b^2}{2} = \frac{b^2 - 2b^2}{4}$

$\Rightarrow ab = {}^{-b^2}/_4$

$\Rightarrow a = {}^{-b}/_4$

Putting $a = {}^{-b}/_4$ in equation (1),

$\Rightarrow z = -\frac{b}{4}x + by + \left(-\frac{b}{4}\right).b$

$\Rightarrow z = -\frac{b}{4}x + by - {}^{b^2}/_4$.................. (3)

Differentiating (3) w.r.t 'b', we get

$\Rightarrow 0 = -\frac{x}{4} + y - \frac{2b}{4} \Rightarrow \frac{b}{2} = (y - {}^x/_4)$

$\Rightarrow b = 2(y - {}^x/_4)$

$a = -\frac{1}{4}2(y - {}^x/_4)$

$= -\frac{1}{2}(y - {}^x/_y)$

$\therefore z = ax + by + ab$

$= -\frac{x}{2}\left(y - \frac{x}{y}\right) + 2\left(y - \frac{x}{y}\right).y + \left(-\frac{1}{2}\left(y - \frac{x}{y}\right).2\left(y - \frac{x}{y}\right)\right)$

$= \frac{-xy}{2} + \frac{x^2}{8} + 2y^2 - \frac{xy}{2} - \left(y - \frac{x}{y}\right)^2$

$= \frac{x^2}{8} + (xy) + 2y^2 - \left(y - \frac{x}{y}\right)^2$

$= \frac{x^2}{8} - xy + 2y^2 - \left(y^2 + \frac{x^2}{16} - 1.4.\frac{x}{y}\right)$

$= \frac{x^2}{8} - xy + 2y^2 - y^2 + \frac{xy}{2} - \frac{x^2}{16}$

$= \frac{x^2}{16} - \frac{1}{2}xy + y^2 = \left(\frac{x}{y} - y\right)^2$

$\therefore z = \left(\frac{x}{4} - y\right)^2$

So option (c) correct and (d) wrong.

10. **Explanation (a), (d)**

$xp^2 + yq^2 + (x + y)pq - u(p + q) + 1 = 0$

$\Rightarrow xp^2 + xpq + yq^2 + ypq + 1 = u(p + q)$

$\Rightarrow uq(q + p) + 1 = u(p + q)$

$\Rightarrow u = px + qy + \frac{1}{p + q}$

This is of the form $u = px + qy + f(p, q)$ i.e Clairaut's form

So, the general solution is $u(x, y) = ax + by + \frac{1}{a+b}$

i.e. option (a) is correct and option (b) wrong.

Charpit's auxiliary equations are,

$\frac{dp}{f_x + pf_u} = \frac{dq}{f_y + qf_u} = \frac{du}{-(pf_p + qf_q)} = \frac{dx}{-f_p} = \frac{dy}{-f_q}$

$\Rightarrow \frac{dp}{p(p+q) - p(p+q)} = \frac{dq}{q(p+q) - q(p+q)} = \frac{dx}{-2px - q(x+y) + u}$

$= \frac{du}{p(2px + (x+y)q - u) + q(2qy + (x+y)p - u)} = \frac{dy}{-2qy - (x+y)p + u}$

So, option (d) is correct and option (c) wrong

Unit 2.3: Second Order Partial Differential Equations and Its Classification

MCQ - Multiple Choice Questions

1. The number of characteristic curves of the PDE $(x^2 + 2y)u_{xx} + (y^3 - y + x)u_{yy} + x^2(y-1)u_{xy} + 3u_x + u = 0$ passing through the point $x = 1, y = 1$ is
(a) 0 (b) 1
(c) 2 (d) 3
[June 2011]

2. A general solution of the second order equation $4u_{xx} - u_{yy} = 0$ is the form $u(x,y) =$
(a) $f(x) + g(y)$
(b) $f(x+2y) + g(x-2y)$
(c) $f(x+4y) + g(x-4y)$
(d) $f(4x+y) + g(4x-y)$
Where f and g are twice differentiable functions.
[June 2011]

3. The complete integral of the PDE
$$\frac{\partial^2 u}{\partial x^2} + 2\frac{\partial^2 u}{\partial x \partial y} + \frac{\partial^2 u}{\partial y^2} = xe^{x+y}$$
Involving arbitrary functions ϕ_1 and ϕ_2 is
(a) $\phi_1(y+x) + \phi_2(y+x) + \frac{1}{4}e^{x+y}$
(b) $\phi_1(y+x) + x\phi_2(y+x) + \frac{(x-1)}{4}e^{x+y}$
(c) $\phi_1(y-x) + \phi_2(y-x) + \frac{1}{4}e^{x+y}$
(d) $\phi_1(y-x) + x\phi_2(y-x) + \frac{(x-1)}{4}e^{x+y}$
[Dec 2011]

4. The second order $PDE\ u_{yy} - yu_{xx} + x^3 u = 0$ is
(a) Elliptic for all $x\epsilon\mathbb{R}, y\epsilon\mathbb{R}$
(b) Parabolic for all $x\epsilon\mathbb{R}, y\epsilon\mathbb{R}$
(c) Elliptic for all $x\epsilon\mathbb{R}, y < 0$
(d) Hyperbolic for all $x\epsilon\mathbb{R}, y < 0$
[June 2012]

5. The partial differential equation $y\frac{\partial^2 u}{\partial x^2} + x\frac{\partial^2 u}{\partial y^2} = 0$ is hyperbolic in
(a) The second and fourth quadrants
(b) The first and second quadrants
(c) The second and third quadrants
(d) The first and third quadrants
[Dec 2012]

6. The partial differential equation $\frac{\partial^2 u}{\partial y^2} - y\frac{\partial^2 u}{\partial x^2} = 0$ has
(a) Two families of real characteristics curve for $y < 0$
(b) No real characteristics for $y > 0$
(c) Vertical lines as a family for characteristics curve for $y = 0$
(d) Branches of quadratic curves as characteristics for $y \neq 0$
[June 2013]

7. Let a, b, c be continuous function defined on $\mathbb{R}^2$. Let V_1, V_2, V_3 be non-empty subset of $\mathbb{R}^2$ such that $V_1 \cup V_2 \cup V_3 = \mathbb{R}^2$ and the PDE $a(x,y)u_{xx} + b(x,y)u_{xy} + c(x,y)u_{yy} = 0$ is elliptic in V_1, parabolic in V_2 and hyperbolic in V_3, then
(a) V_1, V_2 and V_3 are open sets in $\mathbb{R}^2$
(b) V_1, and V_3 are open sets in $\mathbb{R}^2$
(c) V_1, and V_2 are open sets in $\mathbb{R}^2$
(d) V_2 and V_3 are open sets in $\mathbb{R}^2$
[Dec 2013]

8. The PDE $\frac{\partial^2 u}{\partial x^2} + 2\frac{\partial^2 u}{\partial x \partial y} + \frac{\partial^2 u}{\partial y^2} = x$, has
(a) Only one particular integral
(b) A particular integral which is linear in x and y
(c) A particular integral which is a quadratic polynomial is x and y
(d) More than one particular integral
[Dec 2015]

9. Let a, b, c, d be four differentiable functions defined on $\mathbb{R}^2$. Then the partial differential equation $\left(a(x,y)\frac{\partial}{\partial x} + b(x,y)\frac{\partial}{\partial y}\right)\left(c(x,y)\frac{\partial}{\partial x} + d(x,y)\frac{\partial}{\partial y}\right)u = 0$ is
(a) Always hyperbolic (b) Always parabolic
(c) Never parabolic (d) Never elliptic
[June 2016]

10. The PDE $x\frac{\partial^2 u}{\partial x^2} + y\frac{\partial^2 u}{\partial y^2} = 0$
(a) Hyperbolic for $x > 0, y < 0$
(b) Elliptic for $x > 0, y < 0$
(c) Hyperbolic for $x > 0, y > 0$
(d) Elliptic for $x < 0, y > 0$
[Dec 2016]

11. Let D denote the unit disc given by $\{(x,y) | x^2 + y^2 \leq 1\}$ and let D^c be its complement in the plane. The partial differential equation $(x^2 - 1)\frac{\partial^2 u}{\partial x^2} + 2y\frac{\partial^2 u}{\partial x \partial y} - \frac{\partial^2 u}{\partial y^2} = 0$ is
(a) Parabolic for all $(x,y) \in D^c$
(b) Hyperbolic for all $(x,y) \in D$
(c) Hyperbolic for all $(x,y) \in D^c$
(d) Parabolic for all $(x,y) \in D$
[Dec 2017]

12. Consider the PDE
$P(x,y)\frac{\partial^2 u}{\partial x^2} + e^{x^2}e^{y^2}\frac{\partial^2 u}{\partial x \partial y} + Q(x,y)\frac{\partial^2 u}{\partial y^2} + e^{2x} + \frac{\partial u}{\partial x} + e^{y}\frac{\partial u}{\partial y} = 0$
where P and Q are polynomials in two variables with real coefficients. Then which of the following is true for all choices of P and Q?
(a) There exists $R > 0$ such that the PDE is elliptic in $\{(x,y) \in \mathbb{R}^2 : x^2 + y^2 > R\}$
(b) There exists $R > 0$ such that the PDE is hyperbolic in $\{(x,y) \in \mathbb{R}^2 : x^2 + y^2 > R\}$
(c) There exists $R >$ 0such that the PDE is parabolic in $\{(x,y) \in \mathbb{R}^2 : x^2 + y^2 > R\}$
(d) There exists $R > 0$ such that the PDE is hyperbolic in $\{(x,y) \in \mathbb{R}^2 : x^2 + y^2 < R\}$
[June 2019]

13. The second order PDE
$$e^x\frac{\partial^2 U}{\partial x^2} + (x^2 + y^2 - 1)\frac{\partial^2 U}{\partial y^2} = 0\text{is}$$

(a) Elliptic inside the unit circle with centre at $(0,0)$
(b) Hyperbolic outside the unit circle with centre at $(0,0)$
(c) Elliptic outside the unit circle with centre at $(0,0)$
(d) Parabolic for $x, y \in \mathbb{R}$.

[Dec 2019]

14. Consider the second order PDE $au_{xx} + bu_{xy} + au_{yy} = 0$ in $\mathbb{R}^2$. For $a, b \in \mathbb{R}$, which of the following is true?
(a) The PDE is hyperbolic for $b \le 2a$
(b) The PDE is parabolic $b \le 2a$
(c) The PDE is elliptical $|b|, 2|a|$
(d) The PDE is hyperbolic for $|b| < 2|a|$

[SEP 2022]

15. The following partial differential equation $x^2\frac{\partial^2 u}{\partial x^2} - 2xy\frac{\partial^2 u}{\partial x \partial y} - 3y^2\frac{\partial^2 u}{\partial y^2} + \frac{\partial u}{\partial x} - \frac{\partial u}{\partial y} = 0$ is
(a) elliptic in $\{(x,y) \in \mathbb{R}^2 : y > 0\}$
(b) parabolic in $\{(x,y) \in \mathbb{R}^2 : x > 0, y > 0\}$
(c) hyperbolic in $\{(x,y) \in \mathbb{R}^2 : xy \neq 0\}$
(d) parabolic in $\{(x,y) \in \mathbb{R}^2 : xy \neq 0\}$

[DEC-2023]

Answer Key

1	2	3	4	5	6	7
a	b	d	c	a	c	b
8	9	10	11	12	13	14
d	d	a	c	b	c	C
15						
c						

EXPLANATION

1. **Explanation (a)**
$(x^2 + 2y)u_{xx} + (y^3 - y + x)u_{yy} + x^2(y-1)u_{xy} + 3u_x + u = 0 - - - (1)$
Comparing the given equation with $Ar + Bs + Ct + F(x,y,z,p,q) = 0$
$\Rightarrow A = x^2 + 2y,$
$B = x^2(y-1)$
$C = (y^3 - y + x)$
$\Rightarrow B^2 - 4AC = \left(x^2(y-1)\right)^2 - 4(x^2+2y)(y^3 - y + x) - - (2)$
Since the characteristics curve passing through the point $x = 1, y = 1$ Put $x = 1$ and $y = 1$ in equation (2)
we get $B^2 - 4AC = -12 < 0$
⇒ the given PDE is elliptic.
⇒ No real characteristic curves but two imaginary characteristic curve
⇒Number of characteristic curve of PDE is two
Hence, option (c) is correct answer and option a),b) and d) are incorrect.

2. **Explanation (b)**
Consider the given second order PDE
$4u_{xx} - u_{yy} = 0 - - - (1)$
$$(4D^2 - D'^2)y = 0$$
Here put $D = m, D' = 1$ corresponding auxiliary equation is
$4m^2 - 1 = 0$
$\Rightarrow m = -\frac{1}{2}, \frac{1}{2}$
$\Rightarrow m_1 = \frac{1}{2}, m_2 = \frac{1}{2}$
Therefore the general solution of given PDE is $u(x,y) = f_1(y + m_1x) + g_1(y + m_2x)$
$\Rightarrow u(x,y) = f_1\left(y + \frac{1}{2}x\right) + g_1\left(y - \frac{1}{2}x\right)$
$= f(x + 2y) + g(x - 2y)$
Hence, option (b) is correct answer and option a), c) and d) are incorrect.

3. **Explanation (d)**
$\frac{\partial^2 u}{\partial x^2} + 2\frac{\partial^2 u}{\partial x \partial y} + \frac{\partial^2 u}{\partial y^2} = xe^{x+y} - - - (1)$
$(D^2 + 2DD' + D'^2)y = xe^{x+y}\left(\frac{du}{dx} = D, \frac{du}{dy} = D'\right)$
Therefore the corresponding auxiliary equation is
$m^2 + 2m + 1 = 0$
$\Rightarrow m = -1, -1 \Rightarrow m_1 = -1, m_2 = -1$
Complementary function is
$u(x,y) = \phi_1(y + m_1x) + x\phi_2(y + m_2x)$
$= \phi_1(y - x) + x\phi_2(y - x) - - - (2)$
Now find the PI
PI$= \frac{1}{D^2+2DD'+D'^2}xe^{x+y}$
$= e^y\frac{1}{D^2+2D+1}xe^x$
$= e^{x+y}\frac{1}{(D+1)^2 + 2(D+1) + 1}x$
$= e^{x+y}\frac{1}{D^2 + 4D + 4}x$
$= e^{x+y}\frac{1}{4\left(1 + \frac{D^2+4D}{4}\right)}x$
$\frac{e^{x+y}}{4}\left(1 + \frac{D^2 + 4D}{4}\right)^{-1}x$
PI$= (x - 1)\frac{e^{x+y}}{4}$
Now the compete integral of given PDE is
$u(x,y) = C.F + P.I$
$u(x,y) = \phi_1(y - x) + x\phi_2(y - x) + (x - 1)\frac{e^{x+y}}{4}$
From this only option d) is correct answer and a), b), c) are incorrect.

4. **Explanation (c)**
Consider the Given PDE
$u_{yy} - yu_{xx} + x^3y = 0 \ldots\ldots (1)$
Comparing the given equation with standard form of semi-linear PDE
$Ar + Bs + Ct + F(x,y,z,p,q) = 0$
we get,
$A = -y, \quad B = 0, \quad c = 1$
$B^2 - 4AC = -4(-y) = 4y$
Now check the option
If $y < 0$ then $B^2 - 4AC < 0$
We know that if $B^2 - 4AC < 0$

Then the PDE is elliptic

If $y > 0$ then $B^2 - 4AC < 0$

We know that if $B^2 - 4AC < 0$

Then the PDE is parabolic

So above explanation only option (c) is correct

And option (a), (b) and (d) is incorrect

5. **Explanation (a)**

Consider the given PDE

$$y\frac{\partial^2 u}{\partial x^2} + x\frac{\partial^2 u}{\partial y^2} = 0 \;....(1)$$

Comparing the given equation with standard form of semi-linear PDE

$Ar + Bs + Ct + F(x, y, z, p, q) = 0$

$\Rightarrow A = y, B = x, C = 0$

$\Rightarrow c^2 - 4AC = -4xy$

Given PDE is hyperbolic of $c^2 - 4AC > 0$

$c^2 - 4AC = -4xy > 0$

If either $x < 0$ or $y < 0$

⇒ this is possible only in second and fourth quadrant

⇒ Only option (a) is correct answer and b),c) and d) are the incorrect.

6. **Explanation (c)**

Consider the given PDE

$$\frac{\partial^2 u}{\partial y^2} - y\frac{\partial^2 u}{\partial x^2} = 0 \;...(1)$$

Comparing the given equation with standard form of semi-linear PDE

$Ar + Bs + Ct + F(x, y, z, p, q) = 0$

we get,

$\Rightarrow A = -y, B = 0, C = 1$

$\Rightarrow B^2 - 4AC = 0 + 4y$

Now here arises three cases

If $B^2 - 4AC = y < 0 \Rightarrow eliptic$

If $B^2 - 4AC = y > 0$ ⇒Hyperbolic

If $B^2 - 4AC = y = 0$ ⇒parabolic

From above explanation

Option (a) and (b) are incorrect.

Now check remaining option

$A\lambda^2 + B\lambda + C = 0$

$= -y\lambda^2 + 1 = 0$

$$\lambda^2 = \frac{1}{y}$$

$$\lambda = \pm\sqrt{\frac{1}{y}}$$

$$\lambda = \pm\frac{1}{\sqrt{y}}$$

General solution is

$\frac{dy}{dx} = \frac{1}{\sqrt{y}}$ and $\frac{dy}{dx} = -\frac{1}{\sqrt{y}}$

To solve this by separation of variable method

$\sqrt{y}\,dy = dx$

Integrating

$\frac{2y^{\frac{3}{2}}}{3} = x + c$ and

$\frac{dy}{dx} = \frac{1}{\sqrt{y}}$

$\sqrt{y}\,dy = -dx$

Integrating, we get

$\frac{2y^{\frac{3}{2}}}{3} + x = c_2$ and $\frac{24^{3/2}}{3} - x = c_1$

Put $y = 0$

$\Rightarrow x = \pm c$

$c = \{c_1, c_2\}$

⇒ vertical lines are a family of characteristic curve for $y = 0$.

⇒ Option (c) is correct answer and a), b) and d) are incorrect.

7. **Explanation (b)**

Consider the given PDE

$a(x, y)u_{xx} + b(x, y)u_{xy} + c(x, y)u_{yy} = 0 \;...(1)$

Comparing the given equation with standard form of semi-linear PDE

$Ar + Bs + Ct + F(x, y, z, p, q) = 0$

$A = a(x, y), B = b(x, y), C = c(x, y)$

Now V_1 is eliptic in $\mathbb{R}^3$

$V_1 = \{(x, y): B^2 - 4AC < 0\}$

$= \{(x, y): b^2 - 4ac < 0\}$

$\Longrightarrow V_1$ is open set

V_2 is parabolic in $\mathbb{R}^3$

$\Longrightarrow V_2\{(x, y): B^2 - 4AC = 0\}$

$V_2 = \{(x, y): b^2 - 4ac = 0\}$

$\Longrightarrow V_2$ is closed set.

V_3 is hyperbolic in $\mathbb{R}^3$

$\Rightarrow V_3 = \{(x, y): B^2 - 4AC < 0\}$

$V_3 = \{(x, y): b^2 - 4ac < 0\}$

$\Rightarrow V_3$ is hyperbolic in $\mathbb{R}^3$

Only option (b) is correct answer and a), c) and d) are the incorrect.

8. **Explanation (d)**

Consider the given second order PDE

$$\frac{\partial^2 u}{\partial x^2} + 2\frac{\partial^2 u}{\partial x \partial y} + \frac{\partial^2 u}{\partial y^2} = x$$

Now to find the Particular integral

$$PI = \frac{1}{(D + D')^2}x$$

Where, $D = \frac{\partial}{\partial x}$ and $D' = \frac{\partial}{\partial y}$

$$= \frac{1}{D^2}(1 + \frac{D'}{D})^{-2} = \frac{1}{D^2}\left(1 - \frac{2D'}{D}...\right)x = \frac{x^3}{6}$$

$$\text{Or } PI = \frac{1}{D'^2}(1 + \frac{D}{D'})^{-2} = \frac{1}{D'^2}\left(1 - \frac{2D}{D'} + \cdots\right)x$$

$$= \frac{1}{D'^2}(x - 2y)$$

$$= \frac{xy^2}{2} - \frac{y^3}{3}$$

From this, we get more than one PDE option (d) is correct.

9. **Explanation (d)**

Consider the give PDE

$\left(a(x,y)\frac{\partial}{\partial x}+b(x,y)\frac{\partial^2 y}{\partial x\partial y}\right)\left(c(x,y)\frac{\partial}{\partial x}+d(x,y)\frac{\partial}{\partial y}\right)y=0$

$\frac{\partial^2 y}{\partial x^2}+a(x,y)d(x,y)\frac{\partial^2 y}{\partial x\partial y}+b(x,y)c(x,y)\frac{\partial^2 y}{\partial x\partial y}+b(x,y)d(x,y)\frac{\partial^2 y}{\partial y^2}$ ...(1)

Comparing the given equation with standard form of semi-linear PDE

$Ar+Bs+Ct+F(x,y,z,p,q)=0$

$\Rightarrow A=a(x,y)c(x,y)$

$B=a(x,y)d(x,y)+b(x,y)+c(x,y)$

$C=b(x,y)d(x,y)$

Now $B^2-4AC=(ad+bc)^2-4(ac)bd$

$=a^2d^2+b^2c^2+2adbc-4acbd$

$=a^2d^2+b^2c^2-2adbc$

$B^2-4AC=(ad-bc)^2\geq 0\ \forall x,y\in\mathbb{R}^2$

But $B^2-4AC<0$ never possible.

so only option (d) is correct answer and a),b) and c) are incorrect.

10. Explanation (a)

Consider the given PDE

$x\frac{\partial^2 u}{\partial x^2}+y\frac{\partial^2 u}{\partial y^2}=0$ .... (1)

Comparing the given equation with standard form of semi-linear PDE

$Ar+Bs+Ct+F(x,y,z,p,q)=0$

$A=x, C=y,\quad B=0$

Now B^2-4AC

$0-4xy$

$\therefore B^2-4AC=-4xy$

$B^2-4AC=-4xy>0$ if either $x<0$ or $y<0$

$B^2-4AC=-4xy<0$ if $x>0$ and $y>0$

From this,

only option (a) is correct answer and b),c) and d) are incorrect.

11. Explanation (c)

Consider the given PDE

$(x^2-1)\frac{\partial^2 y}{\partial x^2}+2y\frac{\partial^2 y}{\partial x\partial y}-\frac{\partial^2 y}{\partial y^2}=0$ ... (1)

Comparing the given equation with standard form of semi-linear PDE

$Ar+Bs+Ct+F(x,y,z,p,q)=0$

$A=(x^2-1), B=2y, c=-1$

$B^2-4AC=4y^2+4(x^2-1)$

$B^2-4AC=4(x^2+y^2)-4$

D is unit disc

$\{(x,y)|x^2+y^2\leq 1|\}$

$x^2+y^2=1$

$B^2-4AC=4.1-4=0$

$\Rightarrow$ given PDE parabolic in D

if $x^2+y^2=\frac{1}{2}$

$B^2-4AC<0\Rightarrow$ Given PDE is eliptic in D

if $x^2+y^2>1$ in D

Then $B^2-4AC>0$

$\Rightarrow$Given PDE is hyperbolic in D

$\Rightarrow$option (c) is correct answer and a),b) and d) are incorrect.

12. Explanation (b)

Consider the given PDE

$P(x,y)\frac{\partial^2 u}{\partial x^2}+e^{x^2}e^{y^2}\frac{\partial^2 u}{\partial x\partial y}+Q(x,y)\frac{\partial^2 u}{\partial y^2}+e^{2x}+\frac{\partial u}{\partial x}+e^y\frac{\partial u}{\partial y}=0---(1)$

Comparing the given equation with standard form of semi-linear PDE

$Ar+Bs+Ct+F(x,y,z,p,q)=0$

$\Rightarrow A=P(x,y), B=e^{x^2}e^{y^2}, C=Q(x,y)$

Now

$B^2-4AC=\left(e^{x^2+y^2}\right)^2-4PQ$

If $x^2+y^2>R$ and $R>0$

$\Rightarrow$ put $x^2+y^2=1>0$ and $\mathrm{P}=\mathrm{Q}=1$

$\Rightarrow(e)^2-4PQ>0$

$\Rightarrow$ there exist $R>0$ such that the PDE is hyperbolic in $\{(x,y)\in\mathbb{R}^2.x^2+y^2>R\}$

Option b) is the correct answer and option a), c) and d) are the incorrect.

13. Explanation (c)

$e^x\frac{\partial^2 U}{\partial x^2}+(x^2+y^2-1)\frac{\partial^2 U}{\partial y^2}=0$

comparing with the 2nd order equation

$RU_{xx}+SU_{xy}+TU_{yy}+f(x,y,U,U_x,U_y)=0$

$R=e^x,\qquad S=0,\qquad T=(x^2+y^2-1)$

$S^2-4RT=0-e^x(x^2+y^2-1)=-e^x(x^2+y^2-1)$

$e^x>0\ \forall x\in\mathbb{R}$

$\Rightarrow -e^x<0\ \forall x\in\mathbb{R}$

Inside the unit circle $x^2+y^2<1$.

$\Rightarrow x^2+y^2-1<0$

$\Rightarrow C-e^x(x^2+y^2-1)>0$

inside the unit circle so, option (c) wrong.

Now the outside the unit circle $x^2+y^2>1$

$\Rightarrow x^2+y^2-1>0$

So, $-e^x(x^2+y^2-1)<0$

i.e. elliptic outside the unit circle.

Hence option (c) correct and (b) wrong.

14. Explanation: (c)

Given partial differential equation is,

$au_{xx}+bu_{xy}+au_{yy}=0$

Here, $R=a, S=b, T=a$

$\therefore S^2-4RT=b^2-4a^2$

If $S^2-4RT>0\Rightarrow$ Hyperbolic

i.e. $b^2-4a^2>0$

i.e. $b^2>4a^2$

$|b|>2|a|$

& $S^2-4RT<0\Rightarrow$ Elliptic

i.e. $|b|<2|a|$

15. Explanation: (c)

Here $R = x^2,\ S = -2xy,\ T = -3y^2$

Now, $S^2 - 4RT = (-2xy)^2 - 4x^2(-3y^2) = 4x^2y^2 + 12x^2y^2 = 16x^2y^2 > 0$ when $xy \neq 0$.

So, we get the hyperbolic pde.

⇒ option (c) is correct.

MSQ (Multiple Select Questions)

1. The second order partial differential equation $\frac{(x-y)^2}{4}\frac{\partial^2 u}{\partial x^2} + (x-y)\sin(x^2+y^2)\frac{\partial^2 u}{\partial x\partial y} + \cos^2(x^2+y^2)\frac{\partial^2 u}{\partial y^2} + (x-y)\frac{\partial u}{\partial x} + \sin^2(x^2+y^2)\frac{\partial u}{\partial y} + u = 0$ is
(a) Elliptic in the region $\left\{(x,y): x \neq y, x^2+y^2 < \frac{\pi}{6}\right\}$
(b) Hyperbolic in the region $\left\{(x,y): x \neq y, \frac{\pi}{4} < x^2 + y^2 < \frac{3\pi}{4}\right\}$
(c) Elliptic in the region $\left\{(x,y): x \neq y, \frac{\pi}{4} < x^2 + y^2 < \frac{3\pi}{4}\right\}$
(d) Hyperbolic in the region $\left\{(x,y): x \neq y, x^2 + y^2 < \frac{\pi}{4}\right\}$
[Dec 2011]

2. It $u(x,t)$ satisfy the partial differential equation $\frac{\partial^2 u}{\partial t^2} = 4\frac{\partial^2 u}{\partial x^2}$ then $u(x,t)$ can be of the form
(a) $u(x,t) = f(e^{x-2t}) + g(x+2t)$
(b) $u(x,t) = f(x^2 - 4t^2) + g(x^2 + 4t^2)$
(c) $u(x,t) = f(2x - 4t) + g(x + 2t)$
(d) $u(x,t) = f(2x - t) + g(2x + t)$
Where f and g are non-trivial smooth functions.
[Dec 2012]

3. Let $P(x,y)$ be a particular integral of the partial differential equation $\frac{\partial^2 z}{\partial x^2} - \frac{\partial z}{\partial y} = 2y - x^2$
Then $P(2,3)$ equals
(a) 2 (b) 8
(c) 12 (d) 10
[Dec 2013]

4. The PDE $\frac{\partial^2 u}{\partial x^2} + 2\frac{\partial^2 u}{\partial x\partial y} + \frac{\partial^2 u}{\partial y^2} = 0$ is
(a) Parabolic and has characteristic $\xi(x,y) = x + 2y, \eta(x,y) = x - 2y$
(b) Reducible to the canonical form $\frac{\partial^2 u}{\partial \xi^2} = 0$, where $\xi(x,y) = x + 2y$
(c) Reducible to the canonical form $\frac{\partial^2 u}{\partial \eta^2} = 0$, where $\eta(x,y) = x + y$
(d) Parabolic and has the general solution $u = (x-y)f_1(x+y) + f_2(x-y)$, where f_1, f_2, are arbitrary functions.
[June 2014]

5. The second order partial differential equation $u_{xx} + x\,y_{yy} = 0$ is
(a) Elliptic for $x > 0$ (b) Hyperbolic for $x > 0$
(c) Elliptic for $x < 0$ (d) Hyperbolic for $x < 0$
[June 2015]

6. Consider the second order PDE
$$8\frac{\partial^2 z}{\partial x^2} - 2\frac{\partial^2 z}{\partial x\partial y} - 3\frac{\partial^2 z}{\partial y^2} = 0$$
Then which of the following are correct?
(a) The equation is elliptic
(b) The equation is hyperbolic
(c) The general solution is $z = f\left(y - \frac{x}{2}\right) + g\left(y + \frac{3x}{4}\right)$, for atbitrary differentiable function f and g.
(d) The general solution is $z = f\left(y + \frac{x}{2}\right) + g\left(y - \frac{3x}{4}\right)$, for atbitrary differentiable function f and g.
[Dec 2017]

7. Consider the partial differential equations
(i) $\frac{\partial^2 v}{\partial x^2} + 2\frac{\partial^2 v}{\partial x\partial y} + (1 - sgn(y))\frac{\partial^2 v}{\partial y^2} = 0$
(ii) $y\frac{\partial^2 v}{\partial x^2} + x\frac{\partial^2 v}{\partial y^2} = 0$
Which of the following statements are true?
(a) Equation (i) is parabolic for $y > 0$ and elliptic for $y < 0$.
(b) Equation (i) is hyperbolic for $y > 0$ and elliptic for $y < 0$.
(c) Equation (ii) is elliptic in I and III quadrant and hyperbolic in II and IV quadrant.
(d) Equation (ii) is hyperbolic in I and III quadrant and elliptic in II and IV quadrant.
[Nov 2020]

8. Which of the following partial differential equations is NOT PARABOLIC for all $x, y \in \mathbb{R}$?
(a) $x^2\frac{\partial^2 u}{\partial x\partial y} - 2xy\frac{\partial u}{\partial y} + y^2 = 0$
(b) $x^2\frac{\partial^2 u}{\partial x^2} - 2xy\frac{\partial^2 u}{\partial x\partial y} + y^2\frac{\partial^2 u}{\partial y^2} = 0$
(c) $x^2\frac{\partial^2 u}{\partial x^2} + 2xy\frac{\partial^2 u}{\partial x\partial y} + y^2\frac{\partial^2 u}{\partial y^2} = 0$
(d) $x^2\frac{\partial^2 u}{\partial x^2} - 2xy\frac{\partial^2 u}{\partial x\partial y} + y^2\frac{\partial^2 u}{\partial y^2} + x\frac{\partial u}{\partial x} + y\frac{\partial u}{\partial y} = 0$
[Feb 2022]

9. Let $u: \mathbb{R}^3 \to \mathbb{R}$ satisfy $\Delta u = 0$. Define $v(x) = u(Mx)$, where M is the 3×3 matrix
$$M = \begin{pmatrix} 0 & -1 & 0 \\ 1 & 0 & 0 \\ 0 & 0 & 1 \end{pmatrix}$$
Which of the following statement(s) are necessarily true?
(a) $\Delta v = 0$ (b) $\Delta v = v$
(c) $div(M^t M \nabla v) = 0$ (d) $div(M^t M \nabla v) = v$
[SEP 2022]

Answer Key

1	2	3	4	5	6	7	8	9
a, b	a, c	c	c	a, d	b, c	b, c	a	a, c

EXPLANATION

1. Explanation (a), (b)

Consider the given second order PDE

$$\frac{(x-y)^2}{4}\frac{\partial^2 u}{\partial x^2} + (x-y)\sin(x^2+y^2)\frac{\partial^2 u}{\partial x\partial y} + \cos(x^2+y^2)\frac{\partial^2 y}{\partial y^2} + (x-y)\frac{\partial u}{\partial x} + \sin(x^2+y^2)\frac{\partial u}{\partial y} + u = 0$$

Comparing the given equation with standard form of the semi-linear PDE $Ar + Bs + Ct + F(x,y,z,p,q) = 0$

Now find discriminant

$B^2 - 4AC = (x-y)^2 sin^2(x^2+y^2) - 4\frac{(x-y)^2}{4}cos^2(x^2+y^2)$

$B^2 - 4AC = -(x-y)^2 cos2(x^2+y^2)$

$(\because cos^2x\text{-}sin^2x = cos2x)$

We know that,

$(x-y)^2 > 0 \quad \forall x, y \in \mathbb{R} - \{0\}$

Now

Cos$x$ is positive in first and fourth quadrant and negative in second and third quadrant

$\Rightarrow 0 < t < \frac{\pi}{2}$ (In first quadrant)

$\Rightarrow 0 < 2\,(x^2+y^2) < \frac{\pi}{2}$

$\Rightarrow 0 < 2(x^2+y^2) < \frac{\pi}{2}$

$\Rightarrow 0 < (x^2+y^2) < \frac{\pi}{4}$

$\Rightarrow cos2(x^2+y^2)$ is positive

$\Rightarrow B^2 - AC < 0$

$\Rightarrow$ given PDE is eliptic in the region

$\left\{(x,y): x \neq y, x^2+y^2 < \frac{\pi}{6}\right\}$

Now $\frac{\pi}{2} < t < \frac{3\pi}{2}$

$\frac{\pi}{2} < 2 < (x^2+y^2) < \frac{3\pi}{4}$

In this region $cos^2(x^2+y^2)$ is negative

$\Rightarrow B^2 - 4AC > 0$

$\Rightarrow$ give PDE is hyperbolic in the region

$\left\{(x,y): x \neq y, \frac{\pi}{4} < x^2+y^2 < \frac{3\pi}{4}\right\}$

From above explanation

Option (a) and (b) is correct and Option (c) and (d) is incorrect

2. Explanation (a), (c)

$\frac{\partial^2 u}{\partial t^2} = 4\frac{\partial^2 u}{\partial x^2} - - - (1)$

Put $\frac{\partial}{\partial x} = m$ and $\frac{\partial}{\partial t} = 1$

$\Rightarrow$auxiliary equation of (1) is

$4m^2 - 1 = 0$

$\Rightarrow m = \frac{-1}{2}, \frac{1}{2}$

$\Rightarrow u(x,t) = \phi_1\left(x - \frac{1}{2}t\right) + \phi_2\left(x + \frac{1}{2}t\right)$

$= f(2x-t) + g(2x+t) - - - (2)$

Where f and g are arbitrary functions.

Also, let $\frac{\partial}{\partial x} = 1$ and $\frac{\partial}{\partial t} = m$ then the auxiliary equation is

$m^2 - 4 = 0$

$\Rightarrow m = -2, 2$

$\Rightarrow u(x,t) = \Psi_1(x-2t) + \Psi_2(x+2t)$

$= f(e^{x-2t}) + g(x+2t) - - - (3)$

(since f and g are arbitrary functions.)

Hence, options (a) and (c) are correct answer and option b) and d) are incorrect.

3. Explanation (c)

$\frac{\partial^2 z}{\partial x^2} - \frac{\partial z}{\partial y} = 2y - x^2 - - - (1)$

Now find the particular integral is,

$P(x,y) = \frac{1}{D^2 - D'}(2y - x^2)$

$= \frac{1}{D^2}\left[1 - \frac{D'}{D^2}\right]^{-1}(2y - x^2)$

$= \frac{1}{D^2}(2y - x^2 + x^2)$

$= \frac{1}{D^2}2y = yx^2$

$P(2,3) = 3 \times 4 = 12$

Hence, option (c) is correct answer and option a),b) and d) are incorrect.

4. Explanation (c)

$\frac{\partial^2 y}{\partial x^2} + 2\frac{\partial^2 y}{\partial x \partial y} + \frac{\partial^2 y}{\partial y^2} = 0 \ldots (1)$

Comparing the given equation with standard form of semi-linear PDE

$Ar + Bs + Ct + F(x,y,z,p,q) = 0$

$A = 1, B = 2, C = 1$

$\Rightarrow B^2 - 4AC = 4 - 4 = 0$

$\Rightarrow$ Given PDE is parabolic

Now

$A\lambda^2 + B\lambda + c = 0$

$\lambda^2 + 2\lambda + 1 = 0$

$\Rightarrow \lambda = -1, -1$

$\Rightarrow \frac{dy}{dx} = -1$

$dy = -dx$

$n = x + y$ and choose $\xi = x - y$

Now

$\frac{\partial(\xi,\eta)}{\partial(x,y)}\begin{vmatrix}\xi x & \xi y\\ \eta x & \eta y\end{vmatrix} = \begin{vmatrix}1 & -1\\ 1 & 1\end{vmatrix} = 2 \neq 0$

$\Rightarrow$ canonical form is $\frac{\partial^2 u}{\partial \xi^2} = 0$ and $\frac{\partial^2 u}{\partial \eta^2} = 0$

$\Rightarrow$ Only option (c) is correct answer and option a),b) and d) are incorrect.

5. Explanation (a), (d)

Consider the second order

$u_{xx} + x\,y_{yy} = 0 - - - (1)$

Comparing the given equation with standard form of semi-linear PDE

$Ar + Bs + Ct + F(x,y,z,p,q) = 0$

$\Rightarrow A = 1, B = 0, C = x$

Now

$B^2 - 4AC = 0 - 4x$

$B^2 - 4AC = -4x < 0$ if $x > 0$ given PDE is eliptic

$B^2 - 4AC = -4x > 0$ if $x < 0$ given PDE is hyperbolic

From this option (a) and (d) is correct answer and b) and c) are incorrect.

6. Explanation (b), (c)

Given PDE is

$8\frac{\partial^2 z}{\partial x^2} - \frac{2\partial^2 z}{\partial x \partial y} - 3\frac{\partial^2 z}{\partial y^2} = 0 \ldots (1)$

Comparing the given equation with standard form of semi-linear PDE

$Ar + Bs + Ct + F(x,y,z,p,q) = 0$

$B^2 - 4AC = 4 + 4(24) > 0$

$\Rightarrow$PDE is hyperbolic.

$A\lambda^2 + B\lambda + C = 0$

$A = 8, B = -2, C = -3$

$A\lambda^2 + B\lambda + C = 0$

$8\lambda^2 - 2\lambda - 3 = 0$

$8\lambda^2 - 2\lambda - 3 = 0$

$8\lambda^2 + 4\lambda - 6\lambda - 3 = 0$

$4\lambda(2\lambda + 1) - 3(2\lambda + 1) = 0$

$4\lambda - 3 = 0$ or $2\lambda + 1 = 0$

$\Rightarrow \lambda_1 = \frac{3}{4}$ or $\lambda_2 = -\frac{1}{2}$

General solution is

$z = f(y + \lambda_1 x) + g(y + \lambda_2 x)$

$\Rightarrow z = f\left(y - \frac{x}{2}\right) + g\left(y + \frac{3x}{4}\right)$

$\Rightarrow$ Only option (b) and (c) are correct answer and a) and d) are the incorrect.

7. Explanation (b), (c)

Comparing (i) with

$A\,u_{xx} + B\,u_{yy} + C\,u_{yy} + F(x,y,u,u_x,u_y) = 0$

$$\text{Now } sgn(y) = \begin{cases} 1 \text{ if } y > 0 \\ 0 \text{ if } y = 0 \\ -1 \text{ if } y < 0 \end{cases}$$

$$B^2 - 4AC = \begin{cases} 4 - (4.1.0) \text{ if } y > 0 \\ 4 - (4.1.1) \text{ if } y = 0 \\ 4 - (4.1.2) \text{ if } y > 0 \end{cases}$$

$$= \begin{cases} 4 \text{ if } y > 0 \\ 0 \text{ if } y = 0 \\ -4 \text{ if } y < 0 \end{cases}$$

So hyperbolic for $y > 0$ and elliptic for $y < 0$.

i.e. option (b) correct and option (a) Wrong,

Now Comparing (ii) with (*), we get

$A = y, B = 0, C = x$

Now $B^2 - 4\,AC$

$= 0 - (4.y.x) = -4xy$

so $-4xy > 0$ if $(x < 0 \text{ or } y > 0)$

$-4xy < 0$ if $\begin{pmatrix} x > 0 \text{ and } y > 0 \\ x < 0 \text{ and } y < 0 \end{pmatrix}$

So $B^2 - 4\,AC < 0$ in I and III quadrant

$B^2 - 4AC > 0$ in II and IV quadrant

i.e. elliptic in I and III quadrant and hyperbolic in II and IV quadrant.

So option (c) correct and option (d) wrong.

8. Explanation (a)

Consider the standard form of semi-linear PDE is

$Ar + Bs + Ct + F(x,y,z,p,q) = 0$ ...(1)

For option (a)

Comparing equation (1) with

$x^2 \frac{\partial^2 u}{\partial x \partial y} - 2xy \frac{\partial u}{\partial y} + y^2 = 0$

$\Rightarrow B = x^2$

$B^2 - 4AC = x^2 - 0 = x^2$

Which is parabolic only for $x = 0$ not for $R - \{0\}$

Option a) is the correct answer.

For option (b)

$x^2 \frac{\partial^2 u}{\partial x^2} - 2xy \frac{\partial^2 u}{\partial x \partial y} + u^2 \frac{\partial^2 u}{\partial y^2} = 0$

Comparing with equation (1)

$\Rightarrow A = x^2\; B = -2xy\; C = y^2$

$= B^2 - 4ac = 4x^2y^2 - 4x^2y^2 = 0$

= it is parabolic $\forall\, x, y \in R$

For option (c)

$x^2 \frac{\partial^2 u}{\partial x^2} + 2xy \frac{\partial^2 u}{\partial x \partial y} + y^2 \frac{\partial^2 u}{\partial y^2} = 0$

Comparing with equation (1)

$A = x^2\; B = 2xy\; C = y^2$

$= B^2 - 4AC = 4x^2y^2 - 4x^2y^2 = 0$

It is parabolic $\forall\, x, y \in R$

For option (d)

$x^2 \frac{\partial^2 u}{\partial x^2} - 2xy \frac{\partial^2 u}{\partial x \partial y} + y^2 \frac{\partial^2 u}{\partial y^2} + x \frac{\partial u}{\partial x} + y \frac{\partial u}{\partial y} = 0$

Comparing with equation (1)

$A = x^2\;\; B = -2xy\;\; C = y^2$

$= B^2 - 4AC = ux^2y^2 - ux^2y^2 = 0$

It is parabolic $\forall\, x, y \in R$

$\Longrightarrow$ Option (a) is correct answer.

9. Explanation: (a), (c)

Let $X = (x,y,z)$.

Then $v(X) = u(MX) = u\begin{pmatrix} 0 & -1 & 0 \\ 1 & 0 & 0 \\ 0 & 0 & 1 \end{pmatrix}\begin{pmatrix} x \\ y \\ z \end{pmatrix} = u\begin{pmatrix} -y \\ x \\ z \end{pmatrix}$

Therefore, $-v_y = u_x, v_x = u_y, v_z = u_z$ ... (1)

Consider, $\Delta v = v_{xx} + v_{yy} + v_{zz} = u_{yy} + u_{xx} + u_{zz} = 0$ (using (1))

So, option (a) is correct.

Observe, $M^tM = I$

$\therefore \text{div}(M^tM) = \text{div}(v_x, v_y, v_z) = v_{xx} + v_{yy} + v_{zz} = 0$

So, (c) is correct.

Unit 2.4: Heat, Wave and Laplace Equations

MCQ - (Multiple Choice Questions)

1. The function $u(x,t) = \begin{cases} \frac{1}{\sqrt{t}} e^{\frac{-x^2}{4t}} & t > 0, x\in\mathbb{R} \\ 0, & t \le 0, x\in\mathbb{R} \end{cases}$ is a solution of the heat equation in
(a) $\{(x,t): x\in\mathbb{R}, t\in\mathbb{R}\}$
(b) $\{(x,t): x\in\mathbb{R}, t > 0\}$ but not in the set $\{(x,t): x\in\mathbb{R}, t < 0\}$
(c) $\{(x,t): x\in\mathbb{R}, t\in\mathbb{R}\}\backslash\{(0,0)\}$
(d) $\{(x,t): x\in\mathbb{R}, t > -1\}$

[June 2012]

2. Let $u(x,t)$ satisfy the initial boundary value problem
$$\frac{\partial u}{\partial t} = \frac{\partial^2 u}{\partial x^2}; x \in (0,1), t > 0$$
$$u(x,0) = \sin(\pi, x); x\in[0,1]$$
$$u(0,t) = u(1,t) = 0, t > 0$$
Then $x \in (0,1), u\left(x, \frac{1}{\pi^2}\right)$ is equal to
(a) $e\sin(\pi x)$ (b) $e^{-1}\sin(\pi x)$
(c) $\sin(\pi x)$ (d) $\sin(\pi^{-1}x)$

[Dec 2016]

3. Suppose $u \in C^2(\overline{B}), B$ is the unit ball in $\mathbb{R}^2$ satisfies $\Delta u = f$ in $B \propto u + \frac{\partial u}{\partial n} = g$ on $\partial B, \propto > 0$, where n is the unit outward normal to B. If a solution exists then
(a) It is unique
(b) There are exactly two solutions
(c) There are exactly three solutions
(d) There are infinitely many solutions

[June 2017]

4. Let $u(x,t)$ be a solution of the heat equation $\frac{\partial u}{\partial t} = \frac{\partial^2 u}{\partial x^2}$ in a rectangle $[0,\pi] \times [0,T]$ subject to the boundary conditions $u(0,t) = u(\pi,t) = 0$, $0 \le t \le T$ and the intial condition $u(x,0) = \varphi(x), 0 \le x \le \pi$. If $f(x) = u(x,T)$, then which of the following is true for a suitable kernel $k(x,y)$?
(a) $\int_0^\pi k(x,y)\varphi(y)dy = f(x), 0 \le x \le \pi$
(b) $\varphi(x) + \int_0^\pi k(x,y)\varphi(y)dy = f(x), 0 \le x \le \pi$
(c) $\int_0^x k(x,y)\varphi(y)dy = f(x), 0 \le x \le \pi$
(d) $\varphi(x) + \int_0^x k(x,y)\varphi(y)dy = f(x), 0 \le x \le \pi$

[Dec 2017]

5. Let $u(x,t)$ be the solution of the initial value problem
$$u_{tt} - u_{xx} = 0$$
$$u(x,0) = x^3$$
$$u_t(x,0) = \sin x$$
Then $u(\pi,\pi)$ is
(a) $4\pi^3$ (b) π^3
(c) 0 (d) 4

[Dec 2017]

6. Let u be the unique solution of
$$\left.\begin{aligned} \frac{\partial^2 u}{\partial t^2} - \frac{\partial^2 u}{\partial x^2} = 0, x \in \mathbb{R}, t > 0 \\ u(x,0) = f(x), \frac{\partial u}{\partial t}(x,0) = 0, x \in \mathbb{R} \end{aligned}\right\}$$
Where $f: \mathbb{R} \to \mathbb{R}$ satisfies the relations
$$f(x) = x(1-x)\forall x \in [0,1] \text{ and}$$
$$f(x+1) = f(x)\forall x \in \mathbb{R}$$
Then $u\left(\frac{1}{2}, \frac{5}{4}\right)$ is
(a) $\frac{1}{8}$ (b) $\frac{1}{16}$
(c) $\frac{3}{16}$ (d) $\frac{5}{16}$

[June 2018]

7. Let $u(x,t)$ satisfies the IVP:
$$\frac{\partial u}{\partial t} = \frac{\partial^2 u}{\partial x^2}, x \in \mathbb{R}, t > 0$$
$$u(x,0) = \begin{cases} 1, & 0 \le x \le 1 \\ 0, & \text{elsewhere} \end{cases}$$
Then the value of $\lim_{t\to 0^+} u(1,t)$ equals
(a) e (b) π
(c) ½ (d) 1

[Dec 2018]

8. Let $u(x,t)$ be a function that satisfies the PDE $u_{xx} - u_{tt} = e^x + 6t, x \in \mathbb{R}, t > 0$ and the intial conditions $u(x,0) = \sin(x), u_t(x,0) = 0$ for every $x \in \mathbb{R}$
Here subscripts denote partial derivatives corresponding to the variables indicated. Then the value of $u\left(\frac{\pi}{2}, \frac{\pi}{2}\right)$ is
(a) $e^{\frac{\pi}{2}}\left(1 + \frac{1}{2}e^{\frac{\pi}{2}}\right) + \left(\frac{\pi^3+4}{8}\right)$
(b) $e^{\frac{\pi}{2}}\left(1 + \frac{1}{2}e^{\frac{\pi}{2}}\right) + \left(\frac{\pi^3-4}{8}\right)$
(c) $e^{\frac{\pi}{2}}\left(1 - \frac{1}{2}e^{\frac{\pi}{2}}\right) - \left(\frac{\pi^3+4}{8}\right)$
(d) $e^{\frac{\pi}{2}}\left(1 - \frac{1}{2}e^{\frac{\pi}{2}}\right) - \left(\frac{\pi^3-4}{8}\right)$

[Dec 2018]

9. Let u be the unique solution of
$$\left.\begin{aligned} \frac{\partial u}{\partial t} = \frac{\partial^2 u}{\partial x} \text{ where } (x,t) \in (0,1) \times (0,\infty) \\ u(x,0) = \sin \pi x, x \in (0,1) \\ u(0,t) = u(1,t) = 0, t \in (0,\infty) \end{aligned}\right\}$$
. Then which of the following is true?
(a) There exists $(x,t) \in (0,1) \times (0,\infty)$ such that $u(x,t) = 0$
(b) There exists $(x,t) \in (0,1) \times (0,\infty)$ such that $\frac{\partial u}{\partial t}(x,t) = 0$
(c) The function $e^t u(x,t)$ is bounded for $(x,t) \in (0,1) \times (0,\infty)$
(d) There exists $(x,t) \in (0,1) \times (0,\infty)$ such that $u(x,t) > 1$

[June 2019]

10. Let $u(x,y)$ be the solution of $\frac{\partial^2 u}{\partial x^2} + \frac{\partial^2 u}{\partial y^2} = 64$ in the unit disc $\{(x,y);\ x^2 + y^2 < 1\}$& such that u vanished on the boundary of the disc. Then $u\left(\frac{1}{4}, \frac{1}{\sqrt{2}}\right)$ is equal to
(a) 7 (b) 16
(c) −7 (d) −16

[Dec 2019]

11. Let $u(x,t)$ be a smooth solution to the wave equation
$(*) \frac{\partial^2 u}{\partial t^2} - \frac{\partial^2 u}{\partial x^2} = 0$ for $(x,t) \in \mathbb{R}^2$

Which of the following is FALSE?
(a) $u(x-\theta, t)$ also solves the wave equation (*) for any fixed $\theta \in \mathbb{R}$
(b) $\frac{\partial u}{\partial x}$ also solves the wave equation (*)
(c) $u(3x, 9t)$ also solves the wave equation (*)
(d) $u(3x, 3t)$ also solves the wave equation (*)

[SEP 2022]

12. Let $u(x,t)$ be the solution of $u_{tt} - u_{xx} = 0,\ 0 < x < 2,\ t > 0,$

$u(0,t) = 0 = u(2,t), \quad \forall t > 0,$
$u(x,0) = \sin(\pi x) + 2\sin(2\pi x), \quad 0 \le x \le 2,$
$u_t(x,0) = 0, \quad 0 \le x \le 2.$

Which of the following is true?
(a) $u(1,1) = -1.$
(b) $u\left(\frac{1}{2}, 1\right) = 0.$
(c) $u\left(\frac{1}{2}, 2\right) = 1.$
(d) $u_t\left(\frac{1}{2}, \frac{1}{2}\right) = \pi.$

[JUNE 2023]

13. Consider the Cauchy problem for the wave equation

$$\frac{\partial^2 u}{\partial t^2} - 4\frac{\partial^2 u}{\partial x^2} = 0, -\infty < x < \infty, t > 0,$$

$$u(x,0) = \begin{cases} e^{\left(-\frac{1}{x^2}\right)} & x \ne 0 \\ 0 & x = 0 \end{cases}$$

$$\frac{\partial u}{\partial t}(x,0) = x\,e^{-x^2}, x \in \mathbb{R}$$

Which one of the following is true?
(a) $\lim_{t\to\infty} u(5,t) = 1$
(b) $\lim_{t\to\infty} u(5,t) = 2$
(c) $\lim_{t\to\infty} u(5,t) = 1 = \frac{1}{2}$
(d) $\lim_{t\to\infty} u(5,t) = 0$

[DEC 2023]

14. If $u = u(x,t)$ is the solution of the initial value problem

$$\begin{cases} u_t = u_{xx}, x \in \mathbb{R}, t > 0 \\ u(x,0) = \sin(4x) + x + 1, x \in \mathbb{R} \end{cases}$$

satisfying $|u(x,t)| < 3e^{x^2}$ for all $x \in \mathbb{R}$ and $t > 0$, then

(a) $u\left(\frac{\pi}{8}, 1\right) + u\left(-\frac{\pi}{8}, 1\right) = 2$
(b) $u\left(\frac{\pi}{8}, 1\right) = u\left(-\frac{\pi}{8}, 1\right)$
(c) $u\left(\frac{\pi}{8}, 1\right) + 2u\left(-\frac{\pi}{8}, 1\right) = 2$
(d) $u\left(\frac{\pi}{8}, 1\right) = -u\left(-\frac{\pi}{8}, 1\right)$

[JULY 2024]

15. Let $B(0,2) = \{(x,y) \in \mathbb{R}^2 : x^2 + y^2 < 4\}$, and ∂B denote the boundary of $B(0,2)$. Assume $(a, \beta) \ne (0,0), k \in \mathbb{R}$, and u is any solution to

$$\begin{cases} -\Delta u = 0 & \text{in } B(0,2) \\ \alpha u(x,y) + \beta \frac{\partial u}{\partial v}(x,y) = 1 + (x^2 + y^2)k \text{ on } \partial B \end{cases}$$

where $v(x,y)$ is the unit outward normal to $B(0,2)$ at $(x,y) \in \partial B$. Consider the following statements:

S_1: If $\beta = 0$, then there exists a $(x_0, y_0) \in B(0,2)$ such that $|u(x_0,y_0)| = \frac{|1+4k|}{|\alpha|}$.

S_2: If $a = 0$, then $k = -\frac{1}{4}$.

Then
(a) S_1 is true but S_2 is false
(b) S_2 is true but S_1 is false
(c) both S_1 and S_2 are true
(d) both S_1 and S_2 are false

[JULY 2024]

16. Let $u = u(x,t)$ be a solution of the wave equation

$$\frac{\partial^2 u}{\partial t^2} - \frac{\partial^2 u}{\partial x^2} = 0, x \in \mathbb{R}, t > 0$$

satisfying the condition $u(0,t) = 0, \forall t \ge 0$. Then which of the following statements is true?
(a) $u(x,t) = 0$, whenever $x = t$
(b) $u(x,t) = 0$, whenever $x = -t$
(c) $u(-x,t) = u(x,t)$, whenever $x > 0, t > 0$
(d) $u(-x,t) = -u(x,t)$, whenever $0 < x \le t$

[Feb. 2025]

17. Let $u = u(x,t)$ be the solution of

$$\frac{\partial^2 u}{\partial t^2} - \frac{\partial^2 u}{\partial x^2} = 0, x \in \mathbb{R}, t > 0,$$

$u(x,0) = 1 + x^2, x \in \mathbb{R},$

$\frac{\partial u}{\partial t}(x,0) = x + 1, x \in \mathbb{R}.$

Then the value of u(1, 1) is
(a) 2
(b) 3
(c) 4
(d) 5

[June 2025]

18. Let $u(x,t)$ be the solution of the partial differential equation

$$u_t = 16u_{xx} + 2, 0 < x < 7, t > 0$$

satisfying the conditions

$$u_x(0,t) = u(7,t) = 0, t > 0,$$
$$u(x,0) = 0, 0 < x < 7.$$

Then which of the following statements is true?
(a) For each $x \in (0,7), u(x,t) \to 0$ as $t \to \infty$.
(b) For each $x \in (0,7), u(x,t) \to \frac{x^2(7-x)^2}{16}$ as $t \to \infty$.
(c) For each $x \in (0,7), u(x,t) \to \frac{x^2}{16}(7-x)$ as $t \to \infty$.
(d) For each $x \in (0,7), u(x,t) \to \frac{1}{16}(49 - x^2)$ as $t \to \infty$.

[Dec 2025]

19. Let $u(x,t)$ be the solution of the initial value problem

$u_{tt} - u_{xx} = e^{-t}, x \in \mathbb{R}. t > 0,$
$u(x,0) = \cos x, u_t(x,0) = 0, x \in \mathbb{R}.$

Then which of the following statements is true?
(a) For each $x_0 \in \mathbb{R}, e^t u(x_0,t) \to 0$ as $t \to \infty$.
(b) For each $x_0 \in \mathbb{R}, |u(x_0,t)| \to 0$ as $t \to \infty$.
(c) For each $x_0 \in \mathbb{R}$, there exists a $t_0 > 0$ such that $u(x_0,t_0) \ge 4$.
(d) For each $x_0 \in \mathbb{R}$, there exists a $t_0 > 0$ such that $u(x_0,t_0) \le -4$.

[Dec 2025]

Answer Key

1	2	3	4	5	6	7	8	9	10
c	b	a	a	a	c	c	c	c	c
11	12	13	14	15	16	17	18	19	
c	c	a	a	c	d	d	d	c	

EXPLANATION

1. Explanation (c)

Given

$u(x,y) = \frac{1}{\sqrt{t}}\, e^{\frac{-x^2}{4t}}$

$\frac{\partial^2 u}{\partial x^2} = \frac{\partial u}{\partial t}$ is the heat equation .

$\frac{\partial u}{\partial x} = \frac{1}{\sqrt{t}}\, e^{-\frac{x^2}{4t}}\, \frac{(-2x)}{4t}$

$\frac{\partial^2 u}{\partial x^2} = -\frac{2}{\sqrt{t}}\left[e^{-\frac{x^2}{4t}} - \frac{-2x^2}{4t}\, e^{-\frac{x^2}{4t}}\right]\frac{1}{4t}$

$\frac{\partial u}{\partial t} = \frac{1}{\sqrt{t}}\, e^{-\frac{x^2}{4t}}\left(-\frac{x^2}{4}\left(-\frac{1}{t^2}\right)\right) + e^{-\frac{x^2}{4t}} + t^{-3/2}\left(-\frac{1}{2}\right)\Big)$

$= e^{-\frac{x^2}{4t}}\left[\frac{x^2}{4t^2\sqrt{t}} + \left(-\frac{1}{2}\right)t^{\frac{-3}{2}}\right]$

$\frac{\partial u}{\partial t} = e^{-\frac{x^2}{4t}}\left[\frac{x^2}{4t^{\frac{5}{2}}} - \frac{1}{2}\frac{1}{t^{\frac{3}{2}}}\right]$

$\frac{\partial^2 u}{\partial x^2} = e^{-\frac{x^2}{4t}}\left[\frac{x^2}{4t^{\frac{5}{2}}} - \frac{1}{2}\frac{1}{t^{\frac{3}{2}}}\right]$

$\Rightarrow u(x,t) = \frac{1}{\sqrt{t}}\, e^{-\frac{x^2}{4t}}$ is the solution of heat equation in $\{(x,t): x \in \mathbb{R}, t \in \mathbb{R}\}$

Only option (a) is correct answer and b),c) and d) are incorrect.

2. Explanation (b)

Consider the given heat equation

$\frac{\partial u}{\partial t} = \frac{\partial^2 u}{\partial x^2}; x \in (0,1), t > 0$

$u(x,0) = \sin \pi x \qquad x \in [0,1]$

$u(0,t) = u(1,t) = 0, t > 0$

Solution of heat equation is

$u(x,y) = \sum_{n=1}^{\infty} D_n \sin\frac{n\pi x}{l}\, e^{-c\left(\frac{n^2\pi^2}{l^2}\right)t}$

Where $D_n = \frac{2}{l}\int_0^l \sin n\pi x f(x)dx$

Here $c = 1, f(x) = \sin n\pi x$

$$D_n = \frac{2}{l}\int_0^1 \sin n\,\pi x \sin m\pi x\, dx$$

We know that

$\int_0^{\pi} \sin n\pi x \sin mnx\, dx = \begin{cases} \frac{\pi}{2} & if\ m = n \\ 0 & m \neq n \end{cases}$

$D_1 = \frac{2}{1}\int_0^1 \sin \pi x \sin \pi x\, dx$

$D_1 = 1$

$u(x,y) = \sum_{n=1}^{\infty} D_n \frac{\sin n\pi x}{l}\, e^{-c\frac{n^2\pi^2 t}{l}}$

$u(x,y) = D_1 \sin \pi x\, e^{-\pi^2 t}$

$= 1 \sin \pi x\, e^{-\pi^2 t}$

$u(x,y) = \sin \pi x e^{-\pi^2 t}$

$u\left(x, \frac{1}{\pi^2}\right) = \sin \pi\, e^{-1}$

From above,

only option (b) is correct answer and a),c) and d) are the incorrect

3. Explanation (a)

Given

$\alpha y + \frac{\partial y}{\partial n} = g$ on $\partial B\ \alpha > 0$

Where n is the unit outward normal to B and B is unit ball in R^2 satisfies

$\Delta u = f$ in B

The above problem is mixed problem of Dirichlet and Neumann Boundary value problem and it has always unique solution

$\Rightarrow$ Option (a) is correct answer and b), c) and d) are incorrect.

4. Explanation (a)

Given heat equation is

$\frac{\partial u}{\partial t} = \frac{\partial^2 u}{\partial x^2}$

$u(0,t) = u(\pi,t) = 0\ \ 0 \le t \le T$

$u(x,0) = \Phi(x)\ \ 0 \le x \le \pi.$

$u(x,t) = f(x)$

Since solution of heat equation can be written in the form of integral by using green function as if $G(x,y,t)$ be the greens function of the given DE then solution is

$u(x,t)\int_2^{\pi} G(x,y,t)\Phi(y)dy$

$at\ f = t\ u(x,t) = \int_0^H G(x,y,T)\phi(u)dy$

$\Rightarrow f(x) = \int_0^{\pi} k(x,y)\Phi(y)dy$

$where\ k(x,y) = G(x,y,t)$

$\therefore$ Option (a) is correct answer and b), c) and d) are the incorrect.

5. Explanation (a)

Consider the given wave equation,

$u_{tt} - u_{xx} = 0$

$u(x,0) = x^3$

$u_t(x,0) = \sin x \ldots.(1)$

Now

Solution of wave equation is

$u(x,t) = \frac{1}{2}[f(x+ct) + f(x-ct)] + \frac{1}{2}c\int_{x-ct}^{x+ct} g(\xi)d\xi$

From 1)

$c = 1 \qquad g(\xi) = \sin \xi$

$u(x,0) = f(x) = x^3$

$\Rightarrow u(x,t) = \frac{1}{2}[f(x+t) + f(x-t)] + \frac{1}{2}\int_{x-t}^{x+t} g(\xi)d\xi$

$u(\pi,\pi) = \frac{1}{2}[f(2\pi) + f(0)] + \frac{1}{2}\int_0^{2\pi} sin\xi d\xi$

$= \frac{1}{2}[8\pi^3 + 0] + \frac{1}{2}(1-1)$

$= \frac{1}{2}8\pi^3 + 0$

$u(\pi,\pi) = 4\pi^3$

$\Rightarrow$ Only option (a) is correct answer and option b) ,c) and d) are incorrect.

6. Explanation (c)

Consider the given wave equation

$\frac{\partial^2 u}{\partial t^2} = \frac{\partial^2 u}{\partial x^2}$

$u(x,0) = f(x), \frac{\partial y}{\partial t}(x,o) = 0$

Solution of wave equation is

$u(x,t) = \frac{1}{2}[f(x+ct)+f(x-ct)] + \frac{1}{2c}\int_{x-t}^{x+t} g(\xi)d\xi$

Here $c = 1$ and $\frac{\partial y}{\partial t}(x,0) = g(\xi) = 0$

$u(x,y) = \frac{1}{2}[f(x+t)+f(x-t)] + \frac{1}{2}.0$

$= \frac{1}{2}[f(x+t)+f(x-t)]$

$u\left(\frac{1}{2},\frac{5}{4}\right) = \frac{1}{2}\left[f\left(\frac{7}{4}\right)+f\left(-\frac{3}{4}\right)\right]$

$f\left(\frac{7}{4}\right) = f\left(1+\frac{3}{4}\right) = f\left(\frac{3}{4}\right)$

$f\left(-\frac{3}{4}\right) = f\left(1-\frac{3}{4}\right) = f\left(\frac{1}{4}\right)$

$f(x) = x(1-x)$

$f\left(\frac{3}{4}\right) = \frac{3}{4}\left(1-\frac{3}{4}\right)$

$f\left(\frac{3}{4}\right) = \frac{3}{16}$

$f\left(\frac{1}{4}\right) = \frac{1}{4}\left(1-\frac{1}{4}\right) = \frac{3}{16}$

Now

$u\left(\frac{1}{2},\frac{5}{4}\right) = \frac{1}{2}\left(\frac{3}{16}+\frac{3}{16}\right) = \frac{3}{16}$

$\Rightarrow$ Option (c) is correct answer and option a),b) and d) are the incorrect.

7. **Explanation (c)**

$\frac{\partial u}{\partial t} = \frac{\partial^2 u}{\partial x^2}, x \in \mathbb{R}, t > 0$

$u(x,0) = \begin{cases} 1, & 0 \le x \le 1 \\ 0, & elsewhere \end{cases}$

The solution of the problem is given by

$$u(x,t) = \frac{1}{2\sqrt{\pi t}}\int_{-\infty}^{\infty} e^{-\frac{(x-y)^2}{4kt}} f(y)dy$$

$$= \frac{1}{2\sqrt{\pi t}}\int_{-\infty}^{0} e^{-\frac{(x-y)^2}{4kt}} f(y)dy + \frac{1}{2\sqrt{\pi t}}\int_{0}^{1} e^{-\frac{(x-y)^2}{4kt}} f(y)dy$$

$$+ \frac{1}{2\sqrt{\pi t}}\int_{1}^{\infty} e^{-\frac{(x-y)^2}{4kt}} f(y)dy$$

$$u(x,t) = \frac{1}{2\sqrt{\pi t}}\int_{0}^{1} e^{-\frac{(x-y)^2}{4t}} dy$$

Let $\frac{(x-y)}{2\sqrt{t}} = v$

$\frac{-dy}{2\sqrt{t}} = dv$

$$u(x,t) = \frac{1}{2\sqrt{\pi t}}\int_{\frac{x}{2\sqrt{t}}}^{\frac{x-1}{2\sqrt{t}}} (-2\sqrt{t})\, e^{-v^2} dv$$

$$= \frac{1}{\sqrt{\pi}}\int_{\frac{x-1}{2\sqrt{t}}}^{\frac{x}{2\sqrt{t}}} e^{-v^2} dv$$

$$u(1,t) = \frac{1}{\sqrt{\pi}}\int_{0}^{\frac{1}{2\sqrt{t}}} e^{-v^2} dv$$

$\lim_{t\to 0^+} u(1,t) = \frac{1}{\sqrt{\pi}}\int_0^\infty e^{-v^2}\, dv = \frac{1}{\sqrt{\pi}} \times \frac{1}{2}\sqrt{\pi} = \frac{1}{2}$

(since $\int_0^\infty e^{-v^2}\, dv = \frac{1}{2}\sqrt{\pi}$)

Hence, option (c) is correct

8. **Explanation (c)**

$u_{xx} - u_{tt} = e^x + 6t, x \in \mathbb{R}, t > 0$

$\Rightarrow u_{tt} - u_{xx} = -e^x - 6t = F(x,t)$

$u(x,0) = \sin(x) = f(x)$

And $u_t(x,0) = 0 = g(x)$

The solution of the given wave equation is given by,

$$u(x,t) = \frac{1}{2}[f(x+ct)+f(x-ct)] + \frac{1}{2c}\int_{x-ct}^{x+ct} g(y)dy$$

$$+\frac{1}{2c}\iint f(\xi,\tau)d\xi d\tau$$

$$\Rightarrow u(x,t) = \frac{1}{2}[f(x+t)+f(x-t)] + \frac{1}{2c}\int_{x-ct}^{x+ct} 0\, ds$$

$$-\frac{1}{2c}\int_0^t \int_{x-(t-\tau)}^{x+(t-\tau)} (e^\xi + 6\tau)d\xi d\tau$$

$$\Rightarrow u(x,t) = \frac{1}{2}[\sin(x+t)+\sin(x-t)]$$

$$-\frac{1}{2}\int_0^t [e^\xi + 6\tau\xi]_{x-(t-\tau)}^{x+(t-\tau)}$$

$$\Rightarrow u\left(\frac{\pi}{2},\frac{\pi}{2}\right) = \frac{1}{2}[0+0] - \frac{1}{2}\int_0^{\pi/2} [e^\xi + 6\tau\xi]_\tau^{\pi-\tau}\, d\tau$$

$$= \frac{-1}{2}\int_0^{\pi/2} [e^{\pi-\tau} + 6\tau(\pi-\tau) - e^\tau - 6\tau^2]\, d\tau$$

$$\frac{-1}{2}[-e^{\pi-\tau} + 3\pi\tau^2 - 2\tau^3 - e^\tau - 2\tau^3]_0^{\pi/2}$$

$$= \frac{-1}{2}[-e^{\pi-\tau} + 3\pi\tau^2 - 4\tau^3 - e^\tau]_0^{\pi/2}$$

$$= \frac{-1}{2}\left[-e^{\frac{\pi}{2}} + 3\frac{\pi^3}{4} - \frac{\pi^3}{2} - e^{\frac{\pi}{2}} + e^\pi + 1\right]$$

$$= \frac{-1}{2}\left[-2e^{\frac{\pi}{2}} + \frac{\pi^3}{8} + e^\pi + 1\right]$$

$$= \left[-\frac{e^\pi}{2} + e^{\frac{\pi}{2}} - \frac{\pi^3}{8} - \frac{1}{2}\right]$$

$$= e^{\pi/2}\left[1 - \frac{e^{\frac{\pi}{2}}}{2}\right] - \left[\frac{\pi^3+4}{8}\right]$$

Hence, option (c) is correct

9. **Explanation (c)**

$$\left.\begin{aligned} \frac{\partial u}{\partial t} = \frac{\partial^2 u}{\partial x}\ & where\ (x,t) \in (0,1)\times(0,\infty) \\ u(x,0) &= \sin \pi x,\ x \in (0,1) \\ u(0,t) = u(1,t) &= 0,\ t \in (0,\infty) \end{aligned}\right\}$$

The solution of the above wave equation is

$$u(x,t) = \sum_{n=1}^{\infty} B_n \sin\left(\frac{n\pi}{l}\right) x e^{\frac{kn^2\pi^2}{l^2}t}$$

Here, $k = 1, l = 1$ and $f(x) = \sin \pi x$

$$\Rightarrow u(x,t) = \sum_{n=1}^{\infty} B_n \sin(\pi\, x)\, e^{-n^2\pi^2 t}$$

And $B_n = \frac{2}{l}\int_0^l f(x)\sin\left(\frac{n\pi}{l}\right)x\,dx$

$$\Rightarrow B_n = \frac{2}{1}\int_0^1 \sin\pi\, x \sin(n\pi)\, x\, dx$$

Take $\pi x = y$

$\Rightarrow \pi dx = dy$

$$\Rightarrow B_n = \frac{2}{\pi}\int_0^{\pi} \sin(y)\sin(y)\,dy$$

$$B_1 = \frac{2}{\pi}\frac{\pi}{2} = 1$$

If $n \neq 1$, we get $B_n = 0$ by

$$\int_0^{\pi} \sin mx \sin nx\, dx = \begin{cases} 0 & m \neq n \\ \frac{\pi}{2} & m = n \end{cases}$$

$\Rightarrow B_n = 0\forall \mathbb{N}/\{1\}$ and $B_1 = 1$

$\Rightarrow u(x,t) = \sin(\pi x)\, e^{-\pi^2 t}$

Since $e^{-\pi^2} \neq 0$ for any t and $\sin(\pi x) = 0$

If $x = n \in \mathbb{N}$

Hence, $u(x,t) \neq 0$ since $(x,t) \in (0,1) \times (0,\infty)$

Also, $\frac{\partial u}{\partial t} = \sin(\pi x)\, e^{-\pi^2 t}(-\pi^2) \neq 0$

And $e^t u(x,t) = \sin(\pi x)\, e^{(1-\pi^2)t}$

Where $x \in (0,1)$ and $t \in (0,\infty)$

Since, $\sin(\pi x)$ is bounded for $t \in (0,\infty)$

We can observe that $\sin(\pi x)$ can attain maximum value 1 and $e^{-\pi^2 t} < 1$ for $(x,t) \in (0,1) \times (0,\infty)$

So, $u(x,t) \not> 1$

Hence, option (c) is correct

10. Explanation (c)

$u_{xx} + u_{yy} = 64\text{in}\{(x,y)/x^2 + y^2 < 1\}$

$u = 0$ on $\partial D = \{(x,y)/x^2 + y^2 = 1\}$

$u = \underset{\text{Particular}}{\overset{v}{\downarrow}} + w \rightarrow$Homogenous

$u_{xx} + u_{yy} = 64 = v_{xx} + v_{yy} + w_{xx} + w_{yy}$

$v_{xx} + v_{yy} = 64 \qquad w_{xx} + w_{yy} = 0$ on$\Delta°$

$v = P_2(x,y)$

$w = -v$on $\partial\Delta$

$v = a_0 + a_1 x + a_2 x^2 + a_3 xy + a_4 y^2$

$2a_2 + 2a_4 = 64$

$a_2 = 32, \qquad a_4 = 0$

$v = 32x^2 = 32r^2 cos^2\theta, \qquad 0 \leq r < 1$

$w_{xx} + w_{yy} = 0$on$\Delta°$

$x \to r\cos\theta, \qquad y \to r\sin\theta$

$$w_{rr} + \frac{1}{r}w_{r\theta} + \frac{1}{r^2}w_{\theta\theta} = 0$$

$w(-1,\theta) = -32cos^2\theta = -16\cos 2\theta - 16$

$w = R(r)T(\theta)$

$$w(1,\theta) = \frac{A_0}{2} + \sum_{n=1}^{\infty} A_n \cos n\theta + B_n \sin n\theta$$

$= -16 - 16\cos 2\theta$

$A_0 = -32 \qquad A_n = 0\forall n \neq 0, 2$

$A_2 = -16 \qquad B_n = 0\,\forall n$

$w(r,0) = -16 - 16r^2cos^2 0$

$= -16 - 16\left(u^2(2cos^2\theta - 1)\right)$

$= -16 - 16.2x^2 + 16x^2$

$= -16 - 32x^2 + 16x^2 + 16y^2$

$v(x,y) = 32x^2$

$w(x,y) + v(x,y) = u(x,y) = -16 + 16x^2 + 16y^2$

$$u\left(\frac{1}{4}, \frac{1}{\sqrt{2}}\right) = -7$$

11. Explanation: (c)

Given partial differential equation is $\frac{\partial^2 u}{\partial t^2} - \frac{\partial^2 u}{\partial x^2} = 0$.

$u(x,t) = \phi_1(x+t) + \phi_2(x-t)$ is a solution of the given partial differential equation.

Let θ be fixed real number.

$\therefore u(x-\theta,t) = \phi_1(x-\theta+t) + \phi_2(x-\theta-t)$

$u_t = \phi_1'(x-\theta+t) - \phi_2'(x-\theta-t)$

$u_{tt} = \phi_1''(x-\theta+t) + \phi_2''(x-\theta-t)$

$u_x = \phi_1'(x-\theta+t) + \phi_2'(x-\theta-t)$

$u_{xx} = \phi_1''(x-\theta+t) + \phi_2''(x-\theta+t)$

$\Rightarrow u_{tt} - u_{xx} = 0$

(2) $u_x = \phi_1'(x+t) + \phi_2'(x-t)$

Let, $v = \phi_1'(x+t) + \phi_2'(x-t)$

$v_x = \phi_1''(x+t) + \phi_2''(x-t)$

$v_{xx} = \phi_1'''(x+t) + \phi_2'''(x-t)$

$v_{tt} = \phi_1'''(x+t) + \phi_2'''(x-t)$

(3) $u(3x,9t) = \phi_1(3x+9t) + \phi_2(3x-9t)$

$u_x = 3\phi_1'(3x+9t) + 3\phi_2'(3x-9t)$

$u_{xx} = 9\phi_1''(3x+9t) + 9\phi_2''(3x-9t)$

$u_t = 9\phi_1'(3x+9t) - 9\phi_2'(3x-9t)$

$u_{tt} = 81\phi_1''(3x+9t) - 81\phi_2''(3x-9t)$

$\Rightarrow u_{tt} \neq u_{xx}$

$\therefore u(3x,9t)$ is not a solution.

(4) Similarly check $u(3x,3t)$ solves the equation.

So, option (c) is correct.

12. Explanation: (c)

u(x, t)= $\sum_{n=1}^{\infty} A_n \cos\frac{n\pi}{2}t \sin\frac{n\pi}{2}x$

Now,

$A_n = \frac{2}{l}\int_0^l f(x)\sin\frac{n\pi}{l}$ x dx

$= \frac{2}{2}\int_0^2 [\sin\pi x + 2\sin(2\pi x)] \sin\frac{n\pi}{2}$ x dx

Put $\frac{\pi}{2}x = v$

$\Rightarrow \frac{\pi}{2}dx = dv$

$\Rightarrow \frac{2}{\pi}dv = dx$

also; $x = 0 \Rightarrow v = 0$

$x = 2 \Rightarrow v = \pi$

$\therefore A_n = \frac{2}{\pi}\int_0^{\pi} (\sin 2v + 2\sin 4v)\sin nv\, dv$

$\Rightarrow A_2 = 1; A_4 = 2$ and $A_n = 0,\ \forall n \neq 1,4$

$\therefore u(x,t) = \cos\pi t \cdot \sin\pi x + 2\cos 2\pi t \cdot \sin 2\pi x$

$u(1,1) = 0$

$u\left(\frac{1}{2}, 1\right) = -1$

$u\left(\frac{1}{2}, 2\right) = 1$

So, option (c) is correct.

13. Explanation: (a)

Given: $u_{tt} - 4u_{xx} = 0$

$\Rightarrow u_{tt} = 4\,u_{xx}$

$\Rightarrow c^2 = 4 \Rightarrow c = 2$

and $f(x) = \begin{cases} e^{-1/x^2}, x \neq 0 \\ 0, \text{otherwise} \end{cases}$

and $g(x) = xe^{-x^2}$

Now, by D' Alembert's formula, we have,

$$u(x,t) = \frac{1}{2}[f(x+ct) + f(x-ct)] + \frac{1}{2c}\int_{x-ct}^{x+ct} g(y)dy$$

$$= \frac{1}{2}\left[e^{-1(x+2t)^2} + e^{-1/(x-2t)^2}\right] + \frac{1}{4}\int_{x-2t}^{x+2t} ye^{-y^2}dy$$

$\therefore u(s,t) = \frac{1}{2}\left[e^{-1/(s+2t)^2} + e^{-1/(s-2t)^2}\right]$

$+\frac{1}{4}\int_{5-2t}^{5+2t} ye^{-y^2}dy$

Now, we have,

$\lim_{t\to\infty} u(5,t) = \frac{1}{2}[1+1] + \frac{1}{4}\int_{-\infty}^{\infty} y\,e^{-y^2}dy$

$= 1 + \frac{1}{4}\int_{-\infty}^{\infty} y\,e^{-y^2}dy$

Let us substitute $y^2 = v$

$\Rightarrow 2ydy = dv$

$\Rightarrow ydy = \frac{dv}{2}$

$\therefore \lim_{t\to\infty} u(5,t) = 1 + \frac{1}{4}\int_{-\infty}^{\infty} e^{-v}\frac{dv}{2}$

$= 1 + \frac{1}{8}[-e^{-v}]_{-\infty}^{\infty}$

$= 1 - \frac{1}{8}\left(e^{-y^2}\right)_{-\infty}^{\infty}$

$= 1 - \frac{1}{8}[0-0]$

$= 1$

$\Rightarrow$ option (a) is correct.

14. Explanation: (a)

The general solution to the heat equation can be written using the initial condition as:

$$u(x,t) = \int_{-\infty}^{\infty} G(x-t,\xi)u(\xi,0)d\xi$$

where $G(x,\xi)$ is the Green's function for the heat equation.

Now use initial condition:

$$u(x,0) = \sin(4x) + x + 1$$

The solution to the heat equation can be expressed as

$$u(x,t) = \int_{-\infty}^{\infty} G(x-t,\xi)u(\xi,0)d\xi$$

For $u(x,t)$, the solution is

$$u(x,t) = \int_{-\infty}^{\infty} G(x-t,\xi)(\sin(4\xi) + \xi + 1)d\xi$$

where $G(x,t) = \frac{1}{\sqrt{4\pi t}}e^{-\frac{x^2}{4t}}$ is the Green's function.

Now to check the options:

Consider,

$$u(x,t) = \int_{-\infty}^{\infty} \frac{1}{\sqrt{4\pi t}}e^{-\frac{(x-\xi)^2}{4t}}(\sin(4\xi) + \xi + 1)d\xi$$

The integral of $\sin(4\xi)$ will evaluate to zero due to symmetry because it is an odd function. The remaining terms are:

$$u(x,t) = \int_{-\infty}^{\infty} \frac{1}{\sqrt{4\pi t}}e^{-\frac{(x-\xi)^2}{4t}}(\xi + 1)d\xi$$

Since ξ and 1 are not affected by the Gaussian integral, they yield:

$$\int_{-\infty}^{\infty} \frac{1}{\sqrt{4\pi t}}e^{-\frac{(x-\xi)^2}{4t}}d\xi = 1$$

Thus,

$$u(x,t) = x + 1$$

$$\therefore u\left(\frac{\pi}{8},1\right) + u\left(-\frac{\pi}{8},1\right) = \frac{\pi}{8} + 1 + \left(-\frac{\pi}{8} + 1\right) = 2$$

$\therefore$ Option (a) is correct.

15. Explanation: (c)

We have a boundary value problem defined on the disk $B(0,2)$ with the boundary ∂B.

The conditions involve Laplace's equation $-\Delta u = 0$ inside the disk and a boundary condition involving parameters α, β and k.

Statement S_1: If $\beta = 0$, then there exists $(x_0,y_0) \in B(0,2)$ such that $|u(x_0,y_0)| = \frac{|1+4k|}{|\alpha|}$.

When $\beta = 0$, the boundary condition simplifies to $\alpha u(x,y) = 1 + (x^2+y^2)k$ on ∂B.

The maximum value of $|u(x,y)|$ inside the disk would occur at some point and for some (x_0,y_0), we have $|u(x_0,y_0)| = \frac{|1+4k|}{|\alpha|}$. So, S_1 is true.

Statement S_2: If $\alpha = 0$, then $k = -\frac{1}{4}$

When $\alpha = 0$, the boundary condition becomes $\beta\frac{\partial u}{\partial v} = 1 + (x^2+y^2)k$ on ∂B.

If $k = -\frac{1}{4}$, the boundary condition simplifies to $\beta\frac{\partial u}{\partial v} = 0$, implying a constant solution.

The condition $\alpha = 0$ leads directly to $k = -\frac{1}{4}$ because $x^2 + y^2 = 4$ on ∂B.

Hence S_2 is also true.

Therefore option (c) is correct.

16. Explanation: (d)

The general solution of the one-dimensional wave equation is given by d'Alembert's formula:

$$u(x,t) = f(x-t) + g(x+t),$$

where f and g are arbitrary functions.

$$u(0,t) = f(-t) + g(t) = 0, \forall t \geq 0.$$

$$g(t) = -f(-t).$$

$$u(x,t) = f(x-t) - f(-x-t).$$

Option (a): $u(x,t) = 0$, **whenever** $x = t$

$$u(t,t) = f(t-t) - f(-t-t) = f(0) - f(-2t).$$

$$f(0) = f(-2t), \forall t.$$

This is not necessarily true for all functions f.

Option (b): $u(x,t) = 0$, **whenever** $x = -t$

$$u(-t,t) = f(-t-t) - f(t-t) = f(-2t) - f(0).$$

$$f(-2t) = f(0), \forall t.$$

As in Option (a), this is not necessarily true for all functions f.

Option (c): $u(-x,t) = u(x,t)$, **whenever** $x > 0, t > 0$

$$u(-x,t) = f(-x-t) - f(x-t).$$

$$u(x,t) = f(x-t) - f(-x-t),$$

$$u(-x,t) = -u(x,t).$$

This means $u(x,t)$ is an odd function in x, so Option (c) is incorrect.

Option (d): $u(-x,t) = -u(x,t)$, **whenever** $0 < x \le t$

$$u(-x,t) = f(-x-t) - f(x-t) = -u(x,t).$$

This confirms that $u(x,t)$ is indeed an odd function in x, making Option (d) correct.

17. Explanation: (d)

The general solution to the wave equation is given by:

$$u(x,t) = f(x-t) + g(x+t),$$

where f and g are determined by the initial conditions.

Initial condition $u(x,0) = 1 + x^2$:

At $t = 0$, the solution becomes: $u(x,0) = f(x) + g(x) = 1 + x^2$.

So, we have:

$$f(x) + g(x) = 1 + x^2. \quad (1)$$

Initial condition $\frac{\partial u}{\partial t}(x,0) = x + 1$:

Now, differentiate the general solution with respect to t:

$$\frac{\partial u}{\partial t}(x,t) = -f'(x-t) + g'(x+t).$$

At $t = 0$, this becomes:

$$\frac{\partial u}{\partial t}(x,0) = -f'(x) + g'(x) = x + 1.$$

Thus, we have the equation:

$$-f'(x) + g'(x) = x + 1. \quad (2)$$

We now have the system of equations:

1. $f(x) + g(x) = 1 + x^2$,
2. $-f'(x) + g'(x) = x + 1$.

Solve this system to find $f(x)$ and $g(x)$ and hence compute $u(1,1) = 5$.

18. Explanation: (d)

Given PDE

$$u_t = 16u_{xx} + 2, 0 < x < 7, t > 0$$

Boundary conditions

$$u_x(0,t) = 0, u(7,t) = 0$$

Initial condition

$$u(x,0) = 0$$

For heat equations, as $t \to \infty$, the solution approaches a steady state where

$$u_t = 0$$

Find steady state equation

$$16u_{xx} + 2 = 0$$

$$\Rightarrow u_{xx} = -\frac{1}{8}$$

Integrate

$$u_x = -\frac{x}{8} + C_1$$

$$\Rightarrow u = -\frac{x^2}{16} + C_1x + C_2$$

Apply boundary conditions

From $u_x(0,t) = 0$

$$C_1 = 0$$

From $u(7,t) = 0$

$$-\frac{49}{16} + C_2 = 0$$

$$\Rightarrow C_2 = \frac{49}{16}$$

Steady state solution

$$u(x) = \frac{49 - x^2}{16}$$

Hence,

$$u(x,t) \to \frac{49 - x^2}{16} = \frac{1}{16}(49 - x^2) \text{ as } t \to \infty$$

So, the correct option is (4).

19. Explanation: (c)

Given the forced wave equation

$$u_{tt} - u_{xx} = e^{-t}, x \in \mathbb{R}, t > 0$$

with initial conditions

$$u(x,0) = \cos x, u_t(x,0) = 0$$

Write the solution as

$$u(x,t) = v(x,t) + u_p(t)$$

where

- u_p= particular solution for the forcing
- v = solution of the homogeneous wave equation.

Find a particular solution:

Since the RHS depends only on t, try $u_p = u_p(t)$.

Then $u_{xx} = 0$, so

$$u_p''(t) = e^{-t}$$

Integrate twice:

$$u_p(t) = e^{-t}$$

Homogeneous problem

Let $v = u - u_p$.

Then

$$v_{tt} - v_{xx} = 0$$

Initial conditions become

$$v(x,0) = \cos x - 1$$

$$\Longrightarrow v_t(x,0) = 1$$

Use d'Alembert formula

For wave equation

$$v(x,t) = \frac{1}{2}[f(x+t) + f(x-t)] + \frac{1}{2}\int_{x-t}^{x+t} g(s)\,ds$$

where $f(x) = \cos x - 1, g(x) = 1$

First term

$$\frac{1}{2}[(\cos(x+t) - 1) + (\cos(x-t) - 1)]$$

Using identity $\cos(x+t) + \cos(x-t) = 2\cos x \cos t$

we get

$$\cos x \cos t - 1$$

Second term $\frac{1}{2}\int_{x-t}^{x+t} 1\,ds = \frac{1}{2}(2t) = t$

Thus

$$v(x,t) = \cos x \cos t - 1 + t$$

$$u(x,t) = v + u_p = u(x,t) = \cos x \cos t - 1 + t + e^{-t}$$

Behaviour as $t \to \infty$

$$u(x,t) = t + \cos x \cos t - 1 + e^{-t}$$

- t grows to $+\infty$
- cosx cost is bounded between $[-1,1]$
- $e^{-t} \to 0$

Thus $u(x,t) \to \infty$ for every x.

Check statements

(1) $e^t u(x_0,t) \to 0$,
Since $u(x_0,t) \sim t, e^t t \to \infty$
$\Rightarrow$False

(2) $|u(x_0,t)| \to 0$
But $u(x_0,t) \to \infty$
$\Rightarrow$ False

(3) Since $u(x,t) \to \infty$, it will eventually exceed any number.
So there exists t_0 such that
$$u(x_0,t_0) \geq 4$$
$\Rightarrow$ True

(4) The minimum value occurs near $t = 0$:
$$u(x,t) \geq t - 2 + e^{-t}$$
Minimum ≈ -1, so it never reaches -4.
$\Rightarrow$False

So, the correct option is (3).

MSQ (Multiple Select Questions)

1. The PDE
$$\left.\begin{aligned} u_{xx} + u_{yy} + \lambda u = 0,\ 0 < x, y < 1 \\ u(x,0) = u(x,1) = 0,\ 0 \leq x \leq 1 \\ u(0,y) = u(1,y) = 0,\ 0 \leq y \leq 1 \end{aligned}\right\} \text{ has}$$
(a) A unique solution u for any $\lambda \in \mathbb{R}$
(b) Infinitely many solutions for some $\lambda \in \mathbb{R}$
(c) A solution for countably many values of λ
(d) Infinitely many solutions for all $\lambda \in \mathbb{R}$
[June 2011]

2. Let $u(x,t)$ be the solution of the intial boundary value problem
$$\frac{\partial^2 u}{\partial t^2} = \frac{\partial^2 u}{\partial x^2}, 0 < x < \infty, t > 0$$
$$u(x,0) = \cos\left(\frac{\pi x}{2}\right), 0 \leq x < \infty$$
$$\frac{\partial u}{\partial t}(x,0) = 0, \leq x \leq \infty$$
$$\frac{\partial u}{\partial x}(0,t) = 0, t \geq 0$$
Then,
(a) The value of $u(2,2) = -1$
(b) The value of $u(2,2) = 1$
(c) The value of $u\left(\frac{1}{2},\frac{1}{2}\right) = \frac{1}{\sqrt{2}}$
(d) The value of $u\left(\frac{1}{2},\frac{1}{2}\right) = \frac{1}{2}$
[Dec 2011]

3. Let u be a solution of the heat equation
$$\left.\begin{aligned} u_t - u_{xx} = 0\ ; 0 < x < \pi \text{ and } t > 0 \\ u(0,t) = u(\pi,t) = 0\ ; t > 0 \\ u(x,0) = \sin x + \sin 2x\ ;\ 0 \leq x \leq \pi \end{aligned}\right\} \text{ Then}$$
(a) $u(x,t) \to 0$ as $t \to \infty$ for all $x \in (0,\pi)$
(b) $t^2 u(x,t) \to 0$ as $t \to \infty$ for all $x \in (0,\pi)$
(c) $e^2 u(x,t)$ is a bounded function for $x \in (0,\pi), t > 0$
(d) $e^{2t} u(x,t) \to 0$ as $t \to \infty$ for all $x \in (0,\pi)$
[June 2012]

4. Consider the Laplace equation in polar form: $\frac{\partial^2 u}{\partial r^2} + \frac{1}{r}\frac{\partial u}{\partial r} + \frac{1}{r^2}\frac{\partial^2 u}{\partial \theta^2} = 0; 0 < r \leq a, 0 \leq \theta < 2\pi$ Satisfying $u(a,\theta) = f(\theta)$, where f is a given function. Let σ be the separation constant that appears when one uses the method of separation of variables. Then for solution $u(r,\theta)$ to be bounded and also periodic in θ with period 2π,
(a) σ cannot be negative
(b) σ can be zero, and in that case the solution is a constant
(c) σ can be positive, and in the case it must be an integer
(d) The fundamental set of solutions is $\{1, r^n \sin\theta, r^n \cos n\theta\}$, when n is a positive integer
[June 2013]

5. Let the heat equation $\frac{\partial u}{\partial t} = \frac{\partial^2 u}{\partial x_1^2} + \frac{\partial^2 u}{\partial x_2^2} + \frac{\partial^2 u}{\partial x_3^2}$, $t \geq 0, x = (x_1,x_2,x_3) \in \mathbb{R}^3$ admit an exponential function exp $\left(i(\vec{k}\cdot\overline{x} + wt)\right)$ as its solution, where $\vec{k}$ is a non zero constant real vector, and w is constant. Then the solution
(a) Remain constants on certain planes in $\mathbb{R}^3$
(b) Repeats itself after a certain length L
(c) Has, in general, an amplitude decaying exponentially with time t
(d) Is bounded uniformly for $\underset{x}{\to} \in \mathbb{R}^3$ for a fixed t
[June 2013]

6. If the initial value problem for partial differential equation $\frac{\partial u}{\partial t} + \frac{\partial^2 u}{\partial x^2} = 0$; $u(x,0) = \sin(\pi x)$, has a solution of the form $u(x,t) = \phi \sin(\pi x)$, then
(a) ϕ is always negative
(b) ϕ is always positive
(c) ϕ is an increasing function
(d) ϕ is an decreasing function
[Dec 2013]

7. Let $u(x,t)$ be the solution of the equation $\frac{\partial^2 u}{\partial x^2} = \frac{\partial u}{\partial t}$ which tends to zero as $t \to \infty$ and has the value $\cos(x)$ when $t = 0$. Then
(a) $u = \sum_{n=1}^{\infty} a_n \sin(nx + b_n)\, e^{-nt}$ where a_n, b_n are arbitrary constants
(b) $u = \sum_{n=1}^{\infty} a_n \sin(nx + b_n)\, e^{-n^2 t}$ where a_n, b_n are non – zero constants
(c) $u = \sum_{n=1}^{\infty} a_n \cos(nx + b_n)\, e^{-nt}$ where a_n are not all zero and $b_n = 0$ for $n \geq 1$
(d) $u = \sum_{n=1}^{\infty} a_n \cos(nx + b_n)\, e^{-n^2 t}$ where $a_1 \neq 0, a_n = 0$ for $a_n > 1$, and $b_n = 0$ for $n \geq 1$
[June 2014]

8. Let $u(x,y)$ be the solution of the equation $\frac{\partial^2 u}{\partial x^2} + \frac{\partial^2 u}{\partial y^2} = 0$, which tends to zero as $y \to \infty$ and has the value $\sin(x)$ when $y = 0$. Then
(a) $u = \sum_{n=1}^{\infty} a_n \sin(nx + b_n)\, e^{-ny}$ where a_n are arbitrary and b_n are non - zero constants
(b) $u = \sum_{n=1}^{\infty} a_n \sin(nx + b_n)\, e^{-n^2 y}$ where $a_1 = 1$ and $a_n (n > 1) b_n$ are non – zero constants
(c) $u = \sum_{n=1}^{\infty} a_n \sin(nx + b_n)\, e^{-ny}$ where $a_1 = 1, a_n = 0$ for $n > 1$ and $b_n = 0$ for $n \geq 1$
(d) $u = \sum_{n=1}^{\infty} a_n \sin(nx + b_n)\, e^{-n^2 y}$ where $b_n = 0$ for $n \geq 0$ and a_n are all non – zero
[Dec 2015]

9. Let u be the solution of the boundary value problem
$u_{xx} + u_{yy} = 0$ for $0 < x, y < \pi$
$u(x,0) = 0 = u(x,\pi)$ for $0 \le x \le \pi$
$u(0,y) = 0, u(\pi,y) = \sin y + \sin 2y$ for $0 \le y \le \pi$
Then,
(a) $u\left(1,\frac{\pi}{2}\right) = (\sinh(\pi))^{-1}\sinh(1)$
(b) $u\left(1,\frac{\pi}{2}\right) = (\sinh(1))^{-1}\sinh(\pi)$
(c) $u\left(1,\frac{\pi}{4}\right) = (\sinh(\pi))^{-1}(\sinh(1))\frac{1}{\sqrt{2}} + (\sinh(2\pi))^{-1}\sinh(2)$
(d) $u\left(1,\frac{\pi}{4}\right) = (\sinh(1))^{-1}(\sinh(\pi))\frac{1}{\sqrt{2}} + (\sinh(2))^{-1}\sinh(2\pi)$
[June 2016]

10. Let $u: \mathbb{R}\times[0,\infty] \to \mathbb{R}$ be a solution of the initial value problem
$$\left.\begin{aligned} u_{tt} - u_{xx} &= 0, for\ (x,t) \in \mathbb{R}\times(0,\infty) \\ u(x,0) &= f(x), x \in \mathbb{R} \\ u_t(x,0) &= g(x), x \in \mathbb{R}\end{aligned}\right\}$$
Suppose $f(x) = g(x) = 0$ for $x \notin [0,1]$
Then we always have
(a) $u(x,t) = 0$ for all $(x,t) \in (-\infty,0)\times(0,\infty)$
(b) $u(x,t) = 0$ for all $(x,t) \in (1,\infty)\times(0,\infty)$
(c) $u(x,t) = 0$ for all (x,t) satisfying $x + t < 0$
(d) $u(x,t) = 0$ for all (x,t) satisfying $x - t > 1$
[June 2016]

11. Let $u: \mathbb{R}^2\setminus\{(0,0)\} \to \mathbb{R}$ be a C^2 function satisfying $\frac{\partial^2 u}{\partial x^2} + \frac{\partial^2 u}{\partial y^2} = 0$, for all $(x,y) \ne (0,0)$ Suppose u is of the form $u(x,y) = f(\sqrt{x^2+y^2})$, where $f: (0,\infty) \to \mathbb{R}$ is a non – constant function, then
(a) $\lim_{x^2+y^2\to 0} |u(x,y)| = \infty$ (b) $\lim_{x^2+y^2\to 0} |u(x,y)| = 0$
(c) $\lim_{x^2+y^2\to \infty} |u(x,y)| = \infty$ (d) $\lim_{x^2+y^2\to \infty} |u(x,y)| = 0$
[Dec 2016]

12. Consider the wave equation for $u(x,t)$
$$\left.\begin{aligned} \frac{\partial^2 u}{\partial t^2} - \frac{\partial^2 u}{\partial x^2} &= 0 (x,t) \in \mathbb{R}\times(0,\infty) \\ u(x,0) &= f(x), x \in \mathbb{R} \\ \frac{\partial u}{\partial t}(x,0) &= g(x), x \in \mathbb{R}\end{aligned}\right\}$$
Let u_i be the solution of the above problem with $f = f_i$ and $g = g_i$ for $i = 1,2$, where $f_i: \mathbb{R}\to\mathbb{R}$ and $g_i: \mathbb{R}\to\mathbb{R}$ are given C^2 functions satisfying $f_1(x) = f_2(x)$ and $g_1(x) = g_2(x)$, for every $x \in [-1,1]$
Which of the following statements are necessarily true?
(a) $u_1(0,1) = u_2(0,1)$ (b) $u_1(1,1) = u_2(1,1)$
(c) $u_1\left(\frac{1}{2},\frac{1}{2}\right) = u_2\left(\frac{1}{2},\frac{1}{2}\right)$ (d) $u_1(0,2) = u_2(0,2)$
[Dec 2016]

13. If $u(x,t)$ is the solution of $\frac{\partial u}{\partial t} = \frac{\partial^2 u}{\partial x^2}, 0 < x < 1, t > 0$
$$u(x,0) = 1 + x + \sin(\pi x)\cos(\pi x)$$
$$u(0,t) = 1, u(1,t) = 2$$
Then
(a) $u\left(\frac{1}{2},\frac{1}{4}\right) = \frac{3}{2}$ (b) $u\left(\frac{1}{2},\frac{1}{2}\right) = \frac{3}{2}$
(c) $u\left(\frac{1}{4},\frac{3}{4}\right) = \frac{5}{4} + \frac{1}{2}e^{-3\pi^2}$ (d) $u\left(\frac{1}{4},1\right) = \frac{5}{4} + \frac{1}{2}e^{-4\pi^2}$
[June 2018]

14. Let u be the solution of
$$\left.\begin{aligned} \frac{\partial^2 u}{\partial t^2} &= \frac{\partial^2 u}{\partial x^2}, (x,t) \in \mathbb{R}\times(0,\infty) \\ u(x,0) &= f(x), x \in \mathbb{R} \\ u_t(x,0) &= g(x), x \in \mathbb{R}\end{aligned}\right\}$$
Where f, g are in $C^2(\mathbb{R})$ and satisfy the following conditions:
(i) $f(x) = g(x) = 0$ for $x \le 0$
(ii) $0 < f(x) \le 1$ for $x > 0$
(iii) $g(x) > 0$ for $x > 0$
(iv) $\int_0^\infty g(x)dx < \infty$
Then, which of the following statements are true?
(a) $u(x,t) = 0$ for all $x \le 0$ and $t > 0$
(b) u is bounded on $\mathbb{R}\times(0,\infty)$
(c) $u(x,t) = 0$ whenever $x + t < 0$
(d) $u(x,t) = 0$ for some (x,t) satisfying $x + t > 0$
[June 2019]

15. Let u be the solution of the problem
$$\left.\begin{aligned} \frac{\partial^2 u}{\partial x^2} + \frac{\partial^2 u}{\partial y^2} &= 0\ (x,y)\in(0,\pi)\times(0,\pi) \\ u(0,y) = u(\pi,y) &= 0\ y \in (0,\pi) \\ u(x,0) = 0, u(x,\pi) &= \sin(2x),\ x \in (0,\pi)\end{aligned}\right\}$$
Then
(a) $\max\{u(x,y): 0 \le x,y \le \pi\} = 1$
(b) $u(x_0,y_0) = 1$ for some $(x_0,y_0) \in (0,\pi)\times(0,\pi)$
(c) $u(x,y) > -1$ for all $(x,y) \in (0,\pi)\times(0,\pi)$
(d) $\min\{u(x,y): 0 \le x,y \le \pi\} > -1$
[June 2019]

16. Let $u(x,t)$ be the solution of
$$\begin{cases} \frac{\partial^2 u}{\partial t^2} - \frac{\partial^2 u}{\partial x^2} = xt, & -\infty < x < \infty, t > 0 \\ u(x,0) = \frac{\partial u}{\partial y}(x,0) = 0, & -\infty < x < \infty\end{cases}$$
Then $u(2,3)$ is equal to
(a) 9 (b) 1
(c) 27 (d) 12
[Dec 2019]

17. Let $B(0,1) = \{(x,y) \in \mathbb{R}^2: x^2 + y^2 < 1\}$. Consider $U \in C^2\overline{B(0,1)}$ satisfying $\Delta U + \lambda U = 0\ in\ B(0,1)\frac{\partial U}{\partial n} = 0\ on\ \partial(B(0,1))$. Then
(a) $\lambda \ge 0$
(b) $\lambda < 0$
(c) $\lambda = 0 \Rightarrow U = 0$
(d) $\lambda = 0 \Rightarrow U$ is a constant.
[Dec 2019]

18. Consider the Cauchy problem
$$\begin{cases} \frac{\partial^2 u}{\partial x \partial y} = 0, & |x| < 1,\ 0 < y < 1 \\ u(x,x^2) = 0, & \frac{\partial u}{\partial y}(x,x^2) = g(x), |x| < 1\end{cases}$$
Which of the following statements are true?
(a) A necessary condition for a solution to exist is that g is an odd function.

(b) A necessary condition for a solution to exist is that g is an even function.

(c) The solution (if exists) is given by $u(x,y) = 2\int_x^{\sqrt{y}} zg(z)\,dz$

(d) The solution (if it exists) is given by $u(x,y) = 2\int_{\sqrt{y}}^{x^2} zg(z)\,dz$

[Nov 2020]

19. Which of the following are solutions of the Laplace equation $u_{xx} + u_{yy} = 0$ in the unit disk $D\{(x,y): x^2 + y^2 < 1\}$?

(a) $x^5 + 2x^2y^3 - y^5$ (b) $x^2 + 2xy - y^2$

(c) $\cos(y)\,e^x + \sin(x)\,e^y$ (d) $\frac{1+x}{1+2x+x^2+y^2}$

[Nov 2020]

20. Let $u(x,y)$ solve the partial differential equation (PDE) $x^2\frac{\partial^2 u}{\partial x\partial y} + 3y^2u = 0$ with $u(x,0) = e^{1/x}$.

Which of the following statements are true?

(a) The PDE is not linear PDE

(b) $u(1,1) = e^2$

(c) $u(1,1) = e^{-2}$

(d) The method of separation of variables can be utilized to compute the solution $u(x,y)$

[Feb 2022]

21. Let $u = u(x,t)$ be the solution of the initial-boundary value problem

$$\frac{\partial u}{\partial t} = \frac{\partial^2 u}{\partial x^2}, (x,t) \in (0,1)\times(0,\infty),$$
$$u(x,0) = 4x(1-x), x \in [0,1],$$
$$u(0,t) = u(1,t) = 0, t \geq 0.$$

Then which of the following statements are true?

(a) $\lim_{t\to\infty} u(x,t) = 0$ for all $x \in (0,1)$

(b) $u(x,t) = u(1-x,t)$ for all $x \in (0,1), t > 0$

(c) $\int_0^1 (u(x,t))^2\,dx$ is a non-increasing function of t

(d) $\int_0^1 (u(x,t))^2\,dx$ is a non-decreasing function of t

[Feb. 2025]

22. Let $u = u(x,y)$ be the solution of the boundary value problem

$$\frac{\partial^2 u}{\partial x^2} + \frac{\partial^2 u}{\partial y^2} = 0, (x,y) \in (0,1)\times(0,1),$$
$$u(x,0) = e^{\pi x}, u(x,1) = -e^{\pi x}, x \in [0,1],$$
$$u(0,y) = \cos(\pi y) + \sin(\pi y), y \in [0,1],$$
$$u(1,y) = e^{\pi}(\cos(\pi y) + \sin(\pi y)), y \in [0,1].$$

Then there exists a point $(x_0, y_0) \in (0,1)\times(0,1)$ such that

(a) $u(x_0, y_0) = \sqrt{2}e^{\pi}$ (b) $u(x_0, y_0) = e^{\pi}$

(c) $u(x_0, y_0) = -1$ (d) $u(x_0, y_0) = -e^{\pi}$

[Feb. 2025]

23. Suppose $u = u(x,y)$ is the solution of the boundary value problem

$\frac{\partial^2 u}{\partial x^2} + \frac{\partial^2 u}{\partial y^2} + \frac{\partial u}{\partial x} = 0$ in $\{(x,y) \in \mathbb{R}^2: x^2 + y^2 < 1\}$

$u(x,y) = 1 + 2x^2y^2$ on $\{(x,y) \in \mathbb{R}^2: x^2 + y^2 = 1\}$

Then which of the following statements are true?

(a) The minimum value of u is 1

(b) The maximum value of u is 3

(c) The minimum value of u is 2

(d) The maximum value of u is $\frac{3}{2}$

[June 2025]

24. Let $u(x,t)$ be the solution of the initial-boundary value problem

$$u_{tt} - u_{xx} + u_t = 0, 0 < x < \pi, t > 0,$$
$$u(0,t) = 0, u(\pi,t) = 0, t > 0,$$
$$u(x,0) = \sin x, u_t(x,0) = 0, 0 < x < \pi.$$

For $t \geq 0$, define

$$E(t) = \int_0^{\pi} (u_t^2 + u_x^2)\,dx.$$

Then which of the following statements are true?

(a) $E(t) \geq \pi$ for all $t > 0$. (b) $E(t) \leq \pi$ for all $t > 0$.

(c) $E(t) \geq \frac{\pi}{2}$ for all $t > 0$. (d) $E(t) \leq \frac{\pi}{2}$ for all $t > 0$.

[Dec 2025]

25. Consider the boundary value problem (BVP)

$u_{xx} + u_{yy} = 0$ in $\Omega = \{(x,y) \in \mathbb{R}^2: x^2 + y^2 < 1\}$,

$u(x,y) = e^{x+y}$ on $\partial\Omega = \{(x,y) \in \mathbb{R}^2: x^2 + y^2 = 1\}$.

Then which of the following statements are true?

(a) There exists a unique solution to BVP.

(b) The BVP does NOT have a solution.

(c) There exists a solution u to BVP such that $u(x,y) = \frac{1+e}{2}$ for some $(x,y) \in \Omega \cup \partial\Omega$.

(d) There exists a solution u to BVP such that $u(x,y) = \frac{1+e^3}{2}$ for some $(x,y) \in \Omega \cup \partial\Omega$.

[Dec 2025]

Answer Key				
1	2	3	4	5
c	b, d	a, b, c	a, b, c, d	a, b, c, d
6	7	8	9	10
b, c	d	c	a, c	c, d
11	12	13	14	15
a, c	a, c	a, b, c, d	b, c	a, c
16	17	18	19	20
A	a, d	b, c	b, c, d	b, d
21	22	23	24	25
a,b,c	b,c	a, d	b,d	a,c

EXPLANATION

1. **Explanation (c)**

Consider the given PDE

$$u_{xx} + y_{yy} + \lambda u = 0 \quad 0 < x, y < 1$$
$$u(x,0) = u(x,1) = 0 \quad 0 \leq x \leq 1 \quad \text{........ (1)}$$
$$u(0,y) = u(1,y) = 0 \quad 0 \leq y \leq 1$$

To solve this, By separation of variable method

$u(x,y) = X(x)Y(y)$

Equation (1) become

$X''Y + Y''X = -XY\lambda$

$$\frac{X''Y + Y''X}{XY} = -\lambda$$

$$\frac{X''}{X}+\frac{Y''}{Y}=-\lambda$$

X and Y are function of x and y

$\therefore$ *if* $\frac{X''}{X}+\frac{Y''}{Y}=$ *constant*

Then $\frac{X''}{X}$ and $\frac{Y''}{Y}$ both are constant

Consider $\frac{X''}{X}=\lambda_1$ and $\frac{Y''}{Y}=\lambda_2$

$\Rightarrow X''-\lambda_1 X=0$ and $Y''-\lambda_2 Y=0$

Now

$u(x,y)=X(x)Y(y)$

$u(x,0)=X(x)Y(0)=0,\qquad u(0,y)=X(0)Y(0)=0$

$\Rightarrow Y(0)=0\qquad$ and $\qquad X(0)=0$

$u(x,1)=X(x)Y(1)=0\qquad u(1,Y)=X(1)Y(y)=0$

$=y(1)=0$ and $\qquad X(1)=0$

$\Rightarrow X(0)=X(1)=0$ and $Y(0)=Y(1)=0$

This is strum Liouville Boundary value problem

Consider

$X''-X\lambda=0$

Here consider three cases

Case 1: $\lambda=0$

$X''=0$

$X=A+B$

$X=Ax+B$

$X(0)=B=0$

$X(1)=A+B$

$A=0$

$\Rightarrow X(x)=0$

We get trivial solution

Now case 2:

If $\lambda>0$

$\Rightarrow \lambda=\mu^2$

$X''+\mu^2X=0$

$m^2=\pm\mu i$

Complementary function is

$X(x)=c_1\cos\mu x+c_2\sin\mu x$

$X(0)=X(1)=0$

$\Rightarrow c_1=0$

$X(1)=c_2\sin\mu=0$

$\Rightarrow c_2\neq 0,\ \sin\mu=0$

$\sin\mu=\sin n\pi$

$\mu=n\pi$

$\lambda=\mu^2=n^2\pi^2, n\in\mathbb{N}$

$X=c_n\sin n\pi x$

Similarly for y

$Y=c_n\sin m\pi y,\quad m\in\mathbb{N}$

$\Rightarrow u(x,y)=X(x)Y(y)$

$=\sin n\pi x\sin m\pi y\quad \forall\, m,n\in\mathbb{N}$

c_1 is any arbitrary constant

$\Rightarrow$ Here we get infinit solution for $\lambda=n^2\pi^2$

$\Rightarrow$ Option (c) and (d) is correct answer and a) and b) are incorrect.

2. Explanation (b), (d)

Consider the given wave equation

$\frac{\partial^2 y}{\partial t^2}=\frac{\partial^2 y}{\partial x^2}\qquad 0<x<\infty, t>0$

$u(x,0)=\cos\left(\frac{\pi x}{2}\right)\qquad 0\le x\le\infty$

$\frac{\partial u}{\partial t}(x,0)=0,\le x\le\infty$

$\frac{\partial u}{\partial x}(0,t)=0, t\ge 0$

By D' $Alembert's$ $principal$

Solution of wave equation is

$u(x,t)=\frac{1}{2}[f(x+(t)+f(x-t)]+\frac{1}{2c}\int_{x-t}^{x+t}g(s)ds$

Here, $\ c=1$

$u(x,0)=f(x)=\cos\frac{\pi x}{2}$

$\frac{\partial u}{\partial x}(0,t)=g(s)=0$

$u(x,t)=\frac{1}{2}[f(x+t)+f(x-t)]+\frac{1}{2}.0$

$u(x,t)=\frac{1}{2}[f(x+t)+f(x-t)]$

$u(2,2)=\frac{1}{2}(f(4)+f(0))$

$u(2,2)=\frac{1}{2}(1+1)=1$

$u\left[\frac{1}{2},\frac{1}{2}\right]=\frac{1}{2}(0+1)=\frac{1}{2}$

From above

Option (b) and (d) correct answer and option a) and c) are incorrect.

3. Explanation (a), (b), (c)

Consider the given heat equation

$u_t-u_{xx}=0$

$\therefore 0<x<\pi$ and $t>0$

$u(0,t)=u(\pi,t)=0: t>0$

$u(x,0)=\sin x+\sin 2x: 0\le x<\pi$

Solution of heat equation is

$u(x,t)=\sum_{n=1}^{\infty}B_n\sin\frac{n\pi x}{\pi}e^{-c\left(\frac{n^2\pi^2}{\pi^2}\right)t}$

Where $B_n=\frac{2}{\pi}\int_0^{\pi}\sin\frac{n\pi x}{\pi}f(x)$

Here $c=1$, $f(x)=\sin x+\sin 2x$

$u(x,t)=\ \sum_{n=1}^{\infty}B_n\sin nx\, e^{-n^2t}$

$u(x,t)=\ \sum_{n=1}^{\infty}B_n\sin nx\, e^{-n^2t}$

$B_n=\frac{2}{\pi}\int_0^{\pi}\sin\frac{n\pi x}{\pi}f(x)$

$=\frac{2}{\pi}\int_0^{\pi}\sin n\,x\,(\sin x+\sin 2x)$

$=\frac{2}{\pi}\int_0^{\pi}\sin nx\sin x+\frac{2}{\pi}\int_0^{\pi}\sin n\,x\sin 2\,x$

Put $n=1$

$$\Rightarrow B_1=\frac{2}{\pi}\int_0^{\pi}\sin x.\sin x.dx$$

$$+\frac{2}{\pi}\int_0^{\pi}\sin 2x.\sin x.dx$$

$$\Rightarrow B_1=\frac{2}{\pi}.\frac{\pi}{2}+0$$

$\Rightarrow B_1=1$

Put $n=2$

$$\Rightarrow B_2=\frac{2}{\pi}\int_0^{\pi}\sin x.\sin 2\,x.dx$$

$$+\frac{2}{\pi}\int_0^{\pi}\sin 2x.\sin 2x.dx$$

$\Rightarrow B_2 = 0 + \frac{2}{\pi}.\frac{\pi}{2}$

$\Rightarrow B_2 = 1$

$\Rightarrow B_1 = 1$ and $B_2 = 1$ and $B_n = 0 \; \forall \; \mathbb{N} - \{1,2\}$

$\because \int_0^{\pi} \sin mx \sin nx = \begin{cases} \frac{\pi}{2} & if\ m = n \\ 0 & if\ m \neq n \end{cases}$

$\Rightarrow u(x,t) = e^{-t}\sin x + e^{-4t}\sin 2x$

Now check the option

For option (a)

$\lim_{t\to\infty} u(x,t) = \lim_{t\to\infty} |\sin x|e^{-t} + |\sin x|e^{-4t}$

$\Rightarrow$ option (a) is correct.

For option (b)

$\lim_{t\to\infty} t^2u(x,t) = \lim_{t\to\infty} t^2e^{-t}\sin x + t^2e^{-4t}\sin x$

$= 0$

Option b is also correct.

For option c)

$e^2u(x,t) = e^2(e^{-t}\sin x + e^{-4t}\sin 2x)$

$\Rightarrow e^2u(x,t)$ is bounded.

Option c) also correct.

For option d)

$\Rightarrow \lim_{t\to\infty} e^{2t}u(x,t) = \lim_{t\to\infty} e^{2t}(e^{-t}\sin x + e^{-4t}\sin 2x) =$

∞

$\Rightarrow$ option d) is incorrect.

$\Rightarrow$ option a),b) and c) are correct answer and option d)is incorrect.

4. Explanation (a), (b), (c), (d)

Consider the given Laplace equation in polar form

$u(r,\theta) = R(r)H(\theta)$

$\frac{\partial^2 u}{dr^2} = R''(r)H(\theta)$

$\frac{\partial^2 u}{\partial\theta^2} = H''(\theta)R(r)$

$R''(r)H(\theta) + \frac{1}{R(r)}R'(r)H(\theta) + \frac{1}{R^2(r)}H''(\theta)R(r) = 0$

$\Rightarrow \frac{-H''(\theta)}{H(\theta)} = \sigma$

$H''(\theta) + \sigma H(\theta) = 0$

If $\sigma < 0$ then $\sigma = -\mu^2$

$H''(\theta) - \mu^2 H(\theta) = 0$

$H(\theta) = c_1e^{\mu\theta} + c_2e^{-\mu\theta}$

$\Rightarrow R^2(r)R''(r) + R(r)R'(r) = \sigma R(r)$

To solve this,

Put $\log r = z \Rightarrow r = e^z$

We get,

$\Rightarrow R(r) = c_3\cos(\mu\log r) + c_4(\sin(\mu\log r)$

$u(r,\theta) = (c_1e^{\mu\theta} + c_2e^{-\mu\theta})(c_3\cos(\mu\log r) + c_4\sin(\mu\log r))$

$u(a,\theta) = f(\theta) \Rightarrow f(\theta) = (c_1e^{\mu\theta} + c_2e^{-\mu\theta})(c_3\cos(\mu\log a) + c_4\sin(\mu\log a))$

$\Rightarrow u(r,\theta) \equiv 0$

$\frac{R''(r)R^2(r)+r(r)R\prime(r)}{R(r)} = \frac{-H\prime\prime(\theta)}{H(\theta)} = 0$

$H''(\theta) = 0$

$\Rightarrow H(\theta) = c_1 + c_2\theta$

$R''(r)R^2(r) + r(r)R'(r) = 0$

$u(r\theta) = (c_1 + c_2\theta) + (c_3 + c_4 r)$

$u(r\theta)$ is bounded and periodic

$c_4 = 0$ and $c_2 = 0$

$\therefore u(r,\theta) = A$

$u(r,\theta) = A \; (\because c_1c_3 = A)$

Similarly, $u(r,\theta) = Ar^u\cos u\,\theta + Br^{\mu}\sin\mu$

μ should be an integer periodic with period 2π

Option (1), (2), (3) and (4) are correct answer.

5. Explanation (a), (b), (c), (d)

Consider the given heat equation

$\frac{\partial u}{\partial t} = \frac{\partial^2 u}{\partial x_1{}^2} + \frac{\partial^2 u}{\partial x_2^2} + \frac{\partial^2 u}{\partial x_3^2}$ ...(1)

And solution of this equation is

$e^{i(\bar{k}\vec{x}+wt)}$

Here $\bar{x} = (x_1, x_2, x_3)$

$\bar{k} = (k_1, k_2, k_3)$

$e^{i(\bar{x}.\bar{k}+wt)} = e^{i(k_1x_1+k_2x_2+k_3x_3)+wt}$

It is the solution of equation (1),

so it satisfied the equation (1)

$iwe^{i(k_1x_1+k_2x_2+k_3x_3)+wt} = -(k_1^2 + k_2^2 + k_3^2) \times e^{i(wt+k_1x_1+k_2x_2+k_3x_3)}$

$iw + k_1^2 + k_2^2 + k_3^2 = 0$

$\Rightarrow w = k_1 = k_2 + k_3 = 0$

$\Rightarrow e^{io} = 1$ which is constant in x-y plane

$\Rightarrow$Option (a) is correct

Also $e^{i(\bar{k}.\bar{x}+wt)}$ is periodic function in t.

$\Rightarrow$ Option (2) is also correct.

Now $\frac{\partial^2 u}{\partial x^2} = -(k_1^2 + k_2^2 + k_3^2)\,e^{i(\bar{k}.\bar{x}+wt)}$

Which is negative

$\Rightarrow$amplitude decaying exponentially with time t $\Rightarrow$ option (c) is also correct

Now put $t = \propto$ constant

$e^{i(\bar{k}.\vec{x}+wt)} = e^{i(\bar{x}.\bar{k}+wt)} = \cos(\overrightarrow{k}.\vec{x} + w\alpha) + i\sin(\bar{k}.\vec{x} + w\alpha)$ which is bounded uniformly $\forall \; \bar{x} \in R^3$

Option (d) is correct answer and option a),b) and c) are incorrect.

6. Explanation (b), (c)

Consider the given initial value Problem for PDE

$\frac{\partial u}{\partial t} + \frac{\partial^2 u}{\partial x^2} = 0$

$u(x,0) = \sin\pi x$

$u(x,t) = \emptyset(t)\sin(\pi x)$

To solve this by separation of variable method

$\frac{\partial u}{\partial t} = -\frac{\partial^2 u}{\partial x^2}$

$u(x,t) = X(x)T(t)$

$\frac{T'(t)}{T(t)} = -\frac{X''(x)}{X(x)} = k^2 \quad (say)$

$\frac{T'(t)}{T(t)} = k^2$

$\log(T) = k^2t + c_1$

$T(t) = e^{k^2t}c_2$

And

$-X''(x) - X(x)k^2 = 0$

$\Rightarrow X''(x) + X(x)k^2 = 0$

Complementary function is

$X(x) = c_3 \cos kx + c_4 \sin kx$

$u(x,t) = (c_3 \cos kx + c_2 \sin kx)\, e^{k^2 t} c_2$

$u(x,t) = Ae^{k^2 t} \cos kx + Be^{k^2 t} \sin kx$

$u(x,0) = A \cos kx + B \sin kx$

$\sin \pi x = A \cos kx + B \sin kx$

$\Rightarrow A = 0, B = 1$

$k = \pi$

$u(x,t) = e^{\pi^2 t} \sin \pi x$

$\emptyset(t) = e^{\pi^2 t}$, which is always positive and increasing

Hence, option (b) and (c) are correct answer and option (a) and (b) are incorrect.

7. **Explanation (d)**

Consider the given heat equation $\frac{\partial^2 u}{dx^2} = \frac{du}{dt}$

$u(x,t)$ tends to zero as $t \to \infty$ and $u(x,0) = \cos x$

Here $c = 1$

solution *is*

$\Rightarrow u(x) = e^{-\mu^2 t}(A \cos x + B \sin x$

$u(x,0) = \cos x$

$A \cos \mu x + B \sin \mu x = \cos x$

$\Rightarrow \mu = 1, B = 0, A = 1$

$e^{-t} \cos x = u(x,t)$

$u(x,t) = \sum_{n=1}^{\infty} e^{-\mu^2}(A_n \cos \mu x + B_n \sin \mu x) = \cos x$

Therefore $B_n = 0 \quad \mu = 1, A_1 = 1$

$A_2 = A_3 = A_4 = A_5 \ldots\ldots 0$

$\Rightarrow$Option (d) is correct

Now $u = \sum_{n=1}^{\infty} a_n (\cos(nx + B_n)e^{-n^2 t}$

$u = a_1 \cos(x + b_1)e^{-t} + a_2(\cos(2x + b_2)e^{-2t}$

$a_2 = a_3 = \cdots = 0$

$\Rightarrow$ option (c) is correct

$\Rightarrow$ option (c) and d) is correct and Option (a) and (b) are incorrect

8. **Explanation (c)**

Consider the given equation

$\frac{\partial^2 u}{dx^2} + \frac{\partial^2 u}{dy^2} = 0 \ldots (1)$

And $u(x,y)$ tends to zero as $y \to \infty$

$u(x,0) = \sin x$

$u(x,y) = X(x)Y(y)$

$\Rightarrow X''(x)Y(y) + Y''(y)X(x) = 0$

$\Rightarrow \frac{X''(x)}{X(x)} + \frac{Y''(y)}{Y(y)} = 0$

$-\frac{X''(x)}{X(x)} = \frac{Y''(y)}{Y(y)} = k^2$

$\Rightarrow -\frac{X''(x)}{X(x)} = k^2$

$\Rightarrow X''(x) + K^2 X(x) = 0$

$\Rightarrow X(x) = c_1 \cos kx + c_2 \sin kx \ldots. (2)$

$\frac{Y''(y)}{Y(y)} = k^2$

$Y(y) = c_3 e^{-ky} + c_4 e^{ky}$..........................(3)

From equation (2) and (3)

$u(x,y) = X(x)Y(y)$

$u(x,y) = (c_1 \cos kx + c_2 \sin kx)(c_3 e^{-ky} + c_4 e^{ky})$

as $y \to \infty\ u(x,y) \to \infty$

$\Rightarrow c_4 = 0$

$u(x,0) = \sin x$

$\Rightarrow u(x,0) = (c_1 \cos kx + c_2 \sin kx)\, c_3 = \sin x$

$\Rightarrow k = 1, c_3 c_2 = 1, c_1 = 0$

for $k = 1$

$\Rightarrow u(x,y) = c_3 c_2 \sin x e^{-y}$

$y(x,y) = A \sin x e^{-y}\ (\because c_2 c_3 = A)$

From this, option (c) is correct answer and option (a), (b) and (d) incorrect.

9. **Explanation (a), (c)**

Consider the given wave equation with boundary condition

$u_{xx} + u_{yy} = 0$ for $0 < x, y < \pi$

$u(x,0) = 0 = u(x,\pi)$ for $0 \le x \le \pi$

$u(0,y) = 0, u(\pi,y) = \sin y + \sin 2y$ for $0 \le y \le \pi$ (1)

Now substitute the solution

$u(x,y) = (c_1 e^{\mu x} + c_2 e^{-\mu x})(c_3 \cos \mu y + c_4 \sin \mu y)$ (2)

Now using the given boundary condition

$u(x,0) = (c_1 e^{\mu x} + c_2 e^{-\mu x})c_3 = 0$

$c_3 = 0$

$u(x,\pi) = 0 \Rightarrow (c_1 e^{\mu x} + c_2 e^{-\mu x})c_4 \sin \mu\pi = 0$

$\sin \mu\pi = 0 \Rightarrow \mu = n$

$u(0,y) = (c_1 + c_2)c_4 \sin ny = 0 \Rightarrow c_1 + c_2 = 0 \Rightarrow c_1 = -c_2$

Equation (2) become

$u(x,y) = (e^{\mu x} - e^{-\mu x})c_4 \sin \mu y \quad (c_1 = 1)$

General solution is

$$u(x,y) = \sum_{n=1}^{\infty} a_n(e^{\mu x} - e^{-\mu x})\sin \mu y$$

$u(\pi,y) = \sin y + \sin 2y$

$a_1(e^{\pi} - e^{-\pi}) = 1 \Rightarrow a_1 = \frac{1}{2}(\sin h\pi)^{-1}$

$a_2(e^{2\pi} - e^{-2\pi}) = 1 \Rightarrow a_2 = \frac{1}{2}(\sin h2\pi)^{-1}$

$u(x,t) = \frac{1}{2}(\sin h\pi)^{-1}(e^{x} - e^{-x}) \sin y + \frac{1}{2}(\sin h2\pi)^{-1}(e^{2x} - e^{-2x}) \sin 2y$

$u\left(1,\frac{\pi}{2}\right) = \frac{1}{2}(\sin h\,\pi)^{-1}(e - e^{-1}) = \frac{1}{2}(\sin \pi)^{-1} \sin h(1)$

$u\left(1,\frac{\pi}{4}\right) = \frac{1}{2}(\sin h\pi)\,(e - e^{-1}) \sin\frac{\pi}{4} + \frac{1}{2}(\sin h\, 2\pi)\,(e^2 - e^{-2}) \sin\frac{\pi}{2}$

$= (\sin h\pi)^{-1} \sin h(1)\frac{1}{\sqrt{2}} + (\sin h\, 2\pi)^{-1} \sin h(2)$

Option a) and c) are correct answer and b) and d) incorrect.

10. **Explanation (c), (d)**

Consider the given initial value problem

$u_{tt} - u_{xx} = 0$

$u(x,0) = f(x), x \in \mathbb{R}$

$u_t(x,0) = g(x), x \in \mathbb{R}$

Solution of wave equation is

$u(x,t) = \frac{1}{2}(f(x + ct) + f(x - ct) + \frac{1}{2c}\int_{x-t}^{x+t} g(s)ds$

$u(x,t) = \frac{1}{2}[f(x + t) + f(x - t)] + \frac{1}{2}\int_{x-t}^{x+t} g(s)ds \ldots. (1)$

$f(x) = g(x) = 0 \qquad \forall\, x \notin [0,1]$

Now check the option

For option (a)

Take $x = -1.,\quad t = 2$

$f(x+t) = f(1) \neq 0,$ if $x \notin [0,1]$

$\Rightarrow$ Option (a) is incorrect

For option (b)

Take $x = 4, t = 2$

$\Rightarrow f(x-t) = f(2) \neq 0 \quad (\because f(x) = 0 \text{ if } x \in [0,1])$

$\Rightarrow$ Option (b) is incorrect

Now option (c)

$if\ f(x+t) < 0 \Rightarrow f(x+t) = g(x+t) = 0$

$\Rightarrow u(x,t) = 0$ ......from equation (1)

$\Rightarrow$ Option (c) is correct

For option (d)

If $x - t > 1 \Rightarrow f(x-t) = g(x-t) = 0$

$\Rightarrow u(x,t) = 0$

$\Rightarrow$ Option (d) is correct

$\Rightarrow$ Option (c) and option (d) is correct answer and a) and b) are incorrect.

11. Explanation (a), (c)

Consider the given PDE

$$\frac{\partial^2 u}{\partial x^2} + \frac{\partial^2 u}{\partial y^2} = 0$$

also $u(x,y) = f(\sqrt{x^2+y^2})$, since $u(x,y)$ is a function of variables $\sqrt{x^2+y^2}$ .There is solution of Laplace equation.

To solve this,

Take, $u(x,y) = \log(\sqrt{x^2+y^2}) = f(\sqrt{x^2+y^2})$

$$\Rightarrow u(x,y) = \frac{1}{2}\log(x^2+y^2)$$

Differentiating $u(x,y)$ partially w,r. to x and y,we get

$u_{xx} = \left(\frac{y^2-x^2}{(x^2+y^2)^2}\right)$ and $u_{yy} = \left(\frac{-y^2+x^2}{(x^2+y^2)^2}\right)$

Also $u(x,y) = \frac{1}{2}\log(x^2+y^2)$ is a solution of given problem.

From above explanation

$\lim_{x^2+y^2\to 0} |u(x,y)| = \infty$ and $\lim_{x^2+y^2\to\infty} |u(x,y)| = \infty,$

$\Rightarrow$Option a) and c) are the correct answer and b) and d) are incorrect.

12. Explanation (a), (c)

Consider the given wave equation

$$\frac{\partial^2 u}{\partial t^2} - \frac{\partial^2 u}{\partial x^2} = 0, (x,t) \in \mathbb{R} \times (0,\infty)$$

$u(x,0) = f(x), x \in \mathbb{R}$

$\frac{\partial u}{\partial t}(x,0) = g(x), x \in \mathbb{R}$

Also given $f_1(x) = f_2(x)$ and $g_1(x) = g_2(x)$

if $x \in [-1,1]$ (1)

The D'Alembert solution of the given wave equation is

$$u(x,t) = \frac{1}{2}[f(x+ct) + f(x-ct)] + \frac{1}{2c}\int_{x-ct}^{x+ct} g(x)dx$$

From given wave equation,

C=1

$$u_1(x,t) = \frac{1}{2}[f_1(x+t) + f_1(x-t)] + \frac{1}{2}\int_{x-ct}^{x+ct} g(x)dx$$

$$u_2(x,t) = \frac{1}{2}[f_2(x+t) + f_2(x-t)] = +\frac{1}{2}\int_{x-ct}^{x+ct} g_2(x)dx$$

Now check the option,

For option a)

$u_1(0,1) = \frac{1}{2}\ f_1(1) + f_2(-1)]\frac{1}{2}\int_{-1}^{1} g_1(x)dx$

$\Rightarrow u_2(0,1) = \frac{1}{2}[f_2(1) + f_2(-1)] + \frac{1}{2}\int_{-1}^{1} g_2(x)dx$

$f_1 = f_2$ and $g_1 = g_2$ for $x \in [-1,1]$ (given)

From this

option (1) is correct.

For option b)

$$u_1(1,1) = \frac{1}{2}[f_1(2) + f_1(0)]\frac{1}{2}\int_0^2 g_1(x)dx$$

$$u_2(1,1) = \frac{1}{2}[f_2(2) + f_2(0)]\frac{1}{2}\int_0^2 g_2(x)dx$$

From equation (1)

$f_1(2) \neq f_2(2),$

$u_1(1,1) \neq u_2(1,1)$

Option (b) is incorrect.

For option c)

$$u_1\left(\frac{1}{2},\frac{1}{2}\right) = \frac{1}{2}[f_1(1) + f_1(0)] + \frac{1}{2}\int_0^1 g_1(x)dx$$

$\Rightarrow u_2\left(\frac{1}{2},\frac{1}{2}\right) = \frac{1}{2}[f_2(1) + f_2(0)] + \frac{1}{2}\int_0^1 g_2(x)dx$

$u_1\left(\frac{1}{2},\frac{1}{2}\right) = u_2\left(\frac{1}{2},\frac{1}{2}\right)$

Option c) is the correct.

For option d)

$$u_1(0,2) = \frac{1}{2}[f_1(2) + f_1(-2)] + \frac{1}{2}\int_{-2}^{2} g_1(x)dx$$

$$u_2(0,2) = \frac{1}{2}[f_2(2) + f_2(-2)] + \frac{1}{2}\int_{-2}^{2} g_2(x)dx$$

$f_1(2) \neq f_2(2)$ (from (1))

$u_1(0,2) \neq u_2(0,2)$

Option d) is incorrect.

Option a) and c) are correct answer and b), d) are incorrect.

13. Explanation (a), (b), (c), (d)

Consider the given heat equation with boundary condition and non-homogeneous,

$$\frac{\partial u}{\partial t} = \frac{\partial^2 u}{\partial x^2}, 0 < x < 1, t > 0$$

$u(x,0) = 1 + x + \sin(\pi x)\cos(\pi x)$

$u(0,t) = 1, u(1,t) = 2$

is of the form

$$u_{xx} = \frac{1}{k}u_t$$

$u(0,t) = c_1, u(l,t) = c_2, c_1, c_2 \neq 0, u(x,0) = f(x).$

$(non-homogeneous,)$

To solve this,

We need to reduce it homogeneous form

Now, use the transformation

$u(x,t) = v(x,t) + Ax + B$ and reduce equation to the form $v_{xx} = \frac{1}{k}v_t$

$v(0,t) = 0, v(l,t) = 0, v(x,0) = g(x)$

$f(x) = 1 + x + \sin(\pi x)\cos(\pi x)$

$c_1 = 1, c_2 = 2, k = 1, v_{xx} = v_t,$

$v(0,t) = 0, v(1,t) = 0, v(x,0) = g(x), l = 1$

$u(x,t) = v(x,t) + Ax + B$

$\Rightarrow u(0,t) = v(0,t) + B$

$\Rightarrow 1 = 0 + B \Rightarrow B = 1$

Similarly,

$u(1,t) = v(1,t) + Ax + B$

$\Rightarrow 2 = 0 + A + B \Rightarrow A = 1$

$u(x,0) = v(x,0) + Ax + B$

$1 + x + \frac{1}{2}\sin(2\pi x) = v(x,0) + x + 1$

$g(x) + x + 1 \Rightarrow g(x) = \frac{1}{2}\sin(2\pi x)$

$v(x,0) = g(x) = \frac{1}{2}\sin(2\pi x)$

Given equation reduce to

$v_{xx} = v_t,$

$v(0,t) = 0, v(1,t) = 0, (l = 1, k = 1)$

$v(x,0) = g(x) = \frac{1}{2}\sin(2\pi x)$

$v(x,t) = \sum_{n=1}^{\infty} D_n \sin\left(\frac{n\pi x}{l}\right) e^{\frac{-kn^2\pi^2 t}{l^2}}$

$v(x,t) = \sum_{n=1}^{\infty} D_n \sin(n\pi x)\, e^{-n^2\pi^2 t}$

$D_n = \frac{2}{1}\int_0^1 \sin(n\pi x)\frac{1}{2}\sin(2\pi x)dx$

$= \int_0^1 \sin(n\pi x)\sin(2\pi x)dx$

$= \begin{cases} \frac{1}{2}, if\ n = 2 \\ 0, otherwise \end{cases}$

$D_1 = D_3 = D_4 = \cdots 0$ and $D_2 = \frac{1}{2}$

Solution $v(x,t) = \frac{1}{2}\sin(2\pi x)e^{-4\pi^2 t}$

$\Rightarrow u(x,t) = v(x,t) + x + 1$

$\Rightarrow u(x,t) = 1 + x + \frac{1}{2}\sin(2\pi x)e^{-4\pi^2 t}$

Now check the option

For option a)

$u\left(\frac{1}{2},\frac{1}{4}\right) = 1 + \frac{1}{2} + 0 = \frac{3}{2},$

$\Rightarrow$*Option* (a) is correct.

For option b)

$u\left(\frac{1}{2},\frac{1}{2}\right) = \frac{3}{2},$

$\Rightarrow$*Option* (b) is correct.

For option c)

$u\left(\frac{1}{4},\frac{3}{4}\right) = \frac{5}{4} + \frac{1}{2}e^{-3\pi^2}$

$\Rightarrow$Option (3) is correct.

For option d)

$u\left(\frac{1}{4},1\right) = \frac{5}{4} + \frac{1}{2}e^{-4\pi^2}$

$\Rightarrow$ *option* (4) is correct.

$\Rightarrow$ All options are correct answer.

14. Explanation (b), (c)

$$\left.\begin{aligned} \frac{\partial^2 u}{\partial t^2} = \frac{\partial^2 u}{\partial x^2}, \quad (x,t) \in \mathbb{R}\times(0,\infty) \\ u(x,0) = f(x), \quad x \in \mathbb{R} \\ u_t(x,0) = g(x), \quad x \in \mathbb{R} \end{aligned}\right\} --(1)$$

The D'Alembert solution of the given wave equation (1) is

$$u(x,t) = [f(x+ct) + f(x-ct)] + \frac{1}{2c}\int_{x-ct}^{x+ct} g(y)dy..(2)$$

Here $c = 1$

So, $u(x,t) = [f(x+t) + f(f(x-t))] + \frac{1}{2}\int_{x-t}^{x+t} g(y)dy$

(a): It is given that $u(x,t) = 0$; For all $x \le 0$ and $t > 0$

But if we take $x = 0$ and $t = 1$

Then $x + t = 1$ and $x - t = -1$

$\Rightarrow u(0,1) = [f(1) + f(-1)] + \frac{1}{2}\int_{-1}^{1} g(y)dy$

$0 < f(x) \le 1$ for $x > 0$

And $f(-1) = 0$ since $x > 0$

And $g(x) > 0$ for $x > 0$

So, $u(0,1) \ne 0$

So option (a) incorrect.

(b):

Since $0 \le f(x) \le 1$ for all x

And $g(x) = 0$ for $x \le 0$, $\int_0^{\infty} g(x)dx < \infty$

So, $u(x,t)$ is bounded on $\mathbb{R}\times(0,\infty)$;

i.e option (b) correct

(c): When $x + t < 0$

$\Rightarrow x < 0$

$\Rightarrow x - t < 0$

$\Rightarrow f(x+t) = 0$ and $f(x-t) = 0$

Moreover $\int_{x-t}^{x+t} g(y)dy = 0$

$\Rightarrow u(x,t) = 0$

So option (c) correct.

(d): If $x + t > 0$

$\Rightarrow x \ge 0$

$\Rightarrow x + t > 0$ and $x - t \ge 0$

$\Rightarrow f(x+t) > 0$ and $f(x-t) \ge 0$ depending x and t

$\Rightarrow \int_{x-t}^{x+t} g(y)dy > 0$

$\Rightarrow u(x,t) \ne 0$; so option (d) correct.

Hence, option (b) and (c) are correct.

15. Explanation (a), c)

$\frac{\partial^2 u}{\partial x^2} + \frac{\partial^2 u}{\partial y^2} = 0$

Let $u(x,y) = F(x), F(y) = FY(say)$

$\Rightarrow Y\frac{\partial^2 F}{\partial x^2} + F\frac{\partial^2 Y}{\partial y^2} = 0$

$\Rightarrow \frac{1}{F}\frac{d^2 F}{dx^2} = \frac{1}{y}\frac{\partial^2 Y}{\partial y^2} = \lambda$

$\frac{d^2 F}{dx^2} - \lambda F = 0$ and $\frac{\partial^2 Y}{\partial y^2} + \lambda Y = 0$

Case 1: If $\lambda = 0$ then $\frac{d^2 F}{dx^2} = 0$ and $\frac{\partial^2 Y}{\partial y^2} = 0$

$F = Ax + B$ *and* $Y = Cy + D$

$u(x,y) = FY = (Ax+B)(Cy+D)$

$u(0,y) = B(Cy+D) = 0 \to B = 0$

$u(\pi,y) = (A\pi + B)(Cy+D) = 0\backslash$

$\Rightarrow A\pi + B = 0 \Rightarrow a\pi = 0 \Rightarrow A = 0$

Therefore $u(x,y) = 0$ inadmissible.

Case 2: $\lambda > 0, let\ \lambda = k.^2 \frac{d^2F}{dx^2} - k^2F = 0$

Therefore $F_K = A_K \cos h\, kx + B_K \sin h\, kx$

$\frac{d^2dy}{dy^2} + k^2y_=0 \to Y = C_K \cos ky + D_K \sin ky$

Therefore $u(x,y) = FY = (A_k \cos h\, kx + B_K \sin h\, kx)(C_K \cos ky + D_k \sin ky)$

$u(0,y) = A_K(C_K \cos ky + D_K \sin ky) = 0 \to A_K = 0$

$u(\pi,y)B_K \sin h\, kx)(C_K \cos ky + D_k \sin ky) = 0$

$B_K \sin h\, k\pi = 0 \to B_K\left(\frac{e^{k\pi} - e^{-k\pi}}{2}\right) = 0$

$\to B_K = 0$

Therefore $u(x,y) = 0$ inadmissible

Case 3:

$\lambda < 0. Let\ \lambda = -k^2$

$\frac{d^2F}{dx^2} + k^2F = 0 \to F = A_K \cos kx + B_K \sin kx$

$\frac{d^2Y}{dy^2} - k^2Y = 0 \to Y = C_K \cosh ky + D_K \sin h\, ky$

Therefore $u(x,y) = (A_K \cos kx + B_K \sin kx)(\, C_K \cosh ky + D_K \sin h\, ky)$

$u(0,y) = A_K(C_K \cosh ky + D_K \sin h\, ky) \Rightarrow A_K = 0$

$u(\pi,y) = B_K \sin k\pi(\,(C_K \cosh ky + D_K \sin h\, ky) = 0 \to$

$B_K \sin k\pi(= 0 \to \sin k\pi = 0$

$\Rightarrow \sin k\pi = \sin n\pi \Rightarrow k\pi = n\pi \Rightarrow k = n$

$\therefore u(x,y) = B_K \sin nx\, (C_K \cosh ny + D_K \sin h\, ny)$

$u(x,y) = B_K \sin nx\, .\, c_K = 0 \to c_K = 0$

Therefore $u(x,y)B_K \sin nx\; D_k \sin h\, ny$

$= B_K D_K \sin nx \sin h\, ny$

Therefore the general solution is

$u(x,y) = \sum_{n=1}^{\infty} a_n \sin nx \sin h\, ny$

$u(x,\pi) = \sum_{n=1}^{\infty} a_n \sin nx \sin h\, n\pi = \sin 2x$

Comparing $a_1 \sin h\, \pi = 0 \Rightarrow a_1 = 0$

$a_2 \sin 2\pi = 1 \Rightarrow a_2 = \frac{1}{\sin h2\pi}$

$a_3 \sin h\, 3\pi = 0 \Rightarrow a_3 = 0$

i.e. $a_1 = a_3 = a_4 = \cdots 0$

therefore $u(x,y) = a_2\, shin\, h2y. \sin 2x$

$= \frac{1}{\sin h\, 2\pi} \sin h\, 2y. \sin 2x$

1. $0 \le x \le \pi \Rightarrow 0 \le x2 \le 2\pi$
   $-1 \le \sin 2x \le 1$
   $0 \le y \le \pi \Rightarrow 0 \le 2y \le 2\pi$
   $0 \le \sin h\, 2y \le \sin h\, 2\pi,\ since\ \sin hx$ is increasing function
   $0 \le \frac{\sin h\, 2y}{\sin h\, 2\pi} \le 1$
   therefore, $-1 \le \frac{\sin h\, 2y}{\sin h\, 2\pi}. \sin 2x \le 1$
   Max $\{\frac{\sin h\, 2y}{\sin h\, 2\pi}. \sin 2x : 0 \le x,y \le \pi\} = 1$
   So option (1) is correct.
2. For, $0 < x_0 < \pi \to 0 < x_0 < \pi - 1 \le \sin 2x_0 \le 1$
   $0 < y_0 < \pi \Rightarrow 0 < 2y_0 < 2\pi$
   $0 < \sin h\, 2y_0 < \sin h\ 2\pi$, since $\sin h\, x$ isn an increasing function
   $0 < \frac{\sin h2y_0}{\sin h\, 2\pi} < 1$
   Therefore $-1 < \frac{\sin h2y_0}{\sin h\, 2\pi}. \sin 2x_0 < 1$
   So $u(x_0,y_0)$ does not have value 1 for some $(x_0,y_0) \in (0,\pi)\times(0,\pi)$ so, option (b) is incorrect
3. Clearly for above (by case (2) $u(x,y) > -1$ for all $(x,y) \in (0,\pi)\times(0,\pi)$ so option (c) is correct
4. By case (1), min $\{u(x,y): 0 \le x,y \le \pi\} = -1$ so, option (d) is incorrect
   options are (a) and (c) are correct answer.

16. Explanation (a)

$\frac{\partial^2 t}{\partial t^2} - \frac{\partial^2 y}{\partial x^2} = xt, \qquad -\infty < x < \infty, t > 0$

$u(x,0) = \frac{\partial u}{\partial t}(x,0) = 0, \qquad -\infty < x < \infty$

$u(2,3) = ?$

Duhamel's Principle for solving non-homo partial differential equation

$\frac{\partial^2 u}{\partial x^2} - \frac{\partial^2 u}{\partial y^2} = f(x,t)$

$u(x,0) = u_t(x,0)$

$v(x,t,s)$

$\frac{\partial^2 v}{\partial x^2} - \frac{\partial^2 v}{\partial y^2} = 0$

$v(x,0,s) = 0, -\infty < x < \infty$

$v_t(x,0,s) = f(x,s), -\infty < x < \infty$

$u(x,t) = \int_0^t v\,(x, t-s, s)ds$

$v_{xx} = v_{yy},\quad v(x,0,s) = 0$

$v_t(x,0,s) = f(x,s)$

$v(x,t) = \frac{1}{2}[g(x+ct) + g(x-ct)]$

$+\frac{1}{2c}\int_{x-ct}^{x+ct} f\,(x,s)dx$

$= \frac{1}{2}\int_{x-t}^{x+t} xs\, dx\ (as\ c = 1, g\,(x) = 0)$

$= x + s$

$u(x,t) = \int_0^t v\,(x, t-s, s)ds$

$u(x,0) = \frac{\partial u}{\partial t}(x,0) = 0, \qquad -\infty < x < \infty$

$u(2,3) = 9$

17. Explanation (a), (d)

$\Delta U + \lambda U = 0$

$\frac{\partial U}{\partial n} = 0$

The above problem is Neumann –Dirichlet problem in interior circle. And the solution exists for $\lambda \ge 0$

as $\lambda < 0\,; u = ce^{-\lambda n}$ form

then $\frac{\partial U}{\partial n} \nrightarrow 0$

so, option (b) is incorrect.

Now if $\lambda = 0$ then

$\Delta U = 0 \Rightarrow u =$ Constant.

So, option (c) incorrect and (d) correct.

18. Explanation (b), (c)

$\frac{\partial^2 u}{\partial x \partial y} = 0 \Rightarrow \frac{\partial}{\partial x}\left(\frac{\partial u}{\partial y}\right) = 0$

$\Rightarrow \frac{\partial}{\partial x}(g(x)) = 0$

Integrating both sides, we get

$\Rightarrow g(x)$ =Costant.

And every constant function is even

So option (a) wrong and option (b) correct.

(d) If solution exist then $u(x,y) = 2\int_{\sqrt{y}}^{x^2} zg(z)\,dz$

Satisfy $u(x,x^2) = 0$ and

$\frac{\partial u}{\partial y}(x,x^2) = g(x)$

But $u(x,x^2) = 2\int_x^{x^2} zg(z)\,dz$

$= 2.c\frac{z^2}{2}\Big|_x^{x^2}$ ($\because g(z)$ =Constant function)

$= c(x^4 - x^2) \neq 0$

So option (d) not correct.

Now for option (c),

$u(x,y) = 2\int_x^{\sqrt{2}} zg(z)\,dz$ ______ (*)

$\Rightarrow u(x,x^2) = 2\int_x^x zg(z)\,dz = 0$

So first condition $u(x,x^2) = 0$ satisfied

Now differentiating (*) w.r.t y and using Leibnitz rule, we get

$u_y(x,y) = 2.\frac{1}{2\sqrt{y}}\sqrt{y}g(\sqrt{y}) - 0 + 0$

$= g(\sqrt{y})$

$\Rightarrow u_y(x,x^2) = g\left(\sqrt{x^2}\right) = g(x)$

Since option (c) solution satisfy the given equation as well as the initial conditions, we concluded that option (c) correct.

19. Explanation (b), (c), (d)

$u_{xx} + u_{yy} = 0$ ------ (i)

$D\{(x,y): x^2 + y^2 < 1\}$

(a) $u(x,y) = x^5 + 2x^2y^3 - y^5$

$u_x(x,y) = 5x^4 + 4xy^3$

$u_{xx}(x,y) = 20x^3 + 4y^3$

$u_y(x,y) = 6x^2y^2 - 5y^4$

$u_{yy}(x,y) = 12x^2y - 20y^3$

$\therefore u_{xx}(x,y) + u_{yy}(x,y) = 20x^3 + 4y^3 + 12x^2y - 20y^3 \neq 0$

So option (a) not satisfy $u_{xx} + u_{yy} = 0$

Hence option (a) not a solution of (i)

(b) $u(x,y) = x^2 + 2xy - y^2$

$u_x(x,y) = 2x + 2y$

$u_{xx}(x,y) = 2$

$u_y(x,y) = 2x - 2y$

$u_{yy}(x,y) = -2$

$\therefore u_{xx}(x,y) + u_{yy}(x,y) = 2 - 2 = 0$

i.e option (b) is satisfy equation (i)

(c) $u(x,y) = \cos(y)\,e^x + \sin(x)\,e^y$

$u_x(x,y) = e^x\cos(y) + \cos(x)\,e^y$

$u_{xx}(x,y) = e^x\cos(y) - \sin(x)\,e^y$

$u_y(x,y) = -\sin(y)\,e^x + \sin(x)\,e^y$

$u_{yy}(x,y) = -\cos(y)\,e^x + e^y\sin(x)$

$\therefore u_{xx}(x,y) + u_{yy}(x,y) = e^x\cos(y) - \sin(x)\,e^y - \cos(y)\,e^x + \sin(x)\,e^y$

$= 0$

So option (c) satisfy (i) i.e. option (c) is a solution.

(d) $u(x,y) = \frac{1+x}{1+2x+x^2+y^2}$

$u_x(x,y) = \frac{(1+2x+x^2+y^2) - (1+x)(2+2x)}{(1+2x+x^2+y^2)^2}$

$= \frac{1+2x+x^2+y^2-2-2x-2x-2x^2}{(1+2x+x^2+y^2)^2}$

$= \frac{-1-2x-x^2+y^2}{(1+2x+x^2+y^2)^2}$

$u_{xx}(x,y)$

$= \frac{(-2-2x)(1+2x+x^2+y^2)^2 - (-1-2x-x^2+y^2)2(1+2x+x^2+y^2)(2+2x)}{(1+2x+x^2+y^2)^4}$

$= \frac{(-2-2x)(1+2x+x^2+y^2) - (2+2x)(-1-2x-x^2+y^2)}{(1+2x+x^2+y^2)^3}$

$u_y(x,y) = \frac{(1+x).(-1).2y}{(1+2x+x^2+y^2)^2}$

$u_{yy}(x,y)$

$= \frac{-2(1+x)(1+2x+x^2+y^2)^2 + 2y(1+x).2y\,2(1+2x+x^2+y^2)}{(1+2x+x^2+y^2)^4}$

$= \frac{-2(1+x)(1+2x+x^2+y^2) + 4y^2(1+x).2}{(1+2x+x^2+y^2)^3}$

$\therefore u_{xx}(x,y) + u_{yy}(x,y) = 0$

So option (d) also satisfy equation (i) Hence option (d) is a solution.

So options (b), (c) and (d) are correct.

20. Explanation: (b), (d) Given PDE is

$x^2\frac{\partial^2 u}{\partial x\partial y} + 3y^2u = 0$------(1)

By definition of linear PDE

Option a) is incorrect.

Let $u(x,y) = X(x)Y(y)$

$\frac{\partial^2 u}{\partial x\partial y} = X'(x)Y'(y)$

Equation (1) become

$x^2X'Y' = -3y^2XY = 0$

$x^2\frac{X'}{X} = -3y^2XY = c$ (say)

$x^2\frac{X'}{X} = -\frac{3y^2}{Y'}Y = c$

$\frac{x^2}{X}\frac{dX}{dx} = c$

$\frac{dX}{X} = \frac{k}{x^2}dx$

$\log X = -\frac{k}{x} + \log c$

$X = ce^{-\frac{k}{x}}$

$xe^{\frac{k}{x}} = c$

And

$-\frac{3y^2Y}{Y'} = c$

$\frac{Y'}{Y} = \frac{-3y^2}{c}dy$

$\log Y = \frac{-y^3}{c} + \log c_1$

$Y = c_1 e^{-\frac{y^3}{c}}$

$u(X,Y) = X(X)Y(Y)$

$= ce^{-\frac{c}{x}}c_1 e^{-\frac{y^3}{c}}$

$= cc_1 e^{-\frac{c}{x}}e^{-\frac{y^3}{c}}$

$u(X,Y) = Ae^{-\frac{c}{x}}e^{-\frac{y^3}{c}}$

$(\because A = cc_1)$ ------(2)

$u(x,0) = e^{\frac{1}{x}}$ (given)

$u(x,0) = Ae^{-\frac{c}{x}} = e^{\frac{1}{x}}$

$Ae^{-\frac{c}{x}} = e^{\frac{1}{x}}$

$c = -1,\ A = 1,\ \Rightarrow c = c_1 = -1$

Equation (2) become

$u(X,Y) = e^{\frac{1}{x}}e^{y^3}$

$u(X,Y) = e^{\frac{1}{x}+y^3}$

$u(1,1) = e^2$

Option (b) and (d) are correct answer. Given PDE is

$x^2\frac{\partial^2 u}{\partial x\partial y} + 3y^2u = 0$------(1)

By definition of linear PDE

Option a) is incorrect.

Let $u(x,y) = X(x)Y(y)$

$\frac{\partial^2 u}{\partial x\partial y} = X'(x)Y'(y)$

Equation (1) become

$x^2X'Y' = -3y^2XY = 0$

$x^2\frac{X'}{X} = -3y^2XY = c$ (say)

$x^2\frac{X'}{X} = -\frac{3y^2}{Y'}Y = c$

$\frac{x^2}{X}\frac{dX}{dx} = c$

$\frac{dX}{X} = \frac{k}{x^2}dx$

$\log X = -\frac{k}{x} + \log c$

$X = ce^{-\frac{k}{x}}$

$xe^{\frac{k}{x}} = c$

And

$-\frac{3y^2Y}{Y'} = c$

$\frac{Y'}{Y} = \frac{-3y^2}{c}dy$

$\log Y = \frac{-y^3}{c} + \log c_1$

$Y = c_1 e^{-\frac{y^3}{c}}$

$u(X,Y) = X(X)Y(Y)$

$= ce^{-\frac{c}{x}}c_1 e^{-\frac{y^3}{c}} = cc_1 e^{-\frac{c}{x}}e^{-\frac{y^3}{c}}$

$u(X,Y) = Ae^{-\frac{c}{x}}e^{-\frac{y^3}{c}}$

$(\because A = cc_1)$ ------(2)

$u(x,0) = e^{\frac{1}{x}}$ (given)

$u(x,0) = Ae^{-\frac{c}{x}} = e^{\frac{1}{x}}$

$Ae^{-\frac{c}{x}} = e^{\frac{1}{x}}$

$c = -1,\ A = 1,\ \Rightarrow c = c_1 = -1$

Equation (2) become

$u(X,Y) = e^{\frac{1}{x}}e^{y^3}$

$u(X,Y) = e^{\frac{1}{x}+y^3}$

$u(1,1) = e^2$

So, options (b) and (d) are correct.

21. Explanation: (a), (b), (c)

We are given the heat equation (diffusion equation):

$$\frac{\partial u}{\partial t} = \frac{\partial^2 u}{\partial x^2}, (x,t) \in (0,1)\times(0,\infty)$$

with initial condition:

$$u(x,0) = 4x(1-x), x \in [0,1]$$

and boundary conditions:

$$u(0,t) = u(1,t) = 0, t \geq 0.$$

We need to analyze which of the given statements are true.

Statement (a): $\lim_{t\to\infty} u(x,t) = 0$ for all $x \in (0,1)$.

- The given problem represents heat diffusion with Dirichlet boundary conditions.
- The solution can be expressed using separation of variables as a Fourier sine series:

$$u(x,t) = \sum_{n=1}^{\infty} b_n e^{-\lambda_n t}\sin(n\pi x),$$

where $\lambda_n = (n\pi)^2$ are the eigenvalues.

- Since $e^{-\lambda_n t} \to 0$ as $t \to \infty$, the entire solution $u(x,t)$ decays to zero for all $x \in (0,1)$.

Statement (a) is true.

Statement (b): $u(x,t) = u(x,t)$ for all $x \in (0,1), t > 0$.

- This statement is trivial because it just states that $u(x,t)$ is equal to itself, which is always true.

Statement (b) is trivially true.

Statement (c): $\int_0^1 (u(x,t))^2 dx$ is a non-increasing function of t.

- The integral:

$$E(t) = \int_0^1 u^2(x,t)\,dx$$

represents the energy of the system.

- For the heat equation, energy always decreases over time due to the dissipative nature of heat diffusion.
- Taking the time derivative,

$$\frac{d}{dt}E(t) = 2\int_0^1 u(x,t)\frac{\partial u}{\partial t}dx.$$

Using the PDE $\frac{\partial u}{\partial t} = \frac{\partial^2 u}{\partial x^2}$ and integrating by parts (using boundary conditions), we get:

$$\frac{d}{dt}E(t) = -2\int_0^1 \left(\frac{\partial u}{\partial x}\right)^2 dx \le 0.$$

This shows that $E(t)$ is non-increasing over time.

Statement (c) is true.

Statement (d): $\int_0^1 (u(x,t))^2 dx$ is a non-decreasing function of t.

- From Statement (c), we have already shown that $E(t)$ is non-increasing.
- If a function is non-increasing, it cannot be non-decreasing at the same time.

Statement (d) is false.

Thus, options (a), (b) and (c) are correct.

22. Explanation: (b), (c)

The general solution to Laplace's equation can be found using separation of variables or by inspection if the boundary conditions suggest a simple solution.

The function $e^{\pi x}\cos(\pi y)$ and $e^{\pi x}\sin(\pi y)$ are solutions to Laplace's equation.

Verify that the solution to the boundary value problem is $u(x,y) = e^{\pi x}\cos(\pi y) - e^{\pi x}\sin(\pi y)$.

Using this form of solution $u(x,y)$, we can conclude that options (b) and (c) are correct.

23. Explanation: (a), (d) Reason: the PDE $\Delta u + u_x = 0$ is a uniformly elliptic equation with first-order term, so the (strong) maximum principle applies — nonconstant solutions cannot achieve an interior maximum or minimum. Hence the extrema of (u) on the unit disk occur on the boundary $x^2 + y^2 = 1$, where $u|_{\partial D} = 1 + 2x^2y^2$.

On the unit circle put $x = \cos\theta, y = \sin\theta$. Then

$$x^2y^2 = \cos^2\theta\sin^2\theta = \frac{1}{4}\sin^2(2\theta),$$

So $u|_{\partial D} = 1 + \frac{1}{2}\sin^2(2\theta)$.

Thus $\min_{\partial D} u = 1\ when(\sin 2\theta = 0)$ and $\max_{\partial D} u = 1 + \frac{1}{2} = \frac{3}{2}\ when(\sin 2\theta = \pm 1)$. Therefore (1) and (4) hold; (2) and (3) are false.

24. Explanation: (b), (d)

Energy functional

$$E(t) = \int_0^{\pi} (u_t^2 + u_x^2)\, dx$$

Compute the initial energy $E(0)$:

$$u(x,0) = \sin x$$
$$u_x(x,0) = \cos x$$
$$u_t(x,0) = 0$$

Therefore

$$E(0) = \int_0^{\pi} (0 + \cos^2 x)\, dx$$

Using

$$\cos^2 x = \frac{1+\cos 2x}{2}$$

$$E(0) = \int_0^{\pi} \frac{1+\cos 2x}{2}\, dx$$

$$E(0) = \frac{1}{2}\int_0^{\pi} 1\, dx + \frac{1}{2}\int_0^{\pi} \cos 2x\, dx$$

$$E(0) = \frac{\pi}{2}$$

Energy dissipation:

Multiply the PDE by u_t and integrate over $(0, \pi)$:

$$\int_0^{\pi} (u_{tt} - u_{xx} + u_t)u_t\, dx = 0$$

Compute each term:

$$\int_0^{\pi} u_{tt}\, u_t\, dx = \frac{1}{2}\frac{d}{dt}\int_0^{\pi} u_t^2\, dx$$

$$-\int_0^{\pi} u_{xx}\, u_t\, dx = \frac{1}{2}\frac{d}{dt}\int_0^{\pi} u_x^2\, dx$$

(using integration by parts and the boundary conditions)

Thus

$$\frac{d}{dt}\left[\frac{1}{2}\int_0^{\pi} (u_t^2 + u_x^2)\, dx\right] + \int_0^{\pi} u_t^2\, dx = 0$$

Hence

$$\frac{dE}{dt} = -2\int_0^{\pi} u_t^2\, dx \le 0$$

Therefore, the energy is non-increasing:

$$E(t) \le E(0) = \frac{\pi}{2}, t \ge 0$$

Check the options:

(a) $E(t) \ge \pi$— False

(b) $E(t) \le \pi$— True (since $E(t) \le \frac{\pi}{2} < \pi$)

(c) $E(t) \ge \frac{\pi}{2}$— False

(d) $E(t) \le \frac{\pi}{2}$— True

Final answer: (2) and (4)

25. Explanation: (a), (c)

We solve each statement using properties of harmonic functions.

Given the Dirichlet problem

$u_{xx} + u_{yy} = 0$ in $\Omega = (x,y): x^2 + y^2 < 1$

$u(x,y) = e^{x+y}$ on $\partial\Omega = x^2 + y^2 = 1$

This is Laplace's equation in the unit disk with continuous boundary data.

Existence and Uniqueness:

For Laplace's equation on a bounded domain with continuous boundary data, the Dirichlet problem has a unique harmonic solution (Poisson integral formula / maximum principle).

Boundary function e^{x+y} is continuous on the unit circle.

Statement 1 is TRUE

Since existence is guaranteed, Statement 2 is FALSE

For harmonic u:

$\min_{\partial\Omega} u \le u(x,y) \le \max_{\partial\Omega} u$

On the boundary $x^2 + y^2 = 1$.

We examine e^{x+y}.

The quantity $x + y$ on the unit circle satisfies

$-\sqrt{2} \le x + y \le \sqrt{2}$

Thus, $e^{-\sqrt{2}} \le u \le e^{\sqrt{2}}$

Numerically, $e^{-\sqrt{2}} \approx 0.243$, $e^{\sqrt{2}} \approx 4.11$

Now check $\frac{1+e}{2} \approx 1.859$, which lies strictly inside the interval.

Since the harmonic function is continuous and takes values between these extremes, such a value must occur somewhere in the domain.

Statement 3 is TRUE

Compute

$\frac{1+e^3}{2} \approx \frac{1+20.085}{2} \approx 10.54$

But the maximum possible value of u is $e^{\sqrt{2}} \approx 4.11$

Thus $10.54 > 4.11$

Impossible by the maximum principle.

Statement 4 is FALSE

Correct options: (1), (3)

CALCULUS OF VARIATIONS

No. of questions asked from year 2011-2025

Units		2011		2012		2013		2014		2015		2016		2017		2018		2019		2020	2022		2023		2024	2025		
		Jun	Dec	Jun	Dec	Jun	Dec	Jun	Dec	Jun	Dec	Jun	Dec	Jun	Dec	Jun	Dec	Jun	Dec	Nov	Feb	Sep	Jun	Dec	Jul	Feb	Jun	Dec
3.1	Variational Problem and Euler's Equation	2	1	2	2	3	2	2	2	2	2	1	3	2	4	3	2	2	6	6	-	3	3	2	3	3	3	2
3.2	Moving Boundaries Variational Problem	-	1	-	-	-	-	-	-	-	-	2	-	1	-	-	1	1	-	-	-	-	-	-	-	-	-	1

CHAPTER 3

CALCULUS OF VARIATIONS

Unit 3.1: Variational Problems and Euler's Equation

MCQ (Multiple Choice Questions)

1. The variational problem of extremizing the functional $I(y(x)) = \int_0^{2\pi}\left[\left(\frac{d}{dx}y\right)^2 - y^2\right]dx; y(0) = 1,\ y(2\pi) = 1$ has
(a) A unique solution
(b) Exactly two solutions
(c) An infinite number of solutions
(d) No

[June 2011]

2. Suppose any two points $P(x_0, y_0), Q(x_1, y_1)$, and a function $F(x, y, y')$ of three independent variables are given among all curves $y' = \frac{dy}{dx}$. In order to final among all curves $y = y(x)$ joining P and Q that one which furnishes for the definite integral $I(y) = \int_{x_0}^{x_1} F(x, y(x)y'(x))dx$ the smallest value, which of the following assumption suffices:
(a) Function F is the class C^1
(b) Function F is of class C^2 for all systems of value $x, y(x)$ and $y'(x)$ furnished by all of the admissible functions.
(c) Functional F is of class C^3 for all systems of values $x, y(x)$ and $y'(x)$ furnished by all of the admissible functions
(d) It is enough to treat $y(x)$ and F to be of class C^1 only with respect to their arguments.

[Dec 2011]

3. The variational problem of extremizing the functional $I(y(x)) = \int_1^3 y(3x - y)\,dx; y(3) = 4\frac{1}{2}, y(1) = 1$ has
(a) A unique solution
(b) Exactly two solutions
(c) An infinite number of solutions
(d) No solution

[June 2012]

4. Let $J(u) = \int_0^1 \left[u_x^2 + 4\frac{u^2}{x^2}\right] x dx$, where $u(x)$ is a smooth function defined on $[0,1]$ satisfyingu$(0) = 0$ and $u(1) = 1$. Which of the functions minimizes J?
(a) $u(x) = x^2$
(b) $u(x) = \frac{1}{\sqrt{2}}x^2$
(c) $u(x) = \frac{1}{2}x^2$
(d) $u(x) = \frac{1}{4}x^2$

[Dec 2012]

5. Consider the functional

$$I(y) = \int_a^b F(y, y')dx; y' \equiv \frac{dy}{dx}$$

$$y(a) = y_1, y(b) = y_2$$

Where $y \epsilon C^2[a, b], F$ has second order continuous partial derivatives with respect to y, y' and y_1, y_2 are given real numbers. Let $y = y(x)$ be extremizing function for the functional I. Then along the extremizing curve.
(a) F remains constant
(b) $\frac{\partial F}{\partial y} = 0$
(c) $F - y\frac{\partial F}{\partial y'}$ =constant
(d) $F - y'\frac{\partial F}{\partial y'}$ =constant

[June 2013]

6. Consider the functional $J(y) = \int_a^b F(x, y, y')dx$ where $F(x, y, y') = y' + y$ for admissible function y. Then J has
(a) No extremals
(b) Several extremals
(c) $y(x) = e^{-x}$ as an extremal
(d) $y(x) =$ constant as an extremal

[Dec 2013]

7. The curve extremizing the functional $I(y) = \int_1^2 \frac{\sqrt{1+(y'(x))^2}}{x}dx\ y(1) = 0, y(2) = 1$ is
(a) An ellipse
(b) A parabola
(c) A circle
(d) A straight line

[June 2014]

8. Consider the functional $J(y) = y^2(1) + \int_0^1 y'^2(x)dx.\ y(0) = 1$ where $y \epsilon C^2([0,1])$. If y extremizes J then
(a) $y(x) = 1 - \frac{1}{2}x^2$
(b) $y(x) = 1 - \frac{1}{2}x$
(c) $y(x) = 1 + \frac{1}{2}x$
(d) $y(x) = 1 + \frac{1}{2}x^2$

[Dec 2014]

9. The functional $I(y(x)) = \int_a^b (y^2 + y'^2 - 2y\sin x)dx$, has the following extremal with C_1 and C_2 as arbitrary constants
(a) $y = C_1e^{2x} + C_2e^{-2x} + \frac{1}{2}\sin x$
(b) $y = C_1e^{x} + C_2e^{-x} + \frac{1}{2}\sin x$
(c) $y = C_1e^{x} + C_2e^{-x} - \frac{1}{2}\sin x$
(d) $y = C_1e^{2x} + C_2e^{-2x} + \frac{1}{2}\cos x$

[Dec 2015]

10. The curve of fixed length l, that joins the points (0,0) and (1,0), lies above the x-axis and encloses the maximum area between itself and the x-axis, is a segment of
(a) A straight line
(b) A parabola
(c) An ellipse
(d) A circle

[June 2016]

11. If $J[y] = \int_1^2 (y'^2 + 2yy' + y^2)dx, y(1) = 1$ and $y(2)$ is arbitrary then the extremal is
(a) e^{x-1} (b) e^{x+1}
(c) e^{1-x} (d) e^{-x-1}
[Dec 2016]

12. The infimum of $\int_0^1 (u'(t))^2\, dt$ on the class of functions $\{u \epsilon C^1[0,1]$ such that $u(0) = 0$ and $\max_{[0,1]}|u| = 1\}$ is equal to
(a) 0 (b) ½
(c) 1 (d) 2
[June 2017]

13. Let $X = \{u\epsilon C^1[0,1] | u(0) = u(1) = 0\}$ and define $J: X \to \mathbb{R}$ by $J(u) = \int_0^1 e^{-u'(x)^2}\, dx$. Then
(a) J does not attain its infimum
(b) J attains its infimum at a unique $u\epsilon X$
(c) J attains its infimum at exactly two elements $u\epsilon X$
(d) J attains its infimum at infinitely may $u\epsilon X$
[Dec 2017]

14. Consider $J[y] = \int_0^1 [(y') + 2y]dx$ subject to $y(0) = 0, y(1) = 1$. Then inf $J[y]$
(a) Is $\frac{23}{12}$ (b) Is $\frac{21}{24}$
(c) Is $\frac{18}{25}$ (d) Does not exist
[June 2018]

15. Consider the functional $J[y] = \int_0^2 (1 - y'^2)^2 dx$ defined on $\{y\epsilon C[0,2]: y$ is piecewise C^1 and $y(0) = y(2) = 0\}$. Let y_e be a minimizer of the above functional. Then y_e has
(a) A unique corner point
(b) Two corner points
(c) More than two corner points
(d) No corner points
[Dec 2018]

16. Let $x^*(t)$ be the curve which minimizes the functional $J(x) = \int_0^1 [x^2(t) + \dot{x}^2(t)]dt$ satisfying $x(0) = 0. x(1) = 1$. Then the value of $x^*\left(\frac{1}{2}\right)$ is
(a) $\frac{\sqrt{e}}{1+e}$ (b) $\frac{2\sqrt{e}}{1+e}$
(c) $\frac{\sqrt{e}}{1+2e}$ (d) $\frac{2\sqrt{e}}{1+2e}$
[June 2019]

17. Let $y = \phi(x)$ be the extremizing function for the functional $I(y) = \int_0^1 y^2 \left(\frac{dy}{dx}\right) dx$ subject to $y(0) = 0, y(1) = 1$, *Then* $\phi(1/4)$ is equal to
(a) ½ (b) 1/4
(c) 1/8 (d) 1/12
[Dec 2019]

18. The extremal for the following functional

$$\int_0^1 \left(at\, x(t) + (x'(t))^2\right) dt, \alpha \neq 0$$

where $x(0) = 1$ *and* $x'(0) = 0$ is
(a) $\frac{\alpha}{12}t^3 + 1$ (b) $t^3 + \alpha t^2 + 1$
(c) $t^2 + t + 1$ (d) $t^4 + \alpha t^2 + 1$
[Dec 2019]

19. The extremal of the functional $J[y] = \int_0^1 [2(y')^2 + xy]dx, y(0) = 0, y(1) = 1, y \in c^2[0,1]$. Is
(a) $y = \frac{1}{12}x^2 + \frac{11}{12}x$ (b) $y = \frac{1}{3}x^3 + \frac{2}{3}x^2$
(c) $y = \frac{1}{7}x^2 + \frac{6}{7}x$ (d) $y = \frac{1}{24}x^3 + \frac{23}{24}x$
[Nov 2020]

20. The Euler equation satisfied by the extremal of the functional $J[y] = \int_0^5 [y^2 + x^3 y']\, dx$; define a solution curve in the (x, y)- plane which is
(a) Linear (b) quadratic
(c) cubic (d) Trigonometric
[Nov 2020]

21. What is the extremal of the functional $J[y] = \int_{-1}^{0} (12xy - (y')^2)\, dx$ subject to $y(0) = 0$ and $y(-1) = 1$?
(a) $y = x^2$ (b) $y = \frac{2x^2+x^4}{3}$
(c) $y = -x^3$ (d) $y = \frac{(x^2+x^4)}{2}$
[SEP 2022]

22. Consider the variational problem (P)
$J(y(x)) = \int_0^1 [(y')^2 - y|y|y' + xy]\, dx, y(0) = 0, y(1) = 0.$
Which of the following statements is correct?
(a) (P) has no stationary function (extremal).
(b) $y \equiv 0$ is the only stationary function (extremal) for (P).
(c) (P) has a unique stationary function (extremal) y not identically equal to 0.
(d) (P) has infinitely many stationary functions (extremal).
[JUNE 2023]

23. The cardinality of the set of extremals of $J[y] = \int_0^1 (y')^2\, dx$, subject to $y(0) = 1, y(1) = 6, \int_0^1 y dx = 3$ is
(a) 0 (b) 1
(c) 2 (d) countably infinite
[DEC 2023]

24. Let $B(0,1) = \{(x, y) \in \mathbb{R}^2 | x^2 + y^2 < 1\}$ be the open unit disc in $\mathbb{R}^2$, $\partial B(0,1)$ denote the boundary of $B(0,1)$, and v denote unit outward normal to $\partial B(0,1)$. Let $f: \mathbb{R}^2 \to \mathbb{R}$ be a given continuous function. The Euler-Lagrange equation of the minimization problem

$$\min\left\{\frac{1}{2}\iint_{B(0,1)} |\nabla u|^2 dxdy + \frac{1}{2}\iint_{B(0,1)} e^{u^2} dxdy + \int_{\partial B(0,1)} fu\, ds\right\}$$

subject to $u \in C^1\left(\overline{B(0,1)}\right)$ is

(a) $\begin{cases} \Delta u = -ue^{u^2} \text{ in } B(0,1) \\ \frac{\partial u}{\partial v} = f \text{ on } \partial B(0,1) \end{cases}$

(b) $\begin{cases} \Delta u = ue^{u^2} + f \text{ in } B(0,1) \\ u = 0 \text{ on } \partial B(0,1) \end{cases}$

(c) $\begin{cases} \Delta u = ue^{u^2} \text{ in } B(0,1) \\ \frac{\partial u}{\partial v} = -f \text{ on } \partial B(0,1) \end{cases}$

(d) $\begin{cases} \Delta u = ue^{u^2} \text{ in } B(0,1) \\ \frac{\partial u}{\partial v} + u = f \quad \text{on } \partial B(0,1) \end{cases}$

[JULY 2024]

25. The infimum of the set

$$\left\{\int_a^b \sqrt{1+(y'(t))^2}\, dt : y \in C^1[a,b], y(a) = a^2, y(b) = b-5\right\}$$

is

(a) $\frac{19\sqrt{2}}{8}$ (b) $19\sqrt{2}$

(c) $\frac{19}{8}$ (d) $\frac{19}{2\sqrt{2}}$

[JULY 2024]

26. The extremizer of the problem

$$\min\left[\frac{1}{2}\int_{-1}^{1} [(y'(x))^2 + (y(x))^2]dx\right]$$

subject to $y \in C^1[-1,1]$, $\int_{-1}^{1} xy(x)dx = 0$ and $y(-1) = y(1) = 1$ is

(a) $\frac{e}{1+e^2}(e^x + e^{-x}) + x^2 - 1$

(b) $\frac{e}{1+e^2}(e^x + e^{-x}) + 1 - x^2$

(c) $\frac{e}{1+e^2}(e^x + e^{-x})$

(d) $\frac{e}{1+e^2}(e^x + e^{-x}) + \sin(2\pi x)$

[JULY 2024]

27. Let S denote the set of all solutions of the Euler-Lagrange equation of the variational problem:

minimize $J[y] = \int_0^1 (y^2 + (y')^2)\, dx$,

subject to $y(0) = 0, y(1) = 0, \int_0^1 y^2\, dx = 1$.

Then the set $\left\{\varphi\left(\frac{1}{2}\right) : \varphi \in S\right\}$ is equal to

(a) $\{-\sqrt{2}, \sqrt{2}\}$ (b) $\left\{\frac{\sqrt{2}}{k} : k \in \mathbb{Z}, k \neq 0\right\}$

(c) $\left\{\sqrt{\frac{2}{k}} : k \in \mathbb{N}\right\}$ (d) $\{-\sqrt{2}, 0, \sqrt{2}\}$

[Feb. 2025]

28. Let y(x) be the extremal of the functional

$$J[y] = \int_0^{\frac{\pi}{4}} ((y')^2 - 4y^2 + 2xy)\, dx$$

subject to $y(0) = 0, y\left(\frac{\pi}{4}\right) = 1$. Then y(x) is equal to

(a) $\left(1 - \frac{\pi}{4}\right)\sin(2x) + x$ (b) $\left(1 - \frac{\pi}{16}\right)\sin(2x) + \frac{x}{4}$

(c) $\left(1 + \frac{\pi}{4}\right)\sin(2x) - x$ (d) $\left(1 + \frac{\pi}{16}\right)\sin(2x) - \frac{x}{4}$

[June 2025]

29. Suppose $y(x)$ is the extremal of the variational problem

$J(y) = \int_0^4 \frac{(y')^2}{y^2}\, dx$ subject to $y(0) = 1, y(4) = e^8$.

Then which of the following statements is true?

(a) $y(\log_e 2) = 2$. (b) $y(\log_e 3) = 9$.

(c) $y(\log_e 4) = 4$. (d) $y(\log_e 5) = 5$.

[Dec 2025]

ANSWER KEY

1	2	3	4	5	6	7	8	9	10
c	b	d	a	d	a	c	b	b	d

11	12	13	14	15	16	17	18	19	20
c	c	a	a	a	a	a	a	d	b
21	**22**	**23**	**24**	**25**	**26**	**27**	**28**	**29**	
c	c	c	c	a	c	d	b	b	

EXPLANATION

1. Explanation: (c)

Here $f(x,y,y') = y'^2 - y^2$

$y(0) = 1 \quad ; y(2\pi) = 1$

By Euler equation we can find extremal to the functional

We've

$f_y - \frac{d}{dx}(f_{y'}) = 0$

$\Rightarrow -2y - \frac{d}{dx}(2y') = 0$

$\Rightarrow -2y - 2y'' = 0$

$\Rightarrow y'' + y = 0$

$\Rightarrow A.E.$ is given by $m^2 + 1 = 0$

$\therefore y(x) = A\cos x + B\sin x$

$y(0) = 1 = A \Rightarrow A = 1$

$y(2\pi) = 1 = A \Rightarrow A = 1$

$\therefore y(x) = \cos x + B\sin x$

Where B is arbitrary constant

∴ Option (c) is true.

2. Explanation: (b)

Any two points $P(x_0, y_0), Q(x_1, y_1)$, and a function $F(x, y, y')$ of three independent variables are given among all curves $y' = \frac{dy}{dx}$. In order to find among all curves $y = y(x)$ joining P and Q that one which furnishes for the definite integral $I(y) = \int_{x_0}^{x_1} F(x, y(x)y'(x))dx$

Since we need to find the distance between the two point $P(x_0, y_0), Q(x_1, y_1)$, which is of the form of function (x, y, y'), So we must need $y' \in C^2$ i.e $F(x, y, y') \in C^2$

So option (a), (c) discarded and option (d) tells about C^3 so it also discarded.

Hence option (b) correct.

3. Explanation: (d)

$I(y(x)) = \int_1^3 y(3x - y)dx$

$y(3) = 4\frac{1}{2} \quad y(1) = 1$

Here $f(x, y, y') = 3xy - y^2$

By Euler equation -

$fy - \frac{d}{dx}(f_{y'}) = 0$

$\Rightarrow 3x - 2y - \frac{d}{dx}(0) = 0$

$\Rightarrow y = \frac{3}{2}x$

$y(3) = \frac{3}{2}(3) = \frac{9}{2} = 4\frac{1}{2}$

$y(1) = \frac{3}{2}(1) = \frac{3}{2}$

∴ External does not satisfy boundary conditions

∴ Functional has no extremal

So, option (d) is correct.

4. Explanation: (a)

Here, $F(x,u,u_x) = \left[u_x^2 + \frac{4u^2}{x^2}\right]x - - - (1)$

Euler Lagrange equation is given by

$$\frac{\partial F}{\partial u} - \frac{d}{dx}\left(\frac{\partial F}{\partial u_x}\right) = 0$$

$$\Rightarrow \frac{8u}{x} - \frac{d}{dx}(2u_x x) = 0$$

$$\Rightarrow \frac{8u}{x} - 2[xu_{xx} + u_x] = 0$$

$$\Rightarrow 4u - x^2u_{xx} - xu_x = 0$$

$$\Rightarrow x^2u_{xx} + xu_x - 4u = 0 \quad \text{... (2)}$$

Equation (2) is a Cauchy Euler homogeneous equation and using the transformation $x = e^z (=> z = \log x)$, it can be transformed to linear differential equation with constant coefficients, which is $u''(z) - u'(z) + u'(z) - 4u(z) = 0 => u''(z) - 4u(z) = 0 - - - (3)$

The auxiliary equation of (3) is $m^2 - 4 = 0 => m = \pm 2$ and its solution is given by

$u(z) = Ae^{2z} + Be^{-2z}$

$\Rightarrow u(x) = Ax^2 + \frac{B}{x^2}$

Since, $u(0) = 0 \Rightarrow B = 0$

$u(1) = 1 \Rightarrow A = 1$

$\Rightarrow u(x) = x^2$

Option (a) is correct.

5. Explanation: (d)

$$I(y) = \int_a^b F(y,y')dx - - - (1)$$

Note that F is free from x ,so

$$\frac{d}{dx}\left(F - y'\frac{dF}{dy'}\right) - \frac{dF}{dx} = 0$$

But $F = F(y,y') \Rightarrow \frac{dF}{dx} = 0$

$$\Rightarrow \frac{d}{dx}\left(F - y'\frac{dF}{dy}\right) = 0$$

So integrating

$$\Rightarrow \left(F - y'\frac{dF}{dy}\right) = C$$

Hence, option (d) is correct.

6. Explanation: (a)

Here, $F(x,y,y') = y' + y - - - (1)$

Euler's equation is

$$F_y - \frac{d}{dx}\{F_{y'}\} = 0$$

$$\Rightarrow 1 - \frac{d}{dx}(1) = 0$$

$\Rightarrow 1 - 0 = 0$ is absurd

$\Rightarrow$ No extremal exists.

Hence. Option (a) is correct.

7. Explanation: (c)

$$I(y) = \int_1^2 \frac{\sqrt{1+y^2}}{x}dx$$

$y(0) = 0 \quad y(2) = 1$

Euler equation is given by

$$f_y - \frac{d}{dx}(f_{y'}) = 0$$

$$\Rightarrow 0 - \frac{d}{dx}\left\{\frac{1}{x}\frac{2y'}{2\sqrt{1+y'^2}}\right\} = 0$$

$$\Rightarrow \frac{y'}{x\sqrt{1+y'^2}} = C$$

$$\Rightarrow y' = cx\sqrt{1+y'^2}$$

$\Rightarrow y'^2 = c^2x^2(1+y'^2)$ (squaring on either sides)

$$\Rightarrow y'^2 = c^2x^2 + c^2x^2y'^2$$

$$\Rightarrow y'^2(1 - c^2x^2) = c^2x^2$$

$$\Rightarrow y'^2 = \frac{c^2x^2}{(1-c^2x^2)}$$

$$\Rightarrow y' = \frac{cx}{\sqrt{1-c^2x^2}}$$

$\Rightarrow \frac{dy}{dx} = \frac{cx}{\sqrt{1-c^2x^2}} \Rightarrow dy = \frac{cx}{\sqrt{1-c^2x^2}}dx$---------------(1)

$\Rightarrow$ Put $1 - c^2x^2 = t$

$-2c^2xdx = dt$

$cxdx = \frac{dt}{-2c}$

Integrating (1) on on both sides

$y = \int \frac{cx}{\sqrt{1-c^2x^2}}dx$

$y = \int \frac{dt/-2c}{\sqrt{t}} = \frac{-1}{2c}2\sqrt{t} + c_1$

$y = \frac{-\sqrt{t}}{c} + c_1$

$y = \frac{-1}{c}\sqrt{1-c^2x^2} + c_1$

$yc = -1\sqrt{1-c^2x^2} + c\,c_1$

$(yc - cc_1) = -\sqrt{1-c^2x^2}$

$y^2c^2 - 2yc^2c_1 + C_1^2c^2 = 1 - c^2x^2$

$c^2(x^2+y^2) - 2c^2c_1y - 1 = 0$

This is equation of circle

$\therefore$ (*C*) is correct answer.

8. Explanation: (b)

$J(y) = y^2(1) + \int_0^1 y'^2(x)dx.\, y(0) = 1$ where $C^2([0,1])$, we will solve the questions through options

(a) for $y(x) = 1 - \frac{1}{2}x^2 => J[y] = \left(1 - \frac{1}{2}(1)^2\right)^2 + \int_0^1(-x)^2\,dx = \frac{1}{4} + \frac{1}{3} = \frac{7}{12}$

(b) for $y(x) = 1 - \frac{1}{2}x \quad J[y] = \left(1 - \frac{1}{2}(1)\right)^2 + \int_0^1\left(-\frac{1}{2}\right)^2 dx = \frac{1}{4} + \frac{1}{4} = \frac{1}{2}$

(c) for $y(x) = 1 + \frac{1}{2}x => J[y] = \left(1 + \frac{1}{2}(1)\right)^2 + \int_0^1\left(\frac{1}{2}\right)^2 dx = \frac{9}{4} + \frac{1}{4} = \frac{10}{4} = \frac{31}{12}$

(d) for $y(x) = 1 + \frac{1}{2}x^2 => J[y] = \left(1 + \frac{1}{2}(1)\right)^2 + \int_0^1(1)^2\,dx = \frac{9}{4} + 1 = \frac{13}{4}$

$$\frac{1}{2} < \frac{7}{12} < \frac{31}{12} < \frac{13}{4}$$

So, the infimum value is given by option (b).

Hence, option (b) is correct.

9. Explanation: (b)

Here, $F(x,y,y') = y^2 + y'^2 - 2y\sin x$ – – – (1)

Euler's equation is

$$F_y - \frac{d}{dx}\{F_{y'}\} = 0$$

$$(2y - 2\sin x) - \frac{d}{dx}(2y') = 0$$

$$y - \sin x - y'' = 0$$

$$y'' - y = -\sin x \text{ – – – (2)}$$

The solution is $y(x) = C.F + P.I$

The auxiliary equation for (2) is $m^2 - 1 = 0 \Rightarrow m = \pm 1$

$\therefore C.F = C_1e^x + C_2e^{-x}$ and

$$P.I = \frac{1}{(D^2-1)}(-\sin x)$$

$$= -\frac{1}{(D^2-1)}(\sin x) = \frac{-1}{-2}\sin x$$

$$\Rightarrow y(x) = C_1e^x + C_2e^{-x} + \frac{1}{2}\sin x \text{ – – – (3)}$$

Hence, option (b) is correct.

10. Explanation: (d)

Our problem is to maximize

maximize $S = \int_0^1 y\,dx$ – – – (1)

With boundary conditions

$y(0) = 0$ and $y(1) = 0$

Since isoperimetric condition is given by

$$\int_0^1 \sqrt{1 + y'^2}dx = l \text{ – – – (2)}$$

Let $F(x,y,y') = f + \lambda g = y + \lambda\sqrt{(1+y'^2)}$ – – – (3)

Where λ is the Lagrange multiplier.

Now by Euler equation

$$F_y - \frac{d}{dx}\{F_{y'}\} = 0$$

$$\Rightarrow 1 - \frac{d}{dx}\left\{\frac{\lambda y'}{\sqrt{(1+y'^2)}}\right\} = 0$$

Integrating both sides,

$$x - \left\{\frac{\lambda y'}{\sqrt{(1+y'^2)}}\right\} = a$$

$$\Rightarrow (x-a)^2 = \frac{\lambda^2 y'^2}{(1+y'^2)}$$

$$\Rightarrow \frac{1+y'^2}{y'^2} = \frac{\lambda^2}{(x-a)^2}$$

$$\Rightarrow y'^2 = \frac{(x-a)^2}{\lambda^2 - (x-a)^2}$$

$$\Rightarrow \frac{dy}{dx} = \pm\frac{(x-a)}{\sqrt{\lambda^2 - (x-a)^2}}$$

$$\Rightarrow y = b \pm \sqrt{\lambda^2 - (x-a)^2}$$

$$\Rightarrow (y-b)^2 = \lambda^2 - (x-a)^2$$

$$\Rightarrow (x-a)^2 + (y-b)^2 = \lambda^2$$

This is equation of circle with radius λ.

Centre at (a, b)

Using the, boundary conditions $y(0) = 0$, $y(1) = 0$ and $\int_0^1 \sqrt{1+y'^2}dx = 1$,

We can determine value of λ.

Hence, option (d) is correct.

11. Explanation: (c)

$J[y] = \int_1^2 (y'^2 + 2yy' + y^2)dx, y(1) = 1$ and $y(2)$ is arbitrary

The above problem is Free boundary value problem:

Consider $J[y] = \int_a^b F(x,y,y')\,dx$

Where $y(a) = y_1$ and $y(b)$ is determined.

Then, the Euler's equations is

$$F_y - \frac{d}{dx}\{F_{y'}\} = 0$$

And for 2nd boundary condition, we have

$$F_{y'}(b, y(b), y'(b)) = 0$$

Here, $J[y] = \int_1^2 ((y')^2 + 2yy' + y^2)dx$

$y(1) = 1, y(2)$ is arbitrary

$F(x,y,y') = (y')^2 + 2yy' + y^2$

Euler's equation is

$$F_y - \frac{d}{dx}\{F_{y'}\} = 0$$

$$\Rightarrow 2y' + 2y - \frac{d}{dx}(2y' + 2y) = 0$$

$$\Rightarrow 2y' + 2y - 2y'' - 2y' = 0$$

$$\Rightarrow y'' - y = 0 \text{ – – – (1)}$$

The auxiliary equation of (1) is

$\Rightarrow m^2 - 1 = 0$ ... (2)

$\Rightarrow m = \pm 1$

$\Rightarrow y(x) = c_1e^x + c_2e^{-x}$ is the solution of equation (1)

Now, second boundary condition is

$F_{y'}(2, y(2), y'(2)) = 0$

Since, $F_{y'}(x, y(x), y'(x)) = 2y' + 2y$

$\Rightarrow y'(2) + y(2) = 0$

Also, $y'(x) = c_1e^x - c_2e^{-x}$

$\Rightarrow y(2) = c_1e^2 + c_2e^{-2}$

And $y'(2) = c_1e^2 - c_2e^{-2}$

$\therefore 2c_1e^2 = 0$

$\Rightarrow c_1 = 0$

Given $y(1) = 1$

$\Rightarrow c_2e^{-1} = 1$

$\Rightarrow c_2 = e$

$\Rightarrow y(x) = ee^{-x} = e^{1-x}$

Option (c) is correct.

12. Explanation: (c)

$$I[y] = \int_0^1 (u'(t))^2\,dt$$

Euler's equation is

$$\frac{\partial F}{\partial u} - \frac{d}{dt}\left(\frac{\partial F}{\partial u'}\right) = 0$$

$$\Rightarrow 0 - \frac{d}{dx}(2u') = 0$$

$$\Rightarrow u'(t) = c$$

$$\Rightarrow u(t) = ct + d$$

Where, c & d are constants.

Since, $u(0) = 0 \Rightarrow d = 0$

$\Rightarrow u(t) = ct$ and $\max_{[0,1]}|u| = 1$

$\Rightarrow |c| = 1$

$\Rightarrow c = \pm 1$

$\Rightarrow u(t) = \pm t$

$\Rightarrow u'(t) = \pm 1$

$\Rightarrow \int_0^1 (u'(t))^2\, dt = \int_0^1 dt = 1$

$\Rightarrow$ Infimum is 1.

So, option (c) is true.

13. Explanation: (a)

$J(u) = \int_0^1 e^{-u'(x)^2}\, dx$, $u(0) = u(1) = 0$

Euler's equation is

$$\frac{\partial F}{\partial u} - \frac{d}{dx}\left(\frac{\partial F}{\partial u'}\right) = 0 - - - (1)$$

Here, $F(x,u,u') = e^{(-u'(x))^2}$

Since $F(x,u,u')$ is independent of x and u.

So using special forms of (1)

$u''(x) = 0$

$=> u(x) = ax + b$, where a, b arbitrary constants

Now, $u(0) = u(1) = 0$

$\Rightarrow u(x) = 0$

$\Rightarrow X = \{u(x) = 0; \forall x \in [0,1]\}$

Hence, option (a) is correct.

14. Explanation: (a)

$J[y] = \int_0^1 [y'^2 + 2y]dx$, $y(0) = 0, y(1) = 1$

Here $F(x,y,y') = y'^2 + 2y - - - (1)$

Euler's equation is

$$F_y - \frac{d}{dx}\{F_{y'}\} = 0$$

$\Rightarrow 2 - \frac{d}{dx}[2y'] = 0$

$\Rightarrow 2 - 2y'' = 0$

$\Rightarrow y'' = 1 - - - (2)$

Integrating this, we get

$\frac{dy}{dx} = x + a$

Integrating again, we get

$y(x) = \frac{x^2}{2} + ax + b - - - (3)$

Since, $y(0) = 0$ putting in (3)

$\Rightarrow b = 0$

And $y(1) = 1$ in (3) with $b = 0$ we get $1 = \frac{1}{2} + a$.

$\Rightarrow a = \frac{1}{2}$

$\Rightarrow y(x) = \frac{x^2}{2} + \frac{x}{2}$

So, $J[y] = \int_0^1 \left(\left(\frac{x^2}{2} + \frac{x}{2}\right)'\right)^2 + 2\left(\frac{x^2}{2} + \frac{x}{2}\right) dx$

$= \int_0^1 \left(x + \frac{1}{2}\right)^2 + (x^2 + x)dx$

$= \left(\frac{2x^3}{3} + \frac{2x^2}{2} + \frac{1}{4}\right)\Big|_0^1$

$= \frac{23}{12}$

Option (a) is correct.

15. Explanation: (a)

We've, $zF(x,y,y') = (1 - y'^2)^2$

i.e. F is independent of x and y.

So using Euler's equation

$F_y - \frac{d}{dx}\{F_{y'}\} = 0$

We get $y''(x) = 0$

So, $y(x) = Cx + D$, which is a straight line

Since $y(0) = y(2) = 0$

$\Rightarrow C = D = 0$

$\Rightarrow y(x) = 0$

For minimizer, $\frac{\partial F}{\partial y'} = 0$

i.e., $2(1 - y'^2)(-2y') = 0$

$\Rightarrow y'(1 - y'^2) = 0$

$\Rightarrow y' = 0$ or $y'^2 = 1$

Take $y'^2 = 1$ (because $y' = 0$, will give $y(x) = Ax + B$)

$\Rightarrow y' = \pm 1$

$\Rightarrow y(x) = \pm x + c_1$

Since $y(0) = 0 \Rightarrow c_1 = 0$

$y(2) = 0$

$\Rightarrow \pm 2 + c_1 = 0 \Rightarrow c_1 = \pm 2$

Thus, $y_1(x) = \begin{cases} x, & 0 \le x \le k \\ \pm x \pm 2 & k \le x \le 2 \end{cases}$

Since, $x + 2$ and $-(x + 2)$ does not satisfy the given conditions ($y(0) = y(2) = 0$), we shall neglect them

$\Rightarrow y_1(x) = \begin{cases} x & 0 \le x \le k \\ -x + 2 & k \le x \le 2 \end{cases}$

And $y_2(x) = \begin{cases} -x & 0 \le x \le k \\ x - 2 & k \le x \le 2 \end{cases}$

$\Rightarrow y_1(x)$ and $y_2(x)$ both are minimizer of $J[y]$ with unique corner point.

Hence, option (a) is correct.

16. Explanation: (a)

$J(x) = {}_0^1\int [x^2(t) - \dot{x}^2(t)]dt$

$x(0) = 0, x(1) = 1$

Here, $F = x^2 + \dot{x}^2$

Euler equation is given by

$f_x - \frac{d}{dt}\{F_{\dot{x}}\} = 0$

$\Rightarrow 2x - \frac{d}{dt}\{2\dot{x}\} = 0$

$\Rightarrow 2x - 2\ddot{x} = 0$

$\Rightarrow \ddot{x} - x = 0$

$\Rightarrow$Auxillary equation is given by

$m^2 - 1 = 0$

$x(t) = c_1 e^t + c_2 e^{-t}$

$x(0) = 0 \Rightarrow 0 = c_1 + c_2$ ……………(1)

$x(1) = 1 \Rightarrow c_1 e + c_2 e^{-1}$ ……………(2)

Solving (1) and (2) we get

$c_1 = \frac{-e}{1-e^2}$ $c_2 = \frac{e}{1-e^2}$

since given $x^*(t)$ is minimizing curve

$\therefore x^*(t) = \frac{-e}{1-e^2}e^t + \frac{e}{1-e^2}e^{-t}$

$\therefore x^*\left(\frac{1}{2}\right) = \frac{-e}{1-e^2}e^{1/2} + \frac{e}{1-e^2}e^{-1/2}$

$= \frac{-e}{1-e^2}[e^{1/2} - e^{-1/2}]$

$= \frac{ee^{\frac{-1}{2}}}{1-e^2}(1-e)$

$= \frac{\sqrt{e}}{1+e}$

Option (a) is correct

17. Explanation: (a)

f is independent of x

$f - y'\frac{\partial F}{\partial y'}$, =constant

$\Rightarrow y^2y^2 - y'(y^2 2y') = c$

$\Rightarrow y^2y^{\cdot 2} = c$

$\Rightarrow yy' = a$,$\Rightarrow y\frac{dy}{dx} = a$

$\Rightarrow y\,dy = a\,d\,x$

$\Rightarrow y^2/2 \quad = ax + b$

$\because y(0) = 0 \quad \Rightarrow \quad b = 0$

$y(1) = 1 \quad \Rightarrow a = {}^1/_2$

$\Rightarrow y^2/2 \quad = {}^x/_2 \Rightarrow y^2 = x$

$\because y = \phi(x) \Rightarrow \phi(x) = \sqrt{x}$

$\phi(1/4) = \sqrt{1/4}$

$= 1/2$

18. Explanation: (a)

$F(t, x, x') = \alpha t\, x(t) + (x'(t))^2$

Euler-Lagrange's equation is

$\frac{\partial F}{\partial x} - \frac{d}{dt}\left(\frac{\partial F}{\partial x'}\right) = 0$

$\Rightarrow \alpha t - \frac{d}{dt}2x'(t) = 0$

$\Rightarrow \alpha t - 2x''(t) = 0 \Rightarrow x''(t) = \frac{\alpha}{2}t$

Integrating both sides,

$\Rightarrow \; x'(t) = \frac{\alpha}{2}\frac{t^2}{2} + c_1$

Again integrating

$\Rightarrow x(t) = \frac{\alpha}{4}\frac{t^3}{3} + c_1 t + c_2$

$= \frac{\alpha}{12}t^3 + c_1 t + c_2$

Now, $x(0) = \frac{\alpha}{12}.0 + c_1.0 + c_2 \Rightarrow c_2 = 1$

$x'(t) = \frac{\alpha}{4}t^2 + c_1$

$\Rightarrow x'(0) = \frac{\alpha}{4}.0 + c_1 \Rightarrow c_1 = 0$

$\therefore x(t) = \frac{\alpha}{12}t^3 + 1$

So, option (a) correct.

19. Explanation: (d)

Here $F(x, y, y') = 2(y')^2 + xy$ .... (i)

$y(0) = 0, y(1) = 1$ .... (ii)

Euler's equation is,

$\frac{\partial F}{\partial y} - \frac{d}{dx}\left(\frac{\partial F}{\partial y'}\right) = 0$

$\Rightarrow x - \frac{d}{dx}(4y') = 0$

$\Rightarrow x - 4y'' = 0 \Rightarrow 4y'' = x$

$\Rightarrow y'' = {}^x/_4$

Integrating w.r.t x

$\Rightarrow y'(x) = \frac{x^2}{8} + c_1$

Integrating w.r.t x

$\Rightarrow y(x) = \frac{1}{8}\frac{x^3}{3} + c_1 x + c_2$

i.e. $y(x) = \frac{1}{24}x^3 + c_1 x + c_2$ .... (iii)

putting $y(0) = 0$

$\Rightarrow 0 = \frac{1}{24}.0 + c_1.0 + c_2 \Rightarrow c_2 = 0$

So $y(x) = \frac{1}{24}x^3 + c_1 x$

$y(1) = \frac{1}{24} + c_1 \Rightarrow 1 = \frac{1}{24} + c_1$

$\Rightarrow c_1 = 1 - \frac{1}{24} = \frac{23}{24}$

$\therefore y(x) = \frac{1}{24}x^3 + \frac{23}{24}x$

i.e. option (d) correct.

20. Explanation: (b)

$F(x, y, y') = y^2 + x^3 y'$

Euler's equation is

$\frac{\partial F}{\partial y} - \frac{d}{dx}\left(\frac{\partial F}{\partial y'}\right) = 0$

$\Rightarrow 2y - \frac{d}{dx}x^3 = 0 \Rightarrow 02y - 3x^2 = 0$

$\Rightarrow y = \frac{3}{2}x^2$

i.e. the extremal $y = \frac{3}{2}x^2$ is quadratic polynomial.

21. Explanation: (c)

$J[y] = {}_{-1}\int^{0} 12\,xy - y^{1\,2}\,dx \qquad y(0) = 0 \;\; y(-1) = 1$

Here $F = 12\,xy - y'^2$

Euler equation is given by

$F_y - \frac{d}{dx}\{F_{y'}\} = 0$

$\Rightarrow 12\,x - \frac{d}{dx}\{2y'\} = 0$

$\Rightarrow 12x + 2y'' = 0$

$\Rightarrow y'' = -6x$

$\Rightarrow y' = -3x^2 + c_1$

$\Rightarrow y = -x^3 + c_1\,x + c_2$

$y(0) = 0 \Rightarrow C_2 = 0$

$y(-1) = 1 - c_1 = 1 \quad \Rightarrow c_1 = 0$

$\therefore y(x) = -x^3$

22. Explanation: (c)

$J(y(x)) = \int_0^1 [y'^2 - y|y|y' + xy]dx$

Case I: (for positive $|y|$)

$y'^2 - y^2y' + xy$

$=> \frac{\partial f}{\partial y} - \frac{d}{dx}\left(\frac{\partial f}{\partial y'}\right) = 0$

$=> -2yy' + x - \frac{d}{dx}(2y' - y^2) = 0$

$=> -2yy' + x - 2y'' + 2yy' = 0$

$=> y'' = \frac{x}{2}$

$=> y' = \frac{x^2}{4} + a$

$=> y(x) = \frac{x^3}{12} + ax + b$

$y(0) = 0 => b = 0$

$y(1) = 0 => \frac{1}{12} + a = 0$

$=> a = -\frac{1}{12}$

$\therefore y(x) = \frac{x^3}{12} - \frac{1}{12}x = \left(\frac{1}{12}(x^3 - x)\right)$

There is no arbitrary constant, so it gives unique solution.

∴ option (c) correct.

Case II: (for negative $|y|$)

$y'^2 + y^2y' + xy$

$\frac{\partial f}{\partial y} - \frac{d}{dx}\left(\frac{\partial f}{\partial y'}\right) = 0$

$2yy' + x - \frac{d}{dx}(2y' + y^2) = 0$

$2yy' + x - 2y'' - 2y\gamma) = 0$

$\therefore y'' = \frac{x}{2}$

23. Explanation: (b)

Here $f = (y')^2$ and $g = y$

$F = f + \lambda g = y'^2 + \lambda y$

By Euler's - Lagrange equation

$F_y - \frac{d}{dx}F'_y = 0$

$\Rightarrow \lambda - \frac{d}{dx}(2y') = 0$

$\Rightarrow \frac{d}{dx}(2y') = \lambda$

$\Rightarrow 2y'' = \lambda$

$\Rightarrow y'' = \frac{\lambda}{2}$

$\Rightarrow y' = \frac{\lambda}{2}x + c_1$

$\Rightarrow y = \frac{\lambda}{4}x^2 + c_1x + c_2$

Now, $y(0) = 1 \Rightarrow c_2 = 1$

And $y(1) = 6 \Rightarrow 6 = \frac{\lambda}{4} + c_1 + 1 \Rightarrow \lambda + 4c_1 = 20$ ... (1)

Now, we have

$\int_0^1 ydx = 3$

$\Rightarrow \int_0^1 \left[\frac{\lambda}{4}x^2 + c_1x + 1\right] dx = 3$

$\Rightarrow \left[\frac{\lambda}{4}\frac{x^3}{3} + c_1\frac{x^2}{2} + x\right]_0^1 = 3$

$\Rightarrow \frac{\lambda}{12} + \frac{c_1}{2} + 1 = 3$

$\frac{\lambda}{12} + \frac{c_1}{2} = 2$

$\lambda + 6c_1 = 24$ ... (2)

Solving (1) and (2) simultaneously, we get $c_1 = 2$. Put in (2), we get $\lambda = 24 - 6 \times 2 = 12$

$\therefore y(x) = 3x^2 + 2x + 1.$

⇒ option (b) is correct.

24. Explanation: (c)

$I = \min\left\{\frac{1}{2}\left[\iint_{B(0,1)} |\nabla u|^2 + e^{u^2} dxdy + \int_{\partial B(0,1)} 2fu\, ds\right]\right\}$

Here $F = |\nabla u|^2 + e^{u^2} = u_x^2 + u_y^2 + e^{u^2}$ and $F_1 = 2fu$

Euler ostrogradsky equation is

$\frac{\partial F}{\partial u} - \frac{\partial}{\partial x}\left(\frac{\partial F}{\partial u_x}\right) - \frac{\partial}{\partial y}\left(\frac{\partial F}{\partial u_y}\right) = 0$

$\Rightarrow 2ue^{u^2} - \frac{\partial}{\partial x}(2u_x) - \frac{\partial}{\partial y}(2u_y) = 0$

$\Rightarrow \Delta u = ue^{u^2}$ in $B(0,1)$

For $\partial B(0,1)$, $\frac{\partial u}{\partial v} + \frac{1}{2}\left[\frac{\partial F_1}{\partial u} - \frac{d}{ds}\left(\frac{\partial F_1}{\partial u'}\right)\right] = 0$

$\Rightarrow \frac{\partial u}{\partial v} + \frac{1}{2}[2f] = 0$

$\Rightarrow \frac{\partial u}{\partial v} = -f$ on $\partial B(0,1)$.

∴ Option (c) is correct.

25. Explanation: (a)

Here $F = \sqrt{1 + y'^2}, y(a) = a^2, y(b) = b - 5.$

Euler-Lagrange equation is

$\frac{\partial F}{\partial y} - \frac{d}{dx}\left(\frac{\partial F}{\partial y'}\right) = 0$

$\Rightarrow y'' = 0$

$\Rightarrow y = C_1x + C_2$, which is extremal for the given functional.

$\therefore y(a) = C_1a + C_2, y(b) = C_1b + C_2$

Let $\phi_1: y = x^2$ and $\phi_2: y = x - 5$

Transversality condition:

$\phi_1'y' |_{x=a} = -1 \Rightarrow 2xC_1 |_{x=a} = -1$

$\therefore 2aC_1 = -1$

$\phi_2'y' |_{x=b} = -1 \Rightarrow C_1 = -1 \therefore a = \frac{1}{2}$

$\therefore y(a) = a^2 = \frac{1}{4}$

$\therefore y(a) = C_1a + C_2 \Rightarrow C_2 = \frac{3}{4}$

∴ Extremal is $y(x) = -x + \frac{3}{4}$

Now, we have $y(b) = b - 5$ and $y(b) = -b + \frac{3}{4}$

$\therefore b - 5 = -b + \frac{3}{4}$

$\therefore b = \frac{23}{8}$

$\therefore I = \int_a^b \sqrt{1 + (y'(t))^2} dt = \int_{\frac{1}{2}}^{\frac{23}{8}} \sqrt{1 + (-1)^2} dt = \frac{19\sqrt{2}}{8}$

∴ Option (a) is correct.

26. Explanation: (c)

Here $F = \frac{1}{2}(y'^2 + y^2) - \lambda xy$

Euler-Lagrange equation is

$\frac{\partial F}{\partial y} - \frac{d}{dx}\left(\frac{\partial F}{\partial y'}\right) = 0$

$\Rightarrow y - \lambda x - y'' = 0$

$\Rightarrow y'' - y = -\lambda x$

$\Rightarrow y = C_1e^x + C_2e^{-x} + \lambda x$, which is extremal.

Now,

$y(-1) = 1 \Rightarrow C_1e^{-1} + C_2e - \lambda = 1 \ldots (1)$

$y(1) = 1 \Rightarrow C_1e + C_2e^{-1} + \lambda = 1 \ldots (2)$

Adding (1) and (2), we get, $(C_1 + C_2)(e + e^{-1}) = 2$

$\therefore C_1 + C_2 = \frac{2}{e+e^{-1}} \ldots (3)$

$\int_{-1}^{1} xy\,dx = 0$

$\Rightarrow \int_{-1}^{1}(C_1xe^x + C_2xe^{-x} + \lambda x^2)\,dx = 0$

$\Rightarrow \left[C_1(x-1)e^x + C_2(-x-1)e^{-x} + \lambda\frac{x^3}{3}\right]_{-1}^{1} = 0$

$\Rightarrow 2C_1e^{-1} - 2C_2e^{-1} + \frac{2\lambda}{3} = 0$

$\Rightarrow C_1 - C_2 = -\frac{\lambda e}{3} \ldots (4)$

From (3) and (4), we get,

$C_1 = \frac{1}{e+e^{-1}} - \frac{\lambda e}{6}$ and $C_2 = \frac{1}{e+e^{-1}} + \frac{\lambda e}{6}$

Put C_1 and C_2 in (1), we get, $\lambda = 0$.

$\therefore C_1 = C_2 = \frac{1}{e+e^{-1}}$

$\therefore y(x) = C_1e^x + C_2e^{-x} + \lambda x = \frac{1}{e+e^{-1}}(e^x + e^{-x}) = \frac{e}{1+e^2}(e^x + e^{-x})$

27. Explanation: (d)

We introduce λ and modify the functional:

$$J[y] = \int_0^1 ((y')^2 + \lambda y^2)dx.$$

This leads to the Euler-Lagrange equation:

$$y'' - \lambda y = 0.$$

The general solution is:

$$y(x) = A\cos(\sqrt{\lambda}x) + B\sin(\sqrt{\lambda}x).$$

Applying boundary conditions:

1. $y(0) = 0 \Rightarrow A = 0$, so $y(x) = B\sin(\sqrt{\lambda}x)$.
2. $y(1) = 0 \Rightarrow B\sin(\sqrt{\lambda}) = 0$.

Since $B \neq 0$, we get:

$$\sin(\sqrt{\lambda}) = 0 \Rightarrow \sqrt{\lambda} = k\pi, k \in \mathbb{Z}, k \neq 0.$$

Thus, $\lambda_k = k^2\pi^2$ and the solutions are:

$$y_k(x) = B_k\sin(k\pi x).$$

Using the constraint $\int_0^1 y^2dx = 1$:

$$B_k^2\int_0^1 \sin^2(k\pi x)dx = 1.$$

$$B_k^2 \cdot \frac{1}{2} = 1 \Rightarrow B_k = \sqrt{2}.$$

$[\int_0^1 \sin^2(k\pi x)dx = \frac{1}{2}]$

Thus, the solutions are: $y_k(x) = \sqrt{2}\sin(k\pi x)$.

Evaluating $\phi(1/2)$

For $x = 1/2$:

$$\phi_k(1/2) = \sqrt{2}\sin(k\pi/2).$$

Observing the values for different k:

- For $k = 1$, $\sin(\pi/2) = 1 \Rightarrow \sqrt{2}$.
- For $k = 2$, $\sin(\pi) = 0 \Rightarrow 0$.
- For $k = 3$, $\sin(3\pi/2) = -1 \Rightarrow -\sqrt{2}$.
- For $k = 4$, $\sin(2\pi) = 0 \Rightarrow 0$.

This pattern repeats, so values of $\phi(1/2)$ are:

$\{-\sqrt{2}, 0, \sqrt{2}\}$.

28. Explanation: (b)

Euler–Lagrange for $L = (y')^2 - 4y^2 + 2xy$:

$\frac{d}{dx}(2y') + 8y - 2x = 0; \Rightarrow; y'' + 4y = x.$

General solution: $y = C_1\cos(2x) + C_2\sin(2x) + \frac{x}{4}$.

BCs:

$y(0) = 0 \Rightarrow C_1 = 0.$

$y(\pi/4) = 1 \Rightarrow C_2 + \frac{\pi}{16} = 1 \Rightarrow C_2 = 1 - \frac{\pi}{16}.$

Thus $y(x) = (1 - \frac{\pi}{16})\sin(2x) + \frac{x}{4}$, i.e. option (2).

Correct Answer: 2

29. Explanation: (b)

We need the extremal of $J(y) = \int_0^4 \frac{(y')^2}{y^2}dx$

with boundary conditions

$$y(0) = 1, y(4) = e^8$$

Let

$$F = \frac{(y')^2}{y^2}$$

Euler–Lagrange equation:

$$\frac{d}{dx}\left(\frac{\partial F}{\partial y'}\right) - \frac{\partial F}{\partial y} = 0$$

Compute derivatives:

$$\frac{\partial F}{\partial y'} = \frac{2y'}{y^2}, \frac{\partial F}{\partial y} = \frac{2(y')^2}{y^3}$$

Substitute:

$$\frac{d}{dx}\left(\frac{2y'}{y^2}\right) + \frac{2(y')^2}{y^3} = 0$$

Let $u = \ln y$

Then

$$y = e^u, \quad y' = e^u u'$$

Hence $\frac{(y')^2}{y^2} = (u')^2$

So the functional becomes

$$J = \int_0^4 (u')^2dx$$

Euler equation for u:

$$F = (u')^2$$

$$\Rightarrow \frac{d}{dx}(2u') = 0$$

$$\Rightarrow u'' = 0$$

Integrate:

$$u = ax + b$$

Apply boundary conditions

Since $u = \ln y$:

$$y(0) = 1 \Rightarrow u(0) = 0$$

$$y(4) = e^8 \Rightarrow u(4) = 8$$

So, $u = ax$

$$4a = 8 \Rightarrow a = 2$$

Thus

$$u = 2x \Rightarrow y = e^{2x}$$

Check options:

(1) $y(\ln 2)$: $y(\ln 2) = e^{2\ln 2} = 2^2 = 4 \neq 2 \Rightarrow$False.

(2) $y(\ln 3)$: $y(\ln 3) = e^{2\ln 3} = 3^2 = 9 \Rightarrow$True.

(3) $y(\ln 4)$: $y(\ln 4) = e^{2\ln 4} = 4^2 = 16 \neq 4 \Rightarrow$False.
(4) $y(\ln 5)$: $y(\ln 5) = e^{2\ln 5} = 25 \neq 5 \Rightarrow$False.
So, the correct option is (2).

MSQ (Multiple Select Questions)

1. In the Ritz method, seeking an extremum of the functional

$$I(y) = \int_{x_0}^{x_1} F\left(x, y, \frac{dy}{dx}\right) dx; y(x_0) = a, y(x_1) = b$$

The coordinate function/or the admissible function $\phi_i(x), i = 1,2, \ldots$ defined on$[x_0, x_1]$ must be
(a) Linearly independent
(b) Continuous
(c) Smooth
(d) Linearly independent, smooth and the functional be considered not along admissible curves $y = y(x)$ but only along all possible linear combinations of admissible functions.

[June 2011]

2. An approximate solution $z = z_0(x,y)$ to the problem of extremizing the functional $f(z(x,y)) = \iint_D \left[\left(\frac{\partial z}{\partial x}\right)^2 + \left(\frac{\partial z}{\partial y}\right)^2 - 2z\right] dxdy$ where D is the square $-1 \leq x \leq 1, -1 \leq y \leq 1$ and $z = 0$ on the boundary of the square, is of the form
(a) $z_0 = \sum_{i=1}^{n} \alpha_i \phi_i(x,y)$ where α_i are constants and functions ϕ_i are linearly independent in D
(b) $z_0 = \alpha_1 \phi_1(x,y) + \alpha_2 \phi_2(x,y)$ where α_1 and α_2 are constants and ϕ_1 and ϕ_2 have continuous partial derivatives
(c) $z_0 = \alpha\phi(x,y)$ where α is a constant and ϕ is continuous in D
(d) $z_0 = (x^2-1)(y^2-1)/16$

[June 2012]

3. Consider the functional $J = \int_a^b F(x,y,y')dx$ where $F(x,y,y') = (1+y^2)/y'^2$ for admissible functions $y(x)$. Which of the following are extremals for J?
(a) $y(x) = A\sin(x)$
(b) $y(x) = A\sinh(x) + B\cosh(x)$
(c) $y(x) = A\sinh(Ax+B)$
(d) $y(x) = A\sin(x) + B\cos(x)$

[Dec 2012]

4. Let y_{app} be a polynomial approximation, involving only one coordinate function, for the functional $I(y) = \int_0^1 \left(\frac{1}{2}y'^2 - y\right) dx; y(0) = 0, y(1) = 0$, using Rayleigh-Ritz method; here$y\epsilon C^2[0,1]$. If $y_e(x)$ is an exact extremizing function, then y_e and y_{app} are coincident at
(a) $x = 0$ but not at remaining point in $[0,1]$
(b) $x = 1$ but not at remaining points in $[0,1]$
(c) $x = 0$ and $x = 1$, but not at other points in $[0,1]$
(d) All point $x\epsilon[0,1]$

[June 2013]

5. The extremal of $\int_1^2 \frac{\dot{x}^3}{t^3} dt; x(1) = 3, x(2) = 18$ (where $\dot{x} \equiv \frac{dx}{dt}$) using Lagrange's equation is given by which of the following?
(a) $x = t^4 + 2$
(b) $x = \frac{15}{7}t^3 + \frac{6}{7}$
(c) $x = 5t^2 - 2$
(d) $x = 5t^3 + 3$

[June 2013]

6. An extremal of the functional $J(y) = \int_a^b \sqrt{1+|y'(x)|^2}dx$
(a) Is the straight line connecting $(a, y(a))$ and $(b, y(b))$
(b) Is the solution to the differential equation $y' = C\sqrt{1+y'^2}$ for some constant C
(c) Is a solution to $y'' = 0$
(d) Does not exist

[Dec 2013]

7. Let $u(x,y)$ be an extremal of the functional $J(u) = \iint_D \left[\frac{1}{2}u_x^2 + \frac{1}{2}u_y^2 + e^{xy}u\right] dxdy$ where D is the open unit disk in $\mathbb{R}^2$. Then u is satisfies
(a) $u_{xx} + u_{yy} - e^{x+y} = 0$
(b) $u_{xx} + u_{yy} = e^{xy}$
(c) $u_{xx} + u_{yy} = -e^{xy}$
(d) $\iint_D \left[u_{xx} + u_{yy} - e^{xy}\right] h(x,y)dxdy = 0$ for every somooth h vanishing on the boundary of D.

[June 2014]

8. Let $y \in C^2([0,\pi])$ satisfying $y(0) = y(\pi) = 0$ and $\int_0^\pi y^2(x)dx = 1$ extremizes the functional $J(y) = \int_0^\pi (y'(x))^2 dx; y' = \frac{dy}{dx}$. Then
(a) $y(x) = \sqrt{\frac{2}{\pi}}\sin x$
(b) $y(x) = -\sqrt{\frac{2}{\pi}}\sin x$
(c) $y(x) = \sqrt{\frac{2}{\pi}}\cos x$
(d) $y(x) = -\sqrt{\frac{2}{\pi}}\cos x$

[Dec 2014]

9. The extremal of the functional $\int_0^\alpha (y'^2 - y^2)dx$ that passes through (0, 0) and $(\alpha, 0)$ has a
(a) Weak minimum if $\alpha < \pi$
(b) Strong minimum if $\alpha < \pi$
(c) Weak minimum if $\alpha > \pi$
(d) Strong minimum if $\alpha > \pi$

[June 2015]

10. The extremal of the functional $I = \int_0^{x_1} y^2(y')^2 dx$ that passes through (0,0) and (x_1, y_1) is
(a) A constant function
(b) A linear function of x
(c) Part of a parabola
(d) Part of an ellipse

[June 2015]

11. To show the existence of a minimize for the functional $[y] = \int_a^b f(x,y,y')dx$, for which there is a minimizing sequence (φ_n), it is enough to have
(a) (φ_n) is convergent and J is continuous.
(b) (φ_n) is convergent and $J$is differentiable
(c) (φ_n) has a convergent subsequence and $J$is continuous
(d) (φ_n) has a convergent subsequence and $J$is differentiable

[Dec 2015]

12. The functional $J[y] = \int_0^1 (y'^2 + x^2)dx$ where $y(0) = -1$ and $y(1) = 1$ on $y = 2x - 1$ has
(a) Weak minimum (b) Weak maximum
(c) Strong minimum (d) Strong maximum
[Dec 2016]

13. Let $y(x)$ be a piecewise continuously differentiable function on [0,4]. Then the functional $J[y] = \int_0^4 (y' - 1)^2(y' + 1)^2 dx$ attains minimum if $y = y(x)$is
(a) $y = \frac{x}{2}$ $0 \le x \le 4$
(b) $y = \begin{cases} -x & 0 \le x \le 1 \\ x - 2 & 1 \le x \le 4 \end{cases}$
(c) $y = \begin{cases} 2x & 0 \le x \le 2 \\ -x + 6 & 2 \le x \le 4 \end{cases}$
(d) $y = \begin{cases} x & 0 \le x \le 3 \\ -x + 6 & 3 \le x \le 4 \end{cases}$
[Dec 2016]

14. Let B be the unit ball in $\mathbb{R}^2$.
Let $u\epsilon C^2(\overline{B})$ be a minimizer of $I(u) = \int_B (|\nabla u|^2 + fu)dx + \int_{\partial B} au^2 ds$ where f and a are continuous functions in $C^2(\overline{B})$. Let $\vec{n}$ denote the unit outward normal. Which of the following are correct?
(a) $-2\Delta u + f = 0$ in B and $\frac{\partial u}{\partial \vec{n}} + au = 0$ on ∂B
(b) $-2\Delta u + f + a = 0$ in B and $\frac{\partial u}{\partial \vec{n}} = 0$ on ∂B
(c) $-\Delta u + f = 0$ in B and $2\frac{\partial u}{\partial \vec{n}} + au = 0$ on ∂B
(d) $-\Delta u + 2f = 0$ in B and $2\frac{\partial u}{\partial \vec{n}} + au = 0$ on ∂B
[June 2017]

15. Let $X = \{u\epsilon C^1[0,1] | u(0) = 0\}$ and let $I: X \to \mathbb{R}$ be defined as $I(u) = \int_0^1 (u'(t)^2 - u(t)^2)dt$. Which of the following are correct?
(a) I bounded below
(b) I is not bounded below
(c) I is attains its infimum
(d) I does not attain its infimum
[Dec 2017]

16. Let $I: C^1[0,1] \to \mathbb{R}$ be defined as $I(u) := \frac{1}{2}\int_0^1 (u'(t)^2 - 4\pi^2 u(t)^2)dt$
Let us set $(P) m := \inf\{I(u): u\,\epsilon C^1[0,1]: u(0) = u(1) = 0\}$ Let $\overline{u}\epsilon C^1[0,1]$ satisfy the Euler-Lagrange equation associated with (P). Then
(a) $m = -\infty$ i.e. I is not bounded below
(b) $m\epsilon\mathbb{R}$, with $I(\overline{u}) = m$
(c) $m\epsilon\mathbb{R}$, with $I(\overline{u}) > m$
(d) $m\epsilon\mathbb{R}$, with $I(\overline{u}) < m$
[Dec 2017]

17. Let $B = \{(x_1, x_2)\epsilon\mathbb{R}^2 | x_1^2 + x_2^2 < 1\}$, and let $C_{Id}^2(\bar{B}; \mathbb{R}^2) = \{u\epsilon C^2(\bar{B}; \mathbb{R}^2) | u(x_1, x_2) = (x_1, x_2)$ for $(x_1, x_2)\epsilon\partial B\}$. Let $u(u_1, u_2)$ and define $J: C_{Id}^2(\bar{B}; \mathbb{R}^2) \to \mathbb{R}$ by $J(u) = \int_B \left(\frac{\partial u_1}{\partial x_1}\frac{\partial u_2}{\partial x_2} - \frac{\partial u_1}{\partial x_2}\frac{\partial u_2}{\partial x_1}\right) dx_1 dx_2$. Then
(a) $\inf\{J(u): u\epsilon C_{Id}^2(\bar{B}; \mathbb{R}^2)\} = 0$
(b) $J(u) > 0$, for all $u\epsilon C_{Id}^2(\bar{B}; \mathbb{R}^2)$
(c) $J(u) = 1$, for infinitely many $u\epsilon C_{Id}^2(\bar{B}; \mathbb{R}^2)$
(d) $J(u) = \pi$, for all $u\epsilon C_{Id}^2(\bar{B}; \mathbb{R}^2)$
[Dec 2017]

18. The admissible extremal for $J[u] = \int_0^{\log 3} [e^{-x}y'^2 + 2e^x(y' + y)]dx$ where $y(\log 3) = 1$ and $y(0)$ is free is
(a) $4 - e^x$ (b) $10 - e^{2x}$
(c) $e^x - 2$ (d) $e^{2x} - 8$
[June 2018]

19. The extremal of the functional $J[y] = \int_0^1 y'^2(x)dx$ subject to $y(0) = 0, y(1) = 1$ and $\int_0^1 y(x)dx = 0$ is
(a) $3x^2 - 2x$
(b) $8x^3 - 9x^2 + 2x$
(c) $\frac{5}{3}x^4 - \frac{2}{3}x$
(d) $\frac{-21}{2}x^5 + 10x^4 + 4x^3 - \frac{5}{2}x$
[June 2018]

20. The extremals of the functional $J[y] = \int_0^1 [720x^2y - (y'')^2]dx$ subject to $y(0) = y'(0) = y(1) = 0, y'(1) = 6$, are
(a) $x^6 + 2x^3 - 3x^2$ (b) $x^5 + 4x^4 - 5x^3$
(c) $x^5 + x^4 - 2x^3$ (d) $x^6 + 4x^3 - 6x^2$
[Dec 2018]

21. Consider the functional $J[y] = \int_0^1 \left[(y'(x))^2 + (y'(x))^3\right] dx$ subject to $y(0) = 1$ and $y(1) = 2$. Then
(a) There exists an extremal $y \in C^1([0,1]) \backslash C^2([0,1])$
(b) There exists an extremal $y \in C([0,1]) \backslash C^1([0,1])$
(c) Every extremal y belong to $C^1([0,1])$
(d) Every extremal y belongs to $C^2([0,1])$
[June 2019]

22. The minimum if value of the functional
$$I(y) = \int_0^\pi \left(\frac{dy}{dx}\right)^2 dx$$
Subject to $\int_1^\pi y^2(x)dx = 1,\ y(0) = 0$ y (1)is equal to
(a) ½ (b) 1
(c) 2 (d) $^4/_3$
[Dec 2019]

23. Let $y = y(x) \in C^4([0,1])$ be an extremizing function for the functional
$I[y] = \int_0^1 \left[\left(\frac{d^2y}{dx^2}\right)^2 - 2y\right] dx$Satisfying $y(0) = 0 = y(1)$
Then an extremal$y(x)$, satisfying the given conditions at 0 & 1 together with the natural Boundary conditions is given By
(a) $\frac{x}{24}(x - 1)^2$ (b) $\frac{x^2}{24}(x - 1)^2$
(c) $\frac{x}{24}(x^3 - 2x^2 + 1)$ (d) $\frac{x}{24}(x^3 + x^2 - 2)$
[Dec 2019]

24. Consider the problem of minimizing/ maximizing
$$J[y] = \int_0^{\frac{\pi}{8}} (y'^2 + 2yy' - 16y^2)\, dx,$$
Subject to $y(0) = 0, y\left(\frac{\pi}{8}\right) = 1$. Then
(a) Every extremizer of J is a minimizer.
(b) Every extremizer of $J$is a maximizer.
(c) There exists an extremizer of J which is not a minimizer

(d) There exists an extremizer of J which is not a maximizer

[Dec 2019]

25. Is Jacobi's necessary condition satisfied by the admissible external for

$$J[y] = \int_0^b (y'^2 - y^2)\, dx$$

(a) Yes, for all values of b. (b) No for any value of b.
(c) Yes, for $b < \pi$ (d) Yes, for $b \geq \pi$

[Dec 2019]

26. Consider the functional $J[y] = \int_0^{\pi}((y')^2 - ky^2)\,dx$ with the boundary Conditions $y(0) = 0, y(\pi) = 0$.
Which of the following statements are true?
(a) It has a unique extremal for all $k \in \mathbb{R}$.
(b) It has at most one extremal if $\sqrt{k}$ is not an integer.
(c) It has infinitely many extremals if $\sqrt{k}$ is an integer.
(d) It has a unique extremal if $\sqrt{k}$ is an integer.

[Nov 2020]

27. The extremal of the functional
$J[y] = \int_0^1 e^x\sqrt{1+(y')^2}\,dx, y \in c^2[0,1]$ is of the form
(a) $y = \sec^{-1}\left(\frac{x}{c_1}\right) + c_2$, where c_1 and c_2 arbitary constants.
(b) $= \sec^{-1}\left(\frac{x}{c_1}\right) + c_2$; where $|c_1| < 1$ and c_2 is an arbitrary constant.
(c) $y = \tan^{-1}\left(\frac{x}{c_1}\right) + c_2$, where c_1 and c_2 are arbitary constants.
(d) $y = \tan^{-1}\left(\frac{x}{c_1}\right) + c_2$, where $|c_1| > 1$ and c_2 is an arbitary constant.

[Nov 2020]

28. Let B The unit ball in $\mathbb{R}^3$ cantered at origin. The Euler-Lagrange equation corresponding to the functional $I(U) = \frac{1}{2}\int_B |\nabla U|^2 dx - \frac{1}{5}\int_B |U|^5 dx$ is
(a) $\nabla U = U^4$ (b) $\nabla U = -U^4$
(c) $\det(D^2U) = U^4$ (d) $\nabla U = -|U|^3 U$

[Nov 2020]

29. Consider the problem of extremizing the functional $J[y] = \int_1^3 y(3x-y)\,dx$ with Boundary condition $y(1) = 1$and $y(3) = 2$. Which of the following are correct?
(a) There is unique extremal
(b) $y(x) = \frac{3x}{2}$is an extremal
(c) $y(x) = \frac{x}{2} + \frac{1}{2}$is an extremal
(d) There are no extremals

[Nov 2020]

30. If $y(t)$ is a stationary function of $\mathcal{J}[y] = \int_{-1}^{1}(1-x^2)(y')^2dx, y(-1) = 1, y(1) = 1$ subject to $\int_{-1}^{1} y^2 = 1$
Which of the following statements are true?
(a) y is unique
(b) y is always a polynomial of even order
(c) y is always a polynomial of odd order
(d) no such y exists

[SEP 2022]

31. Let $X = \{u \in c^1[0,1]: u(0) = u(1) = 0\}$. Let $I: X \to \mathbb{R}$ be defined as
$I(u) = \int_0^1 e^{-u'(t)^2}dt$, for all $u \in X$.
Let $M = \sup_{f\in X} I[f]$ and $m = \inf_{f\in X} I[f]$.
Which of the following statements are true?
(a) $M = 1, m = 0$ (b) $1 = M > m > 0$
(c) M is attained (d) m is attained

[SEP 2022]

32. Suppose $y(x)$ is an extremal of the following functional
$J(y(x)) = \int_0^1 (y(x)^2 = 4y(x)y'(x) + 4y'(x)^2)dx$
subject to $y(0) = 1$ and $y'(0) = 1/2$.
Which of the following statements are true?
(a) y is a concave function.
(b) y is a convex function.
(c) $(x_1 + x_2) = y(x_1)y(x_2)$ $for\ all\ x_1, x_2\ in\ [0,1]$.
(d) $y(x_1x_2) = y(x_1) + y(x_2)$ $for\ all\ x_1, x_2\ [0,1]$.

[JUNE 2023]

33. Let $y(x)$ and $z(x)$ be the stationary functions (extremals) of the variational problem

$$J(y(x), z(x)) = \int_0^1 [(y')^2 + (z')^2 + y'z']dx$$

Subject to $y(0) = 1, y(1) = 0, z(0) = -1, z(1) = 2$.
Which of the following statements are correct?
(a) $z(x) + 3y(x) = 2$ for $x \in [0,1]$.
(b) $3z(x) + y(x) = 2$ for $x \in [0,1]$.
(c) $y(x) + z(x) = 2x$ for $x \in [0,1]$.
(d) $y(x) + z(x) = x$ for $x \in [0,1]$.

[JUNE 2023]

34. Among the curves connecting the points (1, 2) and (2,8), let γ be the curve on which an extremal of the functional

$$J[y] = \int_1^2 (1 + x^3y')y'\,dx$$

can be attained. Then which of the following points lie on the curve γ?
(a) $(\sqrt{2}, 3)$ (b) $(\sqrt{2}, 6)$
(c) $\left(\sqrt{3}, \frac{22}{3}\right)$ (d) $\left(\sqrt{3}, \frac{23}{3}\right)$

[DEC-2023]

35. Define
$S := \{y \in C^1[-1,1]: y(-1) = -1, y(1) = 3\}$.
Let φ be the extremal of the functional $J: S \to \mathbb{R}$ given by $J[y] = \int_{-1}^{1}[(y')^3 + (y')^2]dx$.
Define $||y||_\infty := \max_{x\in[-1,1]} |y(x)|$ for every $y \in S$ and let
$B_o(\varphi, \varepsilon) := \{y \in S: ||y - \varphi||_\infty < \varepsilon\}$,
$B_1(\varphi, \varepsilon) := \{y \in S: ||y - \varphi||_\infty + ||y' - \varphi'||_\infty < \varepsilon\}$. Then which of the following statements are true?
(a) $\varphi(x) = 2x + 1$ for every $x \in [-1,1]$
(b) There exists $\varepsilon > 0$ such that $J[y] \geq J[\varphi]$ for every $y \in B_o(\varphi, \varepsilon)$
(c) There exists $\varepsilon > 0$ such that $J[y] \geq J[\varphi]$ for every $y \in B_1(\varphi, \varepsilon)$

(d) There exists $\varepsilon > 0$ such that $J[y] \leq J[\varphi]$ for every $y \in B_1(\varphi, \varepsilon)$

[Feb. 2025]

36. For any $b \in \mathbb{R}$, let $S(b)$ denote the set of all broken extremals with one corner of the variational problem
minimize $J[y] = \int_0^1 ((y')^4 - 3(y')^2)\, dx$,
subject to $y(0) = 0, y(1) = b$.
Then which of the following statements are true?
(a) $S(2)$ has exactly two elements
(b) $S\left(\frac{1}{2}\right)$ has exactly one element
(c) $S(2)$ is empty
(d) $S\left(\frac{1}{2}\right)$ has exactly two elements.

[Feb. 2025]

37. For $a, b, c \in \mathbb{R}$, consider the variational problem:
Minimize $J[y] = \int_0^2 [a(y')^2 + 2byy' + cy^2]\, dx$
subject to $y(0) = 10, y(1) = 100$.
Then which of the following statements are true?
(a) If (a, b, c) = (-2, 1, -2), then every admissible extremal is a minimizer
(b) If (a, b, c) = (1,0, 2), then every admissible extremal is a minimizer
(c) If (a, b, c) = (2,-1, 1), then every admissible extremal is a minimizer
(d) If (a, b, c) = (1, -2, 5), then every admissible extremal is a minimizer

[June 2025]

38. For $\alpha \geq 0$, consider the functional
$$J_{\alpha[y]} = \int_1^2 \frac{(y')^2}{x^\alpha} dx$$
defined for all continuously differentiable functions defined on the interval [1, 2] satisfying the conditions $y(1) = 1, y(2) = 2$.
Then which of the following statements are true?
(a) $y(x) = \frac{1}{15}(x^4 + 14)$ is an extremal for J_3
(b) $y(x) = \frac{1}{3}(x^2 + 2)$ is an extremal for J_1
(c) $y(x) = x$ is an extremal for J_0
(d) $y(x) = \frac{1}{2}(x^2 - x + 2)$ is an extremal for J_1

[June 2025]

39. Suppose $y(x)$ is the extremal of the variational problem
$J(y) = \int_0^1 ((y')^2 \sin x + (2\cos x)y)\, dx$
subject to $y(0) = 0, y(1) = 1$.
Then which of the following statements are true?
(a) $y\left(\frac{1}{2}\right) = 1$ (b) $y'(0) = 1$
(c) $y\left(\frac{1}{4}\right) = 2$ (d) $y'\left(\frac{1}{2}\right) = 1$

[Dec 2025]

ANSWER KEY

1	2	3	4	5
a,b,c,d	a,b,c	c	d	a
6	**7**	**8**	**9**	**10**
a,b ,c	b, d	a,b	a,b	c
11	**12**	**13**	**14**	**15**
a,b,c,d	a,c	b,d	a,d	a,c
16	**17**	**18**	**19**	**20**
a	b,d	a	a	a
21	**22**	**23**	**24**	**25**
c, d	b	c,	a,d	c
26	**27**	**28**	**29**	**30**
b,c	NONE	d	d	d
31	**32**	**33**	**34**	**35**
a, c	a, c	a, c	b, c	a, c
36	**37**	**38**	**39**	
c,d	a,b,c,d	a,b,c	b,d	

EXPLANATION

MSQ (Multiple Select Questions)

1. **Explanation: (a), (b), (c), (d)**
$I(y) = \int_{x_0}^{x_1} F\left(x, y, \frac{dy}{dx}\right) dx; y(x_0) = a, y(x_1) = b$
Since in Ritz method coordinate function linearly independent, continuously differentiable so option (a) , (b),(c) are correct .
(d): The coordinate function $\phi_i(x); i = 1, 2 \ldots$
Defined on $[x_0, x_1]$ must be linearly independent, smooth & the functional be considered not along admissible curves $y(x)$ but only along all possible linear combination's admissible functions.
Hence, option (d) is correct.

2. **Explanation: (a), (b), (c)**
From the definition of approximate solution, it is defined as $z = \sum_{i=1}^{n} \alpha_i \phi_i(x, y)$ – – – (1)
where α_i's should be constant, $\phi_i(x, y)$ should be linearly independent and continuous.
So, option (a) correct for $i = 1,2$ option (b) correct and for $i = 1$ option (c) correct.
Let $z_0 = \sum_{i=1}^{n} \alpha_i \phi_i(x, y)$ – – – (2)
be the assumed approximate solution, where α_i's should be constant, $\phi_i(x, y)$ should be linearly independent and continuous.
According to the given D,
$-1 \leq x \leq 1, -1 \leq y \leq 1$ and $z = 0$
$\Rightarrow z = 0$ at $x = \pm 1$ ... (3)
And $z = 0$ at $y = \pm 1$ ... (4)
So, we have to assume such a function which will satisfy these two conditions,
i.e. $z = c(x^2 - 1)(y^2 - 1)$
For option (d) we should have to find value of c.
If $z_x = 2cx(y^2 - 1)$
And $z_y = 2yx(x^2 - 1)$
$f(z(x, y)) = \int_{-1}^{1} \int_{-1}^{1} (2cx(y^2 - 1))^2 + (2yc(x^2 - 1))^2 - 2c(x^2 - 1)(y^2 - 1)\, dx\, dy$
$= 4\left(c^2\left[\frac{4}{3}\left(\frac{1}{5} - \frac{2}{3} + 1\right) + \frac{4}{3}\left(\frac{1}{5} - \frac{2}{2} + 1\right)\right] - 2c\left[\left(\frac{1}{3} - 1\right)\left(\frac{1}{3} - 1\right)\right]\right) = 4\left[c^2 \frac{64}{45} - 2c\frac{4}{9}\right] = \frac{256}{45}c^2 - \frac{32}{9}c$
Now $\frac{df(z(x,y))}{dc} = 0 => \frac{df(z(x,y))}{dc} = \frac{512}{45}c - \frac{32}{9} = 0 =>$
$c = \frac{5}{16}$, so option (d) wrong.

3. **Explanation: (c)**

Here $F(x,y,y') = (1+y^2)/y'^2$,

Since F is free from x

By using special form of Euler's equation

$F - y'F_{y'} = c$

$\Rightarrow \frac{1+y'^2}{(y')^2} - y'\frac{\partial}{\partial y'}\left(\frac{1+y^2}{y'^2}\right) = C$

$\Rightarrow y' = (1+y^2)^{\frac{1}{2}}$

Solving we get

Y(x)= sinh (AX+B)

Option (c) is correct

4. **Explanation: (d)**

For the functional $I(y) = \int_0^1 \left(\frac{1}{2}y'^2 - y\right)dx, y(0) = 0, y(1) = 0$

$F(x,y,y') = \frac{1}{2}y'^2 - y$,

so by Euler's equation

$\frac{\partial F}{\partial y} - \frac{d}{dx}\left(\frac{\partial F}{\partial y'}\right) = 0$

$\Rightarrow y'' + 1 = 0 \Rightarrow y' = -x + c$

$\Rightarrow y = -\frac{x^2}{2} + Ax + B,$

$y(0) = 0 \Rightarrow B = 0$ and $y(1) = 0 \Rightarrow A = \frac{1}{2} \Rightarrow y_n(x) = -\frac{x^2}{2} + \frac{1}{2}x = \frac{1}{2}x(1-x)$. As exact extremising function is of order 2, so by Rayleigh-Ritz method y_{app} which will be also degree 2, will agree with $y_n(x)$ at all points $0 \le x \le 1$ (d) is correct.

5. **Explanation: (a)**

Here $f(t,x,\dot{x}) = \frac{\dot{x}^3}{t^3}$ - - - (1)

Euler's equation for the given functional is

$\frac{dF}{dx} - \frac{d}{dt}\left(\frac{dF}{d\dot{x}}\right) = 0$

$\Rightarrow 0 - \frac{d}{dt}\left(\frac{2\dot{x}}{t^3}\right) = 0$

$\Rightarrow \frac{2\dot{x}}{t^3} = c$

$\Rightarrow 2\dot{x} = ct^3$

$\Rightarrow 2x = \frac{ct^4}{4} + d$

$\Rightarrow x(t) = \frac{ct^4}{8} + \frac{d}{2}$ - - - (2)

$\because x(1) = 3$ and $x(2) = 18$ in equation (2) we have

$\Rightarrow 3 = \frac{c}{8} + \frac{d}{2}$ ... (3)

And $18 = 2c + \frac{d}{2}$ ... (4)

Solving (3) and (4), we get

$c = 8$ and $d = 4$

$\Rightarrow x(t) = t^4 + 2$

So, option (a) is correct.

6. **Explanation: (a), (b), (c)**

Here $F(x,y,y') = \sqrt{1 + (y'(x))^2}$,

Since, $F(x,y,y')$ is free from x & y, the Euler's equation is

$\frac{\partial F}{\partial y} - \frac{d}{dx}\left(\frac{\partial F}{\partial y'}\right) = 0$

$\Rightarrow \frac{\partial F}{\partial y'} = \text{constant}$

$\Rightarrow \frac{y'}{\sqrt{1+(y')^2}} = c$

$\Rightarrow y' = c\sqrt{1+(y')^2}$

$\Rightarrow (y')^2 = (1+(y')^2)c^2$

$\Rightarrow (y')^2 = \frac{c^2}{1-c^2}$

$\Rightarrow y' = \text{constant} = a$, where $a = \sqrt{\frac{c^2}{1-c^2}}$

$\Rightarrow y'' = 0$

$\Rightarrow y(x) = c_2x + c_3$, which is a straight line.

Hence, options (a), (b) and (c) are true.

7. **Explanation: (b), (d)**

$F(x,y,z,p,q) = \frac{1}{2}(p^2 + q^2 + e^{xy}u)$

$\frac{\partial F}{\partial u} - \frac{d}{dx}\left(\frac{\partial F}{\partial p}\right) - \frac{d}{dy}\left(\frac{\partial F}{\partial q}\right) = 0$

$\Rightarrow e^{xy} - u_{xx} - u_{yy} = 0$

$\Rightarrow u_{xx} + u_{yy} = e^{xy}$

(d) is simple property, (b), (d) are true.

Hence options (b), (d) are true.

8. **Explanation: (a), (b)**

Given that $y \in C^2([0,\pi]), y(0) = y(\pi) = 0$ and $\int_0^\pi y^2 dx = 1, f(x,y,y') = (y'(x))^2$

Here, $F(x,y,y') = (y'(x))^2 + \lambda y^2(x)$

The Euler's equation is

$\frac{\partial F}{\partial y} - \frac{d}{dx}\left(\frac{\partial F}{\partial y'}\right) = 0$

$\Rightarrow y'' + \lambda y = 0$ - - - (2)

If $\lambda = 0$, then $y'' = 0$

$\Rightarrow y(x) = Ax + B$

Since $y(0) = 0$

$\Rightarrow B = 0$

Since $y(\pi) = 0$

$A\pi = 0$

$\Rightarrow A = 0$

$\Rightarrow y(x) = 0$

If $\lambda < 0$, take $\lambda = -\mu^2 (\mu \neq 0)$

$\Rightarrow y'' - \mu^2 y = 0 \Rightarrow$ *the auxiliary equation is* $m^2 - \mu^2 = 0 \Rightarrow m = \pm\mu$

$\Rightarrow y(x) = c_1e^{\mu x} + c_2e^{-\mu x}$

Since $y(0) = 0$

$\Rightarrow c_1 + c_2 = 0$

$\Rightarrow c_1 = -c_2$

Since $y(\pi) = 0$

$\Rightarrow c_1e^{\mu\pi} + c_2e^{-\mu\pi} = 0$

$\Rightarrow c_1e^{2\mu\pi} - c_1 = 0$

$\Rightarrow c_1(e^{2\mu\pi} - 1) = 0$

$\Rightarrow c_1 = 0$

$\Rightarrow y(x) = 0$

If $\lambda > 0$, take $\lambda = \mu^2 (\mu \neq 0)$

$\Rightarrow y'' + \mu^2 y = 0 \Rightarrow$ the auxiliary equation is $m^2 + \mu^2 = 0 \Rightarrow m = \pm\mu i$

$\Rightarrow y(x) = A\sin\mu x + B\cos\mu x$

$\Rightarrow y(x) = A\sin\sqrt{\lambda}\,x + B\cos\sqrt{\lambda}\,x$ ... (2)

Where, $\lambda > 0$; A, B are arbitrary constants.

Now $y(0) = 0 \Rightarrow B = 0$

So, $y(x) = A\sin\sqrt{\lambda}\,x$

Also, $y(\pi) = 0$

$\Rightarrow A\sin\sqrt{\lambda}\pi = 0$

If $A = 0 \Rightarrow y(x) = 0$

If $A \neq 0 \Rightarrow \sin\sqrt{\lambda}\pi = 0$

$\Rightarrow \sqrt{\lambda}\pi = n\pi$

$\Rightarrow \lambda = n^2 m\, n \in \mathbb{N}$

Take $n = 1$

$\Rightarrow y(x) = A\sin x$

Also, $\int_0^\pi y^2(x)\,dx = 1$

$$\Rightarrow A^2\int_0^\pi \sin^2 x dx = 1$$

$$\Rightarrow \frac{A^2}{2}\int_0^\pi (1-\cos 2x)\,dx = 1$$

$$\Rightarrow A^2\left[x - \frac{\sin 2x}{2}\right]_0^\pi = 2$$

$$\Rightarrow A^2[\pi - 0] = 2$$

$$\Rightarrow A^2 = \frac{2}{\pi}$$

$$\Rightarrow A = \pm\sqrt{\frac{2}{\pi}}$$

$$\Rightarrow y(x) = \pm\sqrt{\frac{2}{\pi}}\sin x$$

Hence, options (a) and (b) are correct.

9. Explanation: (a), (b)

$f(x, y, y') = y'^2 - y^2 - - - (1)$

By Lagrange condition,

$F_{y'y'} = 2 > 0 \quad \forall y'$

$\Rightarrow$ Strong minimum

$\Rightarrow$ Weak minima.

Hence, option (a) and (b) are correct.

10. Explanation: (c)

Here, $F(x, y, y') = y^2(y')^2$ i.e. free from x

Then, by Euler Lagrange's equation

$$F - y'\frac{\partial F}{\partial y'} = c$$

$\Rightarrow y^2y'^2 - y'(2y^2y') = c$

$\Rightarrow y^2y'^2 - 2y^2y'^2 = c$

$\Rightarrow y^2y'^2 = c_1$

$\Rightarrow yy' = \sqrt{c_1} = c_2$

$$\Rightarrow \int y\cdot dy = \int c_2\,dx$$

$$\Rightarrow \frac{y^2}{2} = c_2 x + d$$

$\Rightarrow y^2 = 2c_2 x + 2d$

Since $y(0) = 0 \Rightarrow d = 0$

$\Rightarrow y^2 = 2c_2 x$

Also, $y(x_1) = y_1$

$\Rightarrow y_1^2 = 2c_2 x_1$

$$\Rightarrow c_2 = \frac{y_1^2}{2x_1}$$

$\Rightarrow y^2 = \frac{y_1^2 x}{x_1}$ which is a parabola ($y^2 = 4ax$; $4a = \frac{y_1^2}{x_1}$)

Thus, option (c) is correct.

11. Explanation: (a), (b), (c), (d)

Given

$J[y] = \int_a^b f(x, y, y')\,dx$ ... (1)

For showing the existence of a minimizer for the functional

(1) it is sufficient to have a convergent subsequence and J is continuous for which these is a minimizing sequence $\langle\phi_n\rangle$,so option (c) correct as other option are implied from (c) so all options are correct.

Hence, option (a), (b), (c) and (d) are correct.

12. Explanation: (a), (c)

Here, $F(x, y, y') = y'^2 + x^2$

$\Rightarrow F_{y'y'} = 2 > 0; \forall y'$

$\Rightarrow$ *functional has* Strong minima

$\Rightarrow$ it also has Weak minima.

Hence, option (a) and (c) are correct.

13. Explanation: (b), (d)

$$J(y) = \int_0^4 (y'-1)^2(y'+1)^2\,dx$$

Here boundary conditions are not given so we proceed without solving from the options to get the minimum as 0.

(a) for $y = \frac{x}{2}; 0 \le x \le 4$

$y' = \frac{1}{2}, (y'-1)^2(y'+1)^2 = \frac{1}{4}\times\frac{9}{4}$

$\Rightarrow J[y] = \int_0^4 \frac{1}{4}\times\frac{9}{4}dx = \frac{9}{4}$

(b) for $y = \begin{cases} -x; & 0 \le x \le 1 \\ x-2; & 1 \le x \le 4 \end{cases}$

$y' = \begin{cases} -1; & 0 \le x \le 1 \\ 1; & 1 \le x \le 4 \end{cases} (y'-1)^2(y'+1)^2 = 0, \forall x \in [0,4]$

$J[y] = \int_0^1 0\,dx + \int_0^4 0\,dx = 0$

(c) for $y = \begin{cases} 2x; & 0 < x \le 2 \\ -x+6; & 2 \le x \le 4 \end{cases}$

$(y'-1)^2(y'+1)^2 = \begin{cases} 9 & 0 < x \le 2 \\ 0, & 2 \le x \le 4 \end{cases}$

$J[y] = \int_0^2 9\,dx + \int_0^4 0\,dx = 18$

(d) for $y = \begin{cases} x; & 0 \le x \le 3 \\ -x+6; & 3 \le x \le 4 \end{cases} (y'-1)^2(y'+1)^2 = 0\ \forall x \in [0,4]$

$J[y] = \int_0^3 0\,dx + \int_0^4 0\,dx = 0$

Option (b) and (d) are correct.

14. Explanation: (a), (d)

Since we know, A minimize R in $C^1(\overline{D})$ of

$E(v) = \int_{\Omega} F(n, v, \nabla v)\,dx - \int_{\partial\Omega} g(u, v)ds$

Is a solution of the given boundary value problem if

$u \in C^2(\overline{D}), \sum_{i=1}^{n} \frac{\partial}{\partial x_i} Fu_{x_i} = F_u$ in Ω

And $\sum_{i=1}^{n} Fu_{xi} v_i = g_u$ on $\partial\Omega$

Where v is the unit normal on the boundary $\partial\Omega$.

Now, $I(u) = \int_B |\nabla u|^2 + fu\,dx + \int_{\partial B} au^2 ds$

$F(x, y, u, u_x, u_y) = u_x^2 + u_y^2 + fu$

$\Rightarrow 2u_x + 2u_y = f$

$\Rightarrow 2\nabla u = f$

$\Rightarrow 2\nabla u - f = 0$

Also, $g = -au^2$

$\sum_{i=1}^{n} Fu_{xi} v_i = g_u$ on $\partial\Omega$

$2u_x + 2u_y = -2au$

$u_x + u_y = au$

$\frac{\partial u}{\partial n} + au = 0$ on ∂B

thus, option (a) and (d) are correct.

15. Explanation: (a), (c)

Here $F(t, u, u') = u'(t)^2 - u(t)^2 - - - (1)$

Euler's equation is

$F_u - \frac{d}{dx}\{F_{u'}\} = 0$

$\Rightarrow -2u - \frac{d}{dt}(2u') = 0$

$\Rightarrow u'' + u = 0 - - - (2)$

Auxiliary equation of (2)$\Rightarrow m^2 + 1 = 0 \Rightarrow m = \pm i$

$\Rightarrow u = A\cos t + B\sin t$

Since, $u(0) = 0 \Rightarrow A = 0$

$\Rightarrow u(t) = B\sin t$

$\Rightarrow I(u) = \int_0^1 (B^2\cos^2 t - B^2\sin^2 t)\,dt$

$= B^2 \int_0^1 \cos 2t\,dt$

$= \frac{B^2 \sin 2}{2}$

As $\frac{\sin 2}{2}$, is positive and B^2 is positive so $I(u)$ is bounded below and attains its infimum.

Hence, $I(u)$ is bounded below and attains its infimum.

Hence, options (a) and (c) are correct.

16. Explanation: (a)

Here $F(t, u, u') = \frac{1}{2}u'(t)^2 - 4\pi^2 u(t)^2 - - - (1)$

Euler's equation is given by

$\frac{\partial F}{\partial u} - \frac{\partial}{\partial t}\left(\frac{\partial F}{\partial u'}\right) = 0$

$\Rightarrow -4\pi^2 u - \frac{d}{dt}(u') = 0$

$\Rightarrow u'' + 4\pi^2 u = 0 - - - -(2)$

Auxiliary equation of (2)$\Rightarrow m^2 + 4\pi^2 = 0 \Rightarrow m = \pm 2\pi i$

$\Rightarrow u(t) = c_1\cos 2\pi t + c_2\sin 2\pi t$

Since, $u(0) = 0 \Rightarrow c_1 = 0$

$\Rightarrow u(t) = c_2\sin 2\pi t\ \forall t \in [0, 1]$

Let $c_2 = 1 \Rightarrow$

$I(u) = \frac{1}{2}\int_0^1((2\pi\cos 2\pi t)^2 - 4\pi^2\sin^2 2\pi t)\,dt$

$= 4\pi^2 \int_0^1 \cos 4\pi t\,dt$

$= \pi[\sin 4\pi t]_0^1$

$= \pi(\sin 4\pi - \sin 0) = 0$

Option (a) is correct.

17. Explanation: (b), (d)

$J(u) = \int_B \left(\frac{\partial u_1}{\partial x_1}\frac{\partial u_2}{\partial x_2} - \frac{\partial u_1}{\partial x_2}\frac{\partial u_2}{\partial x_1}\right) dx_1 dx_2$,

where $B = \{(x_1, x_2) \epsilon \mathbb{R}^2 | x_1^2 + x_2^2 < 1\}$

So $J(u) = x_1^2 + x_2^2 < 1$

$\int_B \left(\frac{\partial u_1}{\partial x_1}\frac{\partial u_2}{\partial x_2} - \frac{\partial u_1}{\partial x_2}\frac{\partial u_2}{\partial x_1}\right) dx_1 dx_2 - - - - - - - (1)$

From question $u(x_1) = x_1$ and $u(x_2) = x_2$ using the above in (1)

$J(u) = \iint_{x_1^2 + x_2^2 < 1} (1.1 - 0.0)dx_1 dx_2 \approx \pi$,

(as $x_1^2 + x_2^2 < 1$, double integral represent area here area inside the unit circle

Now proceeding through options, since J(u) $= \pi > 0$ hence option (b) and (d) correct.

18. Explanation: (a)

Here $F(x, y, y') = e^{-x}y'^2 + 2e^x(y' + y) - - - (1)$

Y(log3)=1 & y(0) is free

Euler's equation is given by

$F_y - \frac{d}{dx}\{F_{y'}\} = 0$

$\Rightarrow 2e^x - \frac{d}{dx}[2e^{-x}y' + 2e^x] = 0$

$\Rightarrow 2e^x + 2e^{-x}y' - 2e^{-x}y'' - 2e^x = 0$

$\Rightarrow y''2e^{-x} - 2e^{-x}y' = 0$

$\Rightarrow 2e^{-x}[y'' - y'] = 0$

$\Rightarrow y'' - y' = 0 - - - (2)$

Auxiliary equation of (2)

$\Rightarrow m^2 - m = 0$

$\Rightarrow m(m - 1) = 0 \Rightarrow m = 0, m = 1$

$\Rightarrow y(x) = c_1 + c_2 e^x$ ... (3)

$\Rightarrow y(\log 3) = c_1 + c_2 e^{\log 3} = c_1 + 3c_2 = 1$ ... (4)

Now second boundary condition

$F_{y'}(0, y(0), y'(0)) = 0$

$\Rightarrow 2y'(0) + 2 = 0$

$\Rightarrow y'(0) = -1$

$\Rightarrow c_2 = -1$

By (4) equation, we get $c_1 = 4$

$\Rightarrow y(x) = 4 - e^x$

Thus, option (a) is correct.

19. Explanation: (a)

$J[y] = \int_0^1 y'^2(x)dx$ subject to $y(0) = 0, y(1) = 1$ and $\int_0^1 y(x)dx = 0$, this problem is an isoperimetric problem.

Let $F(x, y, y') = y'^2 + \lambda y$

Euler's equation is

$\frac{\partial F}{\partial y} - \frac{d}{dx}\left(\frac{\partial F}{\partial y'}\right) = \lambda - \frac{\partial}{dx}(2y)$

$= \lambda - 2y'' = 0$

$\Rightarrow y'' = \dfrac{\lambda}{2}$

Integrating

$\Rightarrow y' = \dfrac{\lambda}{2}x + c_1$

Again integrating

$\Rightarrow y(x) = \dfrac{\lambda x^2}{4} + c_1 x + c_2 - - - (i)$

Given that $y(0) = 0$ and $y(1) = 1$ using in (i)

$\Rightarrow c_2 = 0$ and $\frac{\lambda}{4} + c_1 = 1$

i.e., $c_1 = 1 - \frac{\lambda}{4}$

$\Rightarrow y(x) = \frac{\lambda}{4}x^2 + \left(1 - \frac{\lambda}{4}\right)x3$

Also, $\int_0^1 y(x)\,dx = 0$

$$\int_0^1 \frac{\lambda}{4}x^2 + \left(1 - \frac{\lambda}{4}\right)x\,dx = 0$$

$$\Rightarrow \frac{\lambda}{12} + \frac{\left(1 - \frac{\lambda}{4}\right)}{2} = 0$$

$$\Rightarrow \frac{\lambda}{12} - \frac{\lambda}{8} = -\frac{1}{2}$$

$\Rightarrow \lambda = 12$

$\Rightarrow c_1 = 1 - 3 = -2$

$\Rightarrow y(x) = 3x^2 - 2x$

So, option (a) is correct.

20. Explanation: (a)

Here $F(x, y, y', y'') = 720x^2 y - (y'')^2$

Euler's equation is

$$\frac{\partial F}{\partial y} - \frac{d}{dx}\left(\frac{\partial F}{\partial y'}\right) + \frac{d^2}{dx^2}\left(\frac{\partial F}{\partial y''}\right) = 0$$

$$\Rightarrow 720x^2 - \frac{d}{dx}(0) + \frac{d^2}{dx^2}(-2y'')$$

$\Rightarrow 720\,x^2 - 2y'''' = 0$

$\Rightarrow y^{IV} = 360x^2$

Integrating $\Rightarrow y''' = 120x^3 + c_1$

Integrating $\Rightarrow y'' = 30x^4 + c_1 x + c_2$

Integrating $\Rightarrow y' = 6x^5 + c_1\frac{x^2}{2} + c_2 x + c_3$

Again integrating

$\Rightarrow y(x) = x^6 + c_1\frac{x^3}{6} + c_2\frac{x^2}{2} + c_3 x + c_4 - - - (1)$

Also $y(0) = 0 \Rightarrow c_4 = 0$

And $y'(0) = 0 \Rightarrow c_3 = 0$

Since, $y(1) = 0 \Rightarrow 1 + \frac{c_1}{6} + \frac{c_2}{2} = 0$

$\Rightarrow c_1 + 3c_2 = -6$ ... (2)

Since, $y'(1) = 6 \Rightarrow 6 + \frac{c_1}{2} + c_2 = 6$

$\Rightarrow c_1 + 2c_2 = 0$ ... (3)

Solving equation (2) and (3), we get

$\Rightarrow c_2 = -6$ and $c_1 = 12$

$\Rightarrow y(x) = x^6 + 2x^3 - 3x^2$

Hence, option (a) is correct.

21. Explanation: (c), (d)

Here $f(x, y, y') = (y'(x))^2 + (y'(x))^3 - - - - - - (1)$

From (1) $f(x, y, y')$ *is independent of* x, y, so Euler's equation becomes $y'' = 0 - - - (2)$

Integrating (2) twice we get $y(x) = ax + b$; *where* a, b *arbitary constants* $- - - (3)$

Using the given conditions $y(0) = 1$ and $y(1) = 2$ in (3) we get $b = 1, a = 1$;

$\therefore y(x) = x + 1 - - - (4)$

$y(x) \in C^\infty[0,1]$, *as* $y', y'', y''', - - - - - - -$ *exists.*

So option (a), (b) wrong and (c),(d) correct .

22. Explanation: (b)

By Isoperimetric problem: -

$F = f + \lambda g$

$F = y'^2 + \lambda y^2$

By Euler's Equation: - $\frac{\partial F}{\partial y} - \frac{d}{dx}\left[\frac{\partial F}{\partial y'}\right] = 0$

$\Rightarrow 2\lambda y - \dfrac{d}{dx}(2y') = 0 \Rightarrow y'' = \lambda y$

(i) $\lambda = 0 \;\Rightarrow y'' = 0 \;\Rightarrow y = ax + b$

Using BCs: $a = b = 0 \;\Rightarrow y = 0$

(ii) $\lambda = n^2$: $\;y'' = n^2\,y \Rightarrow \Rightarrow y = G\,e^{nx} + He^{-nx}$

Using BCs :- $G = H = 0 \;\Rightarrow y = 0$

(iii) $\lambda = -n^2 \Rightarrow y'' = -\,n^2\,y$

$\Rightarrow y(x) = G\cos n\,x + H\sin nx\,;\quad n = 1,2,3 \ldots\ldots$

Using $B.C.S \Rightarrow\;\; y(0) = 0, G = 0$

$y(\pi) = 0 \;\Rightarrow H\;\sin\,n\pi = 0$

$\because H \neq 0 \;\Rightarrow \sin n\pi = \sin m\,\pi$

$\Rightarrow n = m\;; m = 1,2,3 \ldots$

$y(x) = H\;\sin n\;mx\;\;; m = 1,2,3\ldots.$

$$\int_0^\pi y^2\,dx = 1 \;\Rightarrow\;\; H^2\int_0^\pi \sin^2\;mx\,dx = 1$$

[$\because \cos 2x = 1 - 2\,\sin^2 x = 2\cos^2 x - 1$]=>

$$H^2\int_0^\pi \frac{1 - \cos 2mx}{2}\,dx = 1$$

$$\Rightarrow H^2\left(\frac{\pi}{2} - 0\right) = 1$$

$\Rightarrow H^2[\pi/2] = 1 \;\;\Rightarrow H^2 = 2/\pi$

External Functional = $\int_0^\pi \left[\frac{dy}{dx}\right]^2\,dx$

$$\because\;\; y = \sqrt{2/\pi}\,\sin mx \Rightarrow \frac{dy}{dx} = m\sqrt{2/\pi}\cos mx$$

$$\Rightarrow F = \int_0^\pi \frac{2m^2}{\pi}\;\cos^2\;mx\;dx$$

$$\Rightarrow F = \frac{2m^2}{\pi}\frac{\pi}{2} = m^2,\;\; m = 1,2,3 \ldots\ldots\ldots.$$

Minimum value of functional attained at $m = 1$ *so minimum value is* 1

23. Explanation: (c)

$y = y(x) \in C^4([0,1])$

$$I\,[y] = \int_0^1 \left[\left(\frac{d^2y}{dx^2}\right)^2 - 2y\right]dx\;, y(0) =$$

Euler's Equation.: -

$$\frac{\partial F}{\partial y} - \frac{d}{dx}\left[\frac{\partial F}{\partial y'}\right] + \frac{d^2}{dx^2}\left[\frac{\partial^2 F}{\partial y'^2}\right] = 0$$

$$\Rightarrow -2 + \frac{d^2}{dx^2}(\,2y'') = 0$$

$\Rightarrow y^{(4)} - 1 = 0$

Integrating both side

$\Rightarrow y'''(x) = x + a$

$\Rightarrow y''(x) = \frac{x^2}{2} + ax + b - - - - - -(1)$

$\Rightarrow y'(x) = \frac{x^3}{6} + \frac{ax^2}{2} + bx + c$

$y = \frac{x^4}{24} + \frac{a}{6}x^3 + \frac{b}{2}x^2 + cx + d - - - - -(2)$

The natural boundary condition is $y''(0) = 0 = y''(1)$ using in (1)

We get $b = 0 ; and\ 0 = \frac{1}{2} + a \Rightarrow a = -\frac{1}{2}$

$\because y(0) = 0 \Rightarrow d = 0\ and\ y(1) = 0 \Rightarrow \frac{1}{24} + \frac{-\frac{1}{2}}{6} + \frac{0}{2} + c = 0 \Rightarrow c = \frac{1}{24}$

$y(x) = \frac{x}{24}(x^3 - 2x^2 + 1)$

So option (c) correct.

24. Explanation: (a), (d)

$F(x, y, y') = y'^2 + 2yy' - 16y^2; y(0) = 0, y\left(\frac{\pi}{8}\right) = 1$

Euler-Lagrange's equation is

$\frac{\partial F}{\partial y} - \frac{d}{dx}\left(\frac{\partial F}{\partial y'}\right) = 0$

$\Rightarrow 2y' - 32y - \frac{d}{dx}(2y' + 2y) = 0$

$\Rightarrow 2y' - 32y - 2y'' - 2y' = 0$

$\Rightarrow y'' + 16y = 0 \quad ....(*)$

The auxiliary equation for (*)

$m^2 + 16 = 0 \Rightarrow m = \pm 4i$

$y(x) = c_1\cos(4x) + c_2\sin(4x)$

$\Rightarrow y(0) = c_1\cos(0) + c_2\sin(0) \Rightarrow 0$

$y(x) = c_2\sin(4x)$

$\Rightarrow y\left(\frac{\pi}{8}\right) = c_2\sin\left(4\,\frac{\pi}{8}\right) = c_2\sin\left(\frac{\pi}{2}\right)$

$\Rightarrow 1 = c_2 .1$

$\Rightarrow c_2 = 1$

$\therefore y(x) = \sin(4x)$

$f(x, y, y') = y'^2 + 2yy' - 16y^2$

$f_{y'}(x, y, y') = 2y' + 2y$

$f_{y'y'}(x, y, y') = 2 > 0$

Hence option (a) correct and option (b) not correct and option incorrect and option (d) correct.

25. Explanation: (c)

$F(x, y, y') = y'^2 - y^2;$

$F_y = -2y, F_{yy} = -2$

$F_{y'} = 2y', F_{y'y'} = 2, F_{yy'} = 0$

Jacobi's condition

$\left[F_{yy} - \frac{d}{dx}F_{yy'}\right]u - \frac{d}{dx}(F_{y'y'}\,u') = 0$

Where $\frac{\partial y(x,c)}{\partial c} = u$ and $u(x_1) = 0$

i.e. $\left[-2 - \frac{d}{dx}(0)\right]u - \frac{d}{dx}(2u') = 0$

$\Rightarrow 2u + 2u'' = 0$

$\Rightarrow u'' + u = 0 \quad ....(*)$

Auxiliary equation of (*) is

$m^2 + 1 = 0 \Rightarrow m = \pm i$

$\therefore lu(x) = c_1\cos x + c_2\sin x$

$u(0) = c_1\cos 0 + c_2\sin 0$

$\Rightarrow 0 = c_1$

$\therefore u(x) = c_2\sin x; where\ c_2 \neq 0 \ ......(**)$

Now for different values of c_2. We get different solution.

So, it $b < \pi$ then we set unique pencil point.

So option (c) correct and option (d) incorrect.

So, as we get one solution only $in(0, \pi)\ and\ b < \pi$. So, option (a), (b) both are incorrect.

26. Explanation: (b), (c)

Here $F(x, y, y') = y'^2 + ky^2$ .... (i)

$y(0) = 0 = y(\pi)$

Euler's-Lagrange's equation is,

$\frac{\partial F}{\partial y} - \frac{d}{dx}\left(\frac{\partial F}{\partial y'}\right) = 0$

$\Rightarrow 2ky - \frac{d}{dx}(2y') = 0$

$\Rightarrow 2ky - 2y'' = 0 \Rightarrow y'' - ky = 0$ .... (ii)

If $k = 0$, then $y'' = 0$

$\Rightarrow y(x) = A + Bx.$

Now $y(0) = A \Rightarrow A = 0$

And $y(\pi) = B\pi \Rightarrow 0 = B$

$\therefore y(x) = 0$

If $k > 0; k = \alpha^2, \alpha \neq 0$

$y'' - \alpha^2 y = 0 \Rightarrow$ auxiliary equation becomes

$m^2 - \alpha^2 = 0 \Rightarrow m = \pm\alpha$

$\therefore y(x) = c_1e^{\alpha x} + c_2e^{-\alpha x}$

$y(0) = c_1 + c_2 \Rightarrow c_1 + c_2 = 0$ .... (iii)

$y(\pi) = c_1e^{\alpha\pi} + c_2e^{-\alpha\pi}$

$\Rightarrow$

$c_1e^{\alpha\pi} + c_2e^{-\alpha\pi} = 0$ ..... (iv)

Solving (iii) and (iv) we set

$c_1 = c_2 = 0 \Rightarrow y(x) = 0$

If $k < 0; k = -\alpha^2;\ \alpha \neq 0$

Then $y'' + \alpha^2 y = 0$

Auxiliary equation becomes,

$m^2 + \alpha^2 = 0$

$\Rightarrow m = \pm\alpha i$

$y(x) = C\cos\alpha x + D\sin\alpha x$

$y(0) = C\cos 0 + D\sin 0 \Rightarrow 0 = C$

$y(x) = D\sin\alpha x$

$\Rightarrow y(\pi) = D\sin\alpha\pi \Rightarrow D\sin\alpha\pi = 0$

$\Rightarrow \sin\alpha\pi = 0 (\because D \neq 0)$

$\Rightarrow \alpha\pi = n\pi; n \in \mathbb{Z}$

$\Rightarrow \alpha = n; n \in \mathbb{Z}$

So $k = \alpha^2 = n^2; n \in \mathbb{Z}$

$\therefore y(x) = D\sin nx; n \in \mathbb{Z}$

So we get infinite many solution if $k = n^2$

Since $\alpha = \sqrt{k} = n$ and $n \in \mathbb{Z}$

Hence option (c) correct.

Since $y = 0$ is also a solution for $k = 0$ or $k < 0$ so we have at most one solution if $\sqrt{k}$ is not an integer i.e. option (b) also correct.

27. Explanation:

Here $F(x, y, y') = e^x\sqrt{1 + (y')^2}$

Euler-Lagrange equation is,

$$\frac{\partial F}{\partial y}-\frac{d}{dx}\left(\frac{\partial F}{\partial y'}\right)=0$$

$$\Rightarrow 0-\frac{d}{dx}\left(\frac{e^x}{2\sqrt{1+(y')^2}}.2y'\right)=0$$

Integrating,

$$\Rightarrow \frac{e^x.y'}{\sqrt{1+(y')^2}}=c_1$$

$$\Rightarrow e^x y'=c_1\sqrt{1+(y')^2}$$

$$\Rightarrow e^{2x}y'^2=c_1^2(1+y'^2)$$

$$\Rightarrow y'^2=\frac{c_1^2}{e^{2x}-c_1^2}$$

$$\therefore y'=\pm\frac{c_1}{e^{2x}-c_1^2}\text{ - - - - - - - - - - - - }(*)$$

$$\Rightarrow y(x)=\int\frac{c_1}{e^{2x}-c_1^2}dx$$

Since any option does not contain the extremal so the options are wrong. But if we moving through options then from option (a)

$$y(x)=\sec^{-1}\left(\frac{x}{c_1}\right)+c_2$$

$$y'(x)=\frac{1}{\left|\frac{x}{c_1}\right|\sqrt{\left(\frac{x}{c_1}\right)^2-1}}=\frac{c_1^2}{|x|\sqrt{x^2-c_1^2}}$$

(a) Not satisfy (*)

(b) $y(x)=\sec^{-1}\left(\frac{x}{c_1}\right)+c_2; |c_1|<1$

$$y'(x)=\frac{c_1^2}{|x|\sqrt{x^2-c_1}}; |c_1|<1$$

Not satisfy (*)

(c) $y(x)=\tan^{-1}\left(\frac{x}{c_1}\right)+c_2$

$$y'(x)=\frac{1}{1+\left(\frac{x}{c_1}\right)^2}=\frac{c_1^2}{x^2+c_1^2}$$

Not satisfy (*)

(d) $y(x)=\tan^{-1}\left(\frac{x}{c_1}\right)+c_2; |c_1|>1$

$y'(x)=\frac{1}{1+\left(\frac{x}{c_1}\right)^2}=\frac{c_1^2}{x^2+c_1^2}$; not satisfy (*)

So no option are correct.

28. Explanation: (d)

29. Explanation: (d)

Here $F(x,y,y')=y(3x-y)$

Euler's Lagrange's equation is

$$\frac{\partial F}{\partial y}-\frac{d}{dx}\left(\frac{\partial F}{\partial y'}\right)=0$$

$$\Rightarrow 3x-2y=0$$

$\Rightarrow y=\frac{3}{2}x$ is an extremal but as it is not satisfy boundary condition $y(1)=1$, so we have no extremal i.e.

Option (d) correct and option (a) and (c) are incorrect.

30. Explanation: (d)

Here $f(x,y,y')=(1-x^2)y'^2$

and $g(x,y,y')=y^2$

Consider $H(x,y,y')=f+\lambda g$

$=(1-x^2)y'^2+\lambda y^2$

Now, necessary condition to have an extremal is

$$\frac{\partial H}{\partial y}-\frac{d}{dx}\left(\frac{\partial H}{\partial y'}\right)=0$$

$$2\lambda y-\frac{d}{dx}(2(1-x^2)y')=0.$$

$$\Rightarrow \lambda y-((1-x^2)y''+2xy')=0$$

$$\Rightarrow (1-x^2)y''-2xy'-\lambda y=0.$$

$$\Rightarrow (x^2-1)y''+2xy'+\lambda y=0$$

whose solutions are Legendre polynomials, which are given by

$$P_n(x)=\frac{1}{2^n n!}\frac{d^n}{dx^n}(x^2-1)^n, n=0,1,2,\cdots$$

$P_0(x)=1$ But $\int_{-1}^{1}(1)dx=2$

Not correct.

$P_1(x)=x$ But $\int_{-1}^{1}x dx=0$

Not possible.

Similarly, for any value of $n, P_n(x)$ does not satisfy condition.

So, such y does not exist.

31. Explanation: (a), (c)

Since F is independent of x & y

$\Rightarrow y(x)=c_1x+c_2$

$\because y(0)=y(1)=1$

$\Rightarrow y(x)=0$

$\because I[0]=\int_0^1 e^{-y'^2}dx=\int_0^1 e^{-0}dx=1$

$M=\sup I[u]=1$

$\because e^{-u'^2}>0$

$\Rightarrow \int_0^1 e^{-u'^2}dx>0$

$\Rightarrow \inf I[u]=0$, but infimum is not attained.

So, (a) and (b) correct.

32. Explanation: (a), (c)

$J(y(x))=\int_0^1 (y(x)^2-4y(x)y'(x)+4y'(x)^2)dx$

$f=y^2-4yy'+4y'^2$

$$\frac{\partial f}{\partial y}-\frac{d}{dx}\left(\frac{\partial f}{\partial y'}\right)=0$$

$$\Rightarrow 2y-4y'-\frac{d}{dx}(-4y+8y')=0$$

$$\Rightarrow 2y-4y'+4y'-8y''=0$$

$$\Rightarrow 4y''-y=0\Rightarrow 4M^2-1=0$$

$$\Rightarrow M=\pm\frac{1}{2}$$

$$\therefore y(x)=C_1e^{\frac{1}{2}x}+C_2e^{-\frac{1}{2}x}$$

$$y(0)=1\Rightarrow C_1+C_2=1$$

$$y'(0)=\frac{1}{2}\Rightarrow\frac{C_1}{2}-\frac{C_2}{2}=\frac{1}{2}=C_1-C_2=1$$

$$\therefore C_1=1, C_2=0$$

$$\therefore y(x)=e^{\frac{1}{2}x}$$

$$y'=\frac{1}{2}e^{\frac{1}{2}x}$$

$$y''(x)=\frac{1}{4}e^{\frac{1}{2}x}>0; \forall x$$

$\therefore y$ is convex

$$y(x_1+x_2)=e^{\frac{x_1+x_2}{2}}$$

$= e^{\frac{x_1}{2}} e^{\frac{x_2}{2}}$

$= y(x_1)y(x_2)$

∴ Option (a) & (c) is correct.

33. Explanation: (a), (c)

$J(y(x), z(x)) = \int_0^1 (y'^2 + z'^2 + y'z')dx$

$y(0) = 1 \quad y(1) = 0$

$z(0) = -1 \quad z(1) = 2$

Given problem is independent of x, y and x, z

∴ Solution is

$y = ax + b\ z = cx + d$

$y(0) = 1 \Rightarrow b = 1\ z(0) = -1$

$y(1) = 0 \Rightarrow a = -1 \Rightarrow d = -1$

$\therefore y(x) = -x + 1\ z(1) = 2$

$\Rightarrow c - 1 = 2 \Rightarrow c = 3$

$\therefore z = 3x - 1$

$\therefore y + z = 2x$

option (c) is correct.

$z + 3y = 3x - 1 - 3x + 3 = 2$

option (a) is correct.

34. Explanation: (b), (c)

Here, $f(x, y, y') = y' + x^3 y'^2$

By Euler-Lagrange's differential equation, we have,

$$\Rightarrow f_y - \frac{d}{dx} f_{y'} = 0$$

$$\Rightarrow 0 - \frac{d}{dx}(1 + 2x^3 y') = 0$$

$$\Rightarrow 1 + 2x^3 y' = c$$

$$\Rightarrow y' = \left(\frac{c-1}{2}\right) \cdot \frac{1}{x^3}$$

$$\Rightarrow y(x) = \left(\frac{c-1}{2}\right) \times \left(-\frac{1}{2}\right) \cdot \frac{1}{x^2} + c_1$$

$$\Rightarrow y(x) = -\left(\frac{c-1}{4}\right) \cdot \frac{1}{x^2} + c_1$$

Now, from given condition, we have,

$y(1) = 2$

$$2 = -\frac{(c-1)}{4} \cdot 1 + c_1$$

$8 = 1 - c + 4c_1$

$4c_1 - c = 7 \qquad \ldots\ldots (1)$

and $y(2) = 8$

$$8 = -\left(\frac{c-1}{4}\right) \cdot \frac{1}{4} + c_1$$

$28 = 1 - c + 16c_1$

$16c_1 - c = 127 \qquad \ldots\ldots (2)$

Solving equation (1) and (2) simultaneously we get

$c_1 = 10$ and $c = 33$

Therefore, $y(x) = -\left(\frac{33-1}{4}\right) \cdot \frac{1}{x^2} + 10$

$$y(x) = \frac{-8}{x^2} + 10$$

a) $(\sqrt{2}, 3)$

i.e. $y(\sqrt{2}) = 3$

$y(\sqrt{2}) = \frac{-8}{2} + 10 = -4 + 10 = 6 \neq 3$

⇒ option (1) is incorrect.

b) $(\sqrt{2}, 6)$

$y(\sqrt{3}) = \frac{-8}{3} + 10 = 6$

Option (b) is correct.

c) $\left(\sqrt{3}, \frac{22}{3m}\right)$

$y(\sqrt{3}) = \frac{-8}{3} + 10 = \frac{22}{3}$

Option (c) is correct, and (d) is incorrect.

35. Explanation: (a), (c)

The functional is given by:

$$J[y] = \int_{-1}^{1} [(y')^3 + (y')^2]dx$$

Using the **Euler-Lagrange equation**, we define:

$$F(y, y') = (y')^3 + (y')^2$$

Since F does not explicitly depend on y, the **first integral condition** applies:

$$\frac{\partial F}{\partial y'} = 3(y')^2 + 2y'$$

$$3(y')^2 + 2y' = C$$

$$3(y')^2 + 2y' - C = 0$$

$$y' = \frac{-2 \pm \sqrt{4 + 12C}}{6}$$

For simplicity, choosing the physically relevant root, let $y' = m$ be constant, so we integrate:

$$y = mx + c$$

Using boundary conditions:

$$y(-1) = -1, y(1) = 3$$

Substituting:

$$-1 = -m + c, 3 = m + c$$

Solving for m and c:

$$m = 2, c = 1$$

Thus, the extremal function is:

$$\phi(x) = 2x + 1$$

Statement (a) is true.

Checking $J[y] \geq J[\phi]$ in $B_0(\phi, \epsilon)$

The set $B_0(\phi, \epsilon)$ contains functions **close to** $\phi(x)$ in the uniform norm, meaning:

$\|y - \phi\|_\infty < \epsilon$.

However, this does not necessarily control the derivative y', which is crucial since $J[y]$ depends on y'. Small deviations in $y(x)$ may lead to larger variations in $J[y]$. Therefore, we **cannot guarantee** $J[y] \geq J[\phi]$ for all $y \in B_0(\phi, \epsilon)$.

Statement (b) is false.

Checking $J[y] \geq J[\phi]$ in $B_1(\phi, \epsilon)$

The set $B_1(\phi, \epsilon)$ controls both $\|y - \phi\|_\infty$ and $\|y' - \phi'\|_\infty$. Since the functional depends on y', small variations in y' will ensure $J[y]$ stays close to $J[\phi]$. By the **local minimality of the extremal**, there exists an $\epsilon > 0$ such that:

$J[y] \geq J[\phi]$ for all $y \in B_1(\phi, \epsilon)$.

Statement (c) is true.

Checking $J[y] \leq J[\phi]$ in $B_1(\phi, \epsilon)$

Since $\phi(x)$ is the extremal function, it minimizes $J[y]$ **locally,** meaning for small perturbations in $B_1(\phi, \epsilon)$, $J[y]$ is **greater than or equal** to $J[\phi]$. This contradicts statement (d), which asserts $J[y] \leq J[\phi]$.

Statement (d) is false.

36. Explanation: (c), (d)

The Euler-Lagrange equation is $\frac{d}{dx}(\frac{\partial f}{\partial y'}) - \frac{\partial f}{\partial y} = 0$.

$f(x,y,y') = y'^4 - 3y'^2$.

$\frac{\partial f}{\partial y'} = 4y'^3 - 6y'$, $\frac{\partial f}{\partial y} = 0$.

$\frac{d}{dx}(4y'^3 - 6y') = 0$.

$4y'^3 - 6y' = C$, where C is a constant.

$2y'^3 - 3y' = C_1$, where $C_1 = \frac{C}{2}$.

The solutions are $y' = k_1, y' = k_2, y' = k_3$, where k_i are roots of $2k^3 - 3k - C_1 = 0$.

$y(x) = kx + D$.

Since $y(0) = 0$, $D = 0$, so $y(x) = kx$.

Let the corner be at $x = c$.

$$y(x) = \begin{cases} k_1 x, & 0 \le x \le c \\ k_2 x + D, & c \le x \le 1 \end{cases}$$

Since $y(0) = 0$, the first part is correct.

$y(c^-) = y(c^+)$, so $k_1 c = k_2 c + D$.

$D = (k_1 - k_2)c$.

$$y(x) = \begin{cases} k_1 x, & 0 \le x \le c \\ k_2 x + (k_1 - k_2)c, & c \le x \le 1 \end{cases}$$

$f(x,y,y'_-) = f(x,y,y'_+)$ implies $k_1^4 - 3k_1^2 = k_2^4 - 3k_2^2$.

$\frac{\partial f}{\partial y'}(x,y,y'_-) = \frac{\partial f}{\partial y'}(x,y,y'_+)$ implies $4k_1^3 - 6k_1 = 4k_2^3 - 6k_2$.

$2k_1^3 - 3k_1 = 2k_2^3 - 3k_2$.

$2k^3 - 3k = C_1$.

k_1 and k_2 are roots of the same equation.

$k_1^4 - 3k_1^2 = k_2^4 - 3k_2^2$ and $2k_1^3 - 3k_1 = 2k_2^3 - 3k_2$.

If $k_1 \ne k_2$, then $k_1 = -k_2$ and $k_1^2 = \frac{3}{2}$.

$k_1 = \pm\sqrt{\frac{3}{2}}$.

$y(1) = b$, so $k_2 + (k_1 - k_2)c = b$.

$k_2(1-c) + k_1 c = b$.

$k_2(1-c) - k_2 c = b$.

$k_2(1-2c) = b$.

$c = \frac{1}{2} - \frac{b}{2k_2}$.

Since $0 < c < 1$, $0 < \frac{1}{2} - \frac{b}{2k_2} < 1$.

$0 < 1 - \frac{b}{k_2} < 2$.

$-1 < -\frac{b}{k_2} < 1$.

$-1 < \frac{b}{k_2} < 1$.

$|b| < |k_2| = \sqrt{\frac{3}{2}}$.

If $|b| < \sqrt{\frac{3}{2}}$, there are two solutions.

If $|b| = \sqrt{\frac{3}{2}}$, there is one solution.

If $|b| > \sqrt{\frac{3}{2}}$, there are no solutions.

For $b = 2$, $|b| > \sqrt{\frac{3}{2}}$, so there are no solutions.

For $b = \frac{1}{2}$, $|b| < \sqrt{\frac{3}{2}}$, so there are two solutions.

Thus, $S(2)$ is empty and $S\left(\frac{1}{2}\right)$ has exactly two elements.

37. Explanation: (a), (b), (c), (d)

38. Explanation: (a), (b), (c)

Reasoning (Euler–Lagrange shortcut).

For $J_\alpha[y] = \int_1^2 \frac{(y')^2}{x^\alpha}, dx$ the integrand does not depend on (y), so

$$\frac{d}{dx}\left(\frac{\partial L}{\partial y'}\right) = 0 \Rightarrow \frac{\partial L}{\partial y'} = \text{constant}.$$

Here $\partial L/\partial y' = 2y'/x^\alpha = C$, so

$$y' = \frac{C}{2}x^\alpha \Rightarrow y(x) = Ax^{\alpha+1} + D$$

$with(A = \frac{C}{2(\alpha+1)})$. Use the boundary conditions $y(1) = 1,; y(2) = 2$ to find (A,D).

- For $\alpha = 3$: $y(x) = Ax^4 + D$. Solving $A + D = 1,; 16A + D = 2$ gives $A = \frac{1}{15},; D = \frac{14}{15}$. So $y = \frac{1}{15}(x^4 + 14)$. (1) **true.**
- For $\alpha = 1$: $y(x) = Ax^2 + D$. Solving $A + D = 1,; 4A + D = 2$ gives $A = \frac{1}{3},; D = \frac{2}{3}$. So $y = \frac{1}{3}(x^2 + 2)$. (2) **true.**
- For $\alpha = 0$: $y(x) = Ax + D$. Solving $A + D = 1,; 2A + D = 2$ gives $A = 1,; D = 0$. So $y = x$. (3) **true.**
- The function in (4) is $\frac{1}{2}(x^2 - x + 2)$, which contains an (x)-term and so is not of the required form $Ax^2 + D$ for $\alpha = 1$; it is not the extremal. (4) **false.**

39. Explanation: (b), (d)

We solve using Euler–Lagrange equation.

Functional: $J(y) = \int_0^1 ((y')^2 \sin x + 2y\cos x)dx$

$$\frac{d}{dx}\left(\frac{\partial F}{\partial y'}\right) - \frac{\partial F}{\partial y} = 0$$

Here

$F = (y')^2 \sin x + 2y\cos x$

$\frac{\partial F}{\partial y'} = 2y'\sin x$

$\frac{\partial F}{\partial y} = 2\cos x$

Differentiate:

$\frac{d}{dx}(2y'\sin x) = 2y''\sin x + 2y'\cos x$

Euler equation:

$2y''\sin x + 2y'\cos x - 2\cos x = 0$

$y''\sin x + y'\cos x - \cos x = 0$

Let $p = y'$

$p'\sin x + p\cos x - \cos x = 0$

$y' = 1 + C\csc x$

Integrate:

$y = x + C\ln(\tan(x/2)) + D$

Apply boundary conditions

$y(0) = 0, y(1) = 1$

This gives C=0, D=0

So, $y = x$

$\therefore y'(x) = 1$

$\therefore y'(0) = 1, y'\left(\frac{1}{2}\right) = 1$

Correct statements: 2 and 4

Unit 3.2: Moving Boundaries Variational Problems

MCQ (Multiple Choice Questions)

1. The curve $y = y(x)$, passing through the point $(\sqrt{3}, 1)$ and defined by the following property (Voltera integral equation of the first kind) $\int_0^y \frac{f(v)dv}{\sqrt{y-v}} = 4\sqrt{y}$, where $f(y) = \sqrt{1+\frac{1}{y'^2}}$, is the part of a

(a) Straight line (b) Circle
(c) Parabola (d) Cycloid

[June 2016]

2. Consider the functional

$$I(y(x)) = \int_{x_0}^{x_1} f(x,y)\sqrt{1+y'^2}e^{\tan^{-1}y'}dx$$

Where $f(x,y) \neq 0$. Let the left end of the extremal be fixed at the point $A(x_0, y_0)$ and the right end $B(x_1, y_1)$ be movable along the curve $y = \Psi(x)$. Then the extremal $y = y(x)$ intersects the curve $y = \Psi(x)$ along which the boundary point $B(x_1, y_1)$ slides at an angle

(a) $\pi/3$ (b) $\pi/2$
(c) $\pi/4$ (d) $\pi/6$

[June 2017]

3. Let $B = \{(x,y) \in \mathbb{R}^2 / x^2 + y^2 \leq 1\}andC = \{(x,y)/x^2 + y^2 = 1\}$and let $f$and g be continuous functions. Let u be the minimizer of the functional

$J[v] = \iint_B (v_x^2 + v_y^2 - 2fv)\,dxdy + \int_C (v^2 - 2gv)\,ds.$

Then u is a solution of

(a) $-\Delta u = f, \frac{\partial u}{\partial n} + u = g$ (b) $\Delta u = f, \frac{\partial u}{\partial n} - u = g$
(c) $-\Delta u = f, \frac{\partial u}{\partial n} = g$ (d) $\Delta u = f, \frac{\partial u}{\partial n} = g$

where $\frac{\partial u}{\partial n}$denotes the directional derivative of u in the direction of the outward drawn normal at$(x,y) \in C$.

[June 2019]

Answer Key		
1	2	3
a	c	a

Explanation

1. **Explanation: (a)**

Here

$$f(y) = \sqrt{1+\frac{1}{y'^2}} --(1) \text{ which is independent of } x, y$$

So, Euler's equation is $y'' = 0$,
Integrating two times, we get,
$y(x) = a + bx$, a and b arbitary constants
As $y(x) = a + bx$ is equation of straight line, so option (a) correct.

2. **Explanation: (c)**

Here $F(x,y,y') = f(x,y)\sqrt{1+y'^2}e^{\tan^{-1}y'}$ ---(1)
$y = \Psi(x)$, $f(x,y) \neq 0$
Transversality condition is $F + (\psi' - y')F_{y'} = 0$

$\Rightarrow f(x,y)\sqrt{1+y'^2}e^{\tan^{-1}y'} + (\psi' - y')f(x,y)\left[\frac{y'}{\sqrt{1+y'^2}}e^{\tan^{-1}y'} + \sqrt{1+y'^2}e^{\tan^{-1}y'}\frac{1}{1+(y')^2}\right] = 0$

$=> f(x,y)e^{\tan^{-1}y'}[1 + (y')^2 + (\psi' - y')(y' + 1)] = 0$
as $f(x,y)e^{\tan^{-1}y'} \neq 0$
$=> [1 + (y')^2 + (\psi' - y')(y' + 1)] = 0$

On simplifying we get $1 = \frac{\psi' - y'}{1+\psi'y'} = \tan\alpha$
as ψ', y' are slopes
$=> \tan\alpha = 1 = \tan\frac{\pi}{4} => \frac{\pi}{4} = \alpha$ so option (c) correct.

3. **Explanation: (a)**

We know, A minimizer$R$ in $C^1(\overline{D})$ of

$$E(v) = \int_\Omega F(n, v, \nabla v)\,dx - \int_{\partial\Omega} g(u,v)\,ds$$

Is a solution of the BVP provided that
$u \in C^2(\overline{D})$, $\sum_{i=1}^n \frac{\partial}{\partial x_i} Fu_{x_i} = F_u$ in Ω
And $\sum_{i=1}^n Fu_{xi}\, v_1 = g_u$ on $\partial\Omega$
Where $v = (v_1, v_2, \dots, v_n)$ is the exterior unit normal at the boundary $\partial\Omega$.

$J[v] = \iint_B (v_x^2 + v_y^2 - 2fv)\,dxdy + \int_C (v^2 - 2gv)\,ds.$
$F = v_x' + v_y' - 2fv$
$\Rightarrow 2v_x + 2v_y - 2f = 0$
$\Rightarrow \Delta v = -f$ on B
$\Rightarrow -\Delta v = f$ on B
$\sum_{i=1}^n Fu_{xi}v_i = g_u$ on $\partial\Omega$
$2v_x + 2v_y = 2v - 2g$ on C
$v_x + v_y = v - g$ on C
$\frac{\Delta v}{\partial n} + v = g$ on C
So, option (a) correct.

MSQ (Multiple Select Questions)

1. Consider the functional $I(y) = \int_{1/2}^{x_1}\sqrt{1+(y')^2}dx$, subject to the condition that the left end of the extremal is fixed at the point$\left(\frac{1}{2}, \frac{1}{4}\right)$ and the right end (x_1, y_1) be movable along the straight line $y = x - 5$.Let$C_1$and C_2 be arbitrary constants. Then

(a) The general solution of the Euler's equation satisfies $2C_1 + 4C_2 = 1$

(b) The transversality condition that holds at the right end yields

$$\sqrt{(1+C_1^2)} + (1 - C_1)\frac{C_1}{\sqrt{1+C_1^2}} = 0$$

(c) The relation $C_1x_1 + C_2 = x_1 - 5$ is true

(d) The extremal is $y = -x + \frac{3}{4}$

[Dec 2011]

2. Let $y = y(x)$ be the extremal of the functional $I[y(x)] = \int_{x_1}^{x_2} \sqrt{1 + \left(\frac{dy}{dx}\right)^2}\, dx$, subject to the condition that the left end of the extremal moves along $y = x^2$, while the right end moves along $x - y = 5$. Then the
   (a) Shortest distance between the parabola and the straight line is $\left(\frac{19\sqrt{2}}{8}\right)$
   (b) Slope of the extremal at (x, y) is $\left(-\frac{3}{2}\right)$
   (c) Point $\left(\frac{3}{4}, 0\right)$ lies on the extremal
   (d) Extremal is orthogonal to the curve $y = \frac{x}{2}$

[June 2016]

3. Consider the functional

$$J[y] = \int_0^1 [(y')^2 - (y')^4]\, dx$$

subject to $y(0) = 0, y(1) = 0$.

A broken extremal is a continuous extremal whose derivative has jump discontinuities at a finite number of points. Then which of the following statements are true?
   (a) There are no broken extremals and $y = 0$ is an extremad
   (b) There is a unique broken extremal
   (c) There exist more than one and finitely many broken extremals
   (d) There exist infinitely many broken extremals

[Dec 2018]

4. Suppose $y(x)$ is the extremal of the variational problem
   $J(y) = \int_0^1 x^2 (y')^2\, dx$
   subject to
   $y(0) = 0, y(1) = 1, \int_0^1 y^2\, dx = \frac{1}{7}$.
   Then which of the following statements are true?
   (a) $y'\left(\frac{1}{2}\right) = \frac{3}{4}$
   (b) $y'\left(\frac{1}{\sqrt{3}}\right) = 1$
   (c) $y'\left(\frac{1}{3}\right) = \frac{1}{3}$
   (d) $y'\left(\frac{1}{4}\right) = \frac{1}{2}$

[Dec 2025]

Answer Key			
1	2	3	4
a, c, d	a, c	d	a,b,c

Explanation

1. **Explanation: (a), (c), (d)**

$$I(y) = \int_{1/2}^{x_1} \sqrt{1 + (y')^2 dx},$$

$F(x, y, y') = \sqrt{1 + (y')^2}$,

Euler equation is

$F_y - \frac{d}{dx}\{F_{y'}\} = 0$

$$\frac{d}{dx}\left(\frac{\partial F}{\partial y'}\right) = 0$$

$$\Rightarrow \frac{y'}{\sqrt{1 + (y'')^2}} = c \Rightarrow \frac{(y')^2}{1 + (y'')^2} = c^2$$

$\Rightarrow y(x) = c_1 x + c_2$.

$\left(\frac{1}{2}, \frac{1}{4}\right) \to (x_1, y_1)$ along $y = x - 5$,

$x - 5 = c_1 x + c_2 \Rightarrow (1 - c_1)x_1 = c_2 + 5$.

Since the extremal is fixed at $\left(\frac{1}{2}, \frac{1}{4}\right), y\left(\frac{1}{2}\right) = \frac{1}{4} \Rightarrow 1 = 2c_1 + 4c_2$. (2) does not hold transversality condition.

$d.\, y = c_1 x + c_2$ and $y = x - 5$, Slope of the first line is c_1 and second line is 1,

they are orthogonal imply $\Rightarrow c_1 = -1$,

$$4c_2 - 2 = 1 \Rightarrow c_2 = \frac{3}{4}$$

$$\therefore y = -x + \frac{3}{4},$$

(a), (c), (d) are true.

2. **Explanation: (a), (c)**

The problem is to extremizing the functional $I[y(x)] = \int_{x_1}^{x_2} \sqrt{1 + (y')^2}\, dx$ subject to the condition that the left end of the extremal moves along $y = x^2$ and the right end moves along

$x - y = 5$

Here $F = \sqrt{1 + (y')^2}$ ------(1)

The functional is independent of x, y so Euler's equation is $y'' = 0$ ------(2)

Integrating (2) two times the Extremal is $y = c_1 x + c_2$

And $y' = c_1$

Since

$\gamma_1(x): y = x^2$

And $\gamma_2(x): y = x - 5$

Here, (x_1, y_1) lies on curve γ_1

And (x_2, y_2) lies on curve γ_2.

Then, transversality condition is

$F + (\phi' - y')F_{y'} = 0$

$$\sqrt{1 + y'^2} + (\phi' - y')\frac{y'}{\sqrt{1 + y'^2}} = 0$$

Using $\gamma_1: y = x^2$

$1 + 2xc_1 = 0$

$1 + c_1 = 0 \quad (\because 1 + \phi' y' = 0)$

$\Rightarrow 1 + 2x_1 c_1 = 0 \qquad c_1 = -1$

$\therefore x_1 = 1/2$

$$y_1 = x_1^2 = \frac{1}{4}$$

$\therefore 1 + y' = 0 (\because 1 + \phi' y' = 0)$

$(x_1, y_1) = \left(\frac{1}{2}, \frac{1}{4}\right)$

$y_1 = c_1 x_1 + c_2$

$$c_2 = \frac{1}{4} + \frac{1}{2} = \frac{3}{4}$$

$$\therefore y = -x + \frac{3}{4}$$

$y_2 = x_2 - 5$

$$y_2 = -x_2 + \frac{3}{4}$$

$(x_2, y_2) = \left(\frac{23}{8}, -\frac{17}{8}\right)$

$$d = \sqrt{\left(\frac{23}{8} - \frac{1}{2}\right)^2 + \left(-\frac{17}{8} - \frac{1}{4}\right)^2}$$

$$= \sqrt{\left(\frac{19}{8}\right)^2 + \left(\frac{19}{8}\right)^2} = \frac{19}{8}\sqrt{2}$$

$y = -x + \frac{3}{4}$ is the extremal the point $(\frac{3}{4}, 0)$ lies on it , so option (a) , (c) correct.

3. Explanation: (d)

Consider the functional $|y| = \int_0^1 [(y')^2 - (y')^4] dx$ subject to

$y(0) = 0, y(1) = 0$

$F(x, y, y') = (y')^2 - (y')^4$, functional is free from x & y.

So, by using euler equation.$y'' = 0$

$\Rightarrow y(x) = c_1 x + c_2$

$y(0) = 0 \Rightarrow c_2 = 0$, So $y(x) = c_1 x$,

$y(1) = 0 \Rightarrow c_1 + c_2 = 0 \Rightarrow c_1 = -c_2$

$$y(x) = \begin{cases} c_1 x, 0 \le x < a \\ c_1(1 - x), a \le x \le 1 \end{cases}$$

$y(x)$ is continuous at $x = a \Rightarrow c_1 a = c_1(1 - a)$

$\Rightarrow a = \frac{1}{2}$

$$\text{Therefore } y(x) = \begin{cases} c_1 x, & 0 \le x < \frac{1}{2} \\ c_1(1 - x), & \frac{1}{2} \le x \le 1 \end{cases}$$

So, there exist infinitely many broken extremals,

Option (d) is correct and Option (a), (b) and (c) are false.

4. Explanation: (a), (b), (c)

First define the augmented functional

$$F(x, y, y') = x^2(y')^2 + \lambda y^2$$

Then apply the Euler–Lagrange equation

$$\frac{d}{dx}\left(\frac{\partial F}{\partial y'}\right) - \frac{\partial F}{\partial y} = 0$$

$$\frac{\partial F}{\partial y'} = 2x^2 y'$$

$$\frac{d}{dx}(2x^2 y') = 4xy' + 2x^2 y''$$

$$\frac{\partial F}{\partial y} = 2\lambda y$$

Substitute: $4xy' + 2x^2 y'' - 2\lambda y = 0$

$\therefore 2xy' + x^2 y'' - \lambda y = 0$

This is a Cauchy–Euler differential equation.

Assume solution $y = x^m$.

Substitute:

$$m(m - 1)x^m + 2mx^m - \lambda x^m = 0$$
$$m^2 + m - \lambda = 0$$

So

$$y = C_1 x^{m_1} + C_2 x^{m_2}$$

Using the boundary condition $y(0) = 0$, the valid extremal becomes

$$y = x^3$$

Check the constraint: $\int_0^1 x^6\, dx = \frac{1}{7}$

So, it satisfies the condition.

Thus, $y' = 3x^2$.

Now check options.

1. $y'\left(\frac{1}{2}\right) = 3\left(\frac{1}{2}\right)^2 = \frac{3}{4}$
True.

2. $y'\left(\frac{1}{\sqrt{3}}\right) = 3\left(\frac{1}{\sqrt{3}}\right)^2 = 1$
True.

3. $y'\left(\frac{1}{3}\right) = 3\left(\frac{1}{3}\right)^2 = \frac{1}{3}$
True.

4. $y'\left(\frac{1}{4}\right) = 3\left(\frac{1}{4}\right)^2 = \frac{3}{16} \ne \frac{1}{2}$
False.

Final answer: 1, 2, 3 are correct.

INTEGRAL EQUATIONS

No. of questions asked from year 2011-2025

Units		2011		2012		2013		2014		2015		2016		2017		2018		2019		2020	2022		2023		2024	2025		
		Jun	Dec	Jun	Dec	Jun	Dec	Jun	Dec	Jun	Dec	Jun	Dec	Jun	Dec	Jun	Dec	Jun	Dec	Nov	Feb	Sep	Jun	Dec	Jul	Feb	Jun	Dec
4.1	Linear Integral Equation of First and Second Kind	-	-	-	1	1	-	1	1	-	-	-	-	1	-	-	1	1	-	-	1	-	-	1	-	-	1	1
4.2	Volterra's and Fredholm Integral Equation	2	2	2	2	1	2	2	1	2	3	1	3	3	2	3	2	-	6	5	1	3	3	2	3	3	2	2

CHAPTER 4

INTEGRAL EQUATIONS

Unit 4.1: Linear Integral Equations of First and Second Kind

MCQ (Multiple Choice Questions)

1. The integral equation
$y(x) = x - \int_1^x xy(t)dt; y \in C^1[1,\infty)$ has the solution
(a) $y = x(1 - In\, x)$
(b) $y = xe^{x-\frac{1}{2}}(x-1) + x$
(c) $y = xe^{(1-x^2)/2}$
(d) $y = x - x(e^{x^2} - e)$

[June 2013]

2. Suppose $x: [0,\infty) \to [0,\infty)$ is continuous and $x(0) = 0$. If $(x(t)^2) \le 2 + \int_0^t x(s)ds, \forall t \ge 0$, then which of the following is TRUE?
(a) $x(\sqrt{2}) \in [0,2]$
(b) $x(\sqrt{2}) \in \left[0, \frac{3}{\sqrt{2}}\right]$
(c) $x(\sqrt{2}) \in \left[\frac{5}{\sqrt{2}}, \frac{7}{\sqrt{2}}\right]$
(d) $x(\sqrt{2}) \in [10, \infty]$

[June 2017]

3. If φ is the solution of
$$\int_0^x (1 - x^2 + t^2)\varphi(t)dt = \frac{x^2}{2},$$
Then $\varphi(\sqrt{2})$ is equal to
(a) $\sqrt{2}e^{\sqrt{2}}$
(b) $\sqrt{2}e^2$
(c) $\sqrt{2}e^{2\sqrt{2}}$
(d) $2e^4$

[Dec 2018]

4. If y is a solution of $y(x) - \int_0^x (x-t)y(t)dt = 1$, then which of the following is true?
(a) y is bounded but not periodic in $\mathbb{R}$
(b) y is periodic in $\mathbb{R}$
(c) $\int_R y(x)dx < \infty$
(d) $\int_R \frac{dx}{y(x)} < \infty$

[June 2019]

5. The value of λ for which the integral equation $y(x) = \lambda \int_0^1 x^2 e^{x+t} y(t)dt$ has a non-zero solution, is
(a) $\frac{4}{1+e^2}$
(b) $\frac{2}{1+e^2}$
(c) $\frac{4}{e^2-1}$
(d) $\frac{2}{e^2-1}$

[DEC-2023]

6. If $y(x)$ is the solution of the integral equation
$$y(x) = x^2 + 2\int_0^1 x\,ty(t)dt,$$
then which of the following statements is true?
(a) $y(0) + y(1) = \frac{1}{2}$
(b) $y(-1) + y(1) = 1$
(c) $y'(0) + y'(1) = \frac{3}{2}$
(d) $y'(-1) + y'(1) = 3$

[June 2025]

7. Suppose $u(x)$ is the solution of the integral equation
$$u(x) = 3 + \int_0^x (x-t)\,u(t)dt.$$
Then which of the following statements is true?
(a) $u(\pi) = 2e^\pi$.
(b) $u'(\pi) = e^\pi$.
(c) $u(\pi) + u'(\pi) = 3e^\pi$.
(d) $u(\pi) - u'(\pi) = e^\pi$.

[Dec 2025]

Answer Key						
1	2	3	4	5	6	7
c	b	b	d	c	d	c

EXPLANATION

1. **Explanation: c)**
Consider the given integral equation
$y(x) = x - x\int_1^x y(t)dt$ .....(1)
$y(x) = f(x) + \lambda \int_a^b k(x.t)y(t)dt$
comparing with equation (1)
$\Rightarrow \lambda = 1, k(x,t) = k_0(x,t) = x$
Now, $k_1(x,t) = \int_t^x k(x,s)k_0(s,t)\, ds$
$\Rightarrow k_1(x,t) = \int_t^x xs\, ds$
$\Rightarrow k_1(x,t) = \frac{x}{2}(x^2 - t^2)$
$k_2(x,t) = \int_t^x k_0(x,s)k_1(s,t)\, ds$
$k_2(x,t) = \int_t^x \frac{xs}{2}(s^2 - t^2)\, ds$
$\Rightarrow k_2(x,t) = \frac{x}{2!}\left(\frac{x^2-t^2}{2}\right)^2$
Similarly,
$k_3(x,t) = \frac{x}{3!}\left(\frac{x^2-t^2}{2}\right)^3$
We know that,
$R(x,t;\lambda) = \sum_{n=0}^{\infty} k_n(x,t)\lambda^n$
$R(x,t;1) = k_0(x,t) + k_1(x,t)\lambda + k_2(x,t)\lambda^2 + k_3(x,t)\lambda^3$ +---
$= x - \frac{x}{2}(x^2 - t^2) + \frac{x}{2!}\left(\frac{x^2-t^2}{2}\right)^2 - \frac{x}{3!}\left(\frac{x^2-t^2}{2}\right)^3 + - - -$
$R(x,t;1) = xe^{\frac{-(x^2-t^2)}{2}}$
$R(x,t;1) = xe^{\frac{(t^2-x^2)}{2}}$
Now $y(x) = f(x) + \lambda \int_a^b R(x,t;\lambda)f(t)dt$

$$y(x) = x - \int_1^x txe^{\frac{(t^2-x^2)}{2}} dt$$

Put $u = \frac{t^2-x^2}{2}$

$du = tdt$

$$y(x) = x - \int_{\frac{1-x^2}{2}}^{0} xe^u du$$

$$y(x) = xe^{\frac{(1-x^2)}{2}}$$

$\Rightarrow$ option c) is the correct answer and a) ,b) and d) are incorrect.

2. Explanation: (b)

We have, $(x(t))^2 \le 2 + \int_0^t x(s)ds$ --- (1)

Consider the equality and apply the Leibniz rule

$\Rightarrow 2x(t)x'(t) = x(t)$

$\Rightarrow x'(t) = \frac{1}{2}$

Integrating,

$\Rightarrow x(t) = \frac{t}{2} + a$ (2)

$x(0) = 0$ (Given)

$\Rightarrow a = 0$

$\Rightarrow x(t) = \frac{t}{2}$

$\Rightarrow x(\sqrt{2}) = \frac{\sqrt{2}}{2} = \sqrt{2}$

From this, option c) and d) are incorrect

Now

Again, consider the equality case

$\Rightarrow \left(\frac{t}{2} + a\right)^2 = 2 + \int_0^t \left(\frac{t}{2} + a\right) ds$ (from (1) and (2))

$\Rightarrow \left(\frac{t}{2} + a\right)^2 = 2 + t^2 + at$

$\Rightarrow a = \pm\sqrt{2}$

$\Rightarrow x(t) = \frac{t}{2} + \sqrt{2}$

$\Rightarrow x(t) = \frac{\sqrt{2}}{2} + \sqrt{2}$

$\Rightarrow x(t) = 2.121$

$\Rightarrow$Option (2) is correct answer and a) c) and d) are incorrect.

3. Explanation: (b)

Given

$$\int_0^x (1 - x^2 + t^2)\phi(t)dt = \frac{x^2}{2} \text{ --- (1)}$$

Differentiating (1) and with the help of Leibnitz rule, we get

$$\int_0^x -2x\phi(t)dt + \phi(x) = \frac{2x}{2}$$

$$\Rightarrow \int_0^x \phi(t)dt = \frac{\phi(x)}{2x} - \frac{1}{2}$$

Again, apply the Leibnitz rule

$$\Rightarrow \phi(x) = \frac{\phi'(x)x - \phi(x)}{2x^2}$$

$$\Rightarrow \phi(x)\left(1 + \frac{1}{2x^2}\right) = \frac{\phi'(x)}{2x}$$

$$\Rightarrow 2x\left(1 + \frac{1}{2x^2}\right) = \frac{\phi'(x)}{\phi(x)}$$

Now integrating both side,

$\Rightarrow x^2 + \log x = \log\phi(x)$

$\Rightarrow \phi(x) = xe^{x^2}$

$\Rightarrow \phi(\sqrt{2}) = \sqrt{2}e^2$

$\Rightarrow$Only option b) is the correct answer and a),c) and d) are incorrect.

4. Explanation: (d)

Consider the given Volterra integral equation

$$y(x) - \int_0^x (x-t)\, y(t)dt = 1$$

$$y(x) = 1 + \int_0^x (x-t)\, y(t)dt$$

$\Rightarrow y(x) = 1 + xy(x)$

$\Rightarrow L(y(x)) = L(1) + L(x)\, L(y(x))$

($\because$ $L(y(x))$ is a Laplace transform)

$$L(y(x)) = \frac{1}{n} + \frac{1}{n^2} L(y(x))$$

$$L(y(x))\left(1 - \frac{1}{n^2}\right) = \frac{1}{n}$$

$$L(y(x)) = \left(\frac{n}{n^2-1}\right)$$

$$L(y(x)) = \frac{n}{(n-1)(n+1)}$$

$$L(y(x)) = \frac{1}{2}\left[\frac{1}{n-1} + \frac{1}{n+1}\right]$$

$$y(x) = \frac{1}{2}\left[L^{-1}\left[\frac{1}{n-1}\right] + L^{-1}\left[\frac{1}{n+1}\right]\right]$$

$$y(x) = \frac{1}{2}[e^x + e^{-x}]$$

Now discuss the option,

As $x \to \infty$ $y(x)$ also tends to ∞

$y(x)$ is not bounded and we know that exponential function never periodic.

$\Rightarrow$Option (a) and (b) are incorrect

Now for option c)

$$\int_{IR} \frac{dx}{y(x)} = \int_{IR} \frac{1}{2}[e^x + e^{-x}]dx$$

$$\int_{IR} \frac{dx}{y(x)} = \frac{1}{2}\int_{-\infty}^{\infty} \frac{1}{e^x + e^{-x}} dx$$

$$\int_{\mathbb{R}} \frac{dx}{y(x)} = \infty$$

$\Rightarrow$option c) is incorrect.

For option d)

$$\int_{\mathbb{R}} \frac{dx}{y(x)} = 2\int_{-\infty}^{\infty} \frac{1}{e^x + e^{-x}} dx$$

$$\int_{\mathbb{R}} \frac{dx}{y(x)} = 2.2\int_0^{\infty} \frac{dx}{e^x + \frac{1}{e^x}}$$

$$= 4\int_0^\infty \frac{e^x}{e^{2x}+1}dx$$

Put $e^x = t$

$\Rightarrow e^x dx = dt$

$$\int_{\mathbb{R}} \frac{dx}{y(x)} = 4\int_1^\infty \frac{dt}{t^2+1}$$

$= 4[\tan^{-1} t]_1^\infty$

$= 4[\tan^{-1}\infty - \tan^{-1} 1]$

$= 4\left[\frac{\pi}{2} - \frac{\pi}{4}\right]$

$= \frac{4\pi}{4} = \pi$

$$\int_{\mathbb{R}} \frac{dx}{y(x)} = \pi < \infty$$

$\Rightarrow$ option d) is correct answer and option a), b) and c) are the incorrect.

5. Explanation: (c)

$y(x) = \lambda \int_0^1 x^2 e^{x+t} y(t)\,dt = \lambda \int_0^1 x^2 e^x \cdot e^t y(t)\,dt$

$\therefore y(x) = \lambda x^2 e^x c$ ... (1), where $c = \int_0^1 e^t y(t)dt$

$\therefore c = \int_0^1 e^t \lambda t^2 e^t c\,dt$ ... from (1)

$$c = \lambda c \int_0^1 e^{2t} t^2 dt$$

$$c = \lambda c \left[\left(\frac{t^2 e^{2t}}{2}\right)_0^1 - \int_0^1 2t\frac{e^{2t}}{2}dt\right]$$

$$c = \lambda c \left[\frac{t^2 e^{2t}}{2} - \frac{te^{2t}}{2} + \frac{e^{2t}}{4}\right]_0^1$$

$$c = \lambda c \left[\frac{e^2}{2} - \frac{e^2}{2} + \frac{e^2}{4} - 0 + 0 - \frac{e^0}{4}\right]$$

$$c = \lambda c \left[\frac{e^2 - 1}{4}\right] \Rightarrow \lambda = \frac{4}{e^2 - 1}$$

$\Rightarrow$ option (c) is correct.

6. Explanation: (d)

Given Equation: $y(x) = x^2 + 2\int_0^1 xty(t), dt.$

We first observe that the integral is independent of x, so we define:

$I = \int_0^1 ty(t), dt.$

Thus, the equation becomes: $y(x) = x^2 + 2xI.$

Substitute $y(t) = t^2 + 2tI$ into the integral to solve for I:

$I = \int_0^1 t(t^2 + 2tI), dt = \int_0^1 t^3, dt + 2I\int_0^1 t^2, dt.$

Compute the integrals:

- $\int_0^1 t^3, dt = \frac{1}{4},$
- $\int_0^1 t^2, dt = \frac{1}{3}.$

Thus: $I = \frac{1}{4} + 2I \cdot \frac{1}{3}.$

$I = \frac{1}{4} + \frac{2I}{3} \Rightarrow 4I = 3 + 8I \Rightarrow 4I = 3 \Rightarrow I = \frac{3}{4}.$

Substitute $I = \frac{3}{4}$ into the equation for $y(x)$:

$y(x) = x^2 + 2x \cdot \frac{3}{4} = x^2 + \frac{3x}{2}.$

Check the statements

1. Statement 1: $y(0) + y(1) = \frac{1}{2}$
   - $y(0) = 0^2 + \frac{3(0)}{2} = 0,$
   - $y(1) = 1^2 + \frac{3(1)}{2} = 1 + \frac{3}{2} = \frac{5}{2},$
   - $y(0) + y(1) = 0 + \frac{5}{2} = \frac{5}{2} \neq \frac{1}{2}$.(False).
2. Statement 2: $y(-1) + y(1) = 1$
   - $y(-1) = (-1)^2 + \frac{3(-1)}{2} = 1 - \frac{3}{2} = -\frac{1}{2},$
   - $y(1) = \frac{5}{2},$
   - $y(-1) + y(1) = -\frac{1}{2} + \frac{5}{2} = 2 \neq 1$.(False).
3. Statement 3: $y'(0) + y'(1) = \frac{3}{2}$
   - $y'(x) = 2x + \frac{3}{2},$
   - $y'(0) = \frac{3}{2},$
   - $y'(1) = 2 + \frac{3}{2} = \frac{7}{2},$
   - $y'(0) + y'(1) = \frac{3}{2} + \frac{7}{2} = 5 \neq \frac{3}{2}$.(False).
4. Statement 4: $y'(-1) + y'(1) = 3$
   - $y'(-1) = 2(-1) + \frac{3}{2} = -2 + \frac{3}{2} = -\frac{1}{2},$
   - $y'(1) = \frac{7}{2},$
   - $y'(-1) + y'(1) = -\frac{1}{2} + \frac{7}{2} = 3$.(True).

The correct statement is Statement 4: 4

7. Explanation: (c)

We are given the integral equation

$$u(x) = 3 + \int_0^x (x - t)u(t)\,dt$$

Using Leibniz rule for differentiation of integrals:

$$u'(x) = \frac{d}{dx}\left[3 + \int_0^x (x-t)u(t)dt\right] = \int_0^x u(t)dt$$

(because $\frac{\partial}{\partial x}(x - t) = 1$ and upper limit gives zero term)

Differentiate again

$$u''(x) = \frac{d}{dx}\left(\int_0^x u(t)dt\right)$$

$$u''(x) = u(x)$$

So the equation becomes the differential equation

$$u''(x) - u(x) = 0$$

General solution:

$$u(x) = Ae^x + Be^{-x}$$

Use initial conditions

From original equation:

At $x = 0$:

$$u(0) = 3$$
$$\Rightarrow A + B = 3$$

Differentiate:

$$u'(x) = Ae^x - Be^{-x}$$

From earlier result $u'(x) = \int_0^x u(t)dt$

Thus

$$u'(0) = 0$$
$$\Rightarrow A - B = 0$$

So

$$A = B$$

Using $A + B = 3$

$$A = B = \frac{3}{2}$$

$$\Rightarrow u(x) = \frac{3}{2}(e^x + e^{-x}) = 3\cosh x$$

At $x = \pi$

$$u(\pi) = \frac{3}{2}(e^\pi + e^{-\pi})$$

$$u'(\pi) = \frac{3}{2}(e^\pi - e^{-\pi})$$

$$\Rightarrow u(\pi) + u'(\pi) = \frac{3}{2}(e^\pi + e^{-\pi}) + \frac{3}{2}(e^\pi - e^{-\pi}) = 3e^\pi$$

MSQ (Multiple Select Questions)

1. The initial value problem

$$\frac{d^2y}{dx^2} + y = 0 ; x > 0$$
$$y(0) = 1, y'(0) = 0,$$

Is equivalent to the Volterra integral equation

(a) $y(x) = 1 + \int_0^x (t - x)y(t)dt$
(b) $y(x) = 1 + \int_0^x (t + x)y(t)dt$
(c) $y(x) = 1 + \int_0^x xty(t)dt$
(d) $y(x) = 1 + \int_0^x (x - t)y(t)dt$

[Dec 2012]

2. If $y : [0, \infty] \to [0, \infty]$ is a continuously differentiable function satisfying $y(t) = y_0 - \int_0^t y(s)ds \ for\ t \geq 0$, then

(a) $y^2(t) = y^2(0) + \left(\int_0^t y(s)ds\right)^2 - 2y(0)\int_0^t y(s)ds$
(b) $y^2(t) = y^2(0) + 2\int_0^t y^2(s)ds$
(c) $y^2(t) = y^2(0) - \int_0^t y(s)ds$
(d) $y^2(t) = y^2(0) - 2\int_0^t y^2(s)ds$

[June 2014]

3. Let $u \in C^2([0,1])$ satisfy for some $\lambda \neq 0$ and $a \neq 0$, $u(x) + \frac{\lambda}{2}\int_0^1 |x - s|u(s)\,ds = ax + b$. Then u also satisfies

(a) $\frac{d^2y}{dx^2} + \lambda u = 0$
(b) $\frac{d^2y}{dx^2} - \lambda u = 0$
(c) $\frac{du}{dx} - \frac{\lambda}{2}\int_0^1 \frac{x-s}{|x-s|} u(s)ds = a$
(d) $\frac{du}{dx} + \frac{\lambda}{2}\int_0^1 \frac{x-s}{|x-s|} u(s)ds = a$

[Dec 2014]

4. Consider the integral equation $\varphi(x) - \frac{e}{2}\int_{-1}^1 xe^t\varphi(t)dt = f(x)$. Then

(a) There exists a continuous function $f: [-1,1] \to (0, \infty)$ for which solution exists
(b) There exists a continuous function $f: [-1,1] \to (-\infty, 0)$ for which solution exists
(c) For $f(x) = e^{-x}(1 - 3x^2)$, a solution exists
(d) For $f(x) = e^{-x}(x + x^3 + x^5)$, a solution exists

5. Consider the integral equation

$$\int_0^x (x - t)\,u(t)dt = x; x \geq 0$$

For continuous functions u defined on $[0, \infty)$. The equation has

(a) A unique bounded solution
(b) No solution
(c) A unique solution u such that $|u(x)| \leq C(1 + |x|)$ for some constant C
(d) more than one solution u such that $|u(x)| \leq c(1 + |x|)$ for some constant C

[Feb 2022]

Answer Key

1	2	3	4	5
a	a, b	a, d	c, d	b

Explanation

1. **Explanation: (a)**

Consider the given initial value problem

$$\frac{d^2y}{dx^2} + y = 0 ; x > 0$$

$$y(0) = 1, y'(0) = 0 \qquad (1)$$

$$\Rightarrow y'' + y = 0$$
$$y''(t) + y(t) = 0$$
$$\Rightarrow y''(t) = -y(t)$$

$$\int_0^x y''(t)\,dt = -\int_0^x y(t)\,dt$$

$$y'(x) - y'(0) = -\int_0^x y(t)\,dt$$

$$y'(x) = -\int_0^x y(t)\,dt \qquad \text{from (1)}$$

$$\int_0^x y'(t) = -\int_0^x\int_0^x y(t)\,dt$$

$$y(x) - y(0) = -\int_0^x (x - t)y(t)dt$$

$$y(x) = 1 - \int_0^x (x - t)(t)\,dt \quad \text{from (1)}$$

$$y(x) = 1 + \int_0^x (t - x)y(t)\,dt$$

⇒ Only option (a) is correct answer and (b), (c)and (d) are incorrect.

2. **Explanation: (a), (b)**

Consider the given volterra integral equation

$$y(t) = y_0 - \int_0^t y(s)\,ds \qquad \text{for } t \geq 0 \quad (1)$$

Differentiating w.r.t. to t

$$y'(t) = -y(t) \qquad \text{(By Leibniz rule)}$$

$$\frac{y'(t)}{y(t)} = -1$$

$$\log y = -t + c_1$$
$$y = e^{-t}c$$
$$y(0) = y_0 \quad \text{from (1)}$$
$$y(0) = c = y_0$$
$$y = e^{-t}y_0$$

$y(t) = y_0 e^{-t}$

For option (a)

$$y(t) = y_0 - \int_0^t y(s)\, ds$$

Squaring both sides, we get,

$$y^2(t) = {y_0}^2 - 2y_0 \int_0^t y(s)\, ds + \left(\int_0^1 y(s)\, ds\right)^2$$

$$y^2(t) = y^2(0) - 2y(0) \int_0^t y(s)\, ds + \left(\int_0^1 y(s)\, ds\right)^2$$

⇒Option (a) is correct.

Now for option (b)

$y^2(t) = y_0^2 e^{-2t} dt$

$$y^2(t) = y^2(0) + 2\int_0^t y^2(s)\, ds$$

$$= y_0^2 + 2\int_0^t y_0^2 e^{-2t}\, dt$$

$$= y_0^2 + 2y_0^2 \left[\frac{e^{-2t}}{2}\right]_0^t$$

$$= y_0^2 + \frac{2y_0^2}{2}[e^{-2t} - 1] \neq y^2(t)$$

⇒Option b is incorrect.

Now option c)

To show

$$y^2(t) = y^2(0) - \int_0^t y(s)\, ds$$

$y^2(t) = y_0 e^{-2t}$

Consider,

$$y^2(0) - \int_0^t y(s)\, ds$$

$$y^2(0) - \int_0^t y(s)\, ds = y_0^2 - \int_0^t y_0 e^{-2t}$$

$$y^2(0) - \int_0^t y(s)\, ds = y_0^2 + y_0\left[\frac{e^{-2t}}{2} - \frac{1}{2}\right]$$

$$y^2(0) - \int_0^t y(s)\, ds = y_0^2 - y_0\left[\frac{e^{-2t}}{2} - \frac{1}{2}\right]$$

$$y^2(t) \neq y^2(0) - \int_0^t y(s)\, ds$$

Option (c) is incorrect.

Now check option (d)

$y^2(t) = y_0 e^{-2t}$

$$y^2(0) - 2\int_0^t y^2(s)\, ds = {y_0}^2 - 2\int_0^t y_0^2 e^{-2s}\, ds$$

$$y^2(0) - 2\int_0^t y^2(s)\, ds = y_0^2 - 2y_0^2[e^{-2t} - 1]$$

$$y^2(0) - 2\int_0^t y^2(s)\, ds = y_0^2 e^{-2t}$$

$$y^2(0) - 2\int_0^t y^2(s)\, ds = y^2(t)$$

⇒ Option d) is also correct.

⇒ Option (a) and (d) are correct and option (c) and (d) are incorrect.

3. Explanation: (a), (d)

Consider the given volterra integral equation

$$u(x) + \frac{\lambda}{2}\int_0^1 |x - s|\, u(s)\, ds = ax + b$$

We know $|x - s| = \begin{cases} x - s & \text{if } x - s \geq 0 \\ s - x & \text{if } x - s < 0 \end{cases}$

$u(x) + \frac{\lambda}{2}\int_0^1 |x - s|\, u(s)\, ds + \frac{\lambda}{2}\int_x^1 |s - x|\, u(s)\, ds = ax + b$

Now differentiating w.r.t to x

$$u'(x) + \frac{\lambda}{2}\int_0^x u(s) ds + \frac{\lambda}{2}\int_x^1 (-1) u(s) ds = a$$

$$u'(x) + \frac{\lambda}{2}\int_0^1 \frac{x - s}{|x - s|} u(s) ds = 0$$

From this option d) is correct and option c) is incorrect

Differentiating equation (2) w.r.t. to x

$$u''(x) + \frac{\lambda}{2}u(x) + \frac{\lambda}{2}u(x) = 0$$

$\Rightarrow u''(x) + \lambda u(x) = 0$

⇒ Option a) is correct and option b) is incorrect.

⇒ Option (a) and (d) are correct answer and b) and c) are the incorrect.

4. Explanation: (c), (d)

Consider the given integral equation

$\phi(x) - \frac{e}{2}\int_{-1}^1 x e^t \phi(t)\, dt = f(x)$-----(1)

$$\Rightarrow \phi(x) = f(x) + \frac{e}{2}\int_{-1}^1 x e^t \phi(t)\, dt$$

Put $c = \int_{-1}^1 e^t \phi(t)\, dt$

$$\Rightarrow \phi(x) = f(x) + \frac{ex}{2}c$$

$$\Rightarrow c = \int_{-1}^1 e^t\left(f(t) - \frac{et}{2}c\right) dt$$

$$\Rightarrow c = \int_{-1}^1 e^t f(t)\, dt - \int_{-1}^1 \frac{e^{t+1} + c}{2} f(t) dt$$

$$\Rightarrow c = \int_{-1}^1 e^t f(t)\, dt + \frac{ec}{2}[te^t]_{-1}^1 - \frac{ec}{2}[e^t]_{-1}^1$$

$$\Rightarrow c = \int_{-1}^1 e^t f(t)\, dt + \frac{ec}{2}[e - e^{-1}] - \frac{ec}{2}[e - e^{-1}]$$

$$\Rightarrow c = \int_{-1}^1 e^t f(t)\, dt + [e + e^{-1} - e + e^{-1}]\frac{ec}{2}$$

$$\Rightarrow c = \int_{-1}^1 e^t f(t)\, dt + c$$

$\Rightarrow \int_{-1}^1 e^t f(t)\, dt = 0$ (2)

Now check the option

For option a)

$f: [-1,1] \to (0, \infty)$ be a continuous function

And we have $f(t) > 0$ for $t \in [-1,1]$

And also $e^t > 0$

$f(t) > 0$ for $t \in [-1,1]$

So, $\int_{-1}^1 e^t f(t) dt > 0$

From equation (2),

we get contradiction, hence initial assumption wrong.

$\Rightarrow$there does not exist a continuous function

$\Rightarrow f: [-1,1] \to (0, \infty)$ for which solution exists.

Option (a) is incorrect

Similarly,

option (b) also incorrect

For option (c)

$f(x) = e^{-x}(1-3x^2)$

$$\int_{-1}^{1} e^t f(t)\, dt = \int_{-1}^{1} e^t e^{-t}(1-3t^2)dt$$

$$= \int_{-1}^{1} (1-3t^2)dt$$

$$= \left[t - \frac{3t^3}{3}\right]_{-1}^{1}$$

$$\Rightarrow \int_{-1}^{1} e^t f(t)\, dt = (1-1) - [-1+1] = 0$$

From equation (2)

$f(x) = e^{-x}(1-3x^2)$ is a solution given equation (1)

For option (d)

$f(x) = e^{-x}(x + x^3 + x^5)$

$$\int_{-1}^{1} e^t f(t)\, dt = \int_{-1}^{1} e^{-t} e^t (t + t^3 + t^5)\, dt$$

$$= \left[\frac{t^2}{2} + \frac{t^4}{4} + \frac{t^6}{6}\right]_{-1}^{1}$$

$$= \frac{1}{2} + \frac{1}{4} + \frac{1}{6} - \left[\frac{1}{2} + \frac{1}{4} + \frac{1}{6}\right]$$

$= 0$

From equation (2)

$f(x) = e^{-x}(x + x^3 + x^5)$

is also a solution of equation (1)

Option (c) and (d) are correct answer and option (a) and (b) are incorrect.

5. **Explanation: (b)**

Consider the given integral equation

$\int_0^x (x-t)\, u(t) dt = x \quad ; x \geq 0 \qquad (1)$

Differentiating equation (1) w. r. to. x with the help of Leibniz rule

$\int_0^x u(t)\, dt = 1 \qquad (2)$

Again, apply Leibniz rule,

$\Rightarrow$ u(x) = 0

$\Rightarrow$ u(t) = 0

$\Rightarrow$ Equation (2) become,

0=1

Which is contradiction

So, it has no solution.

Option (b) is the correct answer.

Unit 4.2: Volterra and Fredholm Integral Equations

MCQ (Multiple Choices Questions)

1. For the Volterra type linear integral equation

$$\phi(x) = x + 2\int_0^x e^{x-\zeta}\,\phi(\zeta)d(\zeta),$$

The resolvent Kernel $R(x,\zeta;2)$ of the kernel $e^{x-\zeta}$ is

(a) $(x-\zeta)^2 e^{2(x-\zeta)}$ (b) $(x-\zeta)e^{x-\zeta}$

(c) $e^{3(x-\zeta)}$ (d) $e^{(x-\zeta)}$

[June 2011]

2. For the linear integral equation

$$\phi(x) = x + \int_0^{1/2} \phi(\xi),$$

The resolvent kernel $R(x,\xi\,;1)$ is

(a) $\frac{1}{2}$ (b) 2

(c) $\frac{3}{2}$ (d) 4

[June 2012]

3. For the homogenous Fredholm integral equation $\phi(x) = \lambda\int_0^1 e^{x+t}\,\phi(t)dt$, a non-trivial solution exists, when λ ahs the value

(a) $\lambda = \frac{2}{e-1}$ (b) $\lambda = \frac{1}{e^2+1}$

(c) $\lambda = \frac{1}{e+1}$ (d) $\lambda = \frac{2}{e^2-1}$

[Dec 2012]

4. The integral equation

$$\varphi(x) = f(x) + \int_0^1 K(x,y)\varphi(y)dy$$

For $K(x,y) = xy^2$ has a solution

(a) $\varphi(x) = f(x)$

(b) $\varphi(x) = K(x,x)$

(c) $\varphi(x) = x^3$

(d) $\varphi(x) = f(x) + \frac{4}{3}\,x\int_0^1 x^2 f(x)dx$

[Dec 2013]

5. The homogeneous integral equation $\varphi(x) - \lambda\int_0^1 (3x-2)t\,\varphi(t)dt = 0$, has

(a) One characteristic numbers

(b) Three characteristic numbers

(c) Two characteristic numbers

(d) No characteristic numbers

[June 2014]

6. Let $y:[0,\infty) \to \mathbb{R}$ be twice continuously differentiable and satisfy $y(x) + \int_0^x (x-S)y(s)ds = x^3/6$. Then

(a) $y(x) = \frac{1}{6}\int_0^x s^3\sin(x-s)ds$

(b) $y(x) = \frac{1}{6}\int_0^x s^3\cos(x-s)ds$

(c) $y(x) = \int_0^x s\sin(x-s)ds$

(d) $y(x) = \int_0^x s\cos(x-s)ds$

[Dec 2014]

7. The integral equation

$$y(x) = \lambda\int_0^1 (3x-2)t\,y(t)dt,$$

With λ as a parameter, has

(a) Only one characteristic number

(b) Two characteristic numbers

(c) More than two characteristic numbers

(d) No characteristic number

[June 2015]

8. The resolvent kernel $R(x,t\,\lambda)$ for the Volterra integral equation $\varphi(x) = x + \lambda\int_a^x \varphi(s)ds$, is

(a) $e^{\lambda(x+t)}$ (b) $e^{\lambda(x-t)}$

(c) $\lambda^{e(x+t)}$ (d) $e^{\lambda xt}$

[Dec 2015]

9. Consider the integral equation

$$y(x) = x^3 + \int_0^x \sin(x-t)y(t)dt, x \in [0,\pi].$$

Then the value of $y(1)$ is

(a) $\frac{19}{20}$ (b) 1

(c) $\frac{17}{20}$ (d) $\frac{21}{20}$

[June 2016]

10. Let ϕ satisfy $\phi(x) = f(x) + \int_0^x \sin(x-t)\phi(t)dt$. Then ϕ is given by

(a) $\phi(x) = f(x) + \int_0^x (x-t)f(t)dt$

(b) $\phi(x) = f(x) - \int_0^x (x-t)f(t)dt$

(c) $\phi(x) = f(x) - \int_0^x \cos(x-t)f(t)dt$

(d) $\phi(x) = f(x) - \int_0^x \sin(x-t)f(t)dt$

[Dec 2016]

11. Let $\phi(x)$ be the solution of $\int_0^x e^{x-t}\,\phi(t)dt = x,\ x > 0$. Then $\phi(1)$ equals

(a) -1 (b) 0

(c) 1 (d) 2

[June 2017]

12. The resolvent Kernel for the integral equation $\Phi(x) = x^2 + \int_0^x e^{t-x}\varphi(t)dt$ is

(a) e^{t-x} (b) 1

(c) e^{x-t} (d) $x^2 + e^{x-t}$

[June 2018]

13. Let ϕ be the solution of

$$\phi(x) = 1 - 2x - 4x^2 + \int_0^x [3 + 6(x-t) - 4(x-t)^2]\,\phi(t)dt$$

Then $\phi(1)$ is equal to

(a) e^{-1} (b) e^{-2}

(c) e (d) e^2

[Dec 2019]

14. If $\phi:[0,1] \to \mathbb{R}$ is continuous and statistics

$$\int_0^x (x-t)^2\ \phi(t)dt = x^4 + x^5, then\ \phi(1) = \_\_$$

(a) 18 (b) 30
(c) 42 (d) 48

[Dec 2019]

15. The solution of the Fredholm integral equation $y(s) = s + 2\int_0^1 (st^2 + s^2t)\, y(t)dt$ is
(a) $y(s) = -(50s + 40s^2)$
(b) $y(s) = 30 + 15s^2$
(c) $y(s) = -(30s + 40s^2)$
(d) $y(s) = (60s + 50s^2)$

[Nov 2020]

16. Consider continuous solutions f of the following integral equation in [0, 1]

$$f^2(t) = 1 + 2\int_0^t f(s)ds\ , \forall t \in [0,1].$$

Which of the following statements are true.
(a) There is no solution.
(b) There is exactly one solution.
(c) There are exactly two solutions.
(d) There are more than two solutions.

[Nov 2020]

17. For any two continuous functions, $g: \mathbb{R} \to \mathbb{R}$, define $f * g(t) = \int_0^t f(s)g(t-s)\, ds$. Which of the following is the value of $f * g(t) = \exp(-t)$ and $g(t) = \sin(t)$?
(a) $\frac{1}{2}[\exp(-t) + \sin(t) - \cos(t)]$
(b) $\frac{1}{2}[-\exp(-t) + \sin(t) - \cos(t)]$
(c) $\frac{1}{2}[\exp(-t) - \sin(t) - \cos(t)]$
(d) $\frac{1}{2}[\exp(-t) + \sin(t) + \cos(t)]$

[SEP 2022]

18. For the unknown $y: [0,1] \to \mathbb{R}$, consider the following two-point boundary value problem:
$$\begin{cases} y''(x) + 2y(x) = 0 & for\ x \in (0,1), \\ y(0) = y(1) = 0 \end{cases}$$
It is given that the above boundary value problem corresponds to the following integral equation:
$y(x) = 2\int_0^1 K(x,t)\, y(t)dt$ for $x \in [0,1]$.
Which of the following is the kernel $K(x,t)$?
(a) $K(x,t) = \begin{cases} t(1-x) & for\ t < x \\ x(1-t) & for\ t > x \end{cases}$
(b) $K(x,t) = \begin{cases} t^2(1-x) & for\ t < x \\ x^2(1-t) & for\ t > x \end{cases}$
(c) $K(x,t) = \begin{cases} \sqrt{t}(1-x) & for\ t < x \\ \sqrt{x}(1-t) & for\ t > x \end{cases}$
(d) $K(x,t) = \begin{cases} \sqrt{t^3}(1-x) & for\ t < x \\ \sqrt{x^3}(1-t) & for\ t > x \end{cases}$

[JUNE 2023]

19. Let u be the solution of the Volterra integral equation

$$\int_0^t \left[\frac{1}{2} + \sin(t-\tau)\right] u(\tau)\, d\tau = \sin t.$$

Then the value of $u(1)$ is
(a) 0 (b) 1
(c) 2 (d) $2e^{-1}$

[July 2024]

20. Let $\lambda \in \mathbb{R}$, and $K: [0,1] \times [0,1] \to \mathbb{R}$ be a function such that every solution of the boundary value problem
$$\frac{d^2u}{dx^2}(x) + \lambda u(x) = 0; \frac{du}{dx}(0) = u(0), \frac{du}{dx}(1) = 0$$
satisfies the integral equation
$$u(x) + \lambda\int_0^1 K(x,t)u(t)\, dt = 0$$
Then
(a) $K(x,t) = \begin{cases} (1+x)(1-t), 0 \le x \le t \le 1 \\ (1+t)(1-x),\ 0 \le t \le x \le 1 \end{cases}$
(b) $K(x,t) = \begin{cases} -1-x, 0 \le x \le t \le 1 \\ -1-t,\ 0 \le t < x \le 1 \end{cases}$
(c) $K(x,t) = \begin{cases} 1-x^2, 0 \le x \le t \le 1 \\ 1-t^2,\ 0 \le t < x \le 1 \end{cases}$
(d) $K(x,t) = \begin{cases} (1+x)(t-1), 0 \le x \le t \le 1 \\ (1+t)(x-1),\ 0 \le t \le x \le 1 \end{cases}$

[Feb. 2025]

21. Let f and K be such that the solution of the initial value problem
$y'' - 3y' + 2y = 4\sin(x), y(0) = 1, y'(0) = -2.$
satisfies the Volterra integral equation
$y(x) = f(x) + \int_0^x K(x,t)\, y(t)\, dt.$
Then which of the following statements are true?
(a) $f'(\pi) = 3$ (b) $f(\pi) + f'(\pi) = 4 - \pi$
(c) $f(\pi) + f'(\pi) = 2 - \pi$ (d) $f(0) + f'(0) = -4$

[June 2025]

Answer Key

1	2	3	4	5	6	7	8	9	10
c	b	d	d	d	c	d	b	d	a
11	12	13	14	15	16	17	18	19	20
b	b	c	c	c	c	a	a	a	B
21									
*									

Explanations

1. **Explanation: (c)**
Consider the given volterra integral equation
$\phi(x) = x + 2\int_0^x e^{x-\xi}\phi(\xi)d\xi$-------(1)
$$y(x) = f(x) + \lambda\int_a^b k(x,\xi)y(\xi)d\xi$$
Comparing with equation (1)
$\Rightarrow f(x) = x\ , \lambda = 2,\ \ k(x,\xi) = e^{x-\xi}$
Now, $k(x,\xi) = k_0(x,\xi) = e^{x-\xi}$
$$k_1(x,\xi) = \int_\xi^x k(x,t)k_0(x,\xi)\, dt$$
$$= \int_\xi^x e^{x-t}e^{t-\xi}\, dt$$
$k_1 = (x-\xi)e^{x-\xi}$

$$k_2 = \int_{\xi}^{x} e^{x-t}e^{t-\xi}(t-\xi)dt$$

$$k_2(x,\xi) = \frac{(x-\xi)^2}{2}e^{x-\xi}$$

Similarly $k_3 = \frac{e^{x-\xi}(x-\xi)^3}{3!}$

We know that,

$$R(x,\zeta;\lambda) = \sum_{n=1}^{\infty} k_n(x,\xi)\lambda^n$$

$$R(x,\xi;2) = k_0(x,\xi) + 2k_1(x,\xi) + 2^2k_2(x,\xi) + 2^3k_3(x,\xi) + ..$$

$$= e^{x-\xi} + 2(x-\xi)e^{x-\xi} + \frac{2^2(x-\xi)^2}{2!}e^{x-\xi} + \frac{2^3e^{x-\xi}(x-\xi)^3}{3!} + \dots$$

$$= e^{x-\xi}\left[1 + \frac{[2(x-\xi)]}{1!} + \frac{[2(x-\xi)]^2}{2!} + \frac{[2(x-\xi)]^3}{3!} + \cdots\right.$$

$$= e^{x-\xi}e^{2(x-\xi)}$$

$$R(x,\xi;2) = e^{3(x-\xi)}$$

Resolvent kernel $R(x,\xi;2)$ of the kernel $e^{(x-\xi)}$ is $e^{3(x-\xi)}$

Only option c) is correct is the correct answer and a),b) and d) are the incorrect.

2. **Explanation: (b)**

Consider the given linear integral equation is

$\phi(x) = x + \int_0^{\frac{1}{2}} \phi(\xi)d\xi$------(1)

$y(x) = f(x) + \lambda \int_a^b \phi(\xi)d\xi,$

comparing with equation (1)

$\Rightarrow \lambda = 1,\ k(x,\xi) = k_0(x,\xi) = 1$

$$k_1(x,\xi) = \int_{\xi}^{x} k(x,t)\,k_0(t,\xi)dt$$

$$k_1(x,\xi) = \int_0^{\frac{1}{2}} 1\,dt = \frac{1}{2}$$

$$k_2(x,\xi) = \int_0^{\frac{1}{2}} k_0(x,t)k_1(t,\xi)\,dt$$

$$k_2(x,\xi) = \frac{1}{4} = \frac{1}{2^2}$$

Similarly $k_3(x,\xi) = \frac{1}{2^3}$

We know that,

$$R(x,\zeta;\lambda) = \sum_{n=0}^{\infty} k_n(x,\xi)\lambda^n$$

$$\Rightarrow R(x,\xi;1) = k_0(x,\xi) + k_1(x,\xi) + k_2(x,\xi) + k_3(x,\xi) + ..$$

$$= 1 + \frac{1}{2} + \frac{1}{2^2} + \frac{1}{2^3} + \cdots ..$$

$$R(x,\xi;1) = \frac{1}{1-\frac{1}{2}} = 2$$

$\Rightarrow$Only option (b) is correct and (a),(b),(d) are incorrect.

3. **Explanation: (d)**

Consider the homogeneous fredholm integral equation

$\phi(x) = \lambda \int_0^1 e^{x+t}\phi(t)dt$------(1)

$$\phi(x) = \lambda e^x \int_0^1 e^t\phi(t)dt$$

Put, $\int_0^1 e^t\phi(t)dt = c$

$$\phi(x) = \lambda e^x c$$

$$e^x\phi(x) = \lambda e^{2x}c$$

$$\int_0^1 e^x\phi(x) = \int_0^1 \lambda e^{2x}c\,dx$$

$$c = \lambda c\left[\frac{e^{2x}}{2}\right]_0^1$$

$$c = \frac{\lambda c}{2}(e^2-1)$$

$$c\left(1 - \frac{\lambda(e^2-1)}{2}\right) = 0$$

$\because$ we choose the non trivial solution

$$\Rightarrow \left(1 - \frac{\lambda(e^2-1)}{2}\right) = 0$$

$$\Rightarrow \frac{\lambda(e^2-1)}{2} = 1$$

$$\Rightarrow \lambda(e^2-1) = 2$$

$$\Rightarrow \lambda = \frac{2}{e^2-1}$$

$\Rightarrow$Only option (d) is correct and option (a),(b),(c) are incorrect.

4. **Explanation: (d)**

Consider the given integral equation

$\phi(x) = f(x) + \int_0^1 k(x,y)\phi(y)dy$-----(1)

$k(x,y) = xy^2$

Now put, $\int_0^1 y^2\phi(y)\,dy = c_1$ (2)

Equation (1) become,

$$\phi(x) = f(x) + c_1x$$

$$x^2\phi(x) = x^2(f(x) + c_1x)$$

$$\int_0^1 x^2\phi(x) = \int_0^1 (x^2f(x) + c_1x^3)\,dx$$

$c_1 = \int_0^1 x^2f(x)\,dx + \frac{c_1}{4}$ from (2)

$$\frac{3}{4}c_1 = \int_0^1 x^2f(x)\,dx$$

$$\Rightarrow c_1 = \frac{4}{3}\int_0^1 x^2f(x)dx$$

$$\Rightarrow \phi(x) = f(x) + \frac{4}{3}x\int_0^1 x^2f(x)dx$$

$\Rightarrow$ Only option (d) is correct answer and option b), c) and d) are the incorrect.

5. **Explanation: (d)**

Consider the given homogeneous integral equation

$$\phi(x) - \lambda\int_0^1 (3x-2)t\,\phi(t)dt = 0$$

$$\Rightarrow \phi(x) = \lambda\int_0^1 (3x-2)t\,\phi(t)dt$$

Put, $c = \int_0^1 t\phi(t)\,dt$

$$\Rightarrow \phi(x) = \lambda(3x-2)c$$

$$\int_0^1 x\phi(x)\,dx = \int_0^1 x\lambda(3x-2)c\,dx$$

$\Rightarrow c = \int_0^1 \lambda x(3x-2)c\,dx$

$c = c\lambda \int_0^1 3x^2 - 2x\,dx$

$c = c\lambda[x^3 - x^2]_0^1$

$\Rightarrow c = 0$

$\Rightarrow \int_0^1 t\phi(t)\,dt = 0$

$\Rightarrow \phi(x) = 0$

From above explanation, we got trivial solution

Therefore, given integral equation has no characteristic numbers.

⇒Only option (d) is correct answer and a), b) and c) are the incorrect.

6. Explanation: (c)

Consider the given volterra integral equation

$y(x) + \int_0^x (x-s)\,y(s)ds = \frac{x^3}{6}$---------(1)

Differentiating equation (1) w.r.to. x

$\Rightarrow y'(x) + \int_0^x y(s)\,ds = \frac{x^2}{2}$

Again differentiate w.r.to. x

$\Rightarrow y'' + y(x) - y(0) = x$

$y(0) = 0$ From equation (1)

$\Rightarrow y''(x) + y(x) = x$

Auxiliary equation of above equation is

$m^2 + 1 = 0$

$m = \pm i$

Complementary function is

$\Rightarrow y(x) = c_1 \cos x + c_2 \sin x$

Fundamental set is $\{\cos x, \sin x\}$

Now find the wronskian

$\begin{vmatrix} \cos x & \sin x \\ -\sin x & \cos x \end{vmatrix} = \cos^2 x + \sin^2 x = 1$

Now, $a(x) = \cos x\; b(x) = \sin x$, R= x

$u(x) = -\int \frac{Rb(x)}{W}dx$

$v(x) = \int \frac{Ra(x)}{W}dx$

$u(x) = -\int \frac{x\sin x}{W}dx$

$v(x) = \int \frac{x\cos x}{W}dx$

$\Rightarrow y(x) = -\cos x \int_0^x s\sin s\,ds + \sin x \int_0^s s\cos s\,ds$

$y(x) = s\int_0^x -\cos x \sin s\,ds + \int_0^x \sin x\cos s\,ds$

$y(x) = s\int_0^x s\sin(x-s)\,ds$

⇒ only option (c)is correct answer and option (a), (b), (d) are incorrect.

7. Explanation: (d)

Consider the given homogeneous integral equation

$\phi(x) - \lambda \int_0^1 (3x-2)t\,\phi(t)dt = 0$

$\Rightarrow \phi(x) = \lambda \int_0^1 (3x-2)t\,\phi(t)dt$

Put $c = \int_0^1 t\phi(t)\,dt$

$\phi(x) = \lambda(3x-2)c$

$\int_0^1 x\phi(x)\,dx = \int_0^1 x\lambda(3x-2)c\,dx$

$c = \int_0^1 \lambda x(3x-2)c\,dx$

$= c\lambda \int_0^1 3x^2 - 2x\,dx$

$= c\lambda[x^3 - x^2]_0^1$

$\Rightarrow c = 0$

$\Rightarrow \int_0^1 t\phi(t)\,dt = 0$

$\Rightarrow \phi(x) = 0$

From above explanation, we got trivial solution

Therefore, given integral equation has no characteristic numbers.

⇒ Only option (d) is correct answer and a), b) and c) are the incorrect.

8. Explanation: (b)

Consider the given volterra integral equation

$\phi(x) = x + \lambda \int_0^x \phi(s)\,ds$

We know that resolvent kernel $R(x,t;\lambda)$is

$R(x,t;\lambda) = \sum_{r=0}^{\infty} \lambda^r k_r(t)$

$k_0(x,t) = 1,\; k_1(x,t) = \int_t^x k(x,s)\,k_1(s,t)ds = (x-t)$

Similarly,

$k_2(x,t) = \frac{(x-t)^2}{2}$

$k_3(x,t) = \frac{(x-t)^3}{3!}$

$\Rightarrow k_r(x,t) = \frac{(x-t)^r}{r!}$

$\Rightarrow R(x,t;\lambda) = \sum_{r=0}^{\infty} \frac{\lambda^r (x-t)^r}{r!} = e^{\lambda(x-t)}$

Only option (b) is correct answer and option (a), (c)&(d) are incorrect.

9. Explanation: (d)

Consider the given volterra integral equation

$y(x) = x^3 + \int_0^x \sin(x-t)\,y(t)\,dt \qquad x \in [0,\pi]$-------(1)

$y(0) = 0$

Now differentiating equation (1) w.r.t. x

We get

$y'(x) = 3x^2 + \frac{d}{dx}\int_0^x \sin(x-t)\,y(t)\,dt$

$y'(x) = 3x^2 + \int_0^x \cos(x-t)\,y(t)dt$-------(2)

$\Rightarrow y'(0) = 0$

Again differentiating equation (2) w.r.t. x we get,

$$y''(x) = 6x - \int_0^x \sin(x-t)\,y(t) + y(x)$$

(By Leibniz rule)

$y''(x) = 6x - \int_0^x \sin(x-t)\,y(t) + x^3 + \int_0^x \sin(x-t)\,y(t)\,dt$ From (1)

$y''(x) = 6x + x^3 \Rightarrow y''(0) = 0$

Now integrating both side

$y'(x) = \frac{6x^2}{2} + \frac{x^4}{4} + a$ --------(3)

Again integrating

$y(x) = x^3 + \frac{x^5}{20} + ax + b$-------(4)

From equation (3)

$$y'(x) = \frac{6x^2}{2} + \frac{x^4}{4} + a$$

$\Rightarrow y'(0) = 0 + 0 + a = 0$

$\Rightarrow a = 0$

And, $y'(0) = 0 + 0 + b = 0$

$\Rightarrow b = 0$

From this, $y(x) = x^3 + \frac{x^5}{20}$

Now find $y(1)$

So put $x = 1$ in above equation

$$y(1) = 1 + \frac{1}{20} = \frac{21}{20}$$

This is the required answer

⇒ only option (d) is correct and (a),(b),(c) are incorrect.

10. Explanation: (a)

Consider the given volterra integral equation

$\phi(x) = f(x) + \int_0^x \sin(x-t)\,\phi(t)dt$-------(1)

$\phi(0) = f(0)$------(2)

Differentiating equation (1) w.r.t. x and also use Leibniz rule

$$\Rightarrow \phi'(x) = f'(x) + \int_0^x \cos(x-t)\,\phi(t)dt$$

$\Rightarrow \phi'(0) = f'(0)$

Again differentiating w..r.t. x and also use Leibniz rule

$$\phi''(x) = f''(x) + \int_0^x -\sin(x-t)\,\phi(t)dt + \phi(x)$$

$\phi''(x) = f''(x) + f(x)$ from equation (1)

$\phi''(t) = f''(t) + f(t)$

now integrating,

$$\int_0^x \phi''(t)\,dt = \int_0^x f''(t)\,dt + \int_0^x f(t)\,dt$$

$$\Rightarrow \phi'(x) - \phi'(0) = f'(x) - f'(0) + \int_0^x f(t)dt$$

$\phi'(t) = f'(t) + \int_0^x f(t)\,dt$ from (3)

Differentiating w.r.t. x

$$\int_0^x \phi'(t)\,dt = \int_0^x f'(t)\,dt + \int_0^x\left[\int_0^x f(t)\,dt\right]dt$$

$$\phi(x) - \phi(0) = f(x) - f(0) + \int_0^x\int_0^x f(t)\,dt\,dt$$

$\phi(x) = f(x) + \int_0^x (x-t)\,f(t)dt$ From (1)

This is the required solution

⇒ only option (a) is correct answer and option (b), (c), (d) are incorrect.

11. Explanation: (b)

We have $\int_0^x e^{x-t}\phi(t)\,dt = x$--------(1)

Differentiating equation (1) w.r.t. to x using Leibniz rule

$$\Rightarrow \int_0^x e^{x-t}\phi(t)\,dt + \phi(x) = 1$$

$\Rightarrow x + \phi(x) = 1$

$\Rightarrow \phi(x) = 1 - x$

$\phi(1) = 1 - 1 = 0$

Option b) is correct answer and a), c) and d) are the incorrect.

12. Explanation: (b)

Consider the given volterra integral equation

$$\phi(x) = x^2 + \int_0^x e^{t-x}\phi(t)\,dt$$

$$y(x) = f(x) + \lambda\int_0^x k(x,t)\phi(t)\,dt$$

Comparing with equation (1)

$f(x) = x^2 k(x,t) = e^{t-x}$ and $\lambda = 1$

$k(x,t) = k_0(x,t) = e^{t-x}$

$$k_1(x,t) = \int_t^x k(x,s)\,k_0(s,t)ds$$

$$k_1(x,t) = \int_t^x e^{(s-x)}e^{t-s}\,ds$$

$$k_1(x,t) = \int_t^x e^{(t-x)}ds$$

$$k_1(x,t) = \frac{(-t+x)(e^{t-x})}{1!} = \frac{(x-t)e^{t-x}}{1!}$$

$$k_2(x,t) = \int_t^x k_0(x,s)\,k_1(s,t)ds$$

$$k_2(x,t) = \int_t^x e^{s-x}(s-t)e^{t-s}\,ds$$

$$k_2(x,t) = \int_t^x e^{(t-x)}(s-t)ds$$

$$k_2(x,t) = e^{t-x}\left[\frac{(s-t)^2}{2}\right]_t^x$$

$$k_2(x,t) = \frac{e^{t-x}}{2}[(x-t)^2] = \frac{e^{t-x}(t+x)^2}{2}$$

Resolvent kernel $R(x,t;\lambda)$

$$R(x,t;\lambda) = \sum_{r=0}^{\infty}\lambda^r k_r(x,t)$$

$= k_0(x,t) + \lambda k_1(x,t) + \lambda^2 k_2(x,t) + ..$

$$R(x,t;1) = e^{t-x} + \frac{(t-x)e^{t-x}}{1!} + \frac{(t-x)^2 e^{t-x}}{2!} + \cdots.$$

$$R(x,t;1) = e^{t-x}\left[1 + \frac{(t-x)}{1!} + \frac{(t-x)^2}{2!} + \cdots\right]$$

$R(x,t;1) = e^{t-x}e^{t+x} = e^0 = 1$

⇒ only option (b) is correct answer and option (a),(c),(d) are incorrect.

13. Explanation (c)

Given

$\phi(x) = 1 - 2x - 4x^2 + \int_0^x (3 + 6(x-t) - 4(x-t)^2]\phi(t)dt \rightarrow (1)$

$\phi'(x) = -2 - 8x + \int_0^x (6 - 8(x-t)]\,\phi(t)dt + 3\phi(x) \rightarrow (2)$

Again,

$\phi''(x) = -8 + \int_0^x (-8)\,\phi(t)dt + 6\phi(x) + 3\phi'(x) \rightarrow (3)$

Again, $\phi'''(x) = -8\phi(x) + 6\phi'(x) + 3\phi''(x) \rightarrow (4)$

$\phi'''(x) = 3\phi''(x) + 8\phi(x) - 6\phi'(x) = 0$

$\Rightarrow \phi'''(x) - 3\phi''(x) - 6\phi'(x) + 8\phi(x) = 0 \rightarrow (5)$

C.F $= \phi(x) = c_1e^x + c_2e^{4x} + c_3e^{-2x} \rightarrow (6)$

$\phi(0) = c_1 + c_2 + c_3 \rightarrow (A)$

From (6) $\Rightarrow \phi'(2) = c_1e^x + 4c_2e^{4x} - 2c_3e^{-2x}$

$\Rightarrow \phi'(0) = c_1 + 4c_2 - 2c_3 \rightarrow (B)$

$\&\phi''(x) = c_1e^x + 16c_2e^{4x} + 4c_3e^{-2x}$

$\Rightarrow \phi''(0) = c_1 + 16c_2 + 4c_3 \rightarrow (3)$

From (1), (2), (3)

$\Rightarrow \phi(0) = 1, \phi'(0) = 1, \phi''(0) = 1$

$\Rightarrow c_1 + c_2 + c_3 = 1$

$c_1 + 4c_2 - 2c_3 = 1$

$c_1 + 16c_2 + 4c_3 = 1$

$\Rightarrow c_1 = 1, c_2 = c_3 = 0$

$\Rightarrow \phi(x) = e^x$

$\Rightarrow \phi(1) = e^1 = e$

$\Rightarrow \phi(1) = e$

14. Explanation: (c)

$$\int_0^x (x-t)^2\,\phi(t)dt = x^4 + x^5,$$

Differentiating both sides with respect to x and using Leibniz rule,

$\Rightarrow 2(x-x)^2\,\phi(x)\frac{\partial x}{\partial x} - 0(x-0)^2\,\phi(0)\frac{\partial 0}{\partial x} + \int_0^x 2(x-t)\,\phi(t)dt = 4x^3 + 5x^4$

$$\Rightarrow 2\int_0^x 2(x-t)\,\phi(t)dt = 4x^3 + 5x^4$$

Again differentiating both side with respect to $x$and using Leibniz rule,

$\Rightarrow 2(x-x)\phi(x)\frac{\partial x}{\partial x} - 2(x-0)\phi(0)\frac{\partial 0}{\partial x} + \int_0^x \phi(t)dt = 12^2 + 20x^3$

$$\Rightarrow 0 - 0 + 2\int_0^x \phi(t)dt = 12^2 + 20x^3$$

$$\Rightarrow \int_0^x \phi(t)dt = 6x^2 + 10x^3$$

Again differentiating and using Leibniz rule,

$\phi(x) = 12x + 30x^2 \Rightarrow \phi(1) = (12.1) + 30.(1)$

$= 12 + 30 = 42$

So, option (c) is correct.

15. Explanation: (c)

$y(s) = s + 2\int_0^1 (st^2 + s^2t)y(t)dt$.............. (i)

$y(s) = s + 2s\int_0^1 t^2y(t)dt + 2s^2\int_0^1 ty(t)dt$.............. (ii)

Let $c_1 = \int_0^1 t^2y(t)dt$ and $c_2 = \int_0^1 ty(t)dt$

So (ii) becomes,

$y(s) = s + 2sc_1 + 2s^2c_2$

Now $c_1 = \int_0^1 t^2(t + 2tc_1 + 2t^2c_2)\,dt$

$$= \int_0^1 t^3dt + \int_0^1 2t^3c_1dt + \int_0^1 2t^4c_2dt$$

$$= \frac{t^4}{4}\Big|_0^1 + 2c_1\frac{t^4}{4}\Big|_0^1 + 2c_2\frac{t^5}{5}\Big|_0^1$$

$$= \frac{1}{4} + 2c_1.\frac{1}{4} + 2c_2\frac{1}{5}$$

$\Rightarrow \left(1 - \frac{1}{2}\right)c_1 - \frac{2}{5}c_2 = 1/_4 \Rightarrow \frac{1}{2}c_1 - \frac{2}{5}c_2 = \frac{1}{4}$.............(iii)

$$c_2 = \int_0^1 t(t + 2tc_1 + 2t^2c_2)dt$$

$$= \int_0^1 t^2(1 + 2c_1)dt + \int_0^1 2t^3c_2dt$$

$$= \frac{1 + 2c_1}{3}t^3|_0^1 + \frac{2}{4}c_2t^4|_0^1$$

$$= \frac{1 + 2c_1}{3}(1 - 0) + \frac{1}{2}c_2(1 - 0)$$

$$c_2 = \frac{1 + 2c_1}{3} + \frac{1}{2}c_2$$

$\Rightarrow \frac{2}{3}c_1 - \frac{1}{2}c_2 = -1/_3$ .... (iv)

Solving (iii) and (iv),

$(iii) - \frac{3}{4}(iv) \Rightarrow \frac{1}{2}c_1 - \frac{2}{5}c_2 - \frac{1}{2}c_1 + \frac{3}{8}c_2 = \frac{1}{4} + \frac{1}{4}$

$\Rightarrow \left(\frac{3}{8} - \frac{2}{5}\right)c_2 = \frac{2}{4} = \frac{1}{2}$

$\Rightarrow \frac{15 - 16}{40}c_2 = 1/_2$

$\Rightarrow c_2 = \frac{-40}{2} = -20$

$\therefore \frac{1}{2}c_1 = \frac{1}{4} + \frac{2}{5}c_2 = \frac{1}{4} + \frac{2}{5} \times (-20) = \frac{1}{4} - 8 = \frac{-31}{4}$

$\Rightarrow c_1 = \frac{-31}{2}$

$\therefore y(s) = s + 2s.\left(\frac{-31}{2}\right) + 2s^2.(-20)$

$= s + (-31)s + (-40s^2)$

$= -30s - 40s^2$

$\therefore$ Option (c) correct.

16. Explanation: (c)

17. Explanation: (a)

$y(t) = \int_0^t e^{-s}\sin(t - s)\,ds$

Using Leibnitz's rule,

$y'(t) = \int_0^t e^{-s}\cos(t - s)\,ds + e^{-t}(0) - 0$

$y''(t) = -\int_0^t e^{-s}\sin(t - s)\,ds + e^{-t}$

$y'' = -y + e^{-t}$

$y'' + y = e^{-t}$

Consider, $y'' + y = 0$

Auxiliary equation: $m^2 + 1 = 0$

$\Rightarrow m = \pm i$

Complementary function: $c_1 \cos t + c_2 \sin t$

Now we obtain particular integral

$y_p = \frac{1}{D^2+1} e^{-t}$

$y_p(t) = \frac{1}{2} e^{-t}$

$\therefore$ General solution is,

$y(t) = c_1 \cos t + c_2 \sin t + \frac{1}{2} e^{-t}$

Now, $y(0) = 0 \Rightarrow 0 = c_1 + \frac{1}{2} \Rightarrow c_1 = -\frac{1}{2}$

$\therefore$ Looking at options & using $y'(0) = 0$

We get $y(t) = \frac{1}{2}[e^{-t} + \sin t - \cos t]$ is the correct answer.

18. Explanation: (a)

Consider the given BVP:

$y'' + 2y = 0$

$y'' = -2y$

Integrating from 0 to x, we get,

$y'(x) - y'(0) = -2 \int_0^x y(t)dt$

Let $y'(0) = \alpha$

$\therefore y'(x) = \alpha - 2 \int_0^x y(t)dt$

Again, integrating from 0 to x,

$y(x) - y(0) = \alpha x - 2 \int_0^x (x-t)y(t)dt$

$y(x) = \alpha x - 2 \int_0^x (x-t)y(t)dt - (1)$

$(\because y(0) = 0)$.

Now given that $y(1) = 0$

$\Rightarrow 0 = \alpha - 2 \int_0^1 (1-t)y(t)dt$

$\Rightarrow \alpha = 2 \int_0^1 (1-t)y(t)dt$

Put this in equation (1), we get,

$y(x) = 2x \int_0^1 (1-t)y(t)dt - 2 \int_0^x (x-t)y(t)dt$

$= 2\left[\int_0^x x(1-t)y(t)dt + \int_x^1 x(1-t)y(t)dt\right]$

$-2 \int_0^x (x-t)y(t)dt$

$= 2 \int_0^x [x(1-t) - (x-t)]y(t)dt \;\; - 2 \int_x^1 (1-t)y(t)dt$

$= 2 \int_0^x (-xt + t)y(t)dt + 2 \int_x^1 x(1-t)y(t)dt$

$y(x) = 2\left[\int_0^x t(1-x)y(t)dt + \int_x^1 x(1-t)y(t)dt\right]$

$K(x,t) = \begin{cases} t, (1-x) \text{ for } t < x \\ x, (1-t) \text{ for } t > x \end{cases}$

So, option (a) is correct.

19. Explanation: (a)

$\int_0^t \left[\frac{1}{2} + \sin(t-\tau)\right] u(\tau)\, d\tau = \sin t$ ... (1)

$\therefore \int_0^t \frac{1}{2} u(\tau)\, d\tau - \sin t = -\int_0^t \sin(t-\tau) u(\tau)\, d\tau$ ... (2)

Using Leibnitz rule, on differentiating (1) with respect to t, we get,

$\int_0^t \cos(t-\tau)u(\tau)\, d\tau + \frac{1}{2}u(t) = \cos t$ ... (3)

Again differentiating with respect to t, we get,

$\int_0^t -\sin(t-\tau)\, u(\tau)\, d\tau + u(t) + \frac{u'(t)}{2} = -\sin t$ ... (4)

From (2) and (4), we get,

$\int_0^t \frac{1}{2} u(\tau)\, d\tau - \sin t + u(t) + \frac{u'(t)}{2} = -\sin t$

$\therefore \int_0^t \frac{1}{2} u(\tau)\, d\tau + u(t) + \frac{u'(t)}{2} = 0$ ... (5)

Differentiating this with respect to t, we get,

$\frac{1}{2}u(t) + u'(t) + \frac{u''(t)}{2} = 0$

$\therefore u(t) + 2u'(t) + u''(t) = 0$

$\therefore u(t) = (c_1 + c_2 t)e^{-t}$

Put $t = 0$ in (3), we get $u(0) = 2$.

Put $t = 0$ in (5), we get $u'(0) = -4$

Using this, we get, $c_1 = 2$ and $c_2 = -2$.

$\therefore u(t) = (2 - 2t)e^{-t}$

$\therefore u(1) = 0$

20. Explanation: (b)

The general solution to the differential equation $\frac{d^2u}{dx^2} + \lambda u(x) = 0$ is:

$$u(x) = A\cos(\sqrt{\lambda}x) + B\sin(\sqrt{\lambda}x),$$

where A and B are constants determined by the boundary conditions.

Using the boundary conditions:

1. $\frac{du}{dx}(0) = u(0)$:

From the derivative of the solution:

$$\frac{du}{dx} = -A\sqrt{\lambda}\sin(\sqrt{\lambda}x) + B\sqrt{\lambda}\cos(\sqrt{\lambda}x),$$

at $x = 0$:

$$\frac{du}{dx}(0) = B\sqrt{\lambda} = A \text{ so } B = \frac{A}{\sqrt{\lambda}}.$$

2. $\frac{du}{dx}(1) = 0$:

From the derivative:

$$\frac{du}{dx}(1) = -A\sqrt{\lambda}\sin(\sqrt{\lambda}) + B\sqrt{\lambda}\cos(\sqrt{\lambda}),$$

and using $B = \frac{A}{\sqrt{\lambda}}$, we get:

$$-A\sqrt{\lambda}\sin(\sqrt{\lambda}) + \frac{A}{\sqrt{\lambda}}\sqrt{\lambda}\cos(\sqrt{\lambda}) = 0.$$

Simplifying this:

$$A\left(\cos(\sqrt{\lambda}) - \sin(\sqrt{\lambda})\right) = 0.$$

This implies $\cos(\sqrt{\lambda}) = \sin(\sqrt{\lambda})$, or $\sqrt{\lambda} = \frac{\pi}{4}, \frac{5\pi}{4}, \ldots$

Thus, we know that λ corresponds to these specific values.

We now use the form of the solution to derive the integral equation. Substituting the solution $u(x)$ into the integral equation:

$$u(x) + \lambda \int_0^1 K(x,t)u(t)\, dt = 0,$$

and using the form of the solution to the differential equation, we can match the behavior of the boundary value problem and the integral equation.

After analyzing the given options for $K(x,t)$, we conclude that **Option (b)** is correct:

$$K(x,t) = \begin{cases} -1-x, & 0 \le x \le t \le 1, \\ -1-t, & 0 \le t \le x \le 1. \end{cases}$$

21. Explanation: (*)

MSQ (MULTIPLE SELECT QUESTIONS)

1. The integral equation, involving a parameter $\lambda, \phi(x) = \cos 2x + \lambda \int_0^\pi \cos(x+\zeta)d\zeta$ has
(a) A Unique solution if $\lambda = 1$, and an infinite numbers of solution if $\lambda = \frac{2}{\pi}$
(b) A unique solution if $\lambda = -1$, and an infinite number of solutions if $\lambda = -\frac{2}{\pi}$
(c) A unique solution if $\lambda \neq \frac{2}{\pi}$
(d) No solution if $\lambda = \pm\frac{2}{\pi}$
[JUNE 2011]

2. The integral equation $y(x) = 1 + \lambda \int_0^{\pi/2} \cos(x - t)y(t)dt$ has
(a) A unique solution for $\lambda \neq 4/(\pi+2)$
(b) A unique solution for $\lambda \neq 4/(\pi-2)$
(c) No solution for $\lambda = 4/(\pi+2)$, but the corresponding homogeneous equation has non-trivial solutions
(d) No solution for $\lambda = 4/(\pi-2)$, but the corresponding homogeneous equation has non-trivial solutions
[Dec 2011]

3. For the integral equation
$$u(x) = f(x) + \lambda \int_a^b K(x,t)u(t)dt$$
To have a continuous solution in the interval $a \le x \le b$, which of the following assumptions are necessary?
(a) $K(x,t) \not\equiv 0$, is real and continuous in the region $a \le x \le b, a \le b$ with $|K(x,t)| \le M$.
(b) $f(x) \not\equiv 0$, is and continuous in the interval $a \le x \le b$.
(c) λ is a constant.
(d) $|\lambda| < \frac{1}{M(b-a)}$.
[Dec 2011]

4. The Integral equation $\phi(x) = \lambda \int_0^\pi K(x,\xi)\phi(\xi)d\xi$
Where λ is a parameter, and
$$K(x,\xi) = \begin{cases} \cos x \sin \xi, for\ 0 \le x < \xi \\ \cos \xi \sin x, for\ \xi \le x \le \pi \end{cases}$$
Leads to a boundary value problem
$$\phi''(x) - f(\lambda)\phi(x) = 0, \phi(\pi) = 0, \phi'(0) = 0$$
Where $f(\lambda)$ is known. Then the boundary value problem has
(a) A unique solution when $f(\lambda) = 0$
(b) Infinite number of solution when $f(\lambda) > 0$
(c) No solution when $f(\lambda) < 0$
(d) A unique solution when $\lambda > 1$
[June 2012]

5. The integral equation
$\varphi(x) - \lambda \int_{-1}^1 \cos[\pi(x-t)]\varphi(t)dt = f(x)$ has
(a) A unique solution for $\lambda \neq 1$ when $f(x) = x$
(b) No solution for $\lambda \neq 1$ when $f(x) = 1$
(c) No solution for $\lambda = 1$ when $f(x) = x$
(d) Infinite number of solutions for $\lambda = 1$ when $f(x) = 1$
[Dec 2012]

6. For the homogenous Fredholm equation
$$y(x) = \lambda \int_0^\pi \sin(x+\zeta)y(\zeta)d\zeta,$$
The Eigen value λ and the corresponding Eigen function $y(x)$, involving arbitrary constants A and B, are
(a) $\lambda = \frac{2}{\pi}, y(x) = A(\sin x - \cos x)$
(b) $\lambda = \frac{-2}{\pi}, y(x) = B(\sin x + \cos x)$
(c) $\lambda = \frac{-2}{\pi}, y(x) = B(\sin x - \cos x)$
(d) $\lambda = \frac{2}{\pi}, y(x) = A(\sin x + \cos x)$
[June 2013]

7. The integral equation
$$\int_a^x K(x,y)\phi(y)dy = f(x)$$
With $K(x,x) \neq 0$, for all x can be transformed to $\phi(x) + \int_0^x G(x,y)\phi(y)dy = g(x)$ where for all x, y
(a) $K(x,y) = 1, g = f'$ and $G(x,y) = \frac{\partial K}{\partial x}(x,y)$
(b) $K(x,x) = 1, g = f$ and $G(x,y) = 0$
(c) $G(x,y) = \frac{1}{K(x,x)}\frac{\partial K}{\partial x}(x,y)$ and $g(x) = \frac{f'(x)}{K(x,x)}$
(d) $G(x,y) = 1$ and $g(x) = f(x)$
[Dec 2013]

8. Let λ_1, λ_2 be the characteristic f_1, f_2 the corresponding eigen functions for the homogenous integral equation $\varphi(x) - \lambda \int_0^1 (xt + 2x^2)\varphi(t)dt = 0$. Then
(a) $\lambda_1 = -18 - 6\sqrt{10}, \lambda_2 = -18 + 6\sqrt{10}$
(b) $\lambda_1 = -36 - 12\sqrt{10}, \lambda_2 = -36 + 12\sqrt{10}$
(c) $\int_0^1 f_1(x)f_2(x)dx = 1$
(d) $\int_0^1 f_1(x)f_2(x)dx = 0$
[June 2014]

9. For the integral equation
$y(x) = 1 + x^3 + \int_0^x K(x,t)y(t)dt$ with kernel $K(x,t) = 2^{x-t}$, the iterated kernel $K_3(x,t)$ is
(a) $2^{x-t}(x-t)^2$
(b) $2^{x-t}(x-t)^3$
(c) $2^{x-t-1}(x-t)^2$
(d) $2^{x-t-1}(x-t)^3$
[June 2015]

10. Let λ_1, λ_2 be the characteristic numbers and f_1, f_2 be the corresponding eigenfunction for the homogeneous integral equation
$$\varphi(x) - \lambda \int_0^1 (2xt + 4x^2)\varphi(t)dt = 0.$$
Then
(a) $\lambda_1 \neq \lambda_2$
(b) $\lambda_1 = \lambda_2$
(c) $\int_0^1 f_1(x)f_2(x)dx = 0$
(d) $\int_0^1 f_1(x)f_2(x)dx = 1$
[Dec 2015]

11. Let $y : [0,\infty) \to [0,\infty)$ be continuously differentiable function satisfying
$y(t) = y(0) + \int_0^t y(s)ds$ for $t \ge 0$. Then
(a) $y^2(t) = y^2(0) + \int_0^t y^2(s)ds$
(b) $y^2(t) = y^2(0) + 2\int_0^t y^2(s)ds$

(c) $y^2(t) = y^2(0) + \int_0^t y(s)ds$

(d) $y^2(t) = y^2(0) + \left(\int_0^t y(s)ds\right)^2 + 2y(0)\int_0^t y(s)ds$

[Dec 2015]

12. Which of the following are the characteristic numbers and the corresponding eigen-function for the Fredholm homogeneous equation whose kernel is
$$K(x,t) = \begin{cases}(x+1)t, 0 \le x \le t \\ (t+1)x, t \le x \le 1\end{cases}?$$
(a) $1, e^x$
(b) $-\pi^2, \pi \sin \pi + \cos \pi x$
(c) $-4\pi^2, \pi \sin \pi x + \pi \cos 2\pi x$
(d) $-\pi^2, \pi \cos \pi x + \sin \pi x$

[Dec 2016]

13. The integral equation
$$\phi(x) - \frac{2}{\pi}\int_0^{\pi} \cos(x+t)\phi(t)dt = f(x)$$
has infinitely many solutions if
(a) $f(x) = \cos x$ (b) $f(x) = \cos 3x$
(c) $f(x) = \sin x$ (d) $f(x) = \sin 3x$

[Dec 2016]

14. The solution for $\lambda = -1$ and $\lambda = 3$ of the integral equation $y(x) = 1 + \lambda\int_0^1 K(x,t)y(t)dt$,
Where $K(x,t) = \begin{cases}\cos h\, x \sinh t, 0 \le x \le t \\ \cosh t \sin h\, x, t \le x \le 1\end{cases}$ are, respectively,
(a) $-\frac{x^2}{2} + \frac{3}{2} - \tanh 1$ and $\frac{1}{4}\left(\frac{3\cos 2x}{\cos 2 - 2\sin 2\tanh 1} + 1\right)$
(b) $-\frac{x^2}{2} + \frac{3}{2} - \tanh 1$ *and* $\frac{1}{4}\left(\frac{3\cosh 2x}{\cosh 2 - 2\sinh 2\tanh 1} + 1\right)$
(c) $\frac{x^2}{2} + \frac{3}{2} - \tanh 1$ *and* $\frac{1}{4}\left(\frac{3\cos 2x}{\cosh 2 - 2\sinh 2\tanh 1} - 1\right)$
(d) $\frac{x^2}{2} + \frac{3}{2} - \tanh 1$ *and* $\frac{1}{4}\left(\frac{3\cos 2x}{\cosh 2 - 2\sinh 2\tanh 1} - 1\right)$

[June 2017]

15. Let $y(x)$ be the solution of the integral equation
$$y(x) = x - \int_0^x xt^2 y(t)dt, x > 0.$$
Then the value of the function $y(x)$ at $x = \sqrt{2}$ is equal to
(a) $\frac{1}{\sqrt{2e}}$ (b) $\frac{e}{2}$
(c) $\frac{\sqrt{2}}{e^2}$ (d) $\frac{\sqrt{2}}{e}$

[June 2017]

16. Let φ be the solution of the integral equation $\frac{1}{2}\varphi(x) - \int_0^1 e^{x-y}\varphi(y)dy = x^2; 0 \le x \le 1$ Then
(a) $\varphi(0) = 20e^{-1} - 8$ (b) $\varphi(0) = 20e - 8$
(c) $\varphi(1) = 22 - 8e$ (d) $\varphi(1) = 22 - 8e^{-1}$

[Dec 2017]

17. Consider a non-zero, real-valued polynomial function $p(x) = a_0 + a_1x + a_2x^2$ of degree at most 2. Let $y = y(x)$ be a solution of the integral equation
$$y = p(x) + \int_0^x y(t)\sin(x-t)\,dt$$
Which of the following statements are necessarily correct?
(a) $y(x)$ is a polynomial function of degree ≤ 2
(b) $y(x)$ is a polynomial function of degree ≤ 4
(c) If $a_1 \neq 0$ and $a_0 + 2a_2 = 0$, then $y'(0) = 0$
(d) If $a_1 \neq 0$ and $a_0 + 2a_2 = 0$, then $y''(0) = 0$

[Dec 2017]

18. Consider the integral equation
$\phi(x) = \lambda\int_0^{\pi}[\cos x\cos t - 2\sin x\sin t]\,\phi(t)dt + \cos 7x, \quad 0 \le x \le \pi$
Which of the following statements are true?
(a) For every $\in \mathbb{R}$, a solution exists
(b) There exists $\lambda \in \mathbb{R}$ such that solution does not exist
(c) There exists $\lambda \in \mathbb{R}$ such that there are more than one but finitely many solutions
(d) There exists $\lambda \in \mathbb{R}$ such that there are infinitely many solutions

[June 2018]

19. The values of λ for which the following equation has a non-trivial solution
$$\phi(x) = \lambda\int_0^{\pi} K(x,t)\phi(t)dt, \quad 0 \le x \le \pi$$
Where $K(x,t) = \begin{cases}\sin x\cos t, 0 \le x \le t \\ \cos x\sin t, t \le x \le \pi\end{cases}$ are.
(a) $\left(n + \frac{1}{2}\right)^2 - 1, n \in \mathbb{N}$
(b) $n^2 - 1, n \in \mathbb{N}$
(c) $\frac{1}{2}(n+1)^2 - 1, n \in \mathbb{N}$
(d) $\frac{1}{2}(2n+1)^2 - 1, n \in \mathbb{N}$

[June 2018]

20. A characteristic number and the corresponding Eigen function of the homogenous Fredholm integer equation with kernel $K(x,t) = \begin{cases}x(t-1), 0 \le x \le t \\ t(x-t), t \le x \le 1\end{cases}$ are
(a) $\lambda = -\pi^2, \varphi(x) = \sin \pi x$
(b) $\lambda = -2\pi^2, \varphi(x) = \sin 2\pi x$
(c) $\lambda = -3\pi^2, \varphi(x) = \sin 3\pi x$
(d) $\lambda = -4\pi^2, \varphi(x) = \sin 2\pi x$

[Dec 2018]

21. If φ is the solution of $\varphi(x) = 1 - 2x - 4x^2 + \int_0^x[3 + 6(x-t) - 4(x-t)^2]\,\varphi(t)dt$,
Then $\varphi(\log 2)$ is equal to
(a) 2 (b) 4
(c) 6 (d) 8

[Dec 2018]

22. The integral equation
$\phi(x) = 1 + \frac{2}{\pi}\int_0^{\pi}(\cos^2 x)\,\phi(t)dt$has
(a) no solution
(b) unique solution
(c) More than one but finitely many solutions
(d) Infinitely many solution

[Dec 2019]

23. Assume that $h_1, h_2, g_1 \& g_2 \in C([a,b])$
Let
$$\phi(x) = f(x) + \lambda\int_a^b [h_1(t)g_1(x) + h_2(t)g_2(x)]\,\phi(t)dt$$

Be an integral equation

Consider the following statements

S_1:- If the given inteqral equation has a solution for some $f \in c[a,b]$ then

$\int_a^b f(t)\, g_1(t)dt = 0 = \int_a^b f(t)\, g_2(t)dt$

S_2:- The given inteqral equation has a unique solution for every $f \in c[a,b]$ if λ is not a characteristic no. of corresponding homogeneous equation

Then

(a) Both S_1&S_2 are true (b) S_1 is true but S_2 is false

(c) S_1 is false but S_2 is true (d) Both S_1&S_2 are false

[Dec 2019]

24. Consider the integral equation

$$\phi(x) - \lambda \int_0^{2\pi} \cos(x-t)\, \phi t dt = f(x), x \in [0, 2\pi]$$

where $f \in c[0, 2\pi]$. Then which of the following statements are true?

(a) If $\lambda = 10$ *and* $f(x) = \cos x$, then the integral equation has a solution.

(b) If $\lambda = \frac{1}{\pi}$ *and* $f(x) = \cos x$, then the integral equation has no solution.

(c) For every $\lambda \in \mathbb{R}$ *and* $f(x) = \cos 2x$, the integral equation has a solution

(d) For every $\lambda \in \mathbb{R}$ *and* $f(x) = \sin 2x$, then the integral equation has unique solution

[Dec 2019]

25. Let $K: [a,b] \times [a,b] \to R$ be a non – zero continuous map with $K(x,t) = K(t,x)$ *for* $t, x \in [a,b]$and $I: C[a,b] \to [a,b]$be the identity operator. Define T,S:C[a, b]→ $C[a,b]$such thatfor $\varphi \in C[a,b], x \in [a,b]$ $(T\varphi)(x) = \int_a^x K(x,t)\varphi(t)dt$, $(S\varphi)(x) = \int_a^b K(x,t)\varphi(t)dt$,

Then which of the following statements are true?

(a) $\forall \lambda \in \mathbb{R}\backslash\{0\}$, the only solution of $(I - \lambda T)\varphi = 0$ *is* $\varphi \equiv 0$

(b) $\forall \lambda \in \mathbb{R}\backslash\{0\}, \forall f \in C[a,b]$, there exists a unique solution of $(I - \lambda T)\varphi = f$

(c) $\forall \lambda \in \mathbb{R}\backslash\{0\}, \forall f \in C[a,b]$, there exists a unique solution of $(I - \lambda S)\varphi = f$

(d) $\exists \lambda \in \mathbb{R}\backslash\{0\}$ such that $(I - \lambda S)\varphi = 0$ has a non – zero solution.

[Dec 2019]

26. For the Fredholm integral equation $y(s) = \lambda \int_0^1 e^s e^t y(t)dt$ which of the following statements are true.

(a) It has a non-trivial solution satisfying $\int_0^1 e^t\, y(t)dt = 0$

(b) Only the trivial solution satisfies $\int_0^1 e^t\, y(t) = 0$

(c) It has non-trivial solution for all $\lambda \neq 0$

(d) It has non-trivial solution if $\lambda = \frac{2}{e^2 - 1}$ and $\int_0^1 e^t\, y(t)dt \neq 0$

[Nov 2020]

27. Let $K(x,y) be$ a kernel in$[0,1] \times [0,1]$,defined as

$$K(x,y) = \begin{cases} x(1-y) & 0 \le x \le y \le 1 \\ y(1-x) & 0 \le y \le x \le 1 \end{cases}$$

And $\mathcal{K}$ be the associated integral operator.

Then $\mathcal{K}: L^2([0,1]) \to L^2([0,1])$

(a) Is positive (b) Is self adjoint

(c) Has a non- zero null space (d) Is onto

[Nov 2020]

28. Let S be the set of all continuous functions $f: [0,1] \to [0, \infty)$ that satisfy

$$\int_0^1 x^2 f(x)\, dx = \frac{1}{2}\int_0^1 x f^2(x)\, dx + \frac{1}{8}$$

Which of the following statements are true

(a) S is empty set

(b) S has at most one element

(c) S has at least one element

(d) S has more than two elements

[Nov 2020]

29. Let $K(x,y)$ be a kernel in $[0,1] \times [0,1]$ defined as $K(x,y) = \sin(2\pi x)\sin(2\pi y)$. Consider the integral operator

$$\mathcal{K}(u)(x) = \int_0^1 u(y)K(x,y)dy$$

Where $u \in C([0,1])$. Which of the following assertions on $\mathcal{K}$ are true?

(a) The null space of $\mathcal{K}$ is infinite dimensional

(b) $\int_0^1 v(x)\mathcal{K}(u)(x)dx = \int_0^1 \mathcal{K}(v)(x)u(x)dx$ for all $u.v \in C([0,1])$

(c) $\mathcal{K}$ has no negative eigenvalue

(d) $\mathcal{K}$ has an eigenvalue grater than 3/4

[Feb 2022]

30. Let g be the solution of the Volterra type integral equation

$g(s) = 1 + \int_0^s (s-t)g(t)dt$; fpr all $s \ge 0$

What is the possible value of $g(1)$?

(a) 2e (b) $e - \frac{1}{e}$

(c) $e + \frac{1}{e}$ (d) $\frac{2}{e}$

[SEP 2022]

31. Consider the following system of integral equations

$\varphi_1(x) = \sin x + \int_0^x \varphi_2(t)\, dt$,

$\varphi_2(x) = 1 - \cos x - \int_0^x \varphi_1(t) dt$.

(a) φ_1 vanishes at atmost countably many points

(b) φ_1 vanishes at uncountably many points

(c) φ_2 vanishes at at most countably many points

(d) φ_2 vanishes at uncountably many points

[SEP 2022]

32. Let $\lambda_1 < \lambda_2$ be two real characteristic numbers for the following homogeneous integral equation:

$$\varphi(x) = \lambda \int_0^{2\pi} \sin(x+t)\varphi(t)\, dt;$$

and let $\mu_1 < \mu_2$ be two real characteristic numbers for the following homogeneous integral equation:

$$\varphi(x) = \mu \int_0^{\pi} \cos(x+t)\psi(t)\, dt;$$

Which of the following statements are true?

(a) $\mu_1 < \lambda_1 < \lambda_2 < \mu_2$ (b) $\lambda_1 < \mu_1 < \mu_2 < \lambda_2$

(c) $|\mu_1 - \lambda_1| = |\mu_2 - \lambda_2|$ (d) $|\mu_1 - \lambda_1| = 2|\mu_2 - \lambda_2|$

[JUNE 2023]

33. Let $K \in C([0,1]\times[0,1])$ satisfy $|K(x,y)| < 1$ for all $x, y \in [0,1]$. For every $g \in C[0,1]$, let us consider the integral equation

$(P_g)\quad f(x) + \int_0^1 K(x,y) f(y) dy = g(x), for\ all\ x \in [0,1].$

Which of the following statements are true?

(a) there exists a $g \in C[0,1]$ for which (P_g) has no solution in $C[0,1]$.

(b) (P_g) has a solution in $C[0,1]$ for infinitely many $g \in C[0,1]$.

(c) the solution of (P_g) in $C[0,1]$ is unique if $g \in C^1[0,1]$.

(d) there exists a $g \in C[0,1]$ for which (P_g) has infinitely many solutions in $C[0,1]$.

[JUNE 2023]

34. Consider the following Fredholm integral equation $y(x) - 3\int_0^1 tx\, y(t)dt = f(x)$, where $f(x)$ is a continuous function defined on the interval [0, 1]. Which of the following choices for $f(x)$ have the property that the above integral equation admits at least one solution?

(a) $f(x) = x^2 - \frac{1}{2}$ (b) $f(x) = e^x$

(c) $f(x) = 2 - 3x$ (d) $f(x) = x - 1$

[DEC-2023]

35. Let y be the solution to the Volterra integral equation $y(x) = e^x + \int_0^x \frac{1+x^2}{1+t^2} y(t)dt$.

Then which of the following statements are true?

(a) $y(1) = \left(1 + \frac{\pi}{4}\right)e$ (b) $y(1) = \left(1 + \frac{\pi}{2}\right)e$

(c) $y(\sqrt{3}) = \left(1 + \frac{3\pi}{4}\right)e^{\sqrt{3}}$ (d) $y(\sqrt{3}) = \left(1 + \frac{4\pi}{3}\right)e^{\sqrt{3}}$

[DEC-2023]

36. For $\lambda \in \mathbb{R}$ such that $|\lambda| < \frac{5}{32}$, let $R(x,t,\lambda)$ and u denote the resolvent kernel and the solution, respectively, of the Fredholm integral equation

$$u(x) = x + \frac{\lambda}{2}\int_{-2}^{2} (xt + x^2t^2)u(t)dt.$$

Then which of the following statements are true?

(a) $R(x,t,\lambda) = \frac{3xt}{3-8\lambda} - \frac{5x^2t^2}{5-32\lambda}$

(b) $R(x,t,\lambda) = \frac{3xt}{3-8\lambda} + \frac{5x^2t^2}{5-32\lambda}$

(c) $u(1) = -\frac{5}{5-32\lambda}$

(d) $u(1) = \frac{3}{3-8\lambda}$

[July 2024]

37. For $c \in \mathbb{R}$, consider the following Fredholm integral equation

$$y(x) = 1 + x + cx^2 + 2\int_0^1 (1-3xt)y(t)dt$$

Then the values of c for which the integral equation admits a solution are

(a) −8 (b) −6

(c) 2 (d) 6

[July 2024]

38. If u is the solution of the Volterra integral equation

$$u(x) = 3 + \sin x + \int_0^x \frac{3+\sin x}{3+\sin t} u(t)dt,$$

Then

(a) $u\left(\frac{\pi}{2}\right) = 4e^{\frac{\pi}{2}}$ (b) $u(\pi) = 3e^{\pi}$

(c) $u(-\pi) = 4e^{-\pi}$ (d) $u\left(-\frac{\pi}{2}\right) = 4e^{\pi}$

[Feb. 2025]

39. The integral equation

$$u(x) = f(x) + \frac{2}{\pi}\int_0^{\pi} \sin(x-t)\, u(t)dt$$

has a unique solution if

(a) $f(x) = \cos x$ (b) $f(x) = \cos 5x$

(c) $f(x) = \sin x$ (d) $f(x) = \sin 5x$

[Feb. 2025]

40. Let u(x) be the solution to the Volterra integral equation

$$u(x) = x^2 + 4\int_0^x (t-x)^2 u(t)dt$$

Then which of the following statements are true?

(a) $u(0) = 0$

(b) $u\left(\frac{2\pi}{\sqrt{3}}\right) = \frac{1}{6}\left(e^{\frac{4\pi}{\sqrt{3}}} - e^{-\frac{2\pi}{\sqrt{3}}}\right)$

(c) $u\left(\frac{\pi}{2\sqrt{3}}\right) = \frac{1}{6}\left(e^{\frac{\pi}{\sqrt{3}}} - \sqrt{3}e^{-\frac{\pi}{2\sqrt{3}}}\right)$

(d) $u\left(\frac{\pi}{2\sqrt{3}}\right) = \frac{1}{6}\left(e^{\frac{\pi}{\sqrt{3}}} + \sqrt{3}e^{-\frac{\pi}{\sqrt{3}}}\right)$

[June 2025]

41. Let $\lambda \in \mathbb{R}$ be such that the integral equation $y(x) = \lambda\int_{-1}^{1}(5xt^3 + 4x^2t + 3xt)\, y(t)dt$ admits a non-trivial solution $y(x)$ such that $y(1) = \frac{5}{2}$.

Then which of the following statements are true?

(a) $y(0) + y'(0) = \frac{3}{2}$ (b) $y\left(\frac{1}{2}\right) + y'\left(\frac{1}{2}\right) = \frac{7}{2}$

(c) $y(-1) + y'(-1) = -1$ (d) $y\left(\frac{1}{3}\right) + y'\left(\frac{1}{3}\right) = \frac{14}{9}$

[Dec 2025]

42. Let $y(x)$ be the solution of the integral equation (IE) $y(x) = e^x + e + 1 + \frac{1}{3}\int_0^1 y(t)\, dt$, and $R\left(x, t, \frac{1}{3}\right)$ be the resolvent kernel associated to IE.

Then which of the following statements are true?

(a) $R\left(0, 1, \frac{1}{3}\right) = \frac{3}{2}$ (b) $R\left(\frac{1}{2}, \frac{1}{2}, \frac{1}{3}\right) = \frac{2}{3}$

(c) $y(1) = 3e + 1$ (d) $y(1) = e + 3$

[Dec 2025]

Answer Key

1	2	3	4	5
a, b	c	a, b, c	a, d	a, c, d
6	7	8	9	10
c, d	c	a, d	c	a, c
11	12	13	14	15
b, d	a, d	b, c, d	b	d
16	17	18	19	20
a, c	b, d	a, d	a	a, d

Answer Key				
21	**22**	**23**	**24**	**25**
a	a	c	a, b, c	a, b, d
26	**27**	**28**	**29**	**30**
b, d	a, b	a, b	a, b, c	*
31	**32**	**33**	**34**	**35**
a, d	a, c	b, c	a, c	b, d
36	**37**	**38**	**39**	**40**
b, d	a	a,b	a,b,c,d	a,b,c
41	**42**			
a,b,c	a,c			

Explanations

1. Explanation: (a), (b)

$$\phi(x) = \cos 2x + \lambda \int_0^{\pi} \cos(x+\zeta)\phi(\zeta)\, d\zeta \; ---(1)$$

$$\phi(x) = \cos 2x + \lambda \int_0^{\pi}(\underbrace{\cos x}_{\alpha_1}\underbrace{\cos\zeta}_{\beta_1} + \underbrace{(-\sin x)}_{\alpha_2}\underbrace{\sin\zeta}_{\beta_2})\phi(\zeta)\, d\zeta$$

$$\Rightarrow \phi(x) = \cos 2x + \lambda\cos x \int_0^{\pi} \cos\zeta\, d\zeta + \lambda \sin x \int_0^{\pi} -\sin\zeta\, d\zeta$$

Let $c_1 = \int_0^{\pi} \cos\zeta\phi(\zeta)\, d\zeta$

And $c_2 = \int_0^{\pi} -\sin\zeta\,\phi(\zeta)d\zeta$

$\Rightarrow \phi(x) = \cos 2x + \lambda\cos x \cdot c_1 + \lambda \sin x \cdot c_2 --(2)$

Now $c_1 = \int_0^{\pi} \cos\zeta\phi(\zeta)d\zeta = \int_0^{\pi}\cos\zeta(\cos 2\zeta + \lambda\cos\zeta \cdot c_1 + \lambda\sin\zeta \cdot c_2)d\zeta = c_1\lambda\frac{\pi}{2}$

$\Rightarrow c_1\left(1-\lambda\frac{\pi}{2}\right) = 0 ---(3)$

And $c_2 = \int_0^{\pi} -\sin\zeta\,\phi(\zeta)d\zeta = \int_0^{\pi} -\sin\zeta(\cos 2\zeta + \lambda\cos\zeta \cdot c_1 + \lambda\sin\zeta \cdot c_2)d\zeta = -c_2\lambda\frac{\pi}{2} - \frac{2}{3}$

$\Rightarrow c_2\left(1+\lambda\frac{\pi}{2}\right) = -\frac{2}{3} ---(4)$

$\lambda = 1 \Rightarrow c_1, c_2$ are unique so option (a) is correct.

$\lambda = -1 \Rightarrow c_1, c_2$ are unique so infinite solution.

$\lambda = \frac{2}{\pi} \Rightarrow c_1$ arbitary , c_2 is unique so infinite solution.

$\lambda = \frac{-2}{\pi} \Rightarrow c_2$ arbitary , c_1 is unique so infinite solution.

Hence option (a) and (b) correct answer and c), d) are incorrect.

2. Explanation: (c)

Consider the given integral equation

$y(x) = 1 + \lambda\int_0^{\frac{\pi}{2}}\cos(x-t)y(t)dt \ldots..(1)$

$\Rightarrow y(x) = 1 + \lambda\int_0^{\pi/2}(\cos x\cos t + \sin x \sin t)\, y(t)dt$

$= 1 + \lambda\int_0^{\frac{\pi}{2}}\cos x\cos t\, y(t)dt + \lambda\int_0^{\frac{n}{2}}\sin x\sin t\, y(t)dt$

$y(x) = 1 + \lambda\cos x\int_0^{\frac{m}{2}}\cos t\, y(t)dt + \lambda\sin x\int_0^{\frac{\pi}{2}}\sin t\, y(t)dt$

$A = \int_0^{\frac{\pi}{2}}\cos t\, y(t)dt \ldots.(3)$

$B = \int_0^{\frac{\pi}{2}}\sin t\, y(t)dt \ldots.(4)$

$\Rightarrow y(x) = 1 + A\lambda\cos x + B\lambda\sin x$

$y(x) = 1 + \lambda A\cos x + \lambda B\sin x$

$\Rightarrow y(t) = 1 + \lambda A\cos t + \lambda B\sin t$

$A = \int_0^{\frac{\pi}{2}}(\cos t + \lambda A\cos^2 t + \frac{\lambda B}{2}\sin 2t)dt$

$A = [\sin t]_0^{\frac{\pi}{2}} + \frac{\lambda A}{2}[t + \sin\frac{2t}{2}]_0^{\frac{\pi}{2}} + \left[\frac{\lambda B(-\cos 2t)}{4}\right]_0^{\frac{\pi}{2}}$

$= 1 + \frac{\lambda A}{2}\frac{\pi}{2} + \frac{\lambda B}{4}(1+1)$

$A = 1 + \frac{\lambda\pi A}{4} + \frac{\lambda B}{2} \ldots.(5)$

$\left[1 - \frac{\lambda\pi}{2}\right]A - \frac{\lambda}{2}B = 1 \quad (6)$

Now

$$B = \int_0^{\frac{\pi}{2}}\sin t(A\, cost\, t + \lambda B\sin t + 1)dt$$

$$B = \int_0^{\frac{\pi}{2}}\left[\frac{\lambda A\sin 2t}{2} + \lambda B\sin^2 t + \sin t\right]dt$$

$$B = \left[-\lambda\frac{A\cos 2t}{4}\right] + \frac{\lambda B}{2}\left[t - \frac{\sin 2t}{2}\right]_0^{\frac{\pi}{2}} + [-\cos t]_0^{\frac{\pi}{2}}$$

$$= \frac{\lambda A}{4}[-1-1] + \frac{\lambda B}{2}\left[\frac{\pi}{2}\right] + 1$$

$$= \frac{2\lambda A}{4} + \frac{\lambda B\pi}{4} + 1$$

$$B = \frac{\lambda A}{2} + \frac{\lambda B\pi}{4} + 1$$

$-\frac{\lambda}{2}A + B\left(1 - \frac{\lambda\pi}{4}\right) = 1 \quad (7)$

From equation (6) and (7)

Let $P = \begin{bmatrix} 1-\frac{\lambda\pi}{4} & -\frac{\lambda}{2} \\ -\frac{\lambda}{2} & 1-\frac{\lambda\pi}{2}\end{bmatrix}$, $Q = \begin{bmatrix} A \\ B\end{bmatrix}$, $R = \begin{bmatrix} 1 \\ 1\end{bmatrix}$

$\Rightarrow [P:Q = R]$

$$\Rightarrow \begin{bmatrix} 1-\frac{\lambda\pi}{4} & -\frac{\lambda}{2} \\ -\frac{\lambda}{2} & 1-\frac{\lambda\pi}{2}\end{bmatrix}\begin{bmatrix} A \\ B\end{bmatrix} = \begin{bmatrix} 1 \\ 1\end{bmatrix}$$

$$\Rightarrow |P| = \begin{vmatrix} 1-\frac{\lambda\pi}{4} & -\frac{\lambda}{2} \\ -\frac{\lambda}{2} & 1-\frac{\lambda\pi}{2}\end{vmatrix} = \left(1-\frac{\lambda\pi}{4}\right)^2 - \frac{\lambda^2}{4}$$

$= \left[1 - \frac{\lambda\pi}{4} + \frac{\lambda}{2}\right]\left[1 - \frac{\lambda\pi}{4} - \frac{\lambda}{2}\right]$

Now, $|P| = 0$

$\Rightarrow 1 - \frac{\lambda\pi}{4} + \frac{\lambda}{2} = 0$ or $1 - \frac{\lambda\pi}{4} - \frac{\lambda}{2} = 0$

$\Rightarrow 1 = \lambda\left(\frac{\pi}{4} - \frac{1}{2}\right)$ or $1 = \lambda\left(\frac{\pi}{4} + \frac{1}{2}\right)$

$\Rightarrow 1 = \lambda\left(\frac{\pi-2}{4}\right)$ or $1 = \lambda\frac{(\pi+2)}{4}$

$\Rightarrow \lambda = \frac{4}{\pi-2}$ or $\lambda = \frac{4}{\pi+2}$

From this $y(x)$ has unique solution if

$\lambda \neq \frac{4}{\pi-2}$ and $\lambda \neq \frac{4}{\pi+2}$

Option (a) and (b) are incorrect.

Now option (c)

Let $\lambda = \frac{4}{\pi+2}$

Equation (6) become $1 - \frac{\pi}{\pi+2}$

$1 - \frac{\pi}{4}\left(\frac{4}{\pi+2}\right) - \frac{B}{2}\left(\frac{4}{\pi+2}\right) = 1$

$A\left(1 - \frac{\pi}{\pi+2}\right) - \frac{2B}{\pi+2} = 1$

$\frac{2A}{\pi+2} - \frac{2B}{\pi+2} = 1$

$\frac{2}{\pi+2}[A - B] = 1 \Rightarrow A - B = \frac{\pi+2}{2}$

Put $\lambda = \frac{4}{\pi+2}$ in equation (7)

$-\frac{4}{\pi+2}\frac{A}{2} + B\left(1 - \frac{\pi}{4}\left(\frac{4}{\pi+2}\right)\right) = 1$

$-\frac{4A}{2(\pi+2)} + \left(1 - \frac{\pi}{\pi+2}\right)B = 1$

$-\frac{2A}{\pi+2} + \frac{2B}{\pi+2} = 1$

$B - A = \frac{\pi+2}{2}$

$\Rightarrow A - B = -\frac{m+2}{2}$ .... (9)

From equation (8) and (9)

$y(x)$ has no solution for $\lambda = \frac{4}{\pi+2}$

Now find the solution homogeneous integral equation corresponding to the given integral equation.

$$P(\lambda) = \begin{vmatrix} 1 - \frac{\lambda\pi}{4} & -\frac{\lambda}{2} \\ -\frac{\lambda}{2} & 1 - \frac{\lambda\pi}{2} \end{vmatrix}$$

If $P(\lambda) = 0$ then the homogeneous part will have non trivial solution.

For $\lambda = \frac{4}{\pi+2}$

$$P\left(\frac{4}{\pi+2}\right) = \begin{vmatrix} \frac{2}{\pi+2} & -\frac{2}{\pi+2} \\ -\frac{2}{\pi+2} & \frac{2}{\pi+2} \end{vmatrix}$$

$$C\left(\frac{4}{\pi+2}\right) = 0$$

$y(x) = \frac{4}{\pi+2}A\sin x + \frac{4}{\pi+2}B\cos x$ is the non trivial solution

For option d) $\lambda = \frac{4}{\pi-2}$

From equation 6) and 7)

$$\begin{bmatrix} 1 - \frac{\lambda\pi}{4} & -\frac{\lambda}{2} \\ -\frac{\lambda}{2} & 1 - \frac{\lambda\pi}{2} \end{bmatrix}\begin{bmatrix} A \\ B \end{bmatrix} = \begin{bmatrix} 1 \\ 1 \end{bmatrix}$$

$R_2 \to R_2 - R_1$

$$\begin{bmatrix} \frac{2}{\pi+2} & -\frac{2}{\pi+2} \\ 0 & 0 \end{bmatrix} = \begin{bmatrix} 1 \\ 0 \end{bmatrix}$$

Rank of above matrix is 1, so, it has infinite solution.

From above explanation only option c) is the correct answer and a), b) and d) are incorrect.

3. Explanation (a), (b), (c)

Consider the given integral equation

$u(x) = f(x) + \lambda \int_a^b k(x,t)\, u(t)dt$------(1)

Solution of given equation (1) is continuous in the interval $a \le x < b$

Now check the option

a) If $k(x,t) = 0$ then integral equation does not exist and if $k(x,t)$ is unbounded then $\int_a^b k(x,t)y(t)dt$ become an improper integral which show that the integral equation does not exist

$\Rightarrow$ Option a) is correct

For option b) if $f(x) = 0$ then integral equation become homogeneous and if $f(x) \neq 0$ is real and continuous in the interval $a \le x \le b$

For option c) we know that λ is given value of integral equation and λ is always constant in the integral equation

For option d) Consider $y(x) = 1 + \int_0^{\frac{\pi}{2}} \sin x\, y(t)dt$ with $y\left(\frac{\pi}{2}\right) = -1$ then $y(x) = 1 + \lambda \sin x$

where $c = \int_0^{\frac{\pi}{2}} y(t)\, dt$

$$c = \int_0^{\frac{\pi}{2}} [1 + \lambda c \sin t]dt$$

$$c = \frac{\pi}{2} + \lambda c$$

Here, $y(x) = 1 + \frac{\lambda\pi}{2(1-\lambda)}\sin x$

But given that

$y\left(\frac{\pi}{2}\right) = -1$

$\Rightarrow \lambda = \frac{4}{4-\pi}$

Now, $\frac{1}{M(b-a)} = \frac{1}{\frac{\pi}{2}-0} = \frac{2}{\pi}$

$|\lambda| = \left|\frac{4}{4-\pi}\right| > \frac{2}{\pi} = \frac{1}{M(b-a)}$

$\Rightarrow$option d) is incorrect.

$\Rightarrow$ option (a),(b) and (c) are correct answer and option (d) is incorrect

4. Explanation: (a), (d) Consider the given integral equation

$\Phi(x) = \lambda \int_0^{\pi} (x,\xi)\Phi(\xi)d\xi$

$$k(x,\xi) = \begin{cases} \cos x \sin\xi & for\ 0 \le x \le \xi \\ \cos\xi \sin x & for\ \xi \le x \le \pi \end{cases} \quad (1)$$

$\Rightarrow \Phi''(x) - f(\lambda)\Phi(x) = 0$

boundary condition

$\Phi(\pi) = 0, \quad \Phi(0) = 0$

$\Rightarrow \Phi(x) = \lambda \int_0^x \cos\xi \sin x\, \Phi(\xi)d\xi +$
$\lambda \int_x^{\pi} \cos x \sin\xi\Phi(\xi)d\xi$

Differentiate above equation w.r.to x with the help of Leibniz rule

$\Rightarrow \Phi'(x) = \lambda \int_0^x \cos x \cos\xi\, \Phi(\xi)d\xi +$
$\lambda \cos x \sin x\, \phi(x) + \lambda \int_x^{\pi} - \sin x \sin\xi\Phi(\xi)d\xi -$
$\lambda \cos x \sin x\, \Phi(x)$

$\Rightarrow \Phi'(x) = \lambda[\int_0^x \cos x \cos\xi\Phi(\xi)d\xi -$
$\int_x^{\pi} \sin x \sin\xi\, \Phi(\xi)d\xi]$

Again differentiate above equation

$\Rightarrow \Phi''(x) = \lambda\left[-\int_0^x \sin x \cos\xi\, \Phi(\xi)d\xi + \cos^2 x\Phi(x)\right]$
$-\lambda \int_x^{\pi} \cos x \sin\xi\Phi(\xi)d\xi + \lambda \sin^2 x\phi(x)$

$\Rightarrow \Phi''(x) = -\Phi(x) + \lambda\Phi(x)$

$\Rightarrow \Phi''(x) - (\lambda - 1)\Phi(x) = 0$

Consider $f(\lambda) = \lambda - 1$

Auxiliary equation is

$m^2 - (\lambda - 1) = 0$

$\Rightarrow m^2 = \lambda - 1$

$\Rightarrow m^2 = f(\lambda)$

Now check the option

For option (1)

$f(\lambda) = 0$

$\Rightarrow m^2 = 0$

$\Rightarrow m = 0,0$

Complementary function is

$\Phi(x) = c_1 + c_2 x$

$\Rightarrow \Phi'(x) = c_1$

$\Phi(\pi) = c_1 + c_2\pi = 0$

And $\Phi'(0) = c_1 = 0$

$\Rightarrow \Phi(\pi) = c_2\Pi = 0$

$\Rightarrow c_2 = 0\ (\because \pi \neq 0)$

$\Rightarrow \Phi(x) = 0$

We get trivial solution.

Option (a) is correct

For option (b)

$f(\lambda) > 0 \Rightarrow m^2 > 0 \Rightarrow m^2 = (\lambda - 1) > 0$

Put $\lambda - 1 = k^2$

$\Rightarrow m^2 = k^2$

$\Rightarrow m = \pm k$

$\Rightarrow \Phi(x) = c_1 e^{kx} + c_2 e^{-kx}$

$\Rightarrow \Phi(\pi) = c_1 e^{k\pi} + c_2 k e^{-kx}$

$\Rightarrow \Phi'(\pi) = c_1 e^{k\pi} + c_2 e^{-k\pi} = 0$

$\Rightarrow \Phi'(0) = c_1\pi - c_2\pi = 0$

$\Rightarrow c_1 = c_2$

$\Rightarrow c_1 e^{k\pi} + c_1 e^{-k\pi} = 0$

$\Rightarrow c_1[e^{k\pi} + e^{-k\pi}]$

$\Rightarrow c_1 = 0\ (\therefore e^{k\pi} + e^{-k\pi} \neq 0)$

$\Phi(x) = 0 \Rightarrow c_2 = 0$

Again get trivial solution

Option (b) is incorrect

For option (c)

If $f(\lambda) < 0$

$\Rightarrow f(\lambda) = \lambda - 1 < 0 \Rightarrow \lambda - 1 = -k^2$

Auxiliary equation is

$m^2 + k^2 = 0$

$\Rightarrow m = \pm ki$

$\Phi(x) = c_1 \cos kx + c_2 \sin kx$

$\Rightarrow \Phi'(x) = -kc_1 \sin kx + c_2\, k \cos kx$

$\Rightarrow \Phi(\pi) = c_1 \cos k\pi + c_2 \sin k\pi = 0$

$\Rightarrow c_1 \neq 0, \cos k\pi = 0$

$\Rightarrow \Phi'(0) = c_2 k cos k0 = 0$

$\Rightarrow c_2 = 0$

$k\pi = \frac{(2n+1)\pi}{2}$

$\Rightarrow k = \frac{2n+1}{2} \Rightarrow \Phi(x) = c_1 \cos\frac{2n+1}{2}\pi$

$\Rightarrow \exists$ infinitely many solution

$\Rightarrow$Option (c) also incorrect.

Now option (d)

From Option (b)

If $f(\lambda) = \lambda - 1 > 0$ then it has unique solution

$\Rightarrow \lambda > 1$ then $\Phi(x)$ has unique solution

$\Rightarrow$Option a) and d) are correct and b) and c) are incorrect.

5. **Explanation (a), (c), (d)**

Consider the given integral equation

$\phi(x) = f(x) + \lambda\int_{-1}^{1} cos[\pi(x-t)]\phi(t)dt$ --- (1)

$\phi(x) = f(x) + \lambda\int_{-1}^{1}(cos\pi x cos\pi t + sin\pi x sin\pi t)\phi(t)dt$ (2)

$\phi(x) = f(x) + \lambda\cos\pi x\int_{-1}^{1}\cos\pi t\,\phi(t)dt + \lambda\sin\pi x\int_{-1}^{1}\sin\pi t\,\phi(t)dt$

Now check the option,

For option a)

$f(x) = x$ and $\lambda \neq 1$

Let $A = \int_{-1}^{1} cos\,\pi t\,\phi(t)dt,\quad B = \int_{-1}^{1}\sin\pi t\,\phi(t)dt$ (3)

$\phi(x) = x + \lambda\, A\cos\pi x + \lambda\, B\sin\pi x$

$A = \int_{-1}^{1} cos\,\pi t(t + \lambda\, A\cos\pi t + \lambda B sin\pi t)\,dt$

$A = \int_{-1}^{1} t\,cos\,\pi t.dt + \lambda A\int_{-1}^{1} cos^2\,\pi t.dt + \lambda B\int_{-1}^{1} cos\,\pi t\sin\pi t.dt$

$\Rightarrow A = \lambda A$

$\Rightarrow A(1-\lambda) = 0$ (4)

And $B = \int_{-1}^{1}\sin\pi t\,[t + \lambda\cos\pi t\,A + \lambda\sin\pi t\,B]dt$

$B = \int_{-1}^{1} t sin\,\pi t + \frac{\lambda}{2}\sin 2\pi t + \lambda B\frac{(1-\cos 2\pi t)}{2}dt$

$= 0 + \frac{-\lambda}{4\pi}[\cos 2\pi t]]_{-1}^{1} + \lambda B - \frac{\lambda B}{2\pi}[\sin 2\pi t]]_{-1}^{1}$

$= \lambda B$

$\Rightarrow B(1-\lambda) = 0$ ...(5)

From equation (4) and (5)

$[P:Q = R]$

Where, $P = \begin{bmatrix}(1-\lambda) & 0\\ 0 & (1-\lambda)\end{bmatrix}, Q = \begin{bmatrix}A\\B\end{bmatrix}, R = \begin{bmatrix}0\\0\end{bmatrix}$

$\Rightarrow \begin{bmatrix}(1-\lambda) & 0\\ 0 & (1-\lambda)\end{bmatrix}\begin{bmatrix}A\\B\end{bmatrix} = \begin{bmatrix}0\\0\end{bmatrix}$

We know that, if $|P| \neq 0$ then we get unique solution

$\Rightarrow (1-\lambda)^2 \neq 0$

$\Rightarrow$ option (a) correct .

For option b)

When $f(x) = 1$ and $\lambda \neq 1$

From equation 2) and 3)

$\Rightarrow \phi(x) = 1 + \lambda A\cos\pi x + \lambda\, B\sin\pi x$

$A = \int_{-1}^{1}\cos\pi t\,[1 + \lambda\, A\cos\pi t + \lambda B\sin\pi t]dt$

$= \int_{-1}^{1}\cos\pi t\,dt + \lambda A\int_{-1}^{1}\cos^2\,\pi t\,.dt + \lambda B\int_{-1}^{1}\cos\,\pi t\sin\,\pi t.dt$

$= \left.\frac{\sin\pi t}{\pi}\right]_{-1}^{1} + \frac{\pi A}{2}\int_{-1}^{1}(cos2\pi t + 1)dt + \frac{\lambda B}{2}\int_{-1}^{1}\sin 2\pi t\,dt$

$= \frac{1}{\pi}[0] + \frac{\lambda A}{2}\left[\frac{sin2\pi t}{2\pi} + t\right]_{-1}^{1} - \frac{\lambda B}{2}\left[\frac{cos2\pi t}{2\pi}\right]_{-1}^{1}$

$= \frac{\lambda A}{2}.2$

$\Rightarrow A = \lambda A$

$\Rightarrow A(1-\lambda) = 0$ ....(6)

And $B = \int_{-1}^{1} sin\pi t[1 + \lambda cos\pi t.A + \lambda sin\pi t.B]dt$

$= \int_{-1}^{1} \sin n\pi t + \frac{\lambda}{2}\sin 2\pi t + \lambda B \frac{(1-\cos 2\pi t)}{2} dt =$

$\frac{-1}{\pi}[\cos\pi t]]_{-1}^{1} \frac{-\lambda}{4\pi}[\cos 2\pi t]]_{-1}^{1} + \lambda B - \frac{\lambda B}{2\pi}[\sin 2\pi t]]_{-1}^{1}$

$= \lambda c_2$

$\Rightarrow B(1-\lambda) = 0$ ...(7)

From equation (6) and (7)

$$[P:Q = R]$$

Where, $P = \begin{bmatrix}(1-\lambda) & 0 \\ 0 & (1-\lambda)\end{bmatrix}$, $Q = \begin{bmatrix}A \\ B\end{bmatrix}$, $R = \begin{bmatrix}0 \\ 0\end{bmatrix}$

We know that, if $|P| \neq 0$ then we get unique solution

$\Longrightarrow (1-\lambda)^2 \neq 0$

$\Longrightarrow$ option (b) is incorrect.

For option c)

When $f(x) = x$ equation is

$\emptyset(x) = x + \lambda A\cos\pi x + \lambda B \sin\pi x$

$$A = \int_{-1}^{1} \cos\pi t\,[t + \lambda A\cos\pi t + \lambda B\sin\pi t]dt$$

$= \int_{-1}^{1} t\cos\pi t.dt + \lambda A\int_{-1}^{1}\cos^2\pi t.dt +$

$\frac{\lambda B}{2}\int_{-1}^{1}\sin 2\pi t.dt$

$= \left[\frac{t\sin\pi t}{\pi} - \frac{1}{\pi}\int_{-1}^{1}\sin\pi t.dt\right]_{-1}^{1} + \frac{\lambda B}{2}\int_{-1}^{1}(\cos 2\pi t + 1)dt$

$-\frac{\lambda B}{2}[\cos 2\pi t]_{-1}^{1}$

$= \lambda A$

$\Rightarrow A(1-\lambda) = 0$ -------(1)

And $B = \int_{-1}^{1}\sin\pi t\,[t + \lambda\cos\pi t\,A + \lambda\sin\pi t\,B)dt$

$= \int_{-1}^{1} t.\sin\pi t.dt + \frac{\lambda}{2}A\int_{-1}^{1}\sin 2\pi t.dt + \frac{\lambda}{4}B\int_{-1}^{1} 1 -$ $\cos 2\pi t.dt$

$= \left[\frac{-t\cos\pi t}{\pi}\right]_{-1}^{1} - \frac{1}{\pi}\int_{-1}^{1}\cos\pi t.dt]$

$+\frac{\pi}{2}A\left[\frac{\cos 2\pi t}{\pi}\right]_{-1}^{1} + \frac{B\lambda}{2}2 - \frac{\lambda B}{4}.\frac{1}{2\pi}[-\sin 2\pi t]_{-1}^{1}$

$= \lambda B - \frac{1}{\pi}[\cos\pi + \cos\pi]$

$= A0 + B(1-\lambda) = \frac{2}{\pi}$

From (1) and (2) we get

$\begin{bmatrix}(1-\lambda) & 0 \\ 0 & (1-\lambda)\end{bmatrix}\begin{bmatrix}A \\ B\end{bmatrix} = \begin{bmatrix}0 \\ \frac{2}{\pi}\end{bmatrix}$

If $\lambda = 1$ then we get $0A + 0B = \frac{2}{\pi}$

Which is not possible

So, no solution for $\lambda = 1$ when $f(x) = x$

$\Longrightarrow$Option c) is correct.

For option d)

From option b)

If $|P| = 0$

$\Rightarrow \lambda = 1$

We get infinite number of solution.

$\Longrightarrow$ option (d) correct

Hence options (a), (c) (d) are correct answer and b) is incorrect.

6. **Explanation: (c) (d)**

Consider the given homogeneous fredhlom equation

$y(x) = \int_0^{\pi}\sin(x+\xi)y(\xi)d\xi$

$$\Rightarrow y(x) = \lambda\int_0^{\pi}\sin x\cos\xi y(\xi)d\xi + \cos x\sin\xi y(\xi)d\xi$$

$= \lambda\sin x\int_0^{\pi}\cos\xi y(\xi)d\xi + \cos x\int_o^{\pi}\sin\xi y(\xi)d\xi$

Now put $A = \lambda\int_0^{\pi}\cos\xi y(\xi)d\xi$

$B = \lambda\int_0^{\pi}\sin\xi y(\xi)d\xi$

$\Rightarrow y(x) = A\sin x + B\cos x$

$B = \lambda\int_0^{\pi}\sin\xi\,(A\sin\xi + B\,os\xi)d\xi$

$\Rightarrow A\lambda\int_o^{H}\frac{\sin 2\xi}{2} + B\cos^2\xi\,d\xi$

$= \lambda A\int_o^{H}\frac{\sin 2\xi}{2}d\xi + \lambda B\int_o^{\pi}\frac{1+\cos 2\xi}{2}d\xi$

$\Rightarrow A = \frac{\lambda B\pi}{2}$

$\Rightarrow A - \frac{\lambda B\pi}{2} = 0$

Now

$B = A\lambda\int_o^{\pi}(\frac{1-\cos 2\xi}{2})d\xi + \lambda B\int_o^{\pi}\frac{\sin 2\xi}{2}d\xi$

$= \frac{A\lambda}{2}\left(\xi - \frac{\sin 2\xi}{2}\right)_0^{\pi} + \frac{\lambda B}{2}\left(-\frac{\cos 2\xi}{2}\right)_0^{\pi}$

$= \frac{A\lambda}{2}\pi + \frac{\lambda B}{2}.0$

$B = \frac{A\lambda h}{2}$

$B - \frac{A\lambda m}{2} = 0$

For non zero solution of above system, determinant of coefficient matrix is zero

$\begin{vmatrix}1 & -\frac{\lambda\pi}{2} \\ \frac{\lambda\pi}{2} & -1\end{vmatrix} = 1 - \frac{\lambda^2 m^2}{4} = 0$

$4 = \lambda^2\pi^2$

$= \lambda = \pm\frac{2}{\pi}$

If $\lambda = -\frac{2}{\pi}$ then $-C_1 = C_2$

$\Rightarrow y(x) = B\,(\sin x - \cos y)$

$\lambda = \frac{2}{\pi}$ then $C_1 = C_2$

$\Rightarrow y\,(x) = A\,(\sin x + \cos x)$

From above explanation,

Option (c) and (d) correct answer and

Option (a) and (b) incorrect.

7. **Explanation: (c)**

Consider the given integral equation

$\int_a^x K(x,y)\phi(y)\,dy = f(x)$ (1)

$$f(x) = \int_a^x K(x,y)\phi(y)\,dy$$

Differentiating equation (1) W.r to x

$f'(x) = \int_a^x \frac{\partial}{\partial x}k(x,y)\,\phi(y)dy + k(x,x)\phi(x)$ (2)

Now Cheek option

For option a)

$\phi(x) + \int_a^x g(x,y)\phi(y)\,dy = g(x)$ (3)

Comparing with equation (2)

$\Rightarrow g(x) = f'(x)$

$\frac{\partial}{\partial x}k(x,y) = G(x,y)\,, k(x,x) = 1$

$\Rightarrow$ option a) is correct

For option b) from option a)

option b) is incorrect.

For option (c)

From equation (2)

$\frac{f'(x)}{k(x,x)} = \int_a^x \frac{1}{k(x.x)} \frac{\partial k}{\partial x}(x,y)\,\phi(y)dy$

Comparing with equation (3)

$\Rightarrow G(x,y) = \frac{1}{K(x,x)} \frac{\partial k}{\partial x}(x,y)$ and

$g(x) = \frac{f(x)}{k(x,x)}$

⇒ Option (c) is correct

For Option d) from above option

option d) is incorrect.

Option c) is the correct answer and option a), b) and d) are incorrect.

8. Explanation: (a), (d)

Consider the given homogeneous integral equation

$\phi(x) = \lambda \int_0^1 (xt + 2x^2)\,\phi(t)dt \;----(1)$

$\phi(x) = \lambda x \int_0^1 t\phi(t)\,dt + +2\lambda x^2 \int_0^1 \phi(t)dt$

Let $A = \int_0^t t\phi(t)dt$ and $B = \int_0^t \phi(t)\,dt$

equation(1) ⇒

$\phi(x) - \lambda Ax + 2B\lambda x^2 = 0$

$\phi(x) = \lambda Ax + 2B\lambda x^2$

$x\phi(x) = \lambda Ax^2 + 2B\lambda x^3$

$A = \int_0^1 t(\lambda At + 2B\lambda t^2)dt$

$A = \left[\frac{\lambda at3}{3} + \frac{2b\lambda t^4}{3}\right]_0^1 = \frac{\lambda A}{3} + \frac{2B\lambda}{4}$

$A\left(1 - \frac{\lambda}{3}\right) - \frac{2B\lambda}{4} = 0$

$A\left(1 - \frac{\lambda}{3}\right) - \frac{B\lambda}{2} = 0$

$B = \int_0^1 (\lambda At + 2B\lambda t^2)dt \frac{\lambda at^2}{2} + \frac{2b\lambda +^3}{3}$

$\Rightarrow B = \left[\frac{\lambda At^2}{2} + \frac{2B\lambda t^3}{3}\right]_0^1$

$B = \frac{\lambda A}{2} + \frac{2B\lambda}{3}$

$-\frac{\lambda A}{2} + \left(1 - \frac{2\lambda}{3}\right)B = 0$

Now find the nonzero solution from equation (2) and (3)

$\begin{vmatrix} 1 - \frac{\lambda}{3} & -\frac{\lambda}{2} \\ -\frac{\lambda}{2} & 1 - \frac{2\lambda}{3} \end{vmatrix} = 0$

$\left(1 - \frac{\lambda}{3}\right))\left(1 - \frac{2\lambda}{3}\right) - \frac{\lambda^2}{4} = 0$

$\frac{\lambda^2}{4} + 1 + \frac{2\lambda^2}{9} - \frac{2\lambda}{3} - \frac{\lambda}{3} = 0$

$\frac{2\lambda^2}{9.} - \lambda - \frac{\lambda^2}{4} + 1 = 0$

$\frac{2\lambda^2}{9} - \lambda + 1 - \frac{\lambda^2}{4} = 0$

$\frac{8\lambda^2}{36} - \frac{9\lambda^2}{36} - \lambda + 1 = 0$

$-\lambda^2 - 36\,\lambda + 36 = 0$

$\lambda^2 + 36\,\lambda - 36 = 0$

Now

$\lambda = \frac{-36 \pm \sqrt{(36)^2 + 4 \times 36}}{2}$

$= -18 \pm \sqrt{360}$

$\lambda = -18 \pm 6\sqrt{10}$

$\lambda = -18 + 6\sqrt{10}\,, -18 - 6\sqrt{10}$

From this,

option a) Is correct and and option b) is incorrect. We know that characteristic function corresponding to distinct eigenfunction are orthogonal

⇒ Option a) and d) is correct and option b),c) are incorrect.

9. Explanation: (c)

Consider the integral equation,

$y(x) = 1 + x^3 + \int_0^x k(x,t)y(t)dt \;---(1)$

$K(x,t) = 2^{x-t}$

$\Rightarrow K(x,t) = k_1(x,t) = 2^{x-t}$

$\Rightarrow k_2(x,t) = \int_t^x k(x,s)k_1(s,t)ds$

$= \int_t^x 2^{x-t}\,2^{s-t}ds$

$k_2(x,t) = 2^{x-t}(x-t)$

$k_3(x,t) = \int_t^x k_1(x,s)k_2(s,t)\,ds$

$= \int_t^x 2^{x-t}\,2^{s-t}(s-t)ds$

$= \int_t^x 2^{x-t}(s-t)ds$

$k_3(x,t) = 2^{x-t}\frac{(x-t)^2}{2}$

$k_3(x,t) = 2^{x-t-1}\frac{(x-t)^2}{2}$

⇒ only option (c) is correct answer and option a),b) and d) are incorrect.

10. Explanation: (a), (c)

Consider the given homogeneous integral equation

$\emptyset(x) = \lambda \int_0^1 (2xt + 4x^2)\,\emptyset(t)dt$

$\emptyset(x) = 2\lambda x \int_0^1 t\phi(t)dt + 4x^2\lambda \int_0^1 \phi(t)dt$

Consider, $A = \int_0^1 t\phi(t)dt$

$B = \int_0^1 \phi(t)\,dt$

$\Rightarrow \phi(x) = 2A\lambda x + 4B\lambda x^2$

$\Rightarrow \phi(t) = 2A\lambda t + 4B\lambda t^2$

$x\phi(x) = \lambda(2x^2A + 4x^3B)$

$x\phi(x) = \lambda(2x^2A + 4x^3B)$

$A = \int_0^1 t(2A\lambda t + 4B\lambda t^2)dt$

$A = \int_0^1 2\lambda At^2 + 4\lambda Bt^3\,dt$

$A = \left[\frac{2\lambda At^3}{3} + \frac{4\lambda Bt^4}{4}\right]_0^1$

$A = \frac{2\lambda}{3}A + \frac{4\lambda B}{4}$

$A = \frac{2\lambda A}{3} + \lambda B$

$A\left(1 - \frac{2\lambda}{3}\right) - \lambda B = 0$ (2)

Now $B = \int_0^1 \lambda\,(2tA + 4t^2B)dt$

$$B = \int_0^1 2\lambda ta + 4\lambda t^2 B\, dt$$

$$b = \left[\frac{2\lambda t^2}{2}A + \frac{4\lambda t^3 B}{3}\right]_0^1$$

$b = \lambda A + \frac{3}{4}\lambda B$

$\left(1 - \frac{4}{3}\lambda\right)B - \lambda A = 0$ (3)

from equation(2) and (3)

Now $\begin{vmatrix} 1 - \frac{2}{3}\lambda & -\lambda \\ -\lambda & 1 - \frac{4}{3}\lambda \end{vmatrix} = 0$

$1 + \frac{8}{9}\lambda^2 - 2\lambda - \lambda^2 = 0$

$\frac{-\lambda^2}{9} - 2\lambda + 1 = 0$

$-\lambda^2 - 18\,\lambda + 9 = 0$

$\lambda^2 + 18\lambda - 9 = 0$

Now

$\lambda = \frac{-18 \pm \sqrt{(18)^2 - 4\times 9}}{2}$

$\lambda = -9 + 3\sqrt{10}$

$\lambda = -9 + 3\sqrt{10}$ *and* $\lambda = -9 - 3\sqrt{10}$

$\Rightarrow$ both eigenvalue are distinct.

$\Rightarrow \lambda_1 \neq \lambda_2$

From this option (a) is correct and option b) is incorrect.

We know that eigenfunctions corresponding to distinct eigenvalue ore orthogonal.

$\Rightarrow$ option (c) is correct and option (d) is incorrect

$\Rightarrow$ option (a)and (c) are the correct answer and (b) and (d) are the incorrect.

11. Explanation: (b), (d)

Consider the given integral equation

$$y(t) = y(0) + \int_0^t y(s)ds = 1$$

Squaring both sides,

$$\Rightarrow y^2(t) = y^2(0) + \left(\int_0^t y(s)ds\right)^2 + 2y(0)\int_0^t y(s)ds$$

$\Rightarrow$Option (4) is correct

Differentiating equation (1)

$\Rightarrow y'(t) = y(t)$

Now integrating,

$y(t) = c\,e^t$

$\Rightarrow y(t) = y(0)e^t$

Now $\left(\int_0^t y(s)ds\right)^2 + 2y(0)\int_0^t y(s)ds$

$= y^2(0)(e^t - 1)^2 + 2y^2(0)(e^t - 1)$

$= y^2(0))(e^t - 1)^2 + 2y^2(0)\frac{(e^{2t-1})}{2}$

$= 2\int_0^t y^2(s)ds$

so $y^2(t) = y^2(0) + 2\int_0^t y^2(s)ds,$

b) is the correct.

Option b) and d) are the correct answer and a), c) are the incorrect.

12. Explanation: (a), (d)

Given

$K(x,t) = \begin{cases}(x+1)t, 0 \le x \le t \\ (t+1)x, t \le x \le 1\end{cases}$ --- (2)

$$\Rightarrow y(x) = \lambda\int_0^1 k(x,t)\,y(t)dt$$

$$\Rightarrow y(x) = \lambda\int_0^x (t+1)x\; y(t)dt + \lambda\int_x^1 (x+1)ty(t)$$

Differentiating above equationw.r.to x

$y'(x) = \lambda\int_0^x (t+1)y(t)dt + \lambda x(x+1)y(x) + \lambda\int_x^1 ty(t)dt - \lambda x(x+1)y(x)$

$$y'(x) = \lambda\int_0^x (t+1)y(t)dt + \lambda\int_x^1 ty(t)dt$$

$y''(x) = \lambda(x+1)y(x) - \lambda xy(x)$

$y''(x) = \lambda y(x)$

$y''(x) - \lambda y(x) = 0$

And $y(0) = y'(0)$

$y(1) = y'(1)$

To solve this consider some cases

Case 1) If $\lambda > 0 \Rightarrow \lambda = \mu^2$

$\Rightarrow y''(x) - \mu^2 y(x) = 0$

Auxiliary equation is

$m^2 - \mu^2 = 0$

Complementary function is

$\Rightarrow y(x) = C_1e^{\mu x} + C_2e^{-\mu x}$

$\Rightarrow y(0) = C_1 + C_2$

$y'(0) = \mu C_1 - \mu C_2$

$\Rightarrow c_1 + c_2 = \mu c_1 - \mu c_2$

$c_1(1-\mu) + c_2(1+\mu) = 0$ (2)

Now,

$y(1) = C_1e^{\mu} + C_2e^{-\mu}$

$y'(1) = \mu C_1e^{\mu} - C_2\mu e^{-\mu}$

$\Rightarrow C_1e^{\mu} + C_2e^{-\mu} = \mu C_1e^{\mu} - C_2\mu e^{-\mu}$

$\Rightarrow C_1(e^{\mu} - \mu e^{\mu}) + C_2(e^{-\mu} + \mu e^{-\mu}) = 0$

$\Rightarrow e^{\mu}C_1(1-\mu) + e^{-\mu}C_2(1+\mu) = 0$ (3)

From and (2) and (3) find the non zero sol^n

$\Rightarrow \begin{vmatrix} 1-\mu & 1+\mu \\ (1-\mu)e^{\mu} & (1+\mu)e^{-\mu}\end{vmatrix} = 0$

$\Rightarrow (1-\mu^2)e^{-\mu} - (1-\mu^2)e^{\mu} = 0$

$(1-\mu^2)[e^{-\mu} - e^{\mu}] = 0$

$\Rightarrow \mu = \pm 1$

$\lambda = \mu^2 = 1$

For $\mu = 1$ in equation (2)

$\Rightarrow C_2 = 0$

$\Rightarrow y(x) = C_1e^{\mu}x$ and C_1 *is orbitorary*

$\Rightarrow$ Option a) is correct.

Case 2) *If* $\lambda < 0$

$\Rightarrow \lambda = -\mu^2$

$\Rightarrow y'' + \mu^2\,y(x) = 0$

Auxiliary equation is

and is $m^2 + \mu^2 = 0$

$\Rightarrow m = \mu i$

Complementary function is

$\Rightarrow y(x) = C_1 \cos \mu x + C_2 \sin\mu x$

Now apply the condition

$y(0) = C_1$

$\Rightarrow C_1 - \mu C_2 = 0 \quad (4)$

$y'(0) = \mu C_2$

$y(1) = C_1 \cos \mu x + C_2 \sin \mu x$

$y'(1) = -\mu C_1 \sin\mu x + \mu C_2 \cos\mu x$

$C_1 \cos \mu + C_2 \sin \mu = -\mu C_1 \sin\mu + \mu C_2 \cos\mu$

$C_1(\cos\mu + \mu \sin\mu) + c_2 (\sin \mu - \mu\cos\mu)$

$= 0 \quad (5)$

$$= \begin{vmatrix} 1 & -\mu \\ \cos\mu + \mu\sin\mu & \sin \mu - \mu\cos\mu \end{vmatrix} = 0$$

$\Rightarrow \sin \mu - \mu\cos\mu + \mu\cos\mu + \mu^2 \sin\mu$

$\Rightarrow \sin \mu (1 + \mu^2) = 0$

$\Rightarrow \sin \mu = 0$

$\Rightarrow \mu = n\pi$

$\Rightarrow \lambda = -n^2\pi^2$

$\Rightarrow y(x) = C_1 \cos n\pi x + C_2 \sin n\pi x$

Also $C_1 = \mu C_2$

$C_1 = n\pi C_2$

For n=1 and $C_2 = 1 \;\; y(x) = \pi \cos\pi x + \sin\pi x$

$\Rightarrow$ Option (a) and option (d) is correct and option (b) and (c) incorrect.

13. Explanation: (b), (c), (d)

Consider the given integral equation is

$$\phi(x) - \frac{2}{\pi}\int_0^{\pi} \cos(x+t)\,\phi(t)dt = f(x) - - - (1)$$

$$\phi(x) = f(x) + \frac{2}{\pi}\int_0^{\pi} \cos(x+t)\,\phi(t)dt$$

$\Rightarrow \phi(x) = f(x) + \frac{2}{\pi}\int_0^{\pi}(\cos x\cos t - \sin x \sin t)\,\phi(t)dt$

To solve this separable kernel method

For the eigenvalue λ

$$\phi(x) = \lambda \int_0^{\pi} (\cos x\cos t - \sin x\sin t)\,\phi(t)dt$$

$\Rightarrow A = \int_0^{\pi} \cos t\, \phi(t)dt$ and

$$B = \int_0^{\pi} \sin t\, \phi(t)dt$$

$$\Rightarrow A = \lambda \int_0^{\pi} \cos t(\cos x\cos t - \sin x\sin t)\,\phi(t)dt$$

$$B = \lambda \int_0^{\pi} \sin t(\cos x\cos t - \sin x\sin t)\,\phi(t)dt$$

$\Rightarrow A = \lambda A \frac{\pi}{2} (2)$

$\Rightarrow B = -\lambda B \frac{\pi}{2} \quad (3)$

Now from (2) and (3)

$$\begin{vmatrix} 1 - \frac{\pi\lambda}{2} & 0 \\ 0 & 1 + \frac{\lambda\pi}{2} \end{vmatrix}$$

$$1 - \left(\frac{\pi\lambda}{2}\right)^2 = 0$$

$$1 = \pm\frac{\lambda\pi}{2}$$

$$\lambda = \frac{2}{\pi}, -\frac{2}{\pi}$$

For $\lambda = \frac{2}{\pi}$

Eigenfunction is

$$\phi(x) = \frac{2}{\pi} A\cos x$$

Put $\frac{2}{\pi} A = 1$

$\Rightarrow \phi(x) = \cos x$

If $\int_0^{\pi} \phi(x) f(x)dx = 0$ then the equation (1) has infinitely many solution

Now Check the option

For option a)

$f(x) = \cos x$

$$\Rightarrow \int_0^{\pi} \cos x \cos x\, dx = \int_0^{\pi} \frac{1+\cos 2x}{2} dx$$

$$= \left[\frac{x}{2} + \frac{\sin 2x}{4}\right]_0^{\pi} = \frac{\pi}{2} \neq 0$$

For option b)

$f(x) = \cos 3x$

$$\Rightarrow \int_0^{\pi} \cos 3x \cos x\, dx = \frac{1}{2}\int_0^{\pi} [\cos 4x + \cos 2x]\, dx$$

$$= \frac{1}{2}\left[\frac{\sin 4x}{4} + \frac{\sin 2x}{2}\right]_0^{\pi} = 0$$

For option c)

$f(x) = \sin x$

$\int_0^{\pi} \sin x\cos x\, dx = \frac{1}{2}\int_0^{\pi} \sin 2x\, dx = \frac{1}{4}(-\cos 2x)_0^{\pi} = 0$

For option d)

$f(x) = \sin 3x$

$$\int_0^{\pi} \sin 3x \cos x\, dx = \frac{1}{2}\int_0^{\pi} (\sin 4x + \sin 2x)\, dx = 0$$

Form above explanation

$\Rightarrow$ Option b),c) and d) are correct answer and a) is incorrect.

14. Explanation: (b)

Consider the given integral equation

$y(x) = 1 + \lambda \int_0^{\pi} k(x,t) y(t)dt$

$k(x,t) = \begin{cases} \cos hx \;\; \sin ht & 0 \le x \le t \\ \cos ht \;\; \sin hx & t \le x \le 1 \end{cases}$

$\Rightarrow y(x) = 1 + \lambda \int_0^{x} \cos ht \sin hx\, y(t)dt +$

$\lambda \int_x^1 \cos hx \sin ht\, y(t)dt$

$= 1 + \lambda \int_0^{x} \cos ht \;\sin hx\, y(t)dt +$

$\lambda \int_x^1 \cos hx \sin ht\, y(t)dt$

Differentiating equation (1) w.r. to x with the help of Leibnitz rule

$y'(x) = \lambda \left[\int_0^x \cos hx \cos ht\, (t)dt + \right.$

$\left.\cos hx \sin hx\, y(x)\right] + \lambda\left[\int_x^1 \sin hx \cos ht\, y(t)dt - \right.$

$\left.\cos hx \sin hx\, y(x)\right]$

Again differentiating with the help of Leibnitz rule

$\Rightarrow y''(x) = \lambda[\int_0^x \sin hx \cos ht\, y(t)dt] +$

$\int_x^1 [\cos hx \cos ht\, y(t)dt\,]$

$\Rightarrow y''(x) = y(x)(\lambda + 1) - 1$

Put $\lambda = -1$ in above equation

$\Rightarrow y''(x) = -1$

Option (c) and (d) ruled out as

$y'' = 1$

For $\lambda = 3$

$y''(x) = 4y(x) - 1$

For option (a)

$$y(x) = \frac{1}{4}\left(\frac{3\cos 2x}{\cos 2 - 2\sin 2\tan h1} + 1\right)$$

$$\Rightarrow y''(x) = \frac{-3\cos 2x}{\cos 2 - 2\sin 2\tan h1}$$

$$\Rightarrow 4y(x) - 1 = \frac{3\cos 2x}{\cos 2 - 2\sin 2\tan h}$$

$\therefore y''(x) \neq 4y(x) - 1$

Hence option (a) is incorrect

$y''(x) = 4y(x) - 1$

$$\Rightarrow y(x) = \frac{1}{4}\left(\frac{3\cos h2x}{\cos h_2 - 2\sin h_2 \tan h_1} + 1\right)$$

Option (b) is correct answer and option (a), (c) and (d) incorrect

15. Explanation: (d)

Consider the given integral equation

$y(x) = x - \int_0^x xt^2 y(t)dt$ --------(1)

$$\Rightarrow y(x) = f(x) + \lambda \int_a^b k(x,t)\emptyset(t)dt$$

Comparing with equation (1)

$\Rightarrow \lambda = -1 \qquad k(x,t) = xt^2$

$k(x,t) = k_0(x,t^2) = xt^2$

Now

$K_1(x,t) = \int_t^x k(x,s)k_0(s,t)ds$

$$K_1(x,t) = \int_t^x xs^2st^2\,ds\frac{s^4}{4}$$

$$K_1(x,t) = xt^2\left[\frac{s^4}{4}\right]_t^x = xt^2\left(\frac{x^4 - t^4}{4}\right)$$

$$K_2(x,t) = \int_t^x k_0(s,t)k_1(s,t)ds$$

$$= xt^2\int_t^x xs^2\,st^2\left(\frac{s^4 - t^4}{4}\right)ds$$

$$= xt^2\int_t^x s^3\left(\frac{s^4 - t^4}{4}\right)ds$$

$$= \frac{xt^2}{4}\left[\frac{s^8}{8} - \frac{t^4s^4}{4}\right]_t^x$$

$$K_2(x,t) = \frac{xt^2}{4}\left[\frac{x^8}{8} - \frac{x^4t^4}{4} - \frac{t^8}{8} + \frac{t^8}{4}\right]$$

$$K_2(x,t) = \frac{xt^2}{4}\left[\frac{x^8 - t^8}{8} - \frac{t^4(x^4 - t^4)}{4}\right]$$

$$= \frac{xt^2}{4}\left[(x^4 - t^4)\left[\frac{x^4 + t^4}{8} - \frac{t^4}{4}\right]\right]$$

$$K_2(x,t) = \frac{xt^4}{4}\left(\frac{x^4 - t^4}{2^3}\right)^2$$

Now find resolvent kernel

$R(x,t;\lambda) = k_0 + \lambda K_1 + \lambda^2 K_2 + ---$

$$= xt^2 - \left(\frac{x^4 - t^4}{4}\right) + \frac{xt^2}{2}\left(\frac{x^4 - t^4}{4}\right)^2 + --$$

$$R(x,t;\lambda) = xt^2 e^{-\left(\frac{x^4 - t^4}{4}\right)}$$

Now $y(x) = x - \int_0^x xt^2 e^{-\left(\frac{x^4 - t^4}{4}\right)}tdt$

$$y(x) = x - x\left(1 - e^{\frac{-x^4}{4}}\right)$$

put $x = \sqrt{2}$

$y(\sqrt{2}) = \frac{\sqrt{2}}{e}$

From this only option d) is correct answer and a), c) and d) incorrect.

16. Explanation (a), (c)

$$\phi(x) = 2x^2 + 2\int_0^1 e^{x-y}\emptyset(y)dy --- (1)$$

Let $c_1 = \int_0^1 e^{-y}\emptyset(y)dy$ then put it in (1)

$\phi(x) = 2x^2 + 2e^x c_1$

$$c_1 = \int_0^1 e^{-y}\emptyset(y)dy$$

$$= \int_0^1 e^{-y}(2y^2 + 2e^y c_1)dy$$

$$= 2\int_0^1 e^{-y}y^2 + c_1 dy$$

$$= 2\left[-\frac{5}{e} + 2 + c_2\right]$$

$$\Rightarrow -c_1 = -\frac{10}{e} + 4$$

$$\Rightarrow c_1 = \frac{10}{e} - 4$$

$$\Rightarrow \phi(x) = 2x^2 + 2e^x\left[\frac{10}{e} - 4\right]$$

$= 2x^2 + 20e^{x-1} - 8e^x$

$\phi(0) = 20e^{-1} - 8$ and $\phi(1) = 22 - 8e$

Hence option (a) & (c) are correct.

17. Explanation: (b), (d)

Consider the given integral equation

$y = p(x) + \int_0^x y(t)\sin(x - t)dt$

$y(x) = p(x) + \int_0^x [\sin x\cos t - \cos x\sin t]\,y(t)at$

Differentiating

$y'(x) = p'(x) + \int_0^x \cos x\cos t\,y(t)dt +$
$\sin x\cos x\,y(x) + \int_0^x \sin x\sin t\,y(t)dt$ ... (2)

$y''(x) = p''(x) + \int_0^x(-\sin x\cos t +$
$\cos x\sin t)y(t)dt + (\cos^2 x + \sin^2 x)\,y(x)$

$y''(x) = p''(x) + y(x) - \int_0^x \sin(x - t)y(t)dt$ .... (3)

$y''(x) = p''(x) + y(x) - [y(x) - p(x)]$

$y''(x) = p''(x) + p(x)$ ... (4)

Now $p(x) = a_0 + a_1x + a_2x^2$ (given)

$p'(x) = a_1 + 2a_2x$

$P''(x) = 2a_2$

From equation (4)

$y''(x) = 2a_2 + a_0 + a_1x + a_2x^2$

$y'(0) = a_1 \qquad y(0) = a_0$

$y'(x) = (2a + a_0)x + \frac{a_1x^2}{2} + a_2\frac{x^3}{3} + c_1$

$y(x) = (2a_2 + a_0)\frac{x^2}{2} + \frac{a_1x^3}{6} + \frac{a_2x^4}{4} + c_1x + c_2$

$y(0) = a_0$

$y'(0) = c_1 = a_1$

$y(x) = (2a_2 + a_0)\frac{x^2}{2} + \frac{a_1x^3}{6} + \frac{ax^4}{4} + a_1x + a_0$

$\Rightarrow y(x)$ is polynomial of degree 4.

$\Rightarrow$ Option (a) is incorrect and option (b) is correct

We know that

$y'(0) = a_1$

From option (c) $a_1 \neq 0$

So $y'(0) = 0 = a_1 \neq 0$

$\Rightarrow y'(0) = 0$ never possible

So option (c) is incorrect

For option (d)

We know that

$y''(x) = q_0 + 2q_2 + q_1x + q_2x^2$

$y''(0) = q_0 + 2q_2$

$y''(0) = 0$

$(\because q_0 + q_2 = 0)$

Option (d) is correct

$\Longrightarrow$ Option (b) and Option (d) is correct and option (a) and (c) incorrect.

18. Explanation: (a), (d)

Consider the given integral equation

$\emptyset(x) = \lambda\int_0^{\pi}[(\cos x\cos t - 2\sin x\sin t]\emptyset(t)dt + \cos 7x$

$\emptyset(0) = 00 \leq x \leq \pi \quad (1)$

Differentiating $w.r.$ to x

$\emptyset'(x) = \lambda\int_0^{\pi}[-\sin x\cos t - 2\cos x\sin t]\emptyset(t)dt - 7\sin x$

$\Rightarrow \emptyset'(\pi) = -1$

Again differentiating w.r. to x with the help of Leibnitz rule

$\emptyset''(x) = \lambda\int_0^{\pi}[-\cos x\cos t + 2\sin x\sin t]\,\emptyset(t)dt - 49\cos 7x$

$\Rightarrow \emptyset''(x) = -\emptyset(x) - 50\cos 7x$

And $\emptyset(0) = 0 \qquad \emptyset'(\pi) = -1$

$\emptyset''(x) + \emptyset(x) = 50\cos 7x$

Auxiliary equation is

$m^2 + 1 = 0$

$\Rightarrow m = \pm i$

Complementary function is

$\emptyset(x) = c_1\cos x + c_2\sin x$

Now Find PI

$PI = \frac{1}{D^2+1} - 50\cos 7x$

$\Rightarrow PI = \frac{-50}{-49+1}\cos 7x$

$\Rightarrow PI = \frac{-50}{-48}\cos 7x = \frac{25}{24}\cos 7x$

$\emptyset(x)$ =CF+PI

$\Rightarrow \emptyset(x) = c_1\cos x + c_2\sin x + \frac{25}{24}\cos 7x$

c_1 and c_2 are arbitrary constant so $\emptyset(x)$ has infinitely many solution $\forall\ \lambda \in \mathbb{R}$

$\Rightarrow$ Option (a) and (d) correct. And option (b) and (c) incorrect.

19. Explanation: (a)

We have

$\emptyset(x) = \int_0^{\pi} k(x,t)\emptyset(t)dt$

Where $k(x,t) = \begin{cases}\sin x & \cos t \quad 0 \leq x \leq t\\ \cos x & \sin t \quad t \leq x \leq \pi\end{cases}$

$\Rightarrow k(x,t) = \begin{cases}\sin t & \cos x \quad 0 \leq t \leq x\\ \cos t & \sin x \quad x \leq t \leq \pi\end{cases}$

Now

$\emptyset(x) =\curlywedge [\int_0^{x}\sin + \cos x\,\emptyset(t)dt + \int_x^{\pi}\cos + \sin x\,\emptyset(t)dt]$

$\emptyset(x) =\curlywedge \int_0^{x}(\sin t + \cos x\,\emptyset(t)dt + \curlywedge \int_x^{\pi}\cos t\sin x\,\emptyset(t\,)dt$

$\Rightarrow \emptyset(0) = 0$ differentiating w. r. to x with the help of Leibnitz rule

$\emptyset'(x) =\curlywedge \int_0^{x}(-\sin x)\sin(\emptyset(t)dt + \sin x - \cos x\,\emptyset(x) +\curlywedge \int_x^{\pi}\cos x\cos t\emptyset(t)dt - \cos x\sin x\,\emptyset(x)$

$= \lambda\int_0^{x}(-\sin x)\sin t\emptyset(t)dt + \int_x^{\pi}\cos x\cos t\emptyset(t)dt$

$\Rightarrow \emptyset'(\pi) = 0$

Again differentiating w. r. to x with the help of Leibnitz rule.

$\emptyset''(x) = \lambda\int_x^{\pi} - \cos x\sin t\,\emptyset(t) - \lambda\sin x\sin x\emptyset(t) + \lambda\int_x^{\pi} - \sin x\cos t\,\emptyset(t)dt - \lambda\cos^2 x\emptyset(x)$

$\emptyset''(x) = \lambda\int_0^{x} - \cos x\, sint\emptyset(t) - \lambda\int_x^{\pi}\sin x\cos t\,\emptyset(t) - \lambda\emptyset(x)$

$\Rightarrow \emptyset''(x) = -\emptyset(x) - \lambda\emptyset(x)$

$\emptyset''(x) = -(\lambda + 1)\emptyset(x)$

$\emptyset''(x) + (1 + \lambda)\emptyset(x) = 0$

This is the sturm Liouville boundary value problem

Now find the eigen value

If $\lambda + 1 = \mu^2$

$\Rightarrow \emptyset''(x) + \mu^2\emptyset(x) = 0$

Auxiliary equation is

$m^2 + \mu^2 = 0$

$\Rightarrow m = \pm\mu i$

Complementary function is

$\emptyset(x) = c_1\cos\mu x + c_2\sin\mu x$

$\emptyset(x) = -\mu c_1\sin\mu x + \mu c_2\cos\mu x$

$\emptyset(0) = c_1 = 0$

$\emptyset(\pi) = \mu c_2\cos\mu\pi = 0$

$c_2 \neq 0$

$\cos\mu\pi \doteq 0$

$\mu\pi = (2n + 1)\frac{\pi}{2}$

$\mu = n + \frac{1}{2}$

$\Rightarrow \emptyset(x) = c_2\sin\left(n + \frac{1}{2}\right)x$

$Now, \lambda + 1 = \mu^2$

$\lambda = -1 + \mu^2$

$\lambda = -1 + \left(n^2 + \frac{1}{4} + n\right)$

$\lambda = \left(n + \frac{1}{2}\right)^2 - 1n \in \mathbb{N}$

$\Longrightarrow$ option a) is the correct answer and option b),c) and d) are incorrect.

20. Explanation: (a), (d)

Given $k(x,t) = \begin{cases} x(t-1) & 0 \le x \le t \\ t(x-1) & t \le x \le 1 \end{cases}$

$\Rightarrow \Phi(x) = \lambda \int_0^1 k(x,t)\Phi(t)dt \ldots.(1)$

$\Phi(x) = \lambda \int_0^x k(x,t)\Phi(t)dt + \lambda \int_x^1 k(x,t)\Phi(t)dt$

$\Phi(x) = \lambda \int_0^x t(x-1)\Phi(t)dt + \lambda \int_x^1 x(t-1)\Phi(t)dt \ldots (2)$

Differentiating above equation x with the help of Leibnitz rule

$\Phi'(x) = \lambda[\int_0^x t\Phi(t)dt + x(x-1)\Phi(x)] + \left[\int_x^1 (t-1)\Phi(t)dt + (-1)x(x-1)\Phi x\right]$

$\Phi'(x) = \lambda\left[\int_0^x t\Phi(t)dt + \int_x^1 (t-1)\Phi(t)dt\right] \ldots (3)$

Again differentiating above equation with the help of Leibnitz rule

$\Phi''(x) = \lambda[x\Phi(x) - (x-1)\Phi(x)]$

$\Phi''(x) = \lambda\Phi(x)$

$\Phi''(x) - \lambda\phi(x) = 0 \ldots (4)$

Now find the solution

There are three possibilities of λ

(1) $\lambda = 0$, straight line

(2) $\lambda = -\mu^2 < 0$, complex

(3) $\lambda = \mu^2 > 0$,exponential

From given option, solution in $\sin x$

So consider $\lambda < 0$

$\Rightarrow$ equation $\lambda = -\mu^2$

$\Phi'' + \mu^2\Phi(x) = 0$

Auxiliary equation is

$m^2 + \mu^2 = 0$

$m = \pm\mu i$

Complementary function is

$\Phi(x) = c_1 \cos \mu x + c_2 \sin \mu x \ldots.. (5)$

From equation (2)

$\Phi(0) = 0$

Equation (5)

$\Rightarrow \Phi(0) = c_1 = 0$

And $\Phi(1) = 0$

$\Rightarrow \Phi(1) = c_2 \sin \mu = 0$

$\Rightarrow c_2 \neq 0, \sin \mu = 0$

$\text{Sin}\,\mu = \sin n\pi$

$\mu = n\pi$

$\Phi(x) = c_2 \sin n\pi x$

$Put\ c_2 = 1 \Rightarrow \Phi(x) = \sin n\pi x$

And $\lambda = -\mu^2 = -n^2\pi^2$

For $n = 1 \Rightarrow \lambda = -\pi^2,\ \Phi(x) = \sin \pi x$

$for\ n = 2 \Rightarrow \lambda = -4\pi^2, \Phi(x) = \sin 2\pi x$

Form this,

only option (a) and (d) is correct answer and option b) and c) are incorrect.

21. Explanation (a)

Given,

$\Phi(x) = 1 - 2x - 4x^2 + \int_0^x [3 + 6(x-t) - 4(x-t)^2]\,\Phi(t)dt$ (1)

$\Phi(0) = 1$

Differentiating equation (1) w.r.to x with the help of Leibnitz rule

$\Phi'(x) = -2 - 8x + \int_0^x (6 - 8(x-t))\ \Phi(t)dt + 3\Phi(x)$

$\Phi'(0) = 1$

again differentiate equation (1) w.r.to x with the help of Leibnitz rule

$$\Phi''(x) = -8 + \int_0^x -8\Phi(t) + 3\Phi'(x) + 6\Phi(x)$$

$\Phi''(0) = 1$

Again differentiating w.r. to x

$\Rightarrow \Phi'''(x) = -8\Phi(x) + 3\Phi''(x) + 6\,\Phi'(x)$

$\rightarrow \Phi'''(x) - 3\Phi''(x) + 8\Phi(x) - 6\Phi'(x) = 0$

$\Rightarrow \Phi'''(x) - 3\Phi''(x) - 6\Phi'(x) + 8\Phi(x) = 0$

Auxiliary equation is

$m^3 - 3m^2 - 6m + 8 = 0$

$\Phi(x) = c_1e^x + c_2e^{4x} + c_3e^{-2x}$

$\Phi'(x) = c_1e^x + 4c_2e^{4x} - 2c_3e^{-2x}$

$\Phi''(x) = c_1e^x + 16c_2e^{4x} + 4c_3e^{-2x}$

$\Phi(0) = c_1 + c_2 + c_3 = 1$ (2)

$\Phi'(0) = c_1 + 4c_2 - 2c_3 = 1$ (3)

$\Phi''(0) = c_1 + 16c_2 + 4c_3 = 1$ (4)

$c_1 = 1 - c_2 - c_3$

$c_1 = -1 - 4c_2 - 2c_3$

$c_1 + 16c_2 + 4c_3 = 1$

From equation 3) and 4)

$\Rightarrow 1 - c_2 - c_3 = 1 - 4c_2 + 2c_3$

$\Rightarrow 3c_2 = 3c_3$

$\Rightarrow c_2 = c_3$

From equation (2)

$\Rightarrow c_1 = 1$ and $c_2 = c_3 = 0$

$\Rightarrow \Phi(x) = c_1e^x$

$\Rightarrow \Phi(\log 2) = c_1e^{\log 2}$

$\Rightarrow = e^{\log 2}$

$\Rightarrow \Phi(\log 2) = 2$

$\Rightarrow$Option a) is the correct answer and option b), c) and are the incorrect.

22. Explanation: (a)

$\phi(x) = 1 + \frac{2}{\pi}\int_0^\pi (\cos^2 x)\,\phi(t)dt \quad \rightarrow (1)$

$\phi(x) = 1 + \frac{2}{\pi}(\cos^2 x).c \quad \rightarrow (2)$

Where $c = \int_0^\pi \phi(t)dt$

$$\Rightarrow c = \int_0^\pi \left(1 + \frac{2c}{\pi}\cos^2 t\right)dt$$

$$\because \cos^2 x = \frac{1 + \cos 2x}{2}$$

$$\therefore c = \int_0^\pi \left[1 + \frac{2c}{\pi}\left\{\frac{1 + \cos 2t}{2}\right\}\right]dt$$

$$c = \int_0^\pi \left[1 + \frac{c}{\pi} + \frac{c\,(\cos 2t)}{\pi}\right]dt$$

$$= \left[1 + \frac{c}{\pi}t + \frac{c}{\pi}\frac{\sin 2t}{2}\right]_0^\pi = \pi + c$$

$\Rightarrow 0 = \pi$ (which is not possible)

$\Rightarrow$ No solution

23. Explanation: (C)

$S_2 :- \phi(x) = \lambda \int_a^b [h_1(t)g_1(x) + h_2(t)g_2(x)]\phi(t)dt$

$\Rightarrow \phi(x) = \lambda[c_1 g_1(x) + c_2 g_2(x)]$

Where $c_1 = \int_a^b h_1(t)\phi(t)dt$

$$c_2 = \int_a^b h_2(t)\phi(t)dt$$

If λ is not characteristic no. of corresponding homogenous equation

$\Rightarrow c_1 = c_2 = 0$

$\Rightarrow \phi(x) = 0$

$\phi(x) = f(x)$

$\Rightarrow$unique solution

$\Rightarrow S_2$truse

Here S_1 is false consider

$$\begin{cases} \phi(x) = 1 + \int_0^\pi \cos(x+t)\,\phi(t)dt \\ \phi(x) = 1 + \int_0^\pi [\cos x \cos t - \sin x \sin t]\,\phi(t)dt \end{cases}$$

$\Rightarrow S_1$ is false statement

24. Explanation: (a), (b), (c)

$\phi(x) = f(x) + \lambda \int_0^{2\pi} \cos(x-t)\,\phi t dt, x \in [0, 2\pi]$ ……. (*)

$\phi(x) = f(x) + \lambda \int_a^b \mathrm{k}(x-t)\,\phi t dt$ ……. (i)

$\phi(x) = \lambda' \int_a^b \mathrm{k}(x-t)\,\phi t dt$ ……. (ii)

NOTE

Ifλ_1, λ_2 are two eigen value of (ii) and λ eigen value in (*)

$\begin{cases} \lambda \neq \lambda_1,\ \lambda \neq \lambda_2 \\ \lambda = \lambda_1 \ or\ \lambda = \lambda_2 \end{cases}$ then unique solution.

$\int_a^b \Psi(x) f(x)dx = 0$has infinite solution.

$\phi(x)$corresponding eigen function forλ_1.

Homogeneous equation of (*) is,

$$\phi(x) = \lambda \int_0^{2\pi} \cos(x-t)\,\phi(t)dt$$

$$= \lambda \int_0^{2\pi} \cos x \cos t\,\phi(t)dt + \lambda \int_0^{2\pi} \sin x \sin t\,\phi(t)dt$$

$\Rightarrow \phi(x) = \lambda \cos x\, \lambda \int_0^{2\pi} \cos t\,\phi(t)dt + \lambda \sin x \int_0^{2\pi} \sin t\,\phi(t)dt$

$\Rightarrow \phi(x) = \lambda \cos x\, c_1 + \lambda \sin x\, c_2$; …… (**)

Where

$$c_1 = \int_0^{2\pi} \cos t\,\phi(t)dt \quad ……(iii)$$

$$c_2 = \int_0^{2\pi} \sin t\,\phi(t)dt \quad …….(iv)$$

$$c_1 = \int_0^{2\pi} \cos t\,(\lambda \cos t\, c_1 + \lambda \sin x\, c_2)dt$$

$$= \lambda c_1 \int_0^{2\pi} \cos^2 t\,dt + \lambda c_2 \int_0^{2\pi} \cos t \sin t\,dt$$

$$= \lambda c_1 \int_0^{2\pi} \frac{1+\cos 2t}{2}dt + \lambda c_2 \int_0^{2\pi} \frac{\sin 2t}{2}dt$$

$$= \frac{\lambda c_1}{2}\left(t + \frac{\sin 2t}{2}\right)|_0^{2\pi} + \frac{\lambda c_2}{2}\frac{-\cos 2t}{2}|_0^{2\pi}$$

$= \frac{\lambda c_1}{2}\left\{(2\pi - 0) + \frac{1}{2}(\sin 4\pi - \sin 0)\right\} + \frac{\lambda c_2}{2}(-\cos 4\pi + \cos 0)$

$$= \pi\lambda c_1 + \frac{\lambda c_2}{4}(-1+1)$$

$\Rightarrow c_1 = \pi\lambda c_1 \Rightarrow c_1(1-\pi\lambda) = 0$

$\Rightarrow c_1(1-\lambda\pi) = 0$ …… (v)

$$c_2 = \int_0^{2\pi} \sin t\,(\lambda \cos t\, c_1 + \lambda \sin x\, c_2)dt$$

$$= \lambda c_1 \int_0^{2\pi} \cos t \sin t\,dt + \lambda c_2 \int_0^{2\pi} \sin^2 t\,dt$$

$$= \lambda c_1 \int_0^{2\pi} \frac{\sin 2t}{2}dt + \lambda c_2 \int_0^{2\pi} \frac{1-\cos 2t}{2}dt$$

$$= \frac{\lambda c_1}{2}\frac{-\cos 2t}{2}|_0^{2\pi} + \frac{\lambda c_2}{2}\left(t - \frac{\sin 2t}{2}\right)|_0^{2\pi}$$

$= \frac{\lambda c_1}{2}[-\cos 4\pi + \cos 0] + \frac{\lambda}{2}c_2\left\{(2\pi - 0) - \frac{1}{2}(\sin(4\pi) - \sin 0)\right\}$

$$= \frac{\lambda}{4}c_1(-1+1)\frac{\lambda}{2}c_2.2\pi - 0$$

$\Rightarrow c_2 = \lambda c_2 \pi \Rightarrow c_2(1-\lambda\pi) = 0$ …… (vi)

Now from (v) and (vi),

$$\begin{vmatrix} 1-\lambda\pi & 0 \\ 0 & 1-\lambda\pi \end{vmatrix} = 0$$

$\Rightarrow (1-\lambda\pi)^2 = 0 \Rightarrow \lambda = \frac{1}{\pi}, \frac{1}{\pi}$

Since we setc_1 *and* c_2 are arbitrary for and $\lambda \in \mathbb{R}$

Let$c_1 = c_2 = \pi$then

$\phi(v) = \cos x + \sin x$

(a) $\lambda = 10$ *then* $10 \neq 1/\pi$ so for any $f(x)$we get unique solution.so, option (a) correct.

(b) $= \frac{1}{\pi}$ *and* $\frac{1}{\pi} = \frac{1}{\pi}$, so we set no solution for $f(x) = \sin x$ *as* $\int_0^{2\pi}(\cos x + \sin x)\cos x \neq 0$.

$\int_0^{2\pi} \cos^2 x\,dx + \int_0^{2\pi} \sin x \cos x = \int_0^{2\pi} \frac{1+\cos 2x}{2}dx + \int_0^{2\pi} \frac{\sin 2x}{2}dx$

$$= \frac{1}{2}x|_0^{2\pi} + \frac{\sin 2x}{2}|_0^{2\pi}\frac{1}{4}\cos 2x\,|_0^{2\pi}$$

$$= \frac{1}{2}(2\pi - 0) + 0 + 0 = \pi \neq 0$$

(c) Let$c_1 = c_2 = \pi$ with

$$\phi(x) = \cos x + \sin x \int_0^{2\pi} \cos 2x\,(\cos x + \sin x)\,dx$$

$$= \int_0^{2\pi} \cos x \cos 2x\,dx + \int_0^{2\pi} \sin x \cos 2x\,dx$$

$= 0 + 0 = 0$

So, the infinite solution for $\lambda = \frac{1}{\pi}$ *and* $\lambda \neq \frac{1}{\pi}$ unique solution.

(d) $\int_0^{2\pi} \sin 2x\,(\cos x + \sin x)\,dx$

$= \int_0^{2\pi} \sin 2x \cos x\,dx + \int_0^{2\pi} \sin 2x \sin x\,dx$

$= 0 + 0 = 0$

So, the infinite solution w. r. $\lambda = \frac{1}{\pi}$ *and* $\lambda \neq \frac{1}{\pi}$ unique solution.

So, option (a), (b), (c) are correct.

25. Explanation: (a), (b), (d)

26. Explanation: (b), (d)

$y(s) = \lambda \int_0^1 e^s e^t y(t)dt$

$= \lambda e^s \int_0^1 e^t y(t)dt = \lambda e^s c_1$

Where $c_1 = \int_0^1 e^t y(t)dt$

$\Rightarrow c_1 = \int_0^1 e^t \lambda e^t c_1 dt$

$= \lambda c_1 \int_0^1 e^{2t} dt$

$= \lambda c_1 \left.\frac{e^{2t}}{2}\right|_0^1 = \lambda c_1 \frac{e^2 - 1}{2}$

$\Rightarrow c_1 = c_1 \cdot \lambda \frac{e^2 - 1}{2}$

$\Rightarrow \lambda = \frac{2}{e^2 - 1}$

If $\int_0^1 e^t y(t)dt = 0 \Rightarrow c_1 = 0$

Then $y(x) = 0$ is the only solution which is the trivial solution.

So we concluded $y(x) = 0$ satisfy $\int_0^1 e^t y(t)dt = 0$

i.e. option (b) correct.

And if $\lambda = \frac{2}{e^2-1}$ and $\int_0^1 e^t y(x)dt \neq 0$ then

We get non-trivial solution i.e.

Option (d) correct.

27. Explanation: (a), (b)

28. Explanation: (a), (b)

29. Explanation: (a),(b),(c)

(a) The null space of $\mathcal{K}$ is infinite dimensional

(b) $\int_0^1 v(x)\mathcal{K}(u)(x)dx = \int_0^1 \mathcal{K}(v)(x)u(x)dx$ for all $u.v \in C([0,1])$

(c) $\mathcal{K}$ has no negative eigenvalue

30. Explanation:

$g(x) = 1 + \int_0^x (x - t)\,g(t)dt, x \geq 0$ ------ (1)

Differentiating with respect to x

$g'(x) = \int_0^x g(t)\,dt$ ------ (2)

Again, differentiating with respect to x we get,

$g''(x) = g(x)$

$\therefore g'' - g = 0$

$\Rightarrow$ Auxiliary equation is,

$m^2 - 1 = 0$

$m = \pm 1$

$\Rightarrow g(x) = c_1 e^x + c_2 e^{-x}$

From (1)

$g(x) = 1$

$c_1 + c_2 = 1$ ------- (3)

Also, from (2)

$g'(0) = 0$

$g'(x) = c_1 e^x - c_2 e^{-x}$

$g'(0) = 0$

$0 = c_1 - c_2$ ------- (4)

Adding (3) and (4)

$2c_1 = 1 \Rightarrow c_1 = \frac{1}{2} \Rightarrow c_2 = \frac{1}{2}$

$\therefore g(x) = \frac{e^x + e^{-x}}{2}$

$g(1) = \frac{e + e^{-1}}{2}$

None of the option is matched.

31. Explanation: (a), (d)

$\phi_1(x) = \sin x + \int_0^x \phi_2(t)dt$ ------ (1)

$\phi_2(x) = 1 - \cos x - \int_0^x \phi_1(t)dt$ ------ (2)

Put (2) in (1) we get

$\phi_1(x) = \sin x + \int_0^x (1 - \cos t - \int_0^x \phi_1(t)dt)\,dt$

$= \sin x + \int_0^x dt - \int_0^x \cos t dt - \int_0^x \int_0^x \phi_1(t)dt^2$

$\phi_1(x) = \sin x + x - \sin x - \int_0^x (x - t)\,\phi_1(t)dt$

$\phi_1(x) = x - \int_0^x (x - t)\,\phi_1(t)dt$

Differentiating with respect to x

$\phi_1'(x) = 1 - [\int_0^x \phi_1(t)dt]$ ------ (3)

Again, differentiating with respect to x

$\phi_1''(x) = -(\phi_1(x))$

$\phi_1'' + \phi_1 = 0$

$\Rightarrow \phi_1(x) = c_1 \cos x + c_2 \sin x$

From (1) $\phi_1(0) = 0$

$\Rightarrow c_1 = 0$

$\therefore \phi_1(x) = c_2 \sin x$

From (3)

$\phi_1'(0) = 1$

$\Rightarrow c_2 = 1$

$\therefore \phi_1(x) = \sin x$

Now from (2)

$\phi_2(x) = 1 - \cos x - \int_0^x \sin t\,dt$

$= 1 - \cos x + (\cos t)_0^x$

$= 1 - \cos x + \cos x - 1$

$\phi_2(x) = 0$

So, option (a) & (d) are correct.

32. Explanation: (a), (c)

Consider the IE I

$\phi(x) = \lambda \int_0^{2\pi} \sin(x + t)\phi(t)dt.$

$\phi(x) = \lambda \int_0^{2\pi} (\sin x\cos t + \cos x\sin t)\phi(t)dt$

$= \lambda \left[\sin x|_0^{2\pi} \cos t\phi(t)dt + \cos x \int_0^{2\pi} \sin t\phi\right.$

$c_1 = \int_0^{2\pi} \cos t\phi(t)dt \,\&\, c_2 = \int_0^{2\pi} \sin t\phi(t)dt$

$\therefore \phi(x) = \lambda(c_1 \sin x + c_2 \cos x) - (3)$

$\therefore \phi(t) = \lambda(c_1 \sin t + c_2 \cos t) - (4)$

Put (4) in (1) we get,

$c_1 = \lambda \int_0^{2\pi} \cos t(c_1 \sin t + c_2 \cos t)dt$

$\Rightarrow c_1 = \lambda\left[\frac{c_1}{2}\int_0^{2\pi} \sin 2t dt + \frac{c_2}{2}\int_0^{2\pi} (1+\cos 2t)dt\right]$

$\Rightarrow c_1 = \lambda c_2 \pi$

$\Rightarrow c_1 - \lambda\pi c_2 = 0 \ldots (5)$

Similarly put (4) in (2) we get

$c_2 = \int_0^{2\pi \sin t} (\lambda c_1 \sin t + \lambda c_2 \cos t)dt$

$= \frac{\lambda c_1}{2}\int_0^{2\pi} (1-\cos 2t)dt + 0$

$c_2 = \lambda\pi c_1$

$\Rightarrow \lambda\pi c_1 - c_2 = 0 \ldots (6)$

from (5) and (6)

$\begin{bmatrix} 1 & -\lambda\pi \\ \lambda\pi & -1 \end{bmatrix}\begin{bmatrix} c_1 \\ c_2 \end{bmatrix} = \begin{bmatrix} 0 \\ 0 \end{bmatrix}$

This system has nontrivial solution if

$-1 + \lambda^2\pi^2 = 0$

$\Rightarrow \lambda^2 = \frac{1}{\pi^2}$

i.e., $\lambda = \pm\frac{1}{\pi}$ characteristic numbers.

Now consider, $\psi(x) = \mu\int_0^{\pi} (\cos x \cos t - \sin x \sin t)\psi(t)dt$

$= \mu\left[\cos x \int_0^{\pi} \cos t\psi(t)dt - \sin x \int_0^{\pi} \sin t\psi(t)dt\right]$

let, $c_1 = \int_0^{\pi} \cos t\psi(t)dt - (1)$

$c_2 = \int_0^{\pi} \sin t\psi(t)dt$ - (2)

$\therefore \psi(x) = \mu[c_1 \cos x - c_2 \sin x]$

$\therefore \psi(t) = \mu[c_1 \cos t - c_2 \sin t]$

Put (3) in (1) we get.

$c_1 = \mu\int_0^{\pi} \cos t(c_1 \cos t - c_2 \sin t)dt$

$= \mu\left[c_1\frac{\pi}{2}\right]$

$\Rightarrow c_1\left(1 - \frac{\mu\pi}{2}\right) = 0 - (4)$

Put (3) in (2) we get,

$c_2 = \mu\int_0^{\pi} \sin t(c_1 \cos t - c_2 \sin t)dt$

$c_2 = -\mu c_2\frac{\pi}{2}$

$\Rightarrow c_2\left(1 + \frac{\mu\pi}{2}\right) = 0 -$ (5)

from (4) $\mu = 2$

from (5) $\mu_1 = \frac{-2}{\pi}$

$\therefore$ We have:

$\lambda_1 = \frac{-1}{\pi}\ \lambda_2 = \frac{1}{\pi}, \mu_1 = \frac{-2}{\pi}, -\mu_2 = 2$

$\therefore \frac{-2}{\pi} < \frac{-1}{\pi} < \frac{1}{\pi} < \frac{2}{\pi}$

2.e. $\mu_1 < \lambda_1 < \lambda_2 < \mu_2$

So, option (a) is correct.

Also, $|\mu_1 - \lambda_1| = |\mu_2 - \lambda_2|$ so option (c) is correct.

33. Explanation: (b), (c)

$|K(x,y)| < 1$

$\therefore K(x,y)$ is bounded $\forall x, y \in [0,1]$

$A = \begin{pmatrix} 1-\lambda\alpha_{11} & -\lambda\alpha_{12} \\ -\lambda\alpha_{21} & 1-\lambda\alpha_2 \end{pmatrix} = \begin{pmatrix} 1-\alpha_{11} & -\alpha_{12} \\ -\alpha_{21} & 1-\alpha_{22} \end{pmatrix}$

As $|K(x,y)| < 1$ so $\alpha_{11} \neq 0\ \alpha_{22} \neq 0$

$\therefore |A| \neq 0\ \rho(A) = 2$

$\therefore$ Options (b) & (c) are correct

$K(x,y) = \frac{x}{2}; f = \frac{x}{2}\ \&\ g = 1$

Let

$A = (1 - \lambda\alpha_{11}); \alpha_{11} = \int_0^1 \frac{x}{2}dx = \frac{1}{4}$

$|A| \neq 0 \therefore \rho(A) = n$

$\therefore$ Options (a) & (d) are incorrect.

34. Explanation: (a), (c)

We have $y(x) = f(x) + 3\int_0^1 tx\, y(t)dt$

$\Rightarrow y(x) = f(x) + 3x\int_0^1 ty(t)dt$

Let $c = \int_0^1 ty(t)dt \ldots (1)$

$\therefore y(x) = f(x) + 3xc$

$\Rightarrow y(t) = f(t) + 3tc$

Now, we will put it in (1),

$\therefore c = \int_0^1 t[f(t) + 3ct]dt$

$c = \int_0^1 [tf(t) + 3ct^2]dt$

$c = \int_0^1 tf(t)dt + c$

$\Rightarrow \int_0^1 tf(t)dt = 0$

(a) $f(x) = x^2 - \frac{1}{2}$

$\Rightarrow \int_0^1 \left(t^3 - \frac{1}{2}t\right)dt = \left[\frac{t^4}{4} - \frac{1}{4}\cdot t^2\right]_0^1 = 0$

$\Rightarrow$ option (a) is correct.

(b) $f(x) = e^x$

$\Rightarrow \int_0^1 te^t dt = [te^t - e^t]_0^1 = e - e = 0 + e = e \neq 0$

$\Rightarrow$ option (b) is incorrect.

(c) $f(x) = 2 - 3x$

$\Rightarrow \int_0^1 (2t - 3t^2)dt = [t^2 - t^3]_0^1 = 1 - 1 = 0$

$\Rightarrow$ option (c) is correct.

(d) $f(x) = x - 1$

$\Rightarrow \int_0^1 (t^2 - t)dt = \left[\frac{t^3}{3} - \frac{t^2}{2}\right]_0^1 = \frac{1}{3} - \frac{1}{2} \neq 0$

$\Rightarrow$ option (d) is incorrect.

35. Explanation: (b), (d)

Here,

$y(x) = e^x + \int_0^x \frac{1+x^2}{1+t^2}y(x)dt \ldots (1)$

Now, by Leibnitz rule, we have,

$\Rightarrow y'(x) = e^x + \int_0^x \frac{2x}{1+t^2}y(t)dt + y(x) - (1)$

$\Rightarrow y'(x) = e^x + 2x\int_0^x \frac{1}{1+t^2}y(t)dt + y(x) \quad \ldots (2)$

Now, from (1) we have,

$y - e^x = (1+x^2)\int_0^x \frac{1}{1+t^2}y(t)dt$

$\Rightarrow \frac{y - e^x}{(1+x^2)} = \int_0^x \frac{1}{1+t^2}y(t)dt$

Put in $eq^n(2)$, we get,

$\Rightarrow y' = e^x + 2x\left(\frac{y - e^x}{1+x^2}\right) + y$

$$\Rightarrow y' = e^x\left(1-\frac{2x}{1+x^2}\right)+\left(\frac{2x}{1+x^2}+1\right)y$$

$$\frac{dy}{dx}-\left(\frac{2x}{1+x^2}+1\right)y = e^x\left(1-\frac{2x}{1+x^2}\right)$$

This is first order linear different equation

Therefore,

$$\text{I.E.} = e^{-\int\left(\frac{2x}{1+x^2}+1\right)dx}$$

$$= e^{-\log(1+x^2)-x} = \frac{1}{1+x^2}e^{-x}$$

Therefore, the general solution is

$$y\cdot\frac{e^{-x}}{1+x^2} = \int\frac{e^{-x}}{1+x^2}\times e^x\left(1-\frac{2x}{1+x^2}\right)dx$$

$$y\cdot\frac{e^{-x}}{1+x^2} = \int\left(\frac{1}{1+x^2}-\frac{2x}{(1+x^2)^2}\right)dx$$

$$y\cdot\frac{e^{-x}}{1+x^2} = \int\frac{dx}{1+x^2}-\int\frac{2x}{(1+x^2)^2}dx$$

$$y.\frac{e^{-x}}{1+x^2} = \tan^{-1}x-\int\frac{2x}{(1+x^2)^2}dx$$

substitute, $1+x^2 = 4$

$\Rightarrow 2xdx = du$

$$y\cdot\frac{e^{-x}}{1+x^2} = \tan^{-1}x-\int\frac{du}{u^2}$$

$$y\cdot\frac{e^{-x}}{1+x^2} = \tan^{-1}x+\frac{1}{u}+c$$

$$y\cdot\frac{e^{-x}}{1+x^2} = \tan^{-1}x+\frac{1}{1+x^2}+c$$

From the given condition, we have

$\Rightarrow y(0) = 1$

$\Rightarrow 1 = 1+c$

$\Rightarrow c = 0$

$$\therefore y\cdot\frac{e^{-x}}{1+x^2} = \tan^{-1}x+\frac{1}{1+x^2}$$

a) Now, Let $x = 1$

$$\Rightarrow \frac{ye^{-1}}{2} = \tan^{-1}(1)+\frac{1}{2}$$

$$\Rightarrow \frac{ye^{-1}}{2} = \frac{\pi}{4}+\frac{1}{2}$$

$$\Rightarrow ye^{-1} = \frac{\pi}{2}+1$$

$$\Rightarrow y = \left(\frac{\pi}{2}+1\right)e$$

$$\Rightarrow y(1) = \left(\frac{\pi}{2}+1\right)\text{e}$$

$\Rightarrow$ option (b) is correct.

b) Let $x = \sqrt{3}$

$$\Rightarrow y\cdot\frac{e^{-\sqrt{3}}}{1+3} = \tan^{-1}(\sqrt{3})+\frac{1}{1+3}$$

$$\Rightarrow y\cdot\frac{e^{-\sqrt{3}}}{4} = \frac{\pi}{3}+\frac{1}{4}$$

$$\Rightarrow y\cdot e^{-\sqrt{3}} = \frac{4\pi}{3}+1$$

$$\Rightarrow y = \left(1+\frac{4\pi}{3}\right)e^{\sqrt{3}}$$

$$\Rightarrow y(\sqrt{3}) = \left(1+\frac{4\pi}{3}\right)e^{\sqrt{3}}$$

Option (d) is correct.

36. Explanation: (b), (d)

Here $K(x,t) = xt+x^2t^2 = k_1(x)k_1(t)+k_2(x)k_2(t)$

$\therefore k_1(x) = x, k_1(t) = t, k_2(x) = x^2, k_2(t) = t^2$

We have

$$R(x,t,\lambda) = \frac{k_1(x)k_1(t)}{1-\frac{\lambda}{2}\cdot\lambda_1}+\frac{k_2(x)k_2(t)}{1-\frac{\lambda}{2}\cdot\lambda_2}\ ...(1)$$

where λ_1 and λ_2 are eigenvalues of $A = \left[a_{ij}\right]_{2\times2}$, where $a_{ij} = \int_{-2}^{2}\left(k_i(t)\right)(y)\cdot\left(k_j(x)\right)(y)\ dy$

Find that $A = \begin{bmatrix}\frac{16}{3} & 0\\ 0 & \frac{64}{5}\end{bmatrix}$, whose eigenvalues are $\lambda_1 = \frac{16}{3}$ and $\lambda_2 = \frac{64}{5}$.

Put λ_1 and λ_2 in (1), to get $R(x,t,\lambda) = \frac{3xt}{3-8\lambda}+\frac{5x^2t^2}{5-32\lambda}$.

Now, $u(x) = x+\frac{\lambda}{2}\int_{-2}^{2}R\cdot t\,dt = x+\frac{\lambda}{2}\left[\frac{16x}{3-8\lambda}\right]$

$\therefore u(1) = \frac{3}{3-8\lambda}$

$\therefore$ Correct options are (b) and (d).

37. Explanation: (a)

Given: $y(x) = 1+x+cx^2+2\int_0^1(1-3xt)y(t)dt$

Here $K(x,t) = 1-3xt = 1\cdot1-3x\cdot t$

Let $F_1 = 1$ $\quad g_1 = 1$

$F_2 = -3x$ $\quad g_2 = t$

Now we calculate $\alpha_{11}, \alpha_{12}, \alpha_{21}, \alpha_{22}, \beta_1, \beta_2$

$\Rightarrow \alpha_{11} = \int_0^1 dx = (x)_0^1 = 1$

$\Rightarrow \alpha_{12} = \int_0^1 -3xdx = -\frac{3}{2}$

$\Rightarrow \alpha_{21} = \int_0^1 xdx = \frac{1}{2}$

$\Rightarrow \alpha_{22} = \int_0^1 -3x^2dx = -1$

$\Rightarrow \beta_1 = \int_0^1(1+x+cx^2)dx = \left[x+\frac{x^2}{2}+\frac{cx^3}{3}\right]_0^1$

$\Rightarrow \beta_1 = \frac{3}{2}+\frac{c}{3}$

$\beta_2 = \int_0^1(x+x^2+cx^3)dx$

$= \frac{1}{2}+\frac{1}{3}+\frac{c}{4}$

$\beta_2 = \frac{5}{6}+\frac{c}{4}$

$$\text{Now,}\begin{bmatrix}1-2 & -2\left(\frac{-3}{2}\right)\\ -2\left(\frac{1}{2}\right) & 1-2(-1)\end{bmatrix}\begin{bmatrix}C_1\\ C_2\end{bmatrix} = \begin{bmatrix}\frac{3}{2}+\frac{1}{3}C\\ \frac{5}{4}+\frac{1}{4}C\end{bmatrix}$$

$$\Rightarrow\begin{bmatrix}-1 & 3\\ -1 & 3\end{bmatrix}\begin{bmatrix}C_1\\ C_2\end{bmatrix} = \begin{bmatrix}\frac{3}{2}+\frac{1}{3}C\\ \frac{5}{6}+\frac{1}{4}C\end{bmatrix}$$

$$AX = B$$

By using RC form

$$\begin{bmatrix}-1 & 3\\ 0 & 0\end{bmatrix}\begin{bmatrix}C_1\\ C_2\end{bmatrix} = \begin{bmatrix}\frac{3}{2}+\frac{1}{3}C\\ -\frac{2}{3}-\frac{1}{12}C\end{bmatrix}$$

$$\Rightarrow\frac{-2}{3}-\frac{1}{12}C = 0$$

$\Rightarrow \frac{C}{12} = -\frac{2}{3}$

$\therefore C = -8$

Hence option (a) is correct.

38. Explanation: (a), (b)

Differentiate the given equation:

$$\frac{d}{dx}u(x) = \frac{d}{dx}\left(3 + \sin x + \int_0^x \frac{3 + \sin x}{3 + \sin t}u(t)dt\right)$$

$$\frac{d}{dx}u(x) = \frac{d}{dx}(3) + \frac{d}{dx}(\sin x) + \frac{d}{dx}\left((3 + \sin x)\int_0^x \frac{1}{3 + \sin t}u(t)dt\right)$$

$$u'(x) = 0 + \cos x + \cos x\int_0^x \frac{1}{3 + \sin t}u(t)dt + (3 + \sin x)\frac{1}{3 + \sin x}u(x)$$

$$u'(x) = \cos x + \cos x\int_0^x \frac{1}{3 + \sin t}u(t)dt + u(x)$$

From the original equation:

$$\int_0^x \frac{3 + \sin x}{3 + \sin t}u(t)dt = u(x) - (3 + \sin x)$$

Divide by $(3 + \sin x)$:

$$\int_0^x \frac{1}{3 + \sin t}u(t)dt = \frac{u(x) - (3 + \sin x)}{3 + \sin x}$$

Substitute this into the differentiated equation:

$$u'(x) = \cos x + \cos x\frac{u(x) - (3 + \sin x)}{3 + \sin x} + u(x)$$

Simplify the equation:

$$u'(x) = \cos x + \frac{\cos x}{3 + \sin x}u(x) - \cos x + u(x) = \left(1 + \frac{\cos x}{3 + \sin x}\right)u(x)$$

$$\frac{u'(x)}{u(x)} = 1 + \frac{\cos x}{3 + \sin x}$$

Integrate both sides:

$$\int \frac{u'(x)}{u(x)}dx = \int \left(1 + \frac{\cos x}{3 + \sin x}\right)dx$$

$\ln|u(x)| = x + \ln|3 + \sin x| + C$

$u(x) = e^{x + \ln|3 + \sin x| + C} = Ae^x(3 + \sin x)$

From the original equation, when $x = 0, u(0) = 3$.

This gives $A = 1$.

$\therefore u(x) = e^x(3 + \sin x)$

$\therefore u\left(\frac{\pi}{2}\right) = 4e^{\frac{\pi}{2}}, u(\pi) = 3e^{\pi}, u(-\pi) = 3e^{-\pi}, u\left(-\frac{\pi}{2}\right) = 2e^{\frac{-\pi}{2}}$

Therefore, options (a) and (b) are correct.

39. Explanation: (a), (b), (c), (d)

Substitute $\sin(x - t) = \sin x\cos t - \cos x\sin t$ into the integral equation:

$$u(x) = f(x) + \frac{2}{\pi}\int_0^{\pi}(\sin x\cos t - \cos x\sin t)u(t)dt$$

$$u(x) = f(x) + \frac{2}{\pi}\sin x\int_0^{\pi}\cos t\, u(t)dt - \frac{2}{\pi}\cos x\int_0^{\pi}\sin t\, u(t)dt$$

Let $A = \int_0^{\pi}\cos t\, u(t)dt$ and $= \int_0^{\pi}\sin t\, u(t)dt$.

$$u(x) = f(x) + \frac{2}{\pi}A\sin x - \frac{2}{\pi}B\cos x$$

Let us analyze the case $f(x) = \cos x$.

Substitute $f(x) = \cos x$:

$$u(x) = \cos x + \frac{2}{\pi}A\sin x - \frac{2}{\pi}B\cos x = (1 - \frac{2}{\pi}B)\cos x + \frac{2}{\pi}A\sin x$$

Substitute $u(x)$ into the expressions for A and B:

$$A = \int_0^{\pi}\cos t\left[(1 - \frac{2}{\pi}B)\cos t + \frac{2}{\pi}A\sin t\right]dt$$

$$B = \int_0^{\pi}\sin t\left[(1 - \frac{2}{\pi}B)\cos t + \frac{2}{\pi}A\sin t\right]dt$$

Evaluating the integrals, we get,

$A = \left(1 - \frac{2}{\pi}B\right)\frac{\pi}{2}$ and $B = \frac{2}{\pi}A\frac{\pi}{2} = A$

Using these two equations, we get $A = B = \frac{\pi}{4}$

Since A and B have unique non-zero solutions, the integral equation has a unique solution when $f(x) = \cos x$.

For $f(x) = \cos 5x$, $f(x) = \sin x$, and $f(x) = \sin 5x$, the same procedure will lead to unique solutions for A and B.

Thus, all options are correct.

40. Explanation: (a), (b), (c)

We solve by Laplace transform. Rewrite the integral as convolution with kernel $k(x) = x^2$:

$$u(x) = x^2 + 4\int_0^x (x - t)^2u(t), dt \Rightarrow U(s) = \mathcal{L}u(s)$$

$$= \frac{2/s^3}{1 - 8/s^3} = \frac{2}{s^3 - 8}.$$

Partial fractions give

$$\frac{2}{s^3 - 8} = \frac{1}{6}\frac{1}{s - 2} - \frac{1}{6}\frac{s + 4}{s^2 + 2s + 4}.$$

Inverting yields the closed form

$$u(x) = \frac{1}{6}(e^{2x} - e^{-x}\cos(\sqrt{3}x) - \sqrt{3}, e^{-x}\sin(\sqrt{3}x)),.$$

Now check the statements:

(a) $u(0) = \frac{1}{6}(1 - 1 - 0) = 0$. **True.**

(b) For $x = \frac{2\pi}{\sqrt{3}}$: $\cos(\sqrt{3}x) = \cos 2\pi = 1, \sin(\sqrt{3}x) = 0$. So $u\left(\frac{2\pi}{\sqrt{3}}\right) = \frac{1}{6}(e^{4\pi/\sqrt{3}} - e^{-2\pi/\sqrt{3}})$, which matches statement (b). **True.**

(c) For $x = \frac{\pi}{2\sqrt{3}}$: $\cos(\sqrt{3}x) = \cos\frac{\pi}{2} = 0, \sin(\sqrt{3}x) = 1$. So $u\left(\frac{\pi}{2\sqrt{3}}\right) = \frac{1}{6}(e^{\pi/\sqrt{3}} - \sqrt{3}, e^{-\pi/(2\sqrt{3})})$, which matches statement (c). **True.**

(d) Statement (d) gives a different expression for $u\left(\frac{\pi}{2\sqrt{3}}\right)$, so **false.**

Final: (a), (b), (c) are true; (d) is false.

41. Explanation: (a), (b), (c)

$y(x) = \lambda\int_{-1}^{1}(5xt^3 + 4x^2t + 3xt)\cdot y(t)\,dt$

Factor x terms outside the integral:

$y(x) = \lambda\left[x\int_{-1}^{1}(5t^3 + 3t)y(t)\,dt + x^2\int_{-1}^{1}4t\cdot y(t)\,dt\right]$

Let, $A = \int_{-1}^{1}(5t^3 + 3t)y(t)dt, B = \int_{-1}^{1}4t\cdot y(t)\,dt$

So, solution has the form: $y(x) = \lambda(Ax + Bx^2)$

Put $y(t) = \lambda(At + Bt^2)$ into A:
$A = \lambda \int_{-1}^{1} (5t^3 + 3t)(At + Bt^2)\, dt$
$= \lambda \int_{-1}^{1} (5At^4 + 5Bt^5 + 3At^2 + 3Bt^3)\, dt$
Key fact: Odd powers like t^3, t^5 integrate to zero over [-1, 1]. Only even powers survive:
$A = \lambda\left[5A \cdot \frac{2}{5} + 3A \cdot \frac{2}{3}\right] = \lambda[2A + 2A] = 4\lambda A$
$\Rightarrow A(1 - 4\lambda) = 0$
Now put $y(t) = \lambda(At + Bt^2)$ into B:
$B = 4\lambda \int_{-1}^{1} t(At + Bt^2)\, dt = 4\lambda \int_{-1}^{1} (At^2 + Bt^3)\, dt$
Again t^3 term vanishes: $B = 4\lambda \cdot A \cdot \frac{2}{3} = \frac{8\lambda A}{3}$
From $A(1 - 4\lambda) = 0$, for non-trivial solution we need $\lambda = \frac{1}{4}$
Substitute $\lambda = \frac{1}{4}$ into B: $B = \frac{8 \cdot \frac{1}{4} \cdot A}{3} = \frac{2A}{3}$
So: $y(x) = \frac{1}{4}\left(Ax + \frac{2A}{3}x^2\right) = \frac{A}{4}\left(x + \frac{2x^2}{3}\right)$
Use $y(1) = \frac{5}{2}$
$y(1) = \frac{A}{4}\left(1 + \frac{2}{3}\right) = \frac{A}{4} \cdot \frac{5}{3} = \frac{5A}{12} = \frac{5}{2}$
$\Rightarrow A = 6, B = 4$
$y(x) = \frac{3x}{2} + x^2$
$y'(x) = \frac{3}{2} + 2x$
Now, check all statements:
Statement 1: $y(0) + y'(0) = \frac{3}{2}$
$y(0) = 0, y'(0) = \frac{3}{2}$
$\therefore y(0) + y'(0) = \frac{3}{2}$
TRUE
Statement 2: $y\left(\frac{1}{2}\right) + y'\left(\frac{1}{2}\right) = \frac{7}{2}$
$y\left(\frac{1}{2}\right) = \frac{3}{4} + \frac{1}{4} = 1, y'\left(\frac{1}{2}\right) = \frac{3}{2} + 1 = \frac{5}{2}$
$\therefore y\left(\frac{1}{2}\right) + y'\left(\frac{1}{2}\right) = 1 + \frac{5}{2} = \frac{7}{2}$
TRUE
Statement 3: $y(-1) + y'(-1) = -1$
$y(-1) = -\frac{3}{2} + 1 = -\frac{1}{2}, y'(-1) = \frac{3}{2} - 2 = -\frac{1}{2}$
$\therefore y(-1) + y'(-1) = -\frac{1}{2} - \frac{1}{2} = -1$
TRUE
Statement 4: $y\left(\frac{1}{3}\right) + y'\left(\frac{1}{3}\right) = \frac{14}{9}$
$y\left(\frac{1}{3}\right) = \frac{1}{2} + \frac{1}{9} = \frac{11}{18}, y'\left(\frac{1}{3}\right) = \frac{3}{2} + \frac{2}{3} = \frac{13}{6}$
$\frac{11}{18} + \frac{39}{18} = \frac{50}{18} = \frac{25}{9} \neq \frac{14}{9}$
FALSE
Correct Answer: Statements 1, 2 and 3 are TRUE. Statement 4 is FALSE.

42. Explanation: (a), (c)
The integral equation is
$$y(x) = e^x + e + 1 + \frac{1}{3}\int_0^1 y(t)dt$$
This is a Fredholm integral equation of second kind with separable kernel.
To recall the structure:
$$y(x) = f(x) + \lambda \int_a^b K(x,t)y(t)dt$$
Here
- $f(x) = e^x + e + 1$
- $K(x,t) = 1$
- $\lambda = \frac{1}{3}$

Let the integral be a constant
Let $C = \int_0^1 y(t), dt$
Then the equation becomes
$$y(x) = e^x + e + 1 + \frac{1}{3}C$$
Integrate both sides from 0 to 1
$$\int_0^1 y(x)dx = \int_0^1 e^x dx + \int_0^1 (e+1)dx + \int_0^1 \frac{1}{3}C dx$$
Compute each term
$$\int_0^1 e^x dx = e - 1$$
$$\int_0^1 (e+1)dx = e + 1$$
$$\int_0^1 \frac{1}{3}C dx = \frac{1}{3}C$$
Thus,
$$C = (e-1) + (e+1) + \frac{1}{3}C$$
$$C = 2e + \frac{1}{3}C$$
$$\frac{2}{3}C = 2e$$
$$C = 3e$$
Substitute back
$$y(x) = e^x + e + 1 + \frac{1}{3}(3e)$$
$$y(x) = e^x + 2e + 1$$
Compute $y(1)$
$$y(1) = e + 2e + 1$$
$$y(1) = 3e + 1$$
So, (3) is true and (4) is false.
Resolvent kernel
For kernel $K(x,t) = 1$,
$$R(x,t,\lambda) = \frac{1}{1-\lambda}$$
Here $\lambda = \frac{1}{3}$
$$R = \frac{1}{1 - \frac{1}{3}} = \frac{3}{2}$$
Thus
$$R(x,t,1/3) = \frac{3}{2}$$
So
$R\left(0, 1, \frac{1}{3}\right) = \frac{3}{2}$ and $R\left(\frac{1}{2}, \frac{1}{2}, \frac{1}{3}\right) = \frac{3}{2}$
So, (1) is true and (2) is false.
Correct options: 1 and 3

NUMERICAL ANALYSIS

No. of questions asked from year 2011-2025

Units		2011		2012		2013		2014		2015		2016		2017		2018		2019		2020	2022		2023		2024	2025		
		Jun	Dec	Jun	Dec	Jun	Dec	Jun	Dec	Jun	Dec	Jun	Dec	Jun	Dec	Jun	Dec	Jun	Dec	Nov	Feb	Sep	Jun	Dec	Jul	Feb	Jun	Dec
5.1	Numerical Solution of Algebraic Equation	1	-	-	-	1	2	-	2	1	-	1	-	1	-	-	-	1	-	-	-	-	-	-	-	-	-	-
5.2	Method of Iteration, NRM and Its Rate of Convergence	1	-	1	2	-	-	3	1	-	3	-	1	-	1	-	1	1	1	3	-	1	2	-	-	-	-	1
5.3	Question Based on Interpolation and Runge Kutta Method	-	1	-	1	2	-	-	-	-	-	2	-	-	-	1	1	-	-	1	1	2	-	2	1	1	-	1
5.4	Question Based on Euler Method & Initial Value Problems	-	-	1	1	-	1	-	1	-	-	-	1	2	-	-	1	-	2	-	1	-	-	1	1	-	2	-
5.5	Question Based On Differentiation, Integration and Gauss-Seidel Iteration	1	1	1	-	-	1	-	-	1	-	1	-	-	2	2	-	1	3	2	1	-	1	-	1	1	-	1

CHAPTER 5

NUMERICAL ANALYSIS

Unit 5.1: Numerical Solutions of Algebraic Equations

MCQ (Multiple Choice Questions)

1. Consider the function $f(x) = e^{-x}$ and its Taylor approximation $g(x)$ of degree 3. For $x = \frac{1}{3}$, $g(x)$ is
(a) Positive and less than 1
(b) Negative and less than -2
(c) Positive and greater than 1
(d) Less than 1 but greater than 0.75

[June 2011]

2. Let $P : \mathbb{R} \to \mathbb{R}$ be a polynomial of the form $P(x) = a_0 + a_1 x + a_2 x^2$, with $a_0, a_1, a_2 \in \mathbb{R}$ and $a_2 \neq 0$. Let $E_1 = \int_0^1 P(x)\,dx - \frac{1}{2}(P(0) + P(1))$, $E_2 = \int_0^1 P(x)\,dx - P\left(\frac{1}{2}\right)$. If $|x|$ is the absolute value of $x \in \mathbb{R}$ then
(a) $|E_1| > |E_2|$
(b) $|E_2| > |E_1|$
(c) $|E_2| = |E_1|$
(d) $|E_2| = 2|E_1|$

[Dec 2014]

3. Let $f : \mathbb{R} \to \mathbb{R}$ be a polynomial of the form $f(x) = a_0 + a_1 x + a_2 x^2$, with $a_0, a_1, a_2 \in \mathbb{R}$ and $a_2 \neq 0$. If $E_1 = \int_{-1}^{1} f(x)\,dx - [f(-1) + f(1)]$, $E_2 = \int_{-1}^{1} f(x)\,dx - \frac{1}{2}\left(f(-1) + 2f(0) + f(1)\right)$ and $|x|$ is the absolute value of $x \in \mathbb{R}$ then
(a) $|E_1| < |E_2|$
(b) $|E_1| = 2|E_2|$
(c) $|E_1| = 4|E_2|$
(d) $|E_1| = 8|E_2|$

[June 2015]

4. Let $f(x) = x^2 + 2x + 1$ and the derivative of f at $x = 1$ is approximated by using the central – difference formula $f'(1) \approx \frac{f(1+h) - f(1-h)}{2h}$ with $h = \frac{1}{2}$. Then the absolute value of the error in the approximation of $f'(1)$ is equal to
(a) 1
(b) $\frac{1}{2}$
(c) 0
(d) $\frac{1}{12}$

[June 2016]

5. The magnitude of the truncation error for the scheme $f'(x) = Af(x) + Bf(x+h) + Cf(x+2h)$ is equal to
(a) $h^2 f'''(\xi)$ if $A = -\frac{5}{6h}, B = \frac{3}{2h}, C = -\frac{2}{3h}$
(b) $h^2 f'''(\xi)$ if $A = \frac{5}{6h}, B = \frac{3}{2h}, C = \frac{2}{3h}$
(c) $h^2 f''(x)$ if $A = -\frac{5}{6h}, B = \frac{3}{2h}, C = -\frac{2}{3h}$
(d) $h^2 f''(x)$ if $A = \frac{5}{6h}, B = \frac{3}{2h}, C = \frac{2}{3h}$

[June 2017]

Answer Key

1	2	3	4	5
a	a	c	c	*

EXPLANATION

1. **Explanation: (a)**
Here $f(x) = e^{-x}$ ... (1)
Differentiating equation (1) w.r.to x, we get
$f'(x) = -e^{-x}$
Again, differentiating above equation w.r.to x, we get
$f''(x) = e^{-x}$
Similarly,
$f'''(x) = -e^{-x}$
Now Taylor's series approximation for $f(x) = e^{-x}$ is
$g(x) = f(0) + (x-0)f'(0) + \frac{1}{2!}(x-0)^2 f''(x) + \frac{1}{3!}(x-0)^3 f'''(0)$
$$g(x) = 1 - x + \frac{1}{2!}x^2 - \frac{1}{3!}x^3$$
$$g\left(\frac{1}{3}\right) = 1 - \left(\frac{1}{3}\right) + \frac{1}{2!}\left(\frac{1}{3}\right)^2 - \frac{1}{3!}\left(\frac{1}{3}\right)^3$$
$g\left(\frac{1}{3}\right) = \frac{58}{81} < 1$ and $g\left(\frac{1}{3}\right) = \frac{58}{81} > 0$
From above explanation,
Only option a) is the correct answer.

2. **Explanation: (a)**
Consider the given polynomial
$P(x) = a_0 + a_1 x + a_2 x^2$, with $a_0, a_1, a_2 \in \mathbb{R}$ and $a_2 \neq 0$
$$E_1 = \int_0^1 P(x)\,dx - \frac{1}{2}(P(0) + P(1))$$
$E_2 = \int_0^1 P(x)\,dx - P\left(\frac{1}{2}\right)$ (given)
Take $P(x) = x^2$
$$E_1 = \int_0^1 x^2\,dx - \frac{1}{2}(0+1)$$
$$E_1 = \frac{-1}{6}$$
And $E_2 = \int_0^1 x^2\,dx - \left(\frac{1}{2}\right)^2$
$$E_2 = \frac{1}{12}$$
$\Rightarrow |E_1| = \frac{1}{6}$
and $|E_2| = \frac{1}{12}$
$\Rightarrow |E_1| > |E_2|$
From above explanation,
Only option a) is the correct answer.

3. **Explanation: (c)**
Consider the given polynomial $f(x) = a_0 + a_1 x + a_2 x^2$, with $a_0, a_1, a_2 \in \mathbb{R}$ and $a_2 \neq 0$

$$E_1 = \int_{-1}^{1} f(x)\,dx - [f(1) + f(1)]$$

$$E_2 = \int_{-1}^{1} f(x)\,dx - \frac{1}{2}(f(-1) + 2f(0) + f(1))$$

Take $f(x) = x^2$

$$E_1 = \int_{-1}^{1} x^2\,dx - [1+1]$$

$$E_1 = \frac{-4}{3}$$

$$E_2 = \int_{-1}^{1} x^2\,dx - \frac{1}{2}(1+0+1)$$

$$E_2 = \frac{1}{3}$$

$|E_1| = \frac{4}{3}$ and $|E_2| = \frac{1}{3}$

$|E_1| = 4|E_2|$

From above explanation

Only option c) is the correct answer.

4. Explanation: (c)

$f(x) = x^2 + 2x + 1$ (1)

$$f'(1) \approx \frac{f(1+h) - f(1-h)}{2h}$$

$h = \frac{1}{2}$ (Given)

$$\Rightarrow f'(1) \approx \frac{f\left(1+\frac{1}{2}\right) - f\left(1-\frac{1}{2}\right)}{2.\frac{1}{2}}$$

$$\Rightarrow f'(1) = f\left(\frac{3}{2}\right) - f\left(\frac{1}{2}\right)$$

$f'(1) = \frac{9}{4} - \frac{1}{4} + 4 - 2$ (from (1))

$f'(1) = 4$

Approximate value= $f'(1) = 4$ (2)

Now differentiating equation 1) w.r.to x, we get

$\Rightarrow f'(x) = 2x + 2$

$\Rightarrow f'(1) = 4$

$\Rightarrow$True value= $f'(1) = 4$ (3)

Now find the absolute error

Absolute error=True value−Approximate value $= 4 - 4$ (from 2) and 3))

$= 0$

From above explanation,

option c) is the correct answer.

5. Explanation: (*)

$f'(x) = Af(x) + Bf(x+h) + Cf(x+2h)$ – – – –(1)

By using Taylor's series expansion of $(x+h)$ and $f(x+2h)$, equation (1) become

$f'(x) = Af(x) + B\{f(x) + hf'(x) + \frac{h^2}{2!}f(x) + \frac{h^3}{3!}f'''(x) + \ldots\} + C\{f(x) + 2hf'(x) + \frac{4h^2}{2!}f(x) + \frac{8h^3}{3!}f'''(x) + \cdots\}$

Now comparing the coefficients, we get

$A + B + C = 0$ ... (1)

$Bh + 2Ch = 1$ .... (2)

$\frac{Bh^2}{2} + 2Ch^2 = 0$ ... (3)

From equation (3),

$B = -4C$ or $C = -\frac{B}{4}$ – – – – – – – –(4)

From equation (2),

$$B = \frac{1}{h} - 2C = \frac{1}{h} + \frac{B}{2}$$

$\Rightarrow B = \frac{2}{h}$ – – – – – –(5)

$\Rightarrow C = -\frac{1}{2h}$ – – – – – – (6)

From equation (1), (5), (6) we get

$$A + \frac{2}{h} - \frac{1}{2h} = 0$$

$$\Rightarrow A = -\frac{3}{2h}$$

$$\Rightarrow A = \frac{-3}{2h}, B = \frac{2}{h}, C = \frac{-1}{2h}$$

So, No any one option is match and its answer marked as (*) in CSIR answer key.

MSQ (Multiple Select Questions)

1. Consider a sufficiently smooth function $f(x)$. A formula for estimating its derivative is given by $\frac{df}{dx} = \frac{1}{4h}[f(x+2h) - f(x-2h)]$ + error term, where $h > 0$. Let $f^{(n)}$ denote the nth derivative of f and let ζ be a point between $x - 2h$ and $x + 2h$. Which of the following expressions for the error term are correct?

(a) $\frac{-f^{(2)}(\zeta)h^2}{2}$ (b) $\frac{-2f^{(3)}(\zeta)h^2}{3}$

(c) $-f^{(1)}(\zeta)h$ (d) $\frac{-f^{(4)}(\zeta)h^4}{12}$

[June 2013]

2. Let $f(x) = e^x$ be approximated by Taylor's polynomial of degree n at the point $x = \frac{1}{2}$ and on the entire interval [0,1]. If the absolute error in this approximation does not exceed 10^{-2}, then the value of n should be taken as

(a) 0 (b) 1

(c) 2 (d) 3

[Dec. 2013]

3. Let $f \in C^3([x_{-1}, x_1])$ where $x_{-1} = x_0 - h$, $x_1 = x_0 + h$ with $h > 0$, $f(x_0) = f_0, f(x_j) = f_j$ for $j = -1,1$ and $f'(x_0) = f_0'$ Then for some $\xi \in (x_{-1}, x_1)$ we have

(a) $f_0' = \frac{f_1 - f_0}{h} - \frac{h^2}{2}f'''(\xi)$ (b) $f_0' = \frac{f_1 - f_{-1}}{h} - \frac{h^3}{3}f'''(\xi)$

(c) $f_0' = \frac{f_1 - f_{-1}}{2h} - \frac{h^2}{6}f'''(\xi)$ (d) $f_0' = \frac{f_1 - f_{-1}}{2h} + \frac{h^3}{6}f'''(\xi)$

[Dec. 2013]

4. Which of the following approximations for estimating the derivative of a smooth function f at point x is order 2 (i.e. the error term is $O(h^2)$)

(a) $f'(x) \approx \frac{f(x+h) - f(x)}{h}$

(b) $f'(x) \approx \frac{f(x+h) - f(x-h)}{2h}$

(c) $f'(x) \approx \frac{3f(x) - 4f(x-h) + f(x-2h)}{2h}$

(d) $f'(x) \approx \frac{-3f(x)+4f(x+h)-f(x+2h)}{2h}$

[Dec. 2014]

5. The values of a, b, c so that the truncation error in the formula $\int_{-h}^{h} f(x)dx = ahf(-h) + bhf(0) + ahf(h) + ch^2 f'(-h) - ch^2 f'(h)$ is minimum, are

(a) $a = \frac{7}{15}, b = \frac{16}{15}, c = \frac{1}{15}$

(b) $a = \frac{7}{15}, b = \frac{16}{15}, c = \frac{-1}{15}$

(c) $a = \frac{7}{15}, b = \frac{-16}{15}, c = \frac{1}{15}$

(d) $a = \frac{7}{15}, b = \frac{-16}{15}, c = \frac{-1}{15}$

[June 2019]

Answer Key

1	2	3	4	5
b	d	c	b, c, d	a

EXPLANATION

1. **Explanation: (b)**

Consider, $\frac{df}{dx} = \frac{1}{4h}[f(x+2h) - f(x-2h)] +$ error term (1)

By using Taylor's series expansion of $(x+2h)$ *and* $f(x-2h)$, equation (1) become

$\frac{df}{dx} = \frac{1}{4h}\Big[f(x) + 2hf'(x) + \frac{(2h)^2}{2!}f(x) + \frac{(2h)^3}{3!}f'''(x) + \cdots - f(x) + 2hf'(x) - \frac{(2h)^2}{2!}f''(x) + \frac{(2h)^3}{3!}f'''(x) - ..\Big] +$ error term

$= f'(x) + \frac{2}{3}h^2 f'''(x) + \cdots +$ error term

$\Rightarrow$ error term $= -\frac{2}{3}h^2 f'''(x)$

$\Rightarrow$ error term $= \frac{-2f^{(3)}(\zeta)h^2}{3}$

From above explanation,

Option b) is the correct answer.

2. **Explanation: (d)**

$f(x) = e^x = 1 + x + \frac{x^2}{2!} + \frac{x^3}{3!} + \cdots$

From Taylor Series error formula at $x = x_0$ is

$R_n = \frac{(x-x_0)^{n+1}}{(n+1)!} f^{n-1}(\xi), x_0 < \xi < x$

So the Error at $x_0 = 0$ is

$\frac{(x-0)^{n+1}}{(n+1)!} f^{n-1}(\xi), 0 < \xi < x$

i.e. $\frac{1}{(n+1)!} x^{n+1} e^{\xi}$

At $x = \frac{1}{2}$; Error $\le \frac{\left(\frac{1}{2}\right)^{n+1}}{(n+1)!}\sqrt{e}$

According to the question absolute error does not exceeds 10^{-2}

$\Rightarrow \frac{1}{(n+1)!\,2^{n+1}}\sqrt{e} \le 10^{-2}$

$(n+1)!\,2^{n+1} \ge 100 \times \sqrt{e}$

$(n+1)!\,2^{n+1} \ge 100 \times 1.414$

$(n+1)!\,2^{n+1} \ge 141$

If $n = 0$ then $2 \ge 141$, which is not possible

If $n = 1$ then $8 \ge 141$, which is not possible

If $n = 2$ then $48 \ge 141$, which is not possible

If $n = 3$ then $384 \ge 141$, which is possible

so option (d) is correct

3. **Explanation: (c)**

To solve this, check all the option

Take option c)

$f_0' = \frac{f_1 - f_{-1}}{2h} - \frac{h^2}{6} f'''(\xi)$

Here $f_1 = f(x_0 + h)$ and $f_{-1} = f(x_0 - h)$

$f_1 - f_{-1} = f(x_0 + h) - f(x_0 - h)$

By using Taylor's series expansion of $f(x_0 + h)$*and*, $f(x_0 - h)$equation (1) become

$f_1 - f_{-1} = 2hf'(x_0) + \frac{(f'''(\xi_1)+f'''(\xi_2))h^3}{3!}$

Here $f'''(x)$ is continuous, the intermediate value theorem can be used to find a value ξ so that

$\frac{f'''(\xi_1) + f'''(\xi_2)}{2} = f'''(\xi)$

$f_1 - f_{-1} = 2hf_0' + \frac{2h^3 f'''(\xi)}{6}$ $(\because f(x_0) = f_0)$

$\Rightarrow f_0' = \frac{f_1 - f_{-1}}{2h} - \frac{h^2}{6} f'''(\xi)$

option a) ,b) and d) are incorrect.

Only option c) is the correct.

4. **Explanation: (b), (c), (d)**

To solve this, check all the option

For option a)

$f'(x) \approx \frac{f(x+h) - f(x)}{h} + \textit{error term}$

By using Taylor's series expansion of $f(x+h)$ above equation become

$f'(x) \approx \frac{f(x) + hf'(x) + \frac{h^2}{2!}f''(x) + \frac{h^3}{3!}f'''(x) + \cdots - f(x)}{h} + \textit{error term}$

$f'(x) = f'(x) + \frac{h}{2!}f''(x) + \ldots + \textit{error term}$

$\Rightarrow \textit{error term} = O(h)$

$\Rightarrow$option a) is incorrect.

Now option b)

$f'(x) \approx \frac{f(x+h) - f(x-h)}{2h} + \textit{error term}$

By using Taylor's series expansion of $f(x+h)$ and $f(x-h)$, we get

$f'(x) = \frac{f(x) + hf'(x) + \frac{h^2}{2!}f''(x) + \frac{h^3}{3!}f'''(x) + \cdots - \left(f(x) - hf'(x) + \frac{h^2}{2!}f''(x) - \frac{h^3}{3!}f'''(x) + \cdots\right)}{2h}$

$\Rightarrow \textit{error term} = \frac{h^2}{3!}f'''(x)$

$\Rightarrow \textit{error term} = O(h^2)$

Option (b) is the correct answer.

For option c)

$$f'(x) \approx \frac{3f(x)-4f(x-h)+f(x-2h)}{2h} + error\ term$$

$$f'(x) \approx \frac{3f(x)-4(f(x)-hf'(x)+\frac{h^2}{2!}f''(x)-\frac{h^3}{3!}f'''(x)+\cdots)+f(x)-(2h)f'(x)+\frac{(2h)^2}{2!}f''(x)-\frac{(2h)^3}{3!}f'''(x)+\cdots}{2h}$$

$$error\ term = \frac{h^2}{3}f'''(x)$$

$$error\ term = O(h^2)$$

Option c) is the correct.

For option d)

$$f'(x) \approx \frac{-3f(x)+4f(x+h)-f(x+2h)}{2h} + error\ term$$

$$f'(x) \approx \frac{-3f(x)+4(f(x)+hf'(x)+\frac{h^2}{2!}f''(x)+\frac{h^3}{3!}f'''(x)+\cdots)-(f(x)+(2h)f'(x)+\frac{(2h)^2}{2!}f''(x)+\frac{(2h)^3}{3!}f'''(x)+\cdots)}{2h}$$

$error\ term = O(h^2)$

So, option (d) correct.

5. **Explanation: (a)** We have,

$\int_{-h}^{h} f(x)dx = ahf(-h)+bhf(0)+ahf(h)+ch^2f'(-h)-ch^2f'(h)$ (1)

When equation 1) is exact for polynomial of as high order as possible then Truncation error in the above formula is minimum

$\int_{-h}^{h} f(x)dx = ahf(-h)+bhf(0)+ahf(h)+ch^2f'(-h)-ch^2f'(h)$

Put $f(x)=1$ in equation (1), we get

$$\Rightarrow \int_{-h}^{h} dx = ah+bh+ah$$

$\Rightarrow 2h = 2ah+bh$

$\Rightarrow 2 = 2a+b$ .... (2)

Put $f(x)=x^2 \Rightarrow f'(x)=2x$ in equation (1), we get

$$\frac{2h^3}{3} = ah^3+0+ah^3-2ch^3-2ch^3$$

$$\frac{2h^3}{3} = 2ah^3-4ch^3$$

$1 = 3a-6c$ (3)

Now put $f(x)=x^4 \Rightarrow f'(x)=4x^3$ in equation (1), we get

$$\frac{2h^5}{5} = ah^5+ah^5-4ch^5-4ch^5$$

$$\frac{2}{5} = 2a-8c$$

$$\frac{1}{5} = a-4c$$

$5a-20c=1$ (4)

From equation (3) and (4) we get

$a=\frac{7}{15}$ and $c=\frac{1}{15}$

Put $a=\frac{7}{15}$ in equation (2) we get

$$b=\frac{16}{15}$$

From above explanation

Only option a) is the correct answer.

Unit 5.2: Methods of Iteration, NRM and Its Rate of Convergence

MCQ – Multiple Choice Questions

1. Let $f(x)=ax+b$ for $a,b \in \mathbb{R}$. Then the iteration $x_{n+1}=f(x_n)$ starting from any given x_0 for $n \geq 0$ converges

(a) For all $a \in \mathbb{R}$ (b) For no $a \in \mathbb{R}$
(c) For $a \in [0,1]$ (d) Only for $a=0$

[June 2014]

2. Let $f(x)=ax+100$ for $a \in \mathbb{R}$. Then the iteration $x_{n+1}=f(x_n)$ for $n \geq 0$ and $x_0=0$ converges for

(a) $a=5$ (b) $a=1$
(c) $a=0.1$ (d) $a=10$

[Dec. 2015]

3. The values of α and β, such that $x_{n+1}=\alpha x_n\left(3-\frac{x_n^2}{a}\right)+\beta x_n\left(1+\frac{a}{x_n^2}\right)$ has 3rd order converges to $\sqrt{a}$, are

(a) $\alpha=\frac{3}{8},\beta=\frac{1}{8}$ (b) $\alpha=\frac{1}{8},\beta=\frac{3}{8}$
(c) $\alpha=\frac{2}{8},\beta=\frac{2}{8}$ (d) $\alpha=\frac{1}{4},\beta=\frac{3}{4}$

[Dec. 2016]

4. The iterative method $x_{n+1}=g(x_n)$ for the solution of $x^2-x-2=0$ converges quadratically in a neighbourhood of the root $x=2$ if $g(x)$ equals

(a) x^2-2 (b) $(x-2)^2-6$
(c) $1+\frac{2}{x}$ (d) $\frac{x^2+2}{2x+1}$

[Dec. 2017]

5. Let $x=\xi$ be a solution of $x^4-3x^2+x-10=0$. The rate of convergence for the iterative method $x_{n+1}=10-x_n^4+3x_n^2$ is equal to

(a) 1 (b) 2
(c) 3 (d) 4

[Dec. 2019]

6. Consider the Newton – Raphson method applied to approximate the square root of a positive number α. A recursion relation for the error $e_n=x_n-\sqrt{\alpha}$

(a) $e_{n+1}=\frac{1}{2}(e_n+\frac{\alpha}{e_n})$ (b) $e_{n+1}=\frac{1}{2}(e_n-\frac{\alpha}{e_n})$
(c) $e_{n+1}=\frac{1}{2}\frac{e_n^2}{e_n+\sqrt{\alpha}}$ (d) $e_{n+1}=\frac{e_n^2}{e_n+\sqrt{\alpha}}$

[Nov. 2020]

7. Let A be the following invertible matrix with real positive entries:

$$A=\begin{pmatrix}1 & 2\\ 8 & 9\end{pmatrix}$$

Let G be the associated Gauss-Seidel iteration matrix. What are the two eigenvalues of G?

(a) 0 and 4/ 3
(b) 0 and -4/3
(c) 0 and 16/9
(d) 4/3 and -4/3

[SEP 2022]

8. Consider the following two sequences $\{a_n\}$ and $\{b_n\}$ given by
$a_n = \frac{1}{n+1} + \frac{1}{n+2} + \cdots + \frac{1}{2n}$,
$b_n = \frac{1}{n}$.
Which of the following statements are true?
(a) $\{a_n\}$ converges to log 2, and has the same convergence rate as the sequence $\{b_n\}$.
(b) $\{a_n\}$ converges to log 4, and has the same convergence rate as the sequence $\{b_n\}$.
(c) $\{a_n\}$ converges to log 2, but does not have the same convergence rate as the sequence $\{b_n\}$.
(d) {a} does not converge.

[JUNE 2023]

ANSWER KEY							
1	2	3	4	5	6	7	8
c	c	b	c	a	c	c	a

EXPLANATION

1. **Explanation: (c)**
Given
$f(x) = ax + b\,; a, b \in \mathbb{R}$
$\Rightarrow f(x_n) = ax_n + b$
And $f'(x_n) = a$
We know that, the iteration $x_{n+1} = f(x_n)$ converges iff
$|f'(x)| < 1$
$\Rightarrow |a| < 1$
$\Rightarrow a \in (-1,1)$
From above explanation, only option c) is the correct answer.

2. **Explanation: (c)**
Given
$f(x) = ax + 100\,; a \in \mathbb{R}$
$\Rightarrow f(x_n) = ax_n + 100$
$\Rightarrow f'(x) = a$
We know that, the iteration $x_{n+1} = f(x_n)$ converges iff
$|f'(x)| < 1$
$\Rightarrow |a| < 1$
$\Rightarrow a \in (-1,1)$
From above explanation,
Only option (c) is the correct answer.

3. **Explanation: (b)**
3rd order convergence of $\sqrt{a}$ is given by
$$x_{n+1} = \frac{1}{8}x_n\left[6 + \frac{3a}{x_n^2} - \frac{x_n^2}{a}\right]$$
$$\Rightarrow x_{n+1} = x_n\left[\frac{6}{8} + \frac{3}{8}\frac{a}{x_n^2} - \frac{1}{8}\frac{x_n^2}{a}\right] \quad \text{... (1)}$$
We've $x_{n+1} = \alpha x_n\left(3 - \frac{x_n^2}{a}\right) + \beta\left(1 + \frac{a}{x_n^2}\right)x_n$
$$\Rightarrow x_{n+1} = x_n\left[3\alpha + \beta - \frac{\alpha}{a}x_n^2 + \beta\frac{a}{x_n^2}\right] \quad \text{... (2)}$$
Comparing equation (1) and (2), we get
$\beta = \frac{3}{8}$ and $\alpha = \frac{1}{8}$
Hence, (b) is correct

4. **Explanation: (c)**
We have,
$x^2 - x - 2 = 0$
By fixed point iteration method
$g(x) = 1 + \frac{2}{x}$
We know that, $x_{n+1} = g(x_n)$ is convergent iff $|g'(x)| < 1$ but $|g'(x)| \neq 0$
$\Rightarrow |g'(x)| = -\frac{2}{x^2}$
$\Rightarrow |g'(2)| = -\frac{2}{2^2}$
$\Rightarrow |g'(2)| < 1$
Similarly, check the remaining option,
Only option (c) is the correct answer.

5. **Explanation: (a)**
Here $x = \varepsilon = \xi$ be a solution of $x^4 - 3x^2 + x - 10 = 0$
Hence $\varepsilon^4 - 3\varepsilon^2 + \varepsilon = 10$
$\Rightarrow \varepsilon = 10 - \varepsilon^4 + 3\varepsilon^2 \quad \text{.....(1)}$
Here $x_{n+1} = 10 - x_n^4 + 3x_n^2$
So for binding the rate of convergence put $x_{n+1} = \varepsilon + \epsilon_{n+1}$ and $x_n = \varepsilon + \epsilon_n$ $\quad (\because \epsilon_n = \text{Error term})$
Now $x_{n+1} = 10 - x_n^4 + 3x_n^2$
$\Rightarrow \varepsilon + \epsilon_{n+1} = 10 - (\varepsilon + \epsilon_n)^4 + 3(\varepsilon + \epsilon_n)^2$
$= 10 - \varepsilon^4 - 4\varepsilon^3\epsilon_n - 6\varepsilon^2\epsilon_n^2 - 4\varepsilon\,\epsilon_n^3$
$- \epsilon_n^4 + 3\varepsilon^2 + 6\varepsilon\,\epsilon_n + 3\,\epsilon_n^2$
$= (10 - \varepsilon^4 + 3\varepsilon^2) + (6\varepsilon - 4\varepsilon^3)\epsilon_n$
$+ (3 - 6\varepsilon^2)\epsilon_n^2 + (-4\varepsilon\,\epsilon_n^3) - \epsilon_n^4$
$= \varepsilon + (6\varepsilon - 4\varepsilon^2)\epsilon_n + (3 - 6\varepsilon^2)\epsilon_n^2 - 4\varepsilon\,\epsilon_4^3 - \epsilon_n^4$
$\therefore \epsilon_{n+1} = (6\varepsilon - 4\varepsilon^3)\epsilon_n + (3 - 6\varepsilon^2)\epsilon_n^2 - 4\varepsilon\,\epsilon_n^3 - \epsilon_n^4$
Since $6\varepsilon - 4\varepsilon^3 \neq 0$
So Rate of convergence is 1
$\Rightarrow$ option (a) correct.

6. **Explanation: (c)**
Since to solve $x^2 - a = 0$, the recursion relation is
$$x_{n+1} = \frac{1}{2}\left(x_n + \frac{a}{x_n}\right)$$
Here given equation is $x^2 - \alpha = 0$, so
$$x_{n+1} = \frac{1}{2}\left(x_n + \frac{\alpha}{x_n}\right)$$
$e_n = x_n - \sqrt{\alpha}$ *(given)*
$\Rightarrow x_n = e_n + \sqrt{\alpha}$
$\Rightarrow x_{n+1} = e_{n+1} + \sqrt{\alpha}$
Therefore $e_{n+1} + \sqrt{\alpha} = \frac{1}{2}\left(e_n + \sqrt{\alpha} + \frac{\alpha}{e_n + \sqrt{\alpha}}\right)$
$$\Rightarrow e_{n+1} = \frac{1}{2}\left\{\frac{(e_n + \sqrt{\alpha})^2 + \alpha}{e_n + \sqrt{\alpha}}\right\} - \sqrt{\alpha}$$
$$\Rightarrow e_{n+1} = \frac{e_n^{\,2} + \alpha + 2e_n\sqrt{\alpha} + \alpha - 2e_n\sqrt{\alpha} - 2\alpha}{2(e_n + \sqrt{\alpha})}$$

$= \frac{e_n^2}{2(e_n + \sqrt{\alpha})}$

From above explanation,

Option (c) is the correct answer.

7. Explanation: (c)

$A = \begin{pmatrix} 1 & 2 \\ 8 & 9 \end{pmatrix}$

G is GSI matrix

$G = -(D+L)^{-1}U$

$= -\begin{pmatrix} 1 & 0 \\ 8 & 9 \end{pmatrix}^{-1} \begin{pmatrix} 0 & 2 \\ 0 & 0 \end{pmatrix}$

$= -\frac{1}{9}\begin{pmatrix} 9 & 0 \\ -8 & 1 \end{pmatrix} \begin{pmatrix} 0 & 2 \\ 0 & 0 \end{pmatrix}$

$= \begin{pmatrix} -1 & 0 \\ \frac{8}{9} & -\frac{1}{9} \end{pmatrix} \begin{pmatrix} 0 & 2 \\ 0 & 0 \end{pmatrix}$

$G = \begin{pmatrix} 0 & -2 \\ 0 & \frac{16}{9} \end{pmatrix}$

So, eigenvalues are $0, \frac{16}{9}$

8. Explanation: (a)

Note:- If x_n is n^{th} iterative value and ϵ is true root of $f(x) = 0$ then if

$\lim_{n\to\infty} \frac{|x_{n+1} - \xi|}{|x_n - \xi|^p} = \lim_{n\to\infty} \frac{\epsilon_{n+1}}{\epsilon_n^p} = \mu$ then order of convergence of iteration method is p and rate of convergence is μ.

$\lim_{n\to\infty} a_n = \lim_{n\to\infty} \frac{1}{n+1} + \frac{1}{n+2} + \cdots + \frac{1}{n+n}$

$= \lim_{n\to\infty} \frac{1}{n}\left[\frac{1}{1+\frac{1}{n}} + \frac{1}{1+\frac{2}{n}} + \cdots + \frac{1}{1+\frac{n}{n}}\right]$

$= \lim_{n\to\infty} \frac{1}{n}\sum_{r=1}^{n} \frac{1}{1+\frac{r}{n}} = \int_0^1 \frac{1}{1+x}dx$

$= \ln(1+x)|_0^1 = \ln 2$

also, $\lim_{n\to\infty} b_n = \lim \frac{1}{n} = 0$

$\lim_{n\to\infty} \left|\frac{b_{n+1} - 0}{b_n - 0}\right| = \lim_{n\to\infty} \frac{\frac{1}{n+1}}{\frac{1}{n}} = 1$

$\Rightarrow$ Rate of convergence of $\{b_n\} = 1$ & order of convergence of $\{b_n\} = 1$.

Also, $\left|\frac{a_{n+1} - \log 2}{a_n - \log 2}\right| = \frac{|a_n - \log 2 + a_{n+1} - a_n|}{|a_n - \log 2|}$

$= \frac{\left|a_n - \log 2 + \frac{1}{(2n+2)(2n+1)}\right|}{|a_n - \log 2|}$

$\Rightarrow \lim_{n\to\infty} \frac{|a_{n+1} - \log 2|}{|a_n - \log 2|} = 1$

=> Rate of convergence of $\{a_n\} = 1$

& order of convergence of $\{a_n\} = 1$

MSQ – Multiple Select Questions

1. Consider the iteration function for Newton's method $g(x) = x - \frac{f(x)}{f'(x)}$ and its application to find (approximate) square root of 2, starting with $x_0 = 2$. Consider the first and the second iterates x_1 and x_2, respectively; then

(a) $1.5 < x_1 \le 2$
(b) $1.5 \le x_1 < 2$
(c) $x_1 \le 1.5; x_2 \le 1.5$
(d) $x_1 = 1.5$; $x_2 < 1$

[June 2011]

2. Consider the function $f(x) = x^2 - x - 2 = 0$ ... (1)
Let $x = g(x)$, so that any fixed point of $g(x)$ is a solution of (1). Then

(a) $g(x) = x - \frac{x^2 - x - 2}{m}, m \in [-a, a]$ is a possible choice where a is positive constant
(b) $g(x) = x^2 - 2, g(x) = 1 + \frac{2}{x}$ are possible choices
(c) $g(x) = x - \frac{x^2 - x - 2}{K}, K \ne 0, K \in \mathbb{R}$ is possible choice
(d) $g(x) = x^2 - 2, g(x) = 1 + \frac{2}{x}$ are the only possible choices

[June 2012]

3. Let f be a continuous map from the interval [0,1] into itself and consider the iteration $x_{n+1} = f(x_n)$. Which of the following maps will yield a fixed point for f?

(a) $f(x) = \frac{x^2}{4}$
(b) $f(x) = \frac{x^2}{8}$
(c) $f(x) = \frac{x^2}{16}$
(d) $f(x) = \frac{x^2}{32}$

[Dec. 2012]

4. Let $f(u) = u^3 - u - 1$

(a) Starting with the initial guess $u^{(0)} = 1.5$, the fixed point iterates of the equation $u = g(u)$, where $g(u) = u^3 - 1$ converges
(b) Starting with initial guess $u^{(0)} = 1.5$, the fixed point iterates of the equation $u = \tilde{g}(u)$, where $\tilde{g}(u) = \sqrt{1 + u^3}$ converges
(c) If u^* is a root of the equation $f(u) = 0$ and $u^* > 1$, then u^* is a stable fixed point of the equation $u = g(u)$
(d) $f(u) = 0$ has a root between 1 and 2

[Dec. 2012]

5. Consider the function $f(x) = \sqrt{2 + x}$ for $x \ge -2$ and the iteration $x_{n+1} = f(x_n)$; $n \ge 0$ for $x_0 = 1$. What are the possible limits of the iteration?

(a) $\sqrt{2 + \sqrt{2 + \sqrt{2 + \cdots}}}$
(b) -1
(c) 2
(d) 1

[June 2014]

6. Consider the iteration $x_{n+1} = \frac{1}{2}\left(x_n + \frac{2}{x_n}\right), n \ge 0$ for a given $x_0 \ne 0$. Then

(a) x_n converges to $\sqrt{2}$ with rate of converges 1
(b) x_n converges to $\sqrt{2}$ with rate of convergence 2
(c) The given iteration is the fixed point iteration for $f(x) = x^2 - 2$
(d) The given iteration is the Newton's method for $f(x) = x^2 - 2$

[June 2014]

7. Let $f: \mathbb{R} \to \mathbb{R}$ be a smooth function with non – vanishing derivative. The Newton's method for finding a root of $f(x) = 0$ is the same as

(a) Fixed point iteration for the map $g(x) = x - f(x)/f'(x)$
(b) Forward Euler method with unit step length for the differential equation $\frac{dy}{dt} + \frac{f(y)}{f'(y)} = 0$
(c) Fixed point iteration for $g(x) = x + f(x)$

(d) Fixed point iteration for $g(x) = x - f(x)$

[Dec. 2014]

8. The iteration $x_{n+1} = \frac{1}{2}\left(x_n + \frac{2}{x_n}\right), n \geq 0$ for a given $x_0 \neq 0$ is an instance of
   (a) Fixed point iteration for $f(x) = x^2 - 2$
   (b) Newton's method for $f(x) = x^2 - 2$
   (c) Fixed point iteration for $f(x) = \frac{x^2+2}{2x}$
   (d) Newton's method for $f(x) = x^2 + 2$

[Dec. 2015]

9. Let $f(x) = \sqrt{x+3}$ for $x \geq -3$ Consider the iteration $x_{n+1} = f(x_n), x_0 = 0 ; n \geq 0$ The possible limits of the iteration are
   (a) -1 (b) 3
   (c) 0 (d) $\sqrt{3+\sqrt{3+\sqrt{3+\cdots}}}$

[Dec. 2015]

10. Let $f: [0,1] \rightarrow [0,1]$ be twice continuously differentiable function with a unique fixed point $f(x_0) = x$. For a given $x_0 \epsilon (0,1)$ consider the iteration $x_{n+1} = f(x_n)$ for $n \geq 0$ If $L = \max_{x\epsilon[0,1]} |f'(x)|$, then which of the following as true?
   (a) *If* $L < 1$, then x_n converges to x.
   (b) x_n converges to x. Provided $L \geq 1$
   (c) The error $e_n = x_n - x$. Satisfies $|e_{n+1}| < L|e_n|$
   (d) If $f'(x_*) = 0$, then $|e_{n+1}| < C|e_n|^2$ for some $C > 0$

[Dec. 2018]

11. Consider the equation $x^2 + ax + b = 0$ which has two real roots α and β. Then which of the following iteration scheme converges when x_0 is chosen sufficiently close to α?
    (a) $x_{n+1} = -\frac{ax_n+b}{x_n}$ *if* $|\alpha| > |\beta|$
    (b) $x_{n+1} = -\frac{x_n^2+b}{a}$, *if* $|\alpha| > 1$
    (c) $x_{n+1} = -\frac{b}{x_n+a}$, *if* $|\alpha| < |\beta|$
    (d) $x_{n+1} = -\frac{x_n^2+b}{a}$, *if* $2|\alpha| < |\beta|$

[June 2019]

12. Fix a $\alpha \in (0,1)$. Consider the iteration defined by (*) $x_{k+1} = \frac{1}{2}(x_k^2 + \alpha), k = 0,1,2, \ldots.$
    The above iteration has two distinct defined points ξ_1 *and* ξ_2 such that $0 < \xi_1 < 1 < \xi_1$.
    Which of the following statements are true?
    (a) The iteration (*) is equivalent to the recurrence relation
    $$x_{k+1} - \xi_1 = \frac{1}{2}(x_k + \xi_1)(x_k - \xi_1), k = 0,1,2, \ldots.$$
    (b) The iteration (*) is equivalent to the recurrence relation
    $$x_{k+1} - \xi_1 = \frac{1}{2}(x_k + \xi_2)(x_k - \xi_1), k = 0,1,2, \ldots.$$
    (c) $0 < x_0 \leq \xi_2$ then $\lim_{k\to\infty} x_k = \xi_1$
    (d) $-\xi_2 < x_0 \leq 0$ then $\lim_{k\to\infty} x_k = \xi_1$

[Nov 2020]

13. Consider the function $F\&[0,1] \rightarrow \mathbb{R}$ defined by
    $$F(x) = \begin{cases} 2^{-\{1+(\log_2(\frac{1}{x})^{\frac{1}{\beta}}\}^\beta} & for\ x \in [0,1] \\ 0 & for\ x = 0 \end{cases}$$
    Where $\beta \in (0, \infty)$ is a parameter. Consider are iterations $x_{k+1} = f(x_k), k = 0,1,2, \ldots\ldots; x_0 > 0$
    Which of the following statements are true about the iteration?
    (a) For $\beta = 1$, The sequence $\{x_k\}$ converges to 0 linearly with asymptotic rate of convergence $\log_{10} 2$.
    (b) For $\beta > 1$, The sequence $\{x_k\}$does not converge to 0.
    (c) For$\beta \in (0,1)$, the sequence $\{x_k\}$ converges to 0 sublinearly.
    (d) For $\beta \in (0,1)$, the sequence $\{x_k\}$ converges to 0 super linearly.

[Nov 2020]

14. Let $f: \mathbb{R} \rightarrow \mathbb{R}$ be defined as $f(x) = \frac{1}{4} + x - x^2$. Given $a \in \mathbb{R}$, let us define the sequence $\{x\}$ by $x_0 = a$ and $x_n = f(x_{n-1})$ for $n \geq 1$. Which of the following statements are true?
    (a) If $a = 0$, then the sequence $\{x_n\}$ converges to $\frac{1}{2}$.
    (b) If $a = 0$, then the sequence $\{x_n\}$ converges to $-\frac{1}{2}$.
    (c) The sequence $\{x_n\}$ converges for every $a \in \left(-\frac{1}{2}, \frac{3}{2}\right)$, and it converges to $\frac{1}{2}$.
    (d) If $a = 0$, then the sequence $\{x_n\}$ does not converge.

[JUNE 2023]

15. Let $\{x_n\}$ be a convergent iterative sequence generated by Newton-Raphson method for solving the equation $\sin x - 1 = 0$ such that $x_n \rightarrow \frac{\pi}{2}$ as $n \rightarrow \infty$. For $n \in N$, let $e_n = x_n - \frac{\pi}{2}$.
    Let $p > 0$ be such that $\lim_{n\to\infty} \frac{|e_{n+1}|}{|e_n|^p}$ exists and is non-zero.
    Then which of the following statements are true?
    (a) $p = 1$ (b) $\lim_{n\to\infty} \frac{|e_{n+1}|}{|e_n|^p} = \frac{1}{2}$
    (c) $p = 2$ (d) $\lim_{n\to\infty} \frac{|e_{n+1}|}{|e_n|^p} = 1$

[Dec 2025]

Answer Key						
1	2	3	4	5	6	7
b,c	b,c	a,b,c,d	d	a,c	b,d	a, b
8	9	10	11	12	13	14
b,c	d	a,c,d	a,c,d	a,c,d	a,c	a, c
15						
a,b						

EXPLANATION

1. **Explanation: (b), (c)**
   We want to find square root of 2 using Newton's method
   Let $f(x) = x^2 - 2$ (1)
   $\Rightarrow f(x_n) = x_n{}^2 - 2$
   By newton's Raphson method
   $$x_{n+1} = x_n - \frac{f(x_n)}{f'(x_n)}$$

$$x_{n+1} = x_n - \frac{x_n^2 - 2}{2x_n}$$

$x_{n+1} = \frac{1}{2}x_n + \frac{1}{x_n}$ (2)

Put n= 0 in equation 2) we get,

$$x_1 = \frac{1}{2}x_0 + \frac{1}{x_0}$$

$$x_1 = \frac{1}{2} \times 2 + \frac{1}{2}$$

$$x_1 = \frac{3}{2}$$

Put n=1 in equation 2) we get

$$x_2 = \frac{1}{2}x_1 + \frac{1}{x_1}$$

$$x_2 = \frac{1}{2} \times \frac{3}{2} + \frac{2}{3}$$

$$x_2 = 1.416$$

From above explanation,

Option b) and c) are the correct answer.

2. Explanation: (b), (c)

Given, $f(x) = x^2 - x - 2 = 0 - - - - - (1)$

For fixed point, $x = g(x)$

$\Rightarrow x^2 - x - 2 = 0$

$\Rightarrow x = x^2 - 2$

$\Rightarrow g(x) = x^2 - 2 - - - - - (2)$

Also $f(x) = x^2 - x - 2 = x(x-1) - 2 = 0$

$\Rightarrow x(x-1) = 2$

$\Rightarrow x - 1 = \frac{2}{x}$

$\Rightarrow x = 1 + \frac{2}{x}$

$\Rightarrow g(x) = 1 + \frac{2}{x} - - - - - - - (3)$

Also, $f(x) = x^2 - x - 2 = 0$

$\Rightarrow \frac{(x^2 - x - 2)}{k} = 0; k \neq 0, k \in R$

$\Rightarrow x - \frac{(x^2 - x - 2)}{k} = x - 0 = x$

$\Rightarrow g(x) = x - \frac{(x^2 - x - 2)}{k} - - - - - - (4)$

From above explanation,

Option b) and c) are the correct answer.

3. Explanation: (a), (b), (c), (d)

We have,

$x_{n+1} = f(x_n)$

We know that, $x_{n+1} = f(x_n)$ is convergent iff $|f'(x)| < 1$ but $|f'(x)| \neq 0$

Now, check the all option

For option (a)

$f(x) = \frac{x^2}{4}$

$\Rightarrow f'(x) = \frac{2x}{4} = \frac{x}{2}$

$\Rightarrow |f'(x)| < \frac{1}{2} < 1$ (on $[0,1]$)

Similarly, for option b), c) and d)

From above explanation,

Options (a), (b), (c) and (d) are correct answer.

4. Explanation: (d)

Given

$f(u) = u^3 - u - 1$

Now check the option

For option a)

For fixed point, $u = g(u)$

$\Longrightarrow g(u) = u^3 - 1$

We know that, $x_{n+1} = g(x_n)$ is convergent iff $|g'(x)| < 1$ but $|g'(x)| \neq 0$

$\Longrightarrow g'(1.5) = 3(1.5)^2 - 1 > 1$

Option a) is incorrect.

For option b)

For fixed point, $u = \tilde{g}(u)$

$\tilde{g}(u) = \sqrt{1 + u^3}$

$\tilde{g}'(u) = \frac{3}{2}\frac{u^2}{\sqrt{1 + u^3}}$

$|\tilde{g}'(1.5)| > 1$

Hence, option (b) is incorrect.

For option c)

u^* do not guarantee convergence for the formula of fixed point, so stability is not guarantee.

For option d)

$f(u) = u^3 - u - 1$

$\Longrightarrow f(1) = -1$ and $f(2) = 5$ as

$f(1)\,f(2) < 0,$

$\Longrightarrow f(u) = 0$, $u \in (1,2)$

So there exist a root of $f(u)$ between 1 and 2.

From above explanation,

Option d) is the correct answer.

5. Explanation: (a), (c)

Consider the given function

$f(x) = \sqrt{2 + x}$ for $x \geq -2$

$\Rightarrow f(x_n) = \sqrt{x_n + 2}$ (1)

$x_{n+1} = f(x_n)$ (Given)

Now, taking limit on both side

$\lim_{n\to\infty} x_{n+1} = \lim_{n\to\infty} \sqrt{x_n + 2}$

$L^2 = L + 2$ ($\because \lim_{n\to\infty} x_{n+1} = L$)

$L^2 - L - 2 = 0$

This is quadratic in L

$$L = \frac{1 \pm \sqrt{1+8}}{2}$$

$L = -1, 2$

By given condition,

$L = -1$ is never possible

$L = 2$

Now, $x_{n+1} = f(x_n)$

$= \sqrt{x_n + 2}$ (from (1))

$= \sqrt{2 + \sqrt{x_{n-1} + 2}}$

$$= \sqrt{2+\sqrt{2+\sqrt{x_{n-1}+2}}}$$

Proceeding, we get

$$x_{n+1} = \sqrt{2+\sqrt{2+\sqrt{2+\cdots}}}$$

Put $L = \sqrt{2+\sqrt{2+\sqrt{2+\cdots}}}$

$\Rightarrow L = \sqrt{2+L}$

$\Rightarrow L^2 - L - 2 = 0$

$\Rightarrow L = 2$

From above explanation,

Option a) and c) are the correct answer.

6. **Explanation: (b), (d)**

Consider the given iteration

$$x_{n+1} = x_n - \frac{f(x_n)}{f'(x_n)}$$

For option d)

Take $f(x) = x^2 - 2$

$f(x_n) = {x_n}^2 - 2$

By newton Raphson method

$$x_{n+1} = x_n - \frac{f(x_n)}{f'(x_n)}$$

$$x_{n+1} = x_n - \frac{(x_n^2-2)}{2x_n}$$

$\Rightarrow x_{n+1} = \frac{1}{2}\left[x_n + \frac{2}{x_n}\right]$ (2)

$\Rightarrow$Given iteration is the newtons method for

$f(x) = x^2 - 2$

Now, $x_{n+1} = \frac{1}{2}\left[x_n + \frac{2}{x_n}\right]$

taking limit on both side and take

$\lim_{n\to\infty} x_{n+1} = L$

$$\Rightarrow \lim_{n\to\infty} x_{n+1} = \lim_{n\to\infty} \frac{1}{2}\left[x_n + \frac{2}{x_n}\right]$$

$$\Rightarrow L = \frac{1}{2}\left[L + \frac{2}{L}\right]$$

$$\Rightarrow 2L = L + \frac{2}{L}$$

$\Rightarrow L = \sqrt{2}$

$\Rightarrow x_n$ converges to $\sqrt{2}$

And we know that rate of convergence of newtons raphson method is 2.

From above explanation,

Option b) and d) are the correct answer.

7. **Explanation: (a), (b)**

We know that, the Newton's method for finding the root of $f(x) = 0$ is

$$x_{n+1} = x_n - \frac{f(x_n)}{f'(x_n)} --- (1)$$

Now check the option,

For option a)

Fixed point iteration for the map

$g(x) = x_{n+1}$

$$g(x) = x_n - \frac{f(x_n)}{f'(x_n)}$$

$\Rightarrow x_{n+1} = x_n - \frac{f(x_n)}{f'(x_n)}$, which is Newton's method formula.

Now,

By Euler method

$$\frac{dy}{dx} = f(x,y)$$

$y_{n+1} = y_n + h\,f(x_n, y_n)$

here h=1,we get

$y_{n+1} = y_n + f(x_n, y_n)$

$$\frac{dy}{dx} = \frac{f(y)}{f'(y)}$$

$$y_{n+1} = y_n - \frac{f(y_n)}{f'(y_n)}$$

Which is same as equation 1)

$g(x) = x_{n+1} = x + f(x_n)$

Which is not same as equation 1

From above explanation,

Option a) and b) are the correct answer.

8. **Explanation: (b), (c)**

Consider the given iteration

$$x_{n+1} = \frac{1}{2}\left(x_n + \frac{2}{x_n}\right), n \ge 0; x \ne 0 --- (1)$$

Now check the option,

For option a)

For fixed point iteration

$$x_{n+1} = f(x_n) = x_n^2 - 2$$

Which is not similar to equation 1)

Option a) is incorrect.

For option b)

$f(x) = x^2 - 2$

By newtons Raphson method

$$x_{n+1} = x_n - \frac{f(x_n)}{f'(x_n)}$$

$$x_{n+1} = x_n - \frac{x_n^2-2}{2x_n}$$

$$x_{n+1} = \frac{1}{2}\left(x_n + \frac{2}{x_n}\right)$$

Which is same as equation 1)

So option b) is the correct answer.

For option c)

For fixed point iteration

$$x_{n+1} = f(x_n) = \frac{x_n^2+2}{2x_n}$$

$$x_{n+1} = \frac{1}{2}\left(x_n + \frac{2}{x_n}\right)$$

Which is same as equation 1)

So option c) is the correct answer.

For option d)

$f(x) = x^2 + 2$

By newtons raphson method

$$x_{n+1} = x_n - \frac{f(x_n)}{f'(x_n)}$$

$$x_{n+1} = x_n - \frac{x_n^2+2}{2x_n}$$

$$x_{n+1} = \frac{x_n}{2} - \frac{1}{x_n}$$

Which is not same as equation 1)
So option d) is incorrect.
From above,
Option b) and c) are the correct answer.

9. Explanation: (d)

Consider the given iteration

$x_{n+1} = f(x_n)$

$= \sqrt{x_n + 3}$ (1)

$x_{n+1} = \sqrt{x_n + 3}$

${x_{n+1}}^2 = x_n + 3$

taking limit on both side and take

$\lim_{n\to\infty} x_{n+1} = L$

$L^2 = L + 3$

$L^2 - L - 3 = 0$ (2)

This is quadratic in L

$$\mathrm{L} = \frac{1 \pm \sqrt{1+12}}{2}$$

$$\mathrm{L} = \frac{1 \pm \sqrt{13}}{2}$$

Now Now, $x_{n+1} = f(x_n)$

$= \sqrt{x_n + 3}$ (from (1))

$= \sqrt{3 + \sqrt{x_{n-1} + 3}}$

$= \sqrt{3 + \sqrt{3 + \sqrt{x_{n-1} + 3}}}$

Proceeding, we get

$x_{n+1} = \sqrt{3 + \sqrt{3 + \sqrt{3 + \cdots}}}$

Put $\mathrm{L} = \sqrt{3 + \sqrt{3 + \sqrt{3 + \cdots}}}$

$\Rightarrow L = \sqrt{3 + L}$

$\Rightarrow L^2 - L - 3 = 0$

Which is same as equation (2)
From above explanation,
Only option d) is the correct answer.

10. Explanation: (a), (c), (d)

$f : [0,1] \to [0,1]$ be twice continuously differentiable function with a unique fixed point $f(x_0) = x$ for all $x_0 \in [0,1]$

For option a)

Consider the given iteration

$x_{n+1} = f(x_n)$

If $L = \max_{x\epsilon[0,1]} |f'(x)|$

We know that,

if $L < 1$, *then* x_n converges to x

Option a) is the correct.

From option a),

Option b) is incorrect.

For option c)

Let α be the root of $f(x)$ and x_n differ from the actual root α by a small quantity e_n

$x_n = \alpha + e_n$

$e_n = x_n - \alpha$

For iteration

$|x_{n+1} - \alpha| \le L|x_n - \alpha|$

(here $f(x) = x, x = \alpha$)

$|e_{n+1} + \alpha - \alpha| \le \mathrm{L}|e_n + \alpha - \alpha|$

$|e_{n+1}| \le \mathrm{L}|e_n|$

From this option c) is correct.

For option d)

If $f'(x) = 0$,

Then we know that

$e_{n+1} \approx \frac{1}{6}\frac{f^4(\alpha)}{f^3(\alpha)} {e_n}^2$ for $x = x_n$

$\Rightarrow e_{n+1} \approx c{e_n}^2$

$\Rightarrow |e_{n+1}| \approx |c{e_n}^2|$

$\Rightarrow |e_{n+1}| \approx c|{e_n}^2|$

Since e_{n+1} and $c{e_n}^2$ are small quantities, $c < 1$ from above option a), c) and d) are the correct answer.

11. Explanation: (a), (c), (d)

Consider the given equation

$x^2 + ax + b = 0$ (1)

α and β are the root of equation 1)

We know that if α and β are the root of equation 1)

Then $\alpha + \beta = -a, \alpha\beta = b$

For option a)

For fixed point iteration,

$x_{n+1} = \varphi(x_n) = \frac{-ax_n + b}{x_n}$

$\varphi(x) = \frac{-ax+b}{x}$

$\varphi'(x) = -\frac{b}{x^2}$

$\varphi'(x) = -\frac{b}{\alpha^2}$ $(\because x_n \to \alpha)$

We know that, $x_{n+1} = \varphi(x_n)$ converges if $|\varphi'(x_n)| < 1$

$\Rightarrow |\varphi'(x)| < 1$

$\Rightarrow \left|-\frac{b}{\alpha^2}\right| = \left|-\frac{\alpha\beta}{\alpha^2}\right| < 1$

$\Rightarrow |\beta| < |\alpha|$

Option a) is the correct answer.

For option b)

$x_{n+1} = -\frac{x_n^2 + b}{a}$

For fixed point iteration

$x_{n+1} = \varphi(x_n)$

$\varphi(x) = -\frac{x^2+b}{a}$

$\varphi'(x) = -\frac{2x}{a}$

We know that,

$x_{n+1} = \varphi(x_n)$ converges if $|\varphi'(x_n)| < 1$

$\left|-\frac{2x}{a}\right| < 1$

$|2x| < |a|$

$2\alpha < (\alpha + \beta)$

$|\alpha| < |\beta|$

So, option b) is incorrect.

In similar way,
Option a), c) and d) are the correct answer.

12. Explanation: (a), (c), (d)

$x_{k+1} = \frac{1}{2}(x_k^2 + \alpha)$, $k = 0,1,2,\ldots$

$\phi(x_n) = \phi(x_k) = \frac{1}{2}(x_k^2 + \alpha)$

So, for convergent, $|\phi'(x_k)| < 1$

$\Rightarrow |x_k| < 1 ; k = 0,1,2,\ldots$

(a) $x_{k+1} = \frac{1}{2}(x_k^2 - \varepsilon_1 x_k + \varepsilon_1 x_k - \varepsilon_1^2) + \varepsilon_1$

$\Rightarrow \phi(x_k) = \frac{1}{2}(x_k^2 - \varepsilon_1^2) + \varepsilon_1$

$\Rightarrow \phi'(x_k) = \frac{1}{2} 2x_k \Rightarrow |\phi'(x_k)| = |x_k| < 1$

So, option (a) is correct.

(b) $x_{k+1} = \frac{1}{2}(x_k^2 - \varepsilon_1 x_k + \varepsilon_2 x_k - \varepsilon_1\varepsilon_2) + \varepsilon_1$

$\Rightarrow \phi(x_k) = \frac{1}{2}(x_k^2 - \varepsilon_1 x_k + \varepsilon_2 x_k - \varepsilon_1\varepsilon_2) + \varepsilon_1$

$\Rightarrow |\phi'(x_k)| = \frac{1}{2}|2x_k - \varepsilon_1 + \varepsilon_2| = \left|x_k - \frac{1}{2}(\varepsilon_1 - \varepsilon_2)\right|$

Since $0 < \varepsilon_1 < 1 < \varepsilon_2$

Let $\varepsilon_1 = {}^1/_2, \varepsilon_2 = 11$

$\Rightarrow |\phi'(x_k)| = \left|x_k + \left(\frac{\varepsilon_2 - \varepsilon_1}{2}\right)\right| = \left|x_k + \frac{21}{4}\right|$

Since for conversance $|x_k| < 1$

$\Rightarrow -1 < x_k < 1$

$\Rightarrow |\phi'(x_k)| > 1$

So option (b) wrong.

(c) $k = 0, x_1 = \frac{1}{2}(x_0^2 + \alpha)$

$\Rightarrow \phi'(x_k) = x_k$

$\Rightarrow |\phi'(x_0)| = x_0 < \varepsilon_2 (\varepsilon_2 > 1)$

So $\lim_{k\to\infty} x_k = \varepsilon_1$ $(\because 0 < \varepsilon_1 < 1) (\therefore 0 < \varepsilon_1 < 1)$

$\therefore$ Option (c) correct

(d) For $k = 0$, $x_1 = \frac{1}{2}(x_0^2 + \alpha)$

$\phi'(x_k)x_k$

$\Rightarrow |\phi'(x_0)| = x_0 \leq 0 \; (\because -\varepsilon_2 < x_0 \leq 0)$

As $0 < \varepsilon_1 < 1 \Rightarrow \lim_{k\to\infty} x_k = \varepsilon_1$

$\therefore$ Option (d) correct.

13. Explanation: (a, c)

For $\beta = 1$, The sequence $\{x_n\}$ converges to 0 linearly with asymptotic rate of convergence $\ln 2$.
Also, when $\beta \in (0,1)$, the sequence $\{x_n\}$ converges to 0
Option (a), (c) are correct

14. Explanation: (a), (c)

$f(x) = \frac{1}{4} + x - x^2 = \frac{1}{4} + \frac{1}{4} - \left(x^2 - x + \frac{1}{4}\right)$

$= \frac{1}{2} - \left(x - \frac{1}{2}\right)^2$ -- (1)

So, $x_{n+1} = f(x_n)$

$\Rightarrow x_{n+1} = \frac{1}{2} - \left(x_n - \frac{1}{2}\right)^2$

$\Rightarrow \left(\frac{1}{2} - x_{n+1}\right) = \left(\frac{1}{2} - x_n\right)^2$ -- (2)

Let $\left|x_n - \frac{1}{2}\right| = \epsilon_n$ (error in nth iteration)

$\Rightarrow \epsilon_{n+1} = \epsilon_n^2$

$\Rightarrow \epsilon_{n+1} = (\epsilon_{n-1})^{2^2}$

$\Rightarrow \epsilon_{n+1} = (\epsilon_0)^{2^{n+1}}$

If $|\epsilon_0| < 1$ then $\lim_{n\to\infty} \epsilon_{n+1} = 0$

So $\{x_n\}$ converges to $\frac{1}{2}$ if $\left|x_0 - \frac{1}{2}\right| < 1$

$\Rightarrow x_0 = a \in \left(\frac{1}{2} - 1, \frac{1}{2} + 1\right)$ i.e. $a \in \left(-\frac{1}{2}, \frac{3}{2}\right)$

15. Explanation: (a), (b)

Newton-Raphson for $f(x) = \sin x - 1 = 0$

At $x^* = \frac{\pi}{2}$:

$f\left(\frac{\pi}{2}\right) = 0$

$f'\left(\frac{\pi}{2}\right) = \cos\left(\frac{\pi}{2}\right) = 0 \leftarrow$ root of multiplicity 2

$f''(\pi/2) = -\sin(\pi/2) = -1 \neq 0$

Since $f'(x^*) = 0$, this is a repeated root → N-R gives linear convergence, not quadratic.

With $e_n = x_n - \pi/2$, expand around $\pi/2$:

$f(x_n) = \sin\left(\frac{\pi}{2} + e_n\right) - 1 = \cos e_n - 1 = -\frac{e_n^2}{2} + \cdots$

$f'(x_n) = \cos\left(\frac{\pi}{2} + e_n\right) = -\sin e_n = -e_n + \cdots$

So: $\frac{f(x_n)}{f'(x_n)} = \frac{-e_n^2/2}{-e_n} = \frac{e_n}{2}$

Therefore: $e_{n+1} = e_n - \frac{e_n}{2} = \frac{e_n}{2}$

$\lim_{n\to\infty} \frac{|e_{n+1}|}{|e_n|^p} = \lim_{n\to\infty} \frac{\frac{1}{2}|e_n|}{|e_n|^p} = \frac{1}{2}\lim_{n\to\infty} |e_n|^{1-p}$

For a finite non-zero limit: $1 - p = 0 \Rightarrow p = 1$, and the limit $= \frac{1}{2}$

Correct answer: Statements 1 and 2 are true.

Unit 5.3: Questions Based on Interpolation and Runge-Kutta Methods

MCQ (Multiple Choice Question)

1. If the points $x_1, x_2, \dots, x_n$ are distinct, then for arbitrary real values $y_1, y_2, \dots, y_n$ the degree of the unique interpolating polynomial $p(x)$ such that $p(x_i) = y_i (1 \le i \le n)$ is
(a) n (b) $n-1$
(c) $\le n-1$ (d) $\le n$
[June 2013]

2. Let $f(x)$ be a polynomial of unknown degree taking the values

x	0	1	2	3
$f(x)$	2	7	13	16

All the fourth divided differences are $-1/6$. Then the coefficient of x^3 is
(a) 1/3 (b) −2/3
(c) 16 (d) −1
[Dec 2018]

3. Let F be an infinitely differentiable. Real valued function on a bounded interval I. take $n \ge 1$ interpolation points $\{x_0, x_1, \dots \dots x_{n-1}\}$. Take n additional interpolation points
$$x_{n+j} = x_j + \in, j = 0,1, \dots, n-1$$
Where $\in > 0$ is such that $\{x_0, x_1, \dots \dots x_{2n-1}\}$ all distinct.
Let P_{2n-1} be the Lagrange interpolation polynomial of degree $2n-1$ with the interpolation points $\{x_0, x_1, \dots \dots x_{n-1}\}$ for the function F, In the $\in \to 0$ limit, The quantity
$$\sup_{x \in I} |P_{2n-1}(x) - q_{2n-1}(x)|$$
(a) Does not necessarily conversant.
(b) converges to $\frac{1}{2^n}$
(c) Converges to 0
(d) *converges to* $\frac{1}{2n+1}$
[Nov 2020]

4. The coefficient of x^3 in the interpolating polynomial for the data is

X	0	1	2	3	4
Y	1	2	1	3	5

(a) $-\frac{1}{3}$ (b) $-\frac{1}{2}$
(c) $\frac{5}{6}$ (d) $\frac{17}{6}$
[DEC-2023]

5. If $p(x)$ is the interpolating polynomial for the data

x	-2	-1	0	1	2
y	-1	3	1	-1	3

then the value of $p\left(\frac{1}{2}\right)$ is
(a) $\frac{-3}{8}$ (b) $\frac{-5}{8}$
(c) $\frac{5}{8}$ (d) $\frac{3}{8}$
[Dec 2025]

Answer Key

1	2	3	4	5
c	b	c	d	a

EXPLANATION

1. **Explanation: (c)**
As it is true that for $n+1$ distinct point we can define a unique interpolating polynomial (x), whose degree is atmost n.
Here given n distinct tabulated points so the degree of the unique polynomial less than equal to $n-1$.
Hence, option (c) is correct

2. **Explanation: (b)**
Newton's divided difference formula, is given by
$f(x) = f(0) + (x-1)\Delta f(0) + (x-1)(x-2)\Delta^2 f(0) + (x-1)(x-2)(x-3)\Delta^3 f(0) - - (i)$

x	f(x)	Δ f(x)	Δ² f(x)	Δ³ f(x)
0	2			
		$\frac{7-2}{1-0} = 5$		
1	7		$\frac{6-5}{2-0} = \frac{1}{2}$	
		$\frac{13-7}{2-1} = 6$		$\frac{\frac{-3}{2} - \frac{1}{2}}{3-0} = \frac{-2}{3}$
2	13		$\frac{3-6}{3-1} = \frac{-3}{2}$	
		$\frac{16-13}{3-2} = 3$		
3	16			

Since we want to find the coefficient of x^3, we need only 4th term of (i) ,
So, we have $(x-1)(x-2)(x-3)\Delta^3 f(0) = \frac{-2}{3}(x-1)(x-2)(x-3)(\text{as}\Delta^3 f(0) = \frac{-2}{3}$, from above difference table)
Hence option (b) is correct.

3. **Explanation: (c)**
We have,
Sup$|p_{2n-1}(x) - q_{2n-1}x| \to 0$
From this, only option c) is the correct answer.

4. **Explanation: (d)**

x	y	Δf	$\Delta^2 f$	$\Delta^3 f$	$\Delta^4 f$
0	1				
1	2	1			
2	3	-1	-2		
3	4	2	3	5	
4	5	2	0	-3	-8

$P(x) = 1 + \frac{x \cdot 1}{1} + \frac{x(x-1)(-2)}{1^2 2!} + \frac{x(x-1)(x-2)}{1^3 \times 3!}(5) +$

$\frac{x(x-1)(x-2)(x-3)}{1^4\times 4!}(-8)$

$= 1 + x + \frac{(x^2-x)(-2)}{2} + \frac{(x^2-x)(x-2)}{6}(5) + \frac{(x^2-x)(x^2-5x+6)}{2^4}(-8)$

$= 1 + x - x^2 + x + \frac{5}{6}(x^3 - 3x^2 + 2x) - \frac{1}{3}(x^4 - 6x^3 + 11x^2 - 6x)$

$= 1 + \frac{17}{3}x - \frac{43}{6}x^2 + \frac{17}{6}x^3 - \frac{1}{6}x^4$

⇒ option (d) is correct.

5. **Explanation: (a)**

Given data:

x	-2	-1	0	1	2
$p(x)$	-1	3	1	-1	3

Assume the interpolating polynomial of degree ≤ 4:

$$p(x) = ax^4 + bx^3 + cx^2 + dx + e$$

Use $x = 0$

$$p(0) = e = 1$$

Substitute remaining values

1. $x = 1: a + b + c + d + 1 = -1 \Rightarrow a + b + c + d = -2$
2. $x = -1: a - b + c - d + 1 = 3 \Rightarrow a - b + c - d = 2$
3. $x = 2: 16a + 8b + 4c + 2d + 1 = 3 \Rightarrow 8a + 4b + 2c + d = 1$
4. $x = -2: 16a - 8b + 4c - 2d + 1 = -1 \Rightarrow 8a - 4b + 2c - d = -1$

Add first two equations:

$$2a + 2c = 0 \Rightarrow c = -a$$

Subtract them:

$$2b + 2d = -4 \Rightarrow b + d = -2$$

Add the last two equations:

$$16a + 4c = 0$$

Substitute $c = -a$:

$$12a = 0 \Rightarrow a = 0$$

Thus $c = 0$.

From $8a + 4b + 2c + d = 1$:

$$4b + d = 1$$

Together with $b + d = -2$:

$$3b = 3 \Rightarrow b = 1, d = -3$$

Thus

$$p(x) = x^3 - 3x + 1$$

$$\Rightarrow p\left(\frac{1}{2}\right) = \left(\frac{1}{2}\right)^3 - 3\left(\frac{1}{2}\right) + 1 = \frac{1}{8} - \frac{3}{2} + 1 = -\frac{3}{8}$$

MSQ (Multiple Select Questions)

1. Consider the interpolation data given below:

x	1	1/2	3
y	3	−10	2

The interpolating polynomial corresponding to this data is given by

(a) $p(x) = -3\left(x - \frac{1}{2}\right)(x-3) - 8(x-1)(x-3) + \frac{2}{5}(x-1)\left(x - \frac{1}{2}\right)$

(b) $q(x) = 3 + 26(x-1) + \frac{-53}{5}(x-1)\left(x - \frac{1}{2}\right)$

(c) $r(x) = \frac{-53}{5}x^2 + \frac{419}{10}x + \frac{-283}{10}$

(d) $p(x)q(x) + r(x)$

[Dec 2011]

2. To compute the value of e^t in the interval [0, 1], pick $t_1 = 0, t_2 = 0.5$ and $t_3 = 1$. Let p be the quadratic polynomial that interpolates e^t, that is $p(t_i) = e^{t_i}, i = 1, 2, 3$. Then

(a) The polynomial p can be written in the form $L_1(t) + e^{1/2}L_2(t) + eL_3(t)$ for some choice of quadratic polynomials L_1, L_2, L_3

(b) If the polynomial p is written in the form $L_1(t) + e^{1/2}L_2(t) + eL_3(t)$, where L_1, L_2 and L_3 are polynomials, then L_1, L_2 and L_3 are uniquely determined

(c) If p is written in the form $L_1(t) + e^{1/2}L_2(t) + eL_3(t)$, then one of L_1, L_2 or L_3 must be linear.

(d) The polynomial p is uniquely determined

[Dec 2012]

3. A Runge-Kutta method for numerically solving the initial-value ordinary differential equation $y' = f(x, y)\,; (x_0) = y_0$ is given by (for h small)

$$y(x+h) = y(x) + W_1F_1(x, y) + W_2F_2(x, y)$$
$$F_1(x, y) = hf(x, y)$$
$$F_2(x, y) = hf(x + \alpha h, y + \beta F_1)\,.$$

The objective is to determine the constants W_1, W_2, α and β such that the above formula is accurate to order 2 (there is, the error term is $O(h^3)$). Which of the following are correct sets of values for these constants?

(a) $W_1 = \frac{1}{2}, W_2 = \frac{1}{2}, \alpha = 1, \beta = 1$

(b) $W_1 = 2, W_2 = 1, \alpha = \frac{1}{2}, \beta = \frac{1}{2}$

(c) $W_1 = \frac{1}{3}, W_2 = \frac{2}{3}, \alpha = \frac{3}{4}, \beta = \frac{3}{4}$

(d) $W_1 = \frac{3}{4}, W_2 = \frac{1}{4}, \alpha = 2, \beta = 2$

[June 2013]

4. Consider the Runge-Kutta method of the form

$$y_{n+1} = y_n + a\kappa_1 + b\kappa_2$$
$$k_1 = hf(x_n, y_n)$$
$$k_2 = hf(x_n + \alpha h, y_n + \beta k_1)$$

to approximate the solution of the initial value problem $y'(x) = f(x, y)(x)), y(x_0) = y_0$. Which of the following choices of a, b, α and β yield a second order method?

(a) $a = \frac{1}{2}, b = \frac{1}{2}, \alpha = 1, \beta = 1$

(b) $a = 1, b = 1, \alpha = \frac{1}{2}, \beta = \frac{1}{2}$

(c) $a = \frac{1}{4}, b = \frac{3}{4}, \alpha = \frac{2}{3}, \beta = \frac{2}{3}$

(d) $a = \frac{3}{4}, b = \frac{1}{4}, \alpha = 1, \beta = 1$

[June 2016]

5. Let $H(x)$ be the cubic Hermite interpolation of $f(x) = x^4 + 1$ on the interval $I = [0, 1]$ interpolating at $x = 0$ and $x = 1$. Then

(a) $\max_{x\in I}|f(x) - H(x)| = \frac{1}{16}$

(b) The maximum of $|f(x) - H(x)|$ is attained at $x = \frac{1}{2}$

(c) $\max_{x\in I}|f(x) - H(x)| = \frac{1}{21}$

(d) The maximum of $|f(x) - H(x)|$ is attained at $x = \frac{1}{4}$

[June 2016]

6. The forward difference operation is defined as $\Delta U_n = U_{n+1} - U_n$. Then which of the following difference equation has an unbounded general solution?
(a) $\Delta^2 U_n - 3\Delta U_n + 2U_n = 0$
(b) $\Delta^2 U_n + \Delta U_n + \frac{1}{4}U_n = 0$
(c) $\Delta^2 U_n - 2\Delta U_n + 2U_n = 0$
(d) $\Delta^2 U_{n+1} - \frac{1}{3}\Delta^2 U_n = 0$

[June 2018]

7. The values of a,b,c,d,e for which the function

$$f(x) = \begin{cases} a(x-1)^2 + b(x-2)^3 & -\infty < x \le 2 \\ c(x-1)^2 + d & 2 \le x \le 3 \\ (x-1)^2 + e(x-3)^3 & 3 \le x < \infty \end{cases}$$

Is a cubic spline are
(a) $a = c = 1, d = 0, b, e$ are arbitrary
(b) $a = b = c = 1, d = 0, e$ are arbitrary
(c) $a = b = c = d = 1, e$ are arbitrary
(d) $a = b = c = d = e = 1$

[Feb 2022]

8. Consider $\alpha = \frac{1+\sqrt{5}}{2}$ and $\beta = \frac{1-\sqrt{5}}{2}$. Define a sequence of numbers F_n as follows:
$F_n = \frac{\alpha^n - \beta^n}{\alpha - \beta}$ for $n = 1,2,\dots$
Let $p: \mathbb{R} \to \mathbb{R}$ be a polynomial of degree at most 2 such that
$p(1) = F_1, p(3) = F_3, p(5) = F_5$
Which of the following statements are TRUE?
(a) $F_n = F_{n-1} + F_{n-2}$, for $n \ge 3$
(b) $p(7) = 13$
(c) $F_n = F_{n-1} + 2F_{n-2}$, for $n \ge 5$
(d) $p(7) = 10$

[SEP 2022]

9. Consider the ODE $\dot{x} = f(t,x)$ in $\mathbb{R}$, for a smooth function f. Consider a general second order Runge-Kutta formula of the form $x(t+h) = x(t) + w_1 h f(t,x) + w_2 h f(t + \alpha h, x + \beta h) + O(h^3)$. Which of the following choices of $(w_1, w_2, \alpha, \beta)$ are correct?
(a) $\left(\frac{1}{2}, \frac{1}{2}, 1, 1\right)$
(b) $\left(\frac{1}{2}, 1, \frac{1}{2}, 1\right)$
(c) $\left(\frac{1}{4}, \frac{3}{4}, \frac{2}{3}, \frac{2}{3}\right)$
(d) $(0,1,1,1)$

[SEP 2022]

10. Consider the initial value problem $\frac{dy}{dx} = f(x,y), f(x_0) = y_0$ where f is a twice continuously differentiable function on a rectangle containing the point (x_0, y_0). With the step-size h, let the first iterate of a second order scheme to approximate the solution of the above initial value problem be given by
$y_1 = y_0 + Pk_1 + Qk_2$, where $k_1 = h f(x_0, y_0), k_2 = hf(x_0 + \alpha_0 h, y_0 + \beta_0 k_1)$ and $P, Q, \alpha_0, \beta_0 \in \mathbb{R}$.
Which of the following statements are correct?
(a) If $\alpha_0 = 2$, then $\beta_0 = 2, P = \frac{3}{4}, Q = \frac{1}{4}$
(b) If $\beta_0 = 2$, then $\alpha_0 = 3, P = \frac{5}{6}, Q = \frac{1}{6}$
(c) If $\alpha_0 = 2$, then $\beta_0 = 2, P = \frac{1}{4}, Q = \frac{3}{4}$
(d) If $\beta_0 = 2$, then $\beta_0 = 3, P = \frac{1}{6}, Q = \frac{5}{6}$

[DEC-2023]

11. Let $g(x)$ be the polynomial of degree at most 4 that interpolates the data

x	-1	0	2	3	6
y	-30	1	c	10	19

If $g(4) = 5$, then which of the following statements are true?
(a) $c = 13$
(b) $g(5) = 6$
(c) $g(1) = 14$
(d) $c = 15$

[JULY 2024]

12. Let $f(x)$ be the polynomial of degree at most 2 that interpolates the data $(-1,2), (0,1)$, and $(1,2)$. If $g(x)$ is a polynomial of degree at most 3 such that $f(x) + g(x)$ interpolates the data $(-1,2), (0,1), (1,2)$, and $(2,17)$, then
(a) $f(5) + g(3) = 50$
(b) $2f(5) - g(3) = 4$
(c) $f(1) + g(3) = 50$
(d) $f(5) + g(3) = 74$

[Feb. 2025]

Answer Key				
1	2	3	4	5
a, b, c	a, b, d	a, c, d	a, c	a, b
6	7	8	9	10
a, c, d	a, c	a, c	a, c	a, b
11	12			
b, c, d	b,c,d			

EXPLANATION

1. **Explanation: (a), (b), (c)**
Given data is

x	1	½	3
y	3	−10	2

$\Rightarrow x_0 = 1,\ x_1 = \frac{1}{2},\ x_2 = 3$ and $y_0 = 3, y_1 = -10, y_2 = 2$

By using Lagrange's interpolation

$$p(x) = \frac{(x-x_1)(x-x_2)}{(x_0-x_1)(x_0-x_2)}y_0 + \frac{(x-x_0)(x-x_2)}{(x_1-x_0)(x_1-x_2)}y_1 + \frac{(x-x_0)(x-x_1)}{(x_2-x_0)(x_2-x_0)}y_2$$

$$p(x) = \frac{\left(x-\frac{1}{2}\right)(x-3)}{\left(1-\frac{1}{2}\right)(1-3)} \times 3 + \frac{(x-1)(x-3)}{\left(\frac{1}{2}-1\right)\left(\frac{1}{2}-3\right)} \times -10 + \frac{(x-1)(x-\frac{1}{2})}{\left(3-\frac{1}{2}\right)(3-1)} \times 2$$

$$p(x) = -3\left(x-\frac{1}{2}\right)(x-3) - 8(x-1)(x-3) + \frac{2}{5}(x-1)\left(x-\frac{1}{2}\right)$$

Also,

$$p(x) = 3 + 26(x-1) + \frac{-53}{5}(x-1)\left(x-\frac{1}{2}\right)$$

$$p(x) = \frac{-53}{5}x^2 + \frac{419}{10}x + \frac{-283}{10}$$

From above explanation,

Option a), b) and c) are the correct answer.

2. **Explanation: (a), (b), (d)**

Given $t_1 = 0, t_2 = 0.5 = \frac{1}{2}, t_3 = 1$

$p(t_i) = e^{t_i}, i = 1, 2, 3$

$\Rightarrow p(t_1) = e^{t_1} = e^0 = 1,$

$p(t_2) = e^{t_2} = e^{1/2},$

$p(t_3) = e^{t_3} = e^1 = e$

Approximation of e^t by the polynomial p(t) gives

$f(t) = L_1(t) + L_2(t)\, e^{1/2} + L_3(t)\, e$

Where,

$L_1(t), L_2(t), L_3(t)$ are the polynomial of degree two (by Lagrange interpolation formula

From above explanation,

Option a), b) and d) are correct answer.

3. **Explanation: (a), (c), (d)**

Given,

$y' = f(x, y)\,;\, y(x_0) = y_0$

$y(x + h) = y(x) + W_1F_1(x, y) + W_2F_2(x, y)$

$F_1(x, y) = hf(x, y)$

$F_2(x, y) = hf(x + \alpha h, y + \beta F_1)$.

Now to find the value of constant, by checking

$(W_1 + W_2) = 1, \alpha W_2 = \frac{1}{2}, \beta W_1 = \frac{1}{2}$

From this,

Option a), c) and d) are the correct answer.

4. **Explanation: (a), (c)**

Given

$y_{n+1} = y_n + a\kappa_1 + b\kappa_2$

$k_1 = hf(x_n, y_n)$

$k_2 = hf(x_n + \alpha h, y_n + \beta k_1)$

$y'(x) = f(x, y)(x)), y(x_0) = y_0$

Now to find the value of constant, by checking

$(a + b) = 1, \alpha b = \frac{1}{2}, \beta a = \frac{1}{2}$

From this,

Option (a) and (c) are correct answer.

5. **Explanation: (a), (b)**

Given that, $H(x)$ be the cubic Hermite interpolation of $f(x) = x^4 + 1$ on the interval $I = [0, 1]$ (1)

$f'(x) = 4x^3$

Given polynomial $f(x)$ interpolating at $x_0 = 0$ and $x_1 = 1$

$\Rightarrow f(x_0) = 1$ and $f(x_1) = 2$

$\Rightarrow f'(x_0) = 0$ and $f'(x_1) = 4$

We know that, Hermite interpolation polynomial is

$H(x) = [1 - 2(x - x_0)l_0'(x_0)](l_0(x_0))^2 f(x_0) + [1 - 2(x - x_1)l_1'(x_1)](l_1(x_1))^2 f(x_1) + (x - x_0)(l_0(x_0))^2 f'(x_0) + (x - x_1)(l_1(x_1))^2 f'(x_1)$ (2)

Where $l_0(x) = \frac{(x - x_1)}{(x_0 - x_1)}$ and $l_1(x) = \frac{(x - x_0)}{(x_1 - x_0)}$

$\Rightarrow l_0(x) = 1 - x$

$l_0'(x) = -1$ and $l_1(x) = x$

$\Rightarrow l_1'(x) = 1$

From above, $H(x)$ become

$H(x) = 2x^3 - x^2 + 1$

$f(x) - H(x) = x^4 + 1 - 2x^3 + x^2 - 1$

$f(x) - H(x) = x^4 - 2x^3 + x^2$

$f(x) - H(x) = x^2(x - 1)^2$

For maximum, $\frac{d}{dx}(f(x) - H(x)) = 0$

$\Rightarrow 2x(x - 1)(2x - 1) = 0$

$\Rightarrow x = 0$ or $x = 1$ or $x = \frac{1}{2}$

at $x = \frac{1}{2}, \frac{d^2}{dx^2}(f(x) - H(x)) < 0$

$|f(x) - H(x)|$ is maximum when $x = \frac{1}{2}$

And its maximum value is $\frac{1}{16}$

From above explanation,

Option a) and b) are correct answer.

6. **Explanation: (a), (c), (d)**

We know that,

$E = \Delta + 1$

Now check the option,

For option (a)

$\Delta^2 U_n - 3\Delta U_n + 2U_n = 0$

$\Rightarrow (E - 1)^2 U_n - 3(E - 1)U_n + 2U_n = 0$

$\Rightarrow (E^2 - 2E + 1)U_n - 3(E - 1)U_n + 2U_n = 0$

$\Rightarrow U_{n+2} - 5U_{n+1} + 6U_n = 0$

Auxiliary equation is

$m^2 - 5m + 6 = 0$

$\Rightarrow (m - 3)(m - 2) = 0$

$\Rightarrow m = 2, 3$

$\Rightarrow U_n = c_1 2^n + c_2 3^n$

as $n \to \infty$ $U_n \to \infty$

Therefore, the solution is unbounded.

For option b)

$\Delta^2 U_n + \Delta U_n + \frac{1}{4} U_n = 0$

$\Rightarrow (E - 1)^2 U_n + (E - 1)U_n + \frac{1}{4} U_n = 0$

$\Rightarrow U_{n+2} - U_{n+1} + \frac{1}{4} U_n = 0$

Auxiliary equation is

$m^2 - m + \frac{1}{4} = 0$

$\Rightarrow \left(m - \frac{1}{2}\right)^2 = 0$

$\Rightarrow U_n = (c_1 + nc_2)\left(\frac{1}{2}\right)^n$

$\Rightarrow U_n \to 0$ as $n \to \infty$

(as $\left(\frac{1}{2}\right) < 1$, so $\left(\frac{1}{2}\right)^n$ tends to 0.)

Therefore, the solution is bounded.

For option c)

$\Delta^2 U_n - 2\Delta U_n + 2U_n = 0$

$\Rightarrow (E - 1)^2 U_n - 2(E - 1)U_n + 2U_n = 0$

$\Rightarrow U_{n+2} - 4U_{n+1} + U_n = 0$

Auxiliary equation is

$m^2 - 4m + 5 = 0$

$\Rightarrow m = (2 \pm i)$

$\Rightarrow U = [c_1\cos(n\theta) + c_2\sin(n\theta)](\sqrt{5})^n$
$\Rightarrow U_n \to \infty$ as $n \to \infty$
as this $c_1\cos(n\theta) + c_2\sin(n\theta)$ is oscillatory and $(\sqrt{5})^n$ *unbounded* as $\sqrt{5} > 1$.
Therefore, the solution is unbounded.
For option d)

$\Delta^2 U_{n+1} - \frac{1}{3}\Delta^2 U_n = 0$

$\Rightarrow (E-1)^2 U_{n+1} - \frac{1}{3}(E-1)^2 U_n = 0$

$\Rightarrow 3U_{n+3} - 7U_{n+2} + 5U_{n+1} - U_n = 0$

Auxiliary equation is

$3m^3 - 7m^2 + 5m - 1 = 1$

$\Rightarrow m = 1, 1, \frac{1}{3}$

$\Rightarrow U_n = c_1 + nc_2\left(\frac{1}{3}\right)^n c_3$

$\Rightarrow U_n \to \infty$ as $n \to \infty$ (as 2nd term unbounded and 3rd term bounded, so it is unbounded.)
Therefore, the solution is unbounded.
From above explanation
Option a), c) and d) are the correct answer.

7. Explanation: (a), (c)
(a) & (c) are correct

8. Explanation: (a), (d)

$\alpha = \frac{1+\sqrt{5}}{2} \mid \beta = \frac{1-\sqrt{5}}{2}$

$F_n = \frac{\alpha^n - \beta^n}{\alpha - \beta}$ $\quad \alpha + \beta = 1$ $\quad \alpha\beta = \frac{1-5}{4} = -1$

$F_1 = 1$

$F_2 = \alpha + \beta = 1$

$F_3 = \frac{(\alpha-\beta)(\alpha^2+\beta^2+\alpha\beta)}{\alpha-\beta} = (1^2+1) = 2$

1,1,2,3,5,8,13

$a + b + c = 1$

$9a + 3b + c = 2 \Rightarrow a = \frac{1}{4}, b = -\frac{1}{2}$

$25a + 5b + c = 5$

$\Rightarrow c = 1 + \frac{1}{2} - \frac{1}{4} = \frac{3}{2} - \frac{1}{4} = \frac{5}{4}$

$p(x) = \frac{1}{4}x^2 - \frac{1}{2}x + \frac{5}{4}$

$p(7) = \frac{4a+5}{4} - \frac{7}{2} = \frac{54-14}{4} = \frac{40}{4} = 10$

9. Explanation: (a), (c)
Consider the DE:

$$\frac{dy}{dx} = f(x, y)$$

$y(x+h) = y(x) + \omega_1 hf(x, y) + \omega_2 hf(x + \alpha h, x + \beta hf) + O(h^3) \ldots (1)$

By 2nd order R-K method:

$y_{n+1} = y_n + \left(1 - \frac{1}{2\alpha}\right)k_1 + \frac{1}{2\alpha}k_2$

$= y_n + \left(1 - \frac{1}{2\alpha}\right)hf(x_n, y_n) + \frac{1}{2\alpha}hf(x_n + \alpha h, y_n + x_k)$

... (2)
Comparing with (1), we get,

$\omega_1 = 1 - \frac{1}{2\alpha}, \omega_2 = \frac{1}{2\alpha}, \alpha = \alpha_1, \beta hf = \alpha k_1$

$\Rightarrow \beta = \frac{\alpha k_1}{hf} = \alpha$

If $\alpha = 1$, then $w_1 = \frac{1}{2}, w_2 = \frac{1}{2}, \beta = \frac{k_1}{hf} = \frac{hf}{hf} = 1$

so option (a) is correct.

If $\alpha = \frac{2}{3}$, then $\omega_1 = \frac{1}{4}, \omega_2 = \frac{3}{4}, \beta = \frac{2}{3}$

So option (c) is correct.
Similarly check that (b) & (d) are incorrect.

10. Explanation: (a), (b)
Similar to the above explanation, here we get,

$P = 1 - \frac{1}{2\alpha}, Q = \frac{1}{2\alpha}, \beta_0 = \alpha_0$

only (a) and (b) satisfies the required equations.

11. Explanation: (b), (c), (d)
We have

x	y	First DD	Second DD	Third DD	Fourth DD
-1	-30				
0	1	31			
3	10	3	-7		
4	5	-5	-2	1	
6	19	7	4	1	0

$\therefore$ Interpolating polynomial $g(x) = -30 + 31(x+1) - 7x(x+1) + x(x+1)(x-3)$

$\therefore c = g(2) = 15, g(1) = 14, g(5) = 6$

12. Explanation: (b), (c), (d)
Given the data points (-1,2), (0,1), (1,2), the polynomial $f(x)$ is a quadratic polynomial that interpolates these points. Let

$$f(x) = ax^2 + bx + c$$

Using the given points:

1. $f(-1) = a(-1)^2 + b(-1) + c = 2 \Rightarrow a - b + c = 2$
2. $f(0) = c = 1$
3. $f(1) = a(1)^2 + b(1) + c = 2 \Rightarrow a + b + c = 2$

Since $c = 1$, substituting it into the other equations:

$$a - b + 1 = 2 \Rightarrow a - b = 1$$
$$a + b + 1 = 2 \Rightarrow a + b = 1$$

Solving for a and b:

$$a = 1, b = 0$$

Thus, $f(x) = x^2 + 1$.
Next, we determine $g(x)$. Since $f(x) + g(x)$ must interpolate (-1,2), (0,1), (1,2), (2,17), we define:

$$h(x) = f(x) + g(x)$$

Since $f(x)$ already satisfies the first three points, $g(x)$ must be zero at $x = -1, 0, 1$, meaning it has factors $(x+1)x(x-1)$. Let

$$g(x) = k(x+1)x(x-1)$$

Using $h(2) = 17$, we calculate:

$$f(2) = 2^2 + 1 = 5$$
$$g(2) = k(2+1)(2)(2-1) = k(3)(2)(1) = 6k$$

Since $h(2) = 17$:

$$5 + 6k = 17$$

$$6k = 12 \Rightarrow k = 2$$

Thus, $g(x) = 2(x+1)x(x-1)$.

Now, computing $f(5)$ and $g(3)$:

$$f(5) = 5^2 + 1 = 26$$

$$g(3) = 2(3+1)(3)(3-1) = 2(4)(3)(2) = 48$$

Now, verifying options:

1. $f(5) + g(3) = 26 + 48 = 74$ (Correct, so Option (d) is valid)
2. $2f(5) - g(3) = 2(26) - 48 = 52 - 48 = 4$ (Correct, so Option (b) is valid)
3. $f(1) + g(3) = 2 + 48 = 50$ (Correct, so Option (c) is valid)
4. $f(5) + g(3) = 74 \neq 50$ (Incorrect, so Option (a) is invalid)

Unit 5.4: Questions Based on Euler Method & Initial Value Problems

MCQ (Multiple Choice Question)

1. Consider a second order ordinary differential Equation (ODE) and its finite difference representation. Identity which of the following statements is correct.
   (a) The finite difference representation is unique
   (b) The finite difference representation is unique for some ODE
   (c) There is no unique finite difference scheme for the ODE
   (d) The uniqueness of a finite difference scheme cannot be determined.

   [June 2012]

2. Consider the initial value problem $\frac{dy}{dx} = x + y, y(0) = 1$. Then the approximate value of the solution $y(x)$ at $x = 0.2$, using improved Euler method, with $h = 0.2$ is
   (a) 1.11 (b) 1.20
   (c) 1.24 (d) 1.48

   [Dec 2013]

3. Using Euler's method with the step size 0.05, the approximate value of the solution for the initial value problem at $\frac{dy}{dx} = \sqrt{3x + 2y + 1}$, $y(1) = 1$ at $x = 1.1$ (rounded off to two decimal places), is
   (a) 1.50 (b) 1.65
   (c) 1.25 (d) 1.15

   [DEC-2023]

4. If the value of the approximate solution of the initial value problem
   $$\begin{cases} y'(x) = x(y(x)+1), & x \in \mathbb{R} \\ y(0) = \beta \end{cases}$$
   at $x = 0.2$ using the forward Euler method with step size 0.1 is 1.02, then the value of β is
   (a) 0 (b) -1
   (c) 2 (d) 1

   [JULY 2024]

Answer Key

1	2	3	4
c	c	c	d

EXPLANATION

1. **Explanation: (c)**

$$y(x+h) = y(x) + h\,y'(x) + \frac{h^2}{2!}y''(x) + O(h^3) \quad ---(1)$$

$$y(x-h) = y(x) - h\,y'(x) + \frac{h^2}{2!}y''(x) + O(h^3) \quad ---(2)$$

Adding (1) and (2), $y''(x) = \frac{1}{h^2}[y(x+h) + y(x-h) - 2y(x)] + O(h^2)$, since $O(h^2)$is not exact value it is an approximation ,so it not guaranteed the uniqueness.

The finite difference representation of a ODE is not unique.

Hence, option (c) is correct.

2. **Explanation: (c)**

$\frac{dy}{dx} = x + y\,; y(0) = 1 \Rightarrow x_0 = 0, y_0 = 1$

And $f(x, y) = x + y$

At $x = 0.2$ and $h = 0.2$

Euler's formula is

$y_{i+1} = y_i + hf(x_i, y_i)$

For $i = 0$

$y_1 = y_0 + hf(x_0, y_0)$

$y_1 = 1 + 0.2(0 + 1) = 1.2$

Now by Euler's improved method

$$y_{i+1} = y_i + \frac{h}{2}(f(x_i, y_i) + f(x_{i+1}, y_{i+1}))$$

Where $x_{i+1} = x_i + h$

So, $x_1 = x_0 + h = 0.2$

$$\Rightarrow y_1 = y_0 + \frac{h}{2}[f(x_0, y_0) + f(x_1, y_1)]$$

$$= 1 + \frac{0.2}{2}[1 + (0.2 + 1.2)]$$

$$= 1 + \frac{0.2}{2}(2.4) = 1.24$$

Hence, option (c) is correct.

3. **Explanation: (c)**

Here $y' = \sqrt{3x + 2y + 1}$ and $y(1) = 1$

$\Rightarrow x_0 = 1$ and $y_0 = 1$ and $h = 0.05$

We have to find $y(1.1)$.

By Euler's method, we have

$y_{n+1} = y_n + hf(x_n, y_n)$

$\therefore x_1 = x_0 + h = 1 + 0.05 = 1.05$ and $x_2 = x_1 + h = 1.05 + 0.05 = 1.1$.

$\therefore y_1 = 1 + (0.05)\sqrt{3(1)+2(1)+1} = 1 + 0.05\sqrt{6} \approx 1.12$ and

$y_2 = 1.12 + (0.05)\sqrt{3\times(1.05)+2\times 1.12+1} = 1.12 + (0.05)\sqrt{6.39} \approx 1.25$

4. **Explanation: (d)**

We have $y_{n+1} = y_n + hf(x_n, y_n), n \geq 0$

Here, $x_0 = 0, y_0 = \beta, h = 0.1, f(x,y) = x(y(x)+1)$

$x_1 = x_0 + h = 0.1, x_2 = x_1 + h = 0.2, y(0.2) = y_2 = 1.02$

Now,

$y_1 = y_0 + hf(x_0, y_0) = \beta + 0.1f(0,\beta) = \beta + 0.1[0(\beta+1)] = \beta$

$y_2 = y_1 + hf(x_1, y_1) = \beta + 0.1f(0.1,\beta) = \beta + 0.1[0.1(\beta+1)]$

$\therefore 1.02 = \beta + 0.01\beta + 0.01$

$\therefore \beta = 1$

MSQ (Multiple Select Question)

1. Consider the ordinary differential equation $\frac{dy}{dx} = \lambda y\,; t > 0, y(0) = 1$, and the Euler scheme with step size h is $\frac{Y_{n+1}-Y_n}{h} = \lambda Y_n\,; n \geq 1$ $Y_0 = 1$. Which of the following are necessarily true for Y_1 which approximates $Y(h) = e^{\lambda h}$?
(a) Y_1 is a polynomial approximation
(b) Y_1 is a rational function approximation
(c) Y_1 is a trigonometric function approximation
(d) Y_1 is a truncation of infinite series

[Dec 2012]

2. Let $y(t)$ satisfy the different equation $y' = \lambda t\,; y(0) = 1$. Then the backward Euler method, for $n \geq 1$ and $h > 0$, $\frac{y_n - y_{n-1}}{h} = \lambda y_n\,; y_0 = 1$ yields
(a) A first order approximation to $e^{\lambda nh}$
(b) A polynomial approximation to $e^{\lambda nh}$
(c) A rational function approximation to $e^{\lambda nh}$
(d) A Chebyshev polynomial approximation to $e^{\lambda nh}$

[Dec 2014]

3. The order of linear multi step method $u_{j+1} = (1-a)u_j + au_{j-1} + \frac{h}{4} + \{(a+3)u'_{j+1} + (3a+1)u'_{j-1}\}$ for solving $u' = f(x,u)$ is
(a) 2 if $a = -1$ (b) 2 if $a = -2$
(c) 3 if $a = -1$ (d) 3 if $a = -2$

[Dec 2016]

4. For a differentiable function $f : \mathbb{R} \to \mathbb{R}$ define the difference quotient $(D_x f)(h) = \frac{f(x+h)-f(x)}{h}\,; h > 0$.
Consider numbers of the form $\hat{h} = h(1+\varepsilon)$ for a fixed $\varepsilon > 0$ let
$e_1(h) = f'(x) - (D_x f)(h)$
$e_2(h) = (D_x f)(h) - (D_x f)(\hat{h})$
$e(h) = e_1(h) + e_2(h)$. If $f(x+\hat{h}) = f(x+h)$, then
(a) $e_1(h) \to 0$ as $h \to 0$
(b) $e_2(h) \to 0$ as $h \to 0$
(c) $e_2(h) \to \varepsilon f'(x)/(1+\varepsilon)$ as $h \to 0$
(d) $e(h) \to 0$ as $h \to 0$

[June 2017]

5. Let y_n satisfy $y_n = y_{n-1} + hy_{n-1}$ with $y_0 = 1$ $(n = 1, 2, \ldots, N)$ and for $0 < h < 1$, $Nh = 1$. Then
(a) $y_N \to e$ as $N \to \infty$ (b) $y_N \to e^n$ as $N \to \infty$
(c) $y_n = (1+h)^n$ (d) $y_n \geq 1$

[June 2017]

6. Let $u(x)$ satisfy the boundary value problem

$$(BVP)\begin{cases} u'' + u' = 0, x \in (0,1) \\ u(0) = 0 \\ u(1) = 1 \end{cases}$$

Consider the finite difference approximation to (BVP)

$$(BVP)_h \begin{cases} \frac{U_{j+1}-2U_j+U_{j-1}}{h^2} + \frac{U_{j+1}-U_{j-1}}{2h} = 0, j = 1, \ldots, N-1 \\ U_0 = 0 \\ U_N = 0 \end{cases}$$

Here U_j is an approximation to $u(x_j)$ where $x_j = jh, j = 0, \ldots, N$ is a partition of $[0,1]$ with $h = 1/N$ for some positive integer N. Then which of the following are true?
(a) There exists a solution to $(BVP)_h$ of the form $U_j = ar^j + b$ for some, $a, b \in \mathbb{R}$ with $r \neq 1$ are r satisfying $(2+h)r^2 - 4r + (2-h) = 0$
(b) $U_j = (r^j - 1)/(r^N - 1)$ where r satisfies $(2+h)r^2 - 4r + (2-h) = 0$ and $r \neq 1$
(c) U is monotonic in x
(d) U_j is monotonic in j

[Dec 2018]

7 Consider the ordinary differential equation

$$\begin{cases} y'(x) + y(x) = 0, \\ y(0) = 1, \end{cases} x > 0,$$

And following numerical scheme to solve the ODE

$$\begin{cases} \frac{Y_{n+1}-Y_{n-1}}{2h} + Y_{n-1} = 0, n \geq 1 \\ Y_0 = 1, \quad Y_1 = 1. \end{cases}$$

If $0 < h < \frac{1}{2}$, then which of the following statements are true?
(a) $(Y_n) \to \infty$ as $n \to \infty$.
(b) $(Y_n) \to 0$ as $n \to \infty$.
(c) (Y_n) is bounded.
(d) $\max_{nh \in [0,T]} |y(nh) - Y_n| \to \infty$ as $T \to \infty$.

[Dec 2019]

8. Consider the first order IVP $y'(x) = -y(x), x > 0, y(0) = 1$ and the corresponding numerical scheme $4\left(\frac{y_{n+1}-y_{n-1}}{2h}\right) - 3\left(\frac{y_{n+1}-y_n}{h}\right) = -y_n$, with $y_0 = 1, y_1 = e^{-h}$. Where h is step size. Then which of the following are correct?
(a) The order of the scheme is 1.
(b) The order of the scheme is 2.
(c) $|y_n - y(nh)| \to \infty$ as $n \to \infty$
(d) $|y_n - y(nh)| \to 0$ as $n \to \infty$

[Dec 2019]

9. Consider the Euler method for integration of the system of differential equations $\dot{x} = -y$
$\dot{y} = x$

Assume that (x_i^n, y_i^n) are the points obtained for $i = 0, 1 \ldots, n^2$ using a time-step $h = 1/n$ starting at the initial point $(x_0, y_0) = (1,0)$. Which of the following statements are true?

(a) The points (x_i^n, y_i^n) lie on a circle of radius 1

(b) $\lim_{n\to\infty}(x_i^n, y_i^n) = (\cos(1), \sin(1))$

(c) $\lim_{n\to\infty}(x_i^n, y_i^n) = (1,0)$

(d) $(x_i^n)^2 + (y_i^n)^2 > 1$ for $i \geq 1$

[Feb 2022]

10. Consider the initial value problem (IVP) $y' + y = 0, y(0) = 1$. Let (y_n) be the iterates of forward Euler method, applied to the IVP, with step h where 0 < h < 1. Then which of the following statements are true?

(a) The sequence (y_n) does NOT converge

(b) $y_n \to 0$ as $n \to \infty$

(c) $0 \leq y_n \leq 1$ for n =0,1,2,.....

(d) $|y(nh) - y_n| \to 0$ as $n \to \infty$

[June 2025]

11. If $\alpha, \beta \in \mathbb{R}$ are such that the equation $\int_0^3 f(x)dx = \frac{3}{2}[f(\alpha) + f(\alpha+\beta)]$ holds for all polynomials f(x) of degree less then or equal to 2, then which of the following statements are true?

(a) $(\alpha, \beta) = \left(\frac{3-\sqrt{3}}{2}, \sqrt{3}\right)$ or $(\alpha, \beta) = \left(\frac{3+\sqrt{3}}{2}, -\sqrt{3}\right)$

(b) $(\alpha, \beta) = \left(\frac{3-\sqrt{2}}{2}, \sqrt{2}\right)$ or $(\alpha, \beta) = \left(\frac{3+\sqrt{2}}{2}, -\sqrt{2}\right)$

(c) $(\alpha, \beta) = \left(\frac{3-\sqrt{5}}{2}, \sqrt{5}\right)$ or $(\alpha, \beta) = \left(\frac{3+\sqrt{5}}{2}, -\sqrt{5}\right)$

(d) $(\alpha, \beta) = \left(\frac{3-\sqrt{7}}{2}, \sqrt{7}\right)$ or $(\alpha, \beta) = \left(\frac{3+\sqrt{7}}{2}, -\sqrt{7}\right)$

[June 2025]

Answer Key

1	2	3	4	5	6
a, d	a, c	b, c	a, c	a, c, d	a, b, c, d
7	8	9	10	11	
b, c	a, c	b, c, d	b,c,d	a	

EXPLANATION

1. **Explanation: (a), (d)**

Consider the given ordinary differential equation

$\frac{dy}{dt} = \lambda y\,; t > 0, y(0) = 1$

By separation of variable method, we get

$\frac{dy}{y} = \lambda dt$

Now, integrating

$\Rightarrow \log y = \lambda t + c$

$y = ce^{\lambda t}$

Now, use the given condition

$y(0) = 1$

Above equation become

$\Rightarrow y = e^{\lambda t} \quad (\because c = 1)$

Now,

$\frac{Y_{n+1} - Y_n}{h} = \lambda Y_n\,; n \geq 1, Y_0 = 1$ (given)

For n=1$\Longrightarrow Y_1 = Y_0 + \lambda h Y_0$

$\Rightarrow Y_1 = 1 + \lambda h$

And $Y(h) = e^{\lambda h}$ (Given)

$\Rightarrow Y(h) = 1 + \lambda h + \frac{(\lambda h)^2}{2!} + \frac{(\lambda h)^3}{3!} + \cdots$

From above explanation,

Y_1 is the only two term of $Y(h)$ and Y_1 is the truncation of $Y(h)$ and polynomial approximation of $Y(h)$

From this option a) and d) are the correct answer.

2. **Explanation: (a), (c)**

Consider the given ordinary differential equation

$\frac{dy}{dt} = \lambda y\,; t > 0, y(0) = 1$

By separation of variable method, we get

$\frac{dy}{y} = \lambda dt$

Now, integrating

$\Rightarrow \log y = \lambda t + c$

$y = ce^{\lambda t}$

Now, use the given condition

$y(0) = 1$

Above equation become

$\Rightarrow y = e^{\lambda t} \quad (\because c = 1)$

Now,

$\frac{y_n - y_{n-1}}{h} = \lambda y_n\,;\ y_0 = 1.$

$\Rightarrow y_n = \frac{y_{n-1}}{1 - \lambda h}$

For n=1

$y_1 = \frac{y_0}{1 - \lambda h}$

$y_1 = \frac{1}{1 - \lambda h}$

$y_1 = (1 - \lambda h)^{-1}$

$y_1 = 1 + \lambda h + \lambda h^2 + \lambda h^3 + \ldots$

and $Y(h) = e^{\lambda h}$

$\Rightarrow Y(h) = 1 + \lambda h + \frac{(\lambda h)^2}{2!} + \frac{(\lambda h)^3}{3!} + \cdots$

From above explanation,

Y_1 is the only two term of $Y(h)$ and Y_1 is the truncation of $Y(h)$ and polynomial approximation of $Y(h)$

Option a) and c) is the correct answer.

3. **Explanation: (b), (c)**

$u_{j+1} = (1-a)u_j + au_{j-1} + \frac{h}{4} + \{(a+3)u'_{j+1} + (3a+1)u'_{j-1}\}$ ------(1)

The general multi step or k-step method for the solution of

$u' = f(x,u), u(x_0) = u_0$ ------(2)

May be written as

$u_{j+1} = a_1u_j + a_2u_{j-1} + \cdots + a_ku_{j-k+1} + h(b_0u'_{j+1} + b_1u'_j + \cdots + b_ku'_{j-k+1})$ ------(3)

And T_{j+1} which is the local truncation error is written as

$T_{j+1} = c_0u(x_j) + c_1hu'(x_j) + c_2h^2u''(x_j) + \cdots + c_ph^pu^{(p)}(x_j) + T_{p+1}$ ------(4)

Where $c_0 = 1 - \sum_{i=1}^{k} a_1$

$c_q = \frac{1}{q!}[1 - \sum_{i=1}^{k} a_i (1-i)^q] - \frac{1}{(q-1)!}\sum_{i=0}^{k} b_i (1-i)^{q-1}, q = 1, 2, \ldots, p$

The linear multi step method is said to be of order p if $c_0 = c_1 = c_2 = \cdots = c_p = 0$ and $c_{p+1} \neq 0$

We are given

$u_{j+1} = (1-a)u_j + au_{j-1} + \frac{h}{4}\{(a+3)u'_{j+1} + (3a+1)u'_{j-1}\}$

$\Rightarrow a_1 = (1-a)$

$a_2 = a$

$b_0 = \frac{a+3}{4}$

$b_1 = 0$

$b_2 = \frac{3a+1}{4}$

Also, $k = 2$

Now, $c_0 = 1 - \sum_{i=1}^{2} a_i$

$= 1 - [a_1 + a_2]$

$= 1 - [1 - a + a]$

$= 0$

$$c_1 = \frac{1}{1!}\left[1 - \sum_{i=1}^{2} a_i (1-i)^1\right] - \frac{1}{0!}\sum_{i=0}^{2} b_i (1-i)^{1-1}$$

$= [1 - [a_1(1-1) + a_2(1-2)]] - 1[b_0(1-0)^0 + b_1(1-1)^0 + b_2(1-2)^{1-1}]$

$= [1 + a_2] - [b_0 + b_2]$

$= 1 + a - \left[\frac{(a+3)}{4} + \frac{3a+1}{4}\right]$

$= 1 + a - [a+1] = 0$

$$c_2 = \frac{1}{2!}\left[1 - \sum_{i=1}^{2} a_i (1-i)^2\right] - \frac{1}{1!}\sum_{i=0}^{2} b_i (1-i)^1$$

$= \frac{1}{2}[1 - [a_1(1-1)^2 + a_2(1-2)^2]] - [b_0(1-0) + b_1(1-1) + b_2(1-2)]$

$= \frac{1}{2}[1 - a_2] - [b_0 - b_2]$

$= \frac{1}{2}[1-a] - \left[\frac{a+3}{4} - \left(\frac{3a+1}{4}\right)\right]$

$= \frac{1}{2}(1-a) - \left(\frac{-2a+2}{4}\right)$

$= \frac{(1-a)}{2} - \frac{(1-a)}{2} = 0$

Similarly,

$c_3 = \frac{1}{3!}[1 - [a_1(1-1) + a_2(1-2)^3]] - \frac{1}{2!}[b_0(1) + b_1 \cdot 0 + b_2(-1)^2]$

$= \frac{1}{6}[1 + \alpha] - \frac{1}{2}[\alpha + 1]$

$= \frac{-1}{3}[1 + \alpha]$

If $a = -1$ then $c_3 = 0$

If $a = -2$ then $c_3 = \frac{1}{3}$

Hence, if $a = -2$

Then $c_0 = c_1 = c_2 = 0$ and $c_3 \neq 0$

Therefore, the order is 2.

Hence, option (b) is correct, option (d) incorrect.

Moreover,

$c_4 = \frac{1}{4!}[1 - [a_2(1-2)^4]]$

$-\frac{1}{3!}[b_0(1) + b_1 \cdot 0 + b_2(-1)^3]$

$= \frac{1}{24}[1-a] - \frac{1}{6}\left[\frac{-2a+2}{4}\right]$

$= -\frac{1}{24}(1-a)$

If $a = -1, c_4 = \frac{-1}{12} \neq 0$

Therefore, order is 3 for $a = -1$

Hence, option (c) is correct and option (a) incorrect.

4. Explanation: (a), (c)

Given, $D_x(f)(h) = \frac{f(x+h) - f(x)}{h}$; $h > 0$

$e_1(h) = f'(x) - (D_x f)(h)$

Taking limit on both side,

$$\lim_{h\to 0} e_1(h) = \lim_{h\to 0} f'(x) - \lim_{h\to 0}\left(\frac{f(x+h) - f(x)}{h}\right)$$

$e_1(h) = f'(x) - f'(x) = 0$

$\Rightarrow e_1(h) \to 0$

Now,

$e_2(h) = (D_x f)(h) - (D_x f)(\hat{h})$

$$\Rightarrow e_2(h) = \left(\frac{f(x+h) - f(x)}{h}\right) - \left(\frac{f(x+\hat{h}) - f(x)}{\hat{h}}\right)$$

$$\Rightarrow e_2(h) = \left(\frac{f(x+h) - f(x)}{h}\right) - \left(\frac{f(x+\hat{h}) - f(x)}{h(1+\varepsilon)}\right)$$

Since $f(x+\hat{h}) = f(x+h)$ (given)

$$\Rightarrow e_2(h) = \left[\frac{f(x+h) - f(x)}{h}\right]\left(1 - \frac{1}{1+\varepsilon}\right)$$

$$\Rightarrow e_2(h) = \left(\frac{\varepsilon}{1+\varepsilon}\right)\left(\frac{f(x+h) - f(x)}{h}\right)$$

As $h \to 0$

$e_2(h) = \left(\frac{\varepsilon}{1+\varepsilon}\right) f'(x)$

$\Rightarrow e(h) \to \left(\frac{\varepsilon}{1+\varepsilon}\right) f'(x)$

From above explanation,

Option a) and c) are the correct answer.

5. Explanation: (a), (c), (d)

We have,

$y_n = y_{n-1} + hy_{n-1}$ with $y_0 = 1$ $(n = 1, 2, \ldots, N)$ and for $0 < h < 1$, $Nh = 1$

Now $y_n = y_{n-1} + hy_{n-1}$

$\Rightarrow y_n = y_{n-1}(1+h)$

For $n = 1$

$y_1 = y_0(1+h)$

$= 1 + h$

$y_2 = y_1(1+h)$

$\Rightarrow y_2 = (1+h)^2$

$\vdots$

$y_k = (1+h)^k$

$\vdots$

$y_n = (1+h)^n$

Now,

$y_N = (1+h)^N = (1+h)^{1/h}$ $(\because Nh = 1)$

$\lim_{N\to\infty} y_N = \lim_{h\to 0}(1+h)^{1/h} = \lim_{h\to\infty}\left(1+\frac{1}{h}\right)^h$ =e

From above explanation,

Options (a), (c), and (d) are correct answer.

6. **Explanation: (a), (b), (c), (d)**

$$(BVP)\begin{cases} u'' + u' = 0, x \in (0,1) \\ u(0) = 0 \\ u(1) = 1 \end{cases} \quad ----(1)$$

And

$$(BVP)_h\begin{cases} \frac{U_{j+1}-2U_j+U_{j-1}}{h^2} + \frac{U_{j+1}-U_{j-1}}{2h} = 0, j = 1,\dots,N-1 \\ U_0 = 0 \\ U_N = 0 \end{cases} \quad -$$

$----(2)$

$$\frac{1}{2h}(u_{j+1}-u_{j-1}) + \frac{1}{h^2}(u_{j+1}-2u_j+u_{j-1}) = 0$$

$$\Rightarrow \left(\frac{1}{2h}-\frac{1}{h^2}\right)u_{j+1} - \frac{2}{h^2}u_j + \left(-\frac{1}{2h}+\frac{1}{h^2}\right)u_{j-1} = 0$$

$$\Rightarrow \left(\frac{h+2}{2h^2}\right)u_{j+1} - \frac{2}{h^2}u_j + \left(-\frac{h+2}{2h^2}\right)u_{j-1} = 0$$

$\Rightarrow (h+2)u_{j+1} - 4u_j + (-h+2)u_{j-1} = 0$...... (3)

Now proceeding through the options by one-one.

Option (a):

Let $u_j = ar^j + b$

$u_{j+1} = ar^{j+1} + b$

$u_{j-1} = ar^{j-1} + b$

$\Rightarrow (h+2)[ar^{j+1}+b] - 4(ar^j+b) + (2-h)[ar^{j-1} + b] = 0$

$\Rightarrow (h+2)ar^{j+1} - 4ar^j + (2-h)ar^{j-1} + (2+h)b - 4b + (2-h)b = 0$

$\Rightarrow [(h+2)r^2 - 4r + (2-h)]ar^{j-1} + 0 = 0$

$\Rightarrow (2+h)r^2 - 4r + (2-h) = 0$

Option (b):

Let $u_j = \frac{r^j-1}{r^N-1}$; $u_{j+1} = \frac{r^{j+1}-1}{r^N-1}$; $u_{j-1} = \frac{r^{j-1}-1}{r^N-1}$

$$\Rightarrow (h+2)\left(\frac{r^{j+1}-1}{r^N-1}\right) - 4\left(\frac{r^j-1}{r^N-1}\right)$$

$$+(2-h)\left(\frac{r^{j-1}-1}{r^N-1}\right) = 0$$

$\Rightarrow (h+2)r^{j+1} - 4r^j + (2-h)r^{j-1}$

$+(h+2-4+2-h)(-1) = 0$

$\Rightarrow (h+2)r^{j+1} - 4r^j + (2-h)r^{j-1} = 0$

$\Rightarrow (h+2)r^2 - 4r + (2-h) = 0, r \neq 1$

Option (c):

$u'' + u' = 0$

$u'' = -u'$

$\frac{u''}{u'} = -1$

Solution is $\log u' = -x + c$

$u' = c_1 e^{-x}$

$u = \frac{c_1}{-1}e^{-x} + c_2$

$u(x) = c_3 e^{-x} + c_2$

$u(0) = 0$

$\Rightarrow c_3 + c_2 = 0$

$c_2 = -c_3$

$u(1) = 1$

$\Rightarrow c_3 e^{-1} + c_2 = 1$

or $c_3(e^{-1} - 1) = 1$

$\Rightarrow c_3 = \frac{1}{e^{-1}-1}$

and $c_2 = \frac{1}{1-e^{-1}}$

$$u(x) = \frac{1}{e^{-1}-1}e^{-x} + \frac{1}{1-e^{-1}}$$

$$u'(x) = \frac{-1}{e^{-1}-1}e^{-x} > 0$$

$\Rightarrow u(x)$ is increasing.

$\Rightarrow u(x)$ is monotonic.

Option (d):

$U_j - U_{j-1} = ar^j - ar^{j-1} = a(r^j - r^{j-1})$

$U_j - U_{j-1} < 0$ if $r < 1$ Hence, decreasing.

$U_j - U_{j-1} > 0$ if $r > 1$ Hence, increasing.

Therefore, U_j is monotonic in J.

Hence, (a), (b), (c) and (d) are correct.

7. **Explanation: (b, c)**

$y' + y = 0\,; y(0) = 1$

$\frac{Y_{n+1} - Y_{n-1}}{2n} + Y_{n-1} = 0\,; n \geq 1 \quad Y_0 = 1, Y_1 = 1$

$\Rightarrow Y_{n+1} = Y_2 = (1-2h)Y_{n-1}$ ... .(1)

$n = 1, Y_2 = (1-2h)Y_0 = 1-2h\ [\because Y_0 = 1]$

$n = 2, Y_3 = (1-2h)Y_1 = (1-2h)\ [\because Y_1 = 1]$

$n = 3, Y_4 = (1-2h)Y_2 = (1-2h)(1-2h)$

$= (1-2h)^2$

$\vdots$

Proceeding in this way,

$Y_n = (1-2h)^{n-2}$

As $0 < h < {}^1/_2$

$\Rightarrow 0 < 2h < 1$

$\Rightarrow -1 < -2h < 0$

$\Rightarrow 0 < 1-2h < 1$

$Y_n = (1-2h)^{n-2}$

$\Rightarrow 0 < Y_n < 1$ ... . (*)

So $\lim_{h-\infty} Y_n \to 0$So option (a) wrong and

Option (b) correct.

From (*) it is cleared that bounded.

i.e. option (c) correct.

$y'(x) + y(x) = 0\,;$

$\Rightarrow \frac{dy}{dx} + y = 0 \;\Rightarrow \frac{dy}{y} = -dx$

$\Rightarrow \log y = -x + \log c$

$\Rightarrow y = ce^{-x}$

$as\ y(0) = 1$

$\Rightarrow y(0) = c\,e^0 \;\Rightarrow 1 + c$

$\therefore y = e^{-x}$

$\Rightarrow y\,(nh) = e^{-nh}$

New $|\,y\,(nh) - Y_n| = |e^{-nh} - (1-2h)^{n-2}|$

$\leq |e^{-nh}| \quad |(1-2h)^{n-2}|$

$\downarrow \quad + \quad \downarrow$

$0 \qquad\quad 0$

So $|Y_n - y(nh)|0\ as\ n \to \infty$

So option (d) wrong.

8. Explanation: (a), (c)

$$4\left(\frac{y_{n+1}-y_{n-1}}{2h}\right)-3\left(\frac{y_{n+1}-y_n}{h}\right)=-y_n$$

$\Rightarrow 2(y_{n+1}-y_{n-1})-3(y_{n+1}-y_n)=-h\,y_n$

$\Rightarrow -y_{n+1}-2y_{n-1}+3y_n=-hy_n$

$\Rightarrow y_{n+1}=(h+3)y_n-2y_{n-1}$

Now for $n=1, y_2=(h+3)y_1-2y_0$

As $y_0=1, y_1=e^{-h}$

$\Rightarrow y_2=(h+3)e^{-h}-2$

$y_3=(h+3)y_2-2y_1$

$=(h+3)[(h+3)e^{-h}-2]-2e^{-h}$

$=(h+3)^2e^{-h}-2(h+3)-2e^{-h}$

$=\{(h+3)^2-2\}e^{-h}-2(3+h)$

So continuing in this way for $n\to\infty$

$y_n\to\infty$

As $y'(x)=-y(x)\Rightarrow\frac{dy}{y(x)}=-dx$, integrating we get

$\log y(x)=-x-\log c$

$\Rightarrow y(x)=ce^{-x}$

$y(0)=1\ \Rightarrow 1=c$

$\therefore y(x)=e^{-x}$

$y(nh)=e^{-nh}$

$\Rightarrow \lim_{n\to\infty} y(nh)=\lim_{h\to\infty} e^{-nh}=0$

Now $|y_n-y(nh)|\to\infty\ as\ y_n\to\infty\ and\ y(nh)\to 0\ as\ n\to\infty$

So, option (c) is correct and option (d) incorrect.

Since first order IVP so option (a) correct and option (b) wrong.

9. Explanation: (b), (c), (d) are true

10. Explanation: (b), (c), (d)

We are asked about the **forward Euler method** applied to

$y'+y=0, y(0)=1$

with step $h\in(0,1)$.

Forward Euler:

$y_{n+1}=y_n+hf(t_n,y_n)=y_n+h(-y_n)=(1-h)y_n.$

With $y_0=1$, we get $y_n=(1-h)^n$.

1. **The sequence (y_n) does NOT converge**
   - Since (0<h<1), we have (0<1-h<1).
   - So $(1-h)^n\to 0$ as $n\to\infty$.

   This **converges**, so statement 1 is **false**.
2. $y_n\to 0$ **as** $n\to\infty$
   - True, as shown above.

   Statement 2 is **true**.
3. $0\le y_n\le 1$ **for** $n=0,1,2,\ldots$
   - $y_n=(1-h)^n\in(0,1]$ for all $n\ge 0$.

   Statement 3 is **true**.
4. $|y(nh)-y_n|\to 0$ **as** $n\to\infty$
   - Exact solution: $y(t)=e^{-t}$.
   - Error at step (n): $|y(nh)-y_n|=|e^{-nh}-(1-h)^n|$.
   - As $n\to\infty$, $e^{-nh}\to 0$, $(1-h)^n\to 0$, so the **error tends to 0.**

   Statement 4 is **true**.

Answer:

True: 2, 3, 4 **False:** 1

11. Explanation: (a)

We require the two-point quadrature with equal weights $w=\frac{3}{2}$ at nodes $x_1=\alpha,; x_2=\alpha+\beta$ to integrate all polynomials of degree ≤ 2 exactly. Matching moments:

(k=0:) (w+w=3) — (holds automatically).

(k=1:)

$$\frac{3}{2}(\alpha+\alpha+\beta)=\int_0^3 x,dx=\frac{9}{2}\Rightarrow 2\alpha+\beta=3. \quad (1)$$

(k=2:)

$$\frac{3}{2}(\alpha^2+(\alpha+\beta)^2)=\int_0^3 x^2,dx=9$$

$$\Rightarrow; 2\alpha^2+2\alpha\beta+\beta^2=6. \quad (2)$$

Solve (1) and (2). From (1) $\beta=3-2\alpha$. Substitute into (2) and solve:

$$2\alpha^2+2\alpha(3-2\alpha)+(3-2\alpha)^2=6,$$

which yields $\alpha=\frac{3\pm\sqrt{3}}{2}$ and corresponding $\beta=\pm\sqrt{3}$ with the sign opposite to the $\pm$ on α. Thus the solutions are

$$(\alpha,\beta)=(\frac{3-\sqrt{3}}{2},\sqrt{3})\text{ or }(\frac{3+\sqrt{3}}{2},-\sqrt{3}).$$

So **only statement (1) is true**; (2),(3),(4) are false.

Unit 5.5: Questions Based On Differentiation, Integration and Gauss-Seidel Iteration

MCQ (Multiple Choice Question)

1. The values of a, b, c such that $\int_0^h f(x)\,dx = h\left\{af(0) + bf\left(\frac{h}{3}\right) + cf(h)\right\}$ is exact for polynomials f of degree as high as possible are
(a) $a = 0, b = \frac{3}{4}, c = \frac{1}{4}$ (b) $a = \frac{3}{4}, b = \frac{2}{4}, c = \frac{1}{4}$
(c) $a = \frac{-2}{4}, b = \frac{3}{4}, c = \frac{1}{4}$ (d) $a = 0, b = \frac{1}{4}, c = \frac{3}{4}$
[June 2018]

2. Consider solving the following system by Jacobi iteration scheme

$$x + 2my - 2mz = 1$$
$$nx + y + nz = 2$$
$$2mx + 2my + z = 1$$

Where $m, n \in \mathbb{Z}$. with any initial vector, the scheme converges provided m, n, satisfy
(a) $m + n = 3$ (b) $m > n$
(c) $m < n$ (d) $m = n$.
[June 2019]

3. Assume that $a, b \in \mathbb{R}\backslash\{0\}$ and $a^2 \neq b^2$. Suppose that the Gauss-seidel method is used to solve the system of equations

$$\begin{bmatrix} a & b \\ b & a \end{bmatrix}\begin{bmatrix} x \\ y \end{bmatrix} = \begin{bmatrix} 1 \\ 1 \end{bmatrix}$$

Then the set of all values of (a, b) such that the method converges for every choice of initial vector is
(a) $\{(a, b) | a^2 < b^2\}$ (b) $\{(a, b) | a < |b|\}$
(c) $\{(a, b) | |b| < |a|\}$ (d) $\{(a, b) | a^2 + b^2 < 1\}$
[Dec 2019]

4. Let $a, b, c \in \mathbb{R}$ be such that the quadrature rule $\int_{-1}^{1} f(x)dx = af(-1) + bf'(0) + cf'(1)$ is exact for all polynomials of degree less than or equal to 2. Then $a + b + c$ equal to
(a) 4 (b) 3
(c) 2 (d) 1
[Feb 2022]

5. Which of the following values of a, b, c and d will produce a quadrature formula
$\int_{-1}^{1} f(x)\,dx \approx af(-1) + bf(1) + cf'(-1) + df'(1)$
that has degree of precision 3?
(a) $a = 1, b = 1, c = \frac{1}{3}, d = -\frac{1}{3}$
(b) $a = -1, b = 1, c = \frac{1}{3}, d = -\frac{1}{3}$
(c) $a = 1, b = 1, c = -\frac{1}{3}, d = \frac{1}{3}$
(d) $a = 1, b = -1, c = \frac{1}{3}, d = -\frac{1}{3}$
[JUNE 2023]

Answer Key

1	2	3	4	5
a	d	c	a	a

EXPLANATION:

1. **Explanation: (a)**
We have,
$$\int_0^h f(x)\,dx = h\left\{af(0) + bf\left(\frac{h}{3}\right) + cf(h)\right\}$$
Let $f(x) = a_0 + a_1x + a_2x^2 + \ldots + a_nx^n$
If $a_n \neq 0$
$\Rightarrow \text{Deg}(f(x)) = n$
Let $f(x) = 1\ \forall x$
$$\Rightarrow \int_0^h 1 \cdot dx = h\{a + b + c\}$$
$\Rightarrow a + b + c = 1$ ... (1)
Let $f(x) = x\ \forall x$
$$\Rightarrow \int_0^h x \cdot dx = h\left\{a \cdot 0 + b \cdot \frac{h}{3} + ch\right\}$$
$$\Rightarrow \frac{h^2}{2} = h^2\left\{\frac{b}{3} + c\right\}$$
$$\Rightarrow \frac{b}{3} + c = \frac{1}{2}$$
$\Rightarrow 2b + 6c = 3$ ... (2)
Let $f(x) = x^2\ \forall x$
$$\Rightarrow \int_0^h x^2\,dx = h\left\{a \cdot 0 + b \cdot \frac{h^2}{9} + ch^2\right\}$$
$$\Rightarrow \frac{h^3}{3} = h^3\left\{\frac{b}{9} + c\right\}$$
$$\Rightarrow \frac{1}{3} = \frac{b}{9} + c$$
$\Rightarrow 3 = b + 9c$ ... (3)
Solving (2) and (3) we get,
$$2b + 18c - 2b - 6c = 6 - 3$$
$\Rightarrow 12c = 3$
$\Rightarrow c = \frac{1}{4}$
Putting $c = \frac{1}{4}$ in (3), $b = \frac{3}{4}$
Now putting value of b, c in (1) we get $a = 0$
So $a = 0, b = \frac{3}{4}$ and $c = \frac{1}{4}$.
from above explanation,
only option a) is the correct answer.

2. **Explanation: (d)**
Consider the given system
$x + 2my - 2mz = 1$
$nx + y + nz = 2$
$2mx + 2my + z = 1$ Where $m, n \in \mathbb{Z}$ (1)
We know that,
In the case of system of equation in three unknowns
$x = \phi_1(x, y, z),\ y = \phi_2(x, y, z),\ z = \phi_1(x, y, z)$
The condition for convergence
$\left|\frac{d\phi_1}{dx}\right| + \left|\frac{d\phi_1}{dy}\right| + \left|\frac{d\phi_1}{dz}\right| < 1$ (2)

$\left|\frac{d\phi_2}{dx}\right| + \left|\frac{d\phi_2}{dy}\right| + \left|\frac{d\phi_2}{dz}\right| < 1$ (3)

$\left|\frac{d\phi_3}{dx}\right| + \left|\frac{d\phi_3}{dy}\right| + \left|\frac{d\phi_3}{dz}\right| < 1$ (4)

From equation (1)

$x = 1 - 2my + 2mz$

$\Rightarrow \phi_1 = 1 - 2my + 2mz$

$\Rightarrow \frac{d\phi_1}{dx} = 0, \frac{d\phi_1}{dy} = -2m, \frac{d\phi_1}{dz} = 2m$

Equation (2) become

$\Rightarrow |0| + |-2m| + |2m| < 1$

$\Rightarrow 4|m| < 1$

$\Rightarrow |m| < \frac{1}{4}$

Now,

$y = 2 - nx - nz$

$\Rightarrow \phi_2 = 2 - nx - nz$

$\Rightarrow \frac{d\phi_2}{dx} = -n, \frac{d\phi_2}{dy} = 0, \frac{d\phi_2}{dz} = -n$

Equation (3) become

$\Rightarrow |-n| + |0| + |-n| < 1$

$\Rightarrow 2|n| < 1$

$\Rightarrow |n| < \frac{1}{2}$

From this,

$|m| < \frac{1}{4}, |n| < \frac{1}{2}$ but m, n ∈ z

So, m=n=0

From above explanation,

Only option d) is the correct answer.

3. Explanation: (c) Since A if A is strictly diagonally dominant matrix, then the Gauss-seidel iteration scheme converses for any initial starting vector.

$A = \begin{bmatrix} a & b \\ b & a \end{bmatrix}$ is strictly diagonally dominant If $|a| > |b|$

So, option (c) correct and option (a), (b) and (d) are wrong.

4. Explanation: (a) We have,

$\int_{-1}^{1} f(x)dx = af(-1) + bf'(0) + cf'(1)$ (1)

Let $f(x)$ be the polynomial of degree less than equal to 2.

Take $f(x) = 1$

$\Rightarrow f'(x) = 0$

Equation (1) become

$\int_{-1}^{1} 1dx = a$

$\Rightarrow 2 = a$ (2)

Take $f(x) = x$

$\Rightarrow f'(x) = 1$

Equation (1) become

$\int_{-1}^{1} x\,dx = -a + b + c$

$\Rightarrow 0 = -a + b + c$

$\Rightarrow -a + b + c = 0$ (2)

Take $f(x) = x^2$

$\Rightarrow f'(x) = 2x$

Equation (1) become

$\int_{-1}^{1} x^2\,dx = a + 2c$

$\Rightarrow \frac{2}{3} = a + 2c$ (4)

From equation (2), (3), and (4)

$\Rightarrow a = 2, b = \frac{8}{3}, c = \frac{-2}{3}$

now,

$a + b + c = 2 + \frac{8}{3} - \frac{2}{3}$

$\Rightarrow a + b + c = 4$

From above explanation,

Only option a) is the correct answer.

5. Explanation: (a)

For degree of precision 3, quadrature formula will give exact results for $f(x) = 1, x, x^2, x^3$

(i) $f(x) = 1$

$\int_{-1}^{1} 1\,dx = a + b \Rightarrow a + b = 2$ -- (1)

(ii) $f(x) = x \Rightarrow f'(x) = 1$

$\int_{-1}^{1} x\,dx = -a + b + c + d$

$\Rightarrow -a + b + c + d = 0$ -- (2)

(iii) $f(x) = x^2 \Rightarrow f'(x) = 2x$

$\int_{-1}^{1} x^2\,dx = a + b - 2c + 2d$

$\Rightarrow a + b - 2c + 2d = \frac{2}{3}$ --- (3)

(iv) $f(x) = x^3 \Rightarrow f'(x) = 3x^2$

$\int_{-1}^{1} f(x)dx = -a + b + 3c + 3d$

$\Rightarrow -a + b + 3c + 3d = 0$ -- (4)

$a = 1; b = 1; c = \frac{1}{3}$ and $d = -\frac{1}{3}$

MSQ (Multiple Select Question)

1. Consider a linear system $Ax = b$ with a computed solution x_c; the error and the residue are defined, respectively by

$$e = x - x_c$$
$$r = Ax - Ax_c$$

Then

(a) A small error necessarily implies a small residue

(b) The error can be larger with relatively small residue

(c) The error can be small with relatively large residue

(d) The error and the residue are always equal.

[June 2011]

2. Let $A = \begin{pmatrix} 1.01 & 0.99 \\ 0.99 & 1.01 \end{pmatrix}, b = \begin{pmatrix} 2 \\ 2 \end{pmatrix}$ and x_0 be the unique solution of the equation $Ax = b$. Let $\hat{x}_1$ and $\hat{x}_2$ be the two approximate solutions $\begin{pmatrix} 1.01 \\ 1.01 \end{pmatrix}$ and $\begin{pmatrix} 2 \\ 0 \end{pmatrix}$. Finally, let $r_1 = Ax_0 - A\hat{x}_1 = b - A\hat{x}_1$ and $r_2 = Ax_0 - A\hat{x}_2 = b - A\hat{x}_2$ be the corresponding residues. Which of the following is/are correct?

(a) $\hat{x}_1$ is a good approximation to x_0 and r_1 is small

(b) $\hat{x}_1$ is not a good approximation to x_0 and r_1 is small

(c) $\hat{x}_2$ is good approximation to x_0 and r_2 is small

(d) $\hat{x}_2$ is not a good approximation to x_0 butr_2 is small.

[Dec 2011]

3. Given that an upper triangular matrix (UTM) is invertible if and only if all its diagonal elements are different from zero, consider the linear system

$$\begin{aligned} 2x_1 + 3x_2 - x_3 &= 5 \\ 4x_1 + 4x_2 - 3x_3 &= 3 \quad (1) \\ -2x_1 + 3x_2 - x_3 &= 1 \end{aligned}$$

Then system (1)

(a) Can be transformed into an UTM but is not invertible because the diagonal entries of the UTM are not different from zero

(b) Is invertible through cannot be transformed into an UTM

(c) Can be transformed into an UTM because above diagonal entries are all different from zero

(d) Can be transformed into an UTM and the solution of UTM is the solution of (1).

[June 2012]

4. Consider a partition of the interval [0, 1] by points of subdivision $0 = x_0, x_1, \ldots, x_n = 1$ with each sub-interval of length h. Let m_i be the midpoint of the ith sub-interval $[x_{i-1}, x_i]$ and $f \in C^2([0,1])$. Then an error bound for the quadrature rule $\int_0^1 f(x)\,dx \approx \sum_{i=1}^{n} f(m_i)\,h$ is

(a) $|f''|_{\max}\frac{h^2}{2}$ (b) $|f''|_{\max}\frac{h^3}{6}$

(c) $|f''|_{\max}\frac{h^2}{24}$ (d) $|f''|_{\max}\frac{h^4}{24}$

[Dec 2013]

5. The following numerical integration formula is exact for all polynomials of degree less than or equal to 3

(a) Trapezoidal rule

(b) Simpson's $1/3^{rd}$ rule

(c) Simpson's $3/8^{rd}$ rule

(d) Gauss-Legendre 2 point formula

[June 2015]

6. Let $f : [0,3] \to \mathbb{R}$ be defined by $f(x) = |1 - |x - 2||$ where $|\cdot|$ denotes the absolute value. Then for the numerical approximation of $\int_0^3 f(x)\,dx$, which of the following statements are true?

(a) The composite trapezoid rule with three equal sub-intervals in exact

(b) The composite midpoint rule with three equal sub-intervals is exact

(c) The composite trapezoid rule with four equal sub-intervals is exact

(d) The composite midpoint rule with four equal sub-intervals is exact

[June 2016]

7. For $f \in C[0,1]$ and $n > 1$, let $T(f) = \frac{1}{n}\left[\frac{1}{2}f(0) + \frac{1}{2}f(1) + \sum_{j=1}^{n-1} f\left(\frac{j}{n}\right)\right]$ be an approximation of the integral $I(f) = \int_0^1 f(x)\,dx$. For which of the following functions f is $T(f) = I(f)$?

(a) $1 + \sin 2\pi nx$ (b) $1 + \cos 2\pi nx$

(c) $\sin^2 2\pi nx$ (d) $\cos^2 2\pi(n+1)x$

[Dec 2017]

8. Consider the linear system $Ax = b$ with $A = \begin{bmatrix} 2 & 1 & -3 \\ 1 & 2 & -2 \\ -3 & -2 & 1 \end{bmatrix}$. Let x_n denote the nth Gauss-Seidel iteration and $e_n = x_n - x$. Let M be the corresponding matrix such that $e_{n+1} = Me_n, n \geq 0$. Which of the following statements are necessarily true?

(a) All eigenvalues of M have absolute value less than 1

(b) There is an eigenvalues of M with absolute value at least 1

(c) e_n converges to 0 as $n \to \infty$ for all $b \in \mathbb{R}^3$ and any e_0

(d) e_n does not converges to 0 as $n \to \infty$ for any $b \in \mathbb{R}^3$ unless $e_0 = 0$.

[Dec 2017]

9. Assume that a non-singular matrix $A = L + D + U$ where L and U are lower and upper triangular matrices respectively with all diagonal entries are zero, and D is a diagonal matrix. Let x^* be the solution of $Ax = b$. Then the Gauss-Seidel iteration method $x^{(k+1)} = Hx^{(k)} + c, k = 0, 1, 2, \ldots$ with $\|H\| < 1$ converges to x^* provided H is equal to

(a) $-D^{-1}(L + U)$ (b) $-(D + L)^{-1}U$

(c) $-D(L + U)^{-1}$ (d) $-(L - D)^{-1}U$.

[June 2018]

10. Consider the integration formula

$$\int_{x_2}^{x_1} f(x)\,dx = \frac{h}{2}[f(x_0) + f(x_1)] + ph^2(f'(x_0) - f'(x_1))$$

Where $h = x_1 - x_0$. Then the constant p such that the above formula give the exact value for highest degree polynomial and degree d of corresponding polynomial are given by,

(a) $p = \frac{1}{6}, d = 4$ (b) $p = \frac{1}{12}, d = 3$

(c) $p = \frac{1}{6}, d = 3$ (d) $p = \frac{1}{12}, d = 4$

[Dec 2019]

11. The values of α, A, β, c for which the quadratic formula $\int_{-1}^{1}(1 - x)f(x)dx = A\,f(-\alpha) + B\,f(0) + Cf(\alpha)$ is exact for polynomials of highest possible degree, are

(a) $\alpha = \sqrt{\frac{3}{5}}, A = \frac{5}{9} + \frac{\sqrt{5}}{3\sqrt{3}}, B = \frac{8}{9}, c = \frac{5}{9} - \frac{\sqrt{5}}{3\sqrt{3}}$

(b) $\alpha = \sqrt{\frac{3}{5}}, A = \frac{5}{9} - \frac{\sqrt{5}}{3\sqrt{3}}, B = \frac{8}{9}, c = \frac{5}{9} + \frac{\sqrt{5}}{3\sqrt{3}}$

(c) $\alpha = \sqrt{\frac{3}{5}}, A = \frac{5}{9}\left(1 - \frac{\sqrt{3}}{\sqrt{5}}\right), B = \frac{8}{9}, c = \frac{5}{9}\left(1 + \frac{\sqrt{3}}{\sqrt{5}}\right)$

(d) $\alpha = \sqrt{\frac{3}{5}}, A = \frac{5}{9} + \left(1 + \frac{\sqrt{3}}{\sqrt{5}}\right), B = \frac{8}{9}, c = \frac{5}{9}\left(1 - \frac{\sqrt{3}}{\sqrt{5}}\right)$

[Dec 2019]

12. Consider the numerical integration formula $\int_{-1}^{1} g(x)dx \approx g(\alpha) + g(-\alpha)$.

Where $\alpha = (0.2)^{\frac{1}{4}}$. which of the following statements are correct?

(a) The integration formula is exact for the polynomials of the form $ax + bx\ for\ all\ a, b \in \mathbb{R}$.

(b) The integration formula is exact for polynomials of the form $a + bx + cx^2$ for $a, b, c \in \mathbb{R}$.

(c) The integration formula is exact for the polynomial of the form $a + bx + cx^2 + dx^3$ for all $a, b, c, d \in \mathbb{R}$.

(d) The integration formula is exact for the polynomials of the form $a + bx + cx^3 + dx^4 + dx^4$ for all $a, b, c, d \in \mathbb{R}$.

[Nov 2020]

13. Let S be the set of continuous functions $F: [0,1] \to [0, \infty]$ that satisfy

$$\int_0^1 x^2 F(x)dx = \frac{1}{2}\int_0^1 xF^2(x)dx = \frac{1}{8}.$$

Which of the following statements are true?

(a) S is an empty set.

(b) S has at most one element.

(c) S has at least one element.

(d) S has more than element.

[Nov 2020]

14. Let S denote the set of all 2×2 matrices A such that the iterative sequence generated by the Gauss-Seidel method applied to the system of linear equations

$$A\begin{pmatrix} x_1 \\ x_2 \end{pmatrix} = \begin{pmatrix} 2 \\ 3 \end{pmatrix}$$

converges for every initial guess. Then which of the following statements are true?

(a) $\begin{pmatrix} 5 & 8 \\ 1 & 2 \end{pmatrix} \in S$ (b) $\begin{pmatrix} 3 & 2 \\ 1 & 2 \end{pmatrix} \in S$

(c) $\begin{pmatrix} -3 & 1 \\ 2 & 3 \end{pmatrix} \in S$ (d) $\begin{pmatrix} 2 & 2 \\ 4 & 3 \end{pmatrix} \in S$

[JULY 2024]

15. If $\lambda \in \mathbb{R}$ and $p \in \mathbb{R}$ are such that the quadrature formula $\int_{x_o}^{x_o+h} f(x)dx \approx \lambda h(f(x_o) + f(x_o + h)) + ph^3(f''(x_o) + f''(x_o + h))$ is exact for all polynomials of degree as high as possible, then

(a) $2\lambda + 24p = 0$ (b) $7\lambda - 12p = 4$

(c) $2\lambda + 24p = -3$ (d) $7\lambda - 12p = 11$

[Feb. 2025]

16. Let S be the set of all 2×2 matrices A such that the iterative sequence generated by the Gauss-Seidel method converges for every initial guess, when employed to solve the system of equations $A\begin{pmatrix} x_1 \\ x_2 \end{pmatrix} = \begin{pmatrix} 1 \\ 2 \end{pmatrix}$.

Then which of the following statements are true?

(a) $\begin{pmatrix} 4 & 1 \\ 2 & 3 \end{pmatrix} \in S$ (b) $\begin{pmatrix} 1 & 2 \\ 3 & 4 \end{pmatrix} \in S$

(c) $\begin{pmatrix} 1 & 5 \\ 1 & 10 \end{pmatrix} \in S$ (d) $\begin{pmatrix} -5 & 2 \\ 1 & -4 \end{pmatrix} \in S$

[Dec 2025]

Answer Key						
1	2	3	4	5	6	7
b, c	a, d	c, d	c	b, c, d	a, b	a
8	9	10	11	12	13	14
b,d	b	b	a, d	a, d	a, b	a, b, c
15	16					
a,b	a,c,d					

EXPLANATION:

1. **Explanation: (b), (c)**

$e = x - x_c$

$r = Ax - Ax_c = A(x - x_c)$

By given equations

We get $e = A^{-1}r$

So if A is non-singular and some elements of A^{-1} are larger then e, may be large even when all then element of r are small. In this case a small change in coefficients of A or b can produce a large change in the solution. Hence, option (b) and (c) are correct.

2. **Explanation: (a), (d)**

Given that, Ax = b has a solution

Where, $A = \begin{pmatrix} 1.01 & 0.99 \\ 0.99 & 1.01 \end{pmatrix}, b = \begin{pmatrix} 2 \\ 2 \end{pmatrix}$

$\hat{x}_1 = \begin{pmatrix} 1.01 \\ 1.01 \end{pmatrix}, \hat{x}_2 = \begin{pmatrix} 2 \\ 0 \end{pmatrix}$

$r_1 = Ax_0 - A\hat{x}_1 = b - A\hat{x}_1$

$= \begin{pmatrix} 2 \\ 2 \end{pmatrix} - \begin{pmatrix} 1.01 & 0.99 \\ 0.99 & 1.01 \end{pmatrix}\begin{pmatrix} 1.01 \\ 1.01 \end{pmatrix}$

$= \begin{pmatrix} 2 \\ 2 \end{pmatrix} - \begin{pmatrix} 2.02 \\ 2.02 \end{pmatrix}$

$= \begin{pmatrix} -0.0200 \\ -0.0200 \end{pmatrix}$

$r_2 = b - A\hat{x}_2 = \begin{pmatrix} 2 \\ 2 \end{pmatrix} - \begin{pmatrix} 1.01 & 0.99 \\ 0.99 & 1.01 \end{pmatrix}\begin{pmatrix} 2 \\ 0 \end{pmatrix}$

$= \begin{pmatrix} 2 \\ 2 \end{pmatrix} - \begin{pmatrix} 2.02 \\ 1.98 \end{pmatrix} = \begin{pmatrix} -0.02 \\ 0.02 \end{pmatrix}$

From above explanation,

Both r_1 and r_2 are small and $\hat{x}_1$ is good approximation to x_0.

Hence, option (a) and (d) are correct answer.

3. **Explanation: (c), (d)**

Given system is

$2x_1 + 3x_2 - x_3 = 5$

$4x_1 + 4x_2 - 3x_3 = 3$

$-2x_1 + 3x_2 - x_3 = 1$ (1)

The augmented matrix of the above system of equation in matrix form is $[A : b] = \begin{bmatrix} 2 & 3 & -1 : 5 \\ 4 & 4 & -3 : 3 \\ -2 & 3 & -1 : 1 \end{bmatrix}$

Row reduced echelon form

$[A : b] = \begin{bmatrix} 2 & 3 & -1 : 5 \\ 4 & 4 & -3 : 3 \\ -2 & 3 & -1 : 1 \end{bmatrix}$

$= \begin{bmatrix} 2 & 3 & -1 : 5 \\ 0 & -2 & -1 : -7 \\ 0 & 6 & -2 : 6 \end{bmatrix}$

$= \begin{bmatrix} 2 & 3 & -1 : 5 \\ 0 & -2 & -1 : -7 \\ 0 & 0 & -5 : -15 \end{bmatrix}$

The system Can be transformed into an UTM because above diagonal entries are all different from zero and the system can be transformed into an UTM and the solution of UTM is the solution of (1).

From this,

Option (c) and (d) are correct answer.

4. Explanation: (c)

We know that, error for Quadrature rule is ,

$|E_m| \le k\left(\frac{b-a}{24n^2}\right)^3$

$= \frac{h^2}{24} kn$

$\Rightarrow |E_m| \le |f''|_{max}\frac{h^2}{24}$

From above explanation,

Only option (c) is correct answer.

5. Explanation: (b), (c), (d)

We know that,

Trapezoidal rule is exact for linear polynomial and Simpson's $1/3^{rd}$ rule, Simpson's $3/8^{rd}$ rule, Gauss-Legendre 2 point formula exact for all polynomials of degree less than or equal to 3.

From above explanation,

Option (b), (c), (d) are correct answer.

6. Explanation: (a), (b)

Given, $f(x) = |1-|x-2||$

Since $f(x) = |1-|x-2||$ is linear polynomial in $[0,1], [1,2], [2,3]$ *and in subinterval* $[0,2], [2,3]$.

We know that, Trapezoidal rule give exact value of integration for polynomials of degree less than equal to 1.

From above explanation,

Option (a) and (b) Correct answer.

7. Explanation: (a)

We have,

$$T(f) = \frac{1}{n}\left[\frac{1}{2}f(0) + \frac{1}{2}f(1) + \sum_{j=1}^{n-1} f\left(\frac{j}{n}\right)\right]$$

$$T(f) = \frac{1}{n}\left[\frac{1}{2}f(0) + \frac{1}{2}f(1)\right] + \frac{1}{n}\left[\sum_{j=1}^{n-1} f\left(\frac{j}{n}\right)\right]$$

$$T(f) = \frac{1}{n}\left[\frac{1}{2}f(0) + \frac{1}{2}f(1)\right] + \frac{1}{n}\left[\sum_{j=1}^{n-1} f\left(\frac{j}{n}\right) - f\left(\frac{n}{n}\right) + f\left(\frac{n}{n}\right)\right]$$

$$T(f) = \frac{1}{n}\left[\frac{1}{2}f(0) + \frac{1}{2}f(1)\right] + \frac{1}{n}\left[\sum_{j=1}^{n} f\left(\frac{j}{n}\right) - f\left(\frac{n}{n}\right)\right]$$

$$T(f) = \frac{1}{n}\left[\frac{1}{2}f(0) + \frac{1}{2}f(1) - f\left(\frac{n}{n}\right)\right] + \frac{1}{n}\left[\sum_{j=1}^{n} f\left(\frac{j}{n}\right)\right]$$

$$T(f) = \frac{1}{n}\left[\frac{1}{2}f(0) - \frac{1}{2}f(1)\right] + \frac{1}{n}\left[\sum_{j=1}^{n} f\left(\frac{j}{n}\right)\right]$$

$$T(f) = \frac{1}{n}\left[\frac{1}{2}f(0) + \frac{1}{2}f(1) - f(1)\right] + \int_0^1 f(x)\,dx$$

$\left(since \;\; \frac{1}{n}\left[\sum_{j=1}^{n} f\left(\frac{j}{n}\right)\right] = \int_0^1 f(x)\,dx\right)$

if $\frac{1}{2}f(0) = \frac{1}{2}f(1)$

$\Rightarrow T(f) = I(f)$

$f(0) = f(1) \quad (1)$

Now check the option

For option a)

$f(x) = 1 + \sin 2\pi nx$

$\Rightarrow f(0) = f(1)$

Similarly, check other option

Only option a) is the correct answer.

8. Explanation: (b), (d)

$$A = \begin{bmatrix} 2 & 1 & -3 \\ 1 & 2 & -2 \\ -3 & -2 & 1 \end{bmatrix}$$

Now reducing the above matrix,

$$= \begin{bmatrix} 2 & 1 & -3 \\ 0 & \frac{3}{2} & \frac{-1}{2} \\ 0 & \frac{-1}{2} & \frac{-7}{2} \end{bmatrix} \begin{matrix} \\ R_2 \to R_2 - \frac{1}{2}R_1 \\ R_3 \to R_3 + \frac{3}{2}R_1 \end{matrix}$$

$$= \begin{bmatrix} 2 & 1 & -3 \\ 0 & \frac{3}{2} & \frac{-1}{2} \\ 0 & 0 & \frac{-11}{3} \end{bmatrix} R_3 \to R_3 + \frac{1}{3}R_2$$

Now from the above all the Eigen values are $2, \frac{3}{2}, \frac{-11}{3}$, so option (a) incorrect and (b) correct.

$e_{n+1} = Me_n$

If $e_0 = 0$

$e_1 = Me_0 = 0$

$e_2 = Me_1 = 0$

So, continuing in this way we concluded that option (d) correct but option (c) incorrect.

9. Explanation: (b)

We know that,

$A = L + D + U$

$|A| \ne 0$

x is solution of $Ax = b$

$(L + D + U)x = b$

$\Rightarrow (L + D)x = -Ux + b$

$\Rightarrow x = (-Ux + b)(L + D)^{-1}$

$\Rightarrow x = -Ux(L + D)^{-1} + b(L + D)^{-1}$

Gauss-Seidel iteration equation is

$x^{(k+1)} = Hx^{(k)} + c\,;\; k = 0, 1, 2, \ldots$

Where $H = -(D + L)^{-1}U$ and $c = (D + L)^{-1}b$

From above explanation,

Only option b) is the correct answer.

10. Explanation: (b)

We solve from options, since $d = 3$ *or* 4, *let* $f(x) = x^3, x_0 = 0, x_1 = 1$ *then* $h = 1 - 0 = 1$

Now,

$$\int_0^1 x^3\,dx = \frac{1}{2}[0 + 1] + p.1(0 - 3)$$

$$\Rightarrow \frac{x^4}{4}\Big|_0^1 = \frac{1}{2} - 3p$$

$$\Rightarrow \frac{1}{4} = \frac{1}{2} - 3p \Rightarrow 3p = \frac{1}{2} - \frac{1}{4} = \frac{1}{4}$$

$$\Rightarrow p = \frac{1}{12}$$

So, for $d = 3, p = \frac{1}{12}$ i.e. option (b) correct and (d) wrong.

Now for $d = 4, f(x) = x^4, x_0 = 0, x_1 = 1, h = 1 - 0 = 1$

$$\therefore \int^{1} x^4\, dx = \frac{1}{2}[0 + 1] + p.1(0 - 4)]$$

$$\Rightarrow \frac{1}{5} = \frac{1}{2} - 4p \Rightarrow 4p = \frac{1}{2} - \frac{1}{5} = \frac{5-2}{10} = \frac{3}{10}$$

$$\Rightarrow p = \frac{3}{40}$$

So when $d = 4, p = \frac{3}{40}$.

So, option (a) and (d) wrong.

11. Explanation: (a, d)

Let $f(x) = 1$

$$\Rightarrow \int_{-1}^{1} (1 - x)dx = A.1 + B.1 + C.1$$

$$\Rightarrow \left[x - \frac{x^2}{2}\right]_{-1}^{1} = A + B + C$$

$$\Rightarrow A + B + C = 2 \ldots\ldots\ldots (x)$$

$f(x) = x$

$$\Rightarrow \int_{-1}^{1} (1 - x)x\, dx = A(-\alpha) + B.0 + C.\alpha$$

$$\Rightarrow \int_{-1}^{1} (x - x^2)dx = -A\,\alpha + x\,\alpha$$

$$\Rightarrow \frac{1}{2}x^2 \int_{-1}^{1} - \frac{x^3}{3}\int_{-1}^{1} = \alpha(-A + c)$$

$$\Rightarrow 0 - \frac{1}{3}(1 + 1) = \alpha\,(-A + c)$$

$$\Rightarrow \alpha(-A + c) = -{}^2/_3 \ldots\ldots (**)$$

Now for $f(x) = x^2$

$$\int_{-1}^{1} (1 - x).x^2\, dx = A\alpha^2 + B.0 + C.\alpha^2$$

$$\Rightarrow \frac{x^3}{3}\int_{-1}^{1} - \frac{x^4}{4}\int_{-1}^{1} = \alpha^2(A + C)$$

$$\Rightarrow \frac{2}{3} - 0 = \alpha^2(A + C)$$

$$\Rightarrow \alpha^2(A + C) = {}^2/_3 \ldots\ldots\ldots\ldots (***)$$

Now from options;

(a) $\alpha = \sqrt{\frac{3}{5}}, A = \frac{5}{9} + \frac{5}{3\sqrt{3}}, B = \frac{8}{9}, c = \frac{5}{9} - \frac{5}{3\sqrt{3}}$

$$A + B + C = \frac{5}{9} + \frac{5}{3\sqrt{3}} + \frac{8}{9} + \frac{5}{9} - \frac{5}{3\sqrt{3}}$$

$$= \frac{18}{9} = 2$$

Now $\alpha\,(C - A) = \sqrt{\frac{3}{5}}\left[\frac{5}{9} - \frac{5}{3\sqrt{3}} - \frac{5}{9} - \frac{5}{3\sqrt{3}}\right]3$

$$= \sqrt{\frac{3}{5}} \times \frac{-2\sqrt{5}}{3\sqrt{3}} = -{}^2/_3$$

$$\alpha^2(A + C) = \frac{3}{5}\left[\frac{5}{9} + \frac{5}{3\sqrt{3}} + \frac{5}{9} - \frac{5}{3\sqrt{3}}\right]$$

$$= \frac{3}{5} \times \frac{10}{9} = \frac{6}{9} = \frac{2}{3}$$

So option (a) correct.

(b) $A + B + C = \frac{5}{9} - \frac{5}{3\sqrt{3}} + \frac{8}{9} + \frac{5}{9} + \frac{5}{3\sqrt{3}} = \frac{18}{9} = 2$

$$\alpha(C - A) = \frac{\sqrt{3}}{5}\left(\frac{5}{9} + \frac{\sqrt{5}}{3\sqrt{3}} - \frac{5}{9} + \frac{\sqrt{5}}{3\sqrt{3}}\right)$$

$$= \sqrt{\frac{3}{5}} \times \frac{\sqrt{5}}{3\sqrt{3}} = \frac{1}{3} \neq -{}^2/_3$$

So option (b) wrong.

(c) $\alpha(C - A) = \sqrt{\frac{3}{5}}\left[\frac{5}{9}\left(1 + \frac{\sqrt{3}}{\sqrt{5}} - 1\,\frac{\sqrt{3}}{\sqrt{5}}\right)\right]$

$$= \sqrt{\frac{3}{5}} . \frac{5}{9} . \frac{2\sqrt{3}}{\sqrt{5}} = \frac{2.3.5}{9.5} = \frac{2}{3} \neq -{}^2/_3$$

So option (c) wrong.

(d) $A + B + C = \frac{5}{9}\left[1 + \frac{\sqrt{3}}{\sqrt{5}} + 1 - \frac{\sqrt{3}}{\sqrt{5}}\right] + \frac{8}{9}$

$$= \frac{10}{9} + \frac{8}{9} = \frac{18}{9} = 2$$

$$\alpha(C - A) = \alpha\,\sqrt{\frac{3}{5}\left[\frac{5}{9}\left(1 - \frac{\sqrt{3}}{\sqrt{5}} - 1 - \frac{\sqrt{3}}{\sqrt{5}}\right)\right]}$$

$$= \frac{\sqrt{3}}{\sqrt{5}} \times \left(\frac{-10}{9}\right) \times \frac{\sqrt{3}}{\sqrt{5}} = \frac{3}{5} \times \left(\frac{-10}{9}\right) = \frac{-6}{9} = -{}^2/_3$$

$$\alpha^2(A + C) = \frac{3}{5}\left[\frac{5}{9}\left(1 - \frac{\sqrt{3}}{\sqrt{5}} + 1 + \frac{\sqrt{3}}{\sqrt{5}}\right)\right]$$

$$= \frac{3}{5} \times \frac{10}{9} = \frac{6}{9} = {}^2/_3$$

So option (d) correct.

Hence option (a) and (d) correct.

12. Explanation: (a), (d)

Now check from options:

(b) Let $a = 0, b = 0, c = 1$

$g(x) = x^2$

$$\int_{-1}^{1} g(x)dx = g(\alpha) + g(-\alpha) \Rightarrow \int_{-1}^{1} x^2\, dx = \alpha^2 + \alpha^2$$

$$\Rightarrow \frac{x^3}{3}\int_{-1}^{1} = 2\alpha^2$$

$$\Rightarrow \frac{2}{3} \neq 2 \times \left(\frac{2}{10}\right)^{1/2}$$

So option (b) discarded

(d) Let $a = 0, b = 0, c = 0, d = 1, \Rightarrow g(x) = x^4 \int_{-1}^{1} x^4\, dx = \frac{x^5}{5}\int_{-1}^{1} {}^2/_{-5}$

$g(\alpha) + g(-\alpha) = \alpha^4 + \alpha^4 = 2\alpha^4 =$

(c) Let $a = 0, b = 0, c = 1, d = 0$

$f(x) = x^2$

$$\int_{-1}^{1} x^2 dx = \frac{x^3}{3}\int_{-1}^{1} = {}^2/_3$$

$$F(\alpha) + f(-\alpha) = \alpha^2 + \alpha^2 + 2\alpha^2 = 2\left(\frac{2}{10}\right)^{1/2}$$

But $\frac{2}{3} \neq 2\left(\frac{2}{10}\right)^{1/2}$;

So option (d) discarded

(a) Let $g(x) = a + bx$

$$\int_{-1}^{1} g(x)dx = \int_{-1}^{1} (a + bx)dx = \left[ax + \frac{b}{2}x^2\right]_{-1}^{1}$$

$$= a(1+1) + \frac{b}{2}(1-1) = 2a$$

$g(\alpha) = a + b\alpha$

$g(-\alpha) = a - b\alpha$

i.e. $\int_{-1}^{1} g(x)dx = 2a = a + b\alpha + a - b\alpha$

$\approx F(\alpha) + F(-\alpha)$

So option (a) correct.

(d) let $g(x) = a + bx + cx^3 + dx^4$

$$\int_{-1}^{1} g(x)dx = \int_{-1}^{1} (a + bx + cx^3 + dx^4)dx$$

$$= \left[ax + \frac{1}{2}x^2 + \frac{c}{4}x^4 + \frac{d}{5}x^5\right]_{-1}^{1}$$

$$= a(1+1) + \frac{b}{2}(1-1) + \frac{c}{4}(1-1) + \frac{d}{5}(1+1)$$

$$= 2a + \frac{2}{5}d$$

$F(\alpha) = a + b\alpha + c\alpha^3 + d\alpha^4$

$F(-\alpha) = a - b - \alpha - c\alpha^3 + d\alpha^4$

$$F(\alpha) + F(-\alpha) = 2a + 2d\,\alpha^4 = 2a + 2d.\frac{2}{10}$$

$$= 2a + \frac{2}{5}\,d$$

∴ Option (d) correct.

13. Explanation: (a), (b) are correct

14. Explanation: (a), (b), (c)

Result 1: If A is strictly diagonally dominant matrix, then Gauss-Seidel iteration method for the system $Ax = b$ converges for any initial approximation.

Matrix in option (b) and (c) is strictly diagonally dominant. So, (b) and (c) are correct.

Result 2: A necessary and sufficient condition for convergence of an iterative method $X^{(k+1)} = HX^{(k)} + C$ is that the eigenvalues of the iteration matrix satisfy $|\lambda_i(H)| < 1, \forall i$.

Gauss-Seidel iteration matrix $H = -(D+L)^{-1}U$

For option (a): $\begin{pmatrix} 5 & 8 \\ 1 & 2 \end{pmatrix} = D + L + U = \begin{pmatrix} 5 & 0 \\ 0 & 2 \end{pmatrix} + \begin{pmatrix} 0 & 0 \\ 1 & 0 \end{pmatrix} + \begin{pmatrix} 0 & 8 \\ 0 & 0 \end{pmatrix}$

$$\therefore H = -\begin{pmatrix} 5 & 0 \\ 1 & 2 \end{pmatrix}^{-1} \begin{pmatrix} 0 & 8 \\ 0 & 0 \end{pmatrix} = \begin{pmatrix} 0 & \frac{-8}{5} \\ 0 & \frac{4}{5} \end{pmatrix},$$

whose eigenvalues are 0 and $\frac{4}{5}$.

∴ Using Result 2, option (a) is correct as well.

For option (d): $\begin{pmatrix} 2 & 2 \\ 4 & 3 \end{pmatrix} = D + L + U = \begin{pmatrix} 2 & 0 \\ 0 & 3 \end{pmatrix} + \begin{pmatrix} 0 & 0 \\ 4 & 0 \end{pmatrix} + \begin{pmatrix} 0 & 2 \\ 0 & 0 \end{pmatrix}$

$$\therefore H = -\begin{pmatrix} 2 & 0 \\ 4 & 3 \end{pmatrix}^{-1} \begin{pmatrix} 0 & 2 \\ 0 & 0 \end{pmatrix} = \begin{pmatrix} 0 & -1 \\ 0 & \frac{4}{3} \end{pmatrix},$$

whose eigenvalues are 0 and $\frac{4}{3}$.

$\because \frac{4}{3} > 1$, using Result 2, option (d) is incorrect.

∴ Correct options are (a), (b) and (c).

15. Explanation: (a), (b)

A quadrature formula is exact for polynomials up to degree n if it integrates polynomials correctly up to that degree.

1. **For $f(x) = 1$:**

$$\int_{x_o}^{x_o+h} 1\,dx = h$$

The quadrature formula simplifies to:

$$2\lambda h = h \Rightarrow \lambda = \frac{1}{2}$$

2. **For $f(x) = x$:**

$$\int_{x_o}^{x_o+h} x\,dx = \frac{h}{2}(2x_o + h)$$

This also holds correctly.

3. **For $f(x) = x^2$:**

$$\int_{x_o}^{x_o+h} x^2\,dx = \frac{1}{3}[(x_o + h)^3 - x_o^3]$$

Matching coefficients gives:

$2\lambda + 24p = 0$

4. **For $f(x) = x^3$:**

$$\int_{x_o}^{x_o+h} x^3\,dx$$

Gives another condition:

$7\lambda - 12p = 4$

Thus, options (a) and (b) are correct.

16. Explanation: (a), (c), (d)

For Gauss–Seidel method, the iterative scheme converges for every initial guess if the spectral radius of the iteration matrix is < 1.

For a 2×2 system,

If the matrix is strictly diagonally dominant (row-wise), Gauss–Seidel definitely converges.

Condition $|a_{ii}| > \sum_{j \neq i} |a_{ij}|$

(i) $\begin{pmatrix} 4 & 1 \\ 2 & 3 \end{pmatrix}$

Row-1 = $|4| > |1|$ $(4 > 1)$

Row-2 = $|3| > |2|$ $(3 > 2)$

Strictly diagonally dominant

Converges

True

(ii) $\begin{pmatrix} 1 & 2 \\ 3 & 4 \end{pmatrix}$

Row-1 = $|1| < |2|$

Row-2 = $|4| > |3|$

Not diagonally dominant.

For this matrix the spectral radius of Gauss–Seidel iteration matrix > 1, so it diverges.

False

(iii) $\begin{pmatrix} 1 & 5 \\ 1 & 10 \end{pmatrix}$

Not diagonally dominant in row-1, so we check Gauss–Seidel iteration matrix.

For Gauss–Seidel iteration, matrix eigenvalue: $\lambda = \frac{bc}{ad}$

Convergence if $\left|\frac{bc}{ad}\right| < 1$

Here

$$\frac{bc}{ad} = \frac{5 \times 1}{1 \times 10} = \frac{1}{2}$$

$$|\lambda| = \frac{1}{2} < 1$$

Converges

True

(iv) $\begin{pmatrix} -5 & 2 \\ 1 & -4 \end{pmatrix}$

Row-1 $= |-5| > |2|$

Row-2 $= |-4| > |1|$

Strictly diagonally dominant.

Converges

True

Final Answer= $(1), (3), (4)$

CLASSICAL MECHANICS

No. of questions asked from year 2011-2025

Units		2011		2012		2013		2014		2015		2016		2017		2018		2019		2020	2022		2023		2024	2025		
		Jun	Dec	Jun	Dec	Jun	Dec	Jun	Dec	Jun	Dec	Jun	Dec	Jun	Dec	Jun	Dec	Jun	Dec	Nov	Feb	Sep	Jun	Dec	Jul	Feb	Jun	Dec
6.1	Classical Mechanics	3	3	2	3	-	2	2	2	2	3	2	2	3	1	2	2	2	2	2	2	-	-	-	2	2	2	1

CHAPTER 6

CLASSICAL MECHANICS

MCQ (Multiple Choice Questions)

1. Which of the following is/are correct
   (a) A free particle in $\mathbb{R}^3$ can have infinite degrees of freedom
   (b) The number of degree of freedom of N particles is greater than 3N
   (c) A system of N particles with k constants has 3N + k degrees of freedom
   (d) A system consisting of three point masses connected by three rigid massless rods has six degrees of freedom.

[June 2011]

2. Which of the following is correct?
   (a) The number of degrees of freedom of a two-particle (connected by a light rod of length L) system in a vertical plane, where one of the particles is constrained to move horizontally, is two
   (b) The number of degrees of freedom of a door swinging on its hinges is three
   (c) The number of independent generalized coordinates needed to specify the simple pendulum moving in a vertical plane is two
   (d) The number of scalar equations needed to determine the motion of an unconstrained N-particle system is N

[Dec. 2011]

3. If the Hamiltonian of a dynamical system is given by H=pq $-q^2$, then as $t \to \infty$
   (a) $q \to \infty, P \to \infty$
   (b) $q \to 0, P \to 0$
   (c) $q \to \infty, P \to 0$
   (d) $q \to 0, P \to \infty$

[June 2012]

4. The total number of vibrational degrees of freedom of a molecule containing n collinear atoms is
   (a) $3n-6$
   (b) $3n-5$
   (c) $3n-2$
   (d) $3n$

[Dec. 2012]

5. Let S be a mechanical system with Lagrangian $L(\vec{q}, \dot{\vec{q}}, t)$ and generalized coordinates $\vec{q} = (q_1, q_2, \ldots, q_n)$. Then the Lagrange equations of motion for S
   (a) constitute a set of n first order ODEs.
   (b) can be transformed to the Hamilton form using Legendre transform.
   (c) are equivalent to a set of n first order ODEs when expressed in terms of Hamiltonian functions.
   (d) is a set of $2n$ second order ODEs.

[Dec 2013]

6. Consider two waves of same angular frequency ω, same angular wave number k, same amplitude a travelling in the positive direction of x-axis with the same speed, and with phase difference ϕ. Then the superposition principle yields a resultant wave with
   (a) Amplitude $2a$ and phase ϕ
   (b) Amplitude $2a$ and phase $\phi/2$
   (c) Amplitude $2a\cos(\phi/2)$ and phase $\phi/2$
   (d) Amplitude $2a\cos(\phi/2)$ and phase ϕ

[June 2014]

7. Consider a body of unit mass falling freely from rest under gravity with velocity v. If the air resistance retards the acceleration by cv where c is a constant, then
   (a) $v = \frac{g}{c}[1 + e^{ct}]$
   (b) $v = \frac{g}{c}[1 + e^{-ct}]$
   (c) $v = \frac{g}{c}[1 - e^{-ct}]$
   (d) $v = \frac{g}{c}[1 - e^{ct}]$

[Dec 2014]

8. Consider two weightless, inextensible rods AB and BC, suspended at A and joined by a flexible joint at B. Then the degrees of freedom of the system is
   (a) 3
   (b) 4
   (c) 5
   (d) 6

[June 2015]

9. A force $5\hat{\imath} - 2\hat{\jmath} + 3\hat{k}$ acts on a particle with position vector $2\hat{\imath} + \hat{\jmath} - 2\hat{k}$. The torque of the force about the origin is
   (a) $\hat{\imath} + 16\hat{\jmath} + 9\hat{k}$
   (b) $-\hat{\imath} - 16\hat{\jmath} - 9\hat{k}$
   (c) $\hat{\imath} + 16\hat{\jmath} - 9\hat{k}$
   (d) $\hat{\imath} - 16\hat{\jmath} + 9\hat{k}$

[Dec 2015]

10. Consider the equations of motion for a system
$$\frac{d}{dt}\left(\frac{\partial L}{\partial \dot{q}_i}\right) - \frac{\partial L}{\partial q_i} = 0,\ i = 1,2,3,\ldots,n$$
Where
$$L = T - V\left[\begin{array}{l} with\ T(t, q_i, \dot{q}_i)\ as\ kinetic\ energy \\ and\ V(t, q_i)\ as\ potential\ energy \end{array}\right], q_i$$
the generalized coordinates, and $\dot{q}_i$ the generalized velocities. Then the equations of motion in the form as above are
   (a) necessarily restricted to a conservative system but there is no unique choice of L.
   (b) not necessarily restricted to a conservative system and there is a unique choice of L.
   (c) necessarily restricted to a conservative system and there is a unique choice of L.
   (d) not necessarily restricted to a conservative system and there is no unique choice of L.

[June 2016]

11. A bead slides without friction on a frictionless wire in the shape of a cycloid with equation $x = a(\theta - \sin\theta), y = a(1 + \cos\theta), 0 \le \theta \le 2\pi$. Then the Lagrangian function is

(a) $ma^2 (1 + \cos\theta)\dot{\theta}^2 - mga(1 + \cos\theta)$
(b) $ma^2 (1 - Cos\,\theta)\dot{\theta}^2 - mga(1 + \cos\theta)$
(c) $ma^2(1 - \cos\theta)\dot{\theta}^2 + mga(1 + \cos\theta)$
(d) $ma^2(1 + \cos\theta)\dot{\theta}^2 - mga(1 - \cos\theta)$

[Dec. 2016]

12. Consider a spherical pendulum consisting of a particle of mass m which moves under gravity on a smooth sphere of radius a. In terms of spherical polar angles θ, ϕ, with θ measured up from the downward vertical, the Lagrangian is given by
(a) $ma\left[\frac{a}{2}(\dot{\theta}^2 + \phi^2 \sin^2\theta) - g\cos\theta\right]$
(b) $ma\left[\frac{a}{2}(\theta^2 + \phi^2 \sin^2\theta) + g\cos\theta\right]$
(c) $ma\left[\frac{a}{2}(\dot{\theta}^2 + \phi^2 \cos^2\theta) - g\sin\theta\right]$
(d) $ma\left[\frac{a}{2}(\dot{\theta}^2 + \phi^2 \cos^2\theta) - g\sin\theta\right]$

[June 2017]

13. A rigid body having one point O fixed and no external torque about O has equal principal moments of inertia. Then the body must rotate with
(a) angular velocity of variable magnitude
(b) angular velocity with constant magnitude
(c) constant angular momentum but varying angular velocity
(d) varying angular momentum with varying angular velocity

[June 2017]

14. Let $I(m)$ denote the moment of inertia of a regular solid tetrahedron about an axis m passing through its centre of gravity. Which of the following is true?
(a) if the axis ℓ passes through a vertex and the axis ℓ' does not pass through a vertex then $I(\ell) > I(\ell')$
(b) if the axis ℓ passes through the mid-point of an edge and ℓ' is any other axis then $I(\ell) > I(\ell')$
(c) $I(\ell)$ is the same for all axes ℓ
(d) if the axis ℓ passes through a vertex and the axis ℓ' does not pass through a vertex then $I(\ell) < I(\ell')$

[Dec. 2017]

15. Given that the Lagrangian for the motion of a simple pendulum is
$$L = \frac{1}{2} m\, l^2\, \dot{\theta}^2 + mgl\cos\theta,$$
where m is the mass of the pendulum bob suspended by a string of length l, g is the acceleration due to gravity and θ is the amplitude of the pendulum from the mean position, then a Hamiltonian corresponding to L is
(a) $H(p,\theta) = \frac{p^2}{2ml^2} + mgl\cos\theta$
(b) $H(p,\theta) = \frac{p^2}{2ml^2} - mgl\cos\theta$
(c) $H(p,\theta) = \frac{p^2}{ml^2} - mgl\cos\theta$
(d) $H(p,\theta) = \frac{3p^2}{2ml^2} + mgl\cos\theta$

[June 2018]

16. Consider the two dimensional motion of a mass m attached to one end of a spring whose other end is fixed. Let k be the spring constant. The kinetic energy T and the potential energy V of the system are given by $T = \frac{1}{2}m\left(\dot{r}^2 + (r\dot{\theta})^2\right)$ and $V = \frac{1}{2}kr^2$. Where $\dot{r} = \frac{dr}{dt}$ and $\dot{\theta} = \frac{d\theta}{dt}$ with t as time. Then which of the following statements is correct?
(a) r is an ignorable coordinate
(b) θ is not an ignorable coordinate
(c) $r^2\dot{\theta}$ remains constant through out the motion
(d) $r\dot{\theta}$ remains constant through out the motion

[Dec. 2018]

17. Suppose a point mass m is attached to one end of a spring of spring constant k. The other end of the spring is fixed on a massless cart that is being moved uniformly on a horizontal plane by an external device with speed v_0. If the position q of the mass in the stationary system is taken as the generalized coordinate, then the Lagrangian of the system is
(a) $\frac{m}{2}\dot{q}^2 - \frac{k}{2}(q - v_0 t)$
(b) $\frac{m}{2}\dot{q}^2 - \frac{k}{2}(q - v_0 t)^2$
(c) $\frac{m}{2}\dot{q}^2 + \frac{k}{2}(q - v_0 t)$
(d) $\frac{m}{2}\dot{q}^2 + \frac{k}{2}(q - v_0 t)^2$

[June 2019]

18. Consider a mass-less infinite straight wire with one end fixed at O. Assume that the wire is rotating in a plane about the point O with constant angular velocity ω. Consider a bead of mass m sliding along the wire in the absence of external forces. Let $r(t)$ denote the distance of the bead from O at time $t \geq 0$, and $\frac{dr}{dt}(0) = 0$. Then which of the following statements is true?
(a) $\exists M > 0, \alpha > 0$ such that $r(t) > Me^{\alpha t}, t > 0$
(b) $r(t) \to$ as $t \to \infty$
(c) $r(t)$ is a constant function
(d) $\frac{dr(t)}{dt}$ changes its sign for some $t > 0$

[Dec. 2019]

19. Consider the solid s made of a material of constant density in the shape of a hemisphere of unit radius: $S = \{(x,y,z)| \, x^2 + y^2 + z^2 \leq 1 \quad z \geq 0\}$.
Which of the following statements is true?
Options
(a) The centre of mass of S is at the origin
(b) The x-axis is a principal axis for S
(c) The moment of inertia tensor of S is not a diagonal matrix
(d) The z-axis is a principal axis for S

[Nov. 2020]

20. A body moves freely in a uniform gravitational field. Which of the following statements is true?
(a) Stable equilibrium of the body is possible
(b) Stable equilibrium of the body is not possible
(c) Stable equilibrium of the body depends on the strength of the field
(d) Equilibrium is metastable

[Feb. 2022]

21. Consider a solid circular cylinder of radius 2 meters and height 3 meters of uniform density. If the density of

the cylinder is $\rho \frac{\text{kg}}{\text{meter}^3}$, then the moment of inertia (in kg meter²) of the cylinder about a diameter of its base is

(a) $48\pi\rho$ (b) $43\pi\rho$
(c) $24\pi\rho$ (d) $4\pi\rho$

[July 2024]

22. Consider a solid torus of constant density ρ, formed by revolving the disc $(y-b)^2 + z^2 \le a^2, x = 0$ about the z axis, where $0 < a < b$. Then the moment of inertia of the solid torus about the z axis is

(a) $2\pi^2 a^2 b^2(4b^2 + 3a^2)\rho$ (b) $\frac{\pi^2}{2} a^2 b(4b^2 + 3a^2)\rho$
(c) $\frac{\pi^2}{2} a^2 b(4a^2 + 3b^2)\rho$ (d) $2\pi^2 a^2 b^2(4a^2 + 3b^2)\rho$

[July 2024]

23. Two blocks of equal mass m are connected by a flexible inelastic cord of mass M. One block is placed on a smooth horizontal table, the other block hangs over the edge. The total potential energy of the entire cord is given by $\frac{-Mg}{2l}x^2$, where x is the distance of the hanging block from the edge of the table, l is the length of the cord, and g is the gravitational acceleration. Then

(a) $\ddot{x} = \frac{l}{g}\frac{ml+Mx}{2m+M}$ (b) $\ddot{x} = \frac{l}{g}\frac{Ml+mx}{m+M}$
(c) $\ddot{x} = \frac{g}{l}\frac{ml+Mx}{m+M}$ (d) $\ddot{x} = \frac{g}{l}\frac{ml+Mx}{2m+M}$

[Feb. 2025]

24. Consider the system of two particles with total kinetic energy

$$T = \frac{5}{2}\dot{x}^2 + l^2\dot{\theta}^2 + 2l\dot{x}\dot{\theta}\cos\theta,$$

and Lagrangian

$$L = \frac{5}{2}\dot{x}^2 + l^2\dot{\theta}^2 + 2l\dot{x}\dot{\theta}\cos\theta + 2gl\cos\theta,$$

where x, θ are generalized coordinates, and g, l are positive constants. Then the non-zero frequency of the normal mode of the system with small oscillations ($|\theta| \ll 1$) is

(a) $\frac{5}{3}\sqrt{\frac{g}{l}}$ (b) $\sqrt{\frac{5g}{3l}}$
(c) $\frac{5}{2}\sqrt{\frac{g}{l}}$ (d) $\sqrt{\frac{5g}{2l}}$

[Feb. 2025]

25. Suppose a dynamical system has the Lagrangian $L = (\dot{q}_1)^2 + (\dot{q}_2)^2 + (\dot{q}_1)^2 + \dot{q}_1\dot{q}_2$
If p_1 and p_2 are momenta conjugate to q_1 and q_2, respectively, then which of the following statements is true?

(a) $\dot{p}_1 = 2q_1, \dot{p}_2 = 0$ (b) $\dot{p}_1 = -q_1, \dot{p}_2 = 0$
(c) $\dot{p}_1 = -\frac{q_1}{2}, p_2 = q_2$ (d) $\dot{p}_1 = q_1, p_2 = -q_2$

[June 2025]

MSQ (Multiple Select Questions)

1. Using Euler's dynamical equation for force- free motion of a rigid body, symmetrical about the Z-principal axis, with angular velocity $\overline{\omega} = (\omega_1, \omega_2, \omega_3)$, where $\omega_i, i = 1, 2, 3$, are the components along the three principal axes, it follows that

(a) ω_i = constant
(b) $\omega_2 = a\sin(\lambda t + b)$ with a, λ, and b as constant
(c) ω_3 = constant
(d) $\omega_1^2 + \omega_2^2$ constant

[June 2011]

2. Consider the force free motion of a rigid body about a fixed point O. Suppose 3A, 5A and 6A are the principal moments of inertia at O, and initially the angular velocity has components $\omega_1 = \sqrt{5}, \omega_2 = 0, \omega_3 = \sqrt{5}$ about the corresponding principal axes; if the body ultimately rotates about the mean axis, then

(a) $\omega_1^2 + \omega_2^2 = 5$ (b) $5\omega_2^2 + g\omega_1^2 = 45$
(c) $\omega_3^2 = \omega_1^2$ (d) $\omega_2^2 \neq \omega_1^2$

[June 2011]

3. Consider the Euler's equations of motion for the free motion of a body relative to its centre of mass O and principal axes OX_1, OX_2, OX_3. If the body is in motion with OX_3 as the axis of symmetry with $\overline{\omega} = (\omega_1, \omega_2, \omega_3)$ and $L = (L_1, L_2, L_3)$ as the angular velocity vector and the angular momentum vector, respectively, then

(a) ω_3 = constant
(b) ω_1 and ω_2 satisfy the simple harmonic motion equation
(c) $\overline{e}_3$, the unit vector along $OX_3, \overline{\omega}$ and $\overline{L}$ lie in the same plane
(d) L_3 = constant

[Dec 2011]

4. Suppose that the potential energy $V(q_1, q_2)$ of a system with generalized coordinates q_1 and q_2 has a minimum at $q_1 = q_2 = 0$ and that $V(0,0) = 0$. Then

(a) the approximate V near (0,0) is a homogeneous quadratic form in q_1 and q_2 assuming that the terms in powers three (or higher) in the small quantities q_1 and q_2 are negligible
(b) if (0,0) is also a minimum point of approximate V, then the quadratic form in the option 1 given above is positive definite
(c) the requirement in the option 2 given above implies that the approximate V takes positive values except when $q_1 = q_2 = 0$
(d) the requirement in the option 2 given above that (0,0) is a minimum point of approximate V implies that $q_1 = q_2 = 0$ yields a strict minimum of the exact V

[Dec 2011]

5. Let L, denote the Lagrangian of a system. Then the

(a) Lagrange's equations are second order differential equations.
(b) Total number of equations is equal to the number of generalized coordinates.
(c) Lagrangian L is not unique in its functional form, but the form of the Lagrange's equation of motion can be preserved.
(d) Lagrangian function is a quadratic function of generalized velocity when the potential exists.

[June 2012]

6. Which of the following is/are correct?
(a) Hamilton's principle follows from the D' Alembert's principle.
(b) Hamilton's principle is not usually applicable to nonholonomic system. Unless a relation connecting the differentials of generalized coordinates is given.
(c) Hamilton's principle follows from Lagrange's equations.
(d) Newton's second law of motion follows from the Hamilton's principle.
[Dec. 2012]

7. The energy of a pendulum executing small oscillations in a Cartesian coordinate system is proportional to
(a) square of the amplitude.
(b) square of the frequency
(c) its mass.
(d) inverse of the product of mass, frequency and amplitude.
[Dec. 2012]

8. Let $H(\vec{q},\vec{p})$ and $L(\vec{q},\dot{\vec{q}})$ denote respectively the Hamiltonian and Lagrangian of an autonomous system with $\vec{p}$ as generalized momentum and $\vec{q}$ the generalized coordinate vector. Then
(a) H remains conserved in the motion.
(b) H is simply the total energy of the system.
(c) $\vec{p}$ is constant if H is independent of $\vec{q}$.
(d) $\vec{p}$ is constant if L is independent of $\vec{q}$.
[Dec 2013]

9. Consider a particle of mass m in simple harmonic oscillation about the origin with spring constant k; then for the Lagrangian L and the Hamiltonian H of the system
(a) $L(x,\dot{x}) = \frac{1}{2}m\dot{x}^2 - \frac{1}{2}k\dot{x}^2, H(x,\dot{x}) = \frac{p^2}{2m} + \frac{1}{2}kx^2; p$ is generalized momentum
(b) $L(x,\dot{x}) = \frac{1}{2}m\dot{x}^2 - \frac{1}{2}kx^2$ And the generalized momentum is p = $m\dot{x}$
(c) $L(x,\dot{x}) = \frac{1}{2}m\dot{x}^2 - \frac{1}{2}kx^2$ And the generalized momentum is $p = m\dot{x}$
(d) $L(x,\dot{x}) = \frac{1}{2}m\dot{x}^2 - \frac{1}{2}kx^2, H(x,\dot{x}) = \frac{m\dot{x}^2}{2} + \frac{1}{2}kx^2$
[June 2014]

10. Consider a particle moving with coordinates $(x(t), y(t))$ on a smooth curve $\phi(x,y) = 0$. If the particle moves from $(x(0),y(0))$ to $(x(\tau),y(\tau))$ $for\ \tau > 0$ such that its kinetic energy is minimized, then
(a) $\frac{\ddot{x}}{\phi_x} = \frac{\ddot{y}}{\phi_y}$
(b) $\dot{x}^2(0) + \dot{y}^2(0) = \dot{x}^2(\tau) + \dot{y}^2(\tau)$
(c) $\dot{x}\phi_x + \dot{y}\phi_y = 0$
(d) $\dot{x}^2(0) = \dot{x}^2(\tau)$
[Dec. 2014]

11. A particle of mass m is constrained to move on the surface of a cylinder $x^2 + y^2 = a^2$ under the influence of a force directed towards the origin and proportional to the distance of the particle from the origin. Then
(a) the angular momentum about z-axis is constant
(b) the angular momentum about z-axis is not constant
(c) the motion is simple harmonic in z-direction
(d) the motion is not simple harmonic in z-direction
[June 2015]

12. Consider a mass m moving in an inverse square central force with characteristic coefficient μ and described by the Lagrangian:
$$L(r,\dot{r},\theta,\dot{\theta}) = \frac{m}{2}(\dot{r}^2 + r^2\dot{\theta}^2) + \frac{\mu m}{r}.$$ Then
(a) The generalized momenta of the system are $p_r = m\dot{r}$ and $P_\theta = mr^2\dot{\theta}$.
(b) The Hamiltonian of the system is $H = \frac{1}{2m}\left[P_r^2 + \frac{p_\theta^2}{r^2}\right] - \frac{1}{2}\frac{\mu m}{r}$.
(c) The Hamiltonian of the system is $H = \frac{1}{2m}\left[P_r^2 + \frac{p_\theta^2}{r^2}\right] - \frac{\mu m}{r}$.
(d) The generalized momenta of the system are $p_r = +m\dot{r}$ and $P_\theta = -mr^2\dot{\theta}$.
[Dec. 2015]

13. Consider the Hamiltonian (H) and the Lagrangian (L) for a free particle of mass m and velocity v. Then
(a) H and L are independent of each other.
(b) H and L are related but have different dependence on v.
(c) H and L are equal.
(d) Both H and L are quadratic in v.
[Dec. 2015]

14. A particle of unit mass moves in the direction of x-axis such that it has the Lagrangian
$$L = \frac{1}{12}\dot{x}^4 + \frac{1}{2}x\dot{x}^2 - x^2.$$
Let $Q = \dot{x}^2\ddot{x}$ represent a force (not arising from a potential) acting on the particle in the x-direction. If $x(0) = 1$ and $\dot{x}(0) = 1$, then the value of $\dot{x}$ is
(a) some non-zero finite value at $x = 0$.
(b) 1 at $x = 1$.
(c) $\sqrt{5}$ at $x = \frac{1}{2}$.
(d) 0 at $x = \sqrt{\frac{3}{2}}$.
[June 2016]

15. Which of the following are canonical transformations? (Where q,p represent generalized coordinate and generalised momentum respectively)
(a) $P = log\ sinp, Q = q\ tan\ p$
(b) $P = qp^2, Q = \frac{1}{p}$
(c) $P = q\cot p, Q = log\left(\frac{1}{q}\sin p\right)$
(d) $P = q^2\ sin\ 2p, Q = q^2\ cos\ 2p$
[Dec. 2016]

16. For a conservative system, the end configurations are fixed and the velocity in the varied motion is such that $T + V = E$. Here T, V and E represent, respectively the kinetic energy, the potential energy and the total energy. If $\delta(A)$ denotes the infinitesimal change in a variable A, and p_α and q_α $(\alpha = 1,2,\ldots,n)$ represent the

generalized momenta and generalized coordinates, respectively, then

(a) $\delta \int T\,dt = 0$

(b) $\delta \int \sum_{\alpha=1}^{n} p_\alpha dq_\alpha = 0$

(c) $\delta \int \sum_{\alpha=1}^{n} q_\alpha dp_\alpha = 0$

(d) $\delta \int \sum_{\alpha=1}^{n} (p_\alpha dq_\alpha + q_\alpha dp_\alpha) = 0$

[June 2017]

17. The Hamiltonian for a simple harmonic oscillator is $H(p,q) = \frac{P^2}{2m} + \frac{k}{2}q^2$. Than a possible Lagrangian corresponding to H can be

(a) $L = \frac{1}{2}\,m\dot{q}^2 - \frac{k}{2}\,q^2$

(b) $L = \frac{1}{2}\,m\dot{q}^2 - \frac{k}{2}\,(q^2 + 3q^2\dot{q})$

(c) $L = \frac{1}{2}\,m\dot{q}^2 + \frac{k}{2}\,q^2$

(d) $L = \frac{1}{2}m\dot{q}^2 + \frac{k}{2}(q^2 + 3q^2\dot{q})$

[June 2018]

18. Consider a point mass of mass m which is attached to a mass-less rigid rod of length a. The other end of the rod is made to move vertically such that its downward displacement from the origin at time t is given by $z(t) = z_0 \cos(\omega t)$. The mass is moving in a fixed plane and its position voctor at time t is given by $\vec{r}(t) = (a\sin\theta(t), z(t) + a\cos\theta(t))$.

Then the equation of motion of the point mass is

(a) $a\frac{d^2\theta}{dt^2} + (g + z_0\omega^2\cos(\omega t))\sin\theta = 0$

(b) $a\frac{d^2\theta}{dt^2} + (g - z_0\omega\cos(\omega t))\sin\theta = 0$

(c) $a\frac{d^2\theta}{dt^2} + (g + z_0^2\omega^2\cos(\omega t))\cos\theta = 0$

(d) $a\frac{d^2\theta}{dt^2} + (g - z_0\,\omega^2\cos(\omega t))\cos\theta = 0$

[Dec. 2018]

19. Let (q,p) be canonical variables. Consider the following transformations

(a) $(Q,P) = (\sqrt{2q e^{\alpha}}\cos p, \sqrt{2q e^{-\alpha}}\sin p), \alpha \in \mathbb{R}$

(b) $(Q,P) = (q\tan p, log(sin\,p))$

(c) $(Q,P) = \left(\frac{1}{p}, qp^2\right)$

Then

(a) only the transformations given in (a) and (b) are canonical

(b) only the transformations given in (b) and (c) are canonical

(c) only the transformations given in (a) and (c) are canonical

(d) all are canonical

[June 2019]

20. Consider a mechanical system whose position is described using the generalized coordinates $q_1, \ldots, q_n$. Let $T(q_1, \ldots, q_n, \dot{q}_1, \ldots, \dot{q}_n)$ be the kinetic energy of the system. If the generalized force $Q_j, 1 \le j \le n$, acting on the system is zero, then the Lagrange equations of motion are

(a) $\frac{d}{dt}\left(\frac{\partial T}{\partial \dot{q}_j}\right) - \frac{\partial T}{\partial q_j} = 0, 1 \le j \le n$

(b) $\frac{d}{dt}\left(\frac{\partial T}{\partial q_j}\right) - \frac{\partial T}{\partial \dot{q}_j} = 0, 1 \le j \le n$

(c) $\frac{\partial}{\partial \dot{q}_j}\left(\frac{dT}{dt}\right) - 2\frac{\partial T}{\partial q_j} = 0, 1 \le j \le n$

(d) $\frac{\partial}{\partial \dot{q}_j}\left(\frac{dT}{dt}\right) - \frac{\partial T}{\partial q_j} = 0, 1 \le j \le n$

[Dec. 2019]

21. Consider a dynamical system with the Lagrangian function $L(q,\dot{q}) = T - U$,

where the kinetic energy

$T = a(q)\dot{q}^2 \ge 0$

and the potential energy $U := U(q) with\ a(q) > 0$.

Which of the following statements are true?

(a) The associated Lagrange's equation is

$$\frac{d}{dt}\frac{\partial L}{\partial \dot{q}} = \frac{\partial L}{\partial q}$$

(b) The associated Lagrange's equation is

$$\frac{d}{dt}\frac{\partial L}{\partial q} = \frac{\partial L}{\partial \dot{q}}$$

(c) The point $(q_0, \dot{q}_o)$ is an equilibrium position of the dynamical system if and only if

$$\dot{q}_o = 0\ and\ \left.\frac{\partial U}{\partial q}\right|_{q=q_0} = 0$$

(d) The point $(q_0, \dot{q}_o)$ is an equilibrium position of the dynamical system if and only if

$$\dot{q}_o = 0\ and\ \left.\frac{\partial U}{\partial q}\right|_{q=q_0} > 0$$

[Nov. 2020]

22. A mass m with velocity v approaches a stationary mass M along the x-axis. The masses bounce of each other elastically. Assume that the motion takes place in one dimension along the x axis, and v_f and V_f represent the final velocities of masses m and M along the x-axis. Which of the following are true

(a) $v_f = v, V_f = v$

(b) $v_f = 0, V_f = v$

(c) $v_f = \frac{(m-M)v}{m+M}, V_f = \frac{2mv}{m+M}$

(d) $v_f = \frac{mv}{m+M}, V_f = \frac{Mv}{m+M}$

[Feb. 2016]

23. Suppose f, g are smooth functions of generalized coordinates $q_1, q_2, \ldots, q_n$ the associated conjugate momenta $p_1, p_2, \ldots, p_n$, and time t. Let [f, g] denote the Poisson bracket of f and g. Suppose H is a Hamiltonian of the system.

Then which of the following statements are true?

(a) $\frac{\partial}{\partial t}[f,g] = \left[\frac{\partial f}{\partial t}, g\right] + \left[f, \frac{\partial g}{\partial t}\right]$

(b) If f is a constant of motion, and f is independent of t, then [H, f] is a constant of motion

(c) $[[H, f.g] + [[g, H.f] + [[f,g], H] = 0$

(d) If f and g are constants of motion, then [f, g] is a constant of motion

[June 2025]

24. A mechanical system is described using generalized position q and generalized momentum p. Let Q and P denote new generalized position and generalized

momentum variables respectively, generated by the generating function $F(g,P) = q^2e^P$ and Q, P are canonical coordinates. Let $G(p,Q)$ be a function such that $G(2,e) = 0$, and it generates the same canonical coordinates Q, P. Then which of the following statements are true?

(a) $G(p,Q) = -Q\left[1 + \log_e\left(\frac{p^2}{4Q}\right)\right]$

(b) $G(p,Q) = -pQ\left[1 + \log_e\left(\frac{Q^2}{4p}\right)\right]$

(c) $p = 2qe^P, Q = q^2e^P$

(d) $p = -2qe^P, Q = -q^2e^P$

[Dec 2025]

Answer Key				
MCQ (Multiple Choice Questions)				
1	2	3	4	5
d	a	a	b	b
6	7	8	9	10
c	c	b	b	d
11	12	13	14	15
b	b	b	d	b
16	17	18	19	20
c	b	a	a	b
21	22	23	24	25
a	b	d	b	a
MSQ (Multiple Select Questions)				
1	2	3	4	5
c, d	a, c, d	a, b, c, d	a, b, c	a, b, c, d
6	7	8	9	10
a, b, c, d	a, b, c	a, b, c, d	a, c, d	d
11	12	13	14	15
a, c	a, c	c, d	b, c, d	a, b, c
16	17	18	19	20
a, b	a, b	a	d	a, c
21	22	23	24	
a, c	c	a,b,c,d	a, c	

EXPLANATIONS

MCQ (Multiple Choice Questions)

1. Explanation: (d)

A system consisting of three point masses connected by three rigid massless rods has six degrees of freedom.

2. Explanation: (a)

3. Explanation: (a)

Given,

$H = pq - q^2$, then as $t \to \infty$

We know Hamilton's equation

$\dot{q} = \frac{\partial H}{\partial p}$ and $\dot{p} = -\frac{\partial H}{\partial q}$

Now, $\dot{q} = \frac{\partial H}{\partial p}$

$\Rightarrow \dot{q} = q$

Integrating, we get

$q = e^t \quad (1)$

Now $\dot{p} = -\frac{\partial H}{\partial q}$

$\Rightarrow \dot{p} = -p + 2q$

$\Rightarrow \dot{p} + p = 2q$

Now find the C.F.

$\Rightarrow \dot{p} + p = 0$

$\Rightarrow p = e^{-t} \quad (2)$

P.I. $= \frac{2}{D^2+1}e^t$

$= \frac{2e^t}{1+1}$

$= e^t \quad (3)$

From (2) and (3)

Solution is

$p(t) = e^{-t} + e^t \quad (4)$

From (1) and (4)

as $t \to \infty \quad q \to \infty$

& as $t \to \infty \quad p \to \infty$

From above explanation,

Option a) is the correct answer.

4. Explanation: (b)

The degrees of freedom for a molecule containing n atoms is $3n$.

If the molecule is linear, the vibrational degrees of freedom $= 3n - 3 - 2$

$= 3n - 5$

5. Explanation: (b)

Given,

S is mechanical system with Lagrangian $L(\vec{q}, \dot{\vec{q}}, t)$ & $\vec{q} = (q_1, q_2, \ldots, q_n)$

we know that,

Lagrange equation of motion constitute n second order ODE.

$\Rightarrow$ Lagrangian can be transformed into Hamiltonian using Legendre Transformation.

So only option (b) is correct answer.

6. Explanation: (c)

$y_1 = a\sin(\omega t - px)$

$y_2 = a\sin(wt - px + \phi)$

Using superposition principle

$y = y_1 + y_2$

$y = a[\sin(\omega t - px) + \sin(\omega t - px + \phi)]$

$y = a\,.2\sin\left[\frac{\omega t - px + \omega t - px + \phi}{2}\right]\cos\left[\frac{\phi}{2}\right]$

$y = 2a\sin\left(\omega t - px + \frac{\phi}{2}\right)\cos\frac{\phi}{2}$

Amplitude $\rightarrow 2a\cos\frac{\phi}{2}$

Phase $\rightarrow \frac{\phi}{2}$

Option (c) is correct.

7. Explanation: (c)

$F = mg - cv$

$m\frac{dV}{dt} = mg - cv$

$\Rightarrow \int_0^v \frac{dV}{g-cv} = \int_0^t dt \quad (\because m = 1)$

$\Rightarrow \left[-\frac{1}{c}\ln(g-cv)\right]_0^v = t$

$\Rightarrow -\frac{1}{c}\ln(g-cv) - \frac{1}{c}\ln g = t$

$\Rightarrow \ln\left(\frac{g-cv}{g}\right) = -ct$

$1 - e^{-ct} = \frac{cv}{g}$

$\Rightarrow v = \frac{g}{c}(1 - e^{-ct})$

Option (c) is correct

8. Explanation: (b)

To specify point B & C we require total 6 co-ordinate

Degree of freedom for system = 6 − 2=4

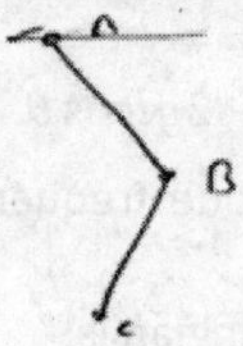

= 4

9. Explanation: (b)

Torque about origin

$\vec{\tau} = (\vec{r} - \vec{r}_0) \times \vec{F}$

$\vec{r} = 2\hat{\imath} + \hat{\jmath} - 2\hat{k}$

$\vec{F} = 5\hat{\imath} - 2\hat{\jmath} + 3\hat{k}$

$\vec{r}_0 = 0\hat{\imath} + 0\hat{\jmath} + 0\hat{k}$

$\vec{\tau} = (2\hat{\imath} + \hat{\jmath} - 2\hat{k}) \times (5\hat{\imath} - 2\hat{\jmath} + 3\hat{k})$

$= -4\hat{k} - 6\hat{\jmath} - 5\hat{k} + 3\hat{\imath} - 10\hat{\jmath} - 4\hat{\imath}$

$\vec{\tau} = -\hat{\imath} - 16\hat{\jmath} - 9\hat{k}$

Option (b) is correct

10. Explanation: (d)

11. Explanation: (b)

Given bead slider without friction on a frictionless wire

$x = a(\theta - \sin\theta) \quad y = a(1 + \cos\theta)$

$0 \le \theta \le \pi$

$L = \frac{1}{2}m(\dot{x}^2 + \dot{y}^2) - mgy$

$\dot{x} = a(\dot{\theta} - \cos\theta\,\dot{\theta})$

$\dot{y} = a(0 - \sin\theta\,\dot{\theta})$

$L = \frac{1}{2}m[a^2\dot{\theta}^2(1-\cos\theta)^2 + a^2\sin^2\theta\,\dot{\theta}^2]$

$-mga(1 + \cos\theta)$

$L = \frac{1}{2}ma^2\dot{\theta}^2[1 + \cos^2\theta - 2\cos\theta + \sin^2\theta]$

$-mga(1 + \cos\theta)$

$L = \frac{1}{2}ma^2\dot{\theta}^2.2(1-\cos\theta) - mga(1+\cos\theta)$

$L = ma^2\dot{\theta}^2(1-\cos\theta) - mga(1+\cos\theta)$

$L = ma^2\ (1 - Cos\,\theta)\dot{\theta}^2 - mga(1+\cos\theta)$

Option b) is the correct answer.

12. Explanation: (b)

13. Explanation: (b)

Angular velocity with constant magnitude

Since rigid body having one point fixed and no external torque. All principle moment of inertia are equal

So option (b) is correct only.

14. Explanation: (d)

15. Explanation: (b)

16. Explanation: (c)

Given $T = \frac{1}{2}m(\dot{r}^2 + r^2\dot{\theta}^2)$

$V = \frac{1}{2}kr^2$

$L = T - V$

$L = \frac{1}{2}m(\dot{r}^2 + r^2\dot{\theta}^2) - \frac{1}{2}kr^2$

θ is ignorable coordinate because $\frac{\partial L}{\partial\theta} = 0$

$P_\theta = \frac{\partial L}{\partial\dot{\theta}} = mr^2\dot{\theta} = constant$

So option (c) is correct.

17. Explanation: (b)

Kinetic energy

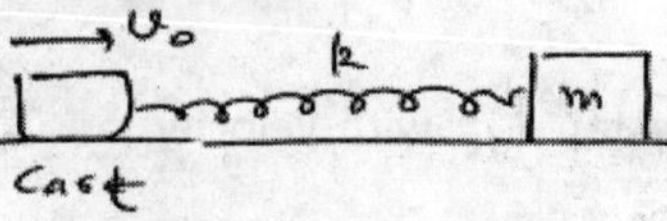

$T = \frac{1}{2}m\dot{q}^2$

$V = \frac{1}{2}k(q - V_0t)^2$

$\frac{m}{2}\dot{q}^2 - \frac{k}{2}(q - v_0t)^2$

18. Explanation: (a)

19. Explanation: (a)

20. Explanation: (b)

When net force on the particle is zero, then it is said to be in equilibrium

→ body moves freely in uniform gravitational field is moving under the action of gravity

So net force on the body is not zero.

⇒ stable equilibrium of the body is not possible.

21. Explanation: (a)

The moment of inertia of the cylinder about a diameter of its base is given by $I = m\left(\frac{r^2}{4} + \frac{h^2}{3}\right)$, where r is radius, h is height and m is mass.

Given $r = 2, h = 3$.

Mass $m = \rho \cdot v$, where v is volume.

Now, $v = \pi r^2 h = 12\pi$.

$\therefore m = 12\pi\rho$

$\therefore I = 12\pi\rho\left(\frac{2^2}{4} + \frac{3^2}{3}\right) = 48\pi\rho.$

22. Explanation: (b)

The moment of inertia I_z for a solid torus of constant density ρ about the z-axis is given by

$$I_z = \rho \cdot V \cdot \left(b^2 + \frac{3a^2}{4}\right)$$

where

V is the volume of the torus,

b is the distance from center of the tube to the z-axis,

a is the radius of the tube,

Now, the volume V of the torus is $V = 2\pi^2 a^2 b$

Substituting the volume into the formula for I_z, we get,

$$I_z = \rho \cdot 2\pi^2 a^2 b \cdot \left(b^2 + \frac{3a^2}{4}\right)$$

$$\therefore I_z = \frac{\pi^2}{2} a^2 b(4b^2 + 3a^2)\rho$$

$\therefore$ Option (b) is correct.

23. Explanation: (d)

The total potential energy of the cord is given by:

$$U = -\frac{Mg}{2l} x^2$$

Since the cord is flexible and inelastic, its distribution affects the dynamics of the system.

Using Lagrangian mechanics, the Lagrangian is:

$$L = T - U$$

The system consists of:

1. Moving block on the table m with velocity $\dot{x}$ $\quad T_{\text{table}} = \frac{1}{2} m\dot{x}^2$
2. Hanging block m with velocity $\dot{x}$ $\quad T_{\text{hanging}} = \frac{1}{2} m\dot{x}^2$
3. Cord of mass M:
   - The cord is assumed to have a linear mass distribution.
   - Part of the cord is on the table, and part of it is hanging.
   - The center of mass of the hanging part moves with velocity $\dot{x}$.
4. Using the center of mass concept, the kinetic energy of the cord can be approximated as:

$$T_{\text{cord}} = \frac{1}{2}\frac{M}{l}(l + x)\dot{x}^2$$

$$T = \frac{1}{2} m\dot{x}^2 + \frac{1}{2} m\dot{x}^2 + \frac{1}{2}\frac{M}{l}(l + x)\dot{x}^2$$

$$T = \frac{1}{2}\left(2m + \frac{M}{l}(l + x)\right)\dot{x}^2$$

The potential energy is given as:

$$U = -\frac{Mg}{2l} x^2$$

Lagrange's equation:

$$\frac{d}{dt}\left(\frac{\partial L}{\partial \dot{x}}\right) - \frac{\partial L}{\partial x} = 0$$

$$\frac{\partial L}{\partial \dot{x}} = \left(2m + \frac{M}{l}(l + x)\right)\dot{x}$$

$$\frac{d}{dt}\left(\left(2m + \frac{M}{l}(l + x)\right)\dot{x}\right)$$

$$= \left(2m + \frac{M}{l}(l + x)\right)\ddot{x} + \frac{M}{l}\dot{x}^2$$

$$\frac{\partial U}{\partial x} = -\frac{Mg}{l} x$$

$$\left(2m + \frac{M}{l}(l + x)\right)\ddot{x} + \frac{M}{l}\dot{x}^2 + \frac{Mg}{l} x = 0$$

Ignoring the $\dot{x}^2$ term for small velocities,

$$\left(2m + \frac{M}{l}(l + x)\right)\ddot{x} = -\frac{Mg}{l} x$$

Solving for $\ddot{x}$,

$$\ddot{x} = \frac{g}{l}\frac{Ml + mx}{2m + M}$$

$$\frac{g}{l}\frac{ml + Mx}{2m + M}$$

which corresponds to Option (d).

24. Explanation: (b)

We are given the Lagrangian of a system with two degrees of freedom:

$$L = \frac{5}{2}\dot{x}^2 + l^2\dot{\theta}^2 + 2l\dot{x}\dot{\theta}\cos\theta + 2gl\cos\theta$$

We need to determine the normal mode frequency for small oscillations ($|\theta| \ll 1$).

The kinetic energy from the given Lagrangian is:

$$T = \frac{5}{2}\dot{x}^2 + l^2\dot{\theta}^2 + 2l\dot{x}\dot{\theta}\cos\theta$$

For small θ, we approximate $\cos\theta \approx 1$, so:

$$T \approx \frac{5}{2}\dot{x}^2 + l^2\dot{\theta}^2 + 2l\dot{x}\dot{\theta}$$

This can be written in matrix form as:

$$T = \frac{1}{2}\begin{bmatrix}\dot{x} \\ \dot{\theta}\end{bmatrix}\begin{bmatrix}5 & 2l \\ 2l & 2l^2\end{bmatrix}\begin{bmatrix}\dot{x} \\ \dot{\theta}\end{bmatrix}$$

Thus, the mass matrix is:

$$M = \begin{bmatrix}5 & 2l \\ 2l & 2l^2\end{bmatrix}$$

The potential energy is:

$$V = -2gl\cos\theta$$

For small θ, using $\cos\theta \approx 1 - \frac{1}{2}\theta^2$, we get:

$$V \approx -2gl\left(1 - \frac{1}{2}\theta^2\right) = -2gl + gl\theta^2$$

Ignoring constant terms, the quadratic potential energy term is:

$$V = \frac{1}{2}(2gl)\theta^2$$

Thus, the stiffness matrix is:

$$K = \begin{bmatrix}0 & 0 \\ 0 & 2gl\end{bmatrix}$$

The equation for normal mode frequencies ω is:

$$\det(K - \omega^2 M) = 0$$

Substituting M and K:

$$\begin{vmatrix}0 - \omega^2(5) & 0 - \omega^2(2l) \\ 0 - \omega^2(2l) & 2gl - \omega^2(2l^2)\end{vmatrix} = 0$$

Expanding the determinant:

$$(-5\omega^2)(2gl - 2l^2\omega^2) - (-2l\omega^2)(-2l\omega^2) = 0$$

$$-10gl\omega^2 + 6l^2\omega^4 = 0$$

Factorizing:

$$\omega^2(-10gl + 6l^2\omega^2) = 0$$

Ignoring the trivial solution $\omega = 0$:

$$6l^2\omega^2 = 10gl$$

$$\omega^2 = \frac{10gl}{6l^2} = \frac{5g}{3l}$$

$$\omega = \sqrt{\frac{5g}{3l}}$$

25. Explanation: (a)

Treat the Lagrangian as $L = (\dot{q}_1)^2 + (\dot{q}_2)^2 + \dot{q}_1\dot{q}_2 +; (q_1)^2$,

so that $V(q) = -(q_1)^2$ would give $\partial L/\partial q_1 = 2q_1$ and $\partial L/\partial q_2 = 0$.

Then the conjugate momenta are $p_1 = \partial L/\partial \dot{q}_1 = 2\dot{q}_1 + \dot{q}_2$ and $p_2 = \partial L/\partial \dot{q}_2 = 2\dot{q}_2 + \dot{q}_1$.

Euler–Lagrange gives $\dot{p}_i = \partial L/\partial q_i$, hence

$\dot{p}_1 = 2q_1, \dot{p}_2 = 0,$

Correct Answer: (a)

MSQ (Multiple Select Questions)

1. Explanation: (c), (d)

Again here is force free motion,

Given, symmetrical about principle Z-axes

$\bar{\omega} = (\omega_1, \omega_2, \omega_3)$

Again write Euler's equation.

$I_1\dot{\omega}_1 = (I_2 - I_3)\omega_2\omega_3$

$I_2\dot{\omega}_2 = (I_3 - I_1)\omega_3\omega_1$

$I_3\dot{\omega}_3 = (I_1 - I_2)\omega_1\omega_2$

Again $I_1 = I_2$ (body is symmetrical about z-axes)

$I_1\dot{\omega}_1 = (I_1 - I_3)\omega_2\omega_3$

$I_1\dot{\omega}_2 = (I_3 - I_1)\omega_3\omega_1$

$\dot{\omega}_3 = 0 \Rightarrow \omega_3 =$ constant

We know that ω_1 & ω_2 will satisfy SHM

$\omega_1 = \cos \Omega t$

$\omega_2 = a \sin \Omega t$

$\omega_1^2 + \omega_2^2 = constant$

$\Rightarrow \omega_2 = a\sin(\lambda t + b)$

Option (c) and (d) are correct.

2. Explanation: (a), (c), (d)

3. Explanation: (a), (b), (c), (d)

Given principle axes \

OX_1, OX_2, OX_3 body is in motion with OX_3 as the axes of symmetry

means $I_1 = I_2$

Euler's equation are

$I_1\dot{w}_1 = (I_2 - I_3)w_2w_3$

$I_2\dot{w}_2 = (I_3 - I_1)w_3w_1$

$I_3\dot{w}_3 = (I_1 - I_2)w_1w_2$

Since $I_1 = I_2$

$\Rightarrow I_1\dot{w}_1 = (I_1 - I_3)w_2w_3$

$I_2\dot{w}_2 = (I_3 - I_1)w_3w_1$

$I_3\dot{w}_3 = 0$

$\Rightarrow w_3 =$ constant

Now put $\frac{I_3 - I_1}{I_1} w_3 = constant = \Omega$

$\dot{w}_1 = -\Omega\, w_2$

$\dot{w}_2 = \Omega\, w_1$

$\Rightarrow \ddot{w}_1 = -\Omega\, \dot{w}_2$

$\ddot{w}_1 + \Omega^2\, w_1 = 0$ SHM

Same way $\ddot{w}_2 + \Omega^2\, w_2 = 0$ SHM

$L_3 = I_3\dot{w}_3 - (I_1 - I_2)\, w_1\, w_2$

$L_3 = 0 = constant$

Option (a), (b), (c), (d) are correct

4. Explanation: (a), (b), (c)

5. Explanation: (a), (b), (c), (d) We know that

$$\frac{d}{dt}\left(\frac{\partial L}{\partial \dot{q}_i}\right) - \frac{\partial L}{\partial q_i} = 0$$

→ From here we can say that this equation is 2nd order differential equation.

→ & Number of equation is equal to the number of generalized co-ordinate

→ We know that Lagrangian is not unique. If we change our reference of potential energy in that case Lagrangian will be difference but Lagrangian equation of motion are preserved

→ Lagrangian is quadratic function of generalized velocity

⇒ All 4 options are correct

6. Explanation: (a), (b), (c), (d)

7. Explanation: (a), (b), (c)

We know for small oscillation case

$E = \frac{1}{2} m\, w^2\, A^2$

$\Rightarrow E \times m, E \times w^2, E \times A^2$

(a), (b) and (a) are correct.

8. Explanation: (a), (b), (c), (d)

Given $H(\vec{q}, \dot{\vec{q}})$ and $L(\vec{q}, \dot{\vec{q}})$

Since H does't depend upon time explicitly

$\Rightarrow H$ is a constant quantity and it represents total energy of the system

We know from Hamilton's equation

$\dot{q} = \frac{\partial H}{\partial p}$ & $\dot{p} = -\frac{\partial H}{\partial q}$

So If H does't depend upon q, then $\vec{p}$ will be constant. & $\dot{\vec{p}} = \frac{\partial L}{\partial q}$

So if L doesn't depend upon $\vec{q}$ then $\vec{p}$ is constant

⇒ All (a), (b), (c), (d) option are correct

9. Explanation: (a), (c),(d)

Consider a particle of mass m in S.H.M.

$T = \frac{1}{2} m\, \dot{x}^2\; V = \frac{1}{2} p\, x^2$

$L = T - V$

$L = \frac{1}{2} m\, \dot{x}^2\, V - \frac{1}{2} p\, x^2$ ...(1)

$p = \frac{\partial L}{\partial \dot{x}} = m\, \dot{x}$

$\Rightarrow \dot{x} = \frac{p}{m}$

$p = m\, \dot{x}$ ...(2)

$H = \dot{x}\, p - L$

$H = \frac{p^2}{m} - \frac{1}{2} m \cdot \frac{p^2}{m^2} + \frac{1}{2} p\, x^2$

$H = \frac{p^2}{2m} + \frac{1}{2}\, p\, x^2$ ...(3)

$H(x,\dot{x}) = \frac{m\dot{x}^2}{2} + \frac{1}{2}p\,x^2$ ...(4)

10. Explanation: (d)

11. Explanation: (a), (c)

Particle is moving on the cylinder

$x^2 + y^2 = a^2$

$x = \delta\cos\phi$

$y = \delta\sin\phi$

Give $F = p\,r$

$V = -\int \vec{F}.d\vec{r}$

$V = \frac{p\,r^2}{2}$ $\{x^2 + y^2 = \delta^2$

$V = \frac{1}{2}\,p\,(x^2 + y^2 + z^2)$

$L = \frac{1}{2}\,m\,[\dot{\delta}^2 + \delta^2\,\dot{\phi}^2 + \dot{z}^2] - \frac{1}{2}p\,(p^2 + z^2)$

Since particle is moving on the surface on the cylinder

$\dot{\delta} = 0$

$\Rightarrow L = \frac{1}{2}\,m\,[\delta^2\,\dot{\phi}^2 + \dot{z}^2] - \frac{1}{2}p\,(\delta^2 + z^2)$

Equation of motion in ϕ

$\frac{d}{dt}\left(\frac{\partial L}{\partial \dot{\phi}}\right) - \frac{\partial L}{\partial \phi} = 0$

$\Rightarrow \frac{d}{dt}(m\,\delta^2\,\dot{\phi}) - 0 = 0$

$\Rightarrow p\phi = constant$

Angular momentum about z-direction is constant

Equation of motion in z

$\frac{d}{dt}\left(\frac{\partial L}{\partial \dot{z}}\right) - \frac{\partial L}{\partial z} = 0$

$\Rightarrow m\,\ddot{z} + p\,z = 0$

So option (a) and (c) are correct.

12. Explanation: (a), (c)

Given $L(r,\dot{r},\theta\dot{\theta}) = \frac{m}{2}(\dot{r}^2 + r^2\,\dot{\theta}^2) + \frac{\mu m}{I}$

$p_r = \frac{\partial L}{\partial \dot{r}} = m\dot{r}, p_\theta = \frac{\partial L}{\partial \dot{\theta}} = mr^2\dot{\theta}$

$H = \frac{1}{2m}\left(p_r^2 + \frac{p_\theta^2}{2r}\right) - \frac{\mu m}{r}$

(a), (c) option are correct

13. Explanation: (c), (d)

14. Explanation: (b), (c), (d)

We know that if force is not arising from potential the Lagrange equation of motion is

$\frac{d}{dt}\left(\frac{\partial L}{\partial \dot{x}}\right) - \frac{\partial L}{\partial x} = 0$

$\frac{d}{dt}\left(\frac{x^3}{3} + x\dot{x}\right) - \left(\frac{\dot{x}^2}{2} - 2x\right) = \dot{x}^2\ddot{x}$

$\dot{x}^2\ddot{x} + \dot{x}^2 + x\ddot{x} - \frac{\dot{x}^2}{2} + 2x = \dot{x}^2\ddot{x}$

$\ddot{x}x + \frac{\dot{x}^2}{2} + 2x = 0$

$2\ddot{x}x + \dot{x}^2 + 4x = 0$

Put $\dot{x} = \sqrt{\delta}$

$\ddot{x} = \frac{1}{2\sqrt{\delta}}\dot{\delta}$

Equation reduces to $\frac{x}{\sqrt{\delta}}\dot{\delta} + \delta + 4x = 0$

$\dot{\delta} = \frac{d\delta}{dt} = \frac{d\delta}{dx}\frac{dx}{dt}$

$= \sqrt{\delta}\frac{d\delta}{dx}$

$x\frac{d\delta}{dx} + \delta + 4x = 0$

$\frac{d\delta}{dx} + \frac{\delta}{x} = -4$

$\delta.x = \int -4xdx + c$

$\delta.x = -2x^2 + c$

$\dot{x}^2 x = -2x^2 + c$

$x(0) = 1 \;\; \dot{x}(0) = 1$

$c = 3$

$\dot{x}^2 x = -2x^2 + 3$

$\dot{x} = \sqrt{\frac{3 - 2x^2}{x}}$

$\dot{x}$ is not define at $x = 0$

When $x = 1 \;\; \dot{x} = \sqrt{1} = 1$

When $x = \frac{1}{2} \;\; \dot{x} = \sqrt{\frac{3-\frac{1}{2}}{\frac{1}{2}}} = \sqrt{5}$

When $x = \sqrt{\frac{3}{2}} \;\; \dot{x} = \sqrt{\frac{3-3}{\sqrt{\frac{3}{2}}}} = 0$

Option (a) (c) and (d) are correct

15. Explanation: (a), (b),(c)

It is given that q and p represent generalised coordinate and generalised momenta respectively

So $\{q,p\} = 1$

If the transformation is canonical then

$\{Q,P\} = 1$

So check for all option

For option (1)

$P = \log\sin p \qquad Q = q\tan p$

$\{Q,P\}$

$\frac{\partial Q}{\partial q}\frac{\partial P}{\partial p} - \frac{\partial Q}{\partial p}\frac{\partial P}{\partial q}$

$\tan p\,.\frac{1}{\sin p}.\cos p - q\sec^2 p \times 0$

$\tan p\,.\cot p - 0$

$= 1$

So first transformation is canonical similarly we can check for all other option

Option (a), (b) and (c) are the correct answer.

16. Explanation: (a), (b) By Hamilton's principle

$\int T\,dt$ is stationary

So, $\delta\int T\,dt = 0$

$T = \frac{\delta}{\alpha}p_\alpha\frac{dq_\alpha}{dt}$

$= \delta\int p_\alpha\,dq_\alpha = 0$

Option (a) and (b) are correct

17. Explanation: (a),(b)

18. Explanation: (a)

Given the mass is moving in plane

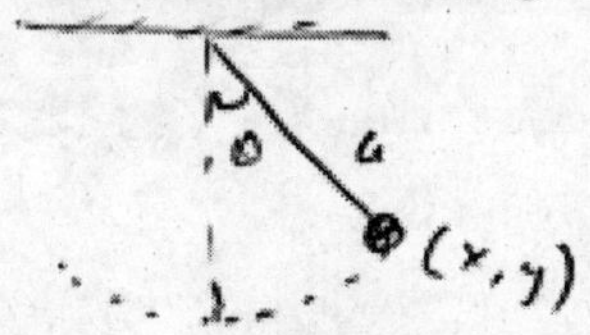

$\vec{r}(l) = (a\sin\theta(t)\, z(t) + \cos\theta(l))$

$z(t) = z_0 \cos\omega t$

$T = \frac{1}{2}m(\dot{x}^2 + \dot{y}^2)$

$x = a\sin\theta$

$\dot{x} = a\cos\dot{\theta}$

$\dot{y} = \dot{z} - a\sin\dot{\theta}$

$\dot{y} = -z_0 \sin\omega t\,(\omega) - a\sin\dot{\theta}$

$T = \frac{1}{2}m[a^2\cos^2\theta\,\dot{\theta}^2 + \omega^2 z_0^2 \sin^2\omega t + a^2\sin^2\theta\,\dot{\theta}^2 +$
$2az_0\omega\dot{\theta}\sin\theta\sin\omega t\,]$

$T = \frac{1}{2}m[a^2\dot{\theta}^2 + \omega^2 z_0^2\sin^2\omega t + 2az_0\omega\dot{\theta}\sin\theta\sin\omega t]$

$V = mgy = -mg\cos\theta$

$L = T - V$

$L = \frac{1}{2}m[a^2\dot{\theta}^2 + \omega^2 z_0^2\sin^2\omega t + 2az_0\omega\dot{\theta}\sin\theta\sin\omega t$
$+mga\cos\theta]$

Equation of motion

$\frac{d}{dt}\left(\frac{\partial L}{\partial\dot{\theta}}\right) - \frac{\partial L}{\partial\theta} = 0$

$\frac{d}{dt}[ma^2\dot{\theta} + ma\omega z_0\sin\theta\sin\omega t]$
$-(ma\omega z_0\dot{\theta}\cos\theta\sin\omega t - mga\sin\theta) = 0$

$ma^2\ddot{\theta} + ma\omega^2 z_0\sin\theta\cos\omega t + ma\omega z_0\dot{\theta}\cos\theta\sin\omega t$
$-ma\omega z_0\dot{\theta}\cos\theta\sin\omega t + mga\sin\theta = 0$

$ma^2\ddot{\theta} + ma\omega^2 z_0\sin\theta\cos\omega t + mga\sin\theta = 0$

$a\frac{d^2\theta}{dt^2} + (\omega^2 z_0\cos\omega t + g)\sin\theta = 0$

Option (a) is correct

19. Explanation: (d)

Given

(a) $(Q, P) = \sqrt{2q}e^{\alpha}\cos p,\ \sqrt{2q}e^{-\alpha}\sin p$

(b) $(Q, P) = (q\tan p, \log(\sin p))$

(c) $(Q, P) = \left(\frac{1}{p}, qp^2\right)$

For canonical transformation

Check {Q, P} =1

For (a)

{Q, P}

$= \frac{\partial Q}{\partial q}\frac{\partial P}{\partial p} - \frac{\partial Q}{\partial p}\frac{\partial P}{\partial q}$

$= \frac{1}{\sqrt{2}\sqrt{q}}e^{\alpha}\cos p.\sqrt{2q}e^{-\alpha}\cos p$

$+\sqrt{2q}e^{\alpha}\sin p, \frac{1}{\sqrt{2q}}e^{-\alpha}\sin p$

$= \cos^2 p + \sin^2 p = 1$

So, (a) transformation is canonical similarly we can check for (b) and (c), (d) Option is correct. All transformations are canonical.

20. Explanation: (a),(c)

Lagrangian equation of motion

$\frac{d}{dt}\left(\frac{\partial T}{\partial\dot{q}_j}\right) - \frac{\partial T}{\partial q_j} = Q_j \quad \forall j = 1,2,\dots,n$

If $Q_j = 0$

$= \frac{d}{dt}\left(\frac{\partial T}{\partial\dot{q}_j}\right) - \frac{\partial T}{\partial q_j} = 0$

$\frac{d}{dt}\left(\frac{\partial T}{\partial\dot{q}_j}\right) = \frac{\partial}{\partial q_j}\left(\frac{dT}{dt}\right) - \frac{\partial T}{\partial q_j}$

$\frac{\partial}{\partial q_j}\left(\frac{dT}{dt}\right) - 2\frac{\partial T}{\partial q_j} = 0$

Option a), c) are correct answer.

21. Explanation: (a),(c)

22. Explanation: (c)

$m \to u \qquad m$ (initially)

$m \to u_f \qquad M \to V_f$ (final)

Using linear momentum conservation

$mu + 0 = mu_f + MV_f$

$\Rightarrow m\,u_f + MV_f = mu \qquad (1)$

Coefficient of Restitution

$e = \frac{V_f - u_f}{u}$

$\Rightarrow V_f - u_f = u \qquad (2)$

$e = 1$ for elastic collision

By equation (1) and (2)

$V_f + \frac{M}{m}V_f = 2u$

$V_f = \left(\frac{2mu}{m+M}\right)$

By equation (2)

$u_f = \frac{2mu}{M+m} - u$

$u_f = \frac{(m-M)u}{(M+m)}$

Option (c) correct

23. Explanation: (a), (b), (c), (d)

Statement (a): $\frac{\partial}{\partial t}[f, g] = \left[\frac{\partial f}{\partial t}, g\right] + \left[f, \frac{\partial g}{\partial t}\right]$

This is **true**. Poisson bracket is linear in each argument, and partial derivatives w.r.t t commute with derivatives w.r.t q_i, p_i.

Statement (b): If f is a constant of motion, and f is independent of t, then $[H, f]$ is a constant of motion

Constant of motion: $\frac{df}{dt} = [f, H] + \frac{\partial f}{\partial t} = 0$. Since f is independent of t, $\frac{\partial f}{\partial t} = 0$, so $[f, H] = 0$.

But $([H, f] = -[f, H] = 0)$. The Poisson bracket with H is zero, so, $([H, f])$ is trivially a constant of motion.

Statement (c): $[[H, f], g] + [[g, H], f] + [[f, g], H] = 0$

This is exactly the **Jacobi identity** with (f, g, H).

Statement (d): If f and g are constants of motion, then $([f, g])$ is a constant of motion

Total derivative:

$$\frac{d}{dt}[f,g] = [[f,g],H] + \frac{\partial}{\partial t}[f,g]$$

Since f and g are constants of motion and independent of t, using Jacobi identity:

$$[[f,g],H] = -([[g,H],f] + [[H,f],g]) = 0$$

So $([f,g])$ is indeed a constant of motion.

Conclusion

All statements **a, b, c, d are true**.

24. Explanation: (a), (c)

Given generating function (Type-2):

$F(q,P) = q^2e^P$

For Type-2 generating function:

$$p = \frac{\partial F}{\partial q}, Q = \frac{\partial F}{\partial P}$$

Find transformation equations

$$p = \frac{\partial}{\partial q}(q^2e^P) = 2qe^P$$

$$Q = \frac{\partial}{\partial P}(q^2e^P) = q^2e^P$$

So

$p = 2qe^P, Q = q^2e^P$

Statement (3) is TRUE

Statement (4) has negative sign → False.

Express (q,P) in terms of (p,Q)

From $Q = q^2e^P$

And $p = 2qe^P$

Divide: $\frac{p^2}{4Q} = e^P$

Thus $P = \ln\left(\frac{p^2}{4Q}\right)$

Relation between generating functions

For transformation from $F(q,P)$ to $G(p,Q)$:

$G = F - pq$

Now

$F = q^2e^P = Q$

Also

$$q = \frac{p}{2e^P} = \frac{2Q}{p}$$

So, $pq = 2Q$

Thus, $G = Q - 2Q = -Q$

Substitute $P = \ln(p^2/4Q)$:

$$G(p,Q) = -Q\left[1 + \ln\left(\frac{p^2}{4Q}\right)\right]$$

Statement (1) is TRUE

Statement (2) False.

Correct answers: (1) and (3)

SECTION - II

STATISTICS

STATISTICS

No. of questions asked from year 2012-2025

Units		2012		2013		2014		2015		2016		2017		2018		2019		2020	2021	2022	2023	2024	2025		
		Jun	Dec	Jun	Dec	Jun	Dec	Jun	Dec	Jun	Dec	Jun	Dec	Jun	Dec	Jun	Dec	Nov	Jun	Sep	Jun	Jul	Feb	Jun	Dec
1	Descriptive statistics	3	1		1	2	-	-	1	-	-	-	-	-	1	-	-	-	-	-	-	-	-	2	1
2	Probability	-	-	1	1	1	1	-	2	2	3	1	3	1	-	-	1	1	1	1	2	1	1	1	3
3	Random variable	4	2	2	2	3	5	4	3	3	-	1	1	3	-	4	2	2	-	2	4	3	2	4	3
4	Distribution theory	3	5	7	5	4	4	8	2	2	3	4	4	4	4	2	2	3	1	6	4	3	2	2	1
5	Estimation theory	5	2	3	3	4	2	2	4	4	3	3	4	4	3	3	5	5	3	3	2	5	5	6	6
6	Testing of hypothesis		2	1	1	3	1	2	3	3	3	3	1	1	2	1	2	1	2	3	3	2	4	3	2
7	Non-parametric	2	-	-	1	1	1	1	-	-	1	-	-	1	-	-	-	1	1	-	-	1	2	-	1
8	Bayesian inference	1	1	1	-	-	3	-	1	1	1	1	1	3	1	1	1	2	2	-	-	2	1	2	2
9	Correlation & regression analysis	2	4	4	2	3	3	4	1	3	2	2	1	-	2	1	-	3	1	3	2	2	3	3	-
10	Design of experiment	1	3	2	2	1	1	1	2	1	2	1	1	1	2	1	4	2	1	-	-	2	1	2	3
11	Sampling	3	1	2	2	2	2	1	1	2	2		2	2	-	2	2	2	1	-	-	1	-	-	1
12	Multivariate analysis	-	2	1	2	1	3	4	6	2	3	3	1	1	1	4	1	2	-	2	2	2	3	1	2
13	Markov chain	2	3	1	2	2	2	2	1	1	1	1	2	2	3	2	3	2	-	2	1	2	2	1	2
14	Linear programming problem	2	1	2	1	1	1		1	1	1	2	-	1	1	2	1	1	-	1	1	1	1	1	1
15	Reliability & queueing theory	2	3	2	3	2	1	1	2	5	1	1	-	-	2	1	1	1	-	-	-	3	2	2	2

DESCRIPTIVE STATISTICS

CHAPTER 1

(JUNE 2012)

1. Suppose that we have a data set consisting of 25 observations, where each value is either 0 or 1.
   (a) The mean of the data cannot be larger than the variance.
   (b) The mean of the data cannot be smaller than the variance.
   (c) The mean being same as the variance implies that the mean is zero.
   (d) The variance will be 0 if and only if the mean is either 1 or 0.

(DEC. 2012)

2. To study the relationship between smoking and lung cancer, 50 adult individuals are randomly selected from the population. For these 50 individuals, the responses to the question (i) "Do your smoke?" (ii) Do you have lung cancer?" lead to the following 2×2 table.

	Lung Cancer		
		Yes	No
Smoking habit	Yes	15	5
	No	10	20

Then which of the following statements are correct at 5% level of significance? (Note: 95th percentile of the chi-square distribution with 1 d.f. is 3.841).
   (a) Lung cancer and smoking habits are significantly related
   (b) Lung cancer and smoking habit are independent
   (c) The proportions of individuals with lung cancer are significantly different in the smoking and non-smoking populations.
   (d) The proportions of smokers in the populations of individuals with or without lung cancer are significantly different.

(JUNE 2012)

3. Consider the following 2 x 2 table of frequencies of voter preferences to two parties classified by gender in an electron. Identify the correct statement:

Gender	Party B	Party C	Total
Male	200	400	600
Female	100	300	400
Total	300	700	1000

   (a) If there is no association between party and gender, the expected frequencies are
   180 420
   120 280
   (b) The chi-square statistic for testing no association is 0.
   (c) Gender and party are not associated.
   (d) Both males and females equally prefer party C

(JUNE 2012)

4. In a system with a single server, suppose that customers arrive at a Poisson rate of 1 person every 12 minutes and are serviced at the Poisson rate of 1 service every 8 minutes. If the arrival rate increases by 20% then in the steady state.
   (a) the increase in the average number of customers in the system is 2.
   (b) the increase in the average number of customers in the system is 4.
   (c) the increase in the average time spent by a customer in the system is 16 minutes.
   (d) the increase in the average time spent by a customer in the system is 24 minutes.

(DEC. 2013)

5. In a 2X2 contingency table if we multiply a particular column by an integer $k(> 1)$then the odds ratio
   (a) will increase
   (b) will decrease
   (c) remains same
   (d) will increase if $k > 2$ and will decrease if $k = 2$

(JUNE 2014)

6. Consider the following three sets of sample observations.
   Sample 1: $x_1, x_2, \dots, x_n$
   Sample 2: $y_1, y_2, \dots, y_m$
   Sample 3: $x_1, x_2, \dots, x_n, y_1, y_2, \dots, y_m$
   Let $\overline{m}_i, \widetilde{m}_i, \widehat{m}_i$ and σ_i^2 denote mean, median, mode and variance respectively of the i^{th}sample for $i = 1, 2, 3$. Assume $\overline{m}_1 = \overline{m}_2$. Which of the following is NOT always true?
   (a) $\overline{m}_3 = \overline{m}_1$
   (b) $\min(\widetilde{m}_1, \widetilde{m}_2) \le \widetilde{m}_3 \le \max(\widetilde{m}_1, \widetilde{m}_2)$
   (c) $\min(\widehat{m}_1, \widehat{m}_2) \le \widehat{m}_3 \le \max(\widehat{m}_1, \widehat{m}_2)$
   (d) $\min(\sigma_1^2, \sigma_2^2) \le \sigma_3^2 \le \max(\sigma_1^2, \sigma_2^2)$

(JUNE 2014)

7. For any set of data, which of the following statements are true?
   (a) Standard deviation $\le \frac{1}{2}$(range)
   (b) Mean absolute deviation about mean $\le$ standard deviation
   (c) Mean absolute deviation about median $\le$ standard deviation

(d) Mean absolute deviation about mode $\leq \frac{1}{2}$(range)

(DEC. 2015)

8. A set of N observations resulted in k distinct values $x_1, x_2, \ldots, x_k$ with respective frequencies $f_1, f_2, \ldots, f_k$, so that $\sum_{i=1}^{k} f_i = N$. Another k observations resulted in observations $x_1, x_2, \ldots, x_k$ once each, so that the modified (new) sample of $N+k$ has observation x_i with frequency $f_i + 1$.
   (a) The new mean is necessarily less than or equal to the original mean
   (b) The new median is necessarily more than or equal to the original median
   (c) The new variance is necessarily less than or equal to the original variance
   (d) The new mode will be same as the original mode.

(JUNE 2018)

9. In a data set with mean 2.5 and standard deviation 0.5.
   (a) the median must be bigger than 2.5
   (b) the median must be smaller than 2.5
   (c) the median must be smaller than 3
   (d) the median must be bigger than 2

(JUNE 2025)

10. A mobile manufacturing company uses two brands of batteries for its mobiles. The life (in years) of batteries of Brand I follows an exponential distribution with the probability density function

$$f(x) = \begin{cases} e^{-x}, & if\ x > 0, \\ 0, & \text{otherwise,} \end{cases}$$

and that of Brand II follows a gamma distribution with the probability density function

$$g(x) = \begin{cases} \frac{x}{4} e^{-\frac{x}{2}} & \text{if } x > 0, \\ 0, & \text{otherwise.} \end{cases}$$

The company uses the batteries of Brands I and II in proportion of 20% and 80% respectively, in its mobiles. The probability that a randomly selected mobile has the battery life more that 2 years is

(a) $\frac{13}{5}e^{-2}$ (b) $\frac{1}{5}(e^{-2} + 2e^{-1})$
(c) $\frac{1}{5}(e^{-2} + 8e^{-1})$ (d) $\frac{1}{5}(4e^{-2} + 2e^{-1})$

(JUNE 2025)

11. Suppose that we have a data set consisting of $2n+1$ observations for some $n \in \mathbb{N}$. Value of each observation is either x or $x + r$, where $x \in \mathbb{N}, r \geq 0$. Then, which of the following statements is always true?
   (a) The mean and median of the data will be different if and only if $r > 0$
   (b) Variance of the data is positive if and only if $r > 0$
   (c) Mean and mode of the data will be same if and only if $r = 0$
   (d) Median and mode of the data will be same for all values of $r \geq 0$

(Dec 2025)

12. Consider a dataset of n observations given by $A = \{x_1, x_2, \ldots, x_n\}$. Create a new dataset, given by $B = \{x_1, x_2, \ldots, x_n, -x_1, -x_2, \ldots, -x_n\}$. Which of the following statements are always true?
   (a) Mean of the observations in dataset B is 0
   (b) Median of the observations in dataset B is 0
   (c) Variance of the observations in dataset $B \geq$ Variance of the observations in dataset A
   (Here variance is calculated with divisor as the number of observations in the corresponding dataset)
   (d) Range of the observations in dataset $B \geq$ Range of the observations in dataset A

Answer Key

1	2	3	4	5	6	7	8	9
b,c,d	a,c,d	a	a,d	c	c	a,b,c	d	c,d
10	11	12						
c	d	a,b,c,d						

:: Explanations ::

1. **Explanation: (b), (c) and (d)**

- We have data set consisting of 25 observations, where each value is either 0 or 1.

So, we can say that each observations are Bernoulli variate i.e. $X_i = 0, 1\ i = 1, 2, .., 25$
X_i represent the ith observation of data set
Mean of data set = Mean of bernoulli distribute.
$X_i = 0$ with probability 1-p
$= 1$ with prob. p ; $0 < p < 1$
Mean $= p$ & variance = $p(1-p)$
$p(1-p) < p$
Mean cannot be smaller than variance
If mean $= 0 \Rightarrow p = 0$
Variance $= 0$
Mean = variance if mean = 0
If mean = 1
Variance = 0
So, option (b), (c) & (d) are correct.

2. **Explanation: (a), (c), (d)**

		Lung cancer Yes	Lung cancer No
Smoking habit	Yes	15	5
	No	10	20

H_0 : Lung cancer and Smoking habit are independent
H_1 : Lung cancer and smoking habit are not independent
Test statistic

$X^2 = \sum \frac{(observed - Expected)^2}{Expected}$ with $d.f = (2-1)(2-1) = 1$

0	ε	$(0-\epsilon)$	$(0-\epsilon)^2$	$\frac{(0-\epsilon)^2}{\varepsilon}$
15	12·5	2·5	6·25	0·5
5	12·5	7·5	56·25	4·5
10	12·5	2·5	6·25	0·5
20	12·5	7·5	56·25	4·5
				10

$\chi^2 = 10 \quad d.f = 1$
Critical value $\chi^2_{0.05,1} = 3.841$
$\chi^2 = 10 > \chi^2_{0.05,1} = 3.841$
We reject null hypothesis
And conclude that lung cancer and smoking habit are significantly related
So, option (a), (c) & (d) are correct

3. **Explanation: (a)**
Expected frequencies,

Gender	Party B	Party C
Male	$\frac{600\times300}{1000} = 180$	$\frac{600\times700}{1000} = 420$
Female	$\frac{400\times300}{1000} = 120$	$\frac{400\times700}{1000} = 280$

Coefficient of association $\theta = \frac{180\times280-120\times420}{180\times280+120\times420} = 0$
If $\theta = 0$ then there is no association between party and gender
Chi-square statistic
$\chi^2 = \sum\frac{(o_i-\epsilon_i)^2}{\epsilon_i} = \frac{(200-180)^2}{180} + \frac{(400-420)^2}{420} + \frac{(100-120)^2}{120} + \frac{(300-280)^2}{280} \neq 0$
So, option (a) is correct.

4. **Explanation: (a), (d)**
5. **Explanation: (c)**
6. **Explanation: (c)**
7. **Explanation: (a), (b), (c)**

8. **Explanation: (d)**
K-distinct values $x_1, x_2, \ldots, x_k$ with respective frequencies $f_1, f_2, \ldots, f_k$, so that $\sum_{i=1}^k f_i = N$
Mean $= \frac{\sum_{i=1}^k f_i x_i}{\sum_{i=1}^k f_i} = m_1 \Rightarrow \sum_{i=1}^k f_i\, x_i = mN$
Now, another k observation resulted in observation $x_1, x_2, \ldots, x_k$ once each, so that modified (new) sample of size $N + K$ has x_i with frequency $f_i + 1$
New mean $= \frac{\sum_{i=1}^k x_i(f_i+1)}{\sum_{i=1}^k (f_i+1)} = \frac{\sum_{i=1}^k x_i f_i + \sum_{i=1}^k x_i}{\sum_{i=1}^k f_i + K} = \frac{m_1 N + \sum_{i=1}^k x_i}{N+K}$
From the we cannot say this value in less than or equal to m
Similarly, we cannot interpret about median variance, but mode will be same because mode represent that sample values which has highest frequency
If x_i is mode having frequency f_i
$\Rightarrow x_i$ is mode having frequency $f_i + 1$
So, option (d) is correct

9. **Explanation: (c), (d)**
Mean $= 2.5$ & standard deviation $= 0.5$
Median must lies between 2 & 3
Median > 2
Median < 3
Option (c) & (d) are correct.

10. **Explanation: (c)**
Brand I (Exponential Distribution):
The life of a battery from Brand I follows an exponential distribution with the probability density function:
$f(x) = \{e^{-x}, \quad \text{if } x > 0, 0, \quad \text{otherwise.}$
The cumulative distribution function (CDF) of Brand I is:
$F_I(x) = P(X \le x) = 1 - e^{-x}$.
Thus, the probability that a battery from Brand I lasts more than 2 years is:
$P(X > 2) = 1 - F_I(2) = e^{-2}$.
Brand II (Gamma Distribution):
The life of a battery from Brand II follows a gamma distribution with the probability density function:
$g(x) = \{\frac{x}{4} e^{-x/2}, \quad \text{if } x > 0, 0, \quad \text{otherwise.}$
This is a gamma distribution with shape parameter $k = 2$ and rate parameter $\lambda = 1/2$.
The cumulative distribution function (CDF) of Brand II, for $x > 0$, is given by:
$F_{II}(x) = 1 - e^{-x/2}\left(1 + \frac{x}{2}\right)$.
Thus, the probability that a battery from Brand II lasts more than 2 years is:
$P(X > 2) = 1 - F_{II}(2) = e^{-1}(1 + 1) = 2e^{-1}$.
Given the proportions in which the company uses the batteries, we have:

- 20% probability that a randomly selected battery is from Brand I,
- 80% probability that a randomly selected battery is from Brand II.

So, the total probability that a randomly selected mobile has a battery life of more than 2 years is the weighted sum of the probabilities for each brand:
$P(\text{Battery Life} > 2) = 0.2 \cdot P(X_I > 2) + 0.8 \cdot P(X_{II} > 2)$.
Substitute the values we calculated:
$P(\text{Battery Life} > 2) = 0.2 \cdot e^{-2} + 0.8 \cdot 2e^{-1}$.
Simplify the expression:
$P(\text{Battery Life} > 2) = 0.2e^{-2} + 1.6e^{-1}$.
Rewriting the expression for clarity: $P(\text{Battery Life} > 2) = \frac{1}{5}(e^{-2} + 8e^{-1})$.
This matches Option 3: 3.

11. **Explanation: (d)**
With $2n + 1$ observations taking only the values x or $x + r$:

- The median is the majority value (since the sample size is odd).
- The mode is also the majority value (unique, because counts can't tie with an odd total).

Hence median = mode for all $r \geq 0$. The other statements fail in simple counterexamples $e.g.$,all values equal when$(k = 0)or(k = 2n + 1)$even with$(r > 0)$.

12. **Explanation: (a), (b), (c), (d)**
Dataset $B = \{x_1, \ldots, x_n, -x_1, \ldots, -x_n\}$

Statement 1: Mean of $B = 0 \rightarrow$ TRUE

$$\bar{x}_B = \frac{\sum_{i=1}^{n} x_i + \sum_{i=1}^{n} (-x_i)}{2n} = \frac{\sum x_i - \sum x_i}{2n} = 0$$

Statement 2: Median of $B = 0 \rightarrow$ TRUE

Dataset B is symmetric about 0 – for every value x_i, its negative $-x_i$ also exists.

In any symmetric distribution about 0, the median = 0.

Statement 3: $Var(B) \geq Var(A) \rightarrow$ TRUE

Since mean of $B = 0$: $\text{Var}(B) = \frac{\sum_{i=1}^{n} x_i^2 + \sum_{i=1}^{n} x_i^2}{2n} = \frac{\sum x_i^2}{n}$

For dataset A with mean $\bar{x}$: $\text{Var}(A) = \frac{\sum x_i^2}{n} - \bar{x}^2$

Therefore: $\text{Var}(B) - \text{Var}(A) = \bar{x}^2 \geq 0$

$\text{Var}(B) \geq \text{Var}(A)$

Statement 4: $Range(B) \geq Range(A) \rightarrow$ TRUE

Let $M = \max\{x_i\}$ and $m = \min\{x_i\}$.

Dataset B contains both x_i and $-x_i$, so it contains M and $-M$, as well as m and $-m$.

$\max(B) = \max(M, -m), \min(B) = \min(m, -M)$

$\text{Range}(B) = \max(M, -m) - \min(m, -M) =$
$\max(M, -m) + \max(M, -m) = 2\max(M, -m)$

$$\text{Range}(A) = M - m$$

Since $2\max(M, -m) \geq M - m$ always holds (as $\max(M, -m) \geq \frac{M-m}{2}$):

$\text{Range}(B) \geq \text{Range}(A)$

Correct Answer: All four statements are always true.

CHAPTER 2

PROBABILITY

(JUNE 2013)

1. Consider the quadratic equation $x^2 + 2Ux + V = 0$ where U and V are chosen independently and randomly from {1, 2, 3} with equal probabilities. Then the probability that the equation has both roots real equals

(a) $\frac{2}{3}$ (b) $\frac{1}{2}$

(c) $\frac{7}{9}$ (d) $\frac{1}{3}$

(DEC. 2013)

2. A popular car comes in both a petrol and diesel version Each of these is further available in 3 models, L, V and Z. Among all owners of the petrol version of this car, 50% have model V and 20% have model Z. Among diesel car customers, 50% have model L and 20% model V. 60% of all customers have bought diesel cars. If a randomly chosen customer has model V, what is the probability that the car is a diesel car?

(a) 3/8 (b) 3/5

(c) 1/5 (d) 2/3

(JUNE 2014)

3. Suppose you have a coin with probability $\frac{3}{4}$ of getting a Head. You toss the coin twice independently. Let $\Omega = \{(H,H),(H,T),(T,H),(T,T)\}$ be the sample space. Then it is possible to have an event $E \subseteq \Omega$ such that

(a) $P(E) = \frac{1}{3}$ (b) $P(E) = \frac{1}{9}$

(c) $P(E) = \frac{1}{4}$ (d) $P(E) = \frac{7}{8}$

(DEC. 2014)

4. Five persons A, B, C, D and E are seated at random on eight numbered chairs which are arranged in a circle. What is the probability that A and B are separated by at least 2 chairs?

(a) 3/7 (b) 4/7

(c) ½ (d) 1/4

(DEC. 2015)

5. From the six letters A, B, C, D, E and F, three letters are chosen at random with replacement. What is the probability that either the word BAD or the word CAD can be formed from the chosen letters?

(a) $\frac{1}{216}$ (b) $\frac{3}{216}$

(c) $\frac{6}{216}$ (d) $\frac{12}{216}$

(DEC. 2015)

6. An urn has 3 red and 6 black balls. Balls are drawn at random one by one without replacement. The probability that second red ball appears at the fifth draw is

(a) $\frac{1}{9!}$ (b) $\frac{4!}{9!}$

(c) $4\left(\frac{6!4!}{9!}\right)$ (d) $\frac{6!4!}{9!}$

(JUNE 2016)

7. Hundred (100) tickets are marked 1,2, ...,100 and are arranged at random. Four tickets are picked from these tickets and are given to four persons A, B, C and D. What is the probability that A gets the ticket with the largest value (among A, B, C, D) and D gets the ticket with the smallest value (among A, B, C, D)?

(a) $\frac{1}{4}$ (b) $\frac{1}{6}$

(c) $\frac{1}{2}$ (d) $\frac{1}{12}$

(JUNE 2016)

8. Let (Ω, F, P) be a probability space and let A be an event with $P(A) > 0$. In which of the following cases does Q define a probability measure on (Ω, f) ?

(a) $Q(D) = P(A \cup D)\ \forall D \in F$

(b) $Q(D) = P(A \cap D)\ \forall D \in F$

(c) $Q(D) = \begin{cases} P(A|D), if\ D \in F\ with\ P(D) > 0 \\ 0, if\ P(D) = 0 \end{cases}$

(d) $Q(D) = P(D|A) \forall D \in F$

(DEC. 2016)

9. There are two boxes. Box 1 contains 2 red balls and 4 green balls. Box 2 contains 4 red balls and 2 green balls. A box is selected at random and a ball is chosen randomly from the selected box. If the ball turns out to be red, what is the probability that Box 1 had been selected?

(a) $\frac{1}{2}$ (b) $\frac{1}{3}$

(c) $\frac{2}{3}$ (d) $\frac{1}{6}$

(DEC. 2016)

10. For any two events A and B, which of the following relations always holds?

(a) $P^2(A \cap B^C) + P^2(A \cap B) + P^2(A^C) \geq \frac{1}{3}$

(b) $P^2(A \cap B^C) + P^2(A \cap B) + P^2(A^C) = \frac{1}{3}$

(c) $P^2(A \cap B^C) + P^2(A \cap B) + P^2(A^C) = 1$

(d) $P^2(A \cap B^C) + P^2(A \cap B) + P^2(A^C) \leq \frac{1}{3}$

(DEC. 2016)

11. A and B play a game of tossing a fair coin. A starts the game by tossing the coin once and B then tosses the coin twice, followed by tossing the coin once and tossing the coin twice and this continues until a head turns up. Whoever gets the first head wins the game. Then,

(a) $P(B\ Wins) > P(A\ Wins)$

(b) $P(B\ Wins) = 2P(A\ Wins)$

(c) $P(A\ Wins) > P(B\ Wins)$

(d) $P(A\ Wins) = 1 - P(B\ Wins)$

(DEC 2017)

12. There are five empty boxes. Balls are placed independently one after another in randomly selected boxes. The probability that the fourth ball is the first to be placed in an occupied box equals

(a) $\frac{4}{5}\left(\frac{3}{5}\right)^2$ (b) $\left(\frac{3}{5}\right)^3$

(c) $\left(\frac{3}{5}\right)^2$ (d) $\left(\frac{4}{5}\right)\left(\frac{3}{5}\right)$

(DEC. 2017)

13. Suppose A, B, C are events in a common probability space with $P(A) = 0.2, P(B) = 0.2, P(C) = 0.3, P(A \cap B) = 0.1, P(A \cap C) = 0.1, P(B \cap C) = 0.1$ Which of the following are possible values of $P(A \cup B \cup C)$?

(a) 0.5 (b) 0.3

(c) 0.4 (d) 0.9

(DEC. 2017)

14. Let S be the set of all 3×3 matrices having 3 entries equal to 1 and 6 entries equal to 0. A matrix M is picked uniformly at random from the set S. Then

(a) $P\{M\ IS\ NONSINGULAR\} = \frac{1}{14}$

(b) $P\{M\ has\ rank\ 1\} = \frac{1}{14}$

(c) $P\{M\ is\ identity\} = \frac{1}{14}$

(d) $P\ \{trace\ (M) = 0\} = \frac{1}{14}$

(JUNE 2017)

15. A box contains 40 numbered red balls and 60 numbered black balls. From the box, balls are drawn one by one at random without replacement till all the balls are drawn. The probability that the last ball drawn is black equals

(a) ${}^1/_{100}$ (b) ${}^1/_{60}$

(c) ${}^3/_5$ (d) ${}^2/_3$

(JUNE 2018)

16. A standard fair die is rolled until some face other than 5 or 6 turns up. Let X denote the face value of the last roll, and $A = \{X \text{ is even}\}$ and $B = \{X \text{ is at most } 2\}$. Then

(a) $P(A \cap B) = 0$ (b) $P(A \cap B) = 1/6$

(c) $P(A \cap B) = 1/4$ (d) $P(A \cap B) = 1/3$

(DEC. 2019)

17. There are three urns U_1, U_2, U_3, each with balls of two colors U_1 contains 2 white balls and 3 black balls, U_2, contains 3 white balls and 2 black balls and U_3 contains 5 white balls and 5 black balls. An urn is chosen at random and a ball is drawn from that urn at random. What is the probability that U_2 was chosen given that the ball picked is black in color?

(a) $\frac{1}{3}$ (b) $\frac{4}{15}$

(c) $\frac{2}{15}$ (d) $\frac{1}{6}$

(NOV. 2020)

18. In an examination involving multiple choice questions, a student works out the solution in 50% of the questions. In the remaining questions the student guesses the answer. However, when the answer is guessed the probability that it is correct is 0.30. When the student works out the solutions it may be wrong with probability 0.10. If the answer to a particular question is correct, what is the probability that the student guessed the answer?

(a) 0.25 (b) 0.50

(c) 0.90 (d) 0.30

(JUNE 2021)

19. A proportion p of a large population has particular disease. A random sample of k people is drawn from the population and their blood samples are combined. An accurate test for the disease applied to the combined blood sample shows a positive result, hence at least one of the k people has the disease. What is the probability that exactly one of the k people has the disease?

(a) $\frac{kp(1-p)^{k-1}}{1-(1-p)^k}$ (b) $\frac{(1-p)^k+kp(1-p)^{k-1}}{1-(1-p)^k}$

(c) $\frac{p}{p+p^2+\cdots+p^k}$ (d) $\frac{1}{k}$

(SEP. 2022)

20. In a random experiment a fair coin is tossed once. Then, an unbiased six faced die is rolled N times, where

$$N = \begin{cases} 100, & if \quad \text{Head appears} \\ 101, & if \quad \text{Tail appears} \end{cases}$$

Let Y denote the total number of times 6 appears out of N. Then P(Head | Y = 15) equals

(a) $\frac{516}{1021}$ (b) $\frac{505}{1021}$

(c) $\frac{201}{1021}$ (d) $\frac{1000}{1021}$

(JUNE 2023)

21. If $f(x)$ is a probability density on the real line, then which of the following is NOT a valid probability density?

(a) $f(x + 1)$ (b) $f(2x)$

(c) $2f(2x - 1)$ (d) $3x^2 f(x^3)$

(JUNE 2023)

22. Let A, B be two events in a discrete probability space with $\mathbb{P}(A) > 0$ *and* $\mathbb{P}(B)0$. Which of the following are necessarily true?

(a) If $\mathbb{P}(A|B) = 0$ then $\mathbb{P}(B \mid A) = 0$.

(b) If $\mathbb{P}(A|B) = 1$ then $\mathbb{P}(B \mid A) = 1$.

(c) If $\mathbb{P}(A|B) > \mathbb{P}(A)$ then $\mathbb{P}(B \mid A) > \mathbb{P}(B)$.

(d) If $\mathbb{P}(A|B) > \mathbb{P}(B)$ then $\mathbb{P}(B \mid A) > \mathbb{P}(A)$.

[JULY-2024]

23. Let A_1, A_2, A_3 be events satisfying $0 < P(A_i) < 1\ for\ i = 1,2,3$. Which of the following statement is true?

(a) $P(A_1|A_2)P(A_2|A_3) \leq P(A_1|A_3)$

(b) $P(A_1|A_2)P(A_3|A_2) \geq P(A_1 \cap A_3|A_2)$

(c) $P(A_1|A_2) + P(A_3|A_2) \geq P(A_1 \cup A_3|A_2)$

(d) $P(A_1|A_2) + P(A_2|A_3) \leq P(A_1|A_3)$

(FEB. 2025)

24. $\lim\limits_{n\to\infty} \int_0^1 \int_0^1 \dots \int_0^1 \frac{x_1^2+\cdots+x_n^2}{x_1+\cdots+x_n} dx_1 \dots dx_n$ equals

(a) 1. 1 (b) 2. $\frac{1}{2}$

(c) 3. 2 (d) 4. $\frac{2}{3}$

(FEB. 2025)

25. Let $U_1, U_2, \dots, U_5$ be 5 urns such that urn U_k contains $2k + k^2$ balls, out of which $2k$ are white balls and k^2 are black balls, $k = 1, 2, \dots, 5$. An urn is selected with probability of selecting urn U_k being proportional to $(k + 2)$. A ball is

chosen randomly from the selected urn. Then, the probability that the urn U_5 was selected, given that the ball drawn is white, is equal to

(a) $\frac{3}{5}$ (b) $\frac{2}{5}$

(c) $\frac{1}{5}$ (d) $\frac{3}{4}$

(JUNE 2025)

26. A biased six-faced die is tossed once. Suppose that the probability of any prime number showing up is twice that of any non-prime number showing up. Then, the probability that an odd number will show up is

(a) $\frac{1}{3}$ (b) $\frac{2}{3}$

(c) $\frac{4}{9}$ (d) $\frac{5}{9}$

(Dec 2025)

27. There are six persons. On each day of the year 2024 at least one of them borrowed money from another. A person P is labeled troublesome in a calendar month M of 2024 if P borrowed from the same person at least twice during the month M. Which of the following statements are necessarily true?
(a) In every calendar month of 2024, at least one person was troublesome.
(b) In any two consecutive calendar months of 2024, at least one person was troublesome in at least one of the two calendar months.
(c) At least one person was troublesome in two calendar months of 2024.
(d) At least one person was troublesome in January 2024.

(Dec 2025)

28. Suppose two fair dice are thrown independently at random. Let X and Y be the numbers on the upper face of the first die and that of the second die, respectively. Then which of the following statements are true?
(a) $P(X-Y=0|X+Y=2)=$
$P(X-Y=0|X+Y=12)$
(b) $E\left(\frac{X-Y}{X+Y}\right)=0$
(c) $\text{Cov}(X+Y,X-Y)=0$
(d) $(X+Y)$ and $(X-Y)$ are independent

(Dec 2025)

29. Let X and Y be two independent random variables such that the moment generating functions of X and Y are

$$M_X(t)=e^{3(e^t-1)},t\in\mathbb{R},$$

and

$$M_Y(t)=\left(\frac{1}{2}e^{-3t}+\frac{1}{2}e^{3t}\right)^2,t\in\mathbb{R},$$

respectively. Then which of the following statements are true?
(a) $P(XY=0)=\frac{1+e^{-3}}{2}$
(b) $E(X+Y)=3$
(c) $\text{Var}(X+Y)=21$
(d) $\text{Cov}(X+Y,X-Y)=0$

Answer Key

1	2	3	4	5	6	7	8	9	10
c	a	c	a	d	c	d	d	b	a
11	12	13	14	15	16	17	18	19	20
c,d	a	a,c	a,b	c	c	b	a	a	a
21	22	23	24	25	26	27	28	29	
b	a,c	c	d	c	d	b,c,d	a,b,c	a,b,c	

:: Explanations ::

1. **Explanation: (c)** Quadratic equation
$x^2+2Ux+V=0$
Where U and V are chosen independently are randomly from $\{1,2,3\}$ with equal probability
The equation has both roots are real if
$\sqrt{4U^2-4V}\geq 0$
$U^2\geq V$
$V=1,U=1,2,3$
$V=2,U=2,3$
$V=3,U=2,3$
Favorable cases = 7
Total case $=3\times 3=9$
Prob. $[U^2\geq V]=\frac{7}{9}$
So, option (c) is correct

2. **Explanation: (a)**
Let the events E_1 and E_2 represent the can in petrol version and diesel version respectively
$P(E_1)=\frac{40}{100}=\frac{2}{5}$ and $P(E_2)=\frac{60}{100}=\frac{3}{5}$
A be an arbitrary events that can of model V
$P(A\mid E_1)=\frac{50}{100}=\frac{1}{2}$ and $P(A\mid E_2)=\frac{20}{100}=\frac{1}{5}$
By Baye's Theorem
$P(E_2\mid A)=\frac{P(E_2).P(A\mid E_2)}{P(E_1)\,P(A|E_1)+P(E_2)\,P(A|E_2)}$
$=\frac{\frac{3}{5}\times\frac{1}{5}}{\frac{2}{5}\times\frac{1}{2}+\frac{3}{5}\times\frac{1}{5}}=\frac{3}{8}$
So, option (a) is correct

3. **Explanation: (c)**
P(head) $=\frac{3}{4}$ and P(Tail) $=\frac{1}{4}$
Toss the coin twice independently
$\Omega=\{(H,H)\ (H,T)\ (T,H)\ (T,T)\}$ be the sample space
$E\subseteq\Omega$
Total outcomes = 4
So, possible prob. Of E be $P(E)=\frac{1}{4}$
So, option (c) is correct

4. **Explanation: (a)**
Five person A, B, C, D and E are seated at random on eight numbered chairs
Total no. of cases 5 person arranged in 8 chair
$=5\times 7\times 6\times 5\times 4$

Favourable cases A and B are separated by at least 2 chair
$= 8 \times 3 \times 6 \times 5 \times 4$
Prob $= \frac{8\times3\times6\times5\times4}{8\times7\times6\times5\times4} = \frac{3}{7}$
So, option (a) is correct

5. Explanation: (d)
From six letter A, B, C, D, E and F, three letter are chosen at random with replacement
Probability that letter 'B' or 'C' select $= \frac{2}{6}$
Probability that letter A is select $= \frac{1}{6}$
Probability that letter D is select $= \frac{1}{6}$
If order does not matter than $3! = 6$ cases are possible
So, probability that either BAD and CAD can be formed $=$
$6 \times \frac{2}{6} \times \frac{1}{6} \times \frac{1}{6} = \frac{12}{216}$
So, option (d) is correct

6. Explanation: (c)
An urn has 3 red and 6 black ball.
Prob. That second red ball appear at the fifth draw= prob. That one red draw in first four draw × prob. That second red ball is drawn in the fifth draw
$= \frac{{}^3C_1 \cdot {}^6C_3}{{}^9C_4} \times \frac{{}^2C_1}{{}^5C_1} = 4\,\frac{6!4!}{9!}$
So, option (c) is correct

7. Explanation: (d)
Let the value of ticket which is given to the person A, B, C and D is respectively X, Y, Z and W
$P(\max(X,Y,Z,W) = X \text{ and } \min(X,Y,Z,W) = W) = P[X > Y > Z > W] + P[X > Z > Y > W]$
$= \frac{1}{4!} + \frac{1}{4!} = \frac{2}{4!} = \frac{2}{24} = \frac{1}{12}$
Option (d) is correct

8. Explanation: (d)

9. Explanation: (b)
Box 1 → 2 red ball and 4 green ball
Box 2 → 4 red ball and 2 green ball
Let the event E_1 & E_2 that represent the box 1 and Box 2 drawn respectively.
$P(E_1) = P(E_2) = \frac{1}{2}$
Let the arbitrary event A represent that drawn ball is red
By Baye's theorem.
$P(E_1|A) = \frac{P(E_1).P(A|E_1)}{P(E_1)P(A|E_1) + P(E_2)P(A|E_2)}$
$= \frac{\frac{1}{2}\times\frac{2}{6}}{\frac{1}{2}\times\frac{2}{6}+\frac{1}{2}\times\frac{4}{6}} = \frac{\frac{2}{6}}{\frac{6}{6}}$
$= \frac{1}{3}$
Option (b) is Correct

10. Explanation: (a)
For any two events A and B.
Let us Suppose $S = \{a, b, c, d\}$
And $A = \{a, b\}$, $B = \{c, d\}$
$A^c = \{c, d\}$ and $B^c = \{a, b\}$
$P^2(A \cap B^c) + P^2(A \cap B) + P(A^c) = \left(\frac{2}{4}\right)^2 + 0 + \left(\frac{2}{4}\right)^2 =$
$\frac{1}{4} + \frac{1}{4} = \frac{1}{2} \geq \frac{1}{3}$
So, option (a) is correct

11. Explanation: (c), (d)
Probability that A wins
$= A + \overline{A}\,\overline{B}\,\overline{B}A + \overline{A}\,\overline{B}\,\overline{B}\,\overline{A}\,\overline{B}\,\overline{B}A + ©$
$= \frac{1}{2} + \left(\frac{1}{2}\right)^4 + \left(\frac{1}{2}\right)^7 + \cdots$
$= \frac{1}{2}\left[1 + \left(\frac{1}{2}\right)^3 + \left(\frac{1}{2}\right)^6 + \cdots\right]$
$= \frac{1}{2} \times \frac{8}{7}$
$= \frac{4}{7}$
$\Rightarrow P(A\ wins) = \frac{4}{7}$
$\therefore P(B\ wins) = 1 - P(A\ wins) = 1 - \frac{4}{7} = \frac{3}{7}$ and
$P(A\ wins) > P(B\ wines)$.
Option (c), (d) are correct

12. Explanation: (a)
There are five empty boxes
Probability that first ball is placed in any 5 empty box
$= \frac{5}{5} = 1$
Probability that second ball is placed in any left 4 empty box $= \frac{4}{5}$
Probability that third ball is placed in any left 3 empty box
$= \frac{3}{5}$
Now,
Probability that the fourth ball is first to be placed In an occupied box =P (1st in 5 empty box) × P(2nd in 4 empty box) × P(3rd in 3 empty box)× P(4th in 3 occupied box)
$= 1 \times \frac{4}{5} \times \frac{3}{5} \times \frac{3}{5} = \frac{4}{5} \times \left(\frac{3}{5}\right)^2$

13. Explanation: (a), (c)
P(A)=0.2, P(B)=0.2, P(C)=0.3
$P(A \cap B) = 0.1, P(A \cap C) = 0.1, P(B \cap C) = 0.1$
By addition theorem of Probability,
$P(A \cup B \cup C) = P(A) + P(B) + P(C) - P(A \cap B) - P(B \cap C) - P(A \cap C) + P(A \cap B \cap C)$
$= 0.2 + 0.2 + 0.3 - 0.1 - 0.1 - 0.1 + P(A \cap B \cap C)$
$P(A \cup B \cup C) = 0.4 + P(A \cap B \cap C)$
$\therefore P(A \cap B \cap C) \geq 0$ & $P(A \cap B \cap C) \leq P(A \cap B)$
So, the possible value of $P(A \cup B \cup C) = 0.4$ or 0.5
Option (a) and (c) are correct.

14. Explanation: (a), (b)
Let S be set of 3×3 matrix having 3 entries equal to 1 and 6 entries equal to 0
Total no. of possible matrix
$= \binom{9}{3} = \frac{9!}{3!\,6!} = \frac{9\times8\times7}{3\times2} = 3 \times 4 \times 7$
No. of possible cares if matrix is non-singular
$= 3 \times 3 \times 1 = 6$

No. of possible can if matrix has rank 1 = 6

No. of possible cases if matrix M is identity = 1

No. of possible cases if trace (M) is 0 is $\binom{6}{3} = \frac{6!}{3!3!} = 20$

P (M is non-singular) $= \frac{6}{3\times4\times7} = \frac{1}{14}$

P (M has rank 1) $= \frac{6}{3\times4\times7} = \frac{1}{14}$

P (M is identity) $= \frac{1}{3\times4\times7} = \frac{1}{84}$

P (trace (M) is 0) $= \frac{20}{3\times4\times7} = \frac{5}{21}$

So, option (a), (b) are correct

15. Explanation: (c)

No. of red balls = 40

No. of black balls = 60

Probability that last ball is black = probability of drawn 59 black & 40 red ball in first 99 ball drawn

$= \frac{{}^{60}C_{59}\ {}^{40}C_{40}}{{}^{100}C_{99}}$

$= \frac{60\times1}{100}$

$= \frac{3}{5}$

Option (c) is correct

16. Explanation: (c)

Let E_1 : 5 or 6 Turns up

E_2 : 2 turns up

$P(E_1) = \frac{2}{6} = \frac{1}{3}$ and $P(E_2) = \frac{1}{6}$

$A \cap B =$ last roll is always 2 as X = 2

$A \cap B$ is similar as $E_2 \cup E_1E_2 \cup E_1E_1E_2 \cup$ ....

$P(A \cap B) = P[E_2] + P[E_1].P(E_2) + P(E_1)P(E_1)P(E_2) + \ldots$

$= \frac{1}{6} + \frac{1}{3}\times\frac{1}{6} + \frac{1}{3^2}\times\frac{1}{6} + \ldots$

$= \frac{1}{6}\left[1 + \frac{1}{3} + \frac{1}{3^2} + \ldots\right]$

$= \frac{1}{6}\left[\frac{1}{1-\frac{1}{3}}\right]$

$= \frac{1}{6}.\frac{3}{2} = \frac{1}{4}$

17. Explanation: (b)

Let the event $E_1 = Urn\ 1 = U_1$

$E_2 = U_2$

$E_3 = U_3$

$E_1 : U_1 : 2W + 3B$

$E_2 : U_2 : 3W + 2B$

$E_3 : U_3 : 5W + 5B$

Suppose an arbitrary event A that represent the picked will is blank in color.

$P(E_1) = P(E_2) = P(E_3) = \frac{1}{3}$

We need to find, Using Baye' x Theorem –

$P(E_2|A) = \frac{P(E_2).P(A|E_2)}{P(E_1)P(A|E_1)+P(E_2)P(A(E_2)+P(E_3.)P(A(E_3)}$

$P(A|E_1) = \frac{3}{5}\ P\ (A|E_2) = \frac{2}{5}$

$P(A|E_3) = \frac{5}{10} = \frac{1}{2}$

$P(E_2|A) = \frac{\frac{1}{3}\times\frac{2}{5}}{\frac{1}{3}\times\frac{3}{5}\times+\frac{1}{3}\times\frac{2}{5}+\frac{1}{3}\times\frac{1}{2}} = \frac{\frac{2}{5}}{\frac{3}{5}+\frac{2}{5}+\frac{1}{2}}$

$= \frac{\frac{2}{5}}{1+\frac{1}{2}} =$

$= \frac{2}{5}\times\frac{2}{3} = \frac{4}{15}$

Option (b) is correct

18. Explanation: (a)

Let E_1 represent those question which are solved by student work out the solution and E_2 represent those remaining question which are quess by student and A be an arbitrary event that represent if the answer to a particular question is correct

$P(E_1) = \frac{50}{100} = 0.5$ and $P(E_2) = \frac{50}{100} = 0.5$

$P(A \mid E_1) = 1 - 0.10 = 0.90$ and $P(A \mid E_2) = 0.30$

By Baye`s Theorem,

$P(E_2 \mid A) = \frac{P(E_2)\cdot P(A \mid E_2)}{P(E_1)\cdot P(A \mid E_1)+P(E_2)\cdot P(A \mid E_2)}$

$= \frac{0.5\times0.30}{0.5\times0.90\times0.5\times0.30}$

$= \frac{0.30}{0.90+0.30} = \frac{0.30}{1.20} = \frac{3}{12} = \frac{1}{4} = 0.25$

Option (a) is correct

19. Explanation: (a)

Let A be the events represents that atleast one of the K people has the disease and B be the event that represent exactly one of the K people has the disease

$P(A|B) = \frac{P(A\cap B)}{P(B)} = \frac{P(A)}{P(B)}$

$P(A) = {}^{K}C_1\, p\, (1-p)^{k-1}$

$P(B) = 1 - P$ (no people has the disease)

$= 1 - (1-p)^k$

$P(A|B) = \frac{{}^{k}C_1\, p(1-p)^{k-1}}{1-(1-p)^k} = \frac{kp\,(1-p)^{k-1}}{1-(1-p)^k}$

So, option (a) is correct

20. Explanation: (a)

Here given coin is fair.

∴ Probability of H = Probability of $T = \frac{1}{2}$

The die is unbiased and six faced.

Let Y be the number of 6 on the upper face of the die.

Thus $p = \frac{1}{6},\ q = 1 - p = 1 - \frac{1}{6} = \frac{5}{6}$

The number of times the die is rolled is

$$N = \begin{cases} 100, & \text{if Head} \\ 101, & \text{if Tail} \end{cases}$$

Thus $Y \rightarrow B(N,p) = B\left(N, \frac{1}{6}\right)$

Then by Bay's theorem $P[\text{ Head} \mid Y = 15]$ is given by

$$\frac{P[Y = 15|\text{ Head}]\cdot P[\text{Head}]}{P[Y = 15|\text{ Head}]\cdot P[\text{ Head}] + P[Y = 15 \mid \text{ Tail}]\cdot P[\text{Tail}]}$$

Consider,

Numerator $= \binom{100}{15}\left(\frac{1}{6}\right)^{15}\left(\frac{5}{6}\right)^{85}.\frac{1}{2}$

and

Denominator

$$=\binom{100}{15}\left(\frac{1}{6}\right)^{15}\left(\frac{5}{6}\right)^{85}\cdot\frac{1}{2}+\binom{101}{15}\left(\frac{1}{6}\right)^{15}\left(\frac{5}{6}\right)^{86}\cdot\frac{1}{2}$$

$$=\frac{1}{2}\cdot\frac{5^{85}}{6^{100}}\left[\frac{100!}{15!\,85!}+\frac{101\times100!}{15!.(86\times85!)}\cdot\frac{5}{6}\right]$$

$$=\frac{1}{2}\cdot\frac{5^{85}}{6^{100}}\frac{100!}{15!\,85!}\left[1+\frac{101}{86}\cdot\frac{5}{6}\right]$$

$$=\frac{1}{2}\cdot\frac{5^{85}}{6^{100}}\binom{100}{15}\left[\frac{86\times6+101\times5}{86\times6}\right]$$

$$\therefore P[\text{ Head }|\,Y=15]=\frac{\text{Numerator}}{\text{Denominator}}$$

$$=\frac{\frac{1}{2}\cdot\frac{5^{85}}{6^{100}}\binom{100}{15}}{\frac{1}{2}\cdot\frac{5^{85}}{6^{100}}\binom{100}{15}\left[\frac{86\times6+101\times5}{86\times6}\right]}$$

$$=\frac{86\times6}{86\times6+101\times5}=\frac{516}{516+505}=\frac{516}{1021}$$

∴ Answer is **Option (a).**

21. Explanation: (b)

$f(x)$ is probability density function but it's not mention than the function is distance or continuous

Let consider f(x) is continuous

i.e. $\int_{-\infty}^{\infty} f(x)\,dx=1\ \&\ f(x)>0$

For (1)

$f(x+1)=f(y)$

$y=x+1$

$dy=dx$

$-\infty<x<\infty\,;-\infty<y<\infty$

$\int_{-\infty}^{\infty} f(y)\,dy=1$ Correct statement

For (2)

$f(2x)=f(y)$

$y=2x$

$dx=\frac{dy}{2}$

$\int_{-\infty}^{\infty} f(y)\frac{dy}{2}=\frac{1}{2}\int_{-\infty}^{\infty} f(y)\,dy=\frac{1}{2}\neq1$

For (3)

$2F(2x-1)=2F(y)$

$y=2x-1$

$dy=2dx$

$dx=\frac{dy}{2}$

$2\int_{-\infty}^{\infty} f(y)\frac{dy}{2}=\frac{2}{2}(1)=1$ Correct statement

For (4)

$3x^2f(x^3)=3x^2f(y)$

$y=x^3$

$dy=3x^2dx\Rightarrow dx=\frac{dy}{3x}$

$3x^2\int_{-\infty}^{\infty} f(y)\frac{dy}{3x^2}=\int f(y)\,dy=1$

∴ Correct statement

∴ Option (b) is correct

$f(2x)$ is not p.d.f.

22. Explanation: (a), (c)

We know that

$P(A)>0\ \&\ P(B)>0$

For (1)

$p(A|B)=\frac{p(A\cap B)}{p(B)}=0$

i.e. $p(A\cap B)=0$

Then,

$\therefore p(B|A)=\frac{p(A\cap B)}{p(B)}=0$

Correct statement

For (2)

$p(A|B)=1$

i.e. $p(A|B)=\frac{p(A\cap B)}{p(B)}=1$

$\Rightarrow p(A\cap B)=p(B)$

$\therefore p(B|A)=\frac{p(A\cap B)}{p(A)}$

$=\frac{p(B)}{p(A)}$

$\neq1$

It's incorrect statement

For (3) $p(A|B)>p(A)$

$\Rightarrow\frac{p(A\cap B)}{p(B)}>p(A)$

$\Rightarrow p(A\cap B)>P(A)p(B)$

Now $p(B|A)=\frac{p(B\cap A)}{p(A)}$

$p(B|A)=\frac{p(A\cap B)}{p(A)}>p(B)$

Correct statement

For (4)

$p(A|B)>p(B)$

$\frac{p(A\cap B)}{p(B)}>p(B)$

$p(A\cap B)>[p(B)]^2$

$\frac{p(A\cap B)}{p(A)}>\frac{[p(B)]^2}{p(A)}\ngtr p(A)$

May or may not be

∴ option (a) & (c) are correct

23. Explanation: (c)

A_1,A_2,A_3be events satisfying $0<P(A_i)<1\ for\ i=1,2,3.$

Let $P(A_1)=x,P(A_2)=y,P(A_3)=z\,;x,y,z>0$

(1) & (4)

Consider a Venn diagram as follows

Note that here $P(A_1\cap A_2)>0\ \&\ P(A_2\cap A_3)>0$ But $P(A_1\cap A_3)=0\ (\because A_1\cap A_3=\phi)$

$\therefore P(A_1\mid A_2)P(A_2\mid A_3)>P(A_1\mid A_3)$

Also note that from the same argument it can be written as

$\therefore P(A_1\mid A_2)+P(A_2\mid A_3)>P(A_1\mid A_3)$

(2) Given

$P(A_1|A_2)P(A_3|A_2)\geq P(A_1\cap A_3|A_2)$

$\Rightarrow P(A_1)P(A_3)\geq P(A_1\cap A_3)$

$\geq P(A_1)+P(A_3)-(2-1)$

(Using the Bonferroni's inequality)

$\Rightarrow P(A_1)P(A_3)\geq P(A_1)+P(A_3)-(2-1)$

$\Rightarrow xz\geq x+z-1$

$\Rightarrow x(z-1)\geq z-1$

$\Rightarrow x\geq1$

But x is a probability. Thus $x\ngtr1$. So we arrived at a contradiction.

(3) Given

$P(A_1|A_2)+P(A_3|A_2)\geq P(A_1\cup A_3\mid A_2)$

$$P(A_1) + P(A_3) \geq P(A_1 \cup A_3)$$
$$= P(A_1) + P(A_3) - P(A_1 \cap A_3)$$
$$\Rightarrow P(A_1 \cap A_3) \geq 0$$

Thus only option (c) is true.

24. Explanation: (d)

Let $S_n = x_1 + \cdots + x_n$. Then the integrand becomes:

$$\frac{x_1^2 + \cdots + x_n^2}{S_n}$$

For large n, by the law of large numbers, the sample mean $\frac{S_n}{n}$ converges to the expected value of x_i, which is:

$$E[x_i] = \int_0^1 x\,dx = \frac{1}{2}$$

Similarly, the sample mean of x_i^2 converges to:

$$E[x_i^2] = \int_0^1 x^2\,dx = \frac{1}{3}$$

$$\frac{x_1^2 + \cdots + x_n^2}{S_n} \approx \frac{n \cdot E[x_i^2]}{n \cdot E[x_i]} = \frac{E[x_i^2]}{E[x_i]} = \frac{\frac{1}{3}}{\frac{1}{2}} = \frac{2}{3}$$

$$\lim_{n\to\infty} \int_0^1 \cdots \int_0^1 \frac{x_1^2 + \cdots + x_n^2}{S_n}\,dx_1 \ldots dx_n = \frac{2}{3}$$

25. Explanation: (c)

The probability of selecting urn U_k is proportional to $(k + 2)$.

Let $P(U_k)$ denote the probability of selecting urn U_k. Then:

$$P(U_k) = \frac{k+2}{S},$$

where S is the normalizing constant:

$$S = \sum_{k=1}^{5} (k+2) = 3 + 4 + 5 + 6 + 7 = 25$$

$$P(U_k) = \frac{k+2}{25}$$

The probability of drawing a white ball from urn U_k is:

$$P(\text{White} \mid U_k) = \frac{2k}{2k + k^2}$$

Using the law of total probability, the total probability of drawing a white ball is:

$$P(\text{White}) = \sum_{k=1}^{5} P(U_k) \cdot P(\text{White} \mid U_k)$$

Substitute $P(U_k) = \frac{k+2}{25}$ and $P(\text{White} \mid U_k) = \frac{2k}{2k+k^2}$:

$$P(\text{White}) = \sum_{k=1}^{5} \frac{k+2}{25} \cdot \frac{2k}{2k + k^2}$$

$$\frac{2k}{2k + k^2} = \frac{2k}{k(2+k)} = \frac{2}{2+k}$$

$$P(\text{White}) = \sum_{k=1}^{5} \frac{k+2}{25} \cdot \frac{2}{2+k} = \sum_{k=1}^{5} \frac{2}{25} = \frac{2}{25} \cdot 5 = \frac{10}{25}$$
$$= \frac{2}{5}$$

We need to find $P(U_5 \mid \text{White})$. Using Bayes' theorem:

$$P(U_5 \mid \text{White}) = \frac{P(\text{White} \mid U_5) \cdot P(U_5)}{P(\text{White})}$$

From Step 1:

$$P(U_5) = \frac{5+2}{25} = \frac{7}{25}$$

From Step 2:

$$P(\text{White} \mid U_5) = \frac{2 \cdot 5}{2 \cdot 5 + 5^2} = \frac{10}{10 + 25} = \frac{10}{35} = \frac{2}{7}$$

From Step 3:

$$P(\text{White}) = \frac{2}{5}$$

Substitute into Bayes' theorem:

$$P(U_5 \mid \text{White}) = \frac{\frac{2}{7} \cdot \frac{7}{25}}{\frac{2}{5}} = \frac{\frac{2}{25}}{\frac{2}{5}} = \frac{2}{25} \cdot \frac{5}{2} = \frac{1}{5}$$

26. Explanation: (d)

Let each non-prime have probability p, each prime $2p$. There are 3 primes 2,3,5 and 3 non-primes 1,4,6, so $3(2p) + 3(p) = 1 \Rightarrow 9p = 1 \Rightarrow p = 1/9$.

Odd numbers: 1,3,5 → $P(1) = 1/9, P(3) = 2/9, P(5) = 2/9$.

So $P(\text{odd}) = 1/9 + 2/9 + 2/9 = 5/9$.

Correct Answer: (d).

27. Explanation: (b), (c), (d)

If no one is troublesome in a month, every borrowing uses a different pair. Since only 30 pairs exist, a month can have at most 30 borrowings without repetition.

So, if a month has more than 30 days (i.e. 31 days), repetition is forced → someone must be troublesome.

Months with 31 days: January, March, May, July, August, October, December = 7 months

Months with ≤ 30 days can avoid troublesome persons (just use each pair at most once per day).

Statement 1: Every month has at least one troublesome person

April has 30 days. We can assign 30 distinct pairs one per day → no pair repeats → nobody troublesome.

→ FALSE

Statement 2: In any two consecutive months, at least one person is troublesome in at least one month

Check every consecutive pair in 2024:

Jan-Feb, Feb-Mar, Mar-Apr, Apr-May, May-Jun, Jun-Jul, Jul-Aug, Aug-Sep, Sep-Oct, Oct-Nov, Nov-Dec

Every single consecutive pair contains at least one 31–day month. That 31-day month always forces a troublesome person (only 30 pairs exist but 31 days).

→ TRUE

Statement 3: At least one person was troublesome in two different months

7 months (the 31-day months) must each have at least one troublesome person, but there are only 6 persons.

By Pigeonhole Principle: at least one person must be troublesome in at least 2 of these 7 months.

→ TRUE

Statement 4: At least one person was troublesome in January

January has 31 days but only 30 distinct pairs exist.

By Pigeonhole: at least one pair repeats → that borrower is troublesome.

→ TRUE

Correct Answer: Statements 2, 3 and 4 are TRUE. Statement 1 is FALSE.

28. Explanation: (a), (b), (c)

Suppose two fair dice are thrown independently at random.

Setup: $X, Y \sim$ Uniform{1,2,3,4,5,6}, independent.

Statement 1: $P(X-Y=0 \mid X+Y=2) = P(X-Y=0 \mid X+Y=12)$ → TRUE

$X+Y=2$: only (1,1) → $X-Y=0$ always. $P=1$

$X+Y=12$: only (6,6) → $X-Y=0$ always. $P=1$

Both equal 1.

Statement 2: $E\left(\frac{X-Y}{X+Y}\right)=0$ → TRUE

Since X and Y are i.i.d., (X,Y) and (Y,X) have the same joint distribution.

$$E\left(\frac{X-Y}{X+Y}\right)=E\left(\frac{Y-X}{Y+X}\right)=-E\left(\frac{X-Y}{X+Y}\right)$$

Therefore $2E\left(\frac{X-Y}{X+Y}\right)=0 \Rightarrow E\left(\frac{X-Y}{X+Y}\right)=0$

Statement 3: $\text{Cov}(X+Y, X-Y)=0$ →TRUE

$\text{Cov}(X+Y, X-Y)=\text{Var}(X)-\text{Var}(Y)=0$

Since X and Y are i.i.d., $\text{Var}(X)=\text{Var}(Y)$.

Statement 4: $(X+Y)$ and $(X-Y)$ are independent → FALSE

Counterexample:

$P(X+Y=2)=\frac{1}{36}$ (only (1,1)), and given $X+Y=2$, we must have $X-Y=0$.

But $P(X-Y=0)=\frac{6}{36}=\frac{1}{6}$

$P(X+Y=2, X-Y=2)=0$

$P(X+Y=2)\cdot P(X-Y=2)=\frac{1}{36}\cdot\frac{5}{36}\neq 0$

So $X+Y$ and $X-Y$ are not independent.

Correct Answer: Statements 1, 2 and 3 are true.

29. Explanation: (a), (b), (c)

Corrected Analysis: $M_Y(t)=\left(\frac{1}{2}e^{-3t}+\frac{1}{2}e^{3t}\right)^2$

Distribution of X

$M_X(t)=e^{3(e^t-1)} \Rightarrow X \sim$ Poisson(3)

$E(X)=3$, $\text{Var}(X)=3$, $P(X=0)=e^{-3}$

$$M_Y(t)=\left(\frac{1}{2}e^{-3t}+\frac{1}{2}e^{3t}\right)^2$$

This is the square of the MGF of a single symmetric variable on $\{-3,3\}$.

So $Y=Y_1+Y_2$ where Y_1, Y_2 are iid with $P=\frac{1}{2}$ on each of $\{-3,3\}$.

Distribution of Y:

Y value	Probability
$-3+(-3)=-6$	$\frac{1}{4}$
$-3+3=0$	$\frac{1}{2}$
$3+3=6$	$\frac{1}{4}$

$P(Y=0)=\frac{1}{2}$

Moments of Y:

$$E(Y)=\frac{1}{4}(-6)+\frac{1}{2}(0)+\frac{1}{4}(6)=0$$

$$E(Y^2)=\frac{1}{4}(36)+\frac{1}{2}(0)+\frac{1}{4}(36)=18$$

$\text{Var}(Y)=18-0=18$

Statement 1: $P(XY=0)=\frac{1+e^{-3}}{2}$

$XY=0 \Leftrightarrow X=0$ or $Y=0$

Since X and Y are independent:

$P(XY=0)=P(X=0)+P(Y=0)-P(X=0)P(Y=0)$

$=e^{-3}+\frac{1}{2}-e^{-3}\cdot\frac{1}{2}$

$=e^{-3}\left(1-\frac{1}{2}\right)+\frac{1}{2}$

$=\frac{e^{-3}}{2}+\frac{1}{2}=\frac{1+e^{-3}}{2}$ →TRUE

Statement 2: $E(X+Y)=3$

$E(X+Y)=E(X)+E(Y)=3+0=3$

TRUE

Statement 3: $\text{Var}(X+Y)=21$

Since X and Y are independent:

$\text{Var}(X+Y)=\text{Var}(X)+\text{Var}(Y)=3+18=21$ →TRUE

Statement 4: $\text{Cov}(X+Y, X-Y)=0$

$\text{Cov}(X+Y, X-Y)=\text{Var}(X)-\text{Cov}(X,Y)+\text{Cov}(Y,X)-\text{Var}(Y)$

$=\text{Var}(X)-\text{Var}(Y)$ (since $\text{Cov}(X,Y)=0$)

$=3-18=-15\neq 0$ →FALSE

Correct answer: statements: 1, 2 and 3

CHAPTER 3

RANDOM VARIABLE

(JUNE 2012)

1. Suppose X and Y are independent random variables where Y is symmetric about 0. Let $U = X + Y$ and $V = X - Y$ then
(a) U and V are always independent
(b) U and V have the same distribution
(c) U is always symmetric about 0
(d) V is always symmetric about 0

(JUNE 2012)

2. Let $F(x,y), G(x)$ and $H(y)$ be the joint c.d.f. of (X, Y), marginal c.d.f. of X and marginal c.d.f. of Y respectively.
Define $U = \begin{cases} 1 \text{ if } X \leq a \\ -1 \text{ if } X > a \end{cases}$ and $V = \begin{cases} 1 \text{ if } Y \leq b \\ -1 \text{ if } y > b \end{cases}$
Where a and b are fixed real numbers. Then
(a) If Cov(U, V)=0 then F(x,y)=G(x)H(y) for all x and y.
(b) If F(x,y)=G(x)H(y) for all x and y then Cov (U, V)=0
(c) If U and V are independent then X and Y are independent.
(d) If X and Y are independent then U and V are independent.

(JUNE 2012)

3. Which of the following conditions imply independence of the random variable X and Y?
(a) p(X>a| Y>a) = P(X>a) for all a $\in \mathbb{R}$
(b) p(X>a| Y<b)=P(X>a) for all a,b $\in \mathbb{R}$
(c) X and Y are uncorrelated
(d) $E[(X-a)(Y-b)] = E(X-a)E(Y-b)$ for all a, b $\in \mathbb{R}$

(JUNE 2012)

4. Let $g(x)=\frac{1}{\sqrt{2\pi}}e^{-\frac{1}{2}x^2}$ for $x \in \mathbb{R}$ and u be a continuous function on $\mathbb{R}$ such that
(i) $u(-x) = -u(x)$, for all $x \in \mathbb{R}$ and u non-zero
(ii) $u(x) = (0)$, for $x \in (-1,1)$
(iii) $|u(x)| \leq \frac{1}{2\sqrt{2\pi e}}$, for all $x \in \mathbb{R}$.
Let $f(x) = g(x) + u(x)$, for all $x \in \mathbb{R}$. Then
(a) f can take negative values
(b) f(x) $>$ 0 for all x and f is not integrable
(c) f is a probability density function on R.
(d) f is an integrable function.

(DEC. 2012)

5. Suppose X_1, X_2, X_3, X_4 are i.i.d. random variables taking values 1 and -1 with probability ½ each. Then $E(X_1 + X_2 + X_3 + X_4)^4$ equals
(a) 4 (b) 76
(c) 16 (d) 12

(DEC. 2012)

6. Let $\{X_n : n \geq 0\}$ and X be random variables defined on a common probability space. Further assume that $X_n's$ are non-negative and X takes values 0 and 1 with probability p and $1-p$ respectively, where $0 \leq p \leq 1$. Which of the following statements are necessarily true?
(a) If $p = 0$ and X_n converges to X in distribution, then X_n converges to X in probability.
(b) If $p = 1$ and X_n converges to X in distribution, then X_n converges to X in probability.
(c) If $0 < p < 1$ and X_n converges to X in distribution, then X_n converges to X in probability.
(d) If X_n converges to X in distribution, then X_n converges to X almost surely.

(JUNE 2013)

7. Consider the following three populations in $\mathbb{R}^2$:
(a) $A_1 = \{(-2,0),(2,0),(0,-2),(0,2),(-1,1),(1,-1),(1,1)\}$
(b) $A_2 = \{(0,0),(-1,1),(1,1),(-2,3),(2,3),(-3,6),(3,6)\}$
(c) $A_3 = \{(-3,0),(-2,0),(0,0),(1,0),(2,0),(3,1)\}$
Suppose one point is selected at random from each population, the point from population A_i being labeled $(X_i, Y_i), i = 1,2,3$. Then the absolute value of Cov(X_i, Y_i) will be highest for
(a) $i = 1$ (b) $i = 2$
(c) $i = 3$ (d) $i = 2$ and $i = 3$

(JUNE 2013)

8. Let X be a non-negative integer valued random variable with probability mass function $f(x)$ satisfying $(x+1)f(x+1) = (\alpha + \beta x) f(x), x = 0,1,2,\ldots, \beta \neq 1$. You may assume that $E(X)$ and $Var(X)$ exist. Then which of the following statements are true?
(a) $E(X) = \frac{\alpha}{1-\beta}$ (b) $E(X) = \frac{\alpha^2}{(1-\beta)(1+\alpha)}$
(c) $Var(X) = \frac{\alpha^2}{(1-\beta)^2}$ (d) $Var(X) = \frac{\alpha}{(1-\beta)^2}$

(DEC. 2013)

9. Let X_1 and X_2 be independent random variables with cumulative distribution functions (cdf) F_1 And F_2 respectively. Let G be the cdf of $X_1 + X_2$ and H be the cdf of X_1X_2.
Identify the correct statements.
(a) If F_1 is a continuous function then so is G.
(b) If F_1 is a continuous function then so is H.
(c) If F_1 is a step function then so is G.
(d) If F_1 is a step function then so is H.

(DEC. 2013)

10. Let X and Y be random variables with $EX^2 < \infty$. Then, we can conclude that
(a) $Var(X) \geq Var(E(X|Y))$
(b) $Var(X) \geq E(Var(X|Y))$
(c) $Var(E(X|Y)) \geq E(Var(X|Y))$
(d) $E(Var(X|Y)) \geq Var(E(X|Y))$
(JUNE 2014)

11. Suppose X, Y and Z are three independent random variables each with finite variance. Let $U = X + Z$ and $V = Y + Z$. Suppose U and V have the same distribution. Then
(a) X and Y have the same distribution
(b) It is possible to have $Corr\ (U, V) < 0$
(c) $U + V$ and $U - V$ are always independent
(d) We must have $Corr\ (U, V) < 0$
(JUNE 2014)

12. Suppose U and V are independent and identically distributed random variables with
$P(U = i) = P(V = i) = \frac{1}{4}$ for $i = 1, 2, 3, 4$.
Consider the triangle T, bounded by the x-axis, y-axis, and the line $Ux + Vy = UV$.
Then which of the following statements are true?
(a) $P(Area(T) < 2) = \frac{5}{16}$ (b) $P(T\ is\ isosceles) = \frac{1}{4}$
(c) $P(Area(T) \leq 8) = 1$ (d) $P(Area(T) > 1) = 1$
(JUNE 2014)

13. A fair coin is tossed repeatedly. Let X be the number of Tails before the first Head occurs. After the first Head occurred, an additional Y tails appear before the next Head occurs. Which of the following statements are true?
(a) $(X\ is\ even, Y\ is\ even) = P(X\ is\ odd, Y\ is\ odd)$
(b) $(X\ is\ even, Y\ is\ even) = P(X\ is\ even, Y\ is\ odd)$
(c) $(X\ is\ even, Y\ is\ even) > P(X\ is\ even, Y\ is\ odd)$
(d) $(X\ is\ even, Y\ is\ even) < P(X\ is\ even, Y\ is\ odd)$
(DEC. 2014)

14. Let X and Y be integer-valued, bounded random variables. Then which of the following statement is FALSE?
(a) $E(X) = \sum_y E(X|Y = y)P(Y = y)$
(b) $V(X) = \sum_y V(X|Y = y)P(Y = y)$
(c) $P(X = x) = \sum_y P(X = x|Y = y)P(Y = y)$
(d) $E(XY) = \sum_y yE(X|Y = y)P(Y = y)$
(DEC. 2014)

15. Suppose X is a random variable such that $E(X) = 0, E(X^2) = 2$ and $E(X^4) = 4$. Then,
(a) $E(X^3) = 0$
(b) $P(X \geq 0) = 1/2$
(c) $X \sim N(0,2)$
(d) X is bounded with probability 1.
(DEC. 2014)

16. Suppose X_1, X_2, X_3 and X_4 are independent and identically distributed random variables, having density function f. Then,
(a) $P(X_4 > \max(X_1, X_2) > X_3) = \frac{1}{6}$
(b) $P(X_4 > \max(X_1, X_2) > X_3) = \frac{1}{8}$
(c) $P(X_4 > X_3 > \max(X_1, X_2)) = \frac{1}{12}$
(d) $P(X_4 > X_3 > \max(X_1, X_2)) = \frac{1}{6}$
(DEC. 2014)

17. Let $X_1, X_2, X_3, \ldots$ be independent random variables with $E(X_k) = 0$ and $Var(X_k) = k$. Let $S_n = \sum_{k=1}^{n} X_k$. Then, as $n \to \infty$,
(a) $\frac{S_n}{n^{3/2}} \to 0$ In probability (b) $\frac{S_n}{n^{3/2}} \to 0$ In distribution
(c) $\frac{S_n X_n}{n^{5/2}} \to 0$ In distribution (d) $\frac{S_n X_n}{n^{5/2}} \to 0$ In probability
(DEC. 2014)

18. Let $\phi(t)$ be a characteristic function of some random variable. Then, which of the following are also characteristic function?
(a) $f(t) = [\phi(t)]^2$ for all $t \in \mathbb{R}$.
(b) $f(t) = |\phi(t)|^2$ for all $t \in \mathbb{R}$.
(c) $f(t) = \phi(-t)$ for all $t \in \mathbb{R}$.
(d) $f(t) = \phi(t + 1)$ for all $t \in \mathbb{R}$.
(JUNE 2015)

19. Suppose X_n, X are random variables such that X_n converges in distribution to X and $(-1)^n X_n$ also converges in distribution to X. Then
(a) X must have a symmetric distribution.
(b) X must be 0.
(c) X must have a density
(d) X^2 must be a constant
(JUNE 2015)

20. Ten balls are put in 6 slots at random. Then the expected total number of balls in the two extreme slots is
(a) 10/6 (b) 10/3
(c) 1/6 (d) 6/10
(JUNE 2015)

21. Let X, Y be independent random variables and let $Z = \frac{X-Y}{2} + 3$. If X has characteristic function φ and Y has characteristic function ψ, then Z has characteristic function θ where
(a) $\theta(t) = e^{-i3t}\varphi(2t)\psi(-2t)$.
(b) $\theta(t) = e^{i3t}\varphi\left(\frac{t}{2}\right)\psi\left(-\frac{t}{2}\right)$.
(c) $\theta(t) = e^{-i3t}\varphi\left(\frac{t}{2}\right)\psi\left(\frac{t}{2}\right)$.
(d) $\theta(t) = e^{i3t}\varphi\left(\frac{t}{2}\right)\psi\left(\frac{-t}{2}\right)$.
(JUNE 2015)

22. Let X and Y be random variables with joint cumulative distribution function F (x, y). Then which of the following condition are sufficient for $(x, y) \in \mathbb{R}^2$ to be a point of continuity of F?
(a) $P(X = x, Y = y) = 0$
(b) Either $P(X = x) = 0$ or $P(Y = y) = 0$
(c) $P(X = x) = 0$ and $P(Y = y) = 0$
(d) $P(X = x, Y \leq y) = 0$ and $P(X \leq x, Y = y) = 0$
(DEC. 2015)

23. Let X be a random variable which is symmetric about 0. Let F be the cumulative distribution function of X. Which of the following statements is always true?
(a) $F(x) + F(-x) = 1$ for all $x \in \mathbb{R}$
(b) $F(x) - F(-x) = 0$ for all $x \in \mathbb{R}$
(c) $F(x) + F(-x) = 1 + P(X = x)$ for all $x \in \mathbb{R}$

(d) $F(x) + F(-x) = 1 - P(X = -x)$ for all $x \in \mathbb{R}$

(DEC. 2015)

24. Let Y_1, Y_2 be two independent random variables taking values -1 and $+1$ with probability $\frac{1}{2}$ each. Define $X_1 = Y_1, X_2 = Y_2, X_3 = X_2X_1, \ldots, X_n = X_{n-1}X_{n-2}$ for $n \geq 3$. Then
(a) $P(X_8 = 1, X_9 = 1, X_{10} = -1) = \frac{1}{4}$
(b) $P(X_8 = 1, X_9 = 1, X_{10} = 1) = \frac{1}{4}$
(c) $P(X_8 = 1, X_9 = 1, X_{10} = -1) = \frac{1}{8}$
(d) $P(X_8 = 1, X_9 = 1, X_{10} = 1) = \frac{1}{8}$

(DEC. 2015)

25. A fair coin in tossed repeatedly. Let X be the number of Tails before the first Head occurs. Let Y denote the number of Tails observed between the occurrence of the first and the second Heads. Let $X + Y = N$. Then, which of the following statements are true:
(a) X and Y are independent random variables with
$$P(X = k) = P(Y = k) = \begin{cases} 2^{-(k+1)} & \text{for } k = 0,1,2 \ldots \\ 0 & \text{otherwise} \end{cases}$$
(b) N has a probability mass function given by
$$P\{N = k\} = \begin{cases} (k-1)2^{-k} & \text{for } k = 2,3,4 \ldots \\ 0 & \text{otherwise} \end{cases}$$
(c) Given $N = n$, the conditional distribution of X and Y are independent
(d) Given $N = n$, $P(X = k) = \begin{cases} \frac{1}{n+1} & \text{for } k = 0,1,2, \ldots, n \\ 0 & \text{otherwise} \end{cases}$

(JUNE 2016)

26. Let X and Y be independent and identically distributed random variables such that.
$P(X = 0) = P(X = 1) = \frac{1}{2}$. Let $Z = X + Y$ and $= |X - Y|$. Then which statement is not correct?
(a) X and W are independent.
(b) Y and W are independent.
(c) Z and W are uncorrelated.
(d) Z and W are independent.

(JUNE 2016)

27. The joint probability density function of (X, Y) is
$$f(x, y) = \begin{cases} 6(1-x)\,;\ 0 < y < x, 0 < x < 1 \\ 0, \textit{otherwise} \end{cases}$$
Which among the following are correct?
(a) X and Y are not independent
(b) $f_Y(y) = \begin{cases} 3(y-1)^2, 0 < y < 1 \\ 0, \textit{ otherwise} \end{cases}$
(c) X and Y are independent
(d) $f_Y(y) = \begin{cases} 3\left(y - \frac{1}{2}y^2\right), 0 < y < 1 \\ 0, \textit{ otherwise} \end{cases}$

(JUNE 2016)

28. $\{X_i\}$ is a sequence of independent and identically distributed random variables with common density function
$$f(x) = \begin{cases} e^{-x}, x > 0 \\ 0, \textit{otherwise} \end{cases}$$
$\{Y_i\}$ is a sequence of independent identically distributed random variables with common density function
$$g(y) = \begin{cases} 4e^{-4y},\ y > 0 \\ 0, \textit{otherwise} \end{cases}$$
Also $\{X_i\}, \{Y_i\}$ are independent families. Let $Z_K = Y_K - 3X_k, k = 1,2, \ldots$. Which among the following are correct?
(a) $P(Z_k > 0) > 0$
(b) $\sum_{k=1}^{n} Z_k \to +\infty$ with probability 1
(c) $\sum_{k=1}^{n} Z_k \to -\infty$ with probability 1
(d) $P(Z_k < 0) > 0$

(JUNE 2017)

29. Let $c \in \mathbb{R}$ be a constant. Let X, Y be random variables with joint probability density function
$$f(x, y) = \begin{cases} cxy, & \text{if } 0 < x < y < 1, \\ 0, & \text{otherwise} \end{cases}$$
Which of the following statements are correct?
(a) $c = \frac{1}{8}$ (b) $c = 8$
(c) X and Y are independent (d) $P(X = Y) = 0$

(DEC. 2017)

30. Let $\psi(t) = e^{-|t| - \frac{t^2}{2}}$ and $\varphi(t) = \frac{e^{-|t|} + e^{-\frac{t^2}{2}}}{2}$. Which of the following is true?
(a) ψ is a characteristic function but φ is not
(b) φ is a characteristic function but ψ is not
(c) both ψ and φ are characteristic functions
(d) neither ψ nor φ is a characteristic function

(JUNE 2018)

31. Let X and Y be two random variables with joint probability density function
$$f(x, y) = \begin{cases} \frac{1}{\pi} & \text{if } 0 \leq x^2 + y^2 \leq 1 \\ 0 & \text{otherwise} \end{cases}.$$
Which of the following statements are correct?
(a) X and Y are independent (b) $P(X > 0) = 1/2$
(c) $E(Y) = 0$ (d) $Cov(X, Y) = 0$

(JUNE 2018)

32. Let X and Y be two random variables satisfying $X \geq 0, Y \geq 0, E(X) = 3, V(X) = 9, E(Y) = 2$ and $V(Y) = 4$. Which of the following statements are correct?
(a) $0 \leq Cov\,(X, Y) \leq 4$ (b) $E(XY) \leq 6$
(c) $V(X + Y) \leq 25$ (d) $E(X + Y)^2 \geq 25$

(JUNE 2018)

33. Let $\{X_i\}_{i \geq 1}$ be a sequence of i.i.d. random variables with $E(X_i) = 0$ and $V(X_i) = 1$. Which of the following are true?
(a) $\frac{1}{n}\sum_{i=1}^{n} X_i^2 \to 0$ in probability
(b) $\frac{1}{n^{3/4}}\sum_{i=1}^{n} X_i \to 0$ in probability
(c) $\frac{1}{n^{1/2}}\sum_{i=1}^{n} X_i \to 0$ in probability
(d) $\frac{1}{n}\sum_{i=1}^{n} X_i^2 \to 1$ in probability

(JUNE 2019)

34. Let X_1, X_2, X_3, X_4, X_5 be $i.i.d.$ random variables having a continuous distribution function. Then

$P(X_1 > X_2 > X_3 > X_4 > X_5)|X_1 = \max(X_1, X_2 \dots X_5)]$equals

(a) $\frac{1}{4}$ (b) $\frac{1}{5}$

(c) $\frac{1}{4!}$ (d) $\frac{1}{5!}$

(JUNE 2019)

35 Consider the function $f(x)$ defined as $f(x) = ce^{-x^4}, x \in \mathbb{R}$ For what value of c is f a probability density function?

(a) $\frac{2}{\Gamma(\frac{1}{3})}$ (b) $\frac{4}{\Gamma(\frac{1}{4})}$

(c) $\frac{3}{\Gamma(\frac{1}{4})}$ (d) $\frac{2}{\Gamma(\frac{1}{4})}$

(JUNE 2019)

36. Let $X_1, X_2 \dots$ be a sequence of independent normally distributed random variables with mean 1 and 1. Let N be a poisson random variable with mean 2, independent of $X_1, X_2 \dots$ Then the variance of $X_1, X_2 + \dots + X_{N+1}$ is

(a) 3 (b) 4

(c) 5 (d) 9

(JUNE 2019)

37. Suppose X, Y are $i.i.d$ Binomial (n, p) random variables. Which of the following are true?

(a) $X + Y \sim Bin(2n, p)$

(b) $(X, Y) \sim Multinomial(2n; p, p)$

(c) $Var(X - Y) = E(X - Y)^2$

(d) $Cov\ (X + Y, X - Y) = 0$

(DEC. 2019)

38. Let X and Y be real-valued independent random variables on Ω. Then which of the following statements are correct?

(a) $E[\cos(tX + uY)] = E[\cos(tX)]E[cos(uy)] - E[\sin(tX)]E[\sin(uy)]$ for all $t, u \in \mathbb{R}$

(b) $If\ X \sim N(2,1) and\ Y \sim N(0,2), then\ Var(X + Y) = 3\ where\ N(\mu, \sigma^2)$ represents Normal distribution with mean μ and variance σ^2

(c) $\{X = a\} \cap \{Y = b\} = \phi\ for\ all\ a, b \in \mathbb{R}$

(d) $P\{\{X = a\} \cap \{Y = b\}) = P(\{X = a\})P(\{Y = b\})\ for\ all\ a, b \in \mathbb{R}$

(DEC. 2019)

39. Let $\{(X_n, Y_n): n \geq 1\}$ and (X, Y) be random variables, on (Ω, F, P). Then which of the following statements are correct?

(a) If $X_n \to X$ amlost surely, $Y_n \to Y$ almost surely, then $X_n + Y_n \to X + Y$ in distribution

(b) If $X_n \to X$ in probability, $Y_n \to Y$ almost surely, then $X_n + Y_n \to X + Y$ in distribution

(c) If $X_n \to X$ in probability, $Y_n \to Y$ in probability, then $X_n + Y_n \to X + Y$ in distribution

(d) If $X_n \to X$ in distribution, $Y_n \to Y$ in distribution, then $X_n + Y_n \to X + Y$ in distribution

(NOV. 2020)

40. Let X and Y be independent random variables with E(X)=E(Y)=0 and Var(x)=Var(Y)=1.
Let Z=X+Y. which of the following statements are correct?

(a) $P(|Z| > \varepsilon) \leq 2/\varepsilon^2$

(b) $E(|Z|) \leq \sqrt{2}$

(c) $E(Z^2) = 2$

(d) $P(Z \leq 0) = P(Z \geq 0)$

(NOV. 2020)

41. For $n > 1$, let $X_1, X_2 \dots, X_n$ be random variables such that $E(X_i) = 0$ and $E(X_i^2) = 1$ for all i and $E(X_i X_j) = \rho$ for all $i \neq j$. Which of the following statements are true?

(a) $\rho = 0$ if and only if $X_1, X_2 \dots, X_n$are independent

(b) $Var(X_1 + X_2 + \dots + X_n) = n$ if and only if $X_1, X_2 \dots, X_n$ are independent

(c) $Var(X_1 + X_2 + \dots + X_n) = n$ if and only if $X_1, X_2 \dots, X_n$ are pairwise independent

(d) $Var(X_1 + X_2 + \dots + X_n) = n$ if and only if $\rho = 0$

[SEP 2022]

42. If the hazard function of a lifetime random variable X is given by $r(x) = \frac{2x}{1+x^2}, x \in (0, \infty)$, indicate the correct options.

(a) Survival function of the random variable X is $S(x) = \frac{1}{1+x^2}, x \in (0, \infty)$

(b) Survival function of the random variable X is $S(x) = \frac{x^2}{1+x^2}, x \in (0, \infty)$

(c) Survival function of the random variable X cannot be determined from the given information

(d) The survival function, density function and distribution function can be determined from the given information

[SEP 2022]

43. Let $\{X_i : i \geq 1\}$ be a sequence of independent and identically distributed Bernoulli random variables with $\mathbb{P}(X_1 = 1) = p \in (0,1)$. Which of the following sequences of estimators are consistent for p as $n \to \infty$?

(a) $\left\{\frac{1}{n}\sum_{i=1}^{n} X_i : n \geq 1\right\}$

(b) $\{0.5(X_n + X_{n+1}): n \geq 1\}$

(c) $\left\{\frac{1}{n}\sum_{i=1}^{n} X_i^i : n \geq 1\right\}$

(d) $\left\{\frac{1}{n}\sum_{i=1}^{n} X_{2i-1}X_{2i} : n \geq 1\right\}$

(JUNE 2023)

44. Suppose $X_1, X_2, \dots, X_n$ are independently and identically distributed $N(\theta, 1)$ random variables, for $\theta \in \mathbb{R}$. Suppose $\bar{X} = n^{-1}\sum_{i=1}^{n} X_i$ denotes the sample mean and let $t_{0.975,n-1}$ denote the 0.975-quantile of a Student's-t distribution with $n - 1$ degrees of freedom. Which of the following statements is true for the following interval $\bar{X} \pm t_{0.975,n-1}\frac{1}{\sqrt{n}}$?

(a) The interval is a confidence interval for θ with confidence level of exactly 0.95.

(b) The interval is a confidence interval for θ with confidence level being less than 0.95.

(c) The interval is a confidence interval for θ with confidence level being more than 0.95.

(d) The interval is not a confidence interval.

(JUNE 2023)

45. Let X_i for $i = 1,2, \dots, 2n, n \geq 1$, be independent random variables each distributed as N(0,1). Which of the following statements are correct?

(a) $(X_1 + \cdots + X_n - X_{n+1} - \cdots - X_{2n})/2n \sim N(0,2)$
(b) $(X_1 - X_2)^2 + (X_3 - X_4)2 + \cdots + (X_{2n-1} - X_{2n})^2 \sim 2\chi_n^2$
(c) $E[max\,(|X_1|, |X_{n+1}|)] = \frac{2}{\sqrt{\pi}}$
(d) $E[max\,(|X_1|, |X_{n+1}|)] = \frac{4}{\sqrt{\pi}}$

(JUNE 2023)

46. Suppose $X_1, X_2, \ldots, X_n$ are independently and identically distributed $N(0, \tau^{-2})$ random variables, for $\tau^{-2} > 0$. Let the prior distribution on τ^{-2} have density $\pi(\tau^2) \propto (1/\tau^2)\alpha$ for some $\alpha > 0$. Which of the following are true?
(a) The prior distribution is an improper distribution for $\alpha > 0$.
(b) The posterior distribution is a proper distribution for all $\alpha > 0$.
(c) Under a squared error loss, the generalized Bayes estimator of τ^2 is $\frac{n/2-\alpha}{\sum_{i=1}^{n} X_i^2/2}$.
(d) The posterior distribution is proper for $\alpha = 1$.

(JUNE 2023)

47. Let X and Y be independent Poisson random variables with parameters 2 and 3, respectively. Which of the following statements are correct?
(a) $Var(X|X + Y = 2) = \frac{12}{25}$
(b) $E\left(\frac{2}{1+X}\middle|X + Y = 2\right) = \frac{98}{3}$
(c) $P(X^2 = 0|X + Y = 2) = e^{-2} + \frac{9}{25}(1 - e^2)$
(d) $X|Y = 3 \sim$Binomial (3,2)

(JULY 2024)

48. Let X be a random variable with cumulative distribution function given by

$$F(x) = \begin{cases} 0, & if\ x < 0 \\ \dfrac{x+1}{3}, & if\ 0 \le x < 1 \\ 1, & if\ x \ge 1 \end{cases}$$

Then the value of $P\left(\frac{1}{3} < X < \frac{3}{4}\right) + P(X = 0)$ is equal to
(a) $\frac{7}{36}$ (b) $\frac{11}{36}$
(c) $\frac{13}{36}$ (d) $\frac{17}{36}$

(July 2024)

49. Let X and Y be jointly distributed continuous random variables with joint probability density function

$$f(x,y) = \begin{cases} \dfrac{x}{y}, & if\ 0 < x < y < 2 \\ 0, & otherwise \end{cases}$$

Which of the following statements are true?
(a) $P\left(X < \frac{1}{2}\middle|Y = 1\right) = \frac{1}{4}$ (b) $E(Y) = \frac{1}{4}$
(c) $\left(X < \frac{Y}{2}\right) = \frac{1}{4}$ (d) $E\left(\frac{Y}{X}\right) = \frac{1}{4}$

(JULY 2024)

50. Let $\{X_n\}_{n\ge1}$ be a sequence of independent and identically distributed random variables with $E(X_1) = 0$ and $Var(X_1) = 1$. Which of the following statements are true?
(a) $\lim_{n\to\infty} P\left(\frac{\sqrt{n}\sum_{i=1}^{n} X_i}{\sum_{i=1}^{n} X_i^2} \le 0\right) = \frac{1}{2}$
(b) $\frac{\sum_{i=1}^{n} X_i}{\sum_{i=1}^{n} X_i^2}$ converges in probability to 0 as $n \to \infty$
(c) $\frac{1}{n}\sum_{i=1}^{n} X_i^2$ converges in probability to 1 as $n \to \infty$
(d) $\lim_{n\to\infty} P\left(\frac{\sum_{i=1}^{n} X_i}{\sqrt{n}} \le 0\right) = \frac{1}{2}$

(FEB. 2025)

51. Suppose that $X \sim$ binomial$(9, \theta), 0.7 < \theta < 1$, and $Y \sim$ Poisson$(\lambda), \lambda > 0$. If $3E(Y) = E(X)$, then which of the following is true?
(a) $Var(X) > 3Var(Y)$
(b) $2Var(Y) < Var(X) < 3Var(Y)$
(c) $Var(Y) < Var(X) < 2Var(Y)$
(d) $Var(X) < Var(Y)$

(FEB. 2025)

52. Let Z_1 and Z_2 be two independent discrete random variables such that Z_1 follows binomial distribution with parameters $n = 2$ and $p = \frac{1}{2}$, and Z_2 follows Poisson distribution with mean 1. Consider the following system of equations with three variables x_1, x_2 and x_3:

$$x_1 - 2x_2 + x_3 = 1$$
$$2x_1 - 5x_2 + 2x_3 = 2$$
$$x_1 + 2x_2 + Z_1x_3 = Z_2.$$

Then, the probability that the given system of equations has infinite number of solutions equals
(a) e^{-1} (b) $\frac{e^{-1}}{2}$
(c) $\frac{e^{-1}}{4}$ (d) $\frac{e^{-1}}{12}$

(JUNE 2025)

53. Let $Z_1, Z_2, \ldots$ be a sequence of independent and identically distributed random variables having discrete uniform distribution over $\{1,2,\ldots,2024\}$. Let $Y_n = \sum_{i=1}^{n} Z_i, n \ge 2$. Further, let X_n be the remainder when Y_n is divided by 2025. Then, which of the following statements is true?
(a) $\lim_{n\to\infty} P(X_n = 0) = \frac{1}{2026}$ (b) $\lim_{n\to\infty} P(X_n = 0) = \frac{1}{2025}$
(c) $\lim_{n\to\infty} P(X_n = 0) = \frac{1}{2024}$ (d) $\lim_{n\to\infty} P(X_n = 0) = \frac{1}{2023}$

(JUNE 2025)

54. Let X and Y be independent Poisson random variables with means 4 and 2, respectively. Then, which of the following statements are true?
(a) The conditional distribution of X given X + Y = 3 is Binomial $\left(3, \frac{1}{3}\right)$
(b) $P(X \le 1|X + Y = 3) = \frac{7}{27}$
(c) $E(X|X + Y = 3) = 2$
(d) The value of the characteristic function of $X + Y$ at the point $t = \pi$ is e^{-12}

(JUNE 2025)

55. Let X be a random variable with the cumulative distribution function

$$F_X(x) = \begin{cases} 0, & if\ x < 0, \\ \dfrac{x+2}{5}, & if\ 0 \le x < 2 \\ 1, & if\ x \ge 2 \end{cases}$$

Then, which of the following statements are true?

(a) $E(X^2) = \frac{4}{3}$

(b) $P\left(\left|X - \frac{4}{5}\right| \geq 1\right) = \frac{19}{25}$

(c) The upper bound of $P\left(\left|X - \frac{4}{5}\right| \geq 1\right)$, using Chebyshev's inequality, is $\frac{52}{75}$

(d) The value of the moment generating function, $M_X(t)$, at t = 1 is $\frac{e^2-1}{5}$

(JUNE 2025)

56. Let X and Y be independent and identically distributed N(0, 1) random variables. Let $S - X^2 + Y^2$ and $T = e^{-(X^2+Y^2)/2}$, Then, which of the following statements are true?

(a) The probability density function of S is $f_s(x) = \begin{cases} \frac{1}{2}e^{-x/2}, & if\ s > 0 \\ 0, & otherwise \end{cases}$

(b) The probability density function of T is $f_x(x) = \begin{cases} 1, & if\ 0 < t < 1 \\ 0, & otherwise \end{cases}$

(c) Var(S) = 2.

(d) $E(T) = \frac{2}{3}$

(Dec 2025)

57. Let $X_1, X_2, \ldots$ be a sequence of independent and identically distributed random variables having Binomial $\left(3, \frac{1}{4}\right)$ distribution. For $j = 1, 2, \ldots$, define

$$Y_j = \begin{cases} 1, & \text{if } X_j \leq \sqrt{5} \\ 0, & \text{otherwise.} \end{cases}$$

If $\frac{1}{n}\sum_{j=1}^{n} Y_j^2$ converges almost surely to a constant c as $n \to \infty$, then the value of c equals

(a) $\frac{1}{64}$ (b) $\frac{37}{64}$

(c) $\frac{63}{64}$ (d) $\frac{27}{32}$

(Dec 2025)

58. Let $\{Y_n, n \geq 1\}$ be a sequence of independent and identically distributed random variables, where $Y_1 \sim$ Bernoulli$\left(\frac{1}{2}\right)$. Define $Z = \sum_{n=1}^{\infty} \frac{4Y_n}{5^n}$. Then, which of the following statements is true?

(a) $P\left(Z \geq \frac{3}{5}\right) = 0.5, P\left(Z = \frac{4}{25}\right) = 0$

(b) $P\left(Z \geq \frac{3}{5}\right) = 0.6, P\left(Z = \frac{4}{25}\right) = 0$

(c) $P\left(Z \geq \frac{3}{5}\right) = 0.7, P\left(Z = \frac{4}{25}\right) = 0.16$

(d) $P\left(Z \geq \frac{3}{5}\right) = 0.8, P\left(Z = \frac{4}{25}\right) = 0.16$

(Dec 2025)

59. Let $\{X_n : n \geq 1\}$ be a sequence of independent and identically distributed random variables, where X_1 has an Exponential distribution with mean 1. Define $T_n = \max\{X_1, X_2, \ldots, X_n\} - \ln n, n \geq 1$.

Suppose $T_n \xrightarrow{d} Y$ as $n \to \infty$. Then which of the following statements are true?

(a) Y has a Double Exponential distribution with location parameter ln(ln 2) and scale parameter 1

(b) Median of $Y = \ln(\ln 2)$

(c) $P(Y \leq 0) = e^{-1}$

(d) The derivative of the cumulative distribution function of Y at ln 3 is $e^{-\frac{1}{3}}$.

Answer Key

1	2	3	4	5	6	7	8	9	10
b	b,d	b	c,d	a	a,b	c	a,d	a	a,b
11	12	13	14	15	16	17	18	19	20
a	a,b,c	c	b	a,b,d	a,c	a,b,c,d	a,b,c	a	b
21	22	23	24	25	26	27	28	29	30
b	c,d	c	b	a,d	d	a,b	a,c,d	b,d	c
31	32	33	34	35	36	37	38	39	40
b,c,d	c,d	b,c,d	c	d	c	a,c,d	a,b,d	a,b,d	a,c
41	42	43	44	45	46	47	48	49	50
d	a,d	a,c	c	b,c	a,d	a	d	a,c	a,b,c,d
51	52	53	54	55	56	57	58	59	
d	b	b	b,c,d	a,c	a,b	c	a	c	

:: Explanations ::

1. **Explanation: (b)**

X and Y are independent random variables where $Y$is symmetric about 0, i.e., $f(-y) = f(y)$

$E(Y) = 0$

$U = X + Y$ and $V = X - Y$

$E(U) = E(X)$ and $E(V) = E(X)$

$E(U) = E(V)$

So, U and V have the same distribution

So, option (b) is correct

2. **Explanation: (b), (d)**

U and V are the function of X and Y respectively. If X and Y independent this implies U and V are independent

$F(x, y) = G(x). H(y)$

$\Rightarrow X$ and Y are independent
$\Rightarrow$ U and Y are independent
$\Rightarrow Co\,(U, V) = 0$
So, option (b) and (d) are correct.

3. Explanation: (b)
$P(X > a|Y > b) = P(x > a)\ \forall\, a, b \in \mathbb{R}$
$\Rightarrow X$ and Y are independent
So, option (b) is correct.

4. Explanation: (c), (d)

5. Explanation: (a)
X_i are iid r.v taking values -1 and 1 with prob $\frac{1}{2}$ each
$X_i = -1$ with prob $\frac{1}{2}$
$= 1$ with prob $\frac{1}{2}$
$i = 1, 2, 3, 4$
Let $Y_1 = X_1 + X_2$
$Y_1 = -2$ with prob $\frac{1}{4}$
$= 0$ with prob. $\frac{1}{2}$
$= 2$ with prob. $\frac{1}{4}$
Similarly let $Y_2 = X_3 + X_4$
$Y_2 = -2$ with prob. $\frac{1}{4}$
$= 0$ with prob. $\frac{1}{2}$
$= 2$ with prob $\frac{1}{4}$
$Z = Y_1 + Y_2$
$Z = -4$ with prob. $\frac{1}{16}$
$= -2$ with prob. $\frac{1}{4}$
$= 0$ with prob. $\frac{3}{8}$
$= 2$ with prob. $\frac{1}{4}$
$= 4$ with prob. $\frac{1}{16}$
$E(X_1 + X_2 + X_3 + X_4)^2 = E(Z^2) = (-4)^2 \times \frac{1}{16} + (2)^2 \times \frac{1}{4} + 0 \times \frac{3}{8} + (2)^2 \times \frac{1}{4} + 4^2 \times \frac{1}{16} = 4$
So, option (a) is correct

6. Explanation: (a), (b)
$X = 0$ with prob. p
$= 1$ with prob. $1 - p$
If $= 0$, $X = 1$
$X_n \xrightarrow{d} X$ and $X_n \xrightarrow{p} 1$ and $X_n \xrightarrow{p} X$
If $= 1$, $X = 0$
$X_n \xrightarrow{d} 0$ and $X_n \xrightarrow{p} 0$ and $X_n \xrightarrow{p} X$
So, option (a) and (b) are correct

7. Explanation: (c)

A_1		
x	y	xy
-2	0	0
2	0	0
0	-2	0
0	2	0
-1	-1	1
-1	1	-1
1	-1	-1
1	1	1
0	**0**	**0**

A_2		
x	y	xy
0	0	0
-1	1	-1
1	1	1
-2	3	-6
2	3	6
-3	6	-18
3	6	18
0	**20**	**0**

A_3		
x	y	xy
-3	0	0
-2	0	0
0	0	0
1	0	0
2	0	0
3	1	3
1	**1**	**3**

$Cov(X_1\,Y_1) = 0 \quad Cov(X_2\,Y_2) = 0 \quad Cov\,(X_3\,Y_3) = \frac{3-1/6}{27-1} \quad Cov(X_3\,Y_3) > 0$
So, $Cov(X_3, Y_3)$ is high among three population $i = 1, 2, 3$
So, option (c) is correct

8. Explanation: (a), (d)
X is non-negative inter-valued random variable with pmf $f(x)$ satisfy
$(x+1)f(x+1) = (\alpha + \beta x)\,f(x); x = 0, 1, 2, \ldots$
$E(X) = \sum_{x=0}^{\infty} x f(x)$
$= f(1) + 2f(2) + 3f(3) + \cdots$
$= \sum_{x=0}^{\infty}(x+1)\,f(x+1)$
$= \sum_{x=0}^{\infty}(\alpha + \beta x)\,f(x)$
$= \sum_{x=0}^{\infty} \alpha f(x) + \sum_{x=0}^{\infty} \beta x\, f(x)$
$= \alpha \sum_{x=0}^{\infty} f(x) + \beta \sum_{x=0}^{\infty} x f(x)$
$E(X) = \alpha + \beta\, E(X)$
$E(X) = \frac{\alpha}{1-\beta}$
$E(X^2) = \sum_{x=0}^{\infty} x^2\, f(x)$
$= 1f(1) + 2^2 f(2) + 3^2 f(3) + \cdots$
$= \sum_{x=0}^{\infty}(x+1)^2\, f(x+1)$
$= \sum_{x=0}^{\infty}(x+1)\,(\alpha + \beta x) f(x)$
$= \alpha \sum_{x=0}^{\infty} x f(x) + \beta \sum_{x=0}^{\infty} x^2\, f(x) + \alpha + \beta \sum_{x=0}^{\infty} x f(x)$
$= (\alpha + \beta)\,E(X) + \beta\,E(X^2) + \alpha$
$E(X^2) = (\alpha + \beta)E(X) + \beta\,E(X^2) + \alpha$

$(1-\beta)\,E(X^2) = (\alpha+\beta)\frac{\alpha}{1-\beta} + \alpha = \frac{\alpha^2+\alpha\beta+\alpha-\alpha\beta}{(1-\beta)}$

$E(X^2) = \frac{\alpha(\alpha+1)}{(1-\beta)^2}$

$Var(X) = E(X^2) - [E(X)]^2 = \frac{\alpha(\alpha+1)}{(1-\beta)^2} - \frac{\alpha^2}{(1-\beta)^2} = \frac{\alpha^2+\alpha-\alpha^2}{(1-\beta)^2}$

$= \frac{\alpha}{(1-\beta)^2}$

$E(X) = \frac{\alpha}{1-\beta}$ and $Var(X) = \frac{\alpha}{(1-\beta)^2}$

So, option (a) and (d) are correct

9. Explanation: (a)

F_1 is continuous function then G is also continuous function

So, option (a) is correct

10. Explanation: (a), (b)

X and Y be random variables with $E(X^2) < \infty$

$Var(X) = Var[E(X|Y)] + E[Var(X|Y)]$

$\therefore \Rightarrow Var(X) \geq Var[E(X|Y)]$

$Var(X) \geq E[Var(X|Y)]$

So, option (a), (b) are correct

11. Explanation: (a)

X, Y and Z are three independent random variables each with finite variance

$U = X + Z$ and $V = Y + Z$

Mgf of U and V are

$M_U(t) = M_{X+Z}(t)$

$M_U(t) = M_X(t)\cdot M_Z(t)$ [X & Z are independent]

and

$M_V(t) = M_{Y+Z}(t)]$

$= M_Y(t)\cdot M_z(t)$ [$\therefore Y$ & Z are independent]

U and V have same distribution this implies the mgf of U & V are equal (same)

$M_U(t) = M_V(t)$

$\Rightarrow M_X(t)\cdot M_Z(t) = M_Y(t)M_Z(t)$

$\Rightarrow M_X(t) = M_Y(t)$

By uniqueness property of mgf, X and Y have same distribution

So, option (a) is correct

12. Explanation: (a), (b), (c)

U and V are iid r.v. with

$P(U = i) = P(V = i) = \frac{1}{4}\,; i = 1,2,3,4$

Consider triangle T, bounded by x-axis, y-axis and the line $Ux + Vy = UV$

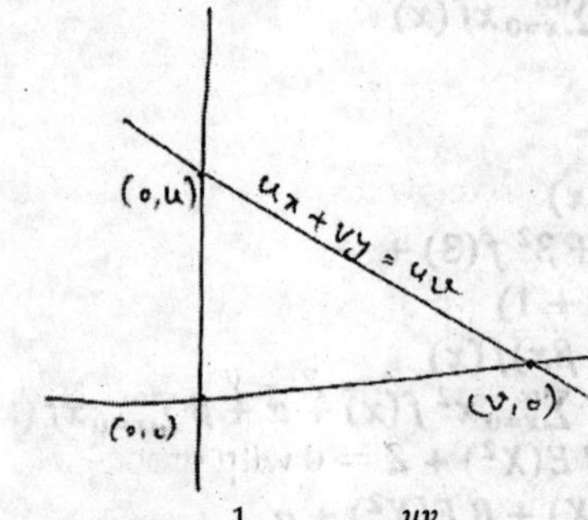

Area of $T = \frac{1}{2}\times uv = \frac{uv}{2}$

Option (a)

$P[Ar(T) < 2] = P\left[\frac{uv}{2} < 2\right] = P[uv < 4] = P[uv = 1] + P[uv = 2] + P[uv = 3]$

$= P(u = 1)\,P(v = 1) + P(u = 1, v = 2) + P(u = 2, v = 1) + P(u = 1, v = 3) + P(u = 3, v = 1)$

$= \frac{1}{4}\times\frac{1}{4} + \frac{1}{4}\times\frac{1}{4} + \frac{1}{4}\times\frac{1}{4} - \frac{1}{4}\times\frac{1}{4} + \frac{1}{4}\times\frac{1}{4} = \frac{5}{16}$

Option (b):

P (T is isosceles) $= P[U = V] = \sum_{i=1}^{4} P(U = V = i)$

$Prob.(T\ is\ isosceles) = P(U = 1, V = 1) + P(U = 2, V = 2) + P(U = 3, V = 3) + P(U = 4, V = 4)$

$= \frac{1}{16} + \frac{1}{16} + \frac{1}{16} + \frac{1}{16} = \frac{4}{16} - \frac{1}{4}$

Option (c):

$P[Ar(T) \leq 8] = P\left[\frac{UV}{2} \leq 8\right] = P[UV \leq 16] = 1$

Option (d):

$P[Ar(T) > 1] = 1 - P[Ar(T) \leq 1] = 1 - P\left[\frac{UV}{2} \leq 1\right]$

$= 1 - P[UV \leq 2]$

$= 1 - \{P(UV = 1) + P(UV = 2)\}$

$= 1 - \left[\frac{1}{16} + \frac{2}{16}\right]$

$\boxed{P(Ar(T) > 1) = \frac{13}{16}}$

So, option (a), (b), (c) are correct

13. Explanation: (c)

14. Explanation: (b)

X and Y be integer – valued, bounded random variable and X and Y discrete random variable

The marginal pmf of X is

$P(X = x) = \sum_y P(X = x, Y = y)$

$P(X = x) = \sum_y P(X = x|Y = y)\,P(Y = y)$

Conditional expectation

$E_y[E_x(X|Y)] = E(X)$

$E(X) = \sum_y E(X|Y = y)\,P(Y = y)$

$E(XY) = E_y[E_x(XY|Y = y)] = E_y[y\,E(X|Y = y)]$

$E(XY) = \sum_y yE(X|Y = y)\,P(Y = y)$

$Var(X) = Var[E(X|Y = y)] + E[Var(X|Y = y)]$

So, option (b) is correct

15. Explanation: (a), (b), (d)

X is a r.v such that $E(X) = 0, E(X^2) = 2$ and $E(X^4) = 4$

$Var(X^2) = E(X^4) - [E(X^2)]^2 = 4 - 2^2 = 0$

$Var(X^2) = 0$

$\Rightarrow X^2$ is constant

Then, $P[X = \pm a] = 1$ and X is bounded

$P[X = -a] = P[X = a] = \frac{1}{2}$

$P(X \geq 0) = \frac{1}{2}$

So, option (a), (b) and (d) are correct

16. Explanation: (a), (c)

X_1, X_2, X_3 and X_4 are iid r.v having density function f,

Total no. of arrangement $X_1, X_2, X_3, X_4 = 4!$

No. of arrangements for $X_4 > \max(X_1, X_2) > X_3 = 4$

$Prob[X_4 > \max(X_1, X_2) > X_3] = \frac{4}{4!} = \frac{1}{6}$

No. of arrangement far $X_4 > X_3 > \max(X_1, X_2) = 2$

$Prob[X_4 > X_3 > \max(X_1, X_2)] = \frac{2}{4!} = \frac{1}{12}$

Option (a) & (c) are correct

17. Explanation: (a), (b), (c), (d)

$E(X_k) = 0$ and $Var(X_k) = k$

$S_n = \sum_{K=1}^{n} X_k$

$E(S_n) = 0$ and $Var(S_n) = \sum_{k=1}^{n} k = \frac{n(n+1)}{2}$

As $\to \infty$; $\frac{S_n}{n^{3/2}} \xrightarrow{p} E\left[\frac{S_n}{n^{3/n}}\right] = \frac{1}{n^{3/2}} E(S_n) = 0$

If $X_n \xrightarrow{p} a \Rightarrow X_n \xrightarrow{d} a$

$\frac{S_n}{n^{3/2}} \xrightarrow{d} 0$

As $\to \infty$; $\frac{S_n X_n}{n^{5/2}} \xrightarrow{p} \frac{1}{n^{3/2}} E(S_n X_n) = \frac{1}{n^{5/2}} E(X_n^2) = \frac{n}{n^{5/2}} = \frac{1}{n^{3/2}} \to 0$

$\frac{S_n X_n}{n^{5/2}} \xrightarrow{p} 0 \Rightarrow \frac{S_n X_n}{n^{5/2}} \xrightarrow{d} 0$

So, option (a), (b), (c) and (d) are correct

18. Explanation: (a), (b), (c)

$\phi(t)$ be a characteristic function of some random variable

Result 1: The product of characteristic function is also characteristic function i.e.

$f(t) = \phi(t) \cdot \phi(t) = [\phi(t)]^2$ is also a characteristic function

$f(t) = |\phi(t)|^2$ is also a characteristic function and $\phi(t)$ is even function, i.e. $\phi(-t) = \phi(t)$

$f(t) = \phi(-t)$ is also a characteristic function

$\phi(0) = 1$

$\phi(1)$ may or may not equal to 1

So, $\phi(t+1)$ is not characteristic function

Option a, b, and c are correct

19. Explanation: (a)

X_n, X are random variable such that

$X_n \xrightarrow{d} X$ and $(-1)^n X_n \xrightarrow{d} X$

n is even then $X_n = (-1)^n X_n = X_n$

n is odd then $X_n = (-1)^n X_n = -X_n$

If X is symmetric distribution then

$\therefore f(x) = f(-x)$

$F(-x) = 1 - F(x)$

X_n and $(-1)^n X_n$ both converges in distribution to X that means X_n and $(-1)^n X_n$ have same density function. So, X must have symmetric distribution

20. Explanation: (b)

Let us suppose X_i represents the number of balls in the i-th slot $(i = 1,2,3,4,5,6)$

According to question, ten balls placed in 6 slots so

$X_1 + X_2 + X_3 + X_4 + X_5 + X_6 = 10$

Now taking expectation both sides

$E[X_1 + X_2 + X_3 + X_4 + X_5 + X_6] = 10$

$6\,E(X_1) = 10$

$E(X_1) = \frac{5}{3} = E(X_6)$

For the two extreme slots

$E[X_1 + X_6] = \frac{5}{3} + \frac{5}{3} = \frac{10}{3}$

So, option (b) is correct

21. Explanation: (b)

Let X and Y be independent random variables

$Z = \frac{X-Y}{2} + 3$

X has the characteristic function ϕ and Y has the characteristic function ψ

The characteristic function of Z is

$\theta_z(t) = \theta_{\left(\frac{X-Y}{2}+3\right)}(t) = E\left[e^{it\left(\frac{X-Y}{2}+3\right)}\right]$

$= E\left[e^{it\left(\frac{X-Y}{2}\right)+3it}\right]$

$= e^{3it} E\left[e^{it\,X/2}\, e^{-it\,Y/2}\right]$

$= e^{3it} E\left[e^{it\,X/2}\right] E\left[e^{it\,Y/2}\right]$

$= e^{3it} \phi(t/2).\psi(-t/2)$

Option (b) is correct

22. Explanation: (c), (d)

X and Y be random variable with joint cumulative distribution function $F(x,y)$.

The sufficient condition for $(x,y) \in R^2$ to be point of continuity of f is the marginal distribution of X and Y should be continuous.

If X is continuous then $P(X = x) = 0$ and Y is continuous then $P(Y = y) = 0$ and

$P(X = x, Y \le y) = 0$ and $P(X \le x, Y = 0) = 0$

So, option (c) and (d) are correct

23. Explanation: (c)

Let X be a random variable which is symmetric about 0 i.e.,

$f(-x) = f(x)$ or $P(X = x) = P(X = -x)$

$F(-x) = P(X \le -x)$ and $F(x) = P(X \le x)$

$F(x) + F(-x) = P(X \le x) + P(X \le -x)$

$= P(X \le x) + P(X \ge x)$

$= P(X \le x) + P(X > x) + P(X = 1) = 1 + P(X = 1)$

$F(x) + F(-x) = 1 + P(X = 1)$

$F(x) - F(-x) = P(X \le x) - P(X \le -x)$

$= P[-x < X \le x] \ne 0$

So, option (c) is correct

24. Explanation: (b)

25. Explanation: (a), (d)

26. Explanation: (d)

X and Y be iid random variable with

$P(X = 0) = P(X = 1) = \frac{1}{2}$

$Z = X + Y$ and $W = |X - Y|$

$X = 0$ with prob. $\frac{1}{2}$ $\quad$ $Z = X + Y$

$X = 1$ with prob. $\frac{1}{2}$ $\quad$ $Z = 0$ with prob. $\frac{1}{4}$

$Y = 0$ with prob. $\frac{1}{2}$ $\quad$ $Z = 1$ with prob. $\frac{1}{2}$

$Y = 1$ with prob. $\frac{1}{2}$ $\quad$ $Z = 2$ with prob. $\frac{1}{4}$

$W = |X - Y|$

$W = 0$ with prob. $\frac{1}{2}$

$W = 1$ with prob. $\frac{1}{2}$

Option (a) if X and W are independent then

$P(X = x, W = w) = P(X = x)\, P(W = w)$

W/X	0	1	P(W=w)
0	¼	¼	½
1	¼	¼	½
P (X=x)	½	½	1

$\therefore P(X = 0, W = 0) = \frac{1}{4}$

$P(X = 0) = P(W = 0) = \frac{1}{2}$

$\therefore P(X = 0, W = 0) = P(X = 0)P(W = 0) = \frac{1}{4}$

$\therefore\Rightarrow P(X = x, W = w) = P(X = x)P(W = w)$

X and W are independent

Option (b) If Y & W are independent

$P(Y = y, W = w) = P(Y = y, W = w)$

W/Y	0	1	P(W=w)
0	¼	¼	½
1	¼	¼	½
P (Y=y)	½	½	½

$\therefore Y$ & W are also independent

Option (c) & (d)

W/Z	0	1	2	P(W=w)
0	¼	0	¼	½
1	0	½	0	½
P (Z=z)	¼	½	¼	1

$\therefore P(Z = 0, W = 0) \neq P(Z = 0).\, P(W = 0)$

$\therefore Z$ & W are not independent

So, option (d) is correct

27. Explanation: (a), (b)

$f(x, y) = 6(1 - x); 0 < y < x; 0 < x < 1$

The marginal pdf of Y is

$f(y) = \int_y^1 f(x, y)\, dx = 6\int_y^1 (1 - x)\, dx = 6\left[x - \frac{x^2}{2}\right]_y^1$

$f(y) = 3(y - 1)^2; 0 < y < 1$

The marginal pdf of X is

$f(x) = \int_0^x f(x, y)\, dy = 6\int_0^x (1 - x)\, dy = 6(1 - x)x$

$f(x) = 6x(1 - x); 0 < x < 1$

$\therefore f(x, y) \neq f(x).f(y)$

So, X and Y are not independent

Then, option (a) and (b) are correct

28. Explanation: (a), (c), (d)

$\{X_i\}$ is sequence of iid r.v. with pdf

$f(x) = e^{-x}; x > 0$

$\{Y_i\}$ is sequence of iid r.v. with pdf

$g(y) = 4\, e^{-4y}; y > 0$

$\{X_i\}, \{Y_i\}$ are independent

$Z_k = Y_k - 3\, X_k;\ k = 1, 2, \ldots$

$P(Z_k > 0) = P(Y_k - 3X_k > 0)$

$= P[Y_k > 3\, X_k]$

$= 4\int_0^\infty \int_{3X_k}^\infty e^{-x}\, e^{-4y}\, dy\, dx$

$= 4\int_0^\infty e^{-x}\left[\frac{e^{4y}}{-4}\right]_{3x}^\infty dy$

$= \int_0^\infty e^{-13x}\, dx = \frac{1}{13}$

$P(Z_k > 0) = \frac{1}{13} > 0$

$P(Z_k < 0) = 1 - \frac{1}{13} = \frac{12}{13} > 0$

$E(X) = 1, E(Y) = \frac{1}{4}$

$E(Z_K) = E(Y_K - 3\, X_K) = \frac{1}{4} - 3 = -\frac{11}{4}$

$E(\sum_{k=1}^n Z_K) = \frac{-11}{4} n$

$\sum_{k=1}^n Z_K \to \lim_{n\to\infty} E[\sum_{k=1}^n Z_K]$ with probability 1

$\sum_{k=1}^n Z_K \to -\infty$ with probability 1

So, option (a), (c), (d) are correct

29. Explanation: (b), (d)

$c \in R$ be a constant

The joint pdf of X and Y is

$f(x, y) = cxy; 0 < x < y < 1$

$\Rightarrow \int_0^1 \int_0^y f(x, y)\, dx\, dy = 1$

$\Rightarrow \int_0^1 \int_0^y cxy\, dx\, dy = 1$

$\int_0^1 cy\left[\frac{x^2}{2}\right]_0^y dy = 1$

$c\int_0^1 \frac{y^3}{2} dy = 1$

$\frac{c}{2}\left[\frac{y^4}{4}\right]_0^1 = 1$

$\frac{c}{8} = 1 \Rightarrow c = 8$

The marginal pdf of X is

$f(x) = \int_x^1 f(x, y)\, dy = \int_x^1 8xy\, dy$

$= 8x\left[\frac{y^2}{2}\right]_x^1$

$f(x) = 4x\,(1 - x)^2; 0 < x < 1$

The marginal pdf of Y is

$g(y) = \int_0^y f(x, y)\, dx$

$= \int_0^y 8xy\, dx$

$= 8y\left[\frac{x^2}{2}\right]_0^y$

$= 8y\,\frac{y^2}{2}$

$g(y) = 4y^3; 0 < y < 1$

$\therefore f(x)\, g(y) \neq f(x, y)$

X & Y are not independent

X and Y are continuous random variable so

$P[X = Y] = 0$

So, option (b) & (d) are correct

30. Explanation: (c)

$\Psi(t) = e^{-|t| - \frac{t^2}{2}}$

Here, $\Psi(0) = 1$ and $|\Psi(t)| = \left|e^{-|t|}.e^{-\frac{t^2}{2}}\right| \leq 1$

$|\Psi(t)| \leq 1$

The necessary condition is satisfied.

Then, $\Psi(t)$ may be the characteristics function of some random variable X

We know that the characteristics function of standard Cauchy variate $\phi_X(t) = e^{-|t|}$

And the characteristics function of standard normal variate is

$\phi_Y(t) = e^{-\frac{1}{2}t^2}$

$\Psi(t) = \phi_X(t).\phi_Y(t)$

$= e^{-|t|}.e^{-\frac{1}{2}t^2}$

$\therefore$ $\Psi(t)$ is the product of characteristics function of standard Cauchy variate & Standard normal variate

So, $\Psi(t)$ is also a characteristic function

Now

$\phi(t) = \frac{e^{-|t|}+e^{-t^2/2}}{2}$

$\varphi(t) = \frac{\phi_X(t)+\phi_Y(t)}{2}$

$\phi(t)$ is the average of characteristics function of standard Cauchy variate and standard normal variate

So, $\varphi(t)$ is also characteristic function

So, option (c) is correct.

31. Explanation: (b), (c), (d)

$f(x,y) = \frac{1}{\pi} \qquad ; 0 \le x^2 + y^2 \le 1$

X and Y are independent if

$f(x,y) = f(x).g(y)$

The marginal pdf of X in

$f(x) = \int_0^{\sqrt{1-x^2}} f(x,y)dy$

$= \frac{1}{\pi}\int_{-\sqrt{1-x^2}}^{\sqrt{1-x^2}} 1\, dy$

$f(x) = \frac{2}{\pi}\sqrt{1-x^2}\,; \ -1 \le x \le 1$

Similarly, the marginal pdf of Y

$g(y) = \frac{2}{\pi}\sqrt{1-y^2}\,; \ -1 \le y \le 1$

$\therefore f(x,y) \neq f(x).g(y)$

$\Rightarrow X$ & Y are not independent

$P(X>0) = \int_0^1 f(x)\,dx = \frac{2}{\pi}\int_0^1 \sqrt{1-x^2}\,dx$

$\therefore \int \sqrt{a^2-x^2}\,dx = \frac{1}{2}x\sqrt{a^2-x^2} + \frac{1}{2}a^2\sin^{-1}\left(\frac{x}{a}\right)$

$\therefore P(X>0) = \frac{2}{\pi}\int_0^1 \sqrt{1-x^2}\partial x = \frac{2}{\pi}\left[\frac{1}{2}x\sqrt{1-x^2} + \frac{1}{2}\sin^{-1}x\right]_0^1$

$= \frac{2}{\pi}\left[\frac{1}{2}\sin^{-1}1 - \sin^{-1}0\right] = \frac{1}{2}$

$P(X>0) = \frac{1}{2}$

$E(Y) = \int_{-1}^1 yf(y)dy$

$= \int_{-1}^1 y\frac{2}{\pi}\sqrt{1-y^2}\,dy$

$= \frac{2}{\pi}\int_{-1}^1 y\sqrt{1-y^2}\,dy$

$E(Y) = 0$

$\text{Cov}(X,Y) = E(XY) - E(X).E(Y)$

$= E(XY)$

$= \iint xyf(x,y)dxdy$

$= \iint xy.\frac{1}{\pi}dxdy = \frac{1}{\pi}\int_{-1}^1\int_{-\sqrt{1-y^2}}^{\sqrt{1+y^2}} xydxdy$

$= \frac{1}{\pi}\int_{-1}^1 y\left[\frac{x^2}{2}\right]_{-\sqrt{1-y^2}}^{\sqrt{1+y^2}} dy$

$= \frac{1}{\pi}\int_{-1}^1 y.0\,dy$

$Cov(X,Y) = 0$

Option (b), (c), (d) are correct

32. Explanation: (c), (d)

$X \ge 0, Y \ge 0$

$E(X) = 3 \ E(Y) = 2$

$Var(X) = 9 \ Var(Y) = 4$

By cauchy – Schwartz inequality

$(E(XY))^2 \le E(X^2).E(Y^2)$

$E(XY) \le \sqrt{E(X^2).E(Y^2)}$

$E(X^2) = Var(X) + [E(X)]^2$

$= 9 + 3^2$

$= 9 + 9$

$E(X^2) = 18$

$E(Y^2) = Var(Y) + [E(Y)]^2$

$= 4 + 2^2$

$= 4 + 4$

$E(Y^2) = 8$

$E(XY) \le \sqrt{18 \times 8} = 3 \times 4$

$E(XY) \le 12$

$E(XY) - E(X).E(Y) \le 12 - E(X).E(Y)$

$Cov(X,Y) \le 12 - 3 \times 2 = 6$

$Cov(X,Y) \le 6$ ... (1)

By Gurland's inequality

$E(XY) \ge E(X).E(Y)$

$E(XY) - E(X)E(Y) \ge 0$

$Cov(XY) \ge 0$ ...(2)

On combine (1) & (2) $0 \le Cov(X,Y) \le 6$

$Var(X+Y) = Var(X) + Var(Y) - 2Cov(X,Y) \le Var(X) + Var(Y)$

$Var(X+Y) \le 13$

So, we can write

$Var(X+Y) \le 25$

$E(X+Y)^2 = E[X^2 + Y^2 + 2XY]$

$= E(X^2) + E(Y^2) + 2E(XY)$

$= 18 + 8 + 2\,E(XY)$

$= 26 + 2E(XY)$

$E(XY) \ge E(X).E(Y) = 3 \times 2 = 6$

$E(XY) \ge 6$

$2E(XY) \ge 12$

$E(X^2) + E(Y^2) + 2E(XY) \ge E(X^2) + E(Y^2) + 12$

$E(X+Y)^2 \ge 26 + 12$

$E(X+Y)^2 \ge 38$

We can write as

$E(X+Y)^2 \ge 25$

So, option (c) & (d) are correct

33. Explanation: (b), (c), (d)

$\{X_i\}_{i\ge1}$ be a sequence of iid random variable with $E(X_i) = 0$ and $Var(X_i) = 1$

By weak law of large number

$\frac{1}{n}\sum X_i^2 \xrightarrow{p} E(X_i^2)$

$\therefore E(X_i^2) = Var(X_i) + [E[X_i]]^2$

$E(X_i^2) = 1$

$\frac{1}{n}\sum X_1^2 \xrightarrow{p} 1$

$\frac{1}{n^{3/4}}\sum X_i \xrightarrow{p} E\left[\frac{1}{n^{3/4}}\sum X_i\right] = 0$

$\frac{1}{n^{3/4}}\sum X_i \xrightarrow{p} 0$

$\frac{1}{n^{1/2}}\sum X_i \xrightarrow{p} 0$

Option (b), (c) & (d) are correct

34. Explanation: (c)

$P[X_1 > X_2 > X_3 > X_4 > X_5 | X_1 = \max(X_1, X_2 \dots X_5)] = \frac{P[X_1>X_2>X_3>X_4>X_5 \cap X_1=max]}{P[X_1=max]}$

$= \frac{P[X_1>X_2>X_3>X_4>X_5]}{P[X_1=max]}$

No. of cases when X_1 is maximum.

$X_1 > X_2 > X_3 > X_4 > X_5$

$X_1 > X_2 > X_3 > X_5 > X_4$

$\vdots$

4! Cases when X_1 is max

$P[X_1 = \max(X_1, X_2 \dots X_5)] = \frac{4!}{5!}$

$P[X_1 > X_2 > X_3 > X_4 > X_5] = \frac{1}{5!}$

$P[X_1 > X_2 > X_3 > X_4 > X_5 | X_1 = \max(X_1, X_2 \dots X_5)] = \frac{\frac{1}{5!}}{\frac{4!}{5!}} = \frac{1}{4!}$

35. Explanation: (d)

$f(x) = Ce^{-x^4}$; $x \in R$

If $f(x)$ is a probability density function then

$\int_{-\infty}^{\infty} f(x) = 1$

$\int_{-\infty}^{\infty} Ce^{-x^4}\, dx = 1$

$C\int_{-\infty}^{\infty} e^{-x^4}\, dx = 1$

$\Rightarrow 2c\int_{-\infty}^{\infty} e^{-x^4} = 1$

Let $x^4 = t$

$4x^3\, dx^2\, dt$

$\therefore 2c\int_0^{\infty} e^{-t}\frac{dt}{4x^3} = 1$

$\therefore \frac{2c}{4}\int_0^{\infty} t^{-3/4} e^{-t}\, dt = 1$

$\frac{2c}{4}\int_0^{\infty} e^{-t}.t^{\frac{1}{4}-1}\, dt = 1$

Using gamma integral,

$\int_0^{\infty} e^{-x}.x^{\lambda-1}\, dx = \Gamma(\lambda)$

$\Rightarrow \frac{c}{2}.\Gamma(\frac{1}{4}) = 1$

$\Rightarrow C = \frac{2}{\Gamma(\frac{1}{4})}$

36. Explanation: (c)

$X_i \sim N(1,1)$

$N \sim P(2)$

$E(X_i) = 1, Var(X_i) = 1$

$E(N) = 2, var(N) = 2$

$X_1 + X_2 + \dots + X_{N+1} \rightarrow$ Stochastic Sum of the random variables

$Var(X_1 + X_2 + \dots + X_{N+1}) = (E(X_i))^2\, Var(N+1) + E(N+1).Var(X_i)$

$= 1^2.2 + [2+1].1$

$= 2 + 3$

$= 5$

Option (c) is correct

37. Explanation: (a), (c), (d)

X, Y *are iid* $\sim B(n,p)$

We know that Binomial random variate follows additive property if probability of success is same

$\therefore X + Y \sim B(2n, p)$

So, option (a) is correct

$Var(X - Y) = Var(X) + Var(Y) - 2\,Cox(X,Y)$

$Cov(X,Y) = 0$ [X & Y *are independent*]

$Var(X - Y) = Var(X) + Var(Y)$

$= npq + npq$

$= 2\,npq$

$E(X - Y)^2 = E[X^2 + Y^2 - 2XY]$

$= E(X^2) + E[Y^2] - 2E(X).E(Y)$

$= npq + (np)^2 + npq + (np)^2 - 2np.np$

$= 2npq + 2(np)^2 - 2(np)^2$

$= 2\,npq$

$\therefore Var(X - Y) = E(X - Y)^2 = 2npq$

$Cov(X + Y, X - Y) = Var(X) - Var(Y) - Cov(X,Y) + Cov(X,Y)$

$= npq - npq$ [$Cov(X + Y, X - Y) = 0$]

So, option (a), (c), (d) are correct.

38. Explanation: (a), (b), (d)

Let X *and* Y are independent random variable

$E[\cos(t\,X + u\,Y)] = E[\cos(tX)\cos(u\,Y) - \sin(t\,X)\sin(uY)]$

($\because \cos(A + B) = \cos A\cos B - \sin A\,\sin B$)

If X & Y are independent then

$E[g(x).h(y)] = E(g(x)).E[h(y)]$

$\Rightarrow E[\cos(tX + uY)] = E[\cos(tX)].E[\cos(uY)] - E[\sin(tX)].E[\sin(uY)]\ \ \forall t, u \in R$

So, option (a) is correct.

For option (b)

$X \sim N(2,1)$ & $Y \sim N(0,2)$

$Var(X) = 1,\ Var(Y) = 2$

$Var(X + Y) = Var(X) + Var(Y) + 2\,cov(X,Y)$

$\text{cov}(X,Y) = 0$ [$\because X$ & Y *are independent*]

$Var(X + Y) = Var(X) + Var(Y)$

$= 1 + 2$

$= 3$

Option (b) is correct

For option (c) & (d)

$P[X = a \cap Y = b] = P[X = a].P[Y = b]$ [$\because X$ & Y *are independent*]

$\neq 0$

$\therefore \{X = a\} \cap \{Y = b\} \neq \phi$

Option (a), (b) & (d) are correct

39. Explanation: (a), (b), (d)

Result (1)

$X_n \xrightarrow{a.s} X$ and $Y_n \xrightarrow{a.s} Y$

Then $a X_n + b Y_n \xrightarrow{a.s} a X + bY \ \forall a, b \in R$

Result (2)

$X_n \xrightarrow{a.s} X \Rightarrow X_n \xrightarrow{P} X \Rightarrow X_n \xrightarrow{D} X$

$\therefore a = 1, b = 1$

$X_n + Y_n \xrightarrow{a.s} X + Y \Rightarrow X_n + Y_n \xrightarrow{D} X + Y$

So, option (a) is correct

Similarly, option (a), (b), (d) are correct but (d) is incorrect because

$X_n \xrightarrow{d} X$ and $X_n \xrightarrow{d} Y \nRightarrow X_n + Y_n \xrightarrow{d} X + Y$

40. Explanation: (a), (c)

Using Chebyshev's Inequality, X be random variable with $E(X) = \mu$ and $Var(X) = \sigma^2$

$P[|X - \mu| \geq K] \leq \frac{Var(X)}{K^2}$ or $P[|X - \mu| < K] \geq 1 - \frac{Var(X)}{K^2}$

Let $Z = X + Y$

$E(Z) = 0; Var(Z) = 2$

For option (a)

$P[|Z - 0| > \varepsilon] \leq \frac{2}{\varepsilon^2}$

$\Rightarrow P[|Z| \geq \varepsilon] \leq \frac{2}{\varepsilon^2}$

Option (a) is correct

For option (b)

$|Z|$ is convex function

So $E(|Z|) \geq |E[Z]|$

$\Rightarrow E[\sqrt{Z^2}] \geq \sqrt{E(Z^2)} = \sqrt{2}$

$E(|Z|) \geq 2$

Option (b) is not correct

For option (c)

$Var(Z) = E(Z^2) - (E(Z))^2$

$Var(Z) = E(Z^2)$

$2 = E(Z^2)$

$\Rightarrow E(Z^2) = 2$

Option (c) is correct

For option (d)

We can't determine the probability, because we don't know about the distribution of Z.

So, option (a), (c) are correct

41. Explanation: (d)

Let $X_1, X_2 \dots X_n$ random variables such that $E(X_i) = 0$ and $E(X_i^2) = 1 \ \forall i, j$ and $E(X_i X_j) = \rho \ \forall i \neq j$

For option (a)

If $\rho = 0$, then $X_1, X_2 \dots X_n$ are not always independent

For option (a) & (c)

$Var(X_1 + X_2 + \dots + X_n) = n$, then $Cov(X_i X_j) = 0$, this does not imply, X_i and X_j are not always independent

For option (d)

If $\rho = 0$ then $Cov(X_i X_j) = 0$

$Var(X_1 + X_2 + \dots + X_n) = \sum Var(X_i) + 2 \sum Cov(X_i X_j)$

$= n \ \{Cov(X_i X_j) = 0\}$

So, option (d) is only correct

42. Explanation: (a), (d)

(III) Hazard rate function $= \lambda(x) = \frac{2x}{1+x^2}$

$\lambda(x) = \frac{2x}{1+x^2}$

Survival function $= s(x)$

$s(x) = P(T > t)$

$= e^{-\int \lambda(x) dx}$

$= e^{-\int \frac{2x}{1+x^2} dx}$

$e^{-\log(1+x^2)}$

$= e^{\log(1+x^2)^{-1}}$

$s(x) = \frac{1}{1+x^2}; x \in (0, \infty)$

As option (1) correct & (2) is incorrect also survival function of random variable is determined

$\therefore$ 3 is incorrect

$s(x) = \frac{1}{1+x^2}$

$s(x)$ is exist

$\Rightarrow$ pdf & D.F. also exist

$s(x) = 1 - F(t)$

$F(t) = 1 - \frac{1}{1+x^2}$

$= \frac{1+x^2-1}{1+x^2}$

$F(t) = \frac{x^2}{1+x^2}$ ---Distribution Function

$\therefore$ F(t) is exist

$f(t) = \frac{-d}{dt} F(t)$

$= -\frac{d}{dt}\left(\frac{x^2}{1+x^2}\right)$

$= -\left[\frac{2x(1+x^2) - x^2(0+2x)}{(1+x^2)^2}\right]$

$f(t) = -\left[\frac{2x+2x^2-2x^3}{(1+x^2)^2}\right]$

$f(t) = \frac{-2x}{(1+x^2)^2}$

$f(t)$ & $F(t)$ both exist.

Option (a) & (d) are correct

43. Explanation: (a), (c)

$X_i \sim$ Bernoulli

$X_i's$ are identifally independent.

$E(X_i) = p$

$v(X_i) = p(1-p) = p - p^2$

Let A is said to consistent estimator of γ

$E(A) = \gamma$

$V(A) \to 0$ as $n \to \infty$

For (1)

$E(1/n \sum X_i) \to p$

$\Rightarrow \frac{1}{n} \sum E(X_i) = \frac{1}{n}(np) = p$

$v\left(\frac{1}{n} \sum X_i\right) = \frac{1}{n^2} np(1-p) = \frac{p(1-p)}{n} \to 0$

$\therefore$ 1st is correct

For (2)

$X_i's$ is sequence of all number but here only X_n & X_{n+1}

$E\left(\frac{X_n + X_{n+1}}{2}\right) = \frac{1}{2}(p + p) = p$

$v\left(\frac{X_n+X_{n+1}}{2}\right)=\frac{1}{4}(pq+pq)\nrightarrow 0$

∴ It's incorrect

For (3)

$E\left(\frac{1}{n}\sum X_i, n\geq 1\right)$

$=E\left(\frac{1}{n}(X_1+X_2^2+X_3^3+\cdots)\right)$

$=\frac{1}{n}E(X_1+X_2^2+X_3^3+\cdots)$ ..... as $E(X_i^2)=(p-p^2)+p^2=p$

$=\frac{1}{n}[E(X_1)+E(X_2^2)+E(X_3^3)+\cdots]$

$=\frac{1}{n}[p+p+p+\cdots.]$

$=\frac{p(n)}{n}$

$=p$

$v\left[\frac{1}{n}(X-1+X_2^2+X_3^3+\cdots)\right]$

$=\frac{1}{n^2}[v(X_1)+v(X_2^2)+v(X_3^3)+\cdots]$ ...X_i's are i.i.d.

$=1/n^2[np(1-p)]$

$=\frac{p(1-p)}{n}\to 0$

Correct option (a) & (c).

44. Explanation: (c)

$x_1, x_2 \ldots\ldots x_n \overset{iid}{\sim} N(\theta,1)$; $\theta\in\mathbb{R}$ & sample mean is,

$\overline{x}=\frac{\sum xi}{n}$; $i=1,2,\ldots.,n$

Here the confidence interval is

$\overline{x}\pm t_{0.975,\ n-1}\cdot\frac{1}{\sqrt{n}}$

∴ level of significance is

$(1-\alpha)=0.975$

$\Rightarrow \alpha=0.225$

i.e. $\alpha=2.25\%$

If the region is

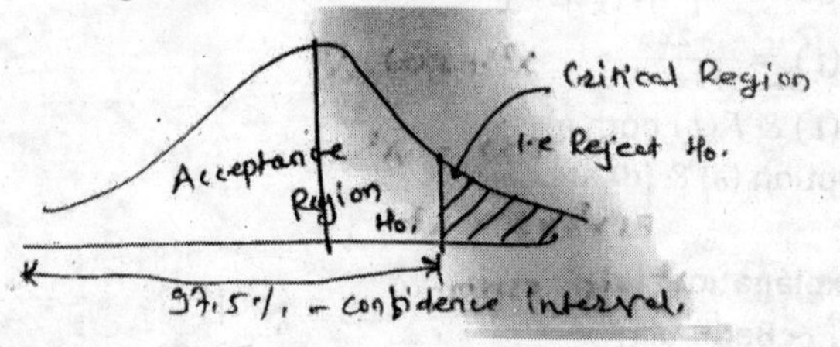

For (1)

Confidence interval is 0.975

∴ It's incorrect statement

For (2)

It's also incorrect option (C.I.=0.975)

For (3)

It's confidence interval being more than 0.95

i.e. 0.95 < 0.975

∴ It's correct statement

For (4)

It's also incorrect option

Option (c) is correct

45. Explanation: (b), (c)

$x_i\sim N(0,1)$; $i=1,2,\ldots\ldots,2n\ n>1$

Let consider $n=1$

$Ix_i\sim N(0,1)$: $i=1,2$

We know that,

$E[\max(x,y)]=\frac{\sqrt{1-\rho}}{\sqrt{\pi}}=\frac{1}{\pi}$

But x_i's are independent therefore correlation is zero.

$\Rightarrow E[\max(|x|,|x_{n+1}|)]=\frac{2}{\pi}$

∴ Option (3) is correct & (4) is incorrect

Let consider,

$E\left(\frac{x_1-x_2}{2}\right)=0$

$v=\left(\frac{x_1-x_2}{2}\right)=\frac{1}{4}[var(x_1)+var(x_2)-2var(x_1x_2)]$

$=\frac{1}{4}[1+1-0]$

$=\frac{1}{2}$

∴ Option (a) is in correct

For (2)

$(x_{2n-1}-x_{2n})^2=(x_1-x_2)^2$; $n=1$

$E(x_1-x_2)=0$

$v(x_1-x_2)=v(x_1)+v(x_2)-2\,cov\,(x_1-x_2)$

$=1+1-0$

$=2$

$x_1-x_2\sim N(0,2)$

$\left(\frac{x_1-x_2}{\sqrt{2}}\right)\sim\chi_1^2$

$\therefore \left(\frac{x_1-x_2}{2}\right)^2\sim\chi_1^2$

$(x_1-x_2)^2\sim 2\chi_1^2$

∴ option (b) is correct

Option (a) & (c) correct

46. Explanation: (a), (d)

For (1)

The prior distribution is improper if the integral of the prior density over the entire parameter space is infinity .in this case

The prior density is proportional to $\left(\frac{1}{\tau^2}\right)^{\alpha}$

The integral $\int_0^\infty\frac{1}{\tau^{2\alpha}}\,d\tau$ diverges α indicating that prior is improper of $\alpha>0$

∴ Statement 1 is true

For (2)

The posterior distribution is proper if the integral of the posterior density over the entire parameter space is finite for this to be true

The likelihood & prior must combine to from a proper posterior.

In this case given the from of the prior & the likelihood (normal dist). The posterior distribution is proper for all $\alpha>0$

∴ The statement also true.

For (3)

The generalized Bayes estimator under squared error loss is given.

$E\left(\frac{\tau^2}{x}\right)=\frac{\frac{n}{2}+\alpha}{\sum x_i^2/2}$

∴ This statement is incorrect.

For (4)

The posterior distribution is proper for $\alpha=1$

This correct statement using 2nd option $\alpha>0$

$\therefore$ option (a), (b), & (d) are correct

47. Explanation: (a)

Option 1:

$X \to P(2), \quad Y \to P(3), \quad X$ & Y are independent.

Then there is a well-known result that if $X \to P(m_1)$, $Y \to P(m_2)$, X and Y are independent then the conditional distribution of X given $X + Y = n$ is Binomial with parameters n & $\frac{m_1}{m_1+m_2}$, n being non-negative integer.

$\therefore$ Variance of Binomial distribution is npq.

Here

$$p = \frac{m_1}{m_1 + m_2}, q = 1 - p = \frac{m_2}{m_1 + m_2}, n = 2, m_1 = 2, m_2 = 3$$

$$\therefore \text{Var}(X|X + Y = 2) = 2 \cdot \frac{2}{5} \cdot \frac{3}{5} = \frac{12}{25}$$

$\therefore$ **Option (a)** is correct.

Option 2:

Here they have given a function of X as $g(X) = \frac{2}{1+X}$.

Now from option (a), we know that X given $X + Y = n$ is $B\left(n, \frac{m_1}{m_1+m_2}\right)$.

As $g(X)$ is a function of X only, so we can safely assign same probability model to $g(X)$ given $X + Y = n$, same as that of X given $X + Y = n$.

$$\therefore E\left(\frac{2}{1+X}\middle| X + Y = 2\right)$$

$$= \sum_x \frac{2}{1+x} P[X = x \mid X + Y = 2]$$

$$= \sum_{x=0}^{2} \frac{2}{1+x}\binom{2}{x}\left(\frac{2}{5}\right)^x\left(\frac{3}{5}\right)^{2-x}$$

$$= 2\binom{2}{0}\left(\frac{2}{5}\right)^0\left(\frac{3}{5}\right)^2 + 1\cdot\binom{2}{1}\left(\frac{2}{5}\right)^1\left(\frac{3}{5}\right)^1 + \frac{2}{3}\binom{2}{2}\left(\frac{2}{5}\right)^2\left(\frac{3}{5}\right)^0$$

$$= 2\left(\frac{3}{5}\right)^2 + 2\left(\frac{2}{5}\right)\left(\frac{3}{5}\right) + \frac{2}{3}\left(\frac{2}{5}\right)^2$$

$$= \frac{18}{25} + \frac{12}{25} + \frac{8}{75} = \frac{54 + 36 + 8}{75}$$

$$= \frac{98}{75} \neq \frac{98}{3} \text{ (Given)}$$

$\therefore$ Option (b) is incorrect.

Option 3:

We have to find $P(X^2 = 0|X + Y = 2)$

$$P(X^2 = 0 \mid X + Y = 2) = P(X = 0 \mid X + Y = 2)$$

Note that here $X \to P(2), x = 0,1,2, \ldots$

So, $X^2 = 0$ is possible if and only if $X = 0$. Thus the above 2 probabilities are same.

Now X given $X + Y = 2 \to B\left(2, \frac{2}{5}\right)$

$\therefore P[X = 0 \mid X + Y = 2] = \binom{2}{0}\left(\frac{2}{5}\right)^0\left(\frac{3}{5}\right)^2 = \frac{9}{25} \neq \left[e^{-2} + \frac{9}{25}(1 - e^2)\right]$ (Given)

Thus, option (c) is incorrect.

For (d) :

As X and Y are independent,

$$P[X \mid Y = y] = P[X = x] \quad \forall x$$

Therefore, option (d) is incorrect.

48. Explanation: (d)

X be a random variable with cumulative distribution function given by

$$F(x) = \begin{cases} 0, & if\ x < 0 \\ \frac{x+1}{3}, & if\ 0 \le x < 1 \\ 1, & if\ x \ge 1 \end{cases}$$

$P\left(\frac{1}{3} < X < \frac{3}{4}\right) = F\left(\frac{3}{4}\right) - F\left(\frac{1}{4}\right) - P\left(X = \frac{3}{4}\right) = F\left(\frac{3}{4}\right) - F\left(\frac{1}{4}\right) - F\left(\frac{3}{4}\right) + F^-\left(\frac{3}{4}\right)$

$= \frac{(3/4)+1}{3} - \frac{(1/3)+1}{3} - \frac{(3/4)+1}{3} + \frac{(3/4)+1}{3} = \frac{7}{12} - \frac{4}{9} - 0 + 0 = \frac{21-16}{36} = \frac{5}{36}$

$$P(X = 0) = F(0) - F^-(0) = \frac{1}{3} - 0 = \frac{1}{3}$$

$$\therefore P\left(\frac{1}{3} < X < \frac{3}{4}\right) + P(X = 0) = \frac{5}{36} + \frac{1}{3} = \frac{17}{36}$$

49. Explanation: (a), (c)

X and Y be jointly distributed continuous random variables with joint probability density function

$$f(x, y) = \begin{cases} \frac{x}{y}, & if\ 0 < x < y < 2 \\ 0, & otherwise \end{cases}$$

(a) The marginal c.d.f. of Y is

$f(y) = \int_0^y f(x, y)\, dx = \int_0^y \frac{x}{y}\, dx = \frac{1}{2y}[x^2]_0^y = \frac{y}{2}\ ; 0 < y < 2$

The conditional c.d.f. of $X \mid Y = y$ is

$$f(x \mid Y = y) = \frac{f(x, y)}{f(y)} = \frac{x/y}{y/2} = \frac{2x}{y^2}\ ; 0 < x < y$$

$$P\left(X < \frac{1}{2}\middle| Y = 1\right) = \int_0^{1/2} f(x \mid Y = 1)\, dx = \int_0^{1/2} \frac{2x}{1^2}\, dx$$

$$= [x^2]_0^{1/2} = \frac{1}{4}$$

(b) $E(Y) = \int_0^2 yf(y)\, dy = \int_0^2 \frac{y^2}{2} dy = \frac{1}{6} \times [y^3]_0^2 = \frac{8}{6} = \frac{4}{3} \neq \frac{1}{4}$

(c) $P\left(X < \frac{Y}{2}\right) = P\left(X < \frac{y}{2} \mid Y = y\right) = \int_0^{y/2} f(x \mid Y = y)\, dx = \int_0^{y/2} \frac{2x}{y^2}\, dx = \frac{1}{y^2}[x^2]_0^{y/2} = \frac{1}{4}$

(d) $E\left(\frac{Y}{X}\right) = \int_0^2 \int_x^2 \frac{y}{x} f(x, y)\, dy\, dx = \int_0^2 \int_x^2 \frac{y}{x} \cdot \frac{x}{y}\, dy\, dx$

$$= \int_0^2 \int_x^2 dy\, dx = \int_0^2 (2 - x)\, dx = \left[2x - \frac{x^2}{2}\right]_0^2$$

$$= 2 \times 2 - \frac{2^2}{2} = 4 - 2 = 2 \neq \frac{1}{4}$$

$\therefore$ **The answer is options (a) and (c).**

50. Explanation: (a), (b), (c), (d)

$\{X_n\}_{n \ge 1}$ be a sequence of independent and identically distributed random variables with $E(X_1) = 0$ and $Var(X_1) = 1$.

(4) $Y_n = \sum_{i=1}^n X_i \Rightarrow E(Y_n) = nE(X_1) = n \times 0 = 0$

$$Var(Y_n) = n \times Var(X_1) = n$$

Then by using the central limit theorem

$$Z_n = \frac{Y_n - E(Y_n)}{\sqrt{Var(Y_n)}} \xrightarrow{d} Z, where\ Z \sim N(0,1)$$

$$\therefore \lim_{n\to\infty} P\left(\frac{\sum_{i=1}^{n} X_i}{\sqrt{n}} \le 0\right) = \Phi(0) = \frac{1}{2}$$

(3) Consider

$$Y_n = \frac{1}{n}\sum_{i=1}^{n} X_i^2 \Rightarrow E(Y_n) = \frac{1}{n} \times n \times E(X_1^2)$$

$$= Var(X_1) + [E(X_1)]^2 = 1 + 0 = 1$$

$$Var(Y_n) = \frac{1}{n^2} \times n \times Var(X_1^2)$$

$$= \frac{1}{n} \times \{E(X_1^4) - [E(X_1^2)]^2\} = \frac{1}{n} \times (3-1) = \frac{2}{n}$$

Consider

$$P\{|Y_n - E(Y_n)| \ge \varepsilon\} \le \frac{Var(Y_n)}{\varepsilon^2}$$

$$= \frac{2}{\varepsilon^2 \times n} \quad (Chebyshev's\ Inequality)$$

$$\lim_{n\to\infty} P\{|Y_n - E(Y_n)| \ge \varepsilon\} = \lim_{n\to\infty} P\{|Y_n - 1| \ge \varepsilon\}$$

$$\le \frac{2}{\varepsilon^2} \lim_{n\to\infty} \frac{1}{n} = 0$$

But the limit value of the probability cannot be less than zero therefore

$$\lim_{n\to\infty} P\{|Y_n - 1| \ge \varepsilon\} = 0$$

$\frac{1}{n}\sum_{i=1}^{n} X_i^2$ converges in probability to 1 as $n \to \infty$.

(2) Consider

$$W_n = \frac{1}{n}\sum_{i=1}^{n} X_i \Rightarrow E(W_n) = \frac{1}{n} \times n \times E(X_1) = 0$$

$$Var(W_n) = \frac{1}{n^2} \times n \times Var(X_1) = \frac{1}{n} \times 1 = \frac{1}{n}$$

Consider

$$P\{|W_n - E(W_n)| \ge \varepsilon\} \le \frac{Var(W_n)}{\varepsilon^2}$$

$$= \frac{1}{\varepsilon^2 \times n} \quad (Chebyshev's\ Inequality)$$

$$\lim_{n\to\infty} P\{|W_n - E(W_n)| \ge \varepsilon\} = \lim_{n\to\infty} P\{|W_n - 0| \ge \varepsilon\}$$

$$\le \frac{1}{\varepsilon^2} \lim_{n\to\infty} \frac{1}{n} = 0$$

But the limit value of the probability cannot be less than zero therefore

$$\lim_{n\to\infty} P\{|W_n - 0| \ge \varepsilon\} = 0$$

$\frac{1}{n}\sum_{i=1}^{n} X_i$ converges in probability to 0 as $n \to \infty$.

Also we have

$\frac{1}{n}\sum_{i=1}^{n} X_i^2$ converges in probability to $1 \ne 0$ as $n \to \infty$.

$$\therefore \frac{\left(\frac{1}{n}\sum_{i=1}^{n} X_i\right)}{\left(\frac{1}{n}\sum_{i=1}^{n} X_i^2\right)} = \frac{\sum_{i=1}^{n} X_i}{\sum_{i=1}^{n} X_i^2} \xrightarrow{p} \frac{0}{1} = 0$$

(1) We have

$$\frac{\sum_{i=1}^{n} X_i}{\sqrt{n}} \xrightarrow{d} Z, where\ Z \sim N(0,1)$$

$\frac{1}{n}\sum_{i=1}^{n} X_i^2$ converges in probability to $1 \ne 0$ as $n \to \infty$.

$$\frac{\frac{\sum_{i=1}^{n} X_i}{\sqrt{n}}}{\frac{1}{n}\sum_{i=1}^{n} X_i^2} = \frac{\sqrt{n}\sum_{i=1}^{n} X_i}{\sum_{i=1}^{n} X_i^2}$$

$$\xrightarrow{d} Z, where\ Z \sim N(0,1) \quad (Use\ Slutkey's\ Theorem)$$

$$\lim_{n\to\infty} P\left(\frac{\sqrt{n}\sum_{i=1}^{n} X_i}{\sum_{i=1}^{n} X_i^2} \le 0\right) = \Phi(0) = \frac{1}{2}$$

51. Explanation: (d)

For a Binomial distribution: $E(X) = 9\theta$ and for a Poisson distribution: $E(Y) = \lambda$.

Using the given equation:

$$3E(Y) = E(X) \Rightarrow 3\lambda = 9\theta \Rightarrow \lambda = 3\theta.$$

For a Binomial distribution: $\text{Var}(X) = 9\theta(1-\theta)$ and for a Poisson distribution: $\text{Var}(Y) = \lambda = 3\theta$.

$$\frac{\text{Var}(X)}{\text{Var}(Y)} = \frac{9\theta(1-\theta)}{3\theta} = 3(1-\theta)$$

Since $0.7 < \theta < 1$, we evaluate $3(1-\theta)$:

- If $\theta = 0.7$, then $3(1-0.7) = 3(0.3) = 0.9$.
- If $\theta = 1$, then $3(1-1) = 0$.

Thus,

$$0 < 3(1-\theta) < 0.9$$

Since $3(1-\theta)$ is always less than 1, we have

$$\frac{\text{Var}(X)}{\text{Var}(Y)} = 3(1-\theta) < 1$$

$\therefore \text{Var}(X) < \text{Var}(Y)$ and option (d) is correct.

52. Explanation: (b)

The coefficient matrix is:

$$A = \begin{bmatrix} 1 & -2 & 1 \\ 2 & -5 & 2 \\ 1 & 2 & Z_1 \end{bmatrix}$$

The augmented matrix is:

$$[A|b] = \begin{bmatrix} 1 & -2 & 1 & 1 \\ 2 & -5 & 2 & 2 \\ 1 & 2 & Z_1 & Z_2 \end{bmatrix}$$

For the system to have infinite solutions, the rank of the coefficient matrix must equal the rank of the augmented matrix but be less than 3. This happens if the determinant of the coefficient matrix is zero, i.e., $\det(A) = 0$.

$$|A| = \begin{vmatrix} 1 & -2 & 1 \\ 2 & -5 & 2 \\ 1 & 2 & Z_1 \end{vmatrix} = -9Z_1 + 9$$

$$-9Z_1 + 9 = 0 \Rightarrow Z_1 = 1$$

Since $Z_1 \sim \text{Binomial}(2,1/2)$, the probability that $Z_1 = 1$ is:

$$P(Z_1 = 1) = \binom{2}{1}\left(\frac{1}{2}\right)^1\left(\frac{1}{2}\right)^1 = 2 \times \frac{1}{2} \times \frac{1}{2} = \frac{2}{4} = \frac{1}{2}$$

Given $Z_1 = 1$, the system has infinite solutions if the augmented matrix remains consistent. Since $Z_2 \sim \text{Poisson}(1)$, the probability of any specific value of Z_2 is:

$$P(Z_2 = Z_2) = e^{-1}\frac{1_2^Z}{Z_2!}.$$

Summing over all possible values of Z_2, the probability remains e^{-1}

Thus, the final probability is:

$$P(Z_1 = 1)P(\text{Consistency}) = \frac{1}{2}e^{-1}$$

53. Explanation: (b)

Let $S_n = \sum_{i=1}^{n} Z_i$ and work mod $m = 2025$. Then $(X_n = S_n \text{mod} 2025)$ is a random walk on the cyclic group $\mathbb{Z}_{2025}$ with transition

$$\Pr(x \to y) = \Pr(Z_1 \equiv y - x!! \text{ (mod 2025)})$$

$$= \begin{cases} \frac{1}{2024}, & y - x \not\equiv 0 \text{ (mod 2025)}, [2pt]0, \end{cases}$$

$y - x \equiv 0$ (mod 2025).

- Stationary distribution. For any (y), $\sum_x \frac{1}{2025}\Pr(x \to y) = \frac{1}{2025}\sum_z \Pr(Z_1 \equiv z) = \frac{1}{2025}$, so the uniform distribution on 0,1, ... ,2024 is stationary.
- Irreducible. Since (1) is in the support of Z_1, every residue is reachable.
- Aperiodic. $\Pr(S_2 \equiv 0) \geq \Pr(Z_1 = a, Z_2 = 2025 - a) > 0$ for any $a \in 1, \ldots ,2024$, and also $\Pr(S_3 \equiv 0) > 0$ (take $Z_1 = a, Z_2 = b, Z_3 \equiv -(a + b) \not\equiv 0$). Having return times 2 and 3 implies period = 1.

Hence the distribution of X_n converges to uniform on $\mathbb{Z} * 2025$, giving

$\lim * n \to \infty \Pr(X_n = 0) = \frac{1}{2025}$.

Correct Answer: b

54. Explanation: (b), (c), (d)

- $X \mid (X + Y = 3) \sim \text{Bin}(3, p)$ with $p = \frac{\lambda_X}{\lambda_X + \lambda_Y} = \frac{4}{4+2} = \frac{2}{3}$.

So (a) claiming Bin(3,1/3) is **false**.
- $P(X \leq 1 \mid X + Y = 3) = P(0) + P(1)$ where with $p = 2/3, ; 1 - p = 1/3$,

$$P(0) = (1/3)^3 = \frac{1}{27}, P(1) = 3 \cdot \frac{2}{3} \cdot \left(\frac{1}{3}\right)^2 = \frac{6}{27},$$

so $P(X \leq 1 \mid \cdot) = \frac{1}{27} + \frac{6}{27} = \frac{7}{27}$. Thus (b) **true.**
- $E[X \mid X + Y = 3] = 3p = 3 \cdot \frac{2}{3} = 2$. So (c) **true**.
- Characteristic function: $\varphi_{X+Y}(t) = \exp 6(e^{it} - 1)$. At $t = \pi$, $e^{i\pi} = -1$, so $\varphi_{X+Y}(\pi) = \exp(6(-2)) = e^{-12}$. Hence (d) **true.**

55. Explanation: (a), (c)

CDF: $F_X(x) = \frac{x+2}{5}$ for $0 \leq x < 2$

Jump at 0: $P(X = 0) = \frac{2}{5}$

PDF on (0,2): $f(x) = \frac{1}{5}$

Jump at 2: $P(X = 2) = \frac{1}{5}$

$$E[X^2] = 0^2 \cdot \frac{2}{5} + \int_0^2 x^2 \cdot \frac{1}{5}\, dx + 4 \cdot \frac{1}{5} = 0 + \frac{8}{15} + \frac{4}{5} = \frac{4}{3}$$

Statement 1: **True**

$P(|X - 4/5| \geq 1)$

$\mu = 4/5, \mu - 1 = -1/5, \mu + 1 = 9/5$

$$P(X \geq 1.8) = \int_{1.8}^{2} \frac{1}{5}dx + \frac{1}{5} = \frac{0.2}{5} + \frac{1}{5} = \frac{6}{25}$$

Statement 2: **False** (says 19/25)

Chebyshev bound

$$\sigma^2 = E[X^2] - \mu^2 = \frac{4}{3} - \frac{16}{25} = \frac{52}{75}$$

Chebyshev: $P(|X - \mu| \geq 1) \leq \sigma^2 = \frac{52}{75}$

Statement 3: **True**

MGF at $t = 1$

$$M_X(1) = \frac{2}{5} + \frac{e^2 - 1}{5} + \frac{e^2}{5} = \frac{1 + 2e^2}{5}$$

Statement 4: **False** (says $(e^2 - 1)/5$)

Final answer: a, c

56. Explanation: (a), (b)

We have $X, Y \overset{\text{i.i.d.}}{\sim} N(0,1)$,

$S = X^2 + Y^2$,

$T = e^{-(X^2+Y^2)/2} = e^{-S/2}$.

Distribution of S

$X^2 \sim \chi_1^2, Y^2 \sim \chi_1^2$, independent $\Rightarrow S \sim \chi_2^2$.

PDF of χ_k^2 is $f(s) = \frac{1}{2^{k/2}\Gamma(k/2)} s^{k/2-1}e^{-s/2}, s > 0$.

For $k = 2$: $\Gamma(1) = 1$, so

$$f_S(s) = \frac{1}{2 \cdot 1} s^{1-1}e^{-s/2} = \frac{1}{2}e^{-s/2}, s > 0.$$

Statement 1: **True.**

Distribution of T

$T = e^{-S/2}, S > 0 \Rightarrow T \in (0,1]$.

CDF: $F_T(t) = P(T \leq t) = P(e^{-S/2} \leq t) = P(-S/2 \leq \ln t) = P(S \geq -2\ln t)$.

For $0 < t < 1, -2\ln t > 0$:

$$F_T(t) = \int_{-2\ln t}^{\infty} \frac{1}{2}e^{-\frac{s}{2}}\, ds = \left[-e^{-\frac{s}{2}}\right]_{-2\ln t}^{\infty}$$

$= 0 - (-e^{\ln t}) = t$.

So $F_T(t) = t$ for $0 < t < 1$, $F_T(t) = 1$ for $t \geq 1$.

PDF: $f_T(t) = 1$ for $0 < t < 1$, 0 otherwise.

Statement 2: **True.**

Variance of S

$S \sim \chi_2^2 \Rightarrow \text{Var}(S) = 2 \cdot 2 = 4$ (since χ_k^2 has mean k, variance $2k$).

So Statement 3 says $\text{Var}(S) = 2 \Rightarrow$ **False.**

$E[T]$

T is uniform on (0,1) from Step 2 $\Rightarrow E[T] = \frac{1}{2}$.

Statement 4 says $E(T) = \frac{2}{3} \Rightarrow$ **False.**

Final answer: a, b.

57. Explanation: (c)

Given $X_j \sim \text{Binomial}\left(3, \frac{1}{4}\right)$.

Y_j is defined as

$$Y_j = \begin{cases} 1, & X_j \leq \sqrt{5} \\ 0, & \text{otherwise} \end{cases}$$

Since $\sqrt{5} \approx 2.236$ and X_j takes integer values 0,1,2,3,

$$X_j \le \sqrt{5} \Rightarrow X_j = 0,1,2$$

Thus, $Y_j = 1$ if $X_j \le 2$, and $Y_j = 0$ if $X_j = 3$.

Because Y_j takes only values 0 and 1,

$$Y_j^2 = Y_j$$

Hence

$$\frac{1}{n}\sum_{j=1}^{n} Y_j^2 = \frac{1}{n}\sum_{j=1}^{n} Y_j$$

By the Strong Law of Large Numbers, the sample mean of i.i.d. variables converges almost surely to the expectation:

$$\frac{1}{n}\sum_{j=1}^{n} Y_j \xrightarrow{\text{a.s.}} E(Y_1)$$

Therefore

$$c = E(Y_1) = P(Y_1 = 1) = P(X_1 \le 2)$$

For $X_1 \sim \text{Bin}(3, \frac{1}{4})$,

$$P(X_1 = 3) = \binom{3}{3}\left(\frac{1}{4}\right)^3 = \frac{1}{64}$$

Thus

$$P(X_1 \le 2) = 1 - \frac{1}{64} = \frac{63}{64}$$

58. Explanation: (a)

Given $Z = \sum_{n=1}^{\infty} \frac{4Y_n}{5^n}, Y_n \sim \text{Bernoulli}\left(\frac{1}{2}\right)$

1. Probability $P\left(Z \ge \frac{3}{5}\right)$

Write the first term separately:

$$Z = \frac{4Y_1}{5} + \sum_{n=2}^{\infty} \frac{4Y_n}{5^n}$$

If $Y_1 = 1$, then

$$Z \ge \frac{4}{5} > \frac{3}{5}$$

If $Y_1 = 0$,

$$Z \le 4\left(\frac{1}{25} + \frac{1}{125} + \cdots\right) = 4\left(\frac{1/25}{1 - 1/5}\right) = \frac{1}{5} < \frac{3}{5}$$

Thus the event occurs only when $Y_1 = 1$.

$$P\left(Z \ge \frac{3}{5}\right) = P(Y_1 = 1) = \frac{1}{2}$$

2. Probability $P\left(Z = \frac{4}{25}\right)$

For $Z = \frac{4}{25}$:

$$Y_1 = 0, Y_2 = 1, Y_n = 0 \text{ for all } n \ge 3$$

This requires infinitely many zeros, whose probability is

$$\left(\frac{1}{2}\right)^{\infty} = 0$$

Hence

$$P\left(Z = \frac{4}{25}\right) = 0$$

Thus,

$$P\left(Z \ge \frac{3}{5}\right) = \frac{1}{2}, P\left(Z = \frac{4}{25}\right) = 0$$

Hence, only Statement 1 is true, so the correct option is (1).

59. Explanation: (c)

Let $X_1, X_2, \ldots$ be i.i.d. Exponential random variables mean (1).

Define

$T_n = \max(X_1, \ldots, X_n) - \ln n$

We find the limiting distribution of T_n.

Distribution of the maximum

For exponential 1: $P(X \le x) = 1 - e^{-x}, x \ge 0$

For the maximum: $P(\max(X_1, \ldots, X_n) \le x) = (1 - e^{-x})^n$

Distribution of T_n

$P(T_n \le y) = P(\max(X_i) \le y + \ln n)$

$= (1 - e^{-(y+\ln n)})^n$

$= (1 - \frac{e^{-y}}{n})^n$

Now take limit $n \to \infty$

$(1 - \frac{e^{-y}}{n})^n \to e^{-e^{-y}}$

Thus, $F_Y(y) = e^{-e^{-y}}$

This is the Gumbel double exponential distribution with

- location (0)
- scale (1)

The location parameter is 0, not $\ln(\ln 2)$.

Statement 1 FALSE

Median of Y:

Median m satisfies

$F_Y(m) = \frac{1}{2}$

$e^{-e^{-m}} = \frac{1}{2}$

$e^{-m} = \ln 2$

$m = -\ln(\ln 2)$

Thus,

Median $= -\ln(\ln 2)$

Statement 2 FALSE

$P(Y \le 0) = F_Y(0) = e^{-e^0} = e^{-1}$

Statement 3 TRUE

Derivative of CDF at $\ln 3$

PDF is derivative of CDF.

$f(y) = e^{-y}e^{-e^{-y}}$

Now evaluate at $y = \ln 3$.

$e^{-y} = e^{-\ln 3} = \frac{1}{3}$

$e^{-e^{-y}} = e^{-1/3}$

Thus

$f(\ln 3) = \frac{1}{3}e^{-1/3}$

Statement 4 FALSE

Final Answer: (3) only

CHAPTER

4

DISTRIBUTION THEORY

(JUNE 2012)

1. Let $X_1, X_2 \dots\dots$ as i.i.d.N(1, 1) random variables. Let $S_n = X_1^2 + X_2^2 + \dots + X_n^2$ for $n \geq 1$. Then $\lim_{\pi\to\infty} \frac{Var(S_n)}{n}$ is
   (a) 4 (b) 6
   (c) 1 (d) 0

(JUNE 2012)

2. Let $X_1, X_2, \dots\dots$ be independent random variable with X_n being uniformly distributed between −n and 3n, n = 1, 2,...... Let $S_N = \frac{1}{\sqrt{N}} \sum_{n=1}^{N} \frac{X_n}{n}$ for N = 1, 2, ... and let F_N be the distribution function of S_N. Also let Φ denote the distribution function of a standard normal random variable. Which of the following is/are true?
   (a) $\lim_{N\to\infty} F_N(0) \leq \Phi(0)$ (b) $\lim_{N\to\infty} F_N(0) \geq \Phi(0)$
   (c) $\lim_{N\to\infty} F_N(1) \leq \Phi(1)$ (d) $\lim_{N\to\infty} F_N(1) \geq \Phi(1)$

(JUNE 2012)

3. Suppose $\varepsilon_1, \varepsilon_2, \dots\dots, \varepsilon_n$ are i.i.d. $N(0, \sigma^2)$. Consider $Y_1, Y_2, \dots\dots, Y_n$ defined $Y_1 = \mu + \varepsilon_1$, $Y_{i+1} - \mu = \rho(Y_i - \mu) + \sqrt{1-\rho^2}\, \varepsilon_{i+1}, i = 1, 2, \dots\dots n-1$.
   Let $T = \frac{1}{n}\sum_{i=1}^{n} Y_i$. Suppose $0 < \rho < 1$ and $\sigma^2 > 0$. Then for $n \geq 2$
   (a) T has a normal distribution
   (b) T has mean μ and variance σ^2/n
   (c) $E(T) = \mu, var\,(T) > \sigma^2/n$
   (d) T follows N (μ, δ^2) where $\delta^2 > \sigma^2/n$

(DEC. 2012)

4. Let $X_1, X_2, \dots$ be i.i.d. standard normal random variables and let $T_n = \frac{X_1^2 + \dots + X_n^2}{n}$. Then
   (a) The limiting distribution of $T_n - 1$ is χ^2 with 1 degree of freedom
   (b) The limiting distribution of $\frac{T_n - 1}{\sqrt{n}}$ is normal with mean 0 and variance 2
   (c) The limiting distribution of $\sqrt{n}(T_n - 1)$ is χ^2 with 1 degree of freedom
   (d) The limiting distribution of $\sqrt{n}(T_n - 1)$ is normal with mean 0 and variance 2

(DEC. 2012)

5. Let X be a binomial random variable with parameters $\left(11, \frac{1}{3}\right)$. At which value(s) of k is $P(X = k)$ maximized?
   (a) $k = 2$ (b) $k = 3$
   (c) $k = 4$ (d) $k = 5$

(DEC. 2012)

6. X, Y, Z are independent random variables with N(0,1) (standard normal) distribution. Let $f: \mathbb{R} \to \mathbb{R}$ be defined by $f(x) = 1$, if $x \geq 0$ and $f(x) = -1$, if $x < 0$. Let U, V, W be defined by $U = |X| \cdot f(Y), V = |Y| \cdot f(X), W = |Z| \cdot f(X)$. Then
   (a) U and V are independent each having a N(0,1) distribution
   (b) U and W are independent each having a N(0,1) distribution
   (c) V and W are independent each having a N(0,1) distribution
   (d) U, V and W are independent random variables.

(DEC. 2012)

7. Let X_1 and X_2 be two independent random variables with $X_1 \sim$ binomial $\left(m, \frac{1}{2}\right)$ and $X_2 \sim$ binomial $\left(n, \frac{1}{2}\right), m \neq n$. Which of the following are always true?
   (a) $2X_1 + 3X_2 \sim$ binomial $\left(2m + 3n, \frac{1}{2}\right)$
   (b) $X_2 - X_1 + m \sim$ binomial $\left(m + n, \frac{1}{2}\right)$
   (c) Conditional distribution of X_2 given $(X_1 + X_2)$ is hypergeometric
   (d) Distribution of $X_1 - X_2$ is symmetric about 0

(DEC. 2012)

8. Let X_1, X_2 and X_3 be independent with $X_1 \sim N(1, 1), X_2 \sim N(-1, 1)$ and $X_3 \sim N(0, 1)$. Let
   $q_1 = \frac{X_1^2 + X_2^2 + 2X_3^2 + 2X_1X_2}{2}$
   $q_2 = \frac{X_1^2 + X_2^2 - 2X_1X_2}{2}$
   Then which of the following statements are always true?
   (a) q_1 has a central chi-square distribution
   (b) q_2 has a central chi-square distribution
   (c) $q_1 + q_2$ has a central chi-square distribution
   (d) q_1 and q_2 are independent

(JUNE 2013)

9. Let $X_1, X_2, \dots, X_n$ be independent and identically distributed random variables each having a uniform distribution on (0, 1). Consider the histogram of these values with k equally spaced class intervals given by $\{(a_i, b_i], i = 1, 2, \dots, k\}$ where $a_i = \frac{i-1}{k}$ and $b_i = a_i + \frac{1}{k}$. Let N_i be the number of values in the interval $(a_i, b_i]$. Then the covariance of N_1 and N_k is
   (a) 0 (b) $-n/k^2$
   (c) n/k^2 (d) 1/2

(JUNE 2013)

10. Let $U_1, U_2, \dots$ be independent and identically distributed random variables each having a uniform distribution on (0, 1). Then $\lim_{n\to\infty} \left(U_1 + \dots + U_n \leq \frac{3}{4}n\right)$
    (a) does not exist (b) exists and equals 0
    (c) exists and equals 1 (d) exists and equals $\frac{3}{4}$

(JUNE 2013)

11. Let X and Y independent random variables each following a uniform distribution on (0, 1). Let $W = X\, I_{\{Y \le X^2\}}$, where I_A denotes the indicator function of the set A. Then which of the following statements are true?
(a) The cumulative distribution function of W is given by $F_W(t) = t^2\, I_{\{0\le t\le 1\}} + I_{\{t>1\}}$
(b) $P[W > 0] = \frac{1}{3}$
(c) The cumulative distribution function of W is continuous
(d) The cumulative distribution function of W is given by $F_W(t) = \left(\frac{2+t^3}{3}\right) I_{\{0\le t\le 1\}} + I_{\{t>1\}}$

(JUNE 2013)

12. Let $X_1, X_2, \ldots$ be independent and identically distributed random variables each following a uniform distribution on (0, 1). Denote $T_n = \max\{X_1, X_2, \ldots, X_n\}$. Then, which of the following statements are true?
(a) T_n converges to 1 in probability
(b) $n(1 - T_n)$ converges in distribution
(c) $n^2(1 - T_n)$ converges in distribution
(d) $\sqrt{n}(1 - T_n)$ converges to 0 in probability

(JUNE 2013)

13. Let $X_1, X_2, \ldots$ be independent random variables each following a normal distribution with unknown mean μ and unknown variance $\sigma^2 > 0$.
Define $\bar{X}_{n=2} = \frac{1}{n-2}\sum_{i=1}^{n-2} X_i$, $T_1 = \frac{\sum_{i=1}^{n-2}(X_i - \bar{X}_{n=2})^2}{n-3}$ and $T_2 = \frac{(X_{n-1} - X_n)}{\sqrt{2}}$; $n > 3$. Then which of the following statements are correct?
(a) T_1 is unbiased for σ^2
(b) $\frac{T_2}{\sqrt{T_1}}$ follows a t distribution with $(n-3)$ degrees of freedom
(c) $\frac{T_2^2}{T_1}$ follows a F distribution with 1 and $(n-3)$ degrees of freedom
(d) $\bar{X}_{n-2}$ is consistent for estimating μ

(JUNE 2013)

14. Let X_1, X_2, X_3, X_4, X_5 be independent and identically distributed random variables each following a uniform distribution on (0, 1), and let M denote their median. Then which of the following statements are true?
(a) $P\left(M < \frac{1}{3}\right) = P\left(M > \frac{2}{3}\right)$
(b) M is uniformly distributed on (0, 1)
(c) $E(M) = E(X_1)$
(d) $V(M) = V(X_1)$

(JUNE 2013)

15. Let $X_1, X_2, \ldots$ be independent random variables each following exponential distribution with mean 1. Then which of the following statements are correct?
(a) $P(X_n > \log n$ for infinitely many $n \ge 1) = 1$
(b) $P(X_n > 2\log n$ for infinitely many $n \ge 1) = 1$
(c) $P(X_n > \frac{1}{2}\log n$ for infinitely many $n \ge 1) = 0$
(d) $P(X_n > \log n, X_{n+1} > \log(n+1)$ for infinitely many $n \ge 1) = 0$

(DEC. 2013)

16. Suppose $D \sim N(0,1)$ and $U = \begin{cases} 1 & if\ D \ge 0 \\ 0 & if\ D < 0 \end{cases}$. Then the correlation coefficient between $|D|$ and U is equal to
(a) 0.5
(b) 0.25
(c) 1
(d) 0

(DEC. 2013)

17. Suppose $X_1, X_2, \ldots, X_n$ are independent and identically distributed random variables each having an exponential distribution with parameter $\lambda > 0$. Let $X_{(1)} \le X_{(2)} \le \cdots \le X_{(n)}$ be the corresponding order statistics. Then the probability distribution of $\frac{X_{(n)} - X_{(n-1)}}{nX_{(1)}}$ is
(a) Chi-square with 1 degree of freedom.
(b) Beta with parameters 2 and 1.
(c) F with parameters 2 and 2.
(d) F with parameters 2 and 1.

(DEC. 2013)

18. Let $X_1, X_2, \ldots$ be independent and identically distributed random variables each having a uniform distribution on $[-1,1]$. For $n \ge 1$, let $S_n = \sum_{i=1}^{n} X_i$ and let $Z_n = S_n/n^p$ for some $p > 0$. Then, as $n \to \infty$.
(a) $Z_n \to 0$almost surely for $p \ge 1$
(b) $Z_n \to 0$ in probability for $\frac{1}{2} < p < 1$
(c) Z_n converges in distribution to a non-degenerate random variable if $p = \frac{1}{2}$
(d) $Z_n \to \infty$ almost surely for $p < \frac{1}{2}$

(DEC. 2013)

19. Let $X_1, X_2, \ldots$ be independent and identically distributed standard normal random variables. Which of the following is true?
(a) $\frac{\sqrt{n}X_1}{X_1^2 + \cdots + X_n^2}$ has a t –distribution with $n-1$ degrees of freedom
(b) $\frac{\sqrt{n}X_1}{X_1^2 + \cdots + X_n^2}$ has a t –distribution with n degrees of freedom
(c) $\frac{\sqrt{n}X_2}{X_2^2 + \cdots + X_{n+1}^2}$ has a t –distribution with n-1 degrees of freedom
(d) $\frac{\sqrt{n}X_2}{X_2^2 + \cdots + X_{n+1}^2}$ has a t –distribution with n degrees of freedom

(DEC. 2013)

20. Let X be a geometric random variable with probability mass function given by
$P(X = k) = (1-p)^k p$ for $k \ge 0$ and $0 < p < 1$. For all $m, n \ge 1$ we have
(a) $P(X > m + n | X > m) = P(X \ge n)$
(b) $P(X > m + n | X > m) = P(X > n)$
(c) $P(X < m + n | X < m) = P(X < n)$
(d) $P(X < m + n | X < m) = P(X \le n)$

(JUNE 2014)

21. Suppose $X_1, X_2, \ldots X_n$ are independent random variables each having a Bin $\left(8, \frac{1}{2}\right)$ distribution. Then $\frac{1}{\sqrt{n}}\sum_{k=1}^{n}(-1)^k X_k$ converges in distribution to

(a) $N(0,1)$ (b) $N(0,2)$
(c) $N(4,2)$ (d) $N(4,1)$

(JUNE 2014)

22. Let X and Y be independent and identically distributed random variables having a normal distribution with mean 0 and variance 1. Define Z and W as follow:

$$\binom{Z}{W} = \begin{cases} \binom{X}{Y} & \text{if } XY > 0 \\ \binom{-X}{Y} & \text{if } X < 0 \text{ and } Y > 0 \\ \binom{X}{-Y} & \text{if } X > 0 \text{ and } Y < 0 \end{cases}. \text{ Then}$$

(a) Z and W are independent
(b) Z has $N(0,1)$ distribution
(c) W has $N(0,1)$ distribution
(d) $Cov(Z,W) > 0$

(JUNE 2014)

23. Let X_n be distributed as a Poisson random variable with parameter n. Then which of the following statements are correct?
(a) $\lim_{n\to\infty} P\left(X_n > n + \sqrt{n}\right) = 0$
(b) $\lim_{n\to\infty} P\left(X_n \le n + \sqrt{n}\right) = 0$
(c) $\lim_{n\to\infty} P\left(X_n \le n\right) = \frac{1}{2}$
(d) $\lim_{n\to\infty} P\left(X_n \le n\right) = 1$

(JUNE 2014)

24. Let X and Y be two independent $N(0,1)$ random variables. Define $U = \frac{X}{Y}$ and $V = \frac{X}{|Y|}$ then
(a) U and V have the same distribution
(b) V has t distribution
(c) $E\left(\frac{V}{U}\right) = 0$
(d) U and V are independent

(DEC. 2014)

25. Let $X_1, X_2, \ldots$ be independent and identically distributed random variables with $E(X_1) = 0$ and Variables with $E(X_i) = 0$ and $\text{Var}(X_i) = 1$ for all i. Let $S_n = X_1 + \cdots + X_n$. Let $\Phi(x)$ denote the cumulative distribution function of a standard normal random variable.
Then, for any $x > 0$, $\lim_{n\to\infty} P(-nx < S_n < nx)$ equals
(a) $2\Phi(x) - 1$ (b) $\Phi(x)$
(c) 1 (d) $1 - \Phi(2x)$

(DEC. 2014)

26. Suppose $X_1, X_2, \ldots$ are random variables on a common probability space with $X_n \sim N(\mu_n, \sigma_n^2)$. Then, X_n converges in probability to 2 if and only if
(a) $\mu_n \to 0$ and $\sigma_n^2 \to 2$
(b) $\mu_n \to 2$ and $\sigma_n^2 \to 0$
(c) $\mu_n \to 0$ and σ_n^2 converges
(d) $\sigma_n^2 \to 0$ and μ_n converges

(DEC. 2014)

27. Suppose that X_1, X_2 and X_3 are independent and identically distributed random variables, each having a Bernoulli distribution with parameter 1/2. Consider the 2 x 2 matrix $A = \begin{pmatrix} X_1 & 0 \\ X_2 & X_3 \end{pmatrix}$. Then, $P(A \text{ is invertible})$ equals
(a) 0 (b) 1
(c) 1/4 (d) 3/4

(DEC. 2014)

28. $N, A_1, A_2 \ldots$ are independent real valued random variables such that $P(N = k) = (1-p)p^k, k = 0,1,2 \ldots$ where $0 < p < 1$, and $\{A_i : i = 1,2,\ldots\}$ is a sequence of independent and identically distributed bounded random variables. Let

$$X(w) = \begin{cases} 0 & \text{If } N(w) = 0 \\ \sum_{j=1}^{k} A_j & \text{If } N(w) = k, k = 1,2,\ldots \end{cases}$$

Which of the following are necessarily correct?
(a) X is a bounded random variable
(b) Moment m_A is the moment function m_X of X is $m_X(t) = \frac{(1-p)}{1-p\, m_A(t)}, t \in \mathbb{R}$, where m_A is the moment generating function of A_1.
(c) Characteristic function $\varphi_X(t) = \frac{(1-p)}{1-p\,\varphi_A(t)}, t \in \mathbb{R}$, where φ_A is the Characteristic function of A_1.
(d) X is symmetric about 0.

(JUNE 2015)

29. Assume that $X\sim$ Binomial (n,p) for some $n \ge 1$ and $0 < p < 1$ and $Y\sim$ Poisson (λ) for some $\lambda > 0$. Suppose $E[X] = E[Y]$. Then
(a) $Var(X) = Var\ (Y)$
(b) $Var(X) < Var\ (Y)$
(c) $Var(X) > Var\ (Y)$
(d) $Var(X)$ may be larger or smaller than $Var(Y)$ depending on the values of n, p and λ.

(JUNE 2015)

30. Suppose $X_i|\theta_i \sim N(\theta_i \sigma^2), i = 1,2$ are independently distributed. Under the prior distribution, θ_1 and θ_2 are i.i.d $N(\mu, \tau^2)$, where σ^2, μ and τ^2 are known. Then which of the following is true about the marginal distributions of X_1 and X_2?
(a) X_1 and X_2 are i.i.d $N(\mu, \tau^2 + \sigma^2)$.
(b) X_1 and X_2 are not normally distributed.
(c) X_1 and X_2 are $N(\mu, \tau^2 + \sigma^2)$ but they are not independent.
(d) X_1 and X_2 are normally distributed but are not identically distributed.

(JUNE 2015)

31. Let $X_1, X_2, \ldots, X_n$ be independent and identically distributed random variables having an exponential distribution with mean $\frac{1}{\lambda}$. Let $S_n = X_1 + X_2 + \ldots + X_n$ and $N = \inf\{n \ge 1 : S_n > 1\}$. Then $Var(N)$ equals
(a) 1 (b) λ
(c) λ^2 (d) ∞

(JUNE 2015)

32. Suppose X has density
$f(x|\theta) = \frac{1}{\theta} e^{-\frac{x}{\theta}}, x > 0$ where $\theta > 0$ is unknown.
Define Y as follows:
$Y = k \text{ if } k \le X < k+1, k = 0, 1, 2 \ldots$
Then the distribution of Y is
(a) Normal (b) Binomial
(c) Poisson (d) Geometric

(JUNE 2015)

33. Let (X, Y) have the joint discrete distribution such that $X \mid Y = y \sim$ Binomials (y, 0.5) and $Y \sim$ poisson $(\lambda), \lambda > 0$ where λ is an unknown parameter. Let $T = T(X, Y)$ be any unbiased estimator of λ Then
(a) $Var(T) \leq Var(Y) for\ all\ \lambda$
(b) $Var(T) \geq Var(Y) for\ all\ \lambda$
(c) $Var(T) \geq \lambda\ for\ all\ \lambda$
(d) $Var(T) = Var(Y) for\ all\ \lambda$

(JUNE 2015)

34. Let X and Y be independent normal random variables with mean 0 and variance 1. Let the characteristics function of XY be denoted by φ Then
(a) $\varphi(2) = 1/2$
(b) φ is an even function
(c) $\varphi(t)\varphi\left(\frac{1}{t}\right) = |t|$ for all $t \neq 0$
(d) $\varphi(t) = E(e^{-t^2 y^2/2})$

(JUNE 2015)

35. Let X_1 *and* X_2 be independent and identically distributed normal random variables with mean 0 and variance 1. Let U_1 *and* U_2 be independent and identically distributed $U(0,1)$ random variables independent of X_1, X_2. Define Z= $\frac{X_1U_1 + X_2U_2}{\sqrt{U_1^2+U_2^2}}$ then
(a) $E(Z) = 0$
(b) $Var(Z) = 1$
(c) Z is standard Cauchy
(d) $Z \sim N(0,1)$

(JUNE 2015)

36. Suppose $X_1, X_2 \ldots$ are independent random variables. Assume that $X_1, X_3, \ldots.$ are identically distributed with mean μ_1 and variance σ_1^2 and $X_2, X_4, \ldots.$ are identically distributed with mean μ_2 and variance σ_2^2.
Let $S_n = X_1 + X_2 + \ldots + X_n$.
Then $\frac{S_n - a_n}{b_n}$ coverges is distribution to N (0, 1) if
(a) $a_n = \frac{n(\mu_1+\mu_2)}{2}$ and $b_n = \sqrt{n}\sqrt{\frac{\sigma_1^2+\sigma_2^2}{2}}$
(b) $a_n = \frac{n(\mu_1+\mu_2)}{2}$ and $b_n = \frac{n(\sigma_1+\sigma_2)}{2}$
(c) $a_n = n(\mu_1 + \mu_2)$ and $b_n = \sqrt{n}\frac{(\sigma_1+\sigma_2)}{2}$
(d) $a_n = n(\mu_1 + \mu_2)$ and $b_n = \sqrt{n}\sqrt{\frac{\sigma_1^2+\sigma_2^2}{2}}$

(DEC. 2015)

37. Let X_i' s be independent random variables such that X_i' are symmetric about 0 and
$Var(X_i) = 2i - 1$, for $i \geq 1$.
Then, $\lim_{n\to\infty} P(X_1 + X_2 + \cdots + X_n > n \log n)$
(a) does not exist (b) equals ½
(c) equals 1 (d) equals 0

(DEC. 2015)

38. Let $X_1, X_2, \ldots$ be independent and identically distributed, each having a uniform distribution on (0, 1). Let $S_n = \sum_{i=1}^{n} X_i$ for $n \geq 1$. Then which of the following statements are true?
(a) $\frac{S_n}{n \log n} \to 0$ as $n \to \infty$ with probability 1
(b) $P\left\{\left\{S_n > \frac{2n}{3}\right\} \text{occurs for infinitely many } n\right\} = 1$
(c) $\frac{S_n}{\log n} \to 0$ as $n \to \infty$ with probability 1
(d) $P\left\{\left\{S_n > \frac{n}{3}\right\} \text{occurs for infinitely many } n\right\} = 1$

(JUNE 2016)

39. Let $X_1 \sim N(0,1)$ and let $X_2 = \begin{cases} -X_1, -2 \leq X_1 \leq 2 \\ X_1,\ otherwise \end{cases}$
Then identify the correct statement.
(a) $corr\ (X_1, X_2) = 1$
(b) X_2 does not have $N(0,1)$ distribution.
(c) (X_1, X_2) has a bivariate normal distribution
(d) (X_1, X_2) does not have a bivariate normal distribution

(JUNE 2016)

40. Suppose $X$and Y are independent and indentically distributed random variables and let $= X + Y$. Then the distribution of Z is in the same family as that of$X$ and$Y$ if$X$ is
(a) Normal (b) Exponential
(c) Uniform (d Binomial

(DEC. 2016)

41. Suppose $X_1, X_2, \ldots, X_n$ is a random sample from a distribution with probability density function
$f(x) = 3x^2 I_{(0,1)}(x)$, where $I_{(0,1)}(Z) = \begin{cases} 1 & if\ z \in (0,1) \\ 0 & otherwise \end{cases}$
What is the probability density function $g(y)$ of $Y = \min\{X_1, X_2, \ldots, X_n\}$?
(a) $g(y) = 3ny^{3n-1} I_{(0,1)}(y)$.
(b) $g(y) = 1 - (1 - y^3)^n I_{(0,1)}(y)$.
(c) $g(y) = (1 - y^3)^n I_{(0,1)}(y)$.
(d) $g(y) = 3ny^2(1 - y^3)^{n-1} I_{(0,1)}(y)$.

(DEC. 2016)

42. Let $\{X_i; i \geq 1\}$ be a sequence of independent random variables each having a normal distribution with mean 2 and variance 5. Then which of the followings are true
(a) $\frac{1}{n}\sum_{1=1}^{n} X_i$ converges in probability to 2
(b) $\frac{1}{n}\sum_{1=1}^{n} X_i^2$ converges in probability to 9
(c) $\left(\frac{1}{n}\sum_{1=1}^{n} X_i\right)^2$ converges in probability to 4
(d) $\sum_{1=1}^{n}\left(\frac{X_i}{n}\right)^2$ converges in probability to 0

(DEC. 2016)

43. Let X be a random variable with a certain non-degenerate distribution. Then identify the correct statements
(a) If X has an exponential distribution then median $(X) < E(X)$
(b) If X has a uniform distribution on an interval$[a, b]$, then $E(X) < median(X)$
(c) If X has a Binomial distribution then $V(X) < E(X)$
(d) If X has a normal distribution, then $E(X) < V(X)$

(JUNE 2017)

44. $X_1, X_2, \ldots.$ are independent identically distributed random variables having common density f. Assume $f(x) = f(-x)$ for all $x \in \mathbb{R}$. Which of the following statements is correct?

(a) $\frac{1}{n}(X_1+\cdots+X_n)\to 0$ in probability
(b) $\frac{1}{n}(X_1+\cdots+X_n)\to 0$ almost surely
(c) $P\left(\frac{1}{\sqrt{n}}(X_1+\cdots+X_n)<0\right)\to\frac{1}{2}$
(d) $\sum_{i=1}^{n} X_i$ has the same distribution as $\sum_{i=1}^{n}(-1)^i X_i$

(JUNE 2017)

45. X and Y are independent random variables each having the density
$f(t)=\frac{1}{\pi}\frac{1}{1+t^2}$; $-\infty<t<\infty$.
Then the density function of $\frac{X+Y}{3}$ for $-\infty<t<\infty$ is given by
(a) $\frac{6}{\pi}\frac{1}{4+9t^2}$ (b) $\frac{6}{\pi}\frac{1}{9+4t^2}$
(c) $\frac{3}{\pi}\frac{1}{1+9t^2}$ (d) $\frac{3}{\pi}\frac{1}{9+t^2}$

(JUNE 2017)

46. Let $\{X_n, n\ge 1\}$ be i.i.d. uniform $(-1,2)$ random variables. Which of the following statements are true?
(a) $\frac{1}{n}\sum_{i=1}^{n} X_i \to 0$ almost surely
(b) $\left\{\frac{1}{2n}\sum_{i=1}^{n} X_{2i}-\frac{1}{2n}\sum_{i=1}^{n} X_{2i-1}\right\}\to 0$ almost surely
(c) $\sup\{X_1, X_2, \ldots\}=2$ almost surely
(d) $\inf\{X_1, X_2, \ldots\}=-1$ almost surely

(JUNE 2017)

47. Suppose X follows an exponential distribution with parameter $\lambda>0$. $Fox\ a>0$. Define the random variable Y by $Y=k$, if $ka\le X<(k+1)a,\ k=0,1,2,\ldots$
Which of the following statement are correct?
(a) $P(4<Y<5)=0$
(b) Y follows an exponential distribution
(c) Y follows a geometric distribution
(d) Y follows a Poisson distribution.

(DEC. 2017)

48. X, Y are independent exponential random variables with means 4 and 5, respectively. Which of the following statements is true?
(a) $X+Y$ is exponential with mean 9
(b) XY is exponential with mean 20
(c) $\max(X,Y)$ is exponential
(d) $\min(X,Y)$ is exponential

(DEC. 2017)

49. Let X and Y be independent exponential random variables. If $E[X]=1$ and $E[Y]=\frac{1}{2}$
then $P(X>2Y|X>Y)$ is
(a) $\frac{1}{2}$ (b) $\frac{1}{3}$
(c) $\frac{2}{3}$ (d) $\frac{3}{4}$

(DEC. 2017)

50. Which of the following are correct?
(a) if X and Y are $N(0,1)$ then $\frac{X+Y}{\sqrt{2}}$ is $N(0,1)$
(b) if X and Y are independent $N(0,1)$ then $\frac{X}{Y}$ has t-distribution
(c) if X and Y are independent Uniform (0,1) then $\frac{X+Y}{2}$ is Uniform (0,1)
(d) if X is Binomial (n,p) then $n-X$ is Binomial $(n,1-p)$

(DEC. 2017)

51. For $n\ge 1$, let X_n be a Poisson random variable with mean n^2. Which of the following are equal to $\frac{1}{\sqrt{2}}\int_2^\infty e^{-x^2/2}dx$
(a) $\lim_{n\to\infty} P\{X_n>(n+1)^2\}$
(b) $\lim_{n\to\infty} P\{X_n\le(n+1)^2\}$
(c) $\lim_{n\to\infty} P\{X_n<(n-1)^2\}$
(d) $\lim_{n\to\infty} P\{X_n<(n-2)^2\}]$

(JUNE 2018)

52. Let X and Y be i.i.d. uniform (0, 1) random variables, Let $Z=\max(X,Y)$ and $W=\min(X,Y)$.
Then $P((Z-W)>1/2)$ is
(a) 1/2 (b) 3/4
(c) 1/4 (d) 2/3

(JUNE 2018)

53. Let X_1, X_2, X_3 be i.i.d. standard normal variables. Which of the following is true?
(a) $\frac{\sqrt{2}|X_1|}{\sqrt{X_2^2+X_3^2}}\sim t_2$ (b) $\frac{X_1-2X_2+X_3}{\sqrt{2}|X_1+X_2+X_3|}\sim t_1$
(c) $\frac{(X_1-X_2)^2}{(X_1+X_2)^2}\sim F_{2,2}$ (d) $\frac{3X_1^2}{X_1^2+X_2^2+X_3^2}\sim F_{1,3}$

(JUNE 2018)

54. Let X and Y be i.i.d. exponential random variables with parameter 1. Define, $W=X+Y$ and $U=X/(X+Y)$. Which of the following are true?
(a) $E(U)=1/2$
(b) U is unform on (0, 1)
(c) W, U are independent
(d) W, U are uncorrelated, but dependent

(JUNE 2018)

55. Suppose that for $n\ge 3$, $X_1, X_2, \ldots, X_n$ are i.i.d. $\sim N(\mu_1,\sigma_1^2)$ and $Y_1, Y_2, \ldots, Y_n$ are i.i.d. $\sim N(\mu_2,\sigma_2^2)$. Assume further that the X_i's and the Y_j's are independent. Let r be the correlation coefficient computed from the bivariate data $(X_1,Y_1),(X_2,Y_2),\ldots,(X_n,Y_n)$. Then
(a) $\frac{r^2(n-2)}{1-r^2}$ has $F_{1,n-2}$ distribution (F- distribution with 1 and $n-2$ d.f.) for all $n\ge 3$
(b) $\frac{r\sqrt{n-2}}{\sqrt{1-r^2}}$ has t_{n-2} distribution (t- distribution with $n-2$ d.f.) for all $n\ge 3$
(c) $\frac{r^2}{1-r^2}$ has the distribution of the square of a Cauchy variable for $n=3$
(d) r^2 has a beta distribution for all $n\ge 3$

(DEC. 2018)

56. Let X and Y be i.i.d. random variables uniformly distributed on (0,4). Then $P(X>Y|X<2Y)$ is.
(a) $\frac{1}{3}$ (b) $\frac{5}{6}$
(c) $\frac{1}{4}$ (d) $\frac{2}{3}$

(DEC. 2018)

57. Suppose $X\sim$ Cauchy (0,1). Then the distribution of $\frac{1-X}{1+X}$ is
(a) Uniform (0,1) (b) Normal (0,1)
(c) Double exponential (0,1) (d) Cauchy (0,1)

(DEC. 2018)

58. Suppose $X_1, X_2 \dots, X_3$ is a random sample for the uniform distribution on (0,2) and $M_n = \max\{X_1, X_2 \dots, X_3\}$ for every positive integer n. Then which of the following statement are true?
(a) $M_n \to 2$ almost surely
(b) $M_n \to 2$ in probability
(c) $M_n \to 2$ in distribution
(d) $\frac{M_n - 2}{\sqrt{n}}$ converges in distribution to normal distribution

(DEC. 2018)

59. Let $X_1, X_2, \dots$ be i.i.d. N (0,1) random variables. Let $S_n = X_1^2 + X_2^2 + \cdots X_n^2, \forall n \geq 1$. Which of the following statements are correct?
(a) $\frac{S_n - n}{\sqrt{2}} \sim N(0,1)$ for all $n \geq 1$
(b) For all $\varepsilon > 0, P\left(\left|\frac{S_n}{n} - 2\right| > \epsilon\right) \to 0 \; as \; n \to \infty$
(c) $\frac{S_n}{n} \to 1$ with probability 1
(d) $P(S_n \leq 1 + \sqrt{n}x) \to P(Y \leq x) \; \forall x \in R$ where $Y \sim N(0,2)$

(JUNE 2019)

60. Suppose a normal $Q - Q$ plot is drawn using a reasonably large sample $x_1, \dots, x_n$ from an unknown probability distribution. For which of the following distribution would you expect the $Q - Q$ plot to be convex (J –shaped)?
(a) Beta (5, 1)
(b) Exponential (1)
(c) Uniform (0,1)
(d) Geometric (1/2)

(JUNE 2019)

61. Let $X_1, X_2, \dots, X_{2n-1} (n > 5)$ be $i.i.d.$ with p.d.f. f_θ, which is symmetric about θ having bounded support. Let $X_{(1)} < X_{(2)} < \cdots < X_{(2n-1)}$ be the order statistics of the random variables $X_1, X_2, \dots, X_{2n-1}$. Which of the following statements are correct?
(a) $X_{(1)} - \theta$ and $\theta - X_{(1)}$ have the same distributioin
(b) $X_{(1)} - \theta$ and $\theta - X_{(2n-1)}$ have the same distribution
(c) The distribution of $X_{(n)}$ is symmetric about θ
(d) $E[X_{(k)} + X_{(2n-k)}]$ is same for all $k = 1,2, \dots, n$

(DEC 2019)

62. Let X and Y be independent Exponential random variables with means $\frac{1}{\lambda}$ and $\frac{1}{\mu}$ respectively with $\neq \mu$. Let f_z (z) denote the density function of Z = X +Y. Then for z>0,
(a) $f_z(z) = (\lambda + \mu)e^{-(\lambda+\mu)z}$
(b) $f_z(z) = \frac{\lambda\mu}{\lambda+\mu} e^{\frac{-\lambda\mu}{e\lambda+\mu}z}$
(c) $f_z(z) = \frac{\lambda\mu}{\lambda-\mu}(e^{-\mu z} - e^{-\lambda z})$
(d) $f_z(z) = \begin{cases} \frac{\lambda\mu}{\lambda-\mu} e^{\frac{-\lambda\mu}{\lambda-\mu}z} \; if \; \lambda > \mu \\ \frac{\lambda\mu}{\mu-\lambda} e^{\frac{-\lambda\mu}{\mu-\lambda}z} \; if \; \mu>\lambda \end{cases}$

(DEC 2019)

63. A random variable T has a symmetric distribution if T and −T have the same distribution. Let X and Y be independent random variables. Then which of the following statements are correct?
(a) If X and Y have the same distribution then X – Y has a symmetric distribution
(b) If X ~ N(3,1) and Y ~ N(2,2), then 2X – 3Y has a symmetric distribution
(c) If X and Y have the same symmetric distribution, then X + Y has a symmetric distribution
(d) If X has a symmetric distribution, then XY has a symmetric distribution

(NOV 2020)

64. Let $X_1, X_2, \dots$ be i.i.d random variables having a $\chi^2 - distribution$ with 5 degree of freedom. Let $a \in R$ be constant. Then the limiting distribution of $a\left(\frac{X_1 + .. + X_n - 5n}{\sqrt{n}}\right)$ is
(a) Gamma distribution for an appropriate value of a
(b) χ^2 –Distribution for an appropriate value of a
(c) Standard normal distribution for an appropriate value of a
(d) A degenerate distribution for an appropriate value of a

(NOV 2020)

65. Suppose that X has uniform distribution on the interval [0,100]. Let Y denote the greatest integer smaller than or equal to X. Which of the following is true?
(a) $P(Y \leq 25) = 1/4$
(b) $P(Y \leq 25) = 26/100$
(c) $E(Y) = 50$
(d) $E(Y) = 101/2$

(NOV 2020)

66. Suppose $X_1, X_2, \dots, X_n$ are i.i.d. random variables with characteristic function $\phi(t; \theta) = E[e^{itX_i}]$ where $\underline{\theta} \epsilon R^k$ is the parameter of the distribution. Let $Z = X_1 + X_2 + \cdots + X_n$. Then for which of the following distributions of X_1 would the characteristic function of Z be of the form $\phi(t; \underline{\alpha})$ for some $\underline{\alpha} \epsilon R^k$?
(a) Negative Binomial
(b) Geometric
(c) Hypergeometric
(d) Discrete Uniform

(JUNE 2021)

67. Suppose that Y has exponential distribution with mean θ and that the conditional distribution of X given $Y = y$ is Normal with mean 0 and variance y, for all $y > 0$. Identify the characteristic function of X (defined as $\phi(t) = \mathbb{E}[e^{itX}]$) from the following.
(a) $e^{-\frac{\theta}{2}t^2}$
(b) $e^{-\frac{1}{2\theta}t^2}$
(c) $\frac{1}{1+\frac{1}{2}\theta t^2}$
(d) $\frac{\theta}{\theta+\frac{1}{2}t^2}$

68. Let $X_1, X_2, \dots. X_n$ be random variable whose marginal distributions are $N(0,1)$. Suppose $E(X_i X_j) =$ for $i, j, i \neq j$. Let $Y = X_1 + X - 2 + \cdots + X_n$ and $V = X_1^2 + X_2^2 + .. + X_n^2$. which of the following statement follow from the give conditions?
(a) Y has normal distribution with mean zero and variance n
(b) V has Chi-square distributon with n degrees of freedom
(c) $E(X_i^3 X_j^3) = 0$ for all $i, j, i \neq j$
(d) $P(|Y| > t) \leq \frac{n}{t^2}$ for all $t > 0$

69. Suppose $X \sim$ Geometric (1/2) (taking values in $\{1,2,3 \ldots,\}$) and conditional on X, the variable Y has Poisson (X) distribution. Similarly suppose $U \sim$ Poisson (1) and conditional on U, the variable V has Geometric $(1/(U+1))$ distribution. Then,

(a) $E[Y] \geq E[V]$ (b) $E[Y] \leq E[V]$
(c) $Var\ [Y] \geq Var[V]$ (d) $Var\ [Y] \leq Var[V]$

[SEP 2022]

70. Let $X_1, \ldots, X_n$ be a random sample from a discrete distribution with probability mass function

$P(X_1 = 1) = \frac{2(1-\theta)}{2-\theta}, P(X_1 = 2) = \frac{\theta}{2-\theta}$

where $\theta \in (0,1)$ is unknown. Let $\overline{X} = \frac{\sum_{i=1}^{n} X_i}{n}$. Then, the method of moments estimator of θ is

(a) $\overline{X}$ (b) $2(1-\overline{X})$
(c) $2\left(1-\overline{X}^{-1}\right)$ (d) $2(2-\overline{X})^{-1}$

[SEP 2022]

71. Suppose that is X is a random variable such that $P(X \in \{0,1,2\}) = 1$. If for some constant c, $P(X = i) = cP(X = i-1), i = 1,2$, then $E[X]$ is

(a) $\frac{1}{1+c+c^2}$ (b) $\frac{c+2c^2}{1+c+c^2}$
(c) $\frac{c+c^2}{1+2c}$ (d) $\frac{3c}{1+2c}$

[SEP 2022]

72. Let $\{X_n : n \geq 1\}$ be a sequence of independent and identically distributed random variables and the probability mass function of X_1 is the following:

$P(X_1 = 1) = P(X_1 = 3) = \frac{1}{2}$.

If $Y_n = X_1 + \cdots + X_n$, then which of the following statements are correct?

(a) $\frac{Y_n}{n}$ converges to 2 in probability
(b) Variance $\left(\frac{Y_n}{n^{\frac{2}{2}}}\right)$ converges to 0, as $n \to \infty$
(c) $\frac{Y_n}{n^{2/2}}$ converges to c probability, where $0 < c < \infty$
(d) $\frac{Y_n}{n^2}$ converges to 0 in probability

[SEP 2022]

73. Let X be a random variable whose distribution is symmetric about -2. Which of the following are true?

(a) If X discrete and $P(X = -2) = \frac{2}{3}$, then $P(X > -2) = 1/6$
(b) If X discrete and $P(X = -2) = \frac{2}{3}$, then $P(X > -2) = 1/2$
(c) If X is absolutely continuous, then $P(X > -2) = 0$
(d) If X is absolutely continuous, then $P(X > -2) = 1/2$

(SEP. 2022)

74. The probability density function of a continuous random variable X is given by

$$f(x) = \begin{cases} e^{-x}, & x > 0 \\ 0, & otherwise \end{cases}$$

Let $Y = [X]$, where $[X]$ denotes the largest integer not exceeding X. Which of the following statements are CORRECT?

(a) $P(Y = 2) = 0$ (b) $P(Y < 1.2) = 1 - e^{-2}$
(c) $E(Y^2) = \frac{e+1}{(e-1)^2}$ (d) $E(Y) = \frac{1}{(e-1)}$

(SEP. 2022)

75. Let $X_1, X_2, \ldots, X_{10}$ be a random sample from Uniform$(0,1)$ and $X_{(1)}, X_{(2)}, \ldots, X_{(10)}$ denote the corresponding order statistics. Which of the following statements are true?

(a) $X_{(1)} \sim Beta(2,9)$
(b) $X_{(10)} - X_{(1)} \sim Beta(11,2)$
(c) $E[X_{(2)}] = \frac{2}{11}$
(d) $Var[X_{(2)}] = \frac{3}{242}$

(JUNE 2023)

76. Let X_1 and X_2 be two independent random variables such that X_1 follows a gamma distribution with mean 10 and variance 10, and $X_2 \sim N(3,4)$. Let f_1 and f_2 denote the density functions of X_1 and X_2 respectively. Define a new random variable Y so that for $y \in \mathbb{R}$, it has density function

$$f(y) = 0.4 f_1(y) + a f_2(y).$$

Which of the following are true?

(a) $q = 0.6$ (b) $E[Y] = 5.8$
(c) $Var(Y) = 3.04$ (d) $Y = 0.4X_1 + qX_2$

(JUNE 2023)

77. Which of the following is a valid cumulative distribution function?

(a) $F(x) = \begin{cases} \frac{1}{2+x^2} & if\ x < 0 \\ \frac{2+x^2}{3+x^2} & if\ x \geq 0 \end{cases}$

(b) $F(x) = \begin{cases} \frac{1}{2+x^2} & if\ x < 0 \\ \frac{2+x^2}{3+2x^2} & if\ x \geq 0 \end{cases}$

(c) $F(x) = \begin{cases} \frac{1}{2+x^2} & if\ x < 0 \\ \frac{2\cos(x)+x^2}{4+x^2} & if\ x \geq 0 \end{cases}$

(d) $F(x) = \begin{cases} \frac{1}{2+x^2} & if\ x < 0 \\ \frac{1+x^2}{4+x^2} & if\ x \geq 0 \end{cases}$

(JUNE 2023)

78. Consider the random sample $\{3,6,9\}$ of size 3 from a normal distribution with mean $\mu \in (-\infty, 5]$ and variance 1. Then the maximum likelihood estimate of μ is

(a) 6 (b) 5
(c) 3 (d) 9

(JUNE 2023)

79. Let $\{X_i : 1 \leq i \leq 2n\}$ be independently and identically distributed normal random variables with mean μ and variance 1, and independent of a standard Cauchy random variable W. Which of the following statistics are consistent for μ?

(a) $n^{-1} \sum_{i=1}^{n} X_i$, (b) $n^{-1} \sum_{i=1}^{2n} X_i$,
(c) $n^{-1} \sum_{i=1}^{n} X_{2i-1}$, (d) $n^{-1}(\sum_{i=1}^{n} X_i, + W)$

(JULY-2024)

80. Let a point P be chosen at random on the line segment AB of length α. Let Z_1 *and* Z_2 denote the lengths of line segments AP and BP respectively. Then the value of $E(|Z_1 - Z_2|)$ is

(a) α (b) 2α

(c) $\frac{\alpha}{2}$ (d) $\frac{2\alpha}{3}$

(JULY 2024)

81. Let $X_1 .... X_{12}$ be a random sample from the $N(2,4)$ distribution and $Y_1, ... Y_{15}$ is be a random sample from the $N(-2,5)$ distribution, where $N(\mu, \sigma^2)$ denotes a normal distribution with mean μ and variance σ^2. Assume that the two random samples are mutually independent. Let

$$\overline{X} = \frac{1}{12}\sum_{i=1}^{12} X_i,\quad S_1^2 = \frac{1}{11}\sum_{i=1}^{12}(X_i - \overline{X})^2$$

$$\overline{Y} = \frac{1}{15}\sum_{j=1}^{15} Y_j,\quad S_2^2 = \frac{1}{14}\sum_{j=1}^{15}(Y_j - \overline{Y})^2.$$

Which of the following statements are true?

(a) The distribution of $\overline{X} + \overline{Y}$ *is* $N\left(0, \frac{2}{3}\right)$

(b) The distribution of $\frac{1}{20}(55S_1^2 + 56S_2^2)$ is x_{26}^2

(c) The distribution of is $\frac{5}{4}\frac{S_1^2}{S_2^2}$ *is* $F_{11,14}$

(d) The distribution of $\frac{2\sqrt{3}\,(\overline{Y}+2)}{S_1}$ *is* t_{14}

(JULY 2024)

82. Let X and Y be independent random variables with $X \sim N(2,4)$ *and* $Y \sim N(-4,9)$ where $N(\mu,\sigma^2)$ denotes a normal distribution with mean μ and variance σ^2. Given $\Phi(1) = 0.8413, \Phi(2) = 0.9772$ *and* $\Phi(3) = 0.9987$ where $\Phi(.)$ is the cumulative distribution function of a standard normal random variable. Which of the following statements are true?

(1) $Var(2X + Y) = 17$

(2) $P(|2X + Y| \leq 15) = 0.9974$

(3) $Cov(3X + 2Y, 3X - 2Y) = 0$

(4) $2X - Y \sim N(0,25)$

(FEB. 2025)

83. Let $X_1, X_2, ..., X_n (n \geq 3)$ be a random sample from a population with absolutely continuous cumulative distribution function $F(\cdot)$. The corresponding order statistics are $X_{1:n} < X_{2:n} < \cdots < X_{r:n} < \cdots < X_{n:n}$. For $r = 2,3$, define, $Y_{r,n} = nF(X_{r:n})$. Suppose that $Y_{r,n}$ converges in distribution to a random variable Y_r as $n \to \infty, r = 2,3$. Then, which of the following statements are true?

(a) Y_2 follows gamma distribution with $E(Y_2) = 2$.

(b) $E(Y_{3,n}) \to 3$ as $n \to \infty$

(c) Y_3 follows beta distribution with $E(Y_3) = \frac{1}{3}$.

(d) $Y_{2,n}$ follows beta distribution with parameters 2 and $n - 1$.

(FEB. 2025)

84. Let X be a random variable with probability density function $f(x) = \frac{1}{\pi(1+x^2)}, x \in \mathbb{R}$. If $Z = \frac{1}{2} + \frac{1}{\pi}\tan^{-1}(X)$, then which of the following statements are true?

(a) $E(Z^m) = \frac{1}{m+1}$ for all $m \in \mathbb{N}$

(b) $E(\Phi^{-1}(Z)) = 0$, where $\Phi(\cdot)$ is the cumulative distribution function of standard normal random variable.

(c) Z is degenerate at 0.

(d) If Z_1 and Z_2 are independent and identically distributed (i.i.d.) random variables having distribution same as the distribution of Z, then $Z = \frac{Z_1+Z_2}{2}$

(JUNE 2025)

85. Let $X_1, X_2, ...$ be a sequence of independent and identically distributed random variables with $E(X_1) = 0, E(X_1^2) = 1, E(X_1^3) = 0, E(X_1^4) = 3$. Let $S_n = \sum_{i=1}^n X_i, T_n = \sum_{i=1}^n X_i^2, U_n = \sum_{i=1}^n X_i^3$ and $V_n = \sum_{i=1}^n X_i^4$. Then, which of the following statements are true?

(a) $\frac{S_n}{\sqrt{n}}$ converges in distribution to a random variable Z, where $Z \sim N(0,1)$

(b) $\frac{T_n - n}{\sqrt{3n}}$ converges in distribution to a random variable Z, where $Z \sim N(0,1)$

(c) $\frac{\sqrt{n}S_n}{T_n}$ converges in distribution to a random variable Z, where $Z \sim N(0,1)$

(d) $\frac{T_n - n}{\sqrt{V_n}}$ converges in distribution to a random variable Z, where $Z \sim N(0,1)$

(JUNE 2025)

86. Let $(X_1,Y_1), (X_2,Y_2), ..., (X_{10},Y_{10})$ be a random sample from a bivariate normal distribution $BVN(\mu_1, \mu_2, \sigma_1^2, \sigma_2^2, \rho)$ with $\mu_1 = 5, \mu_2 = 6, \sigma_1^2 = 4, \sigma_2^2 = 9$ and $\rho = \frac{1}{2}$. Then, which of the following statements are true?

(a) The distribution of $\frac{1}{\sqrt{7}}\sum_{i=1}^{10}(X_i - Y_i + 1)$ is $N(0,10)$

(b) The distribution of $\frac{1}{19}\sum_{i=1}^{10}(X_i + Y_i - 11)^2$ is χ^2 distribution with degrees of freedom 10

(c) The distribution of $\frac{2\sqrt{2}(X_1-5)}{\sqrt{\sum_{i=3}^{10}(X_i-5)^2}}$ is t-distribution with degrees of freedom 9

(d) The distribution of $\frac{2\sum_{i=1}^{3}(Y_i-6)^2}{\sum_{i=4}^{9}(Y_i-6)^2}$ is F-distribution with degrees of freedom 3 and 6.

(Dec 2025)

87. Let X, Y, and Z be independent Normal random variables with means -1, 0, and 1, respectively, and variances 1, 1, and 3, respectively. Which of the following random variables has a Cauchy distribution with location parameter 0 and scale parameter 1?

(a) $\frac{X-1}{|Y|}$ (b) $\frac{X+2Y+Z}{X-2Y+Z}$

(c) $\frac{Z-1}{Y}$ (d) $\frac{X-Y}{X+Y}$

Answer Key

1	2	3	4	5	6	7	8	9	10
b	a,c	a,c,d	d	b,c	a,b	b,c	a,d	d	d
11	**12**	**13**	**14**	**15**	**16**	**17**	**18**	**19**	**20**
d	d	d	d	c,d	d	c	d	b,d	d
21	**22**	**23**	**24**	**25**	**26**	**27**	**28**	**29**	**30**
b	b,c,d	c	a,b,c	c	b	c	c	b	a
31	**32**	**33**	**34**	**35**	**36**	**37**	**38**	**39**	**40**
b	d	b,c	b,d	a,b,d	a	d	a,d	d	a,d
41	**42**	**43**	**44**	**45**	**46**	**47**	**48**	**49**	**50**
d	a,b,c,d	a,c	d	a	b,c,d	a,c	d	d	b,d
51	**52**	**53**	**54**	**55**	**56**	**57**	**58**	**59**	**60**
a,c	c	b	a,b,c	a,b,c,d	a	d	a,b,c	c,d	b,d
61	**62**	**63**	**64**	**65**	**66**	**67**	**68**	**69**	**70**
b,c,d	c	a,b,c,d	c	b	d	c	d	a,b,c,d	c
71	**72**	**73**	**74**	**75**	**76**	**77**	**78**	**79**	**80**
b	a,b,d	a,d	b, c, d	a, c, d	a, b	a	b	a,c,d	C
81	**82**	**83**	**84**	**85**	**86**	**87**			
a,c	b,c	a,b	a,b	a,c	a,b,d	b			

:: Explanations ::

1. **Explanation: (b)**

X_i's are iid $N(1,1)$; $i = 1,2,\ldots.$

$S_n = X_1^2 + X_2^2 + \cdots + X_n^2$

$Var\,(S_n) = Var\,(\sum_{i=1}^n X_i^2) = n\,Var\,(X_i^2)$

$\Rightarrow Var\,(X_i^2) = E(X_i^4) - [E(X_i^2)]^2$

$X_i \sim N(1,1)$

μ_r = r-th moment about mean $1 = E(X-1)^r$

μ_r' = r-th moment about origin $= E(X)^r$

$E(X-1)^4 = \mu_4 = \mu_4' - 4\mu_3'\mu_1' + 6\mu_2'\mu_1'^2 - 3\mu_1'^4$

$\mu_3 = \mu_3' - 3\mu_2'\mu_1' + 2\mu_1'^3$

Odd moments about mean are zero

$\mu_3 = 0$

$\mu_3' - 3\mu_2'\mu_1' + 2\mu_1'^3 = 0$

$\mu_3' = 3\mu_2'\mu_1' - 2\mu_1'^3$

$\mu_1' = E(X_i) = 1$

$\mu_2' = E(X_i^2) = Var\,(X_i) + \left(E(X_i)\right)^2 = 1 + 1$

$\mu_2' = 2$ and $\mu_3' = 3 \times 2 - 2 \times 1 = 4$

$\mu_4 = E(X-1)^4 = 1.3\,\sigma^4 = 3$

$\mu_4' - 4\mu_3' + 6\mu_2'\mu_1'^2 - 3\mu_1'^4 = 3$

$\mu_4' - 4 \times 4 \times 1 + 6 \times 2 \times 1 - 3 \times 1 = 3$

$\mu_4' = 3 + 16 - 6 + 3$

$E(X_i^4) = 10$

$Var\,(X_i^2) = E(X_i^4) - [E(X_i^2)]^2 = 10 - 2^2 = 6$

$\lim_{n\to\infty} \frac{Var\,(S_n)}{n} = \lim_{n\to\infty} \frac{6n}{n} = 6$

So, option (b) is correct

2. **Explanation: (a), (c)**

3. **Explanation: (a), (c), (d)**

$\varepsilon_1, \varepsilon_2, \varepsilon_3, \ldots, \varepsilon_n$ are iid $N(0,\sigma^2)$

$y_1, y_2, y_3, \ldots, y_n$ defined

$y_1 = \mu + \varepsilon_1$

$y_{i+1} - \mu = \rho(y_i - \mu) + \sqrt{1-\rho^2}\,\varepsilon_{i+1}$; $i = 1,2,\ldots,n-1$

$\varepsilon_j \sim N(0,\sigma^2); j = 1,2,\ldots,n$

$E(y_i) = \mu + E(\varepsilon_1) = \mu$

$E[y_{i+1}] = \mu + \rho(E(y_i) - \mu) + \sqrt{1-\rho^2}E(\varepsilon_{i+1})$

$E[y_2] = \mu + \rho(\mu - \mu) + \sqrt{1-\rho^2} \times 0$

$E(y_2) = \mu$

Similarly, $i = 1,2,\ldots,n-1$

$E[y_{i+1}] = \mu$ and $E[y_1] = \mu$

$Var\,(y_1) = Var\,(\varepsilon_1) = \sigma^2$

$Var\,(y_{i+1}) = \rho^2 Var(y_i) + (1-\rho^2)Var(\varepsilon_{i+1})$

$i = 1, Var\,(y_2) = \rho^2\sigma^2 + (1-\rho^2)\sigma^2 = \sigma^2$

$i = 2,3,\ldots,n-1\,; Var\,(y_{i+1}) = \sigma^2$

$y_1, y_2, \ldots, y_n$ are $N(\mu,\sigma^2)$

$T = \frac{1}{n}\sum_{i=1}^n y_i$

$E(T) = \mu$

$Var\,(T) = \frac{1}{n^2} Var\,(\sum_{i=1}^n y_i)$

$= \frac{1}{n^2}\left[\sum_{i=1}^n Var\,(y_i) + 2\sum_{j=1}^n \left(Cov(y_i, y_j)\right)\right]$

$= \frac{1}{n^2}\left[n\sigma^2 + 2\sum_{i=1}^n \left(Cov(y_i y_j)\right)\right] = \delta^2$

$\delta^2 = \frac{\sigma^2}{n} + \frac{2}{n^2}\sum_{i\neq j=1}^n \left(Cov(y_i, y_j)\right)$

$\delta^2 > \sigma^2/n$

$T \sim N(\mu, \delta^2)$

So, option (a), (c) & (d) are correct.

4. **Explanation: (d)**

$X_1, X_2, \ldots$ be iid $N(0,1)$

$T_n = \frac{X_1^2 + \ldots + X_n^2}{n}; X_i \sim N(0,1)$

$X_i^2 \sim \chi^2_{(1)}\,d.f$

$\therefore \sum_{i=1}^n X_i^2 \sim \chi^2_{(n)d.f}$

Using central limit theorem,

Limiting distribution of $\sqrt{n}(T_n - 1)$

$\sqrt{n}(T_n - 1) \xrightarrow{d} N\left[E(\sqrt{n}(T_n-1), Var\left(\sqrt{n}(T_n-1)\right)\right]$

$E\left[\sqrt{n}(T_n-1)\right] = \sqrt{n}[E(T_n) - 1] = \sqrt{n}[1-1] = 0$

$Var\left[\sqrt{n}(T_n-1)\right] = n\,Var\,(T_n) = n \cdot \frac{2n}{n^2} = 2$

$\sqrt{n}(T_n - 1) \xrightarrow{d} N(0,2)$

So, option (d) is correct

5. **Explanation: (b), (c)**

$X \sim B\left(11, \frac{1}{3}\right)$

$(n+1)p = (11+1)\frac{1}{3} = \frac{12}{3} = 4$

$(n+1)p$ is an integer the distribution has bimodal distribution

Mode = 4, 3

$P(X = K)$ is maximum at $K = 3, 4$

So, option (b) & (c) are correct

6. **Explanation: (a), (b)**

7. **Explanation: (b), (c)**

$X_1 \sim B\left(m, \frac{1}{2}\right) X_2 \sim B\left(n, \frac{1}{2}\right)$

Linear combination of binomial variate is not binomial variate if probability of success in variates are different

$2X_2 + 3X_2$ does not follow binomial

$X_1 \sim B\left(m, \frac{1}{2}\right)$

$m - X_1 \sim B\left(m, 1 - \frac{1}{2}\right)$

$X_2+m-X_1 \sim B\left(m+n,\frac{1}{2}\right)$

$P[X_2|X_1+X_2=t]=\frac{P[X_2=x,X_1=t=x]}{P(x_1+\alpha_2=t)}$

$=\frac{{}^nC_x\left(\frac{1}{2}\right)^x\left(\frac{1}{2}\right)^{n-x}{}^mC_{t-x}\left(\frac{1}{2}\right)^m}{{}^{m+n}C_t\left(\frac{1}{2}\right)^{m+n}}$

$=\frac{{}^nC_x\,{}^mC_{t-x}}{{}^{m+n}C_t}$

Which is pmf of hypergeometric distribution

So, option (b) and (c) are correct

8. Explanation: (a), (d)

$X_1 \sim N(1,1)$ and $X_2 \sim N(-1,1)$

X_1, X_2 & X_3 are independent

$X_1+X_2 \sim N(0,2)$ and $\frac{X_1+X_2}{\sqrt{2}} \sim N(0,1)$

$\frac{(X_1+X_2)^2}{2} \sim \chi^2_{1\,d.f}$

$\frac{X_1^2+X_2^2+2X_1X_2}{2} \sim \chi^2_{1\,d.f}$

$X_3^2 \sim \chi^2_{1\,d.f}$

$\frac{X_1^2+X_2^2+2X_1X_2}{2}+X_3^2 \sim \chi^2_{2\,d.f}$

$q_1=\frac{X_1^2+X_2^2+2X_3^2+2X_1X_2}{2} \sim \chi^2_{2\,d.f}$

$Cov(q_1,q_2)=0$

$\Rightarrow q_1$ & q_2 are independent

So, option (a) and (d) are correct

9. Explanation: (d)

10. Explanation: (d)

$U_1, U_2, \dots$ be iid random variable each having a uniform distribution on (0, 1)

$S=U_1+U_2+\dots+U_n$

$U_i \sim U(0,1)\,;\ i=1,2,\dots$

$E(U_i)=\frac{1}{2}\ Var(U_i)=\frac{1}{12}$

$E(S)=\frac{n}{2}\ Var(S)=\frac{n}{12}$

Using CLT,

$\lim_{n\to\infty} P\left[U_1+U_2+\dots+U_n \le \frac{3}{4}n\right]$

$=\lim_{n\to\infty} P\left[\frac{S-E(S)}{\sqrt{Var(S)}} \le \frac{\frac{3}{4}n-\frac{1}{2}n}{\sqrt{\frac{n}{12}}}\right]$

$=\lim_{n\to\infty} P\left[\frac{S-E(S)}{\sqrt{Var(S)}} \le \frac{\sqrt{n}\sqrt{3}}{2}\right]$

$=P[Z\le\infty]=1$

Where Z is standard normal variate

So, option (c) is correct

11. Explanation: (d)

12. Explanation: (d)

$X_i's$ are iid $U(0,1)$ $i=1,2,\dots$

Define $T_n=\max\{X_1,X_2,\dots,X_n\}$

$f(x_i)=1$ and $F(x)=x$

$f(T_n)=n\,t^{n-1}; 0<t<1$ and $F(T_n)=t^n$

$E(T_n)=1$

$T_n \xrightarrow{p} E(T_n)$

$T_n \xrightarrow{p} 1$

T_n converges to 1 in probability

Let $W=n(1-T_n)$

$F_w(\omega)=P[W\le\omega]=P[n(1-T_n)\le\omega]=P\left[T_n\ge 1-\frac{\omega}{n}\right]$

$=1-P\left[T_n\le 1-\frac{\omega}{n}\right]=1-F_{T_n}\left(1-\frac{\omega}{n}\right)$

$=1-\left(1-\frac{\omega}{n}\right)^n$

$\lim_{n\to\infty} F_w(\omega)=1-\lim_{n\to\infty}\left(1-\frac{\omega}{n}\right)^n=1-e^{\omega}$ which is finite

$n(1-T_n)$ is converge in distribution

$V=n^2(1-T_n)$

$F_v(v)=1-\left(1-\frac{v}{n^2}\right)^n$

$\lim_{n\to\infty} F_v(v)=1-\left(1-\frac{v}{n^2}\right)^n$ which is not converges

$\sqrt{n}(1-T_n)\xrightarrow{p} E[\sqrt{n}(1-T_n)]=0$

$\sqrt{n}(1-T_n)\xrightarrow{p} 0$

So, option (a), (b) and (d) are correct

13. Explanation: (d)

$X_1, X_2, \dots$ be independent r.v. each having normal distribution with unknown mean $\mu$and unknown variance $\sigma^2>0$

Sample mean is an unbiased and consistent estimator of μ

$\bar{X}_{n-2}=\frac{1}{n-2}\sum_{i=1}^{n-1}X_i$ is consistent for μ

Sample variance is unbiased and consistent for σ^2

$T_1=\frac{1}{n-3}\sum_{i=1}^{n-2}(X_i-\bar{X}_{n-2})^2$ is unbiased for σ^2

t-distribution is the ratio of standard normal divided by square root of chi-square divided by its d.f.

$T_2=\frac{X_{n-1}-X_n}{\sigma\sqrt{2}} \sim N(0,1)$

$\frac{(n-3)\sum_{i=1}^{n-2}(X_i-\bar{X}_{n-2})^2}{\sigma^2} \sim X^2_{(n-3)}\ d.f.$

So, $\frac{T_2}{\sqrt{T_1}} \sim t_{(n-3)}$

$T_2^2=\left(\frac{X_{n-1}-X_n}{2\sigma^2}\right)^2 \sim X_1^2\ d.f.$

$\frac{T_2^2}{T_1} \sim F_{1,n-3}$

So, option a, b, c and d are correct

14. Explanation: (d)

$X_i's$ $(i=1,2,3,4,5)$ are iid uniformly distributed over (0, 1)

Let M denote their median

The order statistics is

$X_{(1)}\le X_{(2)}\le X_{(3)}\le X_{(4)}\le X_{(5)}$

$M=\left(\frac{n+1}{2}\right)^{th}$ $term=\left(\frac{5+1}{2}\right)^{th}$ $term=3^{rd}$ $term$

$M=X_{(3)}=3^{rd}$ order statistic

The pdf of $X_{(3)}$ is

$g(m)=\frac{1}{\beta(3,3)}F^2(m).f(m).[1-F(m)]^2$

$=30\,m^2.1.[1-m]^2$

$g(m)=30\,m^2(1-m)^2\,;0<m<1$

$P\left(M<\frac{1}{3}\right)=\int_0^{1/3}g(m)\,dm$

$=30\int_0^{1/3}m^2\,(1-m)^2dm$

$=30\int_0^{1/3}(m^4+m^2-2m^3)\,dm$

$=30\left[\frac{m^5}{5}+\frac{m^3}{3}-\frac{2m^4}{4}\right]_0^{1/3}$

$P\left(M<\frac{1}{3}\right)=\frac{17}{81}$

$P\left(M > \frac{2}{3}\right) = \int_{2/3}^{1} g(m)\, dm = \frac{17}{81}$

$\therefore P\left(M < \frac{1}{3}\right) = P\left(M > \frac{2}{3}\right)$

$E(M) = \int_0^1 mg(m)\, dm = 30 \int_0^1 (m^5 + m^3 - 2m^4)\, dm$

$= 30\left[\frac{m^6}{6} + \frac{m^4}{4} - \frac{2m^5}{5}\right]_0^1 = \frac{1}{2}$

$E(X_1) = \frac{1}{2}$ and $E(M) = E(X_1)$

So, option (a) and (c) are correct

15. Explanation: (c), (d)

$X_i \sim \exp(1)\ i = 1, 2, \ldots$

$\lim_{n\to\infty} P(X_n > \log n) = \lim_{n\to\infty} 1 - P(X_n \le \log n)$

$= \lim_{n\to\infty} 1 - F_{X_n}(\log n)$

$= \lim_{n\to\infty} 1 - (1 - e^{-\log n})$

$= \lim_{n\to\infty} 1 - 1 + \frac{1}{n} = 0$

$\lim_{n\to\infty} P[X_n > 2\log n] = \lim_{n\to\infty} 1 - P[X_n \le 2\log n]$

$= \lim_{n\to\infty} 1 - (1 - e^{-2\log n})$

$= \lim_{n\to\infty} \frac{1}{n^2} = 0$

$\lim_{n\to\infty} P\left(X_n > \frac{1}{2}\log n\right) = 0$

$\lim_{n\to\infty} P[X_n > \log n, X_{n+1} > \log(n+1)] = 0$

So, option (c) and (d) are correct

16. Explanation: (d)

17. Explanation: (c)

18. Explanation: (d)

$X_1, X_2 \ldots$ be iid each having uniform $[-1, 1]$

$S_n = \sum_{i=1}^{n} X_i$ and $Z_n = \frac{S_n}{n^p}$

For iid

$Z_n \xrightarrow{a.s.} E(Z_n)$

$E(Z_n) = E\left(\frac{S_n}{n^p}\right) = \frac{1}{n^p} E(S_n) = \frac{1}{n^p}\sum_{i=1}^{n} E(X_i) = 0$

$Z_n \xrightarrow{a.s.} 0$ for all value of p

$Z_n \xrightarrow{a.s.} 0 \Rightarrow Z_n \xrightarrow{p} 0 \Rightarrow Z_n \xrightarrow{d} 0$

So, option a, b and c are correct

19. Explanation: (b), (d)

$X_1, X_2, \ldots$ be iid $N(0, 1)$

$X_i^2 \sim \chi_1^2\ d.f.$

$\sum_{i=1}^{n} X_i^2 \sim \chi_n^2\ d.f.$

$\frac{X_1}{\sqrt{\frac{X_1^2 + X_2^2 + \cdots + X_n^2}{n}}} \sim t_{n\ d.f.}$

$\Rightarrow \frac{\sqrt{n}\, X_1}{\sqrt{X_1^2 + \cdots + X_n^2}} \sim t_{n\ d.f.}$

$\Rightarrow \frac{\sqrt{n}\, X_2}{\sqrt{X_2^2 + \cdots + X_{n+1}^2}} \sim t_{n\ d.f.}$

So, option (b) and (d) are correct

20. Explanation: (d)

$P(X = K) = (1 - P)^K P;\ K = 0, 1, 2, \ldots$

$P[X > m + n \mid X > m] = \frac{P[X > m+n, X > m]}{P(X > m)}$

$= \frac{P(X > m+n)}{P(X > m)} = P(X > n)$

It geometric distribution has memory less property, so

$P(X > m + n \mid X > m) = P(X > n)$

So, option (b) is correct

21. Explanation: (b)

22. Explanation: (b), (c), (d)

23. Explanation: (c)

$X_n \sim P(n)$

$E(X_n) = n\ \&\ Var(X_n) = n$

Using CLT,

(a) $\lim_{n\to\infty} P[X_n > n + \sqrt{n}] = \lim_{n\to\infty} P\left[\frac{X_n - E(X_n)}{\sqrt{n}} > \frac{n + \sqrt{n} - n}{\sqrt{n}}\right]$

$= P[Z > 1] = 1 - \phi(1)$

Where $\phi(\cdot)$ is cdf of standard normal variate

(b) $\lim_{n\to\infty} P[X_n \le n + \sqrt{n}] = \phi(1)$

(d) & (c) $\lim_{n\to\infty} P[X_n \le n] = \lim_{n\to\infty} P\left[\frac{X_n - E(X_n)}{\sqrt{Var(X_n)}} < \frac{n - n}{\sqrt{n}}\right] =$

$P[Z \le 0] = \frac{1}{2}$

So, option (c) is correct

24. Explanation: (a), (b), (c)

X and Y be two independent $N(0, 1)$ random variables

$U = \frac{X}{Y}$ = ratio of two standard normal variate is standard cauchy variate $U \sim C(0, 1)$

Result 1: Standard cauchy is also t-distribution with 1 degree of freedom

$U = \frac{X}{Y} \sim t_{(1)} df$

$V = \frac{X}{|Y|} = \frac{X}{\sqrt{Y^2/1}}$ is the ratio of standard normal divided by sq. root of chi- square divided by d.f

$Y^2 \sim \chi^2_{1\ d.f.}$

$V = \frac{X}{|Y|} = \frac{X}{\sqrt{Y^2/1}} \sim t_{1\ d.f}$

The U and V are same distribution

V has t-distribution with 1 d.f

$E\left[\frac{V}{U}\right] = E\left[\frac{Y}{|Y|}\right] = -1 \times f(y) + 1 \times f(y) = 0$

$E\left[\frac{V}{U}\right] = 0$

U and V are not independent

So, (a), (b), (c) are correct

25. Explanation: (c)

$E(X_i) = 0$ and $Var(X_i) = 1\ \forall\ i$

$S_n = X_1 + X_2 + \ldots + X_n$

$E(S_n) = E(X_1) + E(X_2) + \ldots + E(X_n) = 0$

$Var(S_n) = Var(\sum_{i=1}^{n} X_i) = \sum_{i=1}^{n} Var(X_i) +$
$2\sum_{i\ne j}^{n} Var(X_i X_j) = n + 0$

$Var(S_n) = n$

$\phi(x)$ be the cdf of a standard normal variate

Using central limit theorem,

$\lim_{n\to\infty} P[-nx < S_n < nx] = \lim_{n\to\infty}\left[\frac{-nx - 0}{\sqrt{n}} < \frac{S_n - E(S_n)}{\sqrt{Var(S_n)}} < \frac{nx - 0}{\sqrt{n}}\right] = P[-\infty < z < \infty] = 1$

So, option (c) is correct

26. Explanation: (b)

Suppose $X_1, X_2, \ldots,$ *are* random variables

$X_n \sim N(\mu_n, \sigma_n^2)$

X_n converges in probability to 2

i.e., $X_n \xrightarrow{p} E(X_n)$

Such that as $n \to \infty$ $E(X_n) \to 2$

And $Var(X_n) \to 0$

$\therefore \mu_n \to 2$ and $\sigma_n^2 \to 0$

Then $X_n \xrightarrow{p} 2$

So, option (b) is correct

27. Explanation: (c)

X_1, X_2 and X_3 are iid r.v. each having a Bennoulli distribution with parameter $^1/_2$

$X_i = 0$ with prob. $\frac{1}{2}$

$= 1$ with prob. $\frac{1}{2}$

Matrix $A = \begin{pmatrix} X_1 & 0 \\ X_2 & X_3 \end{pmatrix}$ is invertible iff determinant of A is not equal to zero i.e.

$|A| \neq 0$

$X_1 X_3 \neq 0$

$P[X_1 X_3 \neq 0] = P[X_1 = 1, X_3 = 1]$

$= P[X_1 = 1] P[X_3 = 1]$ $[X_1 \,\&\, X_3 \text{ are independent}]$

$= \frac{1}{2} \times \frac{1}{2} = \frac{1}{4}$

So, option (c) is correct

28. Explanation: (c)

$N, A_1, A_2, \ldots$ are independent r.v such that

$P(N = K) = (1-p)p^k \,; K = \sigma, 1, 2, \ldots ; 0 < p < 1$

$\{A_i ; i = 1, 2, 3, \ldots\}$ is a sequence of iid bounded r.v

$X(\omega) = \begin{cases} 0 & N(\omega) = 0 \\ \sum_{j=1}^{k} A_j & N(\omega) = K, K = 1, 2, 3 \end{cases}$

$K = 1$

$X(\omega) = A_1$ with prob. $(1-p)p$

$= A_1 + A_2$ with prob. $(1-p)p^2$

$= A_1 + A_2 + A_3$ with prob. $(1-p)p^3$

X is not bounded

Mgf of $A_1 = m_A(t)$

Mgf of X is

$m_{(\alpha)}(t) = (1-p) + (1-p)pm_A(t) + (1-p)p^2[m_A(t)]^2 + \cdots$

$= (1-p)[1 + pm_A(t) + [pm_n(t)]^2 + \cdots]$

$= 1 - p\frac{1}{1-pm_A(t)} = \frac{1-p}{1-m_A(t)} \,; t < -\log(1-p)$

The characteristics function of X is

$\phi_x(t) = (1-p) + (1-p)_p\phi_A(t) + (1-p)p^2(\phi_A(t)^2) + \cdots$

$= (1-p)\frac{1}{1-p\,\phi_A(t)} \,; t \in \mathbb{R}$

$= \frac{1-p}{1-p\,\phi_n(t)}, t \in \mathbb{R}$

$E(X) \neq 0, X$ is not symmetric about 0

So, option (c) is correct

29. Explanation: (b)

$X \sim B(n, p)$ for some $n \geq 1$ and $0 < p < 1$

$Y \sim P(\lambda)$ for some $\lambda > 0$

$\therefore E(X) = E(Y)$

$np = \lambda$

$Var(X) = npq < np$ and $Var(Y) = \lambda$

$npq < \lambda$

$Var(X) < Var(Y)$

30. Explanation: (a)

Suppose $X_i | \theta_i \sim N(\theta_i, \sigma^2)$; $i = 1, 2$ are independently distributed

Under prior distribution θ_1 and θ_2 are iid $N(\mu, \tau^2)$

Where σ^2, μ *and* τ^2 are known

To find the marginal distribution of X_1

$f(x_1) = \int_{-\infty}^{\infty} f(x_1, \theta_1)\, d\theta_1$

$= \int_{-\infty}^{\infty} f(x_i|\theta_1) f(\theta_1) d\theta_1$

$= \int_{-\infty}^{\infty} \frac{1}{\sigma\sqrt{2\pi}} \exp\left\{\frac{-1}{2}\left(\frac{x_1-\theta_1}{\sigma}\right)^2\right\} \cdot \frac{1}{\tau\sqrt{2\pi}} \exp\left\{\frac{-1}{2}\left(\frac{\theta_1-\mu}{\tau}\right)^2\right\} d\theta_1$

$= \frac{1}{\sigma\tau\sqrt{2\pi}\sqrt{2\pi}} \int_{-\infty}^{\infty} \exp\left\{\frac{-1}{2}\left(\frac{x_1-\theta_1}{\sigma}\right)^2 + \left(\frac{\theta_1-\mu}{\tau}\right)^2\right\} d\theta_1$

On solving,

$f(x_1) = \frac{1}{2\pi(\sigma^2+\tau^2)} \exp\left\{-\frac{1}{2}\left(\frac{x_1-\mu}{\sigma^2+\tau^2}\right)^2\right\}$

Similarly, $f(x_2) = \frac{1}{2\pi(\sigma^2+\tau^2)} \cdot \exp\left\{-\frac{1}{2}\left(\frac{x_1-\mu}{\sigma^2+\tau^2}\right)^2\right\}$

$X_1|\theta_1$ and $X_2|\theta_2$ are independent

$\Rightarrow X_1$ and X_2 are also independent

The marginal distributions of X_1 and X_2 are independent and identically $N(\mu, \sigma^2 + \tau^2)$ distribute

So, option (a) is correct

31. Explanation: (b)

32. Explanation: (d)

Suppose X has density

$f(x|\theta) = \frac{1}{\theta} e^{-\frac{x}{\theta}} ; x > 0 \,\&\, \theta > 0$

$Y = K$ if $K \leq X < K + 1; K = 0, 1, 2, \ldots$

Therefore

$Y = 0 \,; 0 \leq X < 1$

$Y = 1 \,; 1 \leq X < 2$

$Y = 2 \,; 2 \leq X < 3$

Y is discrete random variate whose sample values are $y = 0, 1, 2, 3, \ldots$

$P(y = 0) = P(0 \leq X < 1)$

$P(y = 1) = P(1 \leq X < 2)$

$P[a \leq X < b] = \int_a^b f(x)\, dx = \int_a^b \frac{1}{\theta} e^{-x/\theta} dx$

$= e^{-\frac{a}{\theta}} - e^{-\frac{b}{\theta}}$

$P(Y = 0) = 1 - e^{-1/\theta}$

$P(Y = 1) = e^{-1/\theta} - e^{-2/\theta}$

$P(Y = 2) = e^{-2/\theta} - e^{-3/\theta}$

$P(Y = y) = e^{-y/\theta} - e^{-(y+1)/\theta}$

$= e^{-y/\theta}[1 - e^{-1/\theta}]$

Let $p = 1 - e^{-1/\theta}$ and $q = e^{-1/\theta}$

Which is pmf of geometric distribution

So, option (d) is correct

33. Explanation: (b), (c)

(X, Y) have joint discrete distribution

$X|Y = y \sim B(y, 0.5)$ and $Y \sim P(\lambda), \lambda > 0$

Let $T = T(X, Y)$ be any unbiased estimator of λ i.e., $E[T(X, Y)] = \lambda$

Now, $X|Y = y \sim B(y, 0.5)$ and $Y \sim P(\lambda)$

$E[X|Y = y] = 0.5\, y = \frac{Y}{2}$ *and* $E(Y) = \lambda$ .... (1)

Using Theorem of conditional expectation, we have

$E(X) = E[E(X|Y = y)] = E[Y/2] = \lambda/2$

$E(2X) = \lambda$ .... (2)

From equation (1) and (2)

$E(2X + Y) = 2\lambda$

$E\left[\frac{2X+Y}{2}\right] = \lambda$

$\therefore T(X,Y) = \frac{2X+Y}{2}$ is an unbiased estimator for λ

$Var(T) = Var\left(\frac{2X+Y}{2}\right)$

$Var(T) = \frac{1}{4}[4Var(X) + Var(Y) + 4\,Cov\,(X,Y)]$

$X|Y = y \sim B(y, 0.5)$

$E(X|Y = y) = Y/2$ and $Var(X|Y = y) = Y/4$

$Var(X) = Var[E(X|Y = y)] + E[Var(X|Y = y)] = Var(Y/2) + E[Y/4]$

$Var(X) = \frac{1}{4} \times \lambda + \frac{1}{4}\lambda = \lambda/2$

$Cov(X,Y) = E(X\,Y) - E(X).E(Y)$

$E(X\,Y) = E[E(XY|Y = y)] = E[Y\,E(X|Y = y)] = \frac{1}{2}E(Y^2) = \frac{1}{2}(\lambda^2 + \lambda)$

$Cov(X,Y) = \frac{1}{2}(\lambda^2 + \lambda) - \frac{\lambda}{2}\lambda = \frac{\lambda^2}{2} + \frac{\lambda}{2} - \frac{\lambda^2}{2} = \frac{\lambda}{2}$

$Var(T) = \frac{1}{4}\left[4 \times \frac{\lambda}{2} + \lambda + 4\frac{\lambda}{2}\right] = \frac{5\lambda}{4}$

$Var(T) = \frac{5\lambda}{4}$ and $Var(Y) = \lambda$

$\therefore Var(T) \geq Var(Y)$

$Var(T) \geq \lambda$

So, option (b) and (c) are correct

34. Explanation: (b), (d)

$X \sim N(0,1)$ and $Y \sim N(0,1)$

X and Y are independent random variable

$\phi(t)$ be the characteristic function of XY

$W = XY$

$\phi_W(t) = E[e^{itw}] = E[e^{itXY}]$

$= E\left[E\left[e^{itXY|Y}\right]\right]$

$= E\left[\exp\left(-\frac{t^2y^2}{2}\right)\right]$

$\phi_W(t) = E[e^{-t^2y^2/2}]$

$\phi(z) = E[e^{-2y^2}] = \int_{-\infty}^{\infty} e^{-2y^2}\frac{1}{\sqrt{2\pi}}e^{-y^2/2}dy$

$= \frac{1}{\sqrt{2\pi}}\int_{-\infty}^{\infty} e^{-5y^2/2}dy = \frac{1}{\sqrt{2\pi}} \times \frac{\sqrt{2\pi}}{\sqrt{5}} = \frac{1}{\sqrt{5}}$

$\phi(z) = \frac{1}{\sqrt{5}}$

The characteristic function is always even function because $\phi(t) = \phi(-t)$

$\phi(t) = E[e^{-t^2y^2/2}]$ and $\phi(1/t) = E[e^{-y^2/2t^2}]$

$\phi(t).\phi(1/t) = E\left[e^{-\frac{t^2y^2}{2} - \frac{y^2}{2t^2}}\right] \neq |t|$

So, option (b) and (d) are correct

35. Explanation: (a), (b), (d)

X_1 and X_2 are i.i.d. $N(0,1)$

U_1 and U_2 be i.i.d. $U(0,1)$

X_1, X_2 are independent of U_1, U_2

Define $Z = \frac{X_1U_1 + X_2U_2}{\sqrt{U_1^2 + U_2^2}}$

$E(Z) = E\left[\frac{X_1U_1 + X_2U_2}{\sqrt{U_1^2 + U_2^2}}\right]$

$= E[X_1] \cdot E\left[\frac{U_1}{U_1^2 + U_2^2}\right] + E[X_2] \cdot E\left[\frac{U_2}{U_1^2 + U_2^2}\right]$

$E(Z) = 0$

$E(Z^2) = E\left[\frac{(X_1U_1 + X_2U_2)^2}{\sqrt{U_1^2 + U_2^2}}\right] = E\left[\frac{X_1^2\,U_1^2 + X_2^2\,U_2^2 + 2X_1X_2U_1U_2}{U_1^2 + U_2^2}\right]$

$= E[X_1^2] \cdot E\left[\frac{U_1^2}{U_1^2 + U_2^2}\right] + E[X_2^2] \cdot E\left[\frac{U_2^2}{U_1^2 + U_2^2}\right] + 2E(X_1)E(X_2)\,E\left(\frac{U_1\,U_2}{U_1^2 + U_2^2}\right)$

$= E\left[\frac{U_1^2}{U_1^2 + U_2^2} + \frac{U_2^2}{U_1^2 + U_2^2}\right]$

$E(Z^2) = 1$

$Var(Z) = E(Z^2) - \left[(E(Z))\right]^2 = 1 - 0$

$Var(Z) = 1$

The mean of Z exists and equal to zero

So, Z cannot be standard Cauchy

Z has mean 0 and variance 1

So, approximate distribution of Z may be standard normal variate

So, option (a), (b) and (d) are correct

36. Explanation: (a)

$X_1, X_2, X_3, \ldots$ are independent random variables.

Assume that X_1, X_3 are identically with mean μ_1 and variance σ_1^2 i.e.,

$E(X_{2i-1}) = \mu_1$ and $Var(X_{2i-1}) = \sigma_1^2$ for $i = 1, 2, \ldots$

$X_2, X_4, \ldots$ are identically with mean μ_2 and variance σ_2^2

$E(X_{2i}) = \mu_2$ and $Var(X_{2i}) = \sigma_2^2; i = 1, 2, \ldots$

$S_n = X_1 + X_2 + \cdots + X_n$, by central limit theorem as n tends to infinity

$$\frac{S_n - a_n}{b_n} \xrightarrow{d} N(0,1)$$

$\therefore\Rightarrow a_n = E(S_n)$ and $b_n = \sqrt{Var(S_n)}$

$E(S_n) = E[X_1 + X_2 + \cdots + X_n]$

$= \mu_1 + \mu_2 + \mu_1 + \mu_2 + \cdots$

$E(S_n) = \frac{n}{2}(\mu_1 + \mu_2)$

$Var(S_n) = Var(X_1 + X_2 + \cdots + X_n)$

$= Var(X_1) + Var(X_2) + \cdots + Var(X_n)$

$= \frac{n}{2}(\sigma_1^2 + \sigma_2^2)$

$a_n = \frac{n}{2}(\mu_1 + \mu_2)$ and $b_n = \sqrt{\frac{n}{2}(\sigma_1^2 + \sigma_2^2)}$

37. Explanation: (d)

Let $X_i's$ be independent random variable such that $X_i's$ are symmetric about 0 and variance $(X_i) = 2i - 1$ for $i \geq 1$

$\therefore E(X_i) = 0$ and $Var(X_i) = 2i - 1$

$S = X_1 + X_2 + \cdots + X_n$

$E(S) = 0$ and $Var(S) = Var(\sum_{i=1}^{n} X_i) = \sum_{i=1}^{n} Var(X_i)$

[$X_i's$ are independent]

$= \sum_{i=1}^{n}(2i - 1) = 2\sum_{i=1}^{n} i - n$

$= \frac{2\,n(n+1)}{2} - n$

$Var(S) = n^2$

Using Central limit theorem,

$\lim_{n\to\infty} P[X_1 + X_2 + \cdots + X_n > n\log n]$

$\lim_{n\to\infty} P[S > n\log n] = \lim_{n\to\infty}\left[Z > \frac{n\log n}{\sqrt{n^2}}\right] = P[Z < \infty] = 0$

So, option (d) is correct

38. Explanation: (a), (d)

$X_i \sim U(0,1)\ i = 1, 2, \ldots$

X_i & are iid random variables and $S_n = \sum_{i=1}^{n} X_i\ for\ n \geq 1$

$E(S_n) = \sum_{i=2}^{n} E(X_i) = \frac{n}{2}$ and $Var(S_n) = \sum_{i=1}^{n} Var(X_i) = \frac{n}{12}$

If X_i & are iid then

$\frac{S_n}{n\log n} \to E\left[\frac{S_n}{n\log n}\right]$ with prob. 1 as $n \to \infty$

$E\left[\frac{S_n}{n\log n}\right] = \frac{1}{n\log n} E(S_n) = \frac{n}{2n\log n} = \frac{1}{2\log n}$

as $n \to \infty$ $E\left[\frac{S_n}{n\log n}\right] = 0$

$\Rightarrow as\ n \to \infty \frac{S_n}{n\log n} \to 0$ with prob. 1

$\frac{S_n}{\log n} \to E\left[\frac{S_n}{\log n}\right]$ with prob. 1

as $n \to \infty$ $\frac{S_n}{\log n} \to \infty$ with prob. 1

option (a) is correct but (c) is incorrect

$\lim_{n\to\infty} P\left[S_n \geq \frac{2n}{3}\right] = \lim_{n\to\infty} P\left[\frac{S_n - E(S_n)}{\sqrt{Var\ (S_n)}} > \frac{\frac{2n}{3} - \frac{n}{2}}{\sqrt{\frac{n}{12}}}\right] = P[Z > \infty] = 0$

$\lim_{n\to\infty} P\left[S_n > \frac{n}{3}\right] = \lim_{n\to\infty} P\left[\frac{S_n - E(S_n)}{\sqrt{Var\ (S_n)}} > \frac{\frac{n}{3} - \frac{n}{2}}{\sqrt{\frac{n}{12}}}\right]$

$= P[Z > -\infty] = 1$

So, option (b) is incorrect and (d) is correct

Finally, option (a) and (d) are correct

39. Explanation: (d)

40. Explanation: (a), (d)

If X and Y are iid random variable and $Z = X + Y$

Normal distribution follows additive property so if X and Y are independent Normal variate then

$X + Y$ is also normal variate

If X and Y are iid random variable

$X, Y \sim B(n, p)$

$X + Y \sim B(2n, p)$

Binomial distribution also follows additive property if probability of success in both random variable is same

Then option (a) & (d) are correct

41. Explanation: (d)

Given $f(x) = 3x^2$; $0 < x < 1$

The cdf of X is

$F(x) = P(X \leq x) = \int_0^x f(x)dx = \int_0^x 3x^2\ dx$

$F\ (x) = x^3$

Let min $(X_1 X_2 \ldots\ldots X_n) = Y$

The cdf is Y is

$G(y) = P(Y \leq y) = 1 - [1 - F_x(y)]^n$

$= 1 - [1 - y^3]^n$

The pdf of Y is

$g(y) = \frac{d}{dy} G(y)$

$= 3ny^2\ (1 - y^3)^{n-1}$; $0 < y < 1$

Option (d) is correct

42. Explanation: (a), (b), (c) & (d)

$X_i \sim N\ (2, 5)$

$E\ (X_i) = 2\ and\ Var\ (X_i) = 5$

$E(X_i^2) = Var\ (X_i) + [E(X_i)]^2$

$= 5 + 2^2$

$= 5 + 4$

$E(X_i^2) = 9$

$\therefore \overline{X} \sim N\left(2, \frac{5}{n}\right)$

$E(\overline{X}) = 2\ \&\ Var\ (\overline{X}) = \frac{5}{n}$

$E\left(\overline{X}^2\right) = Var(\overline{X}) + \left(E(\overline{X})\right)^2$

$= \frac{5}{n} + 4$

X_i `s are iid random variable

Then $\frac{X_1 + X_2 + X_3 + \cdots + X_n}{n} \xrightarrow{P} E(X_i)$

$\frac{1}{n} \sum_{i=1}^{n} X_i \xrightarrow{P} 2$

And $\frac{X_1^2 + X_2^2 + \cdots + X_n{}^2}{n} \xrightarrow{P} E(X_1^2)$

$\frac{1}{n} \sum_{i=1}^{n} X_1^2 \xrightarrow{p} 9$

And $\left(\frac{X_1 + X_2 + \cdots X_n}{n}\right)^2 \xrightarrow{b} E\left(\overline{X}^2\right)$ $as\ n \to \infty$

$\left(\frac{1}{n} \sum X_i\right)^2 \xrightarrow{P} 4 + \frac{5}{n} = 4$

$\sum_{i=1}^{n} \left(\frac{X_1{}^2}{n^2}\right) \xrightarrow{P}$ $\frac{1}{n} E(X_1^2) = \frac{1}{n}\ 9$

$as\ n \to \infty$

$\sum_{i=1}^{n} \frac{X_i{}^2}{n^2} \xrightarrow{p} 0$

Option (a), (b), (c) & (d) are correct.

43. Explanation: (a) & (c)

For option (a)

$X \sim Exponential\ (\lambda)$

$E(X) = \frac{1}{\lambda}$

$Median\ (X) = \frac{\log_e 2}{\lambda}$

$E(X) > Median\ (X)$

For option (b)

$X \sim U\ [a, b]$

$E(X) = \frac{a+b}{2}$

$Median\ (X) = \frac{a+b}{2}$

$Median\ (X) = E(X)$

For option ©

$X \sim B(n, p)$

$E(X) = np$

$Var\ (X) = npq$

$E(X) > Var\ (X)$

For option (d)

$X \sim N\ (\mu, \sigma^2)$

$E(X) = \mu$

$Var\ (X) = \sigma^2$

$E(X) \geq = \leq Var\ (X)$

So, option (a) & (c) are correct.

44. Explanation: (d)

$X_1, X_2, \ldots$ are independent identically distributed random variable having common density function f.

$f(x) = f(-x)$ [Given]

$\Rightarrow X$ and $-X$ have same distribution

So, $\sum_{i=1}^{n} X_i$ and $\sum_{i=1}^{n} (-1)^i X_i$ have same distribution

So, option (d) is correct

45. Explanation: (a)

X and Y are independent random variable each having density

$f(t) = \frac{1}{\pi} \frac{1}{1+t^2}$; $-\infty < t < \infty$

The characteristics function of X and Y is

$\phi_X(t) = e^{-|t|}$ & $\phi_Y(t) = e^{-|t|}$

The characteristics function of $\frac{X+Y}{3}$ is

$\phi_{\frac{X+Y}{3}}(t) = \phi_{X+Y}(t/3) = \phi_X(t/3) \cdot \phi_Y(t/3)$

$= e^{-|t/3|} \cdot e^{-|t/3|}$

$= e^{-\left|\frac{2t}{3}\right|}$

$= \phi_X\left(\frac{2t}{3}\right) = \phi_{\frac{2X}{3}}(t)$

$\phi_{\frac{X+Y}{3}}(t) = \phi_{\frac{2X}{3}}(t)$

Distribution of $\frac{X+Y}{3}$ is same to $\frac{2X}{3}$

$\therefore$ let $U = \frac{2X}{3}$

$X = \frac{3U}{2}$

$\frac{\partial x}{\partial u} = \frac{3}{2}$

The pdf of U is

$g(u) = f(x)\left|\frac{dx}{du}\right|$

$= \frac{1}{\pi}\frac{1}{1+x^2}\frac{3}{2}$

$= \frac{1}{\pi}\frac{1}{1+\left(\frac{3u}{2}\right)^2}\cdot\frac{3}{2}$

$= \frac{1}{\pi}\frac{4}{4+9u^2}\cdot\frac{3}{2}$

$= \frac{6}{\pi}\cdot\frac{1}{4+9u^2}$

Option (a) is correct

46. Explanation: (b), (c) & (d)

$\{X_n; n \geq 1\}$ be iid uniform $(-1, 2)$ random variable

Result: If X_i's are iid then

$\frac{X_1+X_2+\cdots+X_n}{n} \xrightarrow{a.s} E(X_i)$

$X_i \sim U(-1, 2)$

$E(X_i) = \frac{2-1}{2} = \frac{1}{2}$

$\frac{1}{n}\sum_{i=1}^{n} X_i \xrightarrow{a.s} \frac{1}{2}$

$\frac{1}{2n}\left[\sum_{i=1}^{n} X_{2i} - \sum_{i=1}^{n} X_{2i-1}\right] \xrightarrow{a.s} E(X_{2i}) - E(X_{2i-1}) \to \frac{1}{2} - \frac{1}{2}$

$\xrightarrow{a.s} 0$

$X_i \sim U(-1, 2)$; $-1 < X_i < 2$

$\sup\{X_1\, X_2 \ldots\} = 2$ with prob. 1

$\inf\{X_1, X_2 \ldots\} = -1$ with prob. 1

So, option (b), (c) & (d) are correct

47. Explanation: (a) & (c)

$f(x) = \lambda \cdot e^{-\lambda x}; x > 0$

$P(Y = k) = P[ka \leq X \leq (k+1)a]$

$= \int_{ka}^{(k+1)a} f(x)\, dx$

$= \int_{ka}^{(k+1)a} \lambda \cdot e^{-\lambda x}\, dx = \lambda\left[\frac{e^{-\lambda x}}{-\lambda}\right]_{ka}^{(k+1)a}$

$= \left(e^{-\lambda a}\right)^k\left(1 - e^{-\lambda a}\right)$

$= q^k . p\, ; k = 0, 1, 2, \ldots$

Where $q = e^{-\lambda a}$ & $p = 1 - e^{-\lambda a}$

$p + q = 1$

$Y \sim Geom\left(p = 1 - e^{-\lambda a}\right)$

$P[4 < Y < 5] = 0$ because Y is discrete random variable

Option (a) & (c) are correct

48. Explanation: (d)

X and Y are independent exponential random variable with mean 4 and 5 respectively.

Result: $X_1, X_2, X_3, \ldots, X_n$ are exponential random variate with parameter $\lambda_i (i = 1,2, \ldots, n)$

then $\min(X_1, X_2, X_3, \ldots, X_n)$ follows exponential with parameters $(\lambda_1 + \lambda_2 + \cdots \lambda_n) = \sum_{i=1}^{n} \lambda_i$

So, $X \sim$ Exp with mean 4 and $Y \sim$ Exp with mean 5

Then $\min(X, Y) \sim$ Exponential

Option (d) is correct.

49. Explanation: (d)

X and Y be independent exponential random sample

$E(X) = 1$ and $E(Y) = \frac{1}{2}$

$f(x) = e^{-x}; x > 0$

$g(y) = 2e^{-2y}\,; y > 0$

$P[X > 2Y | X > Y] = \frac{P[X>2Y]}{P(X>Y)}$

The joint pdf of X and Y is

$f(x, y) = f(x). g(y) [\because x \text{ and } y \text{ are independent}]$

$= e^{-x} 2. e^{-2y}$

$f(x, y) = 2. e^{-(x+2y)}; (x, y) > 0$

$\therefore P[X > Y] = \int_0^\infty \int_0^y f(x, y) dx\, dy$

$= \int_0^\infty 2. e^{-2y}\left(\int_0^y e^{-x}\, dx\right)dy$

$= \int_0^\infty 2. e^{-2y}(1 - e^{-y})dy$

$= 2\left[\int_0^\infty e^{-2y}\, dy - \int_0^\infty e^{-3y}\, dy\right]$

$= \int_0^\infty 2\, e^{-2y} dy - \int_0^\infty e^{-3y}\, dy$

$= 1 - \left(\frac{e^{-3y}}{-3}\right)_0^\infty = 1 - \frac{1}{3} = \frac{2}{3}$

$P(X > 2Y) = \int_0^\infty \int_0^{2y} f(x, y)\, dx\, dy$

$= \int_0^\infty \int_0^{2y} 2 . e^{-(x+2y)} dx\, dy$

$= \int_0^\infty 2\, e^{-2y}\left(\int_0^{2y} e^{-x} dx\right) dy$

$= \int_0^\infty e^{-2y}\,(1 - e^{-2y})dy$

$= 2\int_0^\infty e^{-2y}\, dy - 2\int_0^\infty e^{-2y}\, dy = 1 - 2\left[\frac{e^{-4y}}{-4}\right]_0^\infty$

$= 1 - 2 \times \frac{1}{4} = 1/2$

$P(X > 2Y) = \frac{1}{2}$

$$P[X > 2Y | X > Y] = \frac{P[X > 2Y]}{P[X > Y]} = \frac{1/2}{2/3} = \frac{3}{4}$$

50. Explanation: (b) and (d)

For option (a)

$X \sim N(0,1)$ and $Y \sim N(0,1)$

X and Y are not independent so we cannot say

$\frac{X+Y}{\sqrt{2}}$ follow $N(0,1)$

So, option (a) is incorrect.

For option (b)

X and Y independent $N(0\,,1)$

We know that ratio of two independent standard normal variate follows standard Cauchy variate

$\frac{X}{Y} \sim C(0,1)$

t- distribution with one degree freedom is similar to standard Cauchy variate

$\frac{X}{Y} \sim t_{1\, d.f}$

So, option (b) is correct.

For option (c)

Uniform distribution does not posses additive property so $\frac{X+Y}{2}$ does not follows $U(0,1)$

So, option (c) is incorrect

For option (d)

$X \sim B(n,p)$

$M_X(t) = (q + +pe^t)^n$

$M_{n-X}(t) = E[e^{t(n-X)}] = e^{nt}E[e^{-tX}]$

$= e^{nt}M_X(-t)$

$= e^{nt}(p + qe^t)^n$

$= (p + qe^t)^n$

which is moment generating function of binomial with parameter n & q

$n - X \sim B(n,q)$

$q = 1 - p$

So, option (d) is correct

Finally, option (b) and (d) are correct

51. Explanation: (a), (c)

$X_n \sim P(n^2)$

$E(X_n) = n^2$ & $Var(X_n) = n^2$

As $n \to \infty$ $\frac{X_n - E(X_n)}{\sqrt{Var(X_n)}} \to N(0,1)$

$\frac{X_n - n^2}{n} \to N(0,1)$

$\frac{1}{\sqrt{2\pi}}\int_2^\infty e^{-x^2/2}\,dx = \lim_{n\to\infty} P[Z_n > 2]$

$= \lim_{n\to\infty} P\left[\frac{X_n - n^2}{n} > 2\right] = \lim_{n\to\infty} P[X_n > n^2 + 2n]$

$= \lim_{n\to\infty} P[X_n > n^2 + 2n + 1 - 1]$

$= \lim_{n\to\infty} P[X_n > (n+1)^2]$

$= \lim_{n\to\infty} P[X_n < (n-1)^2]$

Option (a) and (c) are correct.

52. Explanation: (c)

$X, Y \sim U(0,1)$

$Z = \max(X,Y)$ and $W = \min(X,Y)$

If $X_1, X_2, \ldots. X_n$ are iid $U(0,1)$

Range $R = X_{(n)} - X_{(1)} \sim \beta_1(n-1, 2)$

$n = 2$

$R = \max(X,Y) - \min(X,Y) \sim \beta_1(1,2)$

The pdf of range R is

$f(r) = \frac{1}{\beta(1,2)} r^{1-1}.(1-r)^{2-1}$

$= \frac{1}{\frac{\Gamma 1 \Gamma 2}{\Gamma 3}}(1-r) \quad ; 0 < r < 1$

$f(r) = 2(1-r) \quad ; 0 < r < 1,$

$P[R > 1/2] = \int_{1/2}^1 f(r)dr = 2\int_{1/2}^1 (1-r)\,dr$

$= 2\left[r - \frac{r^2}{2}\right]_{1/2}^1$

$= 2\left[\left(1 - \frac{1}{2}\right) - \left(\frac{1}{2} - \frac{1}{8}\right)\right]$

$= 2\left[\frac{1}{2} - \frac{3}{8}\right]$

$= 2\left[\frac{4-3}{8}\right] = 2.\frac{1}{8}$

$= \frac{1}{4}$

Option (c) is correct

53. Explanation: (b)

X_1, X_2, X_3 are iid standard normal variate

We know that

$\frac{Z}{\sqrt{\chi^2/n}} \sim t_n$ & $\frac{\chi_1^2/n_1}{\chi_2^2/n_2} \sim F_{n_1,n_2}$

For option (a)

$\frac{\sqrt{2}|X_1|}{\sqrt{X_2^2 + X_3^2}} = \frac{\sqrt{X_1^2}}{\sqrt{\frac{X_2^2 + X_3^2}{2}}} \nsim t$

$X_1 \sim N(0,1)$

$X_2^2 \sim \chi^2_{1\,d.f}$

For option (b)

$X_1 - 2X_2 + X_3$

$E(X_1 - 2X_2 + X_3) = 0$

$Var(X_1 - 2X_2 + X_3) = Var(X_1) + 4Var(X_2) + Var(X_3)$

$= 6\,Var(X_1) = 6$

$X_1 - 2X_2 + X_3 \sim N(0,6)$

$\frac{X_1 - 2X_2 + X_3}{\sqrt{6}} \sim N(0,1)$

$X_1 + X_2 + X_3 \sim N(0,3)$

$\frac{X_1 + X_2 + X_3}{\sqrt{3}} \sim N(0,1)$

$\frac{\frac{X_1 - 2X_2 + X_3}{\sqrt{6}}}{\sqrt{\frac{(X_1 + X_2 + X_3)^2}{3}}} \sim t_{1\,d.f}$

$\Rightarrow \frac{X_1 - 2X_2 + X_3}{\sqrt{2}\sqrt{(X_1 + X_2 + X_3)^2}} \sim t_{1\,d.f}$

For option (c)

$X_1 - X_2 \sim N(0,2)$

$X_1 + X_2 \sim N(0,2)$

$\frac{\left(\frac{X_1 - X_2}{\sqrt{2}}\right)^2}{\left(\frac{X_1 + X_2}{\sqrt{2}}\right)^2} = \frac{(X_1 - X_2)^2}{(X_1 + X_2)^2} \sim F_{1,1}$

For option (d)

$X_1^2 \sim \chi^2_{1\,d.f}$

$X_1^2 + X_2^2 + X_3^2 \sim \chi^2_{3\,d.f}$

$\frac{X_1^2}{\frac{X_1^2 + X_2^2 + X_3^2}{3}} \sim F_{1,3}$

$\frac{3X_1^2}{X_1^2 + X_2^2 + X_3^2} \sim F_{1,3}$

So, option (b) is correct

54. Explanation: (a), (b), (c)

X and Y iid exponential random variable with parameter

$X \sim Exp\,(1)$

$Y \sim Exp\,(1)$

$W = X + Y$ & $U = \frac{X}{X+Y}$

X and Y are independent then

$f(x,y) = f(x) \cdot f(y)$

$= e^{-x} \cdot e^{-y}$; if $x, y \geq 0$

$f(x,y) = e^{-(x+y)}$

$W = X + Y$ & $U = \frac{X}{X+Y}$

$X = UW$

$Y = W - UW$

$y = \frac{\partial(x,y)}{\partial(u,w)} = \begin{vmatrix} \frac{\partial x}{\partial u} & \frac{\partial x}{\partial w} \\ \frac{\partial y}{\partial u} & \frac{\partial y}{\partial w} \end{vmatrix} = \begin{vmatrix} w & u \\ -w & 1-u \end{vmatrix}$

$= w(1-u) + uw$

$|J| = w$

The joint pdf of U & W is

$g(U,W) = f(x,y)|J|$

$= e^{-(x+y)}.w$

$g(u,w) = e^{-w}w$

$g(u,w) = w.e^{-u}; 0 < w < \infty$

$0 < u \le 1$

The marginal pdf of U is

$g(u) = \int_0^{\infty} f(u,w)dw$

$= \int_0^{\infty} w.e^{-w}dw$

$g(u) = 1$

$U = \frac{X}{X+Y} \sim U(0,1)$

$E(U) = \frac{0+1}{2} = \frac{1}{2}$

The marginal pdf of W

$g(w) = \int_0^1 w.e^{-w}du$

$g(w) = w.e^{-w}; w \ge 0$

$\therefore g(w).g(u) = g(w,u)$

$\therefore w$ & u are independent

Option (a), (b) & (c) are correct

55. Explanation: (a), (b), (c), (d)

We know that the sample correlation coefficient from an uncorrelated bivariate normal population has the following probability density function is

$$f(r) = \frac{1}{\beta\left(\frac{1}{2},\frac{n-2}{2}\right)}.(1-r^2)^{\frac{(n-4)}{2}}; -1 \le r \le 1$$

Using transformation

$r^2 \sim \beta_1\left(\frac{1}{2},\frac{n-2}{2}\right)$

r^2 has beta distribution of first kind ; $n \ge 3$

So, option (4) is correct

t-test statistic

$t = \frac{r}{\sqrt{1-r^2}}\sqrt{n-2} \sim t_{(n-2)}$ d.f for $\rho = 0$

Relation between t & f-distribution

$t^2 \sim F(1,n)$

$\left(\frac{r}{\sqrt{1-r^2}}\right)^2 (n-2) \sim F_{1,n-2}$

$\frac{r^2}{1-r^2}(n-2) \sim F_{1,n-2}$

So, option (a) & (b) are also correct for $n = 3$

$t = \frac{r}{\sqrt{1-r^2}} \sim t_{1\,d.f} \sim cauchy\ (0,1)$

So, option (a) (b), (c) (d) are correct

56. Explanation: (a)

X and Y are iid random variables uniformly distributed on (0, 4)

$X \sim U(0,4)$

$Y \sim U(0,4)$

$P(X > Y\,|\,X < 2Y) = \frac{P[X>Y \cap X<2Y]}{P[X<2Y]}$

$P[X > Y \cap X > 2Y] = \frac{\frac{1}{2}\times4\times4-\frac{1}{2}\times4\times2}{4\times4} = \frac{1}{4}$

$P[X < 2Y] = \frac{4\times4-\frac{1}{2}\times4\times2}{4\times4} = \frac{3}{4}$

$P(X > Y\,|\,X < 2Y) = \frac{1/4}{3/4} = \frac{1}{3}$

57. Explanation: (d)

$X \sim C(0,1)$

$f(x) = \frac{1}{\pi(1+x^2)}; -\infty < x < \infty$

$Y = \frac{1-X}{1+X} \Rightarrow x = \frac{1-y}{1+y} \Rightarrow \frac{dx}{dy} = \frac{-2}{(1+y)^2}$

The pdf of X is

$g(y) = f(x)\left|\frac{\partial x}{\partial y}\right|$

$= \frac{1}{\pi(1+x^2)}\left|\frac{-2}{(1+y)^2}\right|$

$= \frac{1}{\pi\left(1+\left(\frac{1-y}{1+y}\right)^2\right)}.\frac{2}{(1+y)^2}$

$= \frac{(1+y)^2}{\pi(1+y)^2+(1-y)^2}\frac{2}{(1+y)^2}$

$= \frac{2}{\pi[2(1+y^2)]}$

$= \frac{1}{\pi(1+y^2)}$

$Y \sim C(0,1)$

Option (d) is correct

58. Explanation: (a), (b), (c)

$X_i \sim U(0,2); i = 1,2,\dots n$ and $M_n = \max\{X_1, X_2 \dots X_n\}$

The pdf of X is $f(x_i) = \frac{1}{2}; 0 < x_i < 2$

The cdf $F(x) = \int_0^x f(x)\,dx = \int_0^x \frac{1}{2}dx = \frac{x}{2}$

Then pdf of $M_n = \max\{x_1, x_2 \dots x_n\}$

$g(M_n) = n[F(M_n)]^{n-1} f(M_n)$

$= n\left[\frac{M_n}{2}\right]^{n-1}\frac{1}{2}$

$g(M_n) = \frac{n}{2^n}(M_n)^{n-1}$

Result: X_i's are iid

By law of large number,

$X \xrightarrow{a.s} E(X)$

$\therefore M_n \xrightarrow{a.s} E[M_n]$

$E(M_n) = \int_0^2 M_n\, g(M_n)dM_n$

$= \frac{2n}{n+1}$

As $n \to \infty$ $E(M_n) \to 2$

$\Rightarrow M_n \xrightarrow{a.s} 2$

Result: $X_n \xrightarrow{a.s} X \Rightarrow X_n \xrightarrow{p} X$

$\therefore M_n \xrightarrow{a.s} 2 \Rightarrow M_n \xrightarrow{p} 2$

Result: $X_n \xrightarrow{p} X \Rightarrow X_n \xrightarrow{d} X$

$\therefore M_n \xrightarrow{p} 2 \Rightarrow M_n \xrightarrow{d} 2$

By, CLT, $\frac{M_n - E(M_n)}{\sqrt{Var(M_n)}} \xrightarrow{d} N(0,1)$

$\therefore Var(M_n) = E(M_n^2) - [E(M_n)]^2$

$E(M_n^2) = \frac{4n}{n+2}$

$Var(M_n) = \frac{4n}{n+2} - \left(\frac{2n}{n+1}\right)^2$

$= \frac{4n(n+1)^2 - 4n^2(n+2)}{(n+1)^2(n+2)} \neq n$

$\therefore \frac{M_n - 2}{\sqrt{n}} \xrightarrow{d} N(0,1)$

So, option (a), (b), (c) are correct

59. Explanation: (c), (d)

$X_1, X_2 \dots$ be iid $N(0,1)$

$S_n = X_1^2 + X_2^2 + \dots + X_n^2\ \forall\, n \ge 1$

$X_i \sim N(0,1)$

Let $U_i = X_i^2 \sim \chi_1^2\ d.f$

$S_n = U_1 + U_2 + \dots + U_n$

By additive property of chi-square

$S_n = U_1 + U_2 + \cdots + U_n \sim \chi_n^2\, d.f.$

$E(S_n) = n$

$Var(S_n) = 2n$

$\frac{S_n - E(S_n)}{\sqrt{Var(S_n)}} \sim N(0,1)$

$\frac{S_n - n}{\sqrt{2n}} \sim N(0,1)$

So, option (a) is incorrect

Result 1: $X_i's$ are iid with $E(X_i) < \infty$ then

$\frac{X_1 + X_2 + \cdots X_n}{n} \xrightarrow{a.s} E(X_i)$

Result 2: $\bar{X} \xrightarrow{a.s} E(X_i) \Rightarrow \bar{X} \xrightarrow{p} E(X_i)$

Now, $\frac{U_1 + U_2 + \cdots + U_n}{n} \xrightarrow{a.s} E(U_i)$

$\frac{S_n}{n} \xrightarrow{a.s} E(U_i)$

$\frac{S_n}{n} \xrightarrow{a.s} 1$

Option (c) is correct

$\frac{S_n}{n} \xrightarrow{a.s} 1 \Rightarrow \frac{S_n}{n} \xrightarrow{p} 1$

By Definition of convergence in probability,

$P\left[\left|\frac{S_n}{n} - 1\right| > \varepsilon\right] \to 0$ as $n \to \infty$

So, option (b) is incorrect

$P[S_n \le n + \sqrt{n}x] = P\left[\frac{S_n - n}{\sqrt{2n}} \le \frac{n + \sqrt{n}x - n}{\sqrt{2n}}\right]$

$= P\left[Z \le \frac{x}{\sqrt{2}}\right]$

$= P[\sqrt{2}\, Z \le x]$

$= P[Y \le x]$

$Y = \sqrt{2}\, Z$

$Z \sim N(0,1)$

$E(Y) = 0$

$Var(Y) = 2, Var(Z) = 2$

$Y \sim N(0,2)$

So, option (d) is correct

Finally, option (c) & (d) are correct

60. Explanation: (b), (d) J- shaped distribution are Exponential (1) and Geometric (1/2)

So, option b and d are correct

61. Explanation: (b), (c), (d)

Result: If $X_1, X_2 \ldots\ldots X_n$ having the Pdf $f(x,\theta)$

This pdf is symmetric about $X = \theta$ then

$f_r(x+\theta) = f_{n-r}(\theta - x)$

Acc. To question,

$f_r(\theta + x) = f_{2n-r}(\theta - x) \ldots\ldots\ldots\ldots (1)$

Where $f_k(.)$ represent the pdf of k -th Order statistic

For option (a)

In general, we cannot Say, $X_{(1)} - \theta$ and $\theta - X_{(1)}$ have same distribution

For Option (c)

We Know that

$f(.)$ Symmetric about $x = c$ then

$f(c+x) = f(c-x)$

In The equation (1), put $r = n$, *we get*

$f_n(x+\theta) = f_n(\theta - x)$

$\Rightarrow X_{(n)}$ is symmetric about θ.

For option (b) & (d)

Put $r = k$; $f_k(\theta + x) = f_{2n-k}(\theta - x)$

Case (i)

Let $w = X_{(k)} - \theta$

The pdf of W is

$g(w) = f_k(X_{(k)})\left|\frac{\partial X_{(k)}}{\partial w}\right|$

$= f_k(w+\theta) = f_{2n-k}(\theta - w)$

Case (ii) $u = \theta - X_{(2n-k)}$

$h(u) = f_{2n-k}(X_{(2n-k)})\left|\frac{\partial X_{(2n-k)}}{\partial u}\right|$

$= f_{2n-k}(\theta - u)$

$= f_k(u - \theta)$

$\therefore g(w) = f_{2n-k}(\theta - w)$ & $h(u) = f_{2n-k}(\theta - u)$

$g(x) = f_{2n-k}(\theta - x)$ & $h(x) = f_{2n-k}(\theta - x)$

$\Rightarrow g(x) = h(x)$

$\therefore$ Pdf of w & u are same so

$w = X_{(k)} - \theta$ & $u = \theta - X_{(2n-k)}$ have same disribution

$E[X_{(k)} - \theta] = E[\theta - X_{(2n-k)}] = a$

$E[X_{(k)}] = a + \theta$ are $E[X_{(2n-k)}] = \theta - a$

$E[X_{(k)} + X_{(2n-k)}] = \alpha + \theta + \theta - a = 2\theta \quad \forall k = 1, 2 \ldots n$

So, option (b) , (c) & (d) are correct.

62. Explanation: (c)

$X \sim Exp\ with\ mean \frac{1}{\lambda}$

i.e. $X \sim \exp(\lambda)$

$Y \sim \exp(\mu)$

$Z = X + Y$

The pdf of X is

$f(x) = \lambda e^{-\lambda x}; x > 0$

The pdf of Y is

$f(y) = \mu . e^{-\mu y}; y > 0$

X *and* Y are independent so

The joint pdf of and X and Y is

$f(x,y) = f(x), f(y)$

$= \lambda . e^{-\lambda x}\, \mu . e^{-\mu y}$

$= \lambda\mu\, e^{-\lambda x} . e^{-\mu y}$

Using the transformation to find the pdf of $Z = X + Y$

$Z = X + U$ and $U = Y$

$y = u$ *and* $x = z - u$

The Jacobian

$$J = \frac{\partial(x,y)}{\partial(z,u)} = \begin{vmatrix} \frac{\partial x}{\partial z} & \frac{\partial x}{\partial u} \\ \frac{\partial y}{\partial z} & \frac{\partial y}{\partial u} \end{vmatrix} = \begin{vmatrix} 1 & -1 \\ 0 & 1 \end{vmatrix} - 1$$

$|J| = 1$

The Joint of U and Z is

$g(u,z) = f(x,y)|J|$

$= \lambda\, \mu . e^{-\lambda x} . e^{-\mu y} . 1$

$g(u,z) = \lambda\, \mu . e^{-\lambda(z-u)}\, e^{-\mu u}$

$= \lambda\,\mu\, e^{-\lambda z} . e^{u(\lambda - \mu)}$

$= \lambda\,\mu . e^{-\lambda z} . e^{-u(\mu - \lambda)}$

The marginal pdf of Z is

$g(z) = \int_0^z g(u,z)\, du = \lambda\,\mu \int_0^z e^{-\lambda z} . e^{-u(\mu - \lambda)} . du$

$= \lambda\,\mu\, e^{-\lambda z}\left[\frac{e^{-u(\mu-\lambda)}}{-(\mu-\lambda)}\right]_0^z$

$= \frac{\lambda\,\mu}{\lambda - \mu}\, e^{-\lambda z}\left[e^{-z(\mu - \lambda)} - 1\right]$

$= \frac{\lambda\,\mu}{\lambda - \mu}\left[e^{\lambda z} . e^{-z(\mu . \lambda)} - e^{-\lambda z}\right]$

$g(z) = \frac{\lambda\,\mu}{\lambda - \mu}\left[e^{-\mu z} - e^{-\lambda z}\right]$

So, option (c) is correct

63. Explanation: (a), (b), (c), (d)

X and Y are independent random variable and both have same distribution

For option (a)

$\phi_{X-Y}(t) = E\left[e^{i(x-y)}\right] = E\left[e^{itx}.e^{-ity}\right]$

$= E[e^{itx}]E[e^{-ity}]$

$= \phi_x(t).\phi_{-y}(t)$

X and Y have same distribution

$\Rightarrow -X$ and $-Y$ also have same distribution

$\phi_{X-Y}(t) = \phi_X(t).\phi_{-y}(t)$

$= \phi_Y(t).\phi_{-X}(t)$

$= E[e^{ity}].E[e^{-itx}]$

$= E\left[e^{it(y-x)}\right]$

$= \phi_{Y-X}(t)$

By uniqueness theorem of Characteristic Function

$X - Y$ and $Y - X$ have same distribution

$\therefore X - Y$ has a symmetric distribution

For option (b)

$X \sim N(3,1)$ are $Y \sim N(2,2)$

Linear combination of X and Y i.e $2X - 3Y$ is also normal and normal distribution is symmetric So

$2X - 3Y$ has Symmetric distribution

For option (c)

X and Y have the same symmetric distribution

$\Rightarrow X$ and $-X$ has distribution i.e $\phi_X(t) = \phi_{-X}(t)$

$\Rightarrow Y$ and $-Y$ has same distribution i.e $\phi_Y(t) = \phi_{-Y}(t)$

$\phi_{X+Y}(t) = \phi_X(t).\phi_Y(t)$

$= \phi_{-X}(t).\phi_{-Y}(t)$

$= \phi_{-(X+Y)}(t)$

$(X + Y)$ and $-(X + Y)$ have same distribution

$\therefore X + Y$ has a symmetric distribution

For option (d)

X has symmetric distribution

$f(x) = f(-x)$

$\therefore f(xy) = f(x).f(y)$

$= f(-x).f(y)$

$= f(-xy)$

$\therefore XY$ has symmetric distribution

All option (a), (b), (c), (d) are correct

64. Explanation: (c)

Since $X_1, X_2, ...$ be iid random variable having a χ^2 distribution with 5 d.f. then

$E(X_1) = 5$ and $V(X_1) = 2 \times 5 = 10$

We know that the sum of independent of chi-square variable is also a chi-square variate with d.f. of their sum of degree of freedom.

$\therefore S_n = X_1 + X_2 + \cdots + X_n \sim \chi^2_{5n}$

$E(S_n) = 5n$ and $Var(S_n) = 10n$

Using CLT,

$\frac{S_n - E(S_n)}{\sqrt{Var(S_n)}} \xrightarrow{D} N(0,1)$

$\frac{X_1 + X_2 + \cdots X_n - 5n}{\sqrt{10n}} \xrightarrow{D} N(0,1)$

Thus a $\left(\frac{X_1 + \cdots X_n}{\sqrt{n}}\right) = \frac{X_1 + \cdots X_n - 5n}{\sqrt{10n}} \rightarrow N(0,1)$

If we take $a = \frac{1}{\sqrt{10}} \in R$

Option c is correct

65. Explanation: (b)

$X \sim U[0,100]$

$\Rightarrow f(x) = \frac{1}{100}; 0 \le X \le 100$

Y denote the greatest integer smaller than or equal to X

$\therefore Y = [X]$

$P[Y \le 25] = P\left[[X] \le 25\right] = P[X \in (0,26)]$

$= \int_0^{26} f(x)\,dx = \int_0^{26} \frac{1}{100} dx$

$P[Y \le 25] = \frac{26}{100}$

$E[Y] = E\left[[X]\right] = \int_0^{99} xf(x)\,dx = \int_0^{99} x \cdot \frac{1}{100} dx$

$= \frac{1}{100}\int_0^{99} x\,dx$

$= \frac{1}{100}\left[\frac{x^2}{2}\right]_0^{99}$

$E[Y] = \frac{(99)^2}{2 \times 100}$

Option b is correct

66. Explanation: (d)

Suppose $X_1, X_2, \ldots, X_n$ are i.i.d. random variables with characteristic function $\phi(t;\theta) = E[e^{itX_1}]$ where $\underline{\theta} \in \mathbb{R}^k$.

Let $Z = X_1 + X_2 + \cdots + X_n$

$E[e^{itZ}] = E\left[e^{it(X_1 + X_2 + \cdots + X_n)}\right] =$

$E[e^{itX_1}].E[e^{itX_1}] \ldots E[e^{itX_1}] = \phi(t;\underline{\alpha})$

$\{\because X_1, X_2, \ldots, X_n$ are i.i.d. random variables$\}$

This will be hold only for Negative Binomial distribution when it have i.i.d. random variable or corresponding probability will be same.

Option (d) is correct

67. Explanation: (c)

$Y \sim$ exp with mean θ

$\Rightarrow f(y) = \frac{1}{\theta}e^{-y/\theta}; y > 0$

$X|Y = y \sim N(0,y); y > 0$

The characteristic function of $X|Y = y$ is

$\phi_{X|Y=y} = E[e^{itx}|Y = y] = e^{\frac{-1}{2}yt^2}$

Using theorem of conditional expectation

$E[e^{itx}] = E\left[E(e^{itx}|Y = y)\right] = E\left[e^{\frac{-1}{\alpha}yt^2}\right]$

$= \int_0^{\infty} e^{\frac{-1}{2}yt^2} f(y)dy = \frac{1}{\theta}\int_0^{\infty} e^{-y\left(\theta + \frac{t^2}{2}\right)} dy = \frac{2}{2 + \theta t^2}$

$E[e^{itx}] = \frac{1}{1 + \frac{1}{2}\theta t^2}$ is the characteristic function of X

Option (c) is correct

68. Explanation: (d)

$X_1, X_2, \ldots\ldots, X_n$ be random variables whose marginal distribution are $N(0,1)$ and $E(X_i Y_i) = 0 \; \forall \, i \ne j$

$Y = X_1 + X_2 + \cdots + X_n$ and $V = X_1^2 + X_2^2 + \cdots + X_n^2$

If $X_i's$ are independent then

$\sum_{i=1}^n X_i \sim$ Normal (0, n)

But it is not given that $X_i's$ are independents

So, option (a) is incorrect

$X_i \sim N(0,1) \Rightarrow X_i^2 \sim \chi^2_{1d.f.}$

It is not given that $X_i's$ are independent

We cannot say that $V = \sum_{i=1}^n X_i^2$ follows chi-square

So, option (b) is incorrect

We have given that $E(X_i X_j) = 0 \; \forall \, i \ne j$

It not imply $E(X_i^3\, X_j^3) = 0$

So, option (c) is incorrect

Here, $Y = X_1 + X_2 + \cdots + X_n$

Using Chebyshev's inequality

$P[|Y - E(Y)| > t] \leq \frac{Var(Y)}{t^2}$

$E(Y) = E(X_1 + X_2 + \cdots + X_n) = 0$

$Var(Y) = Var(X_1) + Var(X_2) + \cdots + Var(X_n) + 2\sum_{i=j}^{n} Cov(X_i\, X_j)$

$Cov(X_i\, X_j) = E(X_i\, X_j) - E(X_i)\, E(X_j) = 0 - 0 = 0$

$Var(Y) = \sum_{i=1}^{n} Var(X_i) = n$

$\Rightarrow P[|y| > t] \leq \frac{n}{t^2}$

So, option (d) is correct

69. Explanation: (a), (b),(c), (d)

$X \sim Geom\,(1/2)\,;\, x = 1, 2, 3, \ldots$

$Y|X = x \sim P(X)$ and $U \sim P(1)$ and $V|U \sim Geam\left(\frac{1}{U+1}\right)$

$E(Y) = E[E(X|X)] = E[X] = \frac{1}{1/2} = 2$

$\Rightarrow E(Y) = 2$

$E(V) = E[E(V|V)] = E[U + 1] = E(U) + 1 = 1 + 1$

$E(V) = 2$

$Var(Y) = E[Var(Y|X = x)] + Var[E(Y|X = x)]$

$= E[X] + Var(X] = \frac{1}{1/2} + \frac{1/2}{(1/2)^2}$

$\Rightarrow Var(Y) = 4$

$Var(V) = Var(E[V|U]) + E[Var(V|U)] \quad = Var\,(U + 1) + E\left[\frac{1 - \frac{1}{U+1}}{\frac{1}{(U+1)^2}}\right]$

$= Var(U) + E[U(U + 1)]$

$= 1 + E[U^2] + E(U)$

$= 1 + 2 + 1 = 4$

$\therefore E(Y) = E[V]$ and $Var(Y) = Var(V)$

So, option (a), (b), (c) & (d) are correct

70. Explanation: (c)

Here $X_1, X_2, \ldots, X_n$ are random samples,

$P(X_1 = 1) = \frac{2(1-\theta)}{2-\theta}$

$P(X_1 = 2) = \frac{\theta}{2-\theta}$

Where $\theta \in (0,1)$

And $\overline{X} = \frac{\sum X_i}{n}$

$E(X_1) = \sum_x X \cdot P(X = x)$

$= 1 \cdot P(X_1 = 1) + 2 \cdot P(X_2 = 2)$

$= \frac{2(1-\theta)}{2-\theta} + \frac{2\theta}{2-\theta}$

$= \frac{2-2\theta+2\theta}{2-\theta}$

$E(X_1) = \frac{2}{2-\theta}$

$E(X_1) = \overline{X} = \frac{2}{2-\theta}$

$\overline{X} = \frac{2}{2-\theta}$

$2 - \hat{\theta} = 2(\overline{X})^{-1}$

$\hat{\theta} = 2 - \overline{X}^{-1}$

$\hat{\theta} = 2(1 - \overline{X}^{-1})$

Option (c) is correct

71. Explanation: (b)

X is random variable

$X \in \{0, 1, 2\}$

$P(X \in \{0, 1, 2\}) = 1$

$P(X = i) = cP(X = i - 1)\,;\, i = 1, 2$

Let $i = 1$,

$P(X = 1) = cP(X = 0)$ .... (1)

If $i = 2$,

$P(X = 2) = cP(X = 1)$

$P(X = 2) = c^2P(X = 0)$ ------from (1) ...(2)

But

$P(X \in \{0, 1, 2\}) = 1$

$i.e.\, P(X = 0) + P(X = 1) + P(X = 2) = 1$

$\Rightarrow P(X = 0) + cP(X = 0) + c^2P(X = 0) = 1$

$P(X = 0)(1 + c + c^2) = 1$

$P(X = 0) = \frac{1}{1+c+c^2}$ .... (3)

$\therefore\ eq^n\ (1) \Rightarrow$

$P(X = 1) = cP(X = 0) = \frac{c}{1+c+c^2}$

$P(X = 1) = \frac{c}{1+c+c^2}$

$\therefore eq^n(2) \Rightarrow$

$P(X = 2) = c^2P(X = 0) = \frac{c^2}{1+c+c^2}$

Now

$E(X) = \sum X\, P(X = i)$

$= 0 \cdot P(X = 0) + 1 \cdot P(X = 0) + 2 \cdot P(X = 2)$

$= 0 + \frac{c}{1+c+c^2} + 2 \cdot \frac{c^2}{1+c+c^2}$

$\cdot\, E(X) = \frac{c + 2c^2}{1 + c + c^2}$

Option (b) is correct

72. Explanation: (a), (b), (d)

$\{X_n; n \geq 1\}$ is a sequence of i.i.d. random variables.

The probability mass function of $X_1, P(X_1 = 1) = P(X_1 = 3) = 1/2$

If $A \xrightarrow{P} \vartheta$ iff

$E(A) = \vartheta$ as $n \to \infty$

$V(A) = 0$

i.e. A is coverages to ϑ in probability

X_i	1	3	Total
$P(X_i)$	½	½	1

$E(X_i) = \sum X_i\, P(X_i)$

$= 1P(X_i = 1) + 3P(X_i = 3)$

$= 1\left(\frac{1}{2}\right) + 3\left(\frac{1}{2}\right)$

$E(X_i) = 2$

$E(X_i^2) = \sum X_i^2\, P(X_i = x)$

$= (1)^2P(X_i = 1) + (3)^2P(X_i = 3)$

$= \frac{1}{2} + 9\left(\frac{1}{2}\right)$

$= \frac{10}{2}$

$E(X_1^2) = 5$

$var(X) = E(X_i^2) - [E(X)]^2$

$= 5 - (2)^2$

$var(X) = 1$

$\therefore y_n = X_1 + X_2 + X_3 + \cdots \ldots + X_n$

$E(y_n) = E(\sum X_i) = \sum E\,(X_i)$

$= \sum(2)$

$E(y_n) = 2n$

$var\,(y_n) = \sum var\,(X_i) = n$

Now,

(1) $E\left(\frac{y_n}{n}\right) = \frac{1}{n}.2n = 2$

$v\left(\frac{y_n}{n}\right) = \frac{1}{n^2}.n \to 0$

i.e. 1st correct

(2) $var\left(\frac{y_n}{n^{2/3}}\right)^2$

$= \frac{1}{(n^{2/3})^2} var(y_n)$

$= \frac{1}{n^{4/3}}(n)$

$= \frac{1}{n^{1/3}}$

$\to 0$

i.e. 2nd is also correct

(3) $E\left(\frac{y_n}{n^{2/3}}\right)$

$= \frac{1}{n^{2/3}} E(y_n)$

$= \frac{1}{n^{2/3}}(2n)$

$= 2n^{1/3} \to \infty$

i.e. 3rd is incorrect

(4) $E\left(\frac{y_n}{n^2}\right) = \frac{1}{n^2} E(y_n)$

$= 1/n^2(2n)$

$= \frac{2}{n} \to 0$

And $v\left(\frac{y_n}{n^2}\right) = \frac{1}{n^4} var(y_n)$

$= \frac{1}{n^4}(n)$

$= \frac{1}{n^3} \to 0$

∴ It's correct

The option (a), (b) & (d) are correct

73. Explanation: (a), (d)

X random variable

The distribution is symmetric around -2.

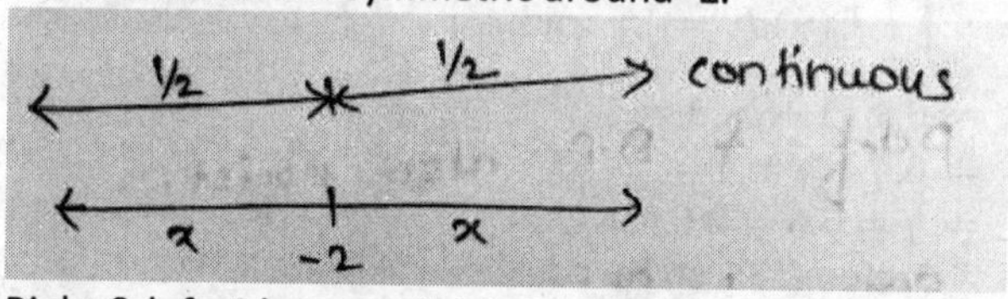

Right & left side area of -2 is same.

Now

$P(X = -2) = 2/3$

$x + 2/3 + x = 1$

$\Rightarrow 2x + 2/3 = 1$

$2x = 1/3$

$x = 1/6$

1st is correct.

Again

$p(X = -2) = 1/2$

$x + 1/2 + x = 1$

$2x = 1 - 1/2$

$2x = 1/2$

$x = 1/4$

$\because P(X = -2) = 1/2$

It's incorrect statement.

If X is continuous random variable then probability is ½ it's clear statement.

∴ 3rd id incorrect statement.

∴ option (a) & (d) are correct.

74. Explanation: (b), (c) & (d)

Given

$$f(x) = \begin{cases} e^{-x} & ; x > 0 \\ 0 & ; \text{otherwise} \end{cases}$$

$$Y = [X],\ y = 0,1,2,\ldots$$

Option (a):

$P[Y = 2] = P[2 \leqslant X < 3] = \int_2^3 e^{-x}\,dx = -e^{-x}|_2^3 =$
$-e^{-3} + e^{-2} \neq 0$ (Given)

∴ Option (a) is incorrect.

Option (b):

$P[Y < 1.2] = P[Y = 0] + P[Y = 1]$

$= P[0 < X < 1] + P[1 \leq X < 2]$

$= P[0 < X < 2]$

$= \int_0^2 e^{-x}dx = -e^{-x}|_0^2$

$= -e^{-2} + e^0 = 1 - e^{-2} = 1 - e^{-2}$ (Given)

∴ **Option (b)** is correct.

Option (d):

$$E(Y) = \sum_{i=0}^{\infty} y_i P[Y = y_i]$$

$= 0 \cdot P[Y = 0] + 1 \cdot P[Y = 1] + 2 \cdot P[Y = 2] + 3 \cdot P[Y = 3] + \cdots$

$= 0 + P[1 \leq X < 2] + 2P[2 \leq X < 3] + 3P[3 \leq X < 4] + \cdots$

$= \int_1^2 e^{-x}dx + 2\int_2^3 e^{-x}dx + 3\int_3^4 e^{-x}dx + \cdots$

$= -e^{-x}|_1^2 + 2(-e^{-x}|_2^3) + 3(-e^{-x}|_3^4) + \cdots$

$= -e^{-2} + e^{-1} + 2(-e^{-3} + e^{-2}) + 3(-e^{-4} + e^{-3}) + \cdots$

$= e^{-1} - e^{-2} + 2e^{-2} - 2e^{-3} + 3e^{-3} - 3e^{-4} + \cdots$

$= e^{-1} + e^{-2} + e^{-3} + e^{-4} + \cdots$

$= \frac{1}{e} + \frac{1}{e^2} + \frac{1}{e^3} + \frac{1}{e^4} + \cdots$

This is a geometric series with common multiplier $\frac{1}{e}$.

Thus it converges to

$$\frac{\frac{1}{e}}{1 - \frac{1}{e}} = \frac{\frac{1}{e}}{\frac{e-1}{e}} = \frac{1}{e-1} = \frac{1}{e-1} \text{ (Given)}$$

Thus, **option (d)** is correct.

Option (c):

$$E(Y^2) = \sum_{i=0}^{\infty} y_i^2 \cdot P[Y = y_i]$$

$= 0 \cdot P[Y = 0] + 1 \cdot P[Y = 1] + 4 \cdot P[Y = 2] + \cdots$

$= 0 + P[1 \leq X < 2] + 4 \cdot P[2 \leq X < 3] + 9 \cdot P[3 \leq X < 4] + \cdots$

$= \int_1^2 e^{-x}dx + 4\int_2^3 e^{-x}dx + 9\int_3^4 e^{-x}dx + \cdots$

$= [-e^{-x}]_1^2 + 4[-e^{-x}]_2^3 + 9 \cdot [-e^{-x}]_3^4 + \cdots$

$= -e^{-2} + e^{-1} + 4(-e^{-3} + e^{-2}) + 9(-e^{-4} + e^{-3}) + \cdots$

$= e^{-1} + 3e^{-2} + 5e^{-3} + 7e^{-4} + \cdots$

This series converges to

$$\frac{e+1}{(e-1)^2}$$

∴ **Option (c)** is correct.

75. Explanation: (a), (c) & (d)

Result - Distribution of rth order statistics.

Let $x_1, x_2, \ldots, x_n$ be random sample from a c.d.f. F(.) and p.d.f. f(.)

Let $X_{(1)}, X_{(2)}, \dots, X_{(n-1)}, X_{(n)}$ be the corresponding order statistics.

Then the p.d.f. of $X_{(r)}$ is given by

$$f_{X_{(r)}}(x) = \frac{n!}{(r-1)!\,(n-r)!} f_X(x)[F_X(x)]^{r-1}[1 - F_X(x)]^{n-r}$$

For option (a):

Here, $n = 10, r = 2$

As $X \sim U(0,1)$

$$f_X(x) = \begin{cases} 1 & ; \quad 0 \le x \le 1 \\ 0 & ; \quad \text{otherwise} \end{cases}$$

$$F_X(x) = \begin{cases} 0; & x < 0 \\ x; & 0 \le x \le 1 \\ 1; & 1 \end{cases}$$

Now p.d.f. of 2nd order statistics $X_{(2)}$ is given by

$$f_{X_{(2)}(x)} = \frac{10!}{(2-1)!\,(10-2)!} \cdot 1 \cdot x^{2-1}(1-x)^{10-2}$$

$$= \frac{1}{\left(\frac{8!}{10!}\right)} x(1-x)^8, 0 < x < 1$$

$$= \frac{1}{B(2,9)} x^{2-1}(1-x)^{9-1}; 0 < x < 1$$

This is the p.d.f. of $B(2,9)$.

Thus, $X_{(2)} \sim B(2,9)$.

Mean of $B(a,b)$ is $\frac{a}{a+b}$ *and* Variance of $B(a,b)$ is $\frac{ab}{(a+b)^2(a+b+1)}$

Here $a = 2, b = 9$

$$E[X_{(2)}] = \frac{2}{11}$$

and

$$\text{Var}[X_{(2)}] = \frac{2 \times 9}{(2+9)^2(2+9+1)} = \frac{18}{1452} = \frac{3}{242}$$

Therefore, **options (a), (c) & (d)** are correct.

In order statistics the distribution of the range $W = X_{(n)} - X_{(1)}$ is given by

$$g_W(w) = n(n-1) \cdot \int_{-\infty}^{\infty} f(u)f(u+w)[F(u+w) - F(u)]^{n-2} du$$

Here $n = 10$.

$\because X \sim U(0,1), \quad X_{(1)}, X_{(n)} \in [0,1]$

$\Rightarrow X_{(n)} - X_{(1)} \in [0,1]$

$\therefore g_W(w) = 10(10-1)\int_0^1 1 \cdot 1 \cdot [u + w - u]^{10-2} du$

$= 10 \times 9 \int_0^1 w^8\, du$

$= 90w^8 \cdot [u]_0^1$

$= 90w^8 \quad ; 0 \le w \le 1$

While the p.d.f of Beta(11,2) is given by

$$f_X(x) = \frac{1}{B(11,2)} x^{11-1}(1-x)^{2-1}, 0 < x < 1$$

$$= 132x^{10}(1-x); 0 < x < 1$$

Thus $W = X_{(n)} - X_{(1)}$ does not follow $B(11,2)$.

So, option (b) is incorrect.

76. Explanation: (a) & (b)

Given $X_1 \rightarrow$ Gamma with mean 10 and Variance 10. $X_2 \rightarrow N(3,4)$. X_1 and X_2 are independent.

$\because$ Mean(Gamma) $= \frac{\lambda}{\alpha}$ and Var(Gamma) $= \frac{\lambda}{\alpha^2}$

If they are equal

$$\frac{\lambda}{\alpha} = \frac{\lambda}{\alpha^2} \Rightarrow \alpha = 1 \Rightarrow \lambda = 10$$

$$\therefore f_1(x_1) = \begin{cases} \frac{1}{\Gamma 10} e^{-x_1} {x_1}^9 \ ; & x_1 \ge 0 \\ 0 & ; \text{otherwise} \end{cases}$$

and

$$f_2(x_2) = \begin{cases} \frac{1}{2\sqrt{2\pi}} e^{-\frac{1}{2}\left(\frac{x_2-3}{2}\right)^2} & ; -\infty < x_2 < \infty \\ 0 & ; \text{otherwise} \end{cases}$$

Define a new random variable Y so that $y \in \mathbb{R}$ with p.d.f. $f(y) = 0.4 f_1(y) + q\, f_2(y), \ -\infty < y < \infty$

Option (a):

Now to find value of q, we use property of p.d.f.

For any p.d.f. $f(y), \quad -\infty < y < \infty$

$$\int_{-\infty}^{\infty} f(y)dy = 1$$

$$\Rightarrow \int_{-\infty}^{\infty} [0.4 f_1(y) + q f_2(y)]dy = 1$$

$$\Rightarrow 0.4 \int_{-\infty}^{\infty} f_1(y)dy + q \int_{-\infty}^{\infty} f_2(y)dy = 1$$

$$\Rightarrow 0.4 \int_{-\infty}^{0} f_1(y)dy + 0.4 \int_0^{\infty} f_1(y)dy + q \int_{-\infty}^{\infty} f_2(y)dy = 1$$

Since in the range $(-\infty, 0)$, $f_1(y) = 0$.

$$\Rightarrow 0 + 0.4 \int_0^{\infty} f_1(y)dy + q \int_{-\infty}^{\infty} f_2(y)dy = 1$$

Note that it is already given that $f_1(y)$ and $f_2(y)$ are p.d.f.'s over their respective ranges.

$$\therefore \int_0^{\infty} f_1(y)dy = 1 \quad \text{and} \quad \int_{-\infty}^{\infty} f_2(y)dy = 1$$

$\Rightarrow 0.4 \cdot 1 + q \cdot 1 = 1$

$\Rightarrow 0.4 + q = 1$

$\Rightarrow q = 0.6 = 0.6$ (Given)

$\therefore$ **Option (a)** is correct.

Option (b):

Now we will use $q = 0.6$ for other options.

$$E(Y) = \int_{-\infty}^{\infty} y\, f(y)dy$$

$$= \int_{-\infty}^{\infty} y\,[0.4\, f_1(y) + 0.6\, f_2(y)]dy$$

$$= 0.4 \int_0^{\infty} y\, f_1(y)dy + 0.6 \int_{-\infty}^{\infty} y f_2(y)dy$$

$= 0.4E_1(Y) + 0.6E_2(Y)$

$= 0.4 \times 10 + 0.6 \times 3$

$= 4 + 1.8 = 5.8 = 5.8$ (Given)

$\therefore$ **Option (b)** is correct.

Option (c):

$$\text{Var (Y)} = E[(Y - E(Y))^2]$$

$= E(Y^2) - [E(Y)]^2$

$= E(Y^2) - (5.8)^2$

$= E(Y^2) - 33.64$

Now,

$$E(Y^2) = \int_{-\infty}^{\infty} y^2 f(y)dy$$

$= \int_{-\infty}^{\infty} y^2[0.4 f_1(y) + 0.6 f_2(y)]dy$

$= 0.4\int_0^{\infty} y^2 f_1(y)dy + 0.6\int_{-\infty}^{\infty} y^2 f_2(y)dy$

By directly using formulae of 2nd order raw moments for Gamma and Normal distributions we get,

$$E(Y^2) = 0.4\left[\frac{\lambda(\lambda+1)}{\alpha^2}\right] + 0.6[\mu^2 + \sigma^2]$$

Here, $\lambda = 10, \alpha = 1, \mu = 3, \sigma^2 = 4$

$= 0.4\left[\frac{10 \times 11}{1}\right] + 0.6[9+4]$

$= 44 + 5.4 + 2.4$

$= 44 + 7.8 = 51.8$

$\therefore$ Var(Y) $= 51.8 - 33.64 = 18.16 \neq 3.04$ (Given)

$\therefore$ Option (c) is incorrect.

77. Explanation: (a)

Here in each case

$f(x) \frac{1}{2+x^2} \quad x \le 0$

So we check

$F(-\infty) = 0$

i.e. Left continuous holds

Now we check eight continuous for each case

i.e $F(\infty) = 1$

Now

$F(x) = \frac{2+x^2}{3+x^2}$

$\lim_{x\to\infty} F(x) \lim_{x\to\infty} \frac{2+x^2}{3+x^2}$

$= \frac{\infty}{\infty}$; here we use L- hospital rule

i.e. $\lim_{x\to\infty} F(x) = \frac{2x}{2x} = 1$

may or may not we satisfied for next

$F(x) \frac{2+x^2}{3+2x^2}$

Using L- hospital again

$= \lim_{x\to\infty} \frac{2x}{4x} = \frac{1}{2} \neq 1$

Now 3rd

$F(x) = \frac{2\cos(x)+x^2}{4+x^2}$

Using L- hospital rule

$\lim_{x\to\infty} F(x) = \lim_{x\to\infty} \frac{-2\sin(x)+2x}{2x} = \lim_{x\to\infty}\left(\frac{-2\sin(x)}{2x} + \frac{2x}{2x}\right) = \lim_{x\to 0}(\frac{-2\sin}{2x}) + 1$

$= -1 + 1 = 0 \neq 1$

For 4th

$F(x) = \frac{1+x^2}{4+x^2}$

$\lim_{x\to\infty} F(x) = \lim_{x\to\infty} \frac{2x}{2x} = 1$

May or may not be.

$\therefore$ We can discover the option (3) & (4)

Now, we check for option (1) & (2) which one the increasing function

i.e. $x < y$

$F(x) < F(y)$

For (4)

$x < 0$

Consider $x = \frac{-1}{2}$ & $y = 1 ; -\frac{1}{2} < 1$

$$F(x)\begin{cases} \frac{1}{2+x^2} = \frac{1}{2+\frac{1}{4}} = \frac{4}{9} = 0.44 \\ \frac{1+x^2}{4+x^2} = \frac{1+1}{4+1} = \frac{2}{5} = 0.4 \end{cases}$$

$\frac{4}{9} \not< \frac{2}{5}$

So 4th also incorrect

Now 1st

$x = -\frac{1}{2}$ & $y = 1$ $\left(i.e. -\frac{1}{2} < 1\right)$

$$F(x) = \begin{cases} \frac{1}{2+x^2} = \frac{1}{2+\left(\frac{1}{2}\right)^2} = \frac{4}{9} \\ \frac{2+X^2}{3+x^2} = \frac{2+1}{3+1} = \frac{3}{4} \end{cases}$$

$\frac{4}{9} < \frac{3}{4}$

$\therefore$ Only 1st is correct

78. Explanation: (b)

The random sample {3, 6, 9} of size 3 from normal distribution with mean $\mu \in (-\infty, 5)$ & variance 1.

i.e. $x \sim N(\mu, 1)$

The M.L.E for mean is,

Mean $= \sum \frac{xi}{n}$

$= \frac{3+6+9}{3}$

$\mu = 6$

But $\mu \in (-\infty, 5)$

$\therefore$ Option (1) & (4) are incorrect

Now option (2) & (3) value are 5 is 3

But maximum value is 5

$\therefore$ Option (b) is correct

79. Explanation: (a), (c), (d)

Here $X_i \sim N(\mu, 1)$ & $W_i \sim Cauchy(\mu, 1)$

Let A is said to be consistent of μ

To check,

$\Rightarrow E(A) = \mu$ as $n \to \infty$ & $v(A) = 0$ as $n \to \infty$

$E(x_i) = \mu$

$E(w_i) = 0$

Let $n = 1$

$n^{-1}\sum^n x_i = x_1 \Rightarrow E(x_i) = (\mu)$

$n^{-1}\sum_{i=1}^{2n} x_i = x_1 + x_2 \Rightarrow E(x_1 + x_2) = 2\mu \neq \mu$

$n^{-1}\sum_{i=1}^{n} x_{2i-1} = x_1 \Rightarrow E(x_1) = \mu$

$n^{-1}(\sum_{i=1}^{n} x_i + w) = x_1 + w \Rightarrow E(x_1 + w) = \mu + 0 = \mu$

Now we check the variance

For (1) $v(n^{-1}\sum x_i) = \frac{1}{n^2}\sum V(x_i) = \frac{1}{n^2}n = \frac{1}{n} \to 0$

For (2) $v(n^{-1}\sum_{i=1}^{2n} x_i) = \frac{1}{n^2} v(x_1 + x_2) = \frac{1}{n^2}[1 + 1 + 2\cos(x_1, x_2)]$

$v(n^{-1}\sum_{i=1}^{2n} x_i) = \sum_{i=1}^{2n}[2 + 0]$ .... independent

$\therefore var(n^{-1}\sum_{i=1}^{2n} x_i) \nrightarrow 0$

For (3)

$var(n^{-1}\sum_{i=1}^{n} x_{2i-1})$

$= \frac{1}{n^2}\sum var(x_i)$

$= \frac{1}{n^2}$

$= \frac{1}{n} \to 0$

For (4)

$var\,[n^{-1}(\sum x_i + w)] = \frac{1}{n^2}var(x_i + w) = \frac{1}{n^2}(n + 0) = \frac{1}{n} \to 0$

80. Explanation: (c)

A point P be chosen at random on the line segment AB of length α.

Let Z_1 and Z_2 denote the lengths of line segments AP and BP respectively.

If $Z_1 = x \Rightarrow Z_2 = \alpha - x \Rightarrow H = |Z_1 - Z_2| = |2x - \alpha| = \begin{cases} 2x-\alpha, & x > \alpha/2 \\ -2x+\alpha, & x \le \alpha/2 \end{cases}$

Note that here

$Z_1 \sim U(0,\alpha)$ & $Z_2 \sim U(0,\alpha)$

$E(H) = E(|Z_1 - Z_2|) = E(|2x-\alpha|)$

$$= \frac{1}{\alpha}\left[\int_{\alpha/2}^{\alpha}(2x-\alpha)\,dx + \int_0^{\alpha/2}(\alpha - 2x)\,dx\right]$$

$$= \frac{1}{\alpha}\left[[x^2 - \alpha x]_{\alpha/2}^{\alpha} + [\alpha x - x^2]_0^{\alpha/2}\right]$$

$$= \frac{1}{\alpha}\left(-\frac{\alpha^2}{4} + \frac{\alpha^2}{2} + \frac{\alpha^2}{2} - \frac{\alpha^2}{4}\right) = \frac{1}{\alpha}\left(\alpha^2 - \frac{\alpha^2}{2}\right) = \frac{1}{\alpha}\times\frac{\alpha^2}{2}$$

$$= \frac{\alpha}{2}$$

81. Explanation: (a),(c)

(a) $\because X_i \sim N(2,4) \Rightarrow \overline{X} \sim N\left(2,\frac{1}{3}\right)$ & $\because$

$Y_j \sim N(-2,5) \Rightarrow \overline{Y} \sim N\left(-2,\frac{1}{3}\right)$

Further the above two samples are independent and so their sample means are also independent.

$$\therefore \overline{X} + \overline{Y} \sim N\left(0,\frac{2}{3}\right)$$

(c) $\frac{11S_1^2}{\sigma_X^2} = \frac{11S_1^2}{4} \sim \chi_{11}^2$ & $\frac{11S_2^2}{\sigma_Y^2} = \frac{14S_2^2}{5} \sim \chi_{14}^2$

Further these two quantities are independent.

Therefore using the definition of F distribution.

$$\frac{\left(\frac{11S_1^2}{4}\right)/11}{\left(\frac{14S_2^2}{5}\right)/14} = \frac{5}{4}\cdot\frac{S_1^2}{S_2^2} \sim F_{11,14}$$

(d) $\overline{Y} \sim N\left(-2,\frac{1}{3}\right) \Rightarrow Z = \sqrt{3}(\overline{Y}+2) \sim N(0,1)$

$\frac{11}{4}S_1^2 \sim \chi_{11}^2$

Thus using the definition of the t distribution

$$\frac{\sqrt{3}(\overline{Y}+2)}{\sqrt{\left(\frac{11}{4}S_1^2/11\right)}} = \frac{2\sqrt{3}(\overline{Y}+2)}{S_1} \sim t_{11}$$

(b) $\frac{1}{20}(55S_1^2 + 56S_2^2) = \left(\frac{55}{20}S_1^2 + \frac{56}{20}S_2^2\right) = \left(\frac{11}{4}S_1^2 + \frac{14}{5}S_2^2\right) \sim \chi_{25}^2$

82. Explanation: (b), (c)

X and Y be independent random variables with $X \sim N(2,4)$ and $Y \sim N(-4,9)$.

(1) $Var(2X+Y) = 4\times Var(X) + Var(Y) = 4\times 4 + 9 = 25 \ne 17$

(4) $2X - Y \sim N(8,25) \not\equiv N(0,25)$

(3) $Cov(3X+2Y, 3X-2Y) = 9\times Cov(X,X) - 6\times Cov(X,Y) + 6\times Cov(X,Y) - 4\times Cov(Y,Y)$

$= 9\times 4 - 4\times 9 = 0$

(4) $2X + Y \sim N(0,25) \Rightarrow Z = \frac{2X+Y}{5} \sim N(0,1)$

$P(|2X+Y| \le 15)) = P(-15 < 2X + Y < 15) = P(-3 < Z < 3) = \Phi(3) - \Phi(-3)$

$= \Phi(3) - 1 + \Phi(3) = 2\Phi(3) - 1 = 2\times 0.9987 - 1 = 0.9974.$

83. Explanation: (a), (b)

We analyze the limiting distribution of the transformed order statistics:

$$Y_{(r,n)} = nF(X_{(r:n)})$$

as $n \to \infty$, for $r = 2,3$.

For a random sample $X_1, X_2, \ldots, X_n$ from a continuous cumulative distribution function (CDF) $F(\cdot)$, the CDF of the r-th order statistic $X_{(r:n)}$ is given by:

$$P(X_{(r:n)} \le x) = \sum_{j=r}^{n}\binom{n}{j}(F(x))^j(1-F(x))^{n-j}.$$

For large n, we consider the transformation:

$$Y_{(r,n)} = nF(X_{(r:n)}).$$

It is known that for large n:

- $Y_{(r,n)}$ converges in distribution to a Gamma(r,1) distribution.
- That is, $Y_r \sim$ Gamma$(r,1)$, which has expectation:

$$E(Y_r) = r.$$

From this:

1. Since $Y_2 \sim$ Gamma(2,1), its expectation is:

$$E(Y_2) = 2.$$

Thus, Statement (a) is true.

2. Since $Y_{(3,n)}$ converges in expectation to $E(Y_3) = 3$,

$$E(Y_{(3,n)}) \to 3 \text{ as } n \to \infty.$$

Thus, Statement (b)) is true.

3. The statement that Y_3 follows a Beta distribution is incorrect because we already established that $Y_r \sim$ Gamma$(r,1)$. Also, its expectation is not 1/3, so Statement (c) is false.
4. The variable $Y_{(2,n)}$ does not follow a Beta distribution; rather, it follows a Gamma (2,1) asymptotically. Hence, Statement (d) is false.

Thus, the correct options are (a) and (b).

84. Explanation: (a), (b)

We have a random variable X with the probability density function (PDF):

$$f(x) = \frac{1}{\pi(1+x^2)}, x \in \mathbb{R}.$$

This is the standard Cauchy distribution with median 0 and mean undefined because the integral $\int xf(x)dx$ does not converge.

We define $Z = \frac{1}{2} + \frac{1}{\pi}\tan^{-1}(X)$.

From probability theory, if $X \sim$ Cauchy(0,1), then:

$$U = \frac{1}{\pi}\tan^{-1}(X) \sim U(0,1).$$

Thus, $Z = \frac{1}{2} + U$.

So, $Z \sim U(0,1)$ (Uniform distribution over [0,1]).

Statement (a):

Since $Z \sim U(0,1)$, we calculate:

$$E[Z^m] = \int_0^1 z^m dz = \frac{1}{m+1}, \text{ for } m > -1.$$

Statement (a) is true.

Statement (b)):

Since $Z \sim U(0,1)$, applying Φ^{-1} (the inverse normal CDF), we get a standard normal distribution:

$$Y = \Phi^{-1}(Z) \sim N(0,1).$$

Since the expectation of a standard normal random variable is 0, we have:

$$E[\Phi^{-1}(Z)] = 0.$$

Statement (b)) is true.

Statement (c):

A degenerate random variable takes only one value with probability 1 (i.e., it's a constant).

Since $Z \sim U(0,1)$, it clearly takes values in the range [0,1] rather than being a single value.

Statement (c) is false.

Statement (d):

If $Z_1, Z_2 \sim U(0,1)$, then their mean $\frac{Z_1+Z_2}{2}$ follows a different distribution (a Beta(2,2) distribution, which is not uniform).

Thus, Z is not equal in distribution to $\frac{Z_1+Z_2}{2}$.

Statement (d) is false.

85. Explanation: (a), (c)

a. **True.** By the classical CLT, $S_n/\sqrt{n} \xrightarrow{d} N(0,1)$ because $[X_i] = 0$, $\text{Var}(X_i) = 1$.

b. **False.** Put $Y_i = X_i^2$. Then $E[Y_i] = 1$ and $\text{Var}(Y_i) = E[X_i^4] - E[X_i^2]^2 = 3 - 1 = 2$. The CLT gives

$$\frac{T_n - n}{\sqrt{2n}} \xrightarrow{d} N(0,1)$$

The given normalization $\sqrt{3n}$ is incorrect, so statement (b) fails.

c. **True.** By LLN, $T_n/n \xrightarrow{P} 1$. Hence

$$\frac{\sqrt{n}S_n}{T_n} = \frac{S_n/\sqrt{n}}{T_n/n} \xrightarrow{d} \frac{N(0,1)}{1} = N(0,1)$$

by Slutsky's theoremsince$(S_n/\sqrt{n} \xrightarrow{d} N(0,1)$ and $T_n/n \xrightarrow{P} 1)$.

d. **False.** Finally, $V_n/n \xrightarrow{p} E[X^4] = 3$, so

$$\frac{T_n - n}{\sqrt{V_n}} \overset{d}{\approx} \frac{T_n - n}{\sqrt{3n}} \xrightarrow{d} N(0, \frac{2}{3}),$$

not $N(0,1)$; hence (4) is false.

86. Explanation: (a), (b), (d)

(a) For each i, $E[X_i - Y_i + 1] = 5 - 6 + 1 = 0$ and $\text{Var}(X_i - Y_i) = 4 + 9 - 2 \cdot (0.5 \cdot 2 \cdot 3) = 7$. So $\sum_{i=1}^{10} (X_i - Y_i + 1) \sim N(0,70)$. Multiplying by $1/\sqrt{7}$ yields $N(0,10)$. True.

(b) For each i, $X_i + Y_i - 11 \sim N(0,19)$ (since $\text{Var}(X_i + Y_i) = 4 + 9 + 2 \cdot 3 = 19$). Hence $\sum_{i=1}^{10} ((X_i + Y_i - 11)^2/19) \sim \chi^2_{10}$. True.

(c) Let $Z_i = (X_i - 5)/2 \sim N(0,1)$. Then $\sum_{i=3}^{10} (X_i - 5)^2 = 4\sum_{i=3}^{10} Z_i^2$ (8 terms). The given statistic equals

$$\frac{2\sqrt{2}, (X_1 - 5)}{\sqrt{\sum_{i=3}^{10} (X_i - 5)^2}} = \frac{2\sqrt{2} \cdot 2Z_1}{2\sqrt{\sum_{i=3}^{10} Z_i^2}} = \frac{\sqrt{8}, Z_1}{\sqrt{\sum_{i=3}^{10} Z_i^2}},$$

which is t-distributed with 8 degrees of freedom, not 9. So (3) is false.

(d) With $W_i = (Y_i - 6)/3 \sim N(0,1)$,

$$\frac{2\sum_{i=1}^{3} (Y_i - 6)^2}{\sum_{i=4}^{9} (Y_i - 6)^2} = \frac{2 \cdot 9\sum_1^3 W_i^2}{9\sum_4^9 W_i^2} = 2\frac{\sum_1^3 W_i^2}{\sum_4^9 W_i^2} = \frac{(\sum_1^3 W_i^2/3)}{(\sum_4^9 W_i^2/6)},$$

which is $F_{3,6}$. True.

87. Explanation: (b)

Use the key property:

If U, V are independent standard normal variables $N(0,1)$, then

$$\frac{U}{V} \sim \text{Cauchy}(0,1)$$

Given: $X \sim N(-1,1), Y \sim N(0,1), Z \sim N(1,3)$

Standardize:

$$X + 1 \sim N(0,1), Y \sim N(0,1), Z - 1 \sim N(0,3)$$

Check Each Option:

Option 1: $\frac{X-1}{|Y|}$

Since

$$X - 1 \sim N(-2,1)$$

This is not centered at 0 and the denominator is $|Y|$(absolute value of a normal variable).

The ratio of a normal variable and $|Y|$does not produce a Cauchy distribution.

⟹ Not Cauchy

Option 2: $\frac{X+2Y+Z}{X-2Y+Z}$

Rewrite:

$$X + 2Y + Z = (X+1) + 2Y + (Z-1)$$
$$X - 2Y + Z = (X+1) - 2Y + (Z-1)$$

Let $U = (X+1) + (Z-1)$

Then

$$U \sim N(0,4), \frac{U}{2} \sim N(0,1)$$

Expression becomes

$$\frac{\frac{U}{2} + Y}{\frac{U}{2} - Y}$$

Let

$$A = \frac{U}{2}, B = Y$$
$$A, B \sim N(0,1)$$

Thus

$$\frac{A+B}{A-B}$$

which follows Cauchy(0,1).

Option 3: $\frac{Z-1}{Y}$

Here

$$Z - 1 \sim N(0,3)$$

Write

$$\frac{Z-1}{Y} = \sqrt{3}\frac{\frac{Z-1}{\sqrt{3}}}{Y}$$

Since

$$\frac{Z-1}{\sqrt{3}} \sim N(0,1)$$

Thus

$$\frac{Z-1}{Y} = \sqrt{3} \times (\text{Cauchy}(0,1))$$

This gives

$$\text{Cauchy}(0, \sqrt{3})$$

Scale parameter is $\sqrt{3}$, not 1.

$\Rightarrow$ Not Cauchy(0,1)

Option 4: $\frac{X-Y}{X+Y}$

Means of numerator and denominator:

$$E(X-Y) = -1$$
$$E(X+Y) = -1$$

They are not centered normals and also not independent. Hence the ratio does not produce a standard Cauchy distribution.

$\Rightarrow$ Not Cauchy

So, the correct option is (2).

CHAPTER 5

ESTIMATION THEORY

(JUNE 2012)

1. Let $X_1, X_2 \dots X_n$ be n (≥ 2) i.i.d. observations from N $(, \sigma^2)$ distribution, where $-\infty < \mu < \infty$ and $0 < \sigma^2 < \infty$ are unknown parameters. Let $\hat{\sigma}^2_{MLE}$ and $\hat{\sigma}^2_{UMVUE}$ denote the maximum likelihood and uniform minimum variance unbiased estimates of σ^2 respectively, Identity the correct statement:
(a) $\hat{\sigma}^2_{MLE}$ has the same variance as that of $\hat{\sigma}^2_{UMVUE}$
(b) $\hat{\sigma}^2_{MLE}$ has the larger variance than that of $\hat{\sigma}^2_{UMVUE}$
(c) $\hat{\sigma}^2_{MLE}$ has the smaller mean squared error than that of $\hat{\sigma}^2_{UMVUE}$
(d) $\hat{\sigma}^2_{MLE}$ and $\hat{\sigma}^2_{UMVUE}$ has the same mean squared error

(JUNE 2012)

2. Suppose X_1 has density $f_1(x) = \frac{1}{\theta} e^{-x/\theta}, x > 0$ and X_2 has density $f_2(x) = \frac{2}{\theta} e^{-2x/\theta}, x > 0$ and X_1, X_2 are independent. Then
(a) $X_1 + X_2$ is sufficient for θ
(b) $X_1 + 2X_2$ is sufficient for θ
(c) $X_1 + 2X_2$ is complete for θ
(d) $\frac{1}{2}(X_1 + 2X_2)$ is unbiased for θ

(JUNE 2012)

3. Suppose that we have $n(\geq 2)$ i.i.d. observations $X_1, X_2, \dots\dots, X_n$ each with a common $N(\mu, \sigma^2)$ distribution, where $-\infty < \mu < \infty$ and $0 < \sigma^2 < \infty$ are both unknown. Then
(a) the maximum likelihood estimate of σ^2 is an unbiased estimate for σ^2.
(b) the uniformly minimum variance unbiased estimate of σ^2 has smaller mean squared error than the maximum likelihood estimate of σ^2.
(c) both the maximum likelihood estimate and the uniformly minimum variance estimate of σ^2 are asymptotically consistent estimates
(d) for any unbiased estimate of σ^2, there is another estimate of σ^2 with a smaller mean squared error.

(JUNE 2012)

4. Let $X_1, X_2, \dots\dots, X_{25}$ be i.i.d. observations from a uniform distribution on the interval $[\theta - 1/2, \theta + 1/2]$ where $-\infty < \theta < \infty$ is an unknown parameter. Then the
(a) sample mean is an unbiased estimate for θ.
(b) sample median is an unbiased estimate for θ.
(c) sample mean is not the uniformly minimum variance unbiased estimate for θ.
(d) sample median is not the uniformly minimum variance unbiased estimate for θ.

(JUNE 2012)

5. Suppose X has density $f(x, \lambda) = \lambda e^{-\lambda x}, x > 0$, where $\lambda > 0$ is unknown. X is discretized to give Y=k if $K < X \leq k+1, k = 0,1,2, \dots\dots$ A random sample $Y_1, Y_2, \dots\dots, Y_n$ is available from the distribution of Y. Let $\bar{Y} = \frac{1}{n}\sum_{i=1}^{n} Y_i$. Then the method of moments estimator $\hat{\lambda}$ of λ is
(a) $\hat{\lambda} = \frac{1}{\bar{Y}}$
(b) $\hat{\lambda} = \frac{1}{\bar{Y}} + 1$
(c) $\hat{\lambda} = In\left(1 + \frac{1}{\bar{Y}}\right)$
(d) the same as the maximum likelihood estimator

(DEC. 2012)

6. The radius of a circle is measured with an error of measurement which is normally distributed with mean 0 and variance σ^2. Let $X_1, \dots, X_n$ be n measurements on the radius. Let $\bar{x}$ and $s^2 = \frac{1}{n-1}\sum(x_i - \bar{x})^2$ be the sample mean and sample variance respectively. Which of the following represents an unbiased estimate of the area of the circle?
(a) $\pi\bar{x}^2$
(b) $\frac{\pi}{n}\sum x_i^2$
(c) $\pi\left[\frac{1}{n}\sum x_i^2 - s^2\right]$
(d) $\pi[\bar{x}^2 - s^2]$

(DEC. 2012)

7. Let $X_1, X_2, \dots, X_n, (n \geq 3)$ be a random sample from uniform $(\theta - 5, \theta - 3)$. Let $X_{(1)}$ and $X_{(n)}$ denote the smallest and largest of the sample values. Then which of following are always true?
(a) $(X_{(1)}, X_{(n)})$ is complete sufficient for θ
(b) $X_1 + X_2 - 2X_3$ is an ancillary statistic
(c) $X_{(n)} + 3$ is unbiased for θ
(d) $X_{(1)} + 5$ is consistent for θ

(JUNE 2013)

8. Suppose X_1 and X_2 are independent and identically distributed random variables each following an exponential distribution with mean θ, i.e., the common pdf is given by
$f_\theta(x) = \frac{1}{\theta} e^{-x/\theta}, 0 < x < \infty, 0 < \theta < \infty$.
Then which of the following is true?
Conditional distribution of X_2 given $X_1 + X_2 = t$ is
(a) exponential with mean $\frac{t}{2}$ and hence $X_1 + X_2$ is sufficient of θ
(b) exponential with mean $\frac{t\theta}{2}$ and hence $X_1 + X_2$ is not sufficient of θ
(c) uniform $(0, t)$ and hence $X_1 + X_2$ is sufficient of θ

(d) uniform $(0, t\theta)$ and hence $X_1 + X_2$ is not sufficient of θ

(JUNE 2013)

9. Let $X_1, \ldots, X_n$ be independent and identically distributed random variables with probability density function $f(x) = \frac{1}{2}\lambda^3 x^2 e^{-\lambda x}; x > 0, \lambda > 0$. Then which of the following statements are true?

(a) $\frac{2}{n}\sum_{i=1}^{n}\frac{1}{X_i}$ is an unbiased estimator of λ

(b) $\frac{3n}{\sum_{i=1}^{n} X_i}$ is an unbiased estimator of λ

(c) $\frac{2}{n}\sum_{i=1}^{n}\frac{1}{X_i}$ is a consistent estimator of λ

(d) $\frac{3n}{\sum_{i=1}^{n} X_i}$ is a consistent estimator of λ

(JUNE 2013)

10. Let $X_1, X_2, \ldots X_n$ be independent and identically distributed random variables each following a uniform distribution on $(\theta - 2, \theta + 2)$. Define $X_{(n)} = \max\{X_1, X_2, \ldots X_n\}$ and $X_{(1)} = \min\{X_1, X_2, \ldots X_n\}$. Then which of the following estimators are maximum likelihood estimators for θ?

(a) $X_{(1)} - 2$

(b) $X_{(n)} + 2$

(c) $\frac{X_{(1)} + X_{(n)}}{2}$

(d) $\frac{1}{4}(X_{(1)} + 2) + \frac{3}{4}(X_{(n)} - 2)$

(DEC. 2013)

11. Consider the following probability mass function $P_{\theta_1,\theta_2}(x)$ where parameter (θ_1, θ_2) take values in the parameter space $\{(\frac{1}{3},3),(\frac{1}{2},2),(2,\frac{1}{2}),(3,\frac{1}{3})\}$

(θ_1,θ_2) / x	$(\frac{1}{3},3)$	$(\frac{1}{2},2)$	$(2,\frac{1}{2})$	$(3,\frac{1}{3})$
1	1/11	1/7	1/8	1/9
2	1/11	1/14	1/16	1/9
3	8/11	5/7	3/4	2/3
4	1/11	1/14	1/16	1/9

Let X be a random observation from this distribution If the observed value of X is 3 then

(a) $MLE\ of\ \theta_1 = 1/3, MLEof\ \theta_2 = 3$

(b) $MLE\ of\ \theta_1 = 1/2, MLEof\ \theta_2 = 2$

(c) $MLE\ of\ \theta_1 = 2, MLEof\ \theta_2 = 1/2$

(d) $MLE\ of\ \theta_1 = 3, MLEof\ \theta_2 = 1/3$

(DEC. 2013)

12. Let $X_1, X_2, \ldots, X_n$ be a random sample from Uniform $(\theta, 3\theta), \theta > 0$. Let $X_{(n)} = \max\{X_1, X_2, \ldots, X_n\}$and $X_{(1)} = \min\{X_1, X_2, \ldots, X_n\}$. Which of the following is/are true?

(a) $\frac{X_{(n)} - X_{(1)}}{2}$ is unbiased for θ

(b) $(X_{(1)}, X_{(n)})$is complete sufficient for θ

(c) $\frac{X_{(n)}}{X_{(1)} + X_{(n)}}$is an ancillary statistic.

(d) $\frac{1}{2n}\sum_{i=1}^{n} X_i$ is unbiased for θ.

(DEC. 2013)

13. Suppose X is an exponential random variable with mean $1/\theta$. Due to round-off X is not observable, and Y defined as below is observed:

$Y = k$ if $k \le Y < k+1, k = 0,1,2 \ldots$

Let $Y_1, Y_2, \ldots, Y_n$ be a random sample from the distribution of Y.

Then a consistent estimator of θ based on $Y_1, Y_2, \ldots, Y_n$ is

(a) $\frac{n}{\sum_{i=1}^{n} Y_i}$
(b) $\ln\left(1 + \frac{n}{\sum_{i=1}^{n} Y_i}\right)$

(c) $\ln\left(1 + \frac{n+1}{\sum_{i=1}^{n} Y_i}\right)$
(d) $\frac{n+1}{\sum_{i=1}^{n} Y_i}$

(JUNE 2014)

14. Let X be a random variable following a Poisson distribution with parameter $\lambda > 0$. To estimate λ^5, consider an estimator $T = X(X-1)(X-2)(X-3)(X-4)$. Which of the following statements is true?

(a) T is not unbiased

(b) T is unbiased but not UMVUE

(c) T is UMVUE

(d) UMVUE for λ^5 does not exist

(JUNE 2014)

15. Suppose $X_1, X_2, \ldots, X_n$ are independent and identically distributed as geometric random variables with parameter p. Let f denote the number $X_i s$ equal to 1. Then which of the following statements are true?

(a) $\frac{f}{n}$ is the maximum likelihood estimator of p.

(b) $\frac{f}{n}$ is an unbiased estimator of p.

(c) $\frac{n-1}{\sum_{i=1}^{n} x_i}$ is the maximum likelihood estimator of p.

(d) $Var\left(\frac{f}{n}\right) = \frac{p(1-p)}{n}$

(JUNE 2014)

16. Consider the following random sample of size 11 from uniform $(\theta - 1, \theta + 1)$ distribution: -0.71, 0.3, -0.4, -0.63, -0.81, -0.7, 0.1, -0.01, -0.02, -0.96, -0.92. Which of the following are maximum likelihood estimates of θ?

(a) -0.96
(b) 0.3

(c) 0.02
(d) -0.54

(JUNE 2014)

17. Let $X_1, X_2, \ldots X_n$ be a random sample from

$$f_\theta(x) = \begin{cases} e^{-(x-\theta)} & x > \theta \\ 0 & x \le \theta \end{cases}$$

Define $X_{(1)} = \min\{X_1, X_2, \ldots X_n\}$.

Which of the following are confidence intervals for θ with confidence coefficient $(1-\alpha)$?

(a) $\left[X_{(1)} + \frac{1}{n}\log\alpha, X_{(1)}\right]$

(b) $\left[X_{(1)} + \frac{1}{n}\log\alpha, X_{(1)} - \frac{1}{n}\log\alpha\right]$

(c) $\left[X_{(1)} + \frac{1}{n}\log\left(\frac{\alpha}{2}\right), X_{(1)} + \frac{1}{n}\log\left(1 - \frac{\alpha}{2}\right)\right]$

(d) $\left[X_{(1)} + \frac{1}{n}\log\alpha, X_{(1)} - \frac{1}{n}\log\left(1 - \frac{\alpha}{2}\right)\right]$

(DEC. 2014)

18. Suppose $X_1, X_2, \ldots X_n$ is a random sample from $U(0,\theta), \theta > 0$. Let $X_{(1)} \le X_{(2)} \le \cdots \le X_{(n)}$ be the order statistics. Consider the two unbiased estimators for $\theta: T_1 = 2\bar{X}$ and $T_2 = \left(\frac{n+1}{n}\right)X_{(n)}$.

Then $\lim_{n\to\infty} \frac{Var(T_2)}{Var(T_1)} =$

(a) 0 (b) 1

(c) ∞ (d) 12

(DEC. 2014)

19. Let $X_1, X_2, \dots, X_n, n \geq 3$, be a random sample from $N(\mu, 1)$ population where μ is unknown. Define $\overline{X}_n = \frac{1}{n}\sum_{i=1}^{n} X_i$. Which of the following are necessarily true?

(a) Covariance $(X_1 - 3X_2 + 2X_3, \overline{X}_n) = 0$

(b) Cramer-Rao lower bound for unbiased estimators of μ is $\frac{1}{n}$

(c) Var $(\overline{X}_n) < Var\left(\frac{X_1+2X_2+3X_3+\cdots+nX_n}{\frac{n(n+1)}{2}}\right)$

(d) $\overline{X}_n$ is a function of any sufficient statistic for μ

(JUNE 2015)

20. Consider a sample of size one, say X from a population with pdf

$$f_\theta(x) = \begin{cases} \frac{2}{\theta^2}(x-\theta) \ ; \theta \leq x \leq 2\theta, \theta > 0 \\ 0 \ ; otherwise \end{cases}$$

Which of the following is/are confidence interval(s) for θ with confidence coefficient $1-\alpha$?

(a) $\left[\frac{X}{2}, \frac{X}{1+\sqrt{\alpha}}\right]$ (b) $\left[\frac{X}{1+\sqrt{1-\frac{\alpha}{2}}}, \frac{X}{1+\sqrt{\frac{\alpha}{2}}}\right]$

(c) $\left[\frac{X}{1+\sqrt{1-\frac{\alpha}{2}}}, X\right]$ (d) $\left[\frac{X}{1+\sqrt{1-\frac{\alpha}{4}}}, \frac{X}{1+\sqrt{\frac{3\alpha}{4}}}\right]$

(JUNE 2015)

21. Consider the pdf

$$f(x;\theta,\sigma) = \frac{0.9}{\sigma}\varphi\left(\frac{x-\theta}{\sigma}\right) +$$

$0.1\,\varphi(x-\theta)$. Where $-\infty < \theta < \infty$ and $\sigma > 0$ are unknown parameters and φ denotes the pdf of N (0,1). Let $X_1, X_2, \dots X_n$ be a random sample from this probability distribution. Then which of the following is (are) correct?

(a) This model is not parametric

(b) Method of moments estimators for θ and σ exists

(c) An unbiased estimator of θ exist

(d) Consistent estimators of θ do not exist

(DEC. 2015)

22. Let $X_1, X_2, \dots, X_n$ be a random sample from uniform $(\theta, 5\theta), \theta > 0$. Define $X_{(1)} = \min\{X_1, X_2, \dots, X_n\}$ and $X_{(n)} = \max\{X_1, X_2, \dots, X_n\}$. Maximum likelihood estimator of θ is

(a) $\frac{X_{(1)}}{5}$ (b) $X_{(n)}$

(c) $X_{(1)}$ (d) $\frac{X_{(n)}}{5}$

(DEC. 2015)

23. Let $X_1, X_2 \dots, X_n$ be a random sample from $U(\theta, \theta+1)$. If $X_{(1)} < X_{(2)} < \cdots < X_{(n)}$ denote the ordered values of $X_1, X_2 \dots, X_n$, then which of the following statements are true?

(a) $(X_{(1)}, X_{(n)} + 1)$ is a jointly sufficient statistics for θ

(b) $X_{(n)} + 1$ is a sufficient statistic for θ

(c) $(X_{(1)}, X_{(n)})$ is a jointly sufficient statistic for θ

(d) $X_{(1)}$ is a sufficient statistic for θ

(DEC. 2015)

24. Consider a region R, which is a triangle with vertices $(0,0), (0,\theta), (\theta,0)$, where $\theta > 0$. A sample of size n is selected at random from this region R. Denote the sample as $\{(X_i, Y_i) : i = 1,2,\dots,n\}$. Then denoting $X_{(n)} = \max(X_1, X_2 \dots, X_n)$ and $Y_{(n)} = \max(Y_1, Y_2 \dots, Y_n)$, which of the following statements are true?

(a) $X_{(n)}$ and $Y_{(n)}$ and independent

(b) MLE of θ is $\frac{X_{(n)}+Y_{(n)}}{2}$

(c) MLE of θ is $\max_{1\leq i\leq n}(X_i + Y_i)$

(d) MLE of θ is $\max\{X_{(n)}, Y_{(n)}\}$

(DEC. 2015)

25. Let $X_1, \dots, X_n$ be independent and identically distributed random variables with $N(\mu, 1)$ distribution. Assume that $\mu \epsilon [0, \infty)$. Let $\hat{\mu}$ be the MLE of μ. Then, which of the following statements are true?

(a) $\hat{\mu} = \max(\overline{X}_n, 0)$

(b) $\hat{\mu}$ is unbiased for μ

(c) $\overline{X}_n$ is sufficient for μ

(d) $\hat{\mu}$ is a consistent estimator of μ

(JUNE 2016)

26. Let $X_1, \dots, X_n$ be a random sample from $N(\theta, 1)$, where $\theta \in \{1,2\}$. Then which of the following statements about the maximum likelihood estimator (MLE) of θ is correct?

(a) MLE of θ does not exist

(b) MLE of θ is $\overline{X}$

(c) MLE of θ exists but it is not $\overline{X}$

(d) MLE of θ is an unbiased estimator of θ

(JUNE 2016)

27. Let $X_1, \dots, X_n$ denote a random sample from a $N(\mu, \sigma^2)$ distribution. Let $\mu \in \mathbb{R}$ be known and $\sigma^2 (> 0)$be unknown. Let $X^2_{n,\alpha/2}$ be an upper $(\alpha/2)^{th}$ percentile point of a x^2_n distribution. Then a $100(1-\alpha)\%$ confidence interval for σ^2 is given by

(a) $\left(\frac{(\sum_1^n x_i^2 - \mu^2)}{X^2_{n,\alpha/2}}, \frac{(\sum_1^n x_i^2 - \mu^2)}{X^2_{n,1-\alpha/2}}\right)$

(b) $\left(\frac{\sum_1^n (x_i^2 - \mu)^2}{(n-1)X^2_{(n-1),\alpha/2}}, \frac{\sum_1^n (x_i^2 - \mu)^2}{(n-1)X^2_{(n-1),1-\alpha/2}}\right)$

(c) $\left(\frac{\sum_1^n (X_i - \bar{X})^2}{nX^2_{n,\alpha/2}}, \frac{\sum_1^n (X_i - \bar{X})^2}{nX^2_{n,1-\alpha/2}}\right)$

(d) $\left(\frac{\sum_1^n (X_i - \mu)^2}{X^2_{n,\alpha/2}}, \frac{\sum_1^n (X_i - \mu)^2}{X^2_{n,1-\alpha/2}}\right)$

(JUNE 2016)

28. Let $X_1, X_2, \dots, X_n$ be a random sample from the following probability density function

$f(x;\mu,\alpha) = \frac{1}{\Gamma(\alpha)}(x-\mu)^{\alpha-1}e^{-(x-\mu)}; x \geq \mu$

Here, $-\infty < \mu < \infty; \alpha > 0$. Then which of the following statements are correct?

(a) The method of moment estimators of neither α nor μ exist.

(b) The method of moment estimator of α exists and it is a consistent estimator ofα .

(c) The method of moment estimator of μ exists and it is a consistent estimator of μ.

(d) The method of moment estimators of both α and μ exist, but they are not consistent.

(JUNE 2016)

29. Let $X_1, X_2, \dots, X_{2n+1}$ be a random sample from a uniform distribution on the interval $(\theta-1, \theta+1)$. Let
$T_1 = \overline{X}$ the sample mean,
$T_2 = \tilde{X}$ the sample median, and $T_3 = \frac{T_1+T_2}{2}$
be three estimators of θ. Then, which of the following statements are correct?
(a) T_1 is consistent for θ.
(b) Both T_1 and T_2 are more efficient than T_3.
(c) All the three estimators are unbiased for θ.
(d) T_2 is a sufficient statistic for θ

(DEC. 2016)

30. $X_1, X_2, \dots, X_n$ are independent and identically distributed $N(\theta, 1)$ random variables, where θ takes only integer values i.e. $\theta \in \{\dots, -2, -1, 0, 1, 2, \dots\}$. Which of the following is the maximum likelihood estimator of θ?
(a) $\overline{X}$
(b) Integer closest to $\overline{X}$
(c) Integer part of $\overline{X}$, (Largest integer $\le \overline{X}$)
(d) median of $(X_1, X_2, \dots, X_n)$

(DEC. 2016)

31. $X_1, X_2, \dots, X_n$ are independent and identically distributed as $N(\mu, \sigma^2), -\infty < \mu < \infty, \sigma^2 > 0$. Then
(a) $\sum_1^n \frac{(X_i-\overline{X})^2}{n-1}$ is the Minimum Variance Unbiased Estimated of σ^2
(b) $\sqrt{\sum_1^n \frac{(X_i-\overline{X})^2}{n-1}}$ is the Minimum Variance Unbiased Estimated of σ
(c) $\sum_1^n \frac{(X_i-\overline{X})^2}{n}$ is the Maximum likelihood Estimate of σ^2
(d) $\sqrt{\sum_1^n \frac{(X_i-\overline{X})^2}{n}}$ is the Maximum likelihood Estimate of σ

(DEC. 2016)

32. Let $X_1, X_2, \dots, X_n$ be independent and identically distributed random variables each following uniform $(1-\theta, 1+\theta)$ distribution, $\theta > 0$.
Define
$X_{(1)} = \min\{X_1, X_2, \dots, X_n\}, X_{(n)} = \max\{X_1, X_2, \dots, X_n\}$
and $\overline{X} = \frac{1}{n}\sum_{i=1}^n X_i$. Which of the following is true?
(a) $(X_{(1)}, \overline{X}, X_{(n)})$ is sufficient for θ
(b) $\frac{1}{2}(X_{(n)} - X_{(1)})$ is unbiased for θ
(c) $\frac{3}{n}\sum_{i=1}^n (X_i-1)^2$ is unbiased for θ^2
(d) $\frac{3}{n}\sum_{i=1}^n (X_i-\overline{X})^2$ is unbiased for θ^2

(JUNE 2017)

33. Suppose $\{X_1, \dots, X_n\}, n \ge 2$, is a random sample from the distribution with probability density function
$$f(x;\theta) = \begin{cases} \frac{\theta^\theta}{\Gamma(\theta)} x^{\theta-1} e^{-x\theta} & ; x > 0 \\ 0 & ; x \le 0 \end{cases}$$
With $\theta > 0$. The the method of moments estimator of θ
(a) does not exist
(b) is $\frac{n}{\sum_{i=1}^n (X_i-1)^2}$
(c) is $\frac{n}{\sum_{i=1}^n (X_i-\overline{X})^2}$
(d) is $\frac{n-1}{\sum_{i=1}^n (X_i-1)^2}$

(JUNE 2017)

34. Let $X_1, X_2, \dots, X_n$ for $n \ge 5$ be a random sample from the distribution with probability density function
$$f(x;\theta) = \begin{cases} e^{-(x-\theta)} & if\ x > \theta \\ 0 & \text{otherwise} \end{cases}$$
For $\theta > 0$. The confidence coefficient of the confidence interval
$\left[\min\{X_1, \dots X_n\} - \frac{\ln 4}{n}, \min\{X_1, .., X_n\} + \frac{\ln 2}{n}\right]$ for θ, is
(a) 0.5
(b) 0.75
(c) 0.95
(d) $1 - \frac{1}{2^n}$

(JUNE 2017)

35. Let $\{X_1, \dots, X_n\}$ be a random sample from the probability density function $f(x;\theta) = \frac{1}{2}e^{-|x-\theta|}; -\infty < x < \infty$ where $\theta \in \mathbb{R}$. Which of the following statements are correct?
(a) The maximum likelihood estimator of θ is $\frac{1}{n}\sum_{i=1}^n X_i$.
(b) $\sum_{i=1}^n X_i$ is a sufficient statistic for θ
(c) The maximum likelihood estimator of θ is a function of a sufficient statistic
(d) There does not exist a uniformly most powerful test for the following testing problem: $H_0 : \theta = 0$ vs $H_1 : \theta \ne 0$

(DEC. 2017)

36. Let $X_1, X_2, \dots$ be a random sample from uniform $(0, 3\theta), \theta > 0$. Define $T_n = \frac{1}{3}\max\{X_1, X_2, \dots X_n\}$. Which of the following is NOT true?
(a) T_n is consistent for θ
(b) T_n is unbiased for θ
(c) T_n is a sufficient statistic
(d) T_n is complete

37. Consider the following regression problem $Y_i = \alpha + \beta_i + \epsilon_i; i = 1, \dots, n$
Here $\epsilon_i; i = 1, 2, \dots, n$ are i.i.d $N(0,1)$ random variables. It is assumed that $\alpha \ne 0$ and β is known. If $\hat{a}_n$ is the MLE of α, which of the following statements is true?
(a) $lim_{n\to\infty} E(\hat{a}_n) \ne \alpha$
(b) $lim_{n\to\infty} E(\hat{a}_n) = 0$
(c) $lim_{n\to\infty} Var(\hat{a}_n) = \infty$
(d) $lim_{n\to\infty} Var(\hat{a}_n) = 0$

(DEC. 2017)

38. Let $X_1, X_2, \dots, X_n$ be a random sample from $f_\theta(x)$, a probability density function or a probability mass function. Define $S_n^2 = \frac{1}{n-1}\sum_{i=1}^n (X_i - \overline{X}_n)^2$, where $\overline{X}_n = \frac{1}{n}\sum_{i=1}^n X_i$. Then S_n^2 is unbiased for θ if
(a) $f_\theta(x) = e^{-\theta}\frac{\theta^x}{x!}, x = 0, 1, 2, \dots .\ and\ \theta > 0$
(b) $f_\theta(x) = \frac{1}{\sqrt{2\pi\sqrt{\theta}}} e^{-\frac{x^2}{2\theta}}, -\infty < x < \infty, \theta > 0$
(c) $f_\theta(x) = \frac{1}{\theta}e^{-\frac{x}{\theta}}, x > 0, \theta > 0$
(d) $f_\theta(x) = \theta e^{-\theta x}, x > 0, \theta > 0$

(DEC. 2017)

39. Consider a Cauchy population with probability density function $f_\theta(x) = \frac{1}{\pi\{1+(x-\theta)^2\}}, -\infty < x < \infty, -\infty < \theta < \infty$ Let $X_1, X_2, \dots, X_n$ be a random sample from the above

population. Which of the following confidence intervals for θ have confidence coefficient $1 - a (0 < a < 1)$?

(a) $\left[X_1 - tan\frac{\pi(1-a)}{2}, X_1 + tan\frac{\pi(1-a)}{2}\right]$

(b) $\left[\frac{X_1+X_2}{2} - tan\frac{\pi(1-a)}{2}, \frac{X_1+X_2}{2} + tan\frac{\pi(1-a)}{2}\right]$

(c) $\frac{X_1+X_2}{2} - tan\frac{5\pi(1-a)}{7}, \frac{X_1+X_2}{2} + tan\frac{2\pi(1-a)}{7}$

(d) $[\frac{X_1+X_2+X_3}{3} - tan\frac{5\pi(1-a)}{7}, \frac{X_1+X_2+X_3}{3} + tan\frac{2\pi(1-a)}{7}]$

(DEC. 2017)

40. Let $X_1, ..., X_n$ be a random sample from $N(\theta, 1), \theta \epsilon [-100,100]$ and let $Y_1, ..., Y_n$ be defined by

$$Y_i = \begin{cases} 0 & If\ X_i < 0 \\ 1 & If\ X_i \geq 0 \end{cases}$$

Suppose $\hat{\theta}_n$ and $\tilde{\theta}_n$ denote the MLEs of based on $\{X_1, ... ,X_n\}$ and on $\{Y_1, ... ,Y_n\}$, respectively. Which of the following statements are true?

(a) $lim_{n\to\infty} E(\hat{\theta}_n) = \theta$

(b) $lim_{n\to\infty} E(\tilde{\theta}_n) = \theta$.

(c) $\hat{\theta}_n$ is a consistent estimator of θ

(d) $\tilde{\theta}_n$ is a consistent estimator of θ

(JUNE 2018)

41. Suppose that the lifetime of an electric bulb follows an exponential distribution with mean θ hours. In order to estimate θ, n bulbs are switched on at the same time. After t hours, $n - m (> 0)$ bulbs are found to be in functioning state. If the lifetimes of the other $m (> 0)$ bulbs are noted as $x_1, x_2, ..., x_m$, respectively, then the maximum likelihood estimate of θ is given by

(a) $\hat{\theta} = \frac{t}{\log\frac{n}{n-m}}$ (b) $\hat{\theta} = \frac{\sum_{i=1}^{m} x_i}{m}$

(c) $\hat{\theta} = \frac{\sum_{i=1}^{m} x_i + (n-m)t}{n}$ (d) $\hat{\theta} = \frac{\sum_{i=1}^{m} x_i + (n-m)t}{m}$

(JUNE 2018)

42. Let $X_1, X_2, ..., X_n$ be i.i.d. uniform (θ_1, θ_2) variables where $\theta_1 < \theta_2$ are unknown parameters. Which of the following is an ancillary statistic?

(a) $\frac{X_{(k)}}{X_{(n)}}$ for any $k < n$

(b) $\frac{X_{(n)} - X_{(k)}}{X_{(n)}}$ for any $k < n$

(c) $\frac{X_{(k)}}{X_{(n)} - X_{(k)}}$ for any $k < n$

(d) $\frac{X_{(k)} - X_{(1)}}{X_{(n)} - X_{(k)}}$ for any k where $1 < k < n$

(JUNE 2018)

43. Let X_1 and X_2 be i.i.d. with probability mass function $f_\theta(x) = \theta^x (1-\theta)^{1-x}; x = 0, 1$ where $\theta \epsilon (0, 1)$. Which of the following statements are true?

(a) $X_1 + 2X_2$ is a sufficient statistic

(b) $X_1 - X_2$ is a sufficient statistic

(c) $X_1^2 + X_2^2$ is a sufficient statistic

(d) $X_1^2 + X_2$ is a sufficient statistic

(JUNE 2018)

44. Let $X_1, X_2, ..., X_n$ be i.i.d. $N(\mu, \sigma^2)$ variables, where μ and σ^2 both are unknown parameters. Consider a confidence interval for σ^2, which is of the form $I_{a,b} = \left[\frac{\Sigma(X_i - \bar{X})^2}{b}, \frac{\Sigma(X_i - \bar{X})^2}{a}\right]$, where $b > a > 0$. Let G_n be the cumulative distribution function of a chi-square random variable with n degrees of freedom. Which of the following statements are true?

(a) It is possible to find a 95% confidence interval of the form $I_{a,b}$, where $ab = 1$.

(b) If $G_{n-1}(a) = 1 - G_{n-1}(b) = 0.025$, then it is the shortest 95% confidence interval.

(c) If it is the shortest 95% confidence interval, then a and b must satisfy the condition $b - a = (n-3)\log\frac{b}{a}$

(d) If $G_{n-1}(b) = 1 - G_{n-1}(a) = 0.95$, then the expected length of a 95% confidence interval of the form $I_{a,b}$ is $(n-1)\left(\frac{1}{a} - \frac{1}{b}\right)\sigma^2$

(DEC. 2018)

45. Given the observation 0.8, 0.71, 0.9, 1.2, 1.68, 1.4, 0.88, 1.62 from the uniform distribution on $(\theta - 0.2, \theta + 0.8)$ with $-\infty < 0 < \infty$, which of the following is a maximum likelihood estimate for θ

(a) 0.7 (b) 0.9

(c) 1.1 (d) 1.3

(DEC. 2018)

46. Let $X_1, X_2, ... X_n$ be a random sample from the distribution with p.d.f.

$$f_\theta(x) = \begin{cases} \frac{1}{\theta}(x_i)^{\frac{1-\theta}{\theta}} & 0 < x < 1 \\ 0 & otherwise, \end{cases} \text{ where } \theta > 0.$$

Then which of the following are true?

(a) $\prod_{i=1}^{n} X_i$ is sufficient for θ.

(b) $-\frac{1}{n}\sum_{i=1}^{n} ln\ X_i$ is sufficient for θ

(c) $\prod_{i=1}^{n} X_i$ is a maximum likelihood estimate for θ

(d) $-\frac{1}{n}\sum_{i=1}^{n} ln\ X_i$ is a maximum likelihood estimate for θ

(DEC. 2018)

47. Let $X_1, X_2, ... X_n$ be a random sample from uniform distribution on $(\theta, \theta + 1)$, where $\theta \in \mathbb{R}$ is an unknown parameter. Let $X_{(1)} < X_{(2)} < \cdots X_{(n)}$ be the corresponding order-statistics. Which of the following are $100(1-a)\%$ confidence intervals for θ

(a) $(-\infty, X_{(n)} - a^{1/n})$ (b) $(X_{(1)} + a^{\frac{1}{n}} - 1, \infty)$

(c) $\left(X_n + \frac{a}{2} - 1, X_n - \frac{a}{2}\right)$ (d) $(-\infty, X_1 - a)$

(JUNE 2019)

48. A random sample of size 7 is drawn from a distribution with p.d.f

$$f_\theta(x) = \begin{cases} \frac{1+x^2}{3\theta(1+\theta^2)} & -2\theta \leq x \leq \theta, \theta > 0 \\ 0, & otherwise \end{cases}$$

And the observations are 12, -54, 26, -2, 24, 17, -39. What is the maximum likelihood estimate of θ?

(a) 3 (b) 4

(c) 5 (d) 9

(JUNE 2019)

49. Let $X_1, X_2, ...$ be $.i.d.$ $N(0, \sigma^2)$, Where $\sigma^2 (> 0)$ is unknown. Consider a class of estimators

$\{T_n = C_n \sum_{i=1}^{n} X_i^2 : C_n > 0, n \geq 1\}$

For σ^2. Then which of the following are true?

(a) T_n is consistent for σ^2 if $C_n = \frac{1}{n-1}$

(b) T_n is unbiased for σ^2 if $C_n = \frac{1}{n}$

(c) T_n is consistent for σ^2 if $C_n = \frac{1}{n+1}$

(d) MSE of T_n is minimised if $C_n = \frac{1}{n+2}$

(JUNE 2019)

50. Let $b_1, b_2, \ldots, b_{10} \sim i.i.d. N(0, \tau^2)$ and $\epsilon_{ij} \sim i.i.d. N(0, \sigma^2)$ for $i - 1, 2, \ldots, 10; j = 1, 2, \ldots, n$, independent of $b_1, b_2, \ldots, b_{10}$. Define $X_{ij} = b_i + \epsilon_{ij}$. As an estimator of σ^2, the statistic $T_n = \frac{1}{10n} \sum_{i=1}^{10} \sum_{j=1}^{n} X_{ij}^2$ is

(a) unbiased

(b) consistent as $n \to \infty$

(c) unbiased only when $\tau^2 = 0$

(d) consistent as $n \to \infty$ only when $\tau^2 = 0$

(DEC. 2019)

51. Let $X_1, X_2, \ldots, X_n$ ($n \geq 2$) be a random sample from a distribution with probability density function f_θ, $\theta > 0$, unknown, where

$$f_\theta(x) \begin{cases} \frac{2(\theta - x)}{\theta^2}, & 0 \leq x \leq \theta \\ 0 & otherwise \end{cases}$$

Let $\bar{X}_n$ be the sample mean and $X_{(n)} = \max\{X_1, X_2, \ldots, X_n\}$. Then which of the following statements is correct?

(a) $X_{(n)}$ is sufficient θ

(b) $X_{(n)}$ is unbiased θ

(c) $3\bar{X}_n$ is unbiased for θ

(d) $3\bar{X}_n$ is sufficient for θ

(DEC. 2019)

52. Let X_1 and X_2, be a random sample of size 2 from Uniform $[0, \theta]$ distribution, $\theta > 0$. Define $M = \max\{X_1, X_2\}$. What is the confidence coefficient of the confidence interval $\left[\frac{3}{7}M, 2M\right]$ for θ?

(a) 0.6285 (b) 0.7539

(c) 0.8333 (d) 0.95

(DEC. 2019)

53. Suppose $X_1, X_2 \ldots, X_n$ are i.i.d Uniform $(\theta, 2\theta), \theta > 0$. Let $X_{(1)} = \min\{X_1, \ldots, X_2\}$ and $X_{(n)} = max\{X_1, \ldots, X_n\}$. Then which of the following statements are correct?

(a) $\{X_{(1)}, X_{(n)}\}$ is jointly sufficient and complete for θ

(b) $\{X_{(1)}, X_{(n)}\}$ is jointly sufficient but not complete for θ

(c) $\frac{X_{(n)}}{2}$ is a maximum likelihood estimator for θ

(d) $X_{(1)}$ is a maximum likelihood estimator for θ

(DEC. 2019)

54. Let $\{X_i : i \geq 1\}$be i.i.d observations with $E(X_i) = 0$ and $var\ (X_i) = \sigma^2 > 0$. Then which of the following statements are correct?

(a) $\frac{1}{n} \sum_{i=1}^{n} (X_{2i-1} - X_{2i})^2$ *is* consistent for σ^2

(b) $\frac{1}{n} \sum_{i=1}^{n} (X_1 - \bar{X})^2$ is consistent for σ^2

(c) $\frac{1}{n} \sum_{i=1}^{n} X_i^2$ is consistent for σ^2

(d) $\frac{1}{n-1} \sum_{i=1}^{n} (X_i - \bar{X})^2$ is consistent for σ^2

(DEC. 2019)

55. Let X_1, X_2 and X_3 be $i.i.d.$ Normal random variables with mean θ and variance θ^2 where $\theta \in \mathbb{R}$ is unknown. Then which of the following statements are correct?

(a) $\frac{X_1 + 2X_2 + 3X_3}{6}$ is unbiased for θ

(b) $\frac{X_1^2 + 4X_2^2 + 9X_3^2}{14}$ is unbiased for θ^2

(c) $\frac{2X_1 + X_3^2}{2}$ is unbiased for $\theta(1 - \theta)$

(d) $X_2\left(1 - \frac{X_2}{2}\right)$ is unbiased for $\theta(1 - \theta)$

(NOV. 2020)

56. Let $X_1, X_2, \ldots, X_n$ be i.i.d random variables with commom pdf $f(\theta) = \frac{(log\theta)\theta^x}{\theta - 1}$ for $0<x<1$ where $\theta > 1$ is an unknown parameter. Then the statistic $T = \sum_{i=1}^{n} X_i$ is

(a) Sufficient, but not complete

(b) Sufficient but not minimal sufficient

(c) Complete sufficient

(d) Neither complete, nor sufficient

(NOV. 2020)

57. Let $X_1, X_2, \ldots, X_n$ be i.i.d. with the common pdf $f(\theta) = \frac{\theta}{x^{\theta+1}}$ for $x > 1$ where $\theta > 1$ is an unknown parameter.

Which of the following estimators of θ are consistent?

(a) $\frac{1}{n} \sum_{i=1}^{n} X_i$ (b) $\frac{1}{n} \sum_{i=1}^{n} log\ (X_i)$

(c) $\frac{n}{\sum_{i=1}^{n} X_i}$ (d) $\frac{n}{\sum_{i=1}^{n} log\ (X_i)}$

(NOV. 2020)

58. Let $X_1, X_2, \ldots, X_n$ be i.i.d. with the common probability mass function

$p(\theta) = \theta^x (1 - \theta)^{1-x}, x = 0$ or 1, and $0 \leq \theta \leq \frac{1}{2}$

Then

(a) The method of moment's estimator of θ is $\frac{1}{2n} \sum_{i=1}^{n} X_i$

(b) The MLE of θ is X_i

(c) The method of moment's estimator of θ is X_i

(d) The MLE of θ is $min\left\{\frac{1}{n} \sum_{i=1}^{n} X_i, \frac{1}{2}\right\}$

(NOV. 2020)

59. Let the pdf of X be $f(\theta) = \frac{2x}{\theta^2}, for\ 0 < x < \theta$, where $\theta > 0$ is unknown parameter. Which of the following are $100(1 - \alpha)\%$ confidence intervals for θ?

(a) $\left[X, \frac{X}{\sqrt{\alpha}}\right]$ (b) [X, 2X]

(c) $\left[\frac{\sqrt{2}}{\sqrt{2-\alpha}} X, \frac{\sqrt{2}}{\sqrt{\alpha}} X\right]$ (d) [0, X]

(NOV. 2020)

60. Let $X_i = \theta + \varepsilon_i, 1 \leq i \leq n$ where $\varepsilon_1, \varepsilon_2, \ldots, \varepsilon_n$ are i.i.d. with pdf $g(\varepsilon) = |\varepsilon|, -1 < \varepsilon < 1$. Let $T_1 = \frac{1}{n} \sum_{i=1}^{n} X_i$ and $T_2 = X_{\left(\left[\frac{3n}{4}\right]+1\right)}$, the sample 75th percentile. Which of the following are correct?

(a) T_1 is a consistent and asymptotically normal estimator of θ

(b) $T_2 - \frac{1}{\sqrt{2}}$ is a consistent and asymptotically normal estimator of θ

(c) The asymptotic variance of T_1 is $\frac{1}{2n}$

(d) The asymptotic variance of T_2 is $\frac{3}{8n}$

(JUNE 2021)

61. Let X_1, X_2, X_3, X_4 be i.i.d. random variables having Uniform distribution on $(0,\theta)$ where $\theta > 0$ is an unknown parameter. Define $X_{(4)} = \max\{X_1, X_2, X_3, X_4\}$. Consider the confidence intervals $I = [2X_{(4)}, 3X_{(4)}]$ and $J = [X_{(4)}, 1 + X_{(4)}]$ for θ. Which of the following is true?
(a) The coverage probabilities of I and J are both independent of θ.
(b) The coverage probability of I is independent of θ but the coverage probability of J is NOT independent of θ
(c) The coverage probability of J is independent of θ but the coverage probability of I is NOT independent of θ
(d) The coverage probabilities of both I and J are NOT independent of θ

(JUNE 2021)

62. Let $X_1, X_2, \ldots, X_n$ be a random sample from exponential distribution with mean θ. Which of the following is NOT a sufficient statistic for θ?
(a) $\frac{1}{X_1+X_2+\ldots+X_n}$
(b) $X_1 + X_2 + \ldots + X_n$
(c) $\frac{X_n}{X_1+X_2+\ldots+X_{n-1}}$
(d) $(X_n, X_1 + X_2 + \cdots + X_{n-1})$

(JUNE 2021)

63. Consider a sequence of i.i.d observations $X_1, X_2, \ldots$ from $N(0,\sigma^2)$. Which of the following are unbiased and consistent estimators of σ?
(a) $\sqrt{\frac{\pi}{2}\frac{1}{n}}\sum_{i=1}^{n}|X_i|$ (b) $\sqrt{\frac{1}{n}\sum_{i=1}^{n}X_i^2}$
(c) $\sqrt{\frac{1}{n-1}\sum_{i=1}^{n}(X_i-\bar{X})^2}$ (d) $\sqrt{\frac{1}{2n}(X_1^2+X_n^2)}$

[SEP 2022]

64. Let $X_1, \ldots, X_n$ be a random sample from $N(\theta,\theta)$ distribution, where $N(\theta,\theta)$ denotes a normal distribution with mean and variance θ; where e satisfies $0 < \theta < \infty$ and is unknown. Then, the maximum likelihood estimate of θ
(a) is $\frac{-1-\left(1+\frac{4}{n}\sum_{i=1}^{n}x_i^2\right)^{\frac{1}{2}}}{2}$ (b) is $\frac{-1+\left(1+\frac{4}{n}\sum_{i=1}^{n}x_i^2\right)^{\frac{1}{2}}}{2}$
(c) does not exist (d) $is\ \max\left(\frac{\sum_{i=1}^{n}x_i}{n},0\right)$

[SEP. 2022]

65. Let $X_1, X_2, \ldots, X_n$ be independent and identically distributed normal random variables with mean μ and variance σ^2. Suppose $(\hat{\mu},\hat{\sigma}^2)$ is the maximum likelihood estimator of (μ,σ^2). Which of the following statements are correct?
(a) $\frac{(n-1)\hat{\sigma}^2}{\sigma^2}$ is a chi-square random variable with $(n-1)$ degrees of freedom
(b) $\hat{\sigma}^2$ is a unbiased estimator of σ^2
(c) Variance of $\hat{\sigma}^2$ tends to 0 as $n \to \infty$
(d) $\frac{n^2\hat{\sigma}^4}{(n-1)(n+1)}$ is an unbiased estimator of σ^4

[SEP. 2022]

66. Let X and Y be independent random variables with $X \sim Uniform\,[0,\theta+3], Y \sim Uniform\,[-\theta-5,0]$, where $\theta \geq -3$. Then the maximum likelihood estimator of θ besed on (X,Y) is
Options:
(a) (5+Y, X-3) (b) (-5-Y, X-3)
(c) (5+Y, X-3) (d) (-5-Y, X-3)

(JUNE 2023)

67. Let X be a Poisson random variable with mean λ. Which of the following parametric function is not estimable?
(a) λ^{-1} (b) λ
(c) λ^2 (d) $e^{-\lambda}$

(JUNE 2023)

68. Consider the simple linear regression model $Y_i = \beta x_i + \epsilon_i$, for $i = 1, \ldots, n$; where $E(\epsilon_i) = 0$, $Cov(\epsilon_i, \epsilon_k) = 0$, if $i \neq k$ and $Var(\epsilon_i) = x_i^2\sigma^2$. The best linear unbiased estimator of β is:
(a) $\frac{\sum_{i=1}^{n}Y_ix_i}{\sum_{i=1}^{n}x_i^2}$ (b) $\frac{\sum_{i=1}^{n}Y_i}{\sum_{i=1}^{n}x_i}$
(c) $\frac{1}{n}\sum_{i=1}^{n}\frac{Y_i}{x_i}$ (d) $\frac{1}{n}\sum_{i=1}^{n}\frac{Y_ix_i}{x_i^2}$

(JULY-2024)

69. Let X_1, X_2 be a random sample from $N(0,\sigma^2)$ distribution, where $\sigma > 0$ and (μ,σ^2) denotes a normal distribution with mean μ and variance σ^2. Suppose, for some constant $c, (c(X_1^2+X_2^2), \infty)$ is a confidence interval for variance σ^2 with confidence coefficient 0.95. Then the value of c is equal to
(a) $-2\,In(0.05)$ (b) $-2\,In(0.95)$
(c) $-\frac{1}{2\,In(0.05)}$ (d) $-\frac{1}{2\,In(0.95)}$

(JULY-2024)

70. Consider a distribution with probability mass function
$$f(x|\theta) = \begin{cases} \frac{1-\theta}{2}, & if\ x = 0 \\ \frac{1}{2} & if\ x = 1 \\ \frac{\theta}{2} & if\ x = 2 \\ 0 & otherwise, \end{cases}$$
where $\theta\epsilon\ (0,1)$ is an unknown parameter. In a random sample of size 100 from the above distribution, the observed counts of 0, 1 and 2 are 20,30 and 50 respectively. Then, the maximum likelihood estimate of θ based on the observed data is
(a) 1 (b) 5/7
(c) 1/2 (d) 2/7

(JULY 2024)

71. Let $X_1 \ldots . X_n$ $(n \geq 3)$ be a random sample from a distribution having probability density function
$$f(x|\theta) = \begin{cases} \theta e^{-\theta x,} & if\ x > 0 \\ 0, & otherwise \end{cases}$$
where $\theta > 0$ is an unknown parameter. Let $T_n = \frac{1}{n}\sum_{i=1}^{n}X_i$. Which of the following statements are true?

(a) Uniformly minimum variance unbiased estimator of θ is $\frac{n-1}{nT_n}$

(b) Cramer-Rao lower bound for the variance of any unbiased estimator of θ is $\frac{\theta^2}{n}$

(c) Uniformly minimum variance unbiased estimator of θ attains the Cramer-Rao lower bound

(d) $\left(1-e^{-\frac{1}{T_n}}\right)$ is a consistent estimator of $P_\theta(X_1 \le 1)$

(JULY 2024)

72. Let $X_1, \ldots, X_n$ $(n \ge 2)$ be a random sample from a $U(-\theta, 2\theta)$ distribution, where $\theta > 0$ is an unknown parameter. Let $\overline{X} = \sum_{i=1}^{n} X_i, X_{(1)} = min\{X_1, \ldots, X_n\}$ *and* $X_{(n)} = max(X_1, \ldots, X_n\}$. Which of the following statements are true?

(a) Maximum likelihood estimator of θ is min $\left\{X_{(1)}, \frac{X_{(n)}}{2}\right\}$

(b) Maximum likelihood estimator of θ is max $\left\{-X_{(1)}, \frac{X_{(n)}}{2}\right\}$

(c) Method of moments estimator of θ is $2\overline{X}$

(d) Method of moments estimator of θ is $\frac{2\overline{X}}{3}$

(JULY 2024)

73. Let $X_1, \ldots, X_n$ be independent and identically distributed $U(0,\theta), \theta > 0$ random variables. Define $X(n) = \max(X_1, \ldots, X_n)$ *and* $X_{(1)} = min\{X_1, \ldots, X_n)$. Which of the following statements are true?

(a) $Cov\left(\frac{X_{(n)}}{X_{(1)}}, X_{(n)}\right) = 0$

(b) $E\left(\frac{X_{(n)}}{X_{(1)}}\right) = \frac{E(X_{(1)})}{E(X_{(n)})}$

(c) $Cov\left(\frac{X_{(n)}}{X_{(1)}}, X_{(n)}\right) = 0$

(d) $Cov\left(In(X_{(1)}) - In(X_{(1)} + X_{(n)}), X_{(n)}\right) < 0$

(FEB. 2025)

74. Let $X_1, X_2, \ldots, X_n (n \ge 2)$ be a random sample from Uniform$(\theta, 1-\theta)$ distribution, where $-\infty < \theta < \frac{1}{2}$. The maximum likelihood estimator of θ is

(a) $\min\{1-\min\{X_1, X_2, \ldots, X_n\}, \max\{X_1, X_2, \ldots, X_n\}\}$

(b) $\max\{1-\min\{X_1, X_2, \ldots, X_n\}, \max\{X_1, X_2, \ldots, X_n\}\}$

(c) $\min\{\min\{X_1, X_2, \ldots, X_n\}, 1-\max\{X_1, X_2, \ldots, X_n\}\}$

(d) $\max\{\min\{X_1, X_2, \ldots, X_n\}, 1-\max\{X_1, X_2, \ldots, X_n\}\}$

(FEB. 2025)

75. Let P be the population proportion of units possessing a certain attribute in a population of N units. Let p be the sample proportion in a simple random sample (without replacement) of n units, $(2 \le n < N)$. Then an unbiased estimator of $P(1-P)$ is

(a) $\frac{(N-n)}{Nn}p(1-p)$ (b) $\frac{(N-n)}{(N-1)n}p(1-p)$

(c) $\frac{n}{(n-1)}p(1-p)$ (d) $\frac{(N-1)n}{N(n-1)}p(1-p)$

(FEB. 2025)

76. Let $X_1, X_2, \ldots, X_{13}$ be independent and identically distributed (i.i.d.) Poisson(θ) random variables, where $\theta > 0$. Then, which of the following statements are true?

(a) $(\sum_{i=1}^{8} X_i)(\sum_{i=8}^{13} X_i)$ is an unbiased estimator of $48\,\theta^2$.

(b) $\frac{1}{13}\sum_{i=1}^{13} X_i$ is method of moments estimator of θ.

(c) There does not exist any unbiased estimator of $e^{-7\theta}$.

(d) $(e^{X_7}, \sum_{i=1}^{6} X_i, \sum_{i=8}^{13} X_i)$ is a sufficient statistic for θ.

(FEB. 2025)

77. Let $X_1, X_2, \ldots, X_n$ be a random sample from an exponential distribution with probability density function

$$f(x|\theta) = \begin{cases} e^{-(x-\theta)} & if\ x \ge \theta \\ 0 & \text{otherwise,} \end{cases}$$

where $\theta \in \mathbb{R}$ is an unknown parameter. If $X_{(1)} = \min\{X_1, X_2, \ldots, X_n\}$, then which of the following statements are true?

(a) $\left(X_{(1)} - \frac{2}{n}\ln 5, X_{(1)}\right)$ is a 97% confidence interval for θ.

(b) $\left(X_{(1)} - \frac{2}{n}\ln 5, X_{(1)}\right)$ is a 96% confidence interval for θ.

(c) $\left(X_{(1)} - \frac{1}{n}\ln 20, X_{(1)}\right)$ is a 95% confidence interval for θ.

(d) $\left(X_{(1)} - \frac{1}{n}\ln 20, X_{(1)}\right)$ is a 96% confidence interval for θ.

(FEB. 2025)

78. Let $X_1, X_2, \ldots, X_n$ be a random sample of size n from $U(\theta, \theta+1)$ distribution, where $\theta \in \mathbb{R}$ is the unknown parameter. If $T_n = \min\{X_1, X_2, \ldots, X_n\}, n = 1, 2, \ldots$, then which of the following statements are true?

(a) T_n is an unbiased estimator of θ.

(b) $\lim_{n\to\infty} E_\theta(T_n) = \theta$ for all $\theta \in \mathbb{R}$.

(c) T_n is a consistent estimator of θ.

(d) $\max\{X_1, X_2, \ldots, X_n)$ is a consistent estimator of θ.

(JUNE 2025)

79. Consider a discrete random variable X with the probability mass function

$$P(X=0) = \frac{\theta}{3}, P(X=1) = 1 - \frac{\theta}{2}, P(X=2) = \frac{\theta}{6},$$

where $\theta \in (0,1)$ is an unknown parameter. In a random sample of size 90 from this distribution, the observed counts for X = 0,1 and 2 are 20, 60 and 10, respectively. Then, the maximum likelihood estimate of θ is

(a) $\frac{1}{3}$ (b) $\frac{1}{2}$

(c) $\frac{2}{3}$ (d) $\frac{3}{4}$

(JUNE 2025)

80. Suppose we want to estimate the population mean $\hat{Y}$ of a variable for a finite population of size 85, with 34 Statisticians and 51 Biologists. We consider the following sampling scheme:

A stratified random sample with 2 strata of Statisticians (Stratum-1) and Biologists (Stratum- 2), where 12 Statisticians and 15 Biologists are drawn from Stratum-1 and Stratum-2, respectively, using SRSWOR scheme. Denote $\hat{y}_S, \hat{y}_B$, and $\hat{y}$ as the mean of the variable among the Statistician sample, Biologist sample, and the combined sample, respectively. Which of the following is an unbiased estimator of $\hat{Y}$?

(a) $\hat{y}$ (b) $\frac{2\hat{y}_S + 3\hat{y}_B}{5}$

(c) $\frac{4\hat{y}_S+5\hat{y}_B}{9}$ (d) $\frac{\frac{\hat{y}_S}{12}+\frac{\hat{y}_B}{15}}{\frac{1}{12}+\frac{1}{15}}$

(JUNE 2025)

81. Let X be a random sample of size 1 from the probability density function

$$f(x|\theta) = \begin{cases} \frac{3}{\theta^3}(\theta - x)^2, & if\ 0 < x < \theta, \\ 0, & \text{otherwise.} \end{cases}$$

If $\left(\frac{X}{1-\lambda_1}, \frac{X}{1-\lambda_2}\right)$ is a confidence interval for with confidence coefficient $1-\alpha$, where $\lambda_i \in (0,1), i = 1,2, \lambda_1 < \lambda_2$, and $\alpha \in (0,1)$, then which of the following statements is true?

(a) $\lambda_2^2 - \lambda_1^2 = 1 - \alpha$ (b) $\lambda_2^3 - \lambda_1^3 = 1 - \alpha$

(c) $\lambda_2^2 - \lambda_1^2 = 4(1-\alpha)$ (d) $\lambda_2^3 - \lambda_1^3 = 9(1-\alpha)$

(JUNE 2025)

82. Let $X_1, X_2, \ldots, X_n$ be independent and identically distributed random variables with the probability density function

$$f(x|\theta) = \begin{cases} e^{-(x-\theta)} & \text{if } x \geq \theta, \\ 0 & \text{otherwise,} \end{cases}$$

where $\theta \in \mathbb{R}$ is the unknown parameter. Further, let $Y = min(X_1, X_2, X_n)$. Which of the following are confidence intervals for θ with the confidence coefficient $(1-\alpha)$, where $\alpha \in (0,1)$?

(a) $\left(Y + \frac{1}{n}In\left(1-\frac{\alpha}{2}\right), Y - \frac{1}{n}In\left(1-\frac{\alpha}{2}\right)\right)$

(b) $\left(Y + \frac{1}{2n}In(\alpha), Y\right)$

(c) $\left(Y + \frac{2}{n}In\left(\frac{\alpha}{2}\right), Y + \frac{2}{n}In\left(1-\frac{\alpha}{2}\right)\right)$

(d) $\left(Y + \frac{1}{n}In\left(\frac{\alpha}{2}\right), Y + \frac{1}{n}In\left(1-\frac{\alpha}{2}\right)\right)$

(JUNE 2025)

83. Let $X_1, X_2, \ldots, X_n$ $(n \geq 3)$ be a random sample from the uniform distribution on the interval $(\theta_1 - \theta_2, \theta_1 + \theta_2)$, where $\theta_1 \in \mathbb{R}$ and $\theta_2 > 0$ are unknown parameters. Let $X_{(j)}$ be the jth order statistic, $j = 1, 2, \ldots, n$, and let $\hat{X} = \frac{1}{n}\sum_{i=1}^{n} X_i$. Here, $(X_{(1)}, X_{(2)})$ is a complete and sufficient statistic for (θ_1, θ_2). Then, which of the following statements are true?

(a) $\hat{X}$ is an unbiased estimator of θ_1

(b) $(\hat{X} - X_{(1)})$ is an unbiased estimator of θ_2

(c) $\frac{X_{(1)}+X_{(2)}}{2}$ is the uniformly minimum variance unbiased estimator of θ_1

(d) $\frac{(n+1)(X_{(n)}-X_{(1)})}{2(n-1)}$ is the uniformly minimum variance unbiased estimator of θ_2

(JUNE 2025)

84. Let $X_1, X_2, \ldots, X_n (n \geq 2)$ be a random sample from a continuous distribution with the probability density function $f(x|\theta) = \frac{1}{2\theta}e^{-\frac{|x-\theta|}{\theta}}, x \in \mathbb{R}$, where $\theta(>0)$ is an unknown parameter. Let $U_n = \frac{1}{n}\sum_{i=1}^{n} X_i, V_n = \frac{1}{n}\sum_{i=1}^{n} X_i^2$, and $S_n^2 = \frac{1}{n-1}\sum_{i=1}^{n}(X_i - U_n)^2$. Then, which of the following statements are true?

(a) U_n is an unbiased estimator of θ

(b) S_n^2 is an unbiased estimator of θ^2

(c) $\frac{1}{3}V_n$ is a consistent estimator of θ^2

(d) The statistic (U_n, V_n) is complete

(Dec 2025)

85. Let X be a Binomial (n,p) random variable, where $n \in \{5,6\}$ and $p \in \left\{\frac{1}{4}, \frac{3}{4}\right\}$. If $X = 3$ is observed, then the maximum likelihood estimate of (n,p) is

(a) $\left(5, \frac{1}{4}\right)$ (b) $\left(5, \frac{3}{4}\right)$

(c) $\left(6, \frac{3}{4}\right)$ (d) $\left(6, \frac{1}{4}\right)$

(Dec 2025)

86. Let X be a single sample from an absolutely continuous distribution with probability density function

$$f(x|\theta) = \begin{cases} \frac{2}{\theta^2}(\theta - x), & \text{if } 0 < x < \theta \\ 0, & \text{otherwise,} \end{cases}$$

where $\theta > 0$ is unknown. Which of the following intervals is a 95% confidence interval for θ?

(a) $\left(X, \frac{X}{1-\sqrt{0.95}}\right)$ (b) $\left(X, \frac{X}{0.95}\right)$

(c) $\left(X, \frac{X}{\sqrt{0.95}}\right)$ (d) $(0.95X, X)$

(Dec 2025)

87. Let $X_1, X_2, X_n, (n \geq 2)$ be a random sample from an Exponential distribution with the probability density function

$$f(x|\mu,\sigma) = \begin{cases} \frac{1}{\sigma}\exp\left(\frac{\mu - x}{\sigma}\right), & \text{if } x > \mu \\ 0, & \text{otherwise} \end{cases}$$

where parameters μ and σ are unknown and positive. Let $\bar{X}_n, S_n^2$ and $X_{1:n}$ denote the sample mean, the sample variance and the sample smallest order statistic, respectively and let $\theta = \frac{\sigma}{\mu}$. Then which of the following statements are true?

(a) $S_n(X_{1:n})^{-1}$ is a consistent estimator of θ

(b) $(\bar{X}_n - X_{1:n})(X_{1:n})^{-1}$ is a consistent estimator of θ

(c) $(\bar{X}_n - X_{1:n})(\bar{X}_n - S_n)^{-1}$ is a consistent estimator of θ

(d) $S_n(\bar{X}_n)^{-1}$ is a consistent estimator of θ

(Dec 2025)

88. Let $X_1, X_2, \ldots, X_n$ $(n \geq 2)$ be a random sample from Uniform$\left[-\frac{3\theta}{2}, \frac{\theta}{2}\right]$ distribution, where $\theta > 0$ is an unknown parameter. Let $\bar{X}, X_{(1)}$ and $X_{(n)}$ denote respectively the mean, the smallest order statistic and the largest order statistic of the sample. Then which of the following statements are true?

(a) The method of moments estimator of θ is $-2\bar{X}$

(b) The method of moments estimator of θ is $2\bar{X}$

(c) The maximum likelihood estimator of θ is $\min\left\{-\frac{2X_{(1)}}{3}, 2X_{(n)}\right\}$

(d) The maximum likelihood estimator of is θ $\max\left\{-\frac{2X_{(1)}}{3}, 2X_{(n)}\right\}$

(Dec 2025)

89. Let $X_1, X_2, \ldots, X_n (n > 5)$ be independent random variables such that $X_t = \alpha + \alpha^2 t + \epsilon_t$, for $t = 1, \ldots, n$,

where, $\epsilon_1, \epsilon_2, \dots, \epsilon_n$ are independent and identically distributed $N(0, \sigma^2)$ random variables. Here $\alpha \in \mathbb{R}$ and $\sigma > 0$ are unknown parameters. Which of the following statements are true?

(a) $(X_1, X_2, \dots, X_n)$ is a sufficient statistic for (α, σ)

(b) $(\sum_{t=1}^{n} X_t, \sum_{t=1}^{n} tX_t, \sum_{t=1}^{n} t^2 X_t^2)$ is a jointly minimal sufficient statistic for (α, σ)

(c) $X_4 - X_3 - X_2 + X_1$ is an ancillary statistic

(d) $\frac{X_4 + X_1 - X_2 - X_3}{X_5 + X_2 - X_3 - X_4}$ is an ancillary statistic

(Dec 2025)

90. Consider the simple linear regression model $Y_i = \beta x_i + \epsilon_i, i = 1, 2, \dots, n$, where $\beta > 0, \sum_{i=1}^{n} x_i^2 > 0$, and the uncorrelated errors $\epsilon_i, i = 1, 2, \dots, n$, have zero mean and finite variance $\sigma^2 (> 0)$. Let $\tilde{\beta}_1 = \sum_{i=1}^{n} a_i^* Y_i$, where a_i^*'s minimize $E(\sum_{i=1}^{n} a_i Y_i - \beta)^2$ with respect to scalars $a_1, a_2, \dots, a_n$. Let $\tilde{\beta}_2$ be the ordinary least squares estimator of β. Which of the following statements are true?

(a) $\mathrm{Var}(\tilde{\beta}_1) > \mathrm{Var}(\tilde{\beta}_2), \mathrm{E}(\tilde{\beta}_1 - \beta)^2 > \mathrm{E}(\tilde{\beta}_2 - \beta)^2$

(b) $\mathrm{Var}(\tilde{\beta}_1) < \mathrm{Var}(\tilde{\beta}_2), \mathrm{E}(\tilde{\beta}_1 - \beta)^2 < \mathrm{E}(\tilde{\beta}_2 - \beta)^2$

(c) $\mathrm{Var}(\tilde{\beta}_1) > \mathrm{Var}(\tilde{\beta}_2), \mathrm{E}(\tilde{\beta}_1) < \mathrm{E}(\tilde{\beta}_2)$

(d) $\mathrm{Var}(\tilde{\beta}_1) < \mathrm{Var}(\tilde{\beta}_2), \mathrm{E}(\tilde{\beta}_1) > \mathrm{E}(\tilde{\beta}_2)$

Answer Key

1	**2**	**3**	**4**	**5**	**6**	**7**	**8**	**9**	**10**
c	b;c,d	c,d	a,b,c,d	c,d	c	b,d	c	a,c,d	c,d
11	**12**	**13**	**14**	**15**	**16**	**17**	**18**	**19**	**20**
c	c,d	a	c	b,d	c,d	a,b,c,d	a	a,b,c,d	a,b,c,d
21	**22**	**23**	**24**	**25**	**26**	**27**	**28**	**29**	**30**
b,c	d	a,c	c	a,c,d	a,c	c	d	b,c	a,c
31	**32**	**33**	**34**	**35**	**36**	**37**	**38**	**39**	**40**
c	b	c,d	b	d	a,b	a,b,c,d	a,b,c,d	b	a,c,d
41	**42**	**43**	**44**	**45**	**46**	**47**	**48**	**49**	**50**
d	d	a,c,d	a,d	b	d	a,b,c,d	d	a,b,c,d	c,d
51	**52**	**53**	**54**	**55**	**56**	**57**	**58**	**59**	**60**
c	b	b,c	b,c,d	a,c,d	c	d	d	a, c	a,b,c
61	**62**	**63**	**64**	**65**	**66**	**67**	**68**	**69**	**70**
b	c	a	b	c, d	d	a	c	c	b
71	**72**	**73**	**74**	**75**	**76**	**77**	**78**	**79**	**80**
b,c,d	b,c	a,b,c	c	d	b,c	b,c	b,c	c	b
81	**82**	**83**	**84**	**85**	**86**	**87**	**88**	**89**	**90**
b	c,d	a,c,d	a,c	b	a	a,b,c	a,d	a,d	b

:: Explanations ::

1. **Explanation: (c)**

X_i 's are iid $N(\mu, \sigma^2)$ $i = 1, 2, .., n$

Where, μ and σ^2 are unknown

$\hat{\sigma}^2_{MLE} = \frac{1}{n} S^2$ is a biased mle of σ^2

$\hat{\sigma}^2_{UMVUE} = \frac{s^2}{n-1}$ is an UMVVE of σ^2

Where $s^2 = \sum_{i=1}^{n} (X_i - \bar{X})^2$

$MSE\ (\hat{\sigma}^2_{MLE}) = Var\left(\frac{s^2}{n}\right) + \left[Bias\left(\frac{s^2}{n}\right)\right]^2$

$= \frac{1}{n^2} Var\ (s^2) + \left[-\frac{1}{n}\sigma^2\right]^2$

$= \frac{2(n-1)}{n^2}\sigma^4 + \frac{1}{n^2}\sigma^4$

MSE $(\hat{\sigma}^2_{MLE}) = \frac{2n-1}{n^2}\sigma^4$

MSE $(\hat{\sigma}^2_{UMVUE}) = Var\left(\frac{s^2}{n-1}\right)$

$= \frac{1}{(n-1)^2} 2(n-1)\sigma^4 = \frac{2}{n-1}\sigma^4$

$\therefore \frac{2n-1}{n^2} < \frac{2}{n-1}$

MSE $(\sigma^2_{MLE}) < MSE(\sigma^2_{UMVUE})$

So, option (c) is correct.

2. **Explanation: (b), (c), (d)**

X_1 has density $f_1(x) = \frac{1}{\theta} e^{-\frac{x_1}{\theta}}$; $x > 0$

X_2 has density $f_2(x) = \frac{2}{\theta} e^{-\frac{2x_2}{\theta}}; x > 0$

X_1 and X_2 are independent.

The likelihood function is

$L(x) = f(x_1, x_2) \qquad = f(x_1) f(x_2)$

$= \frac{1}{\theta} e^{-\frac{x_1}{\theta}} \frac{2}{\theta} e^{-\frac{2x_2}{\theta}}$

$= \frac{2}{\theta^2} e^{-\frac{(x_1 + 2x_2)}{\theta}} : x > 0$

$= g\{x_1 + 2x_2, \theta\}. h(x)$

By factorization theorem, $T = X_1 + 2X_2$ is sufficient for θ

$E[g(T)] = 0$

$\Rightarrow g(T) = 0$

Then, $T = X_1 + 2X_2$ is complete for θ

$E\left[\frac{1}{2}(X_1 + 2X_2)\right] = \frac{1}{2}[E(X_1) + 2E(X_2)] = \frac{1}{2}\left[\theta + 2\frac{\theta}{2}\right] = \theta$

$\Rightarrow \frac{1}{2}(X_1 + 2X_2)$ is an unbiased for θ

So, option b, c and d are correct.

3. **Explanation: (c), (d)**

$X_i \sim N(\mu, \sigma^2)$; $i = 1, 2, .., n$

Where μ and σ^2 are unknown

Maximum likelihood estimator of $\sigma^2 = \frac{1}{n}\sum_{i=1}^{n}(X_i - \bar{X})^2$

which is biased estimators of σ^2

Maximum likelihood estimator of $\sigma^2 = \hat{\sigma}^2_{mle} = \frac{1}{n}\sum_{i=1}^{n}(X_i - \bar{X})^2$

MSE $(\hat{\sigma}^2_{MLE}) = Var\ (\hat{\sigma}^2_{MLE}) + [Bias\ (\hat{\sigma}^2_{MLE})]^2$

$= \frac{1}{n^2} 2(n-1)\sigma^4 + \frac{1}{n^2}\sigma^4 = \frac{2n-1}{n^2}\sigma^4$

MSE $(\hat{\sigma}^2_{MVUE}) = Var\ (\hat{\sigma}^2_{UMVUE}) = \frac{2}{n-1}\sigma^4$

MSE $(\hat{\sigma}^2_{MLE}) < MSE(\hat{\sigma}^2_{UMVUE})$

MLE are consistent estimator

UMVUE are asymptotically consistent

$\lim_{n \to \infty} Var\ (\hat{\sigma}^2_{UMVUE}) = 0$ and $E(\hat{\sigma}^2_{UMVUE}) = \sigma^2$

Both mle & UMVUE are asymptotically constitent estimator

$\hat{\sigma}^2_{MLE} = \frac{1}{n-1}\sum_{i=1}^{n}(X_i - \bar{X})^2$ is an unbiased estimator of σ^2

$\hat{\sigma}^2_{MLE} = \frac{1}{n}\sum_{i=1}^{n}(X_i - \bar{X})^2$ is another estimator (biased) for σ^2

$MSE(\hat{\sigma}^2_{MLE}) < MSE(\hat{\sigma}^2_{UMVUE})$

So, option (c) and (d) are correct.

4. Explanation: (a), (b), (c), (d)

$X_1, X_2, \ldots, X_{25}$ be iid observation form uniform $U\left[\theta - \frac{1}{2}, \theta + \frac{1}{2}\right]$ θ is unknown parameter.

Sample mean $= \overline{X}$

$E(\overline{X}) = \frac{1}{n}\sum_{i=1}^{n} E(X_i) = \frac{1}{25}\sum_{i=1}^{25} E(X_i)$

$= \frac{1}{25}\sum_{i=1}^{25}\left[\frac{\theta+\frac{1}{2}+\theta-\frac{1}{2}}{2}\right] = \theta$

Sample mean is an unbiased estimator of θ. $\overline{X}$ is not function of sufficient estimator so $\overline{X}$ is not an UMVUE for θ

The order statistic are

$X_{(1)} \le X_{(2)} \le \cdots \le X_{(25)}$

Sample median $= \left(\frac{n+1}{2}\right)^{th}$ term $= \left(\frac{25+1}{2}\right)^{th}$ term $= 13^{th}$ term. $= X_{(13)}$

The pdf of $X_{(13)}$ is

$f(X_{(13)}) = \frac{1}{\beta(13,13)} F^{12}(x).f(x)[1 - F(x)]^{12}$

$= \frac{\lfloor 26}{\lfloor 13 \lfloor 13}\left[x - \theta + \frac{1}{2}\right]^{12}\left[1 - x + \theta - \frac{1}{2}\right]^{12}$

$= \frac{25!}{12!12!}\left(\frac{1}{2} + x - \theta\right)^{12}\left(\frac{1}{2} - x + \theta\right)^{12}$

$= \frac{1}{\beta(13,13)}\left(\frac{1}{2} + x - \theta\right)^{12}\left(1 - \left(\frac{1}{2} + x - \theta\right)\right)^{12}$

$E[X_{(13)}] = \int_{\theta-\frac{1}{2}}^{\theta+\frac{1}{2}} x.\frac{1}{\beta(13,13)}\left(\frac{1}{2} + x - \theta\right)^{12}\left[1 - \left(\frac{1}{2} + x - \theta\right)\right]^{12}_{dx}$

Let $\frac{1}{2} + x - \theta = t$

$dx = dt$

$E(X_{(13)}) = \frac{1}{\beta(13,13)}\int_0^1\left(t + \theta - \frac{1}{2}\right) t^{12}(1-t)^{12}\,dt$

$= \frac{1}{\beta(13,13)}\left[\int_0^1 t^{13}(1.t)^{12}\,dt + \left(\theta - \frac{1}{2}\right)\right]\int_0^1 t^{12}(1-t)^{12}dt$

$= \frac{1}{\beta(13,13)}\left[\beta(14,13) + \left(\theta - \frac{1}{2}\right)\beta(13,13)\right]$

$= \frac{\lfloor 26 \ \lfloor 14 . \lfloor 13}{\lfloor 13 \lfloor 13 \lfloor 27} + \theta - \frac{1}{2} = \frac{13}{26} + \theta - \frac{1}{2}$

$= \theta$

$X_{(13)}$ is an unbiased for θ

$X_{(13)}$ is not a function of sufficient

So, $X_{(13)}$ = sample median is not an UMVUE for θ

Option a, b, c and d are correct.

5. Explanation: (c), (d)

$f(x,\lambda) = \lambda e^{-2x}; x > 0, \lambda > 0$ is unknown.

X is discretized to give

$Y = K$ if $K < X \le K + 1; K = 0, 1, 2, \ldots$

$\overline{Y} = \frac{1}{n}\sum_{i=1}^{n} Y_i$

$P(a < X \le b) = F_X(b) - F_X(a) = (1 - e^{-2b}) - (1 - e^{-2a}) - e^{-2a} - e^{-2b}$

$P(K < X \le K+1) = e^{-2k} - e^{-2(K+1)}$

$E(Y) = \sum_{K=0}^{n} K\ P(K < X \le K+1)$

$= (e^{-\lambda} - e^{-2\lambda}) + 2(e^{-2\lambda} - e^{-3\lambda}) + 3(e^{-3\lambda} - e^{-4\lambda}) + \ldots\ldots\ldots$

$= e^{-\lambda} + e^{-2\lambda} + e^{-3\lambda} + \ldots\ldots$

$E(Y) = \frac{e^{-\lambda}}{1-e^{-\lambda}}$

$\overline{Y} = \frac{e^{-\lambda}}{1-e^{-\lambda}}$

$\frac{1}{\overline{Y}} = \frac{1-e^{-\lambda}}{e^{-\lambda}} \Rightarrow \hat{\lambda} = \log\left(1 + \frac{1}{y}\right)$ *is MME* of λ

Which is same as mle of λ

So, option (c) and (d) are correct.

6. Explanation: (c)

7. Explanation: (b), (d)

$X_1, X_2, \ldots X_n$ $(n \ge 3)$ be a random sample form $U(\theta - 5, \theta - 3)$

$f(x) = \frac{1}{2}; \theta - 5 < x_i < \theta - 3$

The likelihood function is

$L = \prod_{i=1}^{n} f(n;)$

$= \frac{1}{2^n}; \theta - 5 \le x_{(1)} \le \ldots < x_{(n)} < \theta - 3$

$= \frac{1}{2^n} I_{(\theta-5, X_{(n)})}(X_{(1)}) \ldots\ldots I_{(X_{(1)},\theta-3)}(X_{(n)})$

$= g(X_{(1)}, X_{(n)}, \theta)\cdot h(x)$

$\therefore (X_{(1)}, X_{(n)})$ is jointly sufficient for θ

$E(X_{(1)}) = \frac{n(\theta-5)+\theta-3}{n+1} = \frac{(n+1)\theta-5n-3}{n+1}$

$E(X_{(1)}) = \theta - \frac{(5n+3)}{n+1}$

$E(X_{(n)}) = \frac{n(\theta-3)+\theta-5}{n+1} = \frac{\theta(n+1)-3n-5}{n+1}$

$E(X_{(n)}) = \theta - \frac{(3n+5)}{n+1}$

$E\left[X_{(n)} + \frac{3n+5}{n+1}\right] = \theta$ ________ (1)

$E\left[X_{(1)} + \frac{5n+3}{n+1}\right] = \theta$ ________ (2)

Subtract equation (1) form equation (2)

$E\left[X_{(1)} + \frac{5n+3}{n+1} - X_{(n)} - \frac{(3n+5)}{n+1}\right] = 0$

$E\left[X_{(1)} - X_{(n)} + 2\frac{(n-1)}{n+1}\right] = 0$

$E\left(g(X_{(1)}, X_{(n)})\right) = 0$

$g(X_{(1)}, X_{(n)}) \ne 0$

$(X_{(1)}, X_{(n)})$ is not complete far θ

$X_{(n)} + 3$ is not unbiased for θ

$E\left[X_{(1)} + \frac{5n+3}{n+1}\right] = \theta$

As $n \to \infty$ and $E[X_{(1)} + 3] = \theta$

$X_{(1)} + 3$ is consistent for θ

The distribution of $X_1 + X_2 - 2X_3$ is independent of θ so, $X_1 + X_2 - 2X_3$ is an ancillary statistic

So, option (b) and (d) are correct

8. Explanation: (c)

X_1 and X_2 are iid random variables each following exponential distribution with mean θ the common pdf is

$f(x) = \frac{1}{\theta} e^{-\frac{x}{\theta}}; 0 < x < \infty, \theta > 0$

Conditional distribution of X_2 given $X_1 + X_2 = t$ is

$P(X_2 \mid X_1 + X_2 = t) = \frac{P(X_2, X_1+X_2=t)}{P(X_1+X_2=t)}$

$X_1 \sim \exp\left(\frac{1}{\theta}\right)$ and $X_2 \sim \exp\left(\frac{1}{\theta}\right)$

X_1 & X_2 are iid

$X_1 + X_2 \sim$ Gamma $\left(\frac{1}{\theta}, 2\right)$

$P(X_1+X_2=t)=\frac{e^{-\frac{t}{\theta}}\cdot t}{\theta^2};t>0$

$P(X_2,X_1+X_2=t)=P(X_2,X_1=t-x_2)=$

$P_{X_1}(x_2)\,P_{X_2}(t-x_2)$

$=\frac{1}{\theta}e^{-\frac{x_2}{\theta}}\frac{1}{\theta}e^{-\frac{(t-x_2)}{\theta}}=\frac{1}{\theta^2}e^{-\frac{t}{\theta}}$

$P(X_2\mid X_1+X_2=t)=\frac{\frac{1}{\theta^2}e^{-\frac{t}{\theta}}}{\frac{1}{\theta^2}t\,e^{-\frac{t}{\theta}}}=\frac{1}{t}0<X_2<t$

$=\frac{1}{t};0<x_2<t$

$X_2\mid X_1+X_2$ is sufficient for θ

So, option (c) is correct

9. Explanation: (a), (c), (d)

$X_i's, i=1,2,\dots,n$ are iid with pdf

$f(x)=\frac{1}{2}\lambda^3.x^2\,e^{-\lambda x},x>0,\lambda>0$

Option (a) and (c)

$E\left[\frac{2}{n}\sum_{i=1}^{n}\frac{1}{X_i}\right]=\frac{2}{n}\sum_{i=1}^{n}E\left[\frac{1}{X_i}\right]$

$E\left[\frac{1}{X}\right]=\int_0^\infty\frac{1}{x}f(x)dx=\frac{\lambda^3}{2}\int_0^\infty x^{2-1}e^{-\lambda x}dx=\frac{\lambda^3}{2}\frac{\sqrt{2}}{\lambda^2}$

[Using Gamma integral]

$=\frac{\lambda}{2}$

$E\left[\frac{2}{n}\sum_{i=1}^{n}\frac{1}{X_i}\right]=\lambda$

$\frac{2}{n}\sum_{i=1}^{n}\frac{1}{X_i}$ is an unbiased estimator of λ

$Var\left(\frac{2}{n}\sum_{i=1}^{n}\frac{1}{X_i}\right)=\frac{4}{n^2}.n\,Var\left(\frac{1}{X_i}\right)=\frac{4}{n}\,Var\left(\frac{1}{X_i}\right)$

As $n\to\infty$, $Var\left(\frac{2}{n}\sum_{i=1}^{n}\frac{1}{X_i}\right)\to 0$

$E\left[\frac{2}{n}\sum_{i=1}^{n}\frac{1}{X_i}\right]\to\lambda$

So, $\frac{2}{n}\sum_{i=1}^{n}\frac{1}{X_i}$ is also consistent estimator of λ

Option (b) and (d)

$E(X_1)=\int_0^\infty x\,f(x)dx=\int_0^\infty x.\frac{\lambda^3}{2}x^2\,e^{-\lambda x}dx$

$=\frac{\lambda^3}{2}\int_0^\infty x^3\,e^{-\lambda x}dx=\frac{3}{\lambda}$

$E\left[\frac{1}{3n}\sum_{i=1}^{n}X_i\right]=\frac{1}{3n}\sum_{i=1}^{n}\frac{3}{\lambda}=\frac{1}{\lambda}$

As $n\to\infty$, $Var\left(\frac{\sum X_i}{3n}\right)\to 0$

$\frac{1}{3n}\sum_{i=1}^{n}X_i$ is consistent for $\frac{1}{\lambda}$

Using invariance property of consistent

$\frac{3n}{\sum X_i}$ is also consistent for λ

But $\frac{3n}{\sum_{i=1}^{n}X_i}$ is not unbiased for λ because unbiased does not follow invariance property

So, option (a), (c) and (d) are correct

10. Explanation: (c), (d)

$X_i\sim U(\theta-2,\theta+2); i=1,2,3,\dots n$

$X_i's$ are iid and $f(x_i)=\frac{1}{4};\ \theta-2\le x_i\le\theta+2$

The likelihood function is

$L(\tilde{x})=\frac{1}{4^n};\ \theta-2<x_{(1)}\le x_{(2)}\le\dots\le x_{(n)}\le\theta+2$

The likelihood function is constant so

$x_{(1)}>\theta-2$ and $x_{(n)}\le\theta+2$

$\theta<X_{(1)}+2\,\theta\ge X_{(n)}-2$

θ lies between

$X_{(n)}-2<\theta<X_{(1)}+2$

Every convex linear combination $(X_{(n)}-2,X_{(1)}+2)$ are mle of θ

The convex linear combination are:

$\alpha.(X_{(n)}-2)+(1-\alpha)(X_{(1)}+2)$

Where $0<\alpha<1$

Then, $\frac{X_{(1)}+X_{(n)}}{2}$ and $\frac{1}{4}(X_{(1)}-2)+\frac{3}{4}(X_{(n)}-2)$ are convex linear combination of the internal

So, option (c) and (d) are correct

11. Explanation: (c)

For observed value of X is 3

$x\ \backslash(\theta_1,\theta_2)$	$\left(\frac{1}{3},3\right)$	$\left(\frac{1}{2},2\right)$	$\left(2,\frac{1}{2}\right)$	$\left(3,\frac{1}{3}\right)$
3	$\frac{8}{11}$	$\frac{5}{7}$	$\frac{3}{4}$	$\frac{2}{3}$

At $(\theta_1,\theta_2)=\left(2,\frac{1}{2}\right)$, the $P_{\theta_1,\theta_2}(x)$ is maximum

Then mle of $\theta_1=2$ and $\theta_2=\frac{1}{2}$

So, option (c) is correct

12. Explanation: (c), (d)

$X_1,X_2,\dots,X_n$ be a random sample from $U(\theta,3\theta),\theta>0$

$X_{(n)}=\max\{X_1,X_2,\dots,X_n\}$ and $X_{(1)}=\min\{X_1,X_2,\dots,X_n\}$

$E(X_{(1)})=\frac{n\theta+3\theta}{n+1}=\frac{\theta(n+3)}{n+1}$

$E(X_{(n)})=\frac{3n\theta+3\theta}{n+1}=\frac{\theta(3n+1)}{n+1}$

$E\left[\frac{X_{(n)}-X_{(1)}}{2}\right]=\frac{1}{2}\left[E(X_{(n)})-E(X_{(1)})\right]$

$=\frac{1}{2}\left[\frac{\theta(3n+1)}{n+1}-\frac{\theta(n+3)}{n+1}\right]$

$=\frac{\theta}{2(n+1)}[3n+1-n-3]$

$=\frac{\theta}{2(n+1)}[2n-2]=\frac{\theta(n-1)}{n+2}$

$\frac{X_{(n)}-X_{(1)}}{2}$ is not an unbiased a function of θ

Likelihood function is

$L=\prod_{i=1}f(x_i)=\frac{1}{(2\theta)^n};\ \theta\le x_{(1)}<\dots;\le x_{(n)}\le 3\theta$

$(X_{(1)},X_{(n)})$ is jointly sufficient for θ

$E[g(X_{(1)},X_{(n)})]=0$

$\Rightarrow g(X_{(1)},X_{(n)})\ne 0$

$(X_{(1)},X_{(n)})$ is not complete

$E\left[\frac{1}{2n}\sum_{i=1}^{n}X_i\right]=\frac{1}{2n}\sum_{i=1}^{n}E(X_i)=\frac{1}{2n}.n2\theta=\theta$

$\frac{1}{2n}\sum_{i=1}^{n}X_i$ is an unbiased estimator of θ

The distribution of $\frac{X_{(n)}}{X_{(1)}+X_{(n)}}$ is independent of θ

So, $\frac{X_{(n)}}{X_{(1)}+X_{(n)}}$ is an ancillary statistic

So, option (c) and (d) are correct

13. Explanation: (b)

X is exponential random variable with mean $1/\theta$

$Y=K$, if $K=Y<K+1, K=0,1,2,\dots$

$P[a\le X<b]=F(b)-F(a)$

$=(1-e^{-\theta b})-(1-e^{-\theta a})$

$=e^{-\theta a}-e^{-\theta b}$

$Y=0$ if $0\le X<1$

$Y=1$ if $1\le X<2$

$Y=2$ if $2\le X<3$

$E(Y)=\sum_{y=0}^{\infty}y\,P(X=y)$

$=1\times P(X=1)+2P(X=2)+3P(Y=3)+\cdots$

$= (e^{-\theta} - e^{-2\theta}) + 2(e^{-2\theta} - e^{-3\theta}) + 3(e^{-3\theta} - e^{-4\theta}) + \dots$

$= e^{-\theta} + e^{-2\theta} + e^{-3\theta} + \cdots$

$= \frac{e^{-\theta}}{1-e^{-\theta}}$

$E(\bar{Y}) = \frac{e^{-\theta}}{1-e^{-\theta}}$

$\bar{Y}$ is consistent estimator of $\frac{e^{-\theta}}{1-e^{-\theta}}$

Consistent estimator has invariance property

$\log\left(1 + \frac{n}{\sum_{i=1}^{\infty} X_i}\right)$ is consistent for θ

So, option (b) is correct

14. Explanation: (c)

X be a random variable having poisson (λ)

To estimate $\lambda^5, T = X(X-1)(X-2)(X-3)(X-4)$

$E(T) = \sum_{x=0}^{\infty} x(x-1)(x-2)(x-3)(x-4) \cdot \frac{e^{-\lambda}.\lambda^x}{x!}$

$= e^{-\lambda} \sum_{x=0}^{\infty} \frac{\lambda^{x-5}}{(x-5)!}$

$= e^{-\lambda} . \lambda^5 \cdot e^{\lambda}$

$E(T) = \lambda^5$

T is an unbiased estimator of λ^5

T is function of complete sufficient for λ, so

T is an UMVUE

So, option (c) is correct

15. Explanation: (b), (d)

$X_i's$ are Geom (p)

$P(X_i = x) = (1-p)^{x-1}p\,;\ x = 1, 2, 3, \dots$

$P(X_i = 1) = p$

$f \to$ no. of $X_i's$ equal to 1

$f = 0, 1, 2, 3, \dots, n$

$f \sim B(n, p)$

$E[f] = np$

$E\left[\frac{f}{n}\right] = p$

$\therefore \frac{f}{n}$ is an unbiased estimate of p

$Var(f) = np(1-p)$

$Var\left(\frac{f}{n}\right) = \frac{1}{n^2} Var(f) = \frac{np(1-p)}{n^2} = \frac{p(1-p)}{n}$

The likelihood function is given by :

$L(p) = (1-p)^{\sum x_i - n} \cdot p$

$\log L = (\sum x_i - n)\log(1-p) + \log p$

$\frac{\partial}{\partial p}\log L = -\frac{(\sum x_i - n)}{1-p} + \frac{1}{p} = 0$

$p = \frac{n}{\sum_{i=1}^{n} X_i}$

m.l.e of $p = \frac{n}{\sum_{i=1}^{n} X_i}$, so option (b) & (d) are correct

16. Explanation: (c), (d)

If $X_1, X_2, \dots . X_n$ be a random sample from $U(\theta - 1, \theta + 1)$ of size 11

$f(x_i) = \frac{1}{2} : \theta - 1 \le x_i \le \theta + 1$

The likelihood

$L = \frac{1}{2^n} : \theta - 1 < x_{(1)} \le \cdots \le x_{(n)} \le \theta + 1$

Likelihood function is constant

$X_{(1)} \ge \theta - 1$ and $X_{(n)} < \theta + 1$

$\theta < X_{(1)} + 1$ and $\theta > X_{(n)} - 1$

$\Rightarrow X_{(n)} - 1 < \theta < X_{(1)} + 1$

$\Rightarrow X_{(1)} - 1 < \theta < X_{(1)} + 1$

$X_{(11)} = 0.3$ and $X_{(1)} = -0.96$

$0.3 - 1 < \theta < -0.96 + 1$

$-0.7 < \theta < 0.04$

The sample value lies between $(-0.7, 0.04)$ are m.l.e of θ

ml.es are 0.02 and -0.54

So, option (c) & (d) are correct

17. Explanation: (a), (b), (c), (d)

$f(x) = e^{-(x-\theta)}\,; x > \theta$

$Y_i = X_i - \theta$

$g(y) = e^{-y}\,; y > 0$

$Y_i \sim Exp\ (1)$

$\min\{Y_1, Y_2, \dots Y_n\} = Y_{(1)} \sim Exp(n)$

Option (a)

$P\left[X_{(1)} + \frac{1}{n}\log\alpha < \theta < X_{(1)}\right] = P[0 < X_{(1)} - \theta < -\frac{1}{n}\log\alpha] = P\left[Y_{(1)} < -\frac{1}{n}\log\alpha\right]$

$= n\int_0^{-\frac{1}{n}\log\alpha} e^{-ny}\,dy = \left[\frac{e^{-ny}}{-1}\right]_0^{-\frac{1}{n}\log\alpha}$

$= 1 - \alpha$

$\therefore \left[X_{(1)} + \frac{1}{n}\log\alpha, X_{(1)}\right]$ is $100(1-\alpha)\%$ confidence interval for θ

Similarly, all other options are also $100(1-\alpha)\%$CI for θ)

So, option a, b, c & d are correct

18. Explanation: (a)

$X_i \sim U(0, \theta) \qquad i = 1, 2, \dots, n, \qquad \theta > 0$

$X_{(1)} \le X_{(2)} \le \ldots \le X_{(n)}$ be the order statistics.

Consider two unbiased estimators of θ is

$T_1 = 2\bar{X}$ and $T_2 = \frac{n+1}{n} X_{(n)}$

$Var(T_1) = 4\,Var(\bar{X})$

$= 4\,Var\left(\frac{1}{n}\sum_{i=1}^{n} X_i\right)$

$= \frac{4}{n} Var(X_i)$

$= \frac{4\theta^2}{12n} = \frac{\theta^2}{3n}$

$Var(T_2) = \frac{(n+1)^2}{n^2} Var(X_{(n)})$

$= \frac{(n+1)^2}{n^2} \cdot \frac{n\,\theta^2}{(n+1)^2(n+2)}$

$= \frac{\theta^2}{n(n+2)}$

$\lim_{n\to\infty} \frac{Var\ (T_2)}{Var\ (T_1)}$

$= \lim_{n\to\infty} \frac{\frac{\theta}{n(n+2)}}{\frac{\theta^2}{3n}}$

$\lim_{n\to\infty} \frac{3}{n+2} = 0$

So, option (a) is correct

19. Explanation: (a), (b), (c), (d)

$X_1, X_2, \dots, X_n, n \ge 3$ be a random sample from $N(\mu, 1)$ population where μ unknown

$Cov\ (X_1 - 3X_2 + 2X_3, \bar{X}_n)$

$= Cov\left(X_1 - 3\,X_2 + 2\,X_3, \frac{X_1 + X_2 + \cdots X_n}{n}\right)$

$= \frac{1}{n}Var(X_1)\frac{-3}{n}Var(X_2) + \frac{2}{n}Var(X_3)$

$= \frac{1}{n} - \frac{3}{n} + \frac{2}{n} = 0\ [Cov\ (X_i, X_j)\ will\ vanish]$

Cramer – Rao lower bound for an unbiased estimator of μ is $\frac{1}{I(\mu)}$

Where $E\left[\frac{\partial}{\partial\mu}\log L\right]^2 = I(\mu) = -E\left[\frac{\partial^2}{\partial\mu^2}\log L\right]$

The likelihood function is

$L = \frac{1}{(2\pi)^{n/2}} \cdot e^{\frac{-1}{2}\sum_{i=1}^{n}(x_i-\mu)^2}$

$\log L = \frac{-n}{2}\log(2\pi) - \frac{1}{2}\sum_{i=1}^{n}(x_i-\mu)^2$

$\frac{\partial}{\partial\mu}\log L = -\sum(x_i-\mu)$

$\frac{\partial^2}{\partial\mu}\log L = -n$

$I(\mu) = n$

CRLB far $\mu = \frac{1}{n}$

$Var\left(\bar{X}_n\right) = \frac{1}{n}$

$$Var\left[\frac{X_1+2X_2+3X_3+\cdots+nX_n}{\frac{n(n+1)}{2}}\right]$$

$$= \frac{4}{n^2(n+1)^2}\frac{n.(n+1)(2n+1)}{6}$$

$= \frac{2(2n+1)}{3n(n+1)}$

$\Rightarrow Var(\bar{X}_n) < Var\left[\frac{X_1+2X_2+3X_3+\ldots+nX_2}{\frac{n(n+1)}{2}}\right]$

$\sum_{i=1}^{n} X_i$ is sufficient for μ

$\therefore \bar{X} = \frac{\sum X_i}{n}$ is a function of sufficient for μ

So, option (a), (b), (c) & (d) are correct

20. Explanation: (a), (b), (c), (d)

$$f_\theta(x) = \frac{2}{\theta^2}(x-\theta);\ \theta \le x \le 2\theta, \theta > 0$$

There is only one sample, so sufficient statistic is X

We need identity the given options is/are confidence interval for θ with confidence coefficient $(1-\alpha)$ or not

If $P[t_1(x) < \theta < t_2(x)] = 1-\alpha$

Then $(t_1(x), t_2(x))$ be the C1 for θ with confidence coefficient $1-\alpha$. Now

Option (a):

$P\left[\frac{X}{2} < \theta < \frac{X}{1+\sqrt{\alpha}}\right] = P\left[\theta(1+\sqrt{\alpha}) < X < 2\theta\right]$

$= \int_{\theta(1+\sqrt{\alpha})}^{2\theta} f(x)\,dx = \frac{2}{\theta^2}\left[\frac{x^2}{2} - \theta x\right]_{\theta(1+\sqrt{\alpha})}^{2\theta}$

$= 1-\alpha$

So, $\left(\frac{X}{2}, \frac{X}{1+\sqrt{\alpha}}\right)$ is $100(1-\alpha)\%$ Confidence interval for θ

Similarly, we can check for option (b), (c), (d)

All are the confidence interval for θ with confidence coefficient $1-\alpha$

Then option (a), (b), (c), (d) are correct.

21. Explanation: (b), (c)

$f(x;\ \theta,\sigma) = \frac{0.9}{\sigma}.\phi\left(\frac{x-\theta}{\sigma}\right) + 0.1\,\phi(x-\theta)$

$X_i \sim N(\theta,\sigma^2)$ with probability 0.9

$X_i \sim N(\theta, 1)$ with probability 0.1

This model is parametric with parameter θ & σ

$\mu_1' = E(X) = 0.9\times\theta + 0.1\times\theta$

$\mu_1' = \theta$

Sample moment $= \bar{X}$

$\hat{\theta} = \bar{X}$

$\mu_2' = 0.9(\sigma^2+\theta^2) + 0.1(\theta^2+1)$

$\mu_2' = 0.9\sigma^2 + 0.1 + \theta^2$

Second sample moment $= \frac{1}{n}\sum_{i=1}^{n} X_i^2$

$\frac{1}{n}\sum X_{i=1}^2 = 0.9\sigma^2 + 1 + \theta^2$

$\frac{1}{n}\sum X_{i=1}^2 - \bar{X}^2 = 0.9 + 1$

$\hat{\sigma}^2 = \frac{1}{0.9}\left[\frac{1}{n}\sum(X_i-\bar{X})^2 - 1\right]$

So, Method of moments estimator for θ and σ exists

$E(\bar{X}) = \theta$

Sample mean is an unbiased and consistent estimator for θ

An unbiased and consistent estimator of θ both exists

So, option (b) and (c) are correct

22. Explanation: (d)

$X_1, X_2, \ldots, X_n$ be a random sample from $U(\theta, 5\theta)$

$f(x_i) = \frac{1}{4\theta};\ \theta < x_i < 5\theta$

The likelihood function

$L = \prod_{i=1}^{n} f(x_i) = \frac{1}{(4\theta)^n};\ \theta \le x_{(1)} \le x_{(2)} \le \cdots \le x_{(n)} \le 5\theta$

L is maximum when θ is minimum

$\theta \le x_{(1)}$ and $x_{(n)} \le 5\theta$

$\frac{X_{(n)}}{5} \le \theta \le X_{(1)}$

L is maximum at $\hat{\theta} = \frac{X_{(n)}}{5}$

So, maximum likelihood estimator of θ is $\hat{\theta} = \frac{X_{(n)}}{5} = \frac{\max\{X_1\ X_2 \ldots X_n\}}{5}$

So, option (d) is correct.

23. Explanation: (a), (c)

$X_1, X_2, \ldots, X_n$ be a random sample from $U(\theta, \theta+1)$

$f(x_i) = 1;\ \theta < x_i < \theta+1$

The likelihood function is

$L = 1;\ \theta \le x_{(1)} \le x_{(2)} \le \cdots \le x_{(n)} \le \theta+1$

$L =$

$1\, I_{(\theta, x_{(n)})}(x_{(1)}) \prod_{i=2}^{n-1} I_{(x_{(1)}, x_{(n-1)})}(x_{(i)})\, I_{(x_{(1)}, \theta+1)}(x_{(n)})$

$= g\{X_{(1)}, X_{(n)}, \theta\}.h(x)$

By factorization theorem, $(X_{(1)}, X_{(n)})$ is jointly sufficient for θ

$\Rightarrow (X_{(1)}, X_{(n)}+1)$ is also sufficient for θ

Option (a), (c) are correct

24. Explanation: (c)

25. Explanation: (a), (c), (d)

$X_1, X_2, \ldots X_n$ be independent and identically random variables with $N(\mu, 1)$

$X_i \sim N(\mu, 1);\ i = 1, 2, \ldots, n\ ;\ \mu \in [0, \infty]$

Let $\hat{\mu}$ be the MLE of μ

We know that MLE's consistent estimator

$\therefore \hat{\mu}$ is also consistent estimator of μ

Sample mean $(\bar{X}_n)$ is consistent estimator of μ

$\mu \ge 0$

$\hat{\mu} = \max\{\bar{X}_n, 0\}$

The likelihood function

$L = \prod_{i=1}^{n} f(x_i) = \prod_{i=1}^{n}\frac{1}{\sqrt{2\pi}}e^{-\frac{1}{2}(x_i-\mu)^2}$

$= \frac{1}{(2\pi)^{n/2}}e^{-\frac{1}{2}\sum_{i=1}^{n}(x_i-\mu)^2}$

$= \frac{1}{(2\pi)^{n/2}}e^{-\frac{1}{2}\left[\sum_{i=1}^{n}x_i^2 + n\mu^2 - 2\mu\sum x_i\right]}$

$= g\{\sum x_i, \mu\}\cdot h(x)$

By factorization theorem

$\therefore \sum_{i=1}^{n} x_i = n\bar{X}_n$ is sufficient for μ

So, option (a), (c) & (d) are correct

26. Explanation: (c)

$X_1, X_2, \dots X_n$ be a random sample from $N(\theta, 1)$ where $\theta \in \{1, 2\}$

MLE of θ is the value of θ at which the likelihood function of the random sample is maximum

$f(x_i) = \frac{1}{\sqrt{2\pi}} e^{\frac{-1}{2}(x_i-\theta)^2}; \ -\infty < x_i < \infty$

The likelihood function is

$L = \prod_{i=1}^{n} f(x_i) = \left(\frac{1}{\sqrt{2\pi}}\right)^n e^{\frac{-1}{2}\sum_{i=1}^{n}(x_i-\theta)^2}$

$\log L = \frac{-n}{2}\log 2\pi - \frac{1}{2}\sum_{i=1}^{n}(x_i-\theta)^2$

$\frac{\partial}{\partial\theta}\log L = \sum_{i=1}^{n} x_i - \theta = 0$

$\therefore \theta = \bar{X}$

But $\therefore \theta \in \{1, 2\}$ θ cannot be equal to $\bar{X}$ so, mle exists but it not equal to $\bar{X}$

27. Explanation: (d)

$X_1, X_2, \dots, X_n$ be a random sample from $N(\mu, \sigma^2)$

$f(x_i) = \frac{1}{\sigma\sqrt{2\pi}} e^{\frac{-1}{2}\left(\frac{x_i-\mu}{\sigma}\right)^2}; -\infty < x < \infty; \mu \in R; \sigma > 0$

μ is known & σ^2 is unknown

As we know $\frac{n s^2}{\sigma^2} \sim \chi^2_{(n)d.f}$

Where $s^2 = \frac{1}{n}\sum_{i=1}^{n}(X_i-\mu)^2$

$P[\chi^2_{n,1-\alpha/2} \le \chi^2 \le \chi^2_{n,\alpha/2}] = 1-\alpha$

$P[\chi^2_{n,1-\frac{\alpha}{2}} \le \frac{n s^2}{\sigma^2} \le \chi^2_{n,\alpha/2}] = 1-\alpha$

$P\left[\frac{n s^2}{\chi^2_{n,\alpha/2}} \le \sigma^2 < \frac{n s^2}{\chi^2_{n,1-\alpha/2}}\right] = 1-\alpha$

The $100(1-\alpha)\%$ Confidence interval for σ^2 is

$\left(\frac{n s^2}{\chi^2_{n,\alpha/2}}, \frac{n s^2}{\chi^2_{n,1-\alpha/2}}\right)$

$\therefore \left(\frac{\sum_{i=1}^{n}(X_i-\mu)^2}{\chi^2_{n,\alpha/2}}, \frac{\sum_{i=1}^{n}(X_i-\mu)^2}{\chi^2_{n,1-\alpha/2}}\right)$ is the $100(1-\alpha)\%$ C1 for σ^2

Option (d) is correct

28. Explanation: (b), (c)

Let $X_1, X_2, \dots X_n$ be a random sample from pdf

$f(x; \mu, \alpha) = \frac{1}{\sqrt{\alpha}}.(x-\mu)^{\alpha-1}e^{-(x-\mu)}; x \ge \mu \ ; -\infty < \mu < \infty$ and $\alpha > 0$

$\mu_1' = E(X) = \int_{\mu}^{\infty} x\frac{1}{\sqrt{\alpha}}(x-\mu)^{\alpha-1}e^{-(x-\mu)}dx$

$= \int_0^{\infty} x\frac{1}{\sqrt{\alpha}}.y^{\alpha-1}.e^{-y}dy \ (\because x-\mu = y)$

$\mu_1' = \int_0^{\infty}(y+\mu)\frac{1}{\sqrt{\alpha}}y^{\alpha-1}.e^{-y}dy$

$= \int_0^{\infty} y\frac{1}{\sqrt{\alpha}}.y^{\alpha-1}.e^{-y}dy + \mu\int_0^{\infty}\frac{1}{\sqrt{\alpha}}.y^{\alpha-1}.e^{-y}dy$

$\mu_1' = \alpha + \mu$

$\mu_2' = \int_r^{\infty} x^2\frac{1}{\sqrt{\alpha}}(x-\mu)^{\alpha-1}.e^{-(x-\mu)}dx$

$= \int_0^{\infty}(y+\mu)^2.\frac{1}{\sqrt{\alpha}}y^{\alpha-1}.e^{-y}dy$

$= \int_0^{\infty} y^2\frac{1}{\sqrt{\alpha}}e^{-y}.y^{\alpha-1}dy + \mu^2\int_0^{\infty}\frac{1}{\sqrt{\alpha}}e^{-y}y^{\alpha-1}dy +$

$2\mu\int_0^{\infty} y\frac{1}{\sqrt{\alpha}}y^{\alpha-1}e^{-y}dy$

$= \alpha(\alpha+1) + \mu^2 + 2\mu\alpha$

$\mu_2' = \alpha(\alpha+1) + \mu^2 + 2\mu\alpha$ and $\mu_1' = \alpha + \mu$

Now, equate these moments to sample moment

First sample moment, $m_1' = \bar{X}$

Second sample moment $m_2' = \frac{1}{n}\sum_{i=1}^{n}X_i^2$

$\bar{X} = \alpha + \mu$

$\bar{X}^2 = \alpha^2 + \mu^2 + 2\mu\alpha$

$\frac{1}{n}\sum_{i=1}^{n}X_i^2 = \alpha^2 + \alpha + \mu^2 + 2\mu\alpha$

$\frac{1}{n}\sum_{i=1}^{n}X_i^2 = \bar{X}^2 + \alpha$

$\hat{\alpha} = \frac{1}{n}\sum_{i=1}^{n}X_i^2 - \bar{X}^2$

$\hat{\alpha} = \frac{1}{n}\sum_{i=1}^{n}(X_i-\bar{X})^2$

$\hat{\mu} = \bar{X} - \hat{\alpha}$

$\hat{\mu} = \bar{X} - \frac{1}{n}\sum_{i=1}^{n}(X_i-\bar{X})^2$

Which is consistent estimator for μ

Option (b) & (c) are correct

Which is consistent estimator for α

29. Explanation: (a), (c)

$X_1, X_2, \dots, X_{2n+1}$ be a random sample from a uniform distribution $U(\theta-1, \theta+1)$

$f(x_i) = \frac{1}{2}; \ \theta-1 < x_i < \theta+1$

$T_1 =$ sample mean $= \bar{X} = \frac{1}{2n+1}\sum_{i=1}^{2n+1}X_i$

$E(T_i) = \frac{1}{2n+1}\sum_{i=1}^{n}E(X_i)$

$E(T_i) = \theta$ and $Var(T_i) = \frac{1}{(2n+1)^2}Var(X_i) = \frac{1}{2n+1}\cdot\frac{4}{12}$

As $n \to \infty$, $E(T_1) = \theta$ and $Var(T_1) = 0$

So T_1 is consistent far θ

T_1 is unbiased far θ

$T_2 =$ sample median $= \left(\frac{2n+1+1}{2}\right)^{th}$ term in the sample $=$ $(n+1)^{th}$ term in the sample$= X_{(n+1)}$

$f(x_{(n+1)}) = \frac{1}{\beta(n+1,n)}\cdot F^n(x)\cdot f(x)\,[1-F(x)]^n$

$= \frac{\Gamma(2n+1)}{\Gamma n\Gamma(n+1)}\cdot\left[\frac{x-\theta+1}{2}\right]^n\cdot\frac{1}{2}\cdot\left[1-\frac{x-\theta+1}{2}\right]^n$

$\Rightarrow E[X_{(n+1)}] = \theta$

$E[T_2] = \theta$

T_2 is unbiased for θ

$T_3 = \frac{T_1+T_2}{2}$

$E(T_3) = \theta$

T_3 is also unbiased for θ

T_1, T_2, T_3 all are unbiased for θ

$Var(T_3) = \frac{1}{4}[Var(T_1) + Var(T_2) + 2Var(T_1\,T_2)]$

We cannot say T_1 & T_2 are more efficient than T_3

$f(x_i) = \frac{1}{2}; \ \theta-1 \le x_i \le \theta+1$

$L = \frac{1}{2^n}: \theta-1 \le x_{(1)} \le x_{(2)} \dots \le x_{(2n+1)} \le \theta+1$

$= \frac{1}{(2)^n} I_{(\theta-1, X_{(2n+1)})}(x_{(1)})\text{h(x)}$

$= g(X_{(1)}, X_{(2n+1)}, \theta)$

$X_{(1)}, X_{(2n+1)}$ is sufficient for θ

So, optional (a) & (c) are correct

30. Explanation: (b)

We know that in case normal distribution $N(\theta, 1)$

M. L E of θ is $\bar{X}$(Sample mean)

$\theta \in \{\dots, -2, -1, 0, 1, 2, \dots\}$

θ takes only integer values

M.L E of θ is the integer closet to $\overline{X}$

So, option (b) is correct

31. Explanation: (a), (c), (d)

$X_i \sim N(\mu, \sigma^2)$; $i = 1,2,\ldots n; -\infty < \mu < \infty ; \sigma^2 > 0$

We Know That, sample variance $S^2 = \frac{1}{n-1}\sum_{i=1}^{n}(X_i - \overline{X})^2$

is complete Sufficient far σ^2

Result: T is complete & Sufficient for θ & $g(.)$ is function & $g(T)$ is an unbiased estimator for θ

Then $g(T)$ is an UMVUE Far θ.

$\therefore E(S^2) = \sigma^2$

$\therefore S^2 = \frac{1}{n-1}\sum_{i=1}^{n}(X_i - \overline{X})^2$ is an UMVUE Far σ^2

$E(S) \neq \sigma$

$So, S = \sqrt{\frac{\sum_{i=1}^{n}(X_i-\overline{X})^2}{n-1}}$ is not an UMVUE Far σ

$$f(x_i) = \frac{1}{\sigma\sqrt{2\pi}}\exp\left\{\frac{-1}{2}\left(\frac{x_i-\mu}{\sigma}\right)^2\right\}$$

$$L = \left(\frac{1}{\sigma\sqrt{2\pi}}\right)^n \exp\left\{\frac{-1}{2\sigma^2}\sum_{i=1}^{n}(x_i-\mu)^2\right\}$$

$$\log L = \frac{-n}{2}\log\sigma^2 + \frac{-n}{2}\log(2\pi) + \frac{-1}{2\sigma^2}\sum_{i=1}^{n}(X_i - \mu)^2$$

$$\frac{\partial^2 L}{\partial\sigma^2} = \frac{-n}{2}\frac{1}{\sigma^2} - \frac{1}{2(\sigma^2)^2}\sum_{i=1}^{n}(X_i - \mu)^2$$

$$\frac{\partial L}{\partial\sigma^2} = 0$$

$$\therefore \hat{\sigma}^2 = \frac{1}{n}\sum_{i=1}^{n}(X_i - \hat{\mu})^2$$

Mle of $\mu = \hat{\mu} = \overline{x}$

$$\sigma^2 = \frac{1}{n}\sum_{i=1}^{n}(x_i - \overline{x})^2$$

MLE of σ^2 is $\frac{1}{n}\sum_{i=1}^{n}(X_i - \overline{X})^2$

MLE's are consistent, So it has invariance property

$\sqrt{\frac{1}{n}\sum(X_i - \overline{X})^2}$ is an MLE far σ

So, option (a), (c), (d) are correct

32. Explanation: (a), (c)

$X_i's$ are © © d $U(1-\theta, 1+\theta)$

$\therefore f(x) = \frac{1}{2\theta}$; $1-\theta < x < 1+\theta$

$E(X_i) = 1$ and $Var(X_i) = \frac{\theta^2}{3}$

$\Rightarrow E(X_i^2) = Var(X_i) + \{E(X_i)\}^2$

$= \frac{\theta^2}{3} + 1^2$

$E(X_i^2) = \frac{\theta^2}{3} + 1$

For option ©

$$E\left[\frac{3}{n}\sum_{i=1}^{n}(X_i - 1)^2\right] = \frac{3}{n}\sum_{i=1}^{n}[EX_i^2 + 1 - 2X_i]$$

$$= \frac{3}{x}\sum_{i=1}^{n}\left[1 + \frac{\theta^2}{3} + 1 - 2\right]$$

$$= 3\left[1 + \frac{\theta^2}{3} - 1\right]$$

$$= \theta^2$$

$\therefore \frac{3}{n}\sum_{i=1}^{n}(X_i - 1)^2$ is an unbiased estimator far θ

For option (4)

$$E\left[\frac{3}{n}\sum_{i=1}^{n}(X_i - \overline{X})^2\right] \neq \theta^2$$

$\frac{3}{n}\sum_{i=1}^{n}(X_i - \overline{X})^2$ is not an unbiased estimator for θ^2

For option (1)

$f(x_i) = \frac{1}{2\theta}$; $1-\theta < x_i < 1+\theta$

The likelihood function is given by

$L = \frac{1}{(2\theta)^n}$; $1-\theta \le x_{(1)} \le x_{(2)} \le \cdots \ldots \le x_{(n)} < 1+\theta$

$L = \frac{1}{(2\theta)^n} I(x_{(1)})_{\{1-\theta, x_{(n)}\}} \ldots\ldots I(x_{(n)})_{\{x_{(1)}, 1+\theta\}}$

$= g\{X_{(1)}, X_{(n)}, \theta\}.h(x)$

$(X_{(1)}, X_{(n)})$ is jointly sufficient for θ

$(X_{(1)}, \overline{X}, X_{(n)})$ is also sufficient for θ

So, option (a) and (c) are correct

33. Explanation: (c)

$$f(x;\theta) = \frac{\theta^\theta}{\Gamma(\theta)}x^{\theta-1}e^{-x\theta}; x > 0$$

Which is pdf of gamma with parameter θ and θ

First moment about origin $= \mu_1' = \frac{\theta}{\theta} = 1$

So, we need second moment to estimate θ

$$\mu_2 = Var(X) = \frac{\theta}{\theta^2} = \frac{1}{\theta}$$

Sample second moment $= \frac{1}{n}\sum_{i=1}^{n}(X_i - \overline{X})^2$

$$\frac{1}{\theta} = \frac{1}{n}\sum_{i=1}^{n}(X_i - \overline{X})^2$$

$$\hat{\theta} = \frac{n}{\Sigma(X_i - \overline{X})^2}$$

Option (c) is correct

34. Explanation: (b)

$f(x,\theta) = e^{-(x-\theta)}$; $x > \theta$

Confidence Interval for θ

$$\left[\min(X_1, X_2, \ldots X_n) - \frac{\log 4}{n}, \min(X_1, X_2, \ldots X_n) + \frac{\log 2}{n}\right]$$

Let $\min(X_1, X_2, \ldots X_n) = Y$

The pdf of Y is

$$g(y) = n[1 - F(y)]^{n-1}f(y)$$

$$= n\left[1 - 1 + e^{-(y-\theta)}\right]^{n-1}e^{-(y-\theta)}$$

$$g(y) = n\,e^{-n(y-\theta)}, y > \theta$$

$$P\left[y - \frac{\log 4}{n} < \theta < y + \frac{\log 2}{n}\right]$$

$$= P\left[\theta - \frac{\log 2}{n} < y < \theta + \frac{\log 4}{n}\right]$$

$$= \int_\theta^{\theta + \frac{\log 4}{n}} g(y)\,dy$$

$$= n\int_\theta^{\theta + \frac{\log 4}{n}} e^{-n(y-\theta)}\,dy$$

$$= n\left[\frac{e^{-n(y-\theta)}}{n}\right]_\theta^{\theta + \frac{\log 4}{n}}$$

$$= e^{-n(\theta-\theta)} - e^{-n\left(\theta + \frac{\log 4}{n} - \theta\right)}$$

$$= 1 - e^{-\log 4}$$

$$= 1 - \frac{1}{4}$$

$$= 1 - 0.25 = 0.75$$

Option (b) is correct

35. Explanation: (c), (d)

$X_1, X_2, \ldots X_n$ be a random sample from distribution with pdf

$f(x) = \frac{1}{2}e^{-|x-\theta|}$; $-\infty < x < \infty$ $\theta \in \mathbb{R}$

The likelihood function is

$$L = \prod_{i=1}^{n} f(x_i)$$

$$= \prod_{i=1}^{n}\frac{1}{2}e^{-|x_i-\theta|} = \left(\frac{1}{2}\right)^n e^{-\sum_{i=1}^{n}|x_i-\theta|}$$

Taking log both sides:

$$\log L = -n\log 2 - \sum_{i=1}^{n}|x_i - \theta|$$

$$\frac{\partial L}{\partial\theta} = 0$$

$\hat{\theta} = \frac{1}{n}\sum_{i=1}^{n}|X_i - \theta|$ is mle of θ

Result: If a sufficient estimate exists, it is function of mle

$\sum_{i=1}^{n} X_i$ is not a function of $\frac{1}{n}\sum_{i=1}^{n}|X_i - \theta|$

$\sum_{i=1}^{n} X_i$ is not sufficient

To that $H_0 : \theta = 0$ against $\theta = \theta_1 > 0$

By Neymann Person Lemma

$\frac{L_1}{L_0} > k$

$\frac{e^{-\sum_{i=1}^{n}|X_i-\theta_1|}}{e^{-\sum_{i=1}^{n}|X_i-\theta_0|}} > k$

$e^{-\{\sum_{i=1}^{n}|X_i-\theta_1| - \sum_{i=1}^{n}|X_i|\}} > k$

Taking log both sides

$\sum_{i=1}^{n}\{|X_i - \theta_1| - |X_i|\} < c$

For $\theta_1 > 0$

$W = \sum_{i=1}^{n}\{|X_i - \theta_1| - |X_i|\} < c$

$\theta_1 < 0$

$W = \sum_{i=1}^{n}\{|X_i - \theta_1| - |X_i|\} > c$

For $\theta_1 \neq 0$ there is not UMP that for testing

$H_0 : \theta = 0$ against $H_1 : \theta \neq 0$

Option (c) & (d) are correct

36. Explanation: (b)

X_1, X_2, X_3 .... be a random sample from uniform $(0, 3\theta)$, $\theta > 0$

$\Rightarrow f(x) = \frac{1}{3\theta}; 0 < x < 3\theta$

Define $T_n = \frac{1}{3}\max\{X_1, X_2, \ldots, X_n\}$

Let $y = \max\{X_1, X_2, \ldots, X_n\}$

The pdf of y is

$g(y) = n(F(y))^{n-1} f(y) = n\left[\frac{y}{3\theta}\right]^{n-1}\cdot\frac{1}{3\theta}$

$g(y) = \frac{n}{(3\theta)^n} y^{n-1}; 0 < y < 3\theta$

$E(Y) = \int_0^{3\theta} y\, g(y)dy = \frac{n}{(3\theta)^n}\int_0^{3\theta} y.y^{n-1}\,dy$

$= \frac{n}{(3\theta)^n}\cdot\left[\frac{y^{n+1}}{n+1}\right]_0^{3\theta}$

$= \frac{n}{n+1}\cdot\frac{(3\theta)^{n+1}}{(3\theta)^n}$

$E(Y) = \frac{3\theta n}{n+1}$ & $Var(Y) = 9\theta^2\left[\frac{n}{n+2} - \frac{n^2}{n+1}\right]$

$E(T_n) = E\left[\frac{Y}{3}\right] = \frac{1}{3}E(Y) = \frac{1}{3}\cdot\frac{3\theta n}{n+1}$

$E(T_n) = \frac{\theta n}{n+1}$

$E(Tn) \neq \theta$

T_n is not an unbiased for θ

So, option (b) is correct.

37. Explanation: (d)

$Y_i = \alpha + \beta_i + \varepsilon_i ; i = 1, 2, \ldots n$

ε_i are iid N(0,1) ; $i = 1,2,\ldots,n$ $\alpha \neq 0$ & β is known

If $\hat{\alpha}_n$ is the maximum likelihood estimate of α

We know that maximum likelihood estimate is consistent estimates so

$\lim_{n\to\infty} E(\hat{\alpha}_n) = \alpha$ and

$\lim_{n\to\infty} Var(\hat{\alpha}_n) = 0$

Option (d) is correct.

38. Explanation: (a), (b)

$X_1, X_2, \ldots, X_n$ be a random sample from $f(x)$, pdf or pmf

Define $S_n^2 = \frac{1}{n-1}\sum_{i=1}^{n}(X_i - \overline{X}_n)^2$, where $\overline{X}_n = \frac{1}{n}\sum_{i=1}^{n} X_i$

S_n^2 is unbiased for θ

$\therefore E(S_n^2) = \sigma^2$

$\therefore \sigma^2 = \theta$

$Var(X_i) = \theta$

For option (a)

$f(x) = e^{-\theta}\frac{\theta^x}{x!}; x = 0, 1, 2 \ldots$

$X \sim P(\theta)$

$\therefore E(S_n^2) = \theta$ for given probability mass function

So, option (a) is correct

For option (b)

$f(x) = \frac{1}{\sqrt{\theta}\sqrt{2\pi}} e^{-\frac{x^2}{2\theta}}$

$X \sim N(0, \theta)$

$Var(X_i) = \theta$

$E(S_n^2) = \theta$

Option (b) is correct.

For option (c)

$f(x) = \frac{1}{\theta}e^{-\frac{x}{\theta}}$

$Var(X_1) = \theta^2$

So, option (c) is incorrect

For Option (d)

$f(x) = \theta.e^{-\theta x} : x > 0$

$Var(X) = \frac{1}{\theta^2}$

$E(S_n^2) = \frac{1}{\theta^2}$

So, option (d) is incorrect

Finally, option (a) & (b) are correct.

39. Explanation: (a), (b), (c), (d)

$f(x) = \frac{1}{\pi[1+[x-\theta]^2]} : < x < \infty$

If (t_1, t_2) be the $100(1-\alpha)$ % Confidence Interval for θ then

$P(t_1 < \theta < t_2) = 1 - \alpha$

$P\left[X_1 - \tan\frac{\pi(1-\alpha)}{2} < \theta < X_1 + \tan\frac{\pi(1-\alpha)}{2}\right]$

$= P\left[\theta - \tan\frac{\pi(1+\alpha)}{2} < X_1 < \theta + \tan\frac{\pi(1-\alpha)}{2}\right]$

$= \int_{\theta-\tan\frac{\pi(1-\alpha)}{2}}^{\theta+\tan\frac{\pi(1-\alpha)}{2}} f(x)dx$

$= \frac{1}{\pi}\int_{\theta-\tan\frac{\pi(1-\alpha)}{2}}^{\theta+\tan\frac{\pi(1-\alpha)}{2}} \frac{1}{1+(x-\theta)^2}dx$

$= \frac{1}{\pi}\left(tan^{-1}(x-\theta)\right)_{\theta-\tan\frac{\pi(1-\alpha)}{2}}^{\theta+\tan\frac{\pi(1-\alpha)}{2}}$

$= \frac{1}{\pi}\left[\frac{\pi(1-\alpha)}{2} + \frac{\pi(1-\alpha)}{2}\right] = 1 - \alpha$

$\left[X_1 - \tan\frac{\pi(1-\alpha)}{2}, X_1 + \tan\frac{\pi(1-\alpha)}{2}\right]$ be the $100(1-\alpha)\%$ CI for θ

For option (b):

$\overline{X} = \frac{X_1+X_2}{2} \sim$ Cauchy $(\theta, 1)$

$P\left[\frac{X_1+X_2}{2} - \tan\frac{\pi(1-\alpha)}{2} < \theta < \frac{X_1+X_2}{2} + \tan\frac{\pi(1+\alpha)}{2}\right]$

$= P\left[\theta - \tan\frac{\pi(1-\alpha)}{2} < \frac{X_1+X_2}{2} < \theta + \tan\frac{\pi(1-\alpha)}{2}\right]$

$= \int_{\theta-\tan\frac{\pi(1-\alpha)}{2}}^{\theta+\tan\frac{\pi(1-\alpha)}{2}} f(\overline{x})\, d\overline{x}$

$= 1 - \alpha$

$\left[\frac{X_1+X_2}{2} - \tan\frac{\pi(1-\alpha)}{2}, \frac{X_1+X_2}{2} + \tan\frac{\pi(1-\alpha)}{2}\right]$ be the 100 $(1 - \alpha)\%$ *Confidence Interval* for θ

Similarly for option (c) & (d)

$\left[\frac{X_1+X_2}{2} - \tan\frac{5\pi(1-\alpha)}{2}, \frac{X_1+X_2}{2} + \tan\frac{2\pi(1-\alpha)}{7}\right]$ be the 100 $(1 - \alpha)\%$ *Confidence Interval* for θ

$\left[\frac{X_1+X_2+X_3}{3} - \tan\frac{5\pi(1-\alpha)}{2}, \frac{X_1+X_2+X_3}{3} + \tan\frac{5\pi(1-\alpha)}{2}\right]$ be the 100 $(1 - \alpha)\%$ *Confidence Interval* for θ

Option (a), (b), (c), (d) are correct.

40. Explanation: (a), (b), (c), (d)

$X_i \sim N(\theta, 1)\,;\ \theta \in [-100, 100]$

$Y_i = \begin{cases} 0 & \text{if } X_i < 0 \\ 1 & \text{if } X_i \geq 0 \end{cases}$

$\hat{\theta}_n$ and $\tilde{\theta}_n$ denote the maximum likelihood estimate of θ based X_i's and Y_i's respectively

We know that maximum likelihood estimate's are consistent $\hat{\theta}_n$ and $\hat{\theta}_n$ are consistent estimate for θ

$\lim_{n\to\infty} E(\hat{\theta}_n) = \theta$ and $\lim_{n\to\infty} Var(\hat{\theta}_n) = 0$

$\lim_{n\to\infty} E(\tilde{\theta}_n) = \theta$ & $\lim_{n\to\infty} Var(\tilde{\theta}_n) = 0$

So, option (a), (b), (c) & (d) are correct.

41. Explanation: (d)

If the recorded lifetime of m bulbs are $x_1, x_2, \dots x_m$ and their sum is $\sum_{t=1}^{m} x_t$, then the lifetime function of the sample data is

$L(\theta) = \frac{1}{\theta^m} e^{-\sum_{t=1}^{m} x_t/\theta} \left[e^{-\frac{t}{\theta}}\right]^{n-m}$

$\log L = -m\log\theta - \frac{\sum_{t=1}^{m} x_t}{\theta} - \frac{t(n-m)}{\theta}$

$\frac{\partial}{\partial\theta}\log L = \frac{-m}{\theta} + \frac{\sum_{t=1}^{m} x_t}{\theta^2} + \frac{t(n-m)}{\theta^2}$

$\therefore \frac{\partial \log L}{\partial\theta} = 0$

$\theta = \frac{\sum_{t=1}^{m} x_t + (n-m)t}{m}$

$\frac{\partial^2 \log L}{\partial\theta^2} < 0$ at θ

m.l.e of $\hat{\theta} = \frac{\sum_{t=1}^{m} x_t + (n-m)t}{m}$

option (d) is correct

42. Explanation: (d)

$X_i \sim U(\theta_1, \theta_2)\,;\ \theta_1 < \theta_2$

If the given ancillary statistic then it should be distribution free Parameter

$X_i \sim (\theta_1, \theta_2)$

Let $\theta_1 = \theta$ & $\theta_2 = \theta + 1$

$X_i \sim (\theta, \theta + 1)$

$\theta < x < \theta + 1 \qquad f(x) = 1$

$0 < x - \theta < 1$

Let $y_i = x_i - \theta$

$G(y) = P[Y \leq y]$

$= P[X_i - \theta \leq y]$

$= P[X_i \leq y + \theta]$

$= F_X(y + \theta)$

$= y + \theta - \theta$

$= y$

Which is distribution free

$Y_{(i)} = X_{(i)} - \theta$ which is free from θ

For option (a)

$\frac{X_{(k)}}{X_{(n)}} \neq \frac{X_{(k)}-\theta}{X_{(n)}-\theta}$

That means $\frac{X_{(k)}}{X_{(n)}}$ is not parameter free, so,

$\frac{X_{(k)}}{X_{(n)}}$ is not ancillary statistic

For option (b)

$\frac{X_{(n)}-X_{(k)}}{X_{(n)}} \neq \frac{(X_{(n)}-\theta)-(X_{(k)}-\theta)}{X_{(n)}-\theta}$

$\therefore \frac{X_{(n)}-X_{(k)}}{X_{(n)}}$ is not ancillary statistic

For option (c)

Similarly, $\frac{X_{(k)}}{X_{(n)}-X_{(k)}}$ is not ancillary

For option (d)

$\frac{X_{(k)}-X_{(1)}}{X_{(n)}-X_{(k)}} = \frac{(X_{(k)}-\theta)-(X_{(1)}-\theta)}{(X_{(n)}-\theta)-(X_{(k)}-\theta)} = \frac{Y_{(k)}-Y_{(1)}}{Y_{(n)}-Y_{(k)}}$ is parameter free distribution so $\frac{X_{(k)}-X_{(1)}}{X_{(n)}-X_{(k)}}$ is an ancillary statistic

43. Explanation: (a), (c), (d)

X_1 & X_2 are iid with pmf

$f_a(x) = \theta^x(1-\theta)^{1-x}\,;\ x = 0, 1\,;\ \theta \in (0, 1)$

The likelihood function is

$L = f(x_1).f(x_2)$

$= \theta^{x_1}(1-\theta)^{1-x_1}\theta^{x_2}(1-\theta)^{1-x_2}$

$= \theta^{x_1+x_2}(1-\theta)^{2-(x_1+x_2)}$

$= \left(\frac{\theta}{1-\theta}\right)^{x_1+x_2}(1-\theta)^2$

$g(x_1 + x_2, \theta).\hbar(x)$

By factorization theorem,

$X_1 + X_2$ is sufficient function θ

$\Rightarrow X_1 + 2X_2$ is also sufficient for θ

$X_1 = 0 \Rightarrow X_1^2 = 0$

$X_1 = 1 \Rightarrow X_1^2 = 1$

$\Rightarrow X_1^2 + X_2^2$ is also sufficient for θ

$\Rightarrow X_1^2 + X_2$ is also sufficient for θ

Option (a), (c) & (d) are correct

44. Explanation: (a), (d)

45. Explanation: (b)

$X_i \sim U(\theta - 0.2, \theta + 0.8)\ i = 1, 2, \dots 8$

$\theta - 0.2 < x_i < \theta + 0.8$

$\theta - 0.2 < x_{(1)} \leq x_{(2)} \leq \dots \leq x_{(8)} < \theta + 0.8$

$x_{(1)} > \theta - 0.2$ and $X_{(8)} < \theta + 0.8$

$\theta < X_{(1)} + 0.2$ and $\theta > X_{(8)} - 0.8$

Acc. to given observations

$x_{(1)} = 0.71$ and $X_{(8)} = 1.68$

$\theta < 0.71 + 0.2 \qquad \theta > 1.68 - 0.8$

$\theta < 0.91$ and $\theta > 0.88$

$0.88 < \theta < 0.91$

Acc. to option

0.9 is lies in the above interval

So, mle of θ is 0.9

46. Explanation: (d)

$f(x_i) = \frac{1}{\theta}(x_i)^{\frac{1-\theta}{\theta}}$

The likelihood function is

$L = \prod_{i=1}^{n} f(x_i)$

$= \prod_{i=1}^{n} \frac{1}{\theta}(x_i)^{\frac{1-\theta}{\theta}}$

$= \frac{1}{\theta^n} (\prod_{i=1}^n x_i)^{\frac{1-\theta}{\theta}}$

For MLE,

$\frac{\partial}{\partial\theta} \log L = 0$ & $\frac{\partial^2}{\partial\theta^2} \log L < 0$

$\therefore \log L = -n \log\theta + \frac{1-\theta}{\theta} \sum_{i=1}^n \log x_i$

$\frac{\partial}{\partial\theta} \log L = \frac{-n}{\theta} - \frac{1}{\theta^2} \sum_{i=1}^n \log x_i$

$\frac{\partial}{\partial\theta} \log L = 0$

$\frac{n}{\theta} = -\frac{1}{\theta^2} \sum \log x_i$

m.l.e of θ i.e., $\hat{\theta} = \frac{-1}{n} \sum_{i=1}^n \log x_i$

$\hat{\theta} = \frac{-1}{n} \sum_{i=1}^n \log x_i = \frac{-1}{n} \log(\prod_{i=1}^n x_i)$

We know that m.l.e. has a property of invariance i.e.,

T_n is m.l.e. of θ

$\Rightarrow g(T_n)$ is also m.l.e. of $g(\theta)$

$\therefore \frac{-1}{n} \sum \log(X_i) = \frac{-1}{n} \log(\prod_{i=1}^n x_i)$ is m.l.e. of θ

$\Rightarrow \prod_{i=1}^n x_i$ is m.l.e. of $e^{-n\theta}$

$\therefore$ option (c) is incorrect & (d) is correct

Result:

If likelihood function is expressed in form of

$L = c(\theta) \cdot h(x) \cdot e^{Q(\theta)T(x)}$

$\Rightarrow T(x)$ is complete sufficient

We have

$L = \frac{1}{\theta^n} (\prod_{i=1}^n x_i)^{\frac{1-\theta}{\theta}}$

$= \frac{1}{\theta^n} e^{\log(\prod_{i=1}^n x_i)^{\frac{1-\theta}{\theta}}}$

$= \frac{1}{\theta^n} e^{\frac{1-\theta}{\theta} \log(\prod_{i=1}^n x_i)}$

$= \frac{1}{\theta} e^{\frac{1-\theta}{\theta} \sum_{i=1}^n \log x_i}$

$\therefore T(x) = \sum \log x_i$ is complete sufficient for θ

47. Explanation: (a), (b) (c), (d)

$X_i \sim U(\theta, \theta+1)$

$f(x_i) = 1 : \theta < x_i < \theta + 1$

CDF of X is

$F(x) = \int_\theta^x f(t)\,dt = \int_\theta^x 1\,dt = x - \theta$

The pdf of Largest order statistic $X_{(n)} = Y$ is

$g(y) = n[f(y)]^{n-1}.f(y)$

$\quad = n.(y-\theta)^{n-1}$

$g(y) = n(y-\theta)^{n-1}$

For option (a)

According to question

$P[-\infty < \theta < X_{(n)} - \alpha^{1/n}] = P[X_{(n)} > \theta + \alpha^{1/n}]$

$= P(Y > \theta + \alpha^{1/n})$

$= \int_{\theta+\alpha^{1/n}}^{\theta+1} g(y)\,dy$

$= n \int_{\theta+\alpha^{1/n}}^{\theta+1} (y-\theta)^{n-1}\,dy$

$= n \left[\frac{(y-\theta)^n}{n}\right]_{\theta+\alpha^{1/n}}^{\theta+1}$

$= (\theta + 1 - \theta)^n - (\theta + \alpha^{1/n} - \theta)^n$

$P[-\infty < \theta < X_{(n)} - \alpha^{1/n}] = 1 - \alpha$

$\therefore 100(1-\alpha)\%\ CI\ for\ \theta : (-\infty, \quad X_{(n)} + \alpha^{1/n})$

So, option (a) is correct

For option (b)

$X_{(1)} = \min(X, X_2, \dots, X_n) = U$

The pdf of U is

$h(u) = n[1 - F(u)]^{n-1} f(u)$

$= n(1 - u + \theta)^{n-1} \cdot 1$

$= n[1 - u + \theta]^{n-1}$

$P[X_{(1)} + \alpha^{1/n} - 1 < \theta < \infty] = P[X_{(1)} < \theta + 1 - \alpha^{1/n}]$

$= \int_\theta^{\theta+1-\alpha^{1/n}} h(u)\,du$

$= n \int_\theta^{\theta+1-\alpha^{1/n}} (1 - u + \theta)^{n-1}\,du$

$= n \left[\frac{(1-u+\theta)^{n-1+1}}{n}\right]_\theta^{\theta+1-\alpha^{1/n}}$

$= 1 - \alpha$

So, $100(1-\alpha)\%\ CI\ for\ \theta$ is $[X_{(1)} + \alpha^{1/n} - 1, \infty]$

So, option (b) is correct

For option (c)

$P\left[X_n + \frac{\alpha}{2} - 1 < \theta < X_n - \frac{\alpha}{2}\right]$

$= P\left[\theta + \frac{\alpha}{2} < X_n < \theta + 1 - \frac{\alpha}{2}\right]$

$= \int_{\theta+1-\alpha/2}^{\theta+\alpha/2} f(x)\,dx$

$= \int_{\theta+1-\alpha/2}^{\theta+\alpha/2} 1\,dx$

$= 1 - \alpha$

$100(1-\alpha)\%\ CI\ for\ \theta$ is $\left[X_n + \frac{\alpha}{2} - 1, X_n - \frac{\alpha}{2}\right]$

So, option (c) is also correct

For option (d)

$P[-\infty < \theta < X_1 - \alpha] = P[X_1 > \theta + \alpha]$

$= \int_{\theta+\alpha}^{\theta+1} f(n)\,dx = \int_{\theta+\alpha}^{\theta+1} 1\,dx$

$= [x]_{\theta+\alpha}^{\theta+1}$

$= \theta + 1 - \theta - \alpha$

$= 1 - \alpha$

So, option (d) is also correct.

48. Explanation: (d)

$f(x) = \frac{1+x^2}{3\theta(1+\theta^2)}$; $-2\theta \le x \le \theta$; $\theta > 0$

The likelihood function

$L = \prod_{i=1}^7 f(x_i)$

$= \prod_{i=1}^7 \frac{1+x_i^2}{3\theta(1+\theta^2)}$

$L = \frac{1}{(3\theta(1+\theta^2))^7} : \prod_{i=1}^7 (1 + x_i^2) : -2\theta \le x_{(1)} \le x_{(2)} < \dots.. < x_{(7)} \le \theta$

L is maximum when θ is minimum

$-2\theta \le x_{(1)} \le x_{(2)} \le \dots \le x_{(7)} \le \theta$

$x_{(1)} \ge -2\theta$ and $\theta \ge x_{(7)}$

According to given sample value

$x_{(1)} = -54$ and $x_{(7)} = 26$

$-54 \ge -2\theta \qquad \theta \ge 26$

$\theta \ge 27$ and $\theta \ge 26$

Min. value if θ is 27

mle of θ is 27

Option (d) is correct

49. Explanation: (a), (b), (c) & (d)

$T_n = \{C_n ; \sum_{i=1}^n X_i^2 : C_n > 0 ; n \ge 1\}$

$X_i \sim N(0, \sigma^2)$

$E(X_i) = 0, \qquad Var(X_i) = \sigma^2$

$E(X^2) = \sigma^2$

T_n is consistent for σ^2 is
$E(T_n) = \sigma^2 \; as\, n \to \infty$
$V(T_n) = 0 \; as\, n \to \infty$
$\chi^2 = \sum_{i=1}^{n}\left(\frac{X_i - 0}{\sigma}\right)^2 \sim \chi^2_{(n)\,\partial f}$
$E(T_n) = E[C_n \sum_{i=1}^{n} X_i^2]$
$= C_n E[\sigma^2\chi^2]$
$= C_n\sigma^2.n$
$= n.C_n\,\sigma^2$
$E(T_n) = \sigma^2 \Rightarrow T_n$ is unbiased for σ^2 for this $C_n = \frac{1}{n}$
Let us take $C_n = \frac{1}{n-1}$
$E(T_n) = \frac{n}{n-1}\sigma^2 \; and$
$Var\,(T_n) = Va(C_n \sum X_i^2)$
$= C_n^2.Va(\sigma^2\chi^2)$
$= C_n^2\,\sigma^4.2n$
$E(T_n) = \sigma^2$ as $n \to \infty$
$C_n = \frac{1}{n-1}$
$Var\,(T_n) = \frac{1}{(n-1)^2}.2n.\sigma^4$
as $n \to \infty\; Var\,(T_n) \to 0$
$C_n = \frac{1}{n+1}$
$E(T_n) = \sigma^2 \; as\, n \to \infty$
$Var\,(T_n) = 0 \; as\, n \to \infty$
$MSE(T_n) = Var\,(T_n) + \{Bias(T_n)\}^2$
$Var\,(T_n) = Var\,(C_n \sum X_i^2) = C_n^2\, Var\,(\sigma^2\chi^2)$
$= C_n^2\,\sigma^4.2n$
$= 2n\,C_n^2\,\sigma^4$
$Bias(T_n) = E(T_n) - \sigma^2$
$= n\,C_n\sigma^2 - \sigma^2$
$= \sigma^2 C_n(n-1)$
$MSE(T_n) = 2n\,C_n^2\,\sigma^4 + \{\sigma^2[n\,C_n - 1]\}^2$
Differentiate w.r.t C_n
$\frac{\partial}{\partial\, C_n} MSE(T_n) = 4n(n\,\sigma^4 + 2\sigma^4(n\,C_n - 1).n = 0$
$2n\,\sigma^4\,[2\,C_n + nC_n - 1] = 0$
$C_n = \frac{1}{n+2}$
$at\; C_n = \frac{1}{n+2}$
$\frac{\partial^2}{\partial\, C_n^2} MSE\,(T_n) > 0$
So, $C_n = \frac{1}{n+2}\; MSE$ is minimised
Then option (a), (b), (c) & (d) are correct

50. Explanation: (c), (d)
$bi \sim N\,(0, \tau^2) \quad \forall\, i = 1,2 \ldots 10$
$\epsilon_{ij} \sim N\,(0, \sigma^2) \;\; ; j = 1,2 \ldots .n$
Define $X_{ij} = b + \varepsilon_{ij}$
$E\,[X_{ij}] = E\,[bi] + E[E_{ij}]$
$= 0 + 0$
$E[X_{ij}] = 0$
$Var\,(X_{ij}) = Var\,(bi) + Var\,(\varepsilon_{ij})$
$= \tau^2 + \sigma^2$
$E\,[X_{ij}^2] = \tau^2 + \sigma^2$
$T_n = \frac{1}{10\,n}\; \sum_{i=1}^{10}\sum_{j=1}^{n} E({X_{ij}}^2)$
$= \frac{1}{10\,n}.10n\,(\tau^2 + \sigma^2)$
$= \sigma^2 + \tau^2$
T_n *is not an unbiased for* σ^2
If $\tau^2 = 0$ then T_n is unbiased for σ^2
as $n \to \infty$
T_n is not consistent for σ^2
When $\tau^2 = 0$
$E(T_n) = \sigma^2$ as $n \to \infty$
$Var\,(T_n) = Var\,\left(\frac{1}{10n}\sum_{i=1}^{10}\sum_{j=1}^{n} X_{ij}\right)$
$X_{ij} \sim N\,(0, \tau^2 + \sigma^2)$
$\chi^2 = \sum\sum\left(\frac{X_{ij} - 0}{\sigma^2 + \tau^2}\right)^2 \sim \chi^2_{(10n)\,d.f}$
$Var\,(T_n) = \left(\frac{1}{10n}\right)^2 Var\,[(\sigma^2 + \tau^2)\chi^2]$
$= \frac{1}{100n^2}(\sigma^2 + \tau^2)^2.Var\,(\chi^2)$
$= \frac{1}{10n^2}(\sigma^2 + \tau^2)^2.2.10\text{n} = \frac{2}{10\,n}(\sigma^2 + \tau^2)^2$
When $\tau^2 = 0$, Var $(T_n) = \frac{1}{5n}\sigma^4$
$as\; n \to \infty,\, Var\,(T_n) = 0$
So, $\tau^2 = 0$ *then* T_n *is consistent for* σ^2
So, option (c) & (d) are correct.

51. Explanation: (c)
If $X_1\, X_2 \ldots X_n\; (n \geq 2)$ be a random sample with Pdf
$f(x) = \frac{2(\theta - x)}{\theta^2} \quad ; 0 \leq x \leq \theta$
Let $\overline{X}_n$ be the sample mean and $X_{(n)} = \max(X_1\, X_2 \ldots X_n)$
First, we check for unbiasedness,
$E[\overline{X}_n] = E\left[\frac{1}{n}\sum_{i=1}^{n} X_i\right] = \frac{1}{n}\;\sum_{i=1}^{n} E\,(X_i)$
$E(X_i) = \int_0^\theta x.f(x)\,\partial\, x = \int_0^\theta \frac{2}{\theta^2} x(\theta - x)dx$
$= \frac{2}{\theta^2}\int_0^\theta(\theta x - x^2)\partial\, x$
$= \frac{2}{\theta^2}\left[\frac{\theta x^2}{2} - \frac{x^3}{3}\right]_0^\theta$
$= \frac{2}{\theta^2}\left[\frac{\theta^3}{2} - \frac{\theta^3}{3}\right]$
$= \frac{1}{\theta^2}.\frac{\theta^3}{3}$
$E[X_i] = \frac{\theta}{3}$
$E\,[\overline{X}_n] = \frac{1}{n}\sum_i E\,(X_i) = \frac{\theta}{3}$
$E[\overline{X}_n] = \frac{\theta}{3}$
$E[3\overline{X}_n] = \theta$
$\therefore 3\,\overline{X}_n$ is an unbiased estimator for θ
So, option (c) is correct

52. Explanation: (b)
$X_i \sim U\,[0, \theta]$
$M = \max[X_1 X_2]$
Confidence interval $= \left[\frac{3}{7}M, 2M\right]$
$P\left[\frac{3}{7}M \leq \theta \leq 2M\right] = ?$
$P\left[\frac{3}{7} \leq \frac{\theta}{M} \leq 2\right] = P\left[\frac{7}{3} > \frac{M}{\theta} > \frac{1}{2}\right] = P\left[\frac{1}{2}\,\theta < M < \frac{7}{3}\theta\right]$
Now final pdf of M = $\max[X_1 X_2]$
$f\,(x_{(n)}) = n\,[F(x)]^{n-1}.f(x) \;\; ; \;\; 0 < X_{(n)} < \theta$
$= 2.\left[\frac{x}{\theta}\right]^{2-1}\frac{1}{\theta}$
$= \frac{2}{\theta^2}x$

$P\left[\frac{1}{2}\theta < M < \frac{7}{3}\theta\right] = \int_{\theta/2}^{\theta} x\,dx = \frac{2}{\theta^2}\left[\frac{x^2}{2}\right]_{\theta/2}^{\theta}$

$= \frac{1}{\theta^2}\left[\theta^2 - \frac{\theta^2}{4}\right]$

$= 0.75$

So, option (b) is correct

53. Explanation: (b), (c)

$X_i \sim U(\theta, 2\theta)$

$f(x_i) = \frac{1}{\theta} \;:\; \theta < x_i < 2\theta \;\; \forall \; i = 1,2,\dots n$

The likelihood function is

$L = \prod_{i=1}^{n} f(x_i) = \frac{1}{\theta^n} \;:\; \theta < x_1 < x_2 < \cdots x_n < 2\theta$

$L = \frac{1}{\theta^n} \;:\; \theta \le x_{(1)} \le x_{(2)} \le \cdots < x_{(n)} < 2\theta$

$L = \frac{1}{\theta^n}\; I(x_{(1)})_{(\theta, x_{(n)})} \cdot I(x_{(n)})_{(x_{(1)}, 2\theta)}$

$= g(\theta, X_{(1)}, X_{(n)})$

By factorization Theorem.

$(X_{(1)}, X_{(n)})$ is jointly sufficient for θ.

For completeness, we need a function of $X_{(1)}, X_{(n)}$, for this

Let $y = X_{(1)}$ and $u = X_{(n)}$

$g(y) = n f(y)[1 - F(y)]^{n-1}$

$g(y) = n\frac{1}{\theta}\left[1 - \left(\frac{y-\theta}{\theta}\right)\right]^{n-1}$

$E[y] = \int_{\theta}^{2\theta} y\, g(y)\, dy$

$= \frac{n}{\theta}\int_{\theta}^{\theta} y.\left[1 - \frac{y-\theta}{\theta}\right]^{n-1} dy$

$E(y) = n\,\theta\left[\frac{2}{n} - \frac{1}{n+1}\right]$

$= \frac{\theta(n+2)}{n+1}$

$h(u) = n f(u)\,[F(u)]^{n-1}$

$h(u) = n\frac{1}{\theta}.\left[\frac{u-\theta}{\theta}\right]^{n-1}$

$E(u) = \int_{\theta}^{2\theta} u\, h(u) du$

$= \frac{n}{\theta}\int_{\theta}^{2\theta} u\left(\frac{u-\theta}{\theta}\right)^{n-1} du$

$E(u) = \frac{\theta(n+2)}{n+1}$

$\therefore E(y) = E[u]$

$E[y - u] = 0$

So, $E\left[X_{(1)} - X_{(n)}\right] = 0$

$\therefore X_{(n)} - X(1) \ne 0$

So, $(X_{(1)}, X_{(n)})$ is sufficient but not complete for θ.

Now, $L = \frac{1}{\theta^n}$; $\theta < X_{(1)} \le X_{(2)} \dots \le 2\theta$

$X_{(1)} \ge \theta$ and $2\theta > X_{(n)}$

$\theta < X_{(1)}$ and $\theta > \frac{X_{(n)}}{2}$

$\frac{X_{(n)}}{2} < \theta < X_{(1)}$

$L = \frac{1}{\theta^n}$ is maximum when θ is minimum

θ is minimum at $\frac{X_{(n)}}{2}$

So, m.l.e is $\frac{X_{(n)}}{2}$

Option (b) and (c) is correct

54. Explanation: (b), (c), (d)

X_i `s be iid observations $E(X_i) = 0$ & $Var(X_i) = \sigma^2$

For option (a)

$T_1 = \frac{1}{n}\sum_{i=1}^{n}(X_{2i-1} - X_{2i})^2$

$\frac{X_{2i-1} - X_{2i} - E[X_{2i-1} - X_{2i}]}{\sqrt{Var(X_{2i-1} - X_{2i})}} \sim N(0,1)$

$U_i = \frac{X_{2i-1} - X_{2i}}{\sigma\sqrt{2}} \sim N(0,1)$

$U_i^2 = \frac{(X_{i-1} - X_{2i})^2}{2\,\sigma\,2} \sim \chi^2_{1\,d.f}$

$\chi^2 = \sum_{i=1}^{n} U_i^2 = \frac{1}{2\sigma 2}\sum_{i=1}^{n}(X_{2i-1} - X_{2i})^2 \sim \chi^2_{n\,d.f}$

T_1 is consistent for σ^2 if

$E(T_1) = \sigma^2$ as $n \to \infty$

$Var(T_1) = 0$ as $n \to \infty$

$E(T_1) = E\left[\frac{1}{n}\sum_{i=1}^{n}(X_{2i=1} - X_{2i})^2\right]$

$= \frac{1}{n}E[2\sigma^2\chi^2] = \frac{1}{n}.2\sigma^2 E[\chi^2] = \frac{2\sigma^2}{n}.n$

$= 2\sigma^2$

$E(T_i) \ne \sigma^2$ or $n \to \infty$

T_1 is not consistent for σ^2

For option (b)

$T_2 = \frac{1}{n}\sum_{i=1}^{n}(X_i - \overline{X})^2$

We know that

$\sum_{i=1}^{n}\left(\frac{X_i - \overline{X}}{\sigma}\right)^2 \sim \chi^2_{(n-1)d.f}$

$T_2 = \frac{1}{n}\sigma^2.\chi^2_{(n-1)d.f}$

$E(T_2) = \frac{1}{n}\sigma^2 E(\chi^2_{n-1})$

$= \frac{n-1}{n}\sigma^2$

5	6	7	8	9	10
$\frac{1}{10}$	$\frac{1}{10}$	$\frac{1}{10}$	$\frac{1}{10}$	$\frac{1}{10}$	$\frac{1}{10}$
$\frac{5}{55}$	$\frac{6}{55}$	$\frac{7}{55}$	$\frac{8}{55}$	$\frac{9}{55}$	$\frac{10}{55}$
$\frac{50}{55}$	$\frac{60}{55}$	$\frac{70}{55}$	$\frac{80}{55}$	$\frac{90}{55}$	$\frac{100}{55}$

$E(T_2) = \sigma^2$ As $n \to \infty$

$Var(T_2) = \frac{\sigma^4}{n^2}Var(\chi^2_{n-1})$

$= \frac{\sigma^4}{n^2}.2(n-1)$

$Var(T_2) = 0$ as $n \to \infty$

So, T_2 is consistent for σ^2

For option (c)

$T_3 = \frac{1}{n}\sum_{i=1}^{n} X_i^2$

$\sum_{i=1}^{n}\left(\frac{X_i}{\sigma}\right)^2 \sim X^2_{(n)d.f}$

$T_3 = \frac{\sigma^2}{n}\chi^2$

$E(T_3) = \frac{\sigma^2}{n}.n = \sigma^2$

$Var(T_3) = \frac{\sigma^4}{n^2}.Var(\chi^2)$

$= \frac{\sigma^4.2n}{n^2}$

$Var(T_3) = 0$ as $n \to \infty$

T_3 is consistent for σ^2

For option (d)

$T_4 = \frac{1}{n-1}\sum_{i=1}^{n}(X_i - \overline{X})^2$

$\sum_{i=1}^{n}\frac{(X_i - \overline{X})^2}{\sigma^{-2}} \sim \chi^2_{(n-1)\,d.f}$

$E\,[T_4] = E\left[\frac{\sigma^2}{n-1}\chi^2\right]$

$= \frac{\sigma^2}{n-1}E[\chi^2]$

$= \frac{\sigma^2}{n-1}n-1 = \sigma^2$

$Var\,(T_4) \to 0\; or\; n \to \infty$

T_4 is consistent for σ^2

So, option b,c,d are correct

55. Explanation: (a), (c), (d)

$X_i \sim N\,(\theta, \theta^2)\,;\; i = 1,2,3$

For option (a)

$T_1 = \frac{X_1+2X_2+3X_3}{6}$

$E[T_1] = E\left[\frac{X_1+2X_2+3X_3}{6}\right] = \frac{1}{6}[E(X_1) + 2E(X_2) + 3E(X_3)]$

$= \frac{1}{6}[\theta + 2\theta + 3\theta] = \theta$

$\therefore \frac{X_1+2X_2+3X_3}{6}$ is unbiased for θ

For option (b)

$T_2 = \frac{X_1^2+4X_2^2+9X_3^2}{14}$

$\therefore E[X_1] = \theta\;\&\; Var\,(X_1) = \theta^2$

$\therefore E(X_1^2) = Var\,(X_1) + (E[X_1])^2$

$= \theta^2 + \theta^2$

$= 2\theta^2$

$E\,[T_2] = \frac{1}{14}[E(X_1^2) + 4E(X_2^2) + 9E(X_3^2)]$

$= \frac{1}{14}[2\,\theta^2 + 4.2\theta^2 + 9.2\,\theta^2]$

$\neq \theta^2$

$T_2 = \frac{X_1^2+4X_2^2+9X_3^2}{14}$ is not unbiased for θ^2

For option (c)

$T_3 = \frac{2X_1+X_3^2}{2}$

$E[T_3] = \frac{1}{2}[2E[X_1] + E[X_3^2]]$

$= \frac{1}{2}[2.\theta + 2\,\theta^2]$

$= \theta + \theta^2$

$= \theta(1+\theta)$

$T_3 = \frac{2X_1+X_3^2}{2}$ is an unbiased for $\theta(1+\theta)$

For option (d)

$T_4 = X_2\left(1 - \frac{X_2}{2}\right)$

$T_4 = X_2 - \frac{1}{2}X_2^2$

$E[T_4] = E[X_2] - \frac{1}{2}E[X_2^2]$

$= \theta - \frac{1}{2}.2\theta^2$

$= \theta(1-\theta)$

$T_4 = X_2\left(1 - \frac{X_2}{2}\right)$ is an unbiased for $\theta(1-\theta)$

So, option, (a), (c), (d) are correct

56. Explanation: (c)

Let $X_1, X_2 \ldots X_n$ be i.i.d. random variables with common pdf $f(x) = \frac{(\log\theta)\,\theta^x}{\theta-1}$

The likelihood function is

$L(x,\theta) = \prod_{i=1}^{n} f(x_i, \theta)$

$= \prod_{i=1}^{x} \frac{(\log\theta)\theta^{x_i}}{\theta-1}$

$= \left(\frac{\log\theta}{\theta-1}\right)^n \theta^{\sum_{i=1}^{n} x_i}$

$= g(\sum x_i, \theta)\, h(x)$

Using factorization Theorem

$T = \sum_{i=1}^{n} X_i$ is sufficient for θ

Let the function of T be $g(T)$

$\therefore E[g(T)] = 0$

$\Rightarrow g(T) = 0$

Then we can say that T is complete

So $T = \sum X_i$ is sufficient & complete for θ

Option (c) is correct

57. Explanation: (d)

Let $X_1, X_2, \ldots, X_n$ be i.i.d. with the common pdf $f(x|\theta) = \frac{\theta}{x^{\theta+1}}$, for $x > 1$ where $\theta > 1$ is an unknown parameter.

$E(\log x) = \int_1^\infty \log x\, f(x)dx = \int_1^\infty \log x \frac{\theta}{x^{\theta+1}} d$

$= \int_0^\infty e^{-\theta t}\, e^{2-1} dt = \frac{1}{\theta}$

Therefore $\frac{1}{n}\sum_{i=1}^{n}\log(X_i) \to \frac{1}{\theta} \Rightarrow \frac{n}{\sum_{i=1}^{n}\log(X_i)} \to \frac{1}{\frac{1}{\theta}} = \theta$

We know that convergence in probability implies consistency

Thus $\frac{n}{\sum_{i=1}^{n}\log(X_i)}$ is consistent for θ

Option (d) is correct.

58. Explanation: (d)

Let $X_1, X_2, \ldots, X_n$ be i.i.d. with the common probability mass function

$p(x|\theta) = \theta^x\,(1-\theta)^{1-x}, x = 0$ or 1, and $0 \le \theta \le \frac{1}{2}$

Likelihood function

$L(X;\,\theta) = \prod_{i=1}^{n} p(x_i|\theta) = \theta^{\sum_{i=1}^{n} x_i}(1-\theta)^{n-\sum_{i=1}^{n} x_i}$

$\frac{\partial}{\partial\theta}\log L(X;\theta) = 0$

$\Rightarrow \frac{\sum_{i=1}^{n} x_i}{\theta} + \frac{n-\sum_{i=1}^{n} x_i}{1-\theta} = 0$

$\Rightarrow \hat{\theta}_{MLE} = \frac{1}{n}\sum_{i=1}^{n} X_i$

Since MLE of θ will be $\frac{1}{n}\sum_{i=1}^{n} X_i$ when $0 \le \theta \le 1$

But $0 \le \theta \le \frac{1}{2}$, then $\hat{\theta}_{MLE} = \min\left\{\sum_{i=1}^{n} X_i, \frac{1}{2}\right\}$ because $0 < \hat{\theta}_{MLE} \le \frac{1}{2}$

Similarly, $\hat{\theta}_{MME} = \frac{1}{n}\sum_{i=1}^{n} X_i$ when $0 \le \theta \le 1$

But $0 \le \theta \le \frac{1}{2}$. Then method of moment's estimator of θ is $\min\left\{\sum_{i=1}^{n} X_i, \frac{1}{2}\right\}$ because $0 < \hat{\theta}_{MME} \le \frac{1}{2}$.

Option (d) is correct.

59. Explanation: (a), (c)

$f(x|\theta) = \frac{2x}{\theta^2}$, for $0 < x < \theta$, where $\theta > 0$

Let $u = \frac{x}{\theta} \Rightarrow x = u\theta \Rightarrow dx = \theta du$

$f(u) = f(x|\theta)\left|\frac{dx}{du}\right| = \frac{2x}{\theta^2}\,\theta = 2u; 0 < u < 1$

For option (a)

$P\left(X \le \theta \le \frac{X}{\sqrt{\alpha}}\right) = P\left(1 \le \frac{\theta}{X} \le \frac{1}{\sqrt{\alpha}}\right) = P\left(\sqrt{\alpha} \le \frac{X}{\theta} \le 1\right)$

$= P(\sqrt{\alpha} \le u \le 1) = \int_{\sqrt{\alpha}}^{1} f(u)\,du$

$= \int_{\sqrt{\alpha}}^{1} 2u\,du = 2\left[\frac{u^2}{2}\right]_{\sqrt{\alpha}}^{1} = 1\;\alpha$

For option (b)

$P(X \le \theta \le 2X) = P\left(1 \le \frac{\theta}{X} \le 2\right) = P\left(\frac{1}{2} \le \frac{X}{\theta} \le 1\right)$

$= P\left(\frac{1}{2} \le u \le 1\right) = \int_{½}^{1} f(u)\, du$

$= \int_{1/2}^{1} 2u\, du = 2\left[\frac{u^2}{2}\right]_{1/2}^{1} = 1 - \frac{1}{4} = \frac{3}{4}$

For option (c)

$$P\left(\frac{\sqrt{2}}{\sqrt{2-\alpha}} X \le \theta \le \frac{\sqrt{2}}{\sqrt{\alpha}} X\right) = P\left(\frac{\sqrt{2}}{\sqrt{2-\alpha}} \le \frac{\theta}{X} \le \frac{\sqrt{2}}{\sqrt{\alpha}}\right)$$

$$= P\left(\frac{\sqrt{\alpha}}{\sqrt{2}} \le \frac{X}{\theta} \le \frac{\sqrt{2-\alpha}}{\sqrt{2}}\right)$$

$$= P\left(\frac{\sqrt{\alpha}}{\sqrt{2}} \le u \le \frac{\sqrt{2-\alpha}}{\sqrt{2}}\right)$$

$$= \int_{\frac{\sqrt{\alpha}}{\sqrt{2}}}^{\frac{\sqrt{2-\alpha}}{\sqrt{2}}} f(u)\, d = \int_{\frac{\sqrt{\alpha}}{\sqrt{2}}}^{\frac{\sqrt{2-\alpha}}{\sqrt{2}}} 2u\, du$$

$$= 2\left[\frac{u^2}{2}\right]_{\frac{\sqrt{\alpha}}{\sqrt{2}}}^{\frac{\sqrt{2-\alpha}}{\sqrt{2}}} = \frac{2-\alpha}{2} - \frac{\alpha}{2} = 1 - \alpha$$

For option (d)

$P(0 \le \theta \le X) = P\left(0 \le \frac{\theta}{x} \le 1\right) = P\left(1 \le \frac{X}{\theta} < \infty\right) =$

$P(1 \le u < \infty) = \int_{1}^{\infty} f(u)\, du = 0$

Option (a) and (c) are correct.

60. Explanation: (a), (b), (c) and (d)

$T_1 = \frac{1}{n}\sum_{i=1}^{n} X_i$ and $T_2 = X_{\left(\left[\frac{3n}{4}\right]+1\right)}$, the sample 75th percentile

$\mu_x = E(X) = E(\theta + \varepsilon) = \theta + E(\varepsilon) = \theta$

$\sigma_x^2 = V(X) = v(\theta + \varepsilon) = V(\varepsilon) = \frac{1}{2}$

Using CLT

$\frac{T_1 - \theta}{\frac{1}{\sqrt{2n}}} = \sqrt{2n}(T_1 - \theta) \to N(0,1)$

$E(T_1) \to \theta \;\&\; Var(T_1) = \frac{1}{2n} \to 0$

Therefore

T_1 is a consistent and asymptotically normal estimator of θ the asymptotic variance of T_1 is $\frac{1}{2n}$

Asymptotically distribution of sample quartile

Let $X_i (i = 1, 2, \dots, n) \sim i.i.d$ with cdf $F(x)$ and continuous density $f(x)$. If $f(\mu_\theta) > 0$, then

$\sqrt{n}(\hat{\mu}_\theta - \mu_\theta) \to N\left(0, \frac{\theta(1-\theta)}{\{f(\mu_\theta)\}^2}\right)$

$\hat{\mu}_\theta \to$ Sample Quantile ; $\mu_\theta \to$ Population Quantile

T_2 = 75th percentile = 3rd quantile = $Q_3 \Rightarrow \Pr(X < Q_3) = \frac{3}{4}$

$$Q_3 = \theta + \frac{1}{\sqrt{2}} \Rightarrow \sqrt{n}\left[T_2 - \left(\theta + \frac{1}{\sqrt{2}}\right)\right] \to N\left(0, \frac{\frac{3}{4}\left(1-\frac{3}{4}\right)}{\left\{f\left(\theta + \frac{1}{\sqrt{2}}\right)\right\}^2}\right) = N\left(0, \frac{3}{8}\right)$$

Where,

$f(x) = g(\varepsilon)\left|\frac{d\varepsilon}{dx}\right| = |x - \theta|;\ \theta - 1 < x < \theta + 1$

$E\left(T_2 - \frac{1}{\sqrt{2}}\right) \to \theta \;\&\; Var\left(T_2 - \frac{1}{\sqrt{2}}\right) = Var(T_2) = \frac{3}{8n} \to 0$

Therefore

(1) $T_2 - \frac{1}{\sqrt{2}}$ is a consistent and asymptotically normal estimator of θ

(2) The asymptotic variance of T_2 is $\frac{3}{8n}$

Option (a), (b), (c) and (d) are correct.

61. Explanation: (b)

Let X_1, X_2, X_3, X_4 be iid random variables having uniform distribution on $(0, \theta), \theta > 0$ is an unknown parameter

Here, $I = \left[2X_{(4)}, 3X_{(4)}\right]$ is the confidence interval with confidence coefficient α_1

$\alpha_1 = P\left[2X_{(4)} < \theta < 3X_{(4)}\right]$

$= P\left[\frac{\theta}{3} < X_{(4)} \le \frac{\theta}{2}\right]$

$X_{(4)}$ is the largest order statistic with pdf

$f(x_{(4)}) = 4[F(x)]^{4-1} f(x) = 4\left[\frac{x}{\theta}\right]^3 \frac{1}{\theta} = \frac{4}{\theta^4} x_{(4)}^3$

$f(x_{(4)}) = \frac{4}{\theta^4} x_{(4)}^3;\ 0 < x_{(4)} < \theta$

$\alpha_1 = P\left[\frac{\theta}{3} < X_{(4)} < \frac{\theta}{2}\right] = \int_{\theta/3}^{\theta/2} f(x_{(4)})\, dx_{(4)}$

$= \frac{4}{\theta^4}\int_{\theta/3}^{\theta/2} x_{(4)}^3\, dx_{(4)}$

$\alpha_1 = 0.05$

Which is independent of parameter θ

Here $J = \left[X_{(4)}, 1 + X_{(4)}\right]$ be the confidence interval with confidence (coverage probability), α_2

$\alpha_2 = P[X_{(4)} \le \theta \le 1 + X_{(4)}] = P\left[0 \le \theta - X_{(4)} \le 1\right]$

$= P\left[\theta - 1 \le X_{(4)} \le \theta\right]$

$= \int_{\theta-1}^{\theta} f(x_{(4)})\, dx_{(4)} = \frac{4}{\theta^4}\int_{\theta-1}^{\theta} x_{(4)}^3\, dx_{(4)}$

$= \frac{\theta^4 - (\theta-1)^4}{\theta^4}$

Which is dependent of parameter of θ

$\Rightarrow$ Coverage probability of I is independent of θ but coverage probability of J is dependent of θ

So, option (b) is correct

62. Explanation: (c)

Let $X_1, X_2, \dots, X_n$ be a random sample from exponential distribution with mean θ

The pdf of exponential distribution is

$f(x_i) = \frac{1}{\theta} e^{-x_i/\theta};\ x_i > \theta$

The likelihood function is

$L = \prod_{i=1}^{n} f(x_i) = \prod_{i=1}^{n} \frac{1}{\theta} e^{-x_i/\theta}$

$= \frac{1}{\theta^n} e^{-\frac{1}{\theta}\sum_{i=1}^{n} x_i}.1$

$= g\{\sum_{i=1}^{n} x_i, \theta\}.h(\tilde{x})$

Where $g\{\sum_{i=1}^{n} x_i, \theta\}$ is the function of sample value through parameter θ and $h(x)$ is the only function of $\tilde{x}$

$\Rightarrow$ function of sufficient statistic is also sufficient for θ

$\Rightarrow \frac{1}{\sum_{i=1}^{n} X_1}$ is sufficient for θ

$(X_n, X_1 + X_2 + \dots + X_{n-1})$ is also sufficient for θ

But $\frac{X_n}{X_1 + X_2 + \dots + X_{n-1}}$ is not a function of $\sum_{i=1}^{n} X_i$ so

$\frac{X_n}{X_1 + X_2 + \dots + X_{n-1}}$ is not sufficient statistic for θ

So, option (c) is correct

63. Explanation: (a)

$X_i's \sim N(0, \sigma^2)$ are independent

For option (a):

$T_1 = \sqrt{\frac{\pi}{2}}.\frac{1}{n}\sum_{i=1}^{n} |X_i|$

$E(T_1) = \sqrt{\frac{\pi}{2}}.\frac{1}{n}\sum_{i=1}^{n} E|X_i| = \sqrt{\frac{\pi}{2}}.\frac{1}{n}.n.\sqrt{\frac{2}{\pi}}$

$$\left[E|X_i| = \sqrt{\frac{2}{\pi}}\sigma\right]$$

$E(T_1) = \sigma$

T_1 is an unbiased estimator of σ

$Var(T_1) = \frac{\pi}{2}.\frac{1}{n^2}.n\,Var(|X_i|)$

$Var(|X_i|) = E(X_i^2) - \{E\,|X_i|\}^2 = \sigma^2 - \frac{2}{\pi}\sigma^2$

$Var(T_1) = \frac{\pi}{2}.\frac{1}{n}.\sigma^2\left(1 - \frac{2}{\pi}\right)$

As $n \to \infty, Var(T_1) \to 0$

So T_1 is consistent estimator for σ

T_1 is an unbiased & consistent for σ

For option (b): $T_2 = \sqrt{\frac{1}{n}\sum_{i=1}^{n} X_i^2}$

$T_2^2 = \frac{1}{n}\sum_{i=1}^{n} X_i^2$

$E[T_2^2] = \frac{1}{n}.n.\sigma^2 = \sigma^2$

T_2^2 is an unbiased for σ^2

But unbiased estimator does not follow invariance property so

$E(T_2) \neq \sigma$

So, T_2 is not an unbiased estimator for σ

Similarly, $\sqrt{\frac{1}{n}\Sigma(X_i - \bar{X})^2}$ and $\sqrt{\frac{1}{2n}(X_1^2 + X_2^2)}$ is not an unbiased estimator for σ

So, option (a) is correct

64. Explanation: (b)

Here $X_i \sim N(\theta, \theta)$

i.e. $mean = variance = \theta$ is same in given

$var\,(X) = E(X^2) - [E(X)]^2$

$E(X^2) = var(X) + [E(X)]^2$

$E(X^2) = \theta + \theta^2$ .... (1)

For (1)

$\theta = \frac{-1-(1+4/n\sum x_i^2)^{1/2}}{2}$

But $\theta \in (0, \infty)$

So the option is incorrect.

Similarly

For (4)

Max $\left(\frac{\Sigma x_i}{n}, 0\right)$

Here max point is of $\theta = 0$

but $0 < \theta < \infty \Rightarrow \theta > 0$

∴ It's also incorrect

For (2)

assume

$\theta = \frac{-1+(1+4/n\sum x_i^2)^{1/2}}{2}$

$\theta + \frac{1}{2} = \frac{1+(1+4/n\sum x_i^2)^{1/2}}{2}$

$2\left(\theta + \frac{1}{2}\right) = (1 + 4/n\sum X_i^2)^{1/2}$

$(2\theta + 1)^2 = (1 + 4/n\sum X_i^2)$

$4\theta^2 + 4\theta + 1 = 1 + 4/n\sum X_i^2$

$4(\theta^2 + \theta) = 4/n\sum X_i^2 + 1 - 1$

$\theta^2 + \theta = \frac{4\sum X_i^2}{4n}$

$(\theta^2 + \theta) = \frac{\sum X_i^2}{n}$

$\Rightarrow E(X^2) = \theta^2 + \theta$ .... (2)

By eq^n (a) & (b)

θ exists & it's MLE

$\hat{\theta} = \frac{-1+(1+4/n\sum X_i^2)^{1/2}}{2}$

65. Explanation: (c), (d).

We know that if $X_1, X_2, \ldots .X_n$ are i. i. d. $N(\mu, \sigma^2)$.

Then the M.L.E. of μ and σ^2 is given by

$$\hat{\mu} = \bar{x} \text{ and } \hat{\sigma}^2 = \sum_i \frac{(x_i - \bar{x})^2}{n}$$

Option (b) :

$$E(\hat{\sigma}^2) = E\left[\sum_{i=1}^{n}\frac{(x_i - \bar{x})^2}{n}\right]$$

Consider

$$\sum (x_i - \mu)^2 = \sum [(x_i - \bar{x}) + (\bar{x} - \mu)]^2$$

$= \sum [(x_i - \bar{x})^2 + (\bar{x} - \mu)^2 + 2(x_i - \bar{x})(\bar{x} - \mu)]$

$= \Sigma(x_i - \bar{x})^2 + n(\bar{x} - \mu)^2 + 2\Sigma[x_i\bar{x} - x_i\mu - \bar{x}^2 + \mu\bar{x}]$

$= \Sigma(x_i - \bar{x})^2 + n(\bar{x} - \mu)^2 + 2[n\bar{x}^2 - n\mu\bar{x} - n\bar{x}^2 + n\mu\bar{x}]$

$= \Sigma(x_i - \bar{x})^2 + n(\bar{x} - \mu)^2$

$\therefore n\hat{\sigma}^2 = \Sigma(x_i - \mu)^2 - n(\bar{x} - \mu)^2$

Taking expectation on both sides.

$nE(\hat{\sigma}^2) = \Sigma E(x_i - \mu)^2 - nE(\bar{x} - \mu)^2$

$= n\sigma^2 - n\left(\frac{\sigma^2}{n}\right)$

$= n\sigma^2 - \sigma^2$

$= \sigma^2(n - 1)$

$\Rightarrow E(\hat{\sigma}^2) = \sigma^2\left(\frac{n-1}{n}\right) \neq \sigma^2\ (Given)$

Therefore $\hat{\sigma}^2$ is not an unbiased estimator of σ^2.

∴ Option (b) is incorrect.

Option 4 :

$$E(\hat{\sigma}^4) = E[(\hat{\sigma}^2)^2]$$

We know that $n\hat{\sigma}^2/\sigma_2^2 \sim \chi_{n-1}^2$

$\therefore Var(n\hat{\sigma}^2/\sigma^2) = \frac{n^2}{\sigma^4}Var(\hat{\sigma}^2)$

Now

$$Var(\hat{\sigma}^2) = E[(\hat{\sigma}^2)^2] - [E(\hat{\sigma}^2)]^2$$

$= E[\hat{\sigma}^4] - \left[\sigma^2\left(\frac{n-1}{n}\right)\right]^2$

$= E(\hat{\sigma}^4) - \sigma^4\left(\frac{n-1}{n}\right)^2$

$\therefore Var\left(\frac{n\hat{\sigma}^2}{\sigma^2}\right) = \frac{n^2}{\sigma^4}\left[E(\hat{\sigma}^4) - \sigma^4\left(\frac{n-1}{n}\right)^2\right]$

$$2(n-1) = \frac{n^2}{\sigma^4}E(\hat{\sigma}^4) - (n-1)^2$$

$\Rightarrow \frac{n^2}{\sigma^4}E(\hat{\sigma}^4) = 2(n-1) + (n-1)^2$

$= (n-1)(2 + n - 1)$

$= (n-1)(n+1)$

$\therefore E(\hat{\sigma}^4) = \sigma^4\left(\frac{(n-1)(n+1)}{n^2}\right)$

$\Rightarrow \frac{n^2}{(n-1)(n+1)}E(\hat{\sigma}^4) = \sigma^4$

$\therefore E\left[\frac{n^2\hat{\sigma}^4}{(n-1)(n+1)}\right] = \sigma^4$

Therefore **option (d)** is correct.

Option (c):

$\because \frac{n\hat{\sigma}^2}{\sigma^2} \sim \chi^2_{n-1}$

$\therefore Var\left[\frac{n\hat{\sigma}^2}{\sigma^2}\right] = 2(n-1)$

$\Rightarrow \frac{n^2}{\sigma^4} Var(\hat{\sigma}^2) = 2(n-1)$

$\Rightarrow Var(\hat{\sigma}^2) = \sigma^4 \frac{2(n-1)}{n^2}$

$= 2\sigma^4\left(\frac{1}{n} - \frac{1}{n^2}\right)$

Applying limit as $n \to \infty$ on both sides.

$$\lim_{n\to\infty} Var(\hat{\sigma}^2) = \lim_{n\to\infty}\left[2\sigma^4\left(\frac{1}{n} - \frac{1}{n^2}\right)\right]$$

$= 2\sigma^4 \lim_{n\to\infty}\left(\frac{1}{n} - \frac{1}{n^2}\right)$

$= 2\sigma^4.0$

$= 0$

$\therefore$ **Option (c)** is correct.

Option (a):

Let us assume that

$$\frac{(n-1)\hat{\sigma}^2}{\sigma^2} \sim \chi^2_{n-1}$$

$\therefore E\left[\frac{(n-1)\hat{\sigma}^2}{\sigma^2}\right] = n-1$

$\Rightarrow \frac{(n-1)}{\sigma^2} E[\hat{\sigma}^2] = n-1$

$\Rightarrow \frac{(n-1)}{\sigma^2}\left(\frac{n-1}{n}\right)\sigma^2 = (n-1)$

$\Rightarrow n-1 = n$ So we arrived at a contradiction.

This is so because our original assumption must be wrong.

Thus $\frac{(n-1)\hat{\sigma}^2}{\sigma^2}$ does not follow χ^2_{n-1}.

$\therefore$ Option (a) is incorrect.

66. Explanation: (d)

Let X & Y are independent random variables.

$X \sim U[0, \theta+3]$, $Y \sim U[-\theta-5, 0]$, $\theta \geqslant -3$

$$L(\theta, x, y) = f(x, y)$$

$= f(x)\cdot f(y)$

$\because X$ & Y are independent.

$= \frac{1}{\theta+3}\cdot\frac{1}{\theta+5}; \ \theta \geqslant -3;\ 0 \le x \le \theta+3;\ -\theta-5 \le y \le 0$

Taking log on both sides

$$\log L(\theta, x, y) = -\log(\theta+3) - \log(\theta+5)$$

Differentiating on both the sides w.r.t. θ and equating to 0.

$$\frac{\partial \ln(\theta, x, y)}{\partial\theta} = \frac{-1}{\theta+3} - \frac{1}{\theta+5} = 0$$

$\Rightarrow \frac{-\theta-5-\theta-3}{(\theta+3)(\theta+5)} = 0$

$\Rightarrow \frac{-2(\theta+4)}{(\theta+3)(\theta+5)} = 0 \Rightarrow \theta = -4$

But given that $\theta \geqslant -3$. Thus calculus method does not provide us maximum $L(\theta)$ in the given parameter space.

Note that here ranges of both X & Y involve parameter θ.

$$0 \leqslant x \leqslant \theta+3 \ \ \& \ -\theta-5 \leqslant y \leqslant 0$$

$\Rightarrow x-3 \le \theta \ \& \ -5-y \le \theta$ (1)

Now observe that $L(\theta, x, y) = \frac{1}{(\theta+3)(\theta+5)}$ will be maximum when the denominator will be minimum. This is possible only when θ will take its possible lower limit based on (X,Y).

From Equ. (1) we get the minimum value of θ under given (X,Y) which is (−5 − Y, X − 3).

Thus answer is **option (d)**.

67. Explanation: (a)

Here $x \sim$ Poisson$(mean = \lambda)$

$\therefore E(x) = \lambda$, $v(x) = \lambda$

$\therefore E(x) = \lambda$

We have to find X where the function is estimable

Now $E(x) = \lambda$

$\therefore \lambda$ is estimable for X

$\therefore$ The statement is true

For λ^2

$E(x^2) = [E(x)]^2 + var(x)$

$E(x^2) = \lambda^2 + \lambda$

$E(x^2) = \lambda^2 + E(x)$ .... $\therefore E(x) = var(x)$

$E(x^2) - E(x) = \lambda^2$

$E(x^2 - x) = \lambda^2$

$\therefore \lambda^2$ is estimable for $x^2 - x$

For $e^{-\lambda}$

$E(f(x)) = \sum f(x).p(x)$

$= \sum(-1)^x e^{\lambda}\frac{e^{-\lambda}\lambda^x}{x!}$ ..... ; $f(x) = (-1)^x e^{\lambda}$

$= \frac{\sum(-1)\lambda^x}{x!}$

$= e^{-\lambda}$

$\therefore e^{-\lambda}$ is estimable for $(-1)^x e^{\lambda}$

$\therefore$ Above $\lambda, \lambda^2, e^{-\lambda}$ are estimable function

$\therefore \lambda^{-1}$ is not estimable function

$\therefore$ Option (a) is correct

68. Explanation: (c)

The simple linear regression model is

$y_i = \beta x_i + \epsilon_i$; $i = 1, 2, \ldots. n$

$E(\epsilon_i) = 0$

$cov(\epsilon_i, \epsilon_k) = 0$; $i \neq k$

$var(\epsilon_i) = xi^2\sigma^2$

We know that

If $y = \beta_0 + \beta_1 x + \epsilon$ & $\epsilon \sim N(0, \sigma^2)$

Then $\widehat{\beta_1} = \frac{\sum(x_i-\bar{x})(y_i-\bar{y})}{\sum(x-i-\bar{x})^2}$

$\beta_0 = \bar{y} - \widehat{\beta_1 \bar{x}}$

But $var(\epsilon_i)$ isw given $x_1^2\sigma^2$

$\therefore$ we consider

$y_i = \beta x_i + \epsilon_i$

Divide by x_i

$\frac{y_i}{x_i} = \beta + \frac{\epsilon_i}{x_i}$

$E\left(\frac{y_i}{x_i}\right) = \beta + 0 = \beta$

$\& V\left(\frac{y_i}{x_i}\right) = 0 + v\left(\frac{\epsilon_i}{x_i}\right)$

$= \frac{1}{x_i^2} v(\epsilon_i)$

$v\left(\frac{y_i}{x_i}\right) = \frac{1}{x_i^2}(\sigma^2 x_i^2) = \sigma^2$

i.e. $\frac{y_i}{x_i} \sim N(0, \sigma^2)$

Now we check the option

$E\left(\frac{y_i}{x_i}\right) = \sum \frac{y_i/x_i}{n} = \frac{1}{n}\sum \frac{y_i}{x_i} = \beta$

$\therefore \frac{1}{n}\sum \frac{y_i}{x_i}$ is unbiased estimated for β

$\therefore$ Option (c) is correct.

69. Explanation: (c)

X_1, X_2 be a random sample from $N(0, \sigma^2)$ distribution, where $\sigma > 0$.

Suppose, for some constant c, $(c(X_1^2 + X_2^2), \infty)$ is a confidence interval for variance σ^2 with confidence coefficient 0.95.

$\because X_1, X_2 \sim N(0, \sigma^2) \Rightarrow \frac{X_1}{\sigma}, \frac{X_2}{\sigma} \sim N(0,1) \Rightarrow \frac{X_1^2}{\sigma^2}, \frac{X_2^2}{\sigma^2} \sim \chi_1^2$

Since X_1 & X_2 are independent as they are the random variable hence X_1^2 & X_2^2 are also independent.

$\Rightarrow \frac{X_1^2}{\sigma^2} + \frac{X_2^2}{\sigma^2} = \frac{X_1^2 + X_2^2}{\sigma^2} = \frac{Y}{\sigma^2} \sim \chi_2^2 \equiv Exp\left(\frac{1}{2}\right)$

Given that $(c(X_1^2 + X_2^2), \infty)$ is a 95% confidence interval for σ^2.

$P(c(X_1^2 + X_2^2) < \sigma^2) = 0.95 \Rightarrow P\left(\frac{Y}{\sigma^2} < \frac{1}{c}\right) = 0.95$

$\Rightarrow P\left(\chi_2^2 < \frac{1}{c}\right) = 0.95$

$\Rightarrow 1 - e^{-\frac{1}{2c}} = 0.95 \Rightarrow e^{-\frac{1}{2c}} = 0.05 \Rightarrow -\frac{1}{2c} = \ln 0.05$

$\Rightarrow c = -\frac{1}{2\ln 0.05}$

70. Explanation: (b)

$$f(x|\theta) = \begin{cases} \frac{1-\theta}{2}, & if\ x = 0 \\ \frac{1}{2} & if\ x = 1 \quad \theta \in (0,1) \\ \frac{\theta}{2} & if\ x = 2 \\ 0 & otherwise, \end{cases}$$

A random sample of size 100 from the above distribution, the observed counts of 0, 1 and 2 are 20,30 and 50 respectively.

The likelihood is given by

$$L(\theta, \underline{x}) = \prod_{i=1}^{100} f(x_i \mid \theta) = \left(\frac{1-\theta}{2}\right)^{20} \times \left(\frac{1}{2}\right)^{30} \times \left(\frac{\theta}{2}\right)^{50}$$

$\log L(\theta, \underline{x}) = 20\log(1-\theta) + 50\log\theta + constants$

$\frac{\partial}{\partial\theta}\log L(\theta, \underline{x}) = -\frac{20}{1-\theta} + \frac{50}{\theta} = 0$

$\Rightarrow -20\theta + 50 - 50\theta = -70\theta + 50$

$= 0 \Rightarrow \hat{\theta} = \frac{5}{7}$

71. Explanation: (b), (c), (d)

$X_1, \ldots, X_n$ $(n \geq 3)$ be a random sample from a distribution having probability density function

$$f(x \mid \theta) = \begin{cases} \theta e^{-\theta x}, & if\ x > 0 \\ 0, & otherwise \end{cases}; \ \theta > 0$$

Let $T_n = \frac{1}{n}\sum_{i=1}^n X_i$.

$\because X_i \sim Exp(\theta) \Rightarrow nT_n$

$= \sum_{i=1}^n X_i \sim Gamma(scale = \theta, shape = n)$

$\Rightarrow \frac{1}{nT_n} = \frac{1}{\sum_{i=1}^n X_i} \sim Inverse\ Gamma(scale = \theta, shape = n)$

$\Rightarrow E\left(\frac{1}{nT_n}\right) = E\left(\frac{1}{\sum_{i=1}^n X_i}\right) = \frac{\theta}{(n-1)} \Rightarrow E\left(\frac{(n-1)}{nT_n}\right) = \theta$

$\Rightarrow Var\left(\frac{1}{nT_n}\right) = Var\left(\frac{1}{\sum_{i=1}^n X_i}\right) = \frac{\theta^2}{(n-1)^2(n-2)}$

$\Rightarrow Var\left(\frac{(n-1)}{nT_n}\right) = (n-1)^2 Var\left(\frac{1}{nT_n}\right)$

$= (n-1)^2 \times \frac{\theta^2}{(n-1)^2(n-2)} = \frac{\theta^2}{n-2}$

The p.d.f. of the X is

$f(x, \theta) = \theta e^{-\theta x} \Rightarrow \log f(x, \theta)$

$= \log\theta - \theta x \Rightarrow \frac{\partial}{\partial\theta}\log f(x, \theta) = \frac{1}{\theta} - x$

$\Rightarrow \frac{\partial^2}{\partial\theta^2}\log f(x, \theta) = -\frac{1}{\theta^2}$

$E\left(\frac{\partial^2}{\partial\theta^2}\log f(x, \theta)\right) = -\frac{1}{\theta^2} \Rightarrow -nE\left(\frac{\partial^2}{\partial\theta^2}\log f(x, \theta)\right) = \frac{n}{\theta^2}$

Thus the Cramer-Rao lower bound for estimating the variance of any unbiased estimator of θ is

$\frac{(\theta')^2}{(n/\theta^2)} = \frac{\theta^2}{n}$

As the variance of $\frac{n-1}{nT_n}$ is does not attain the Cramer-Rao lower bound. Thus the $\frac{n-1}{nT_n}$ is not a UMVUE of θ.

The option (3) follows from the theory of UMVUE as it is one of the definitions of the UMVUE.

(d) Note that the sample moments are consistent estimators of their corresponding population moments. Thus

T_n is a consistent estimator for $E(X) = \frac{1}{\theta}$

$P_\theta(X_1 \leq 1) = F(1) = 1 - e^{-\theta} = 1 - e^{-\frac{1}{(1/\theta)}}$

Note that $1 - e^{-\frac{1}{(1/\theta)}}$ is a continuous function of $\frac{1}{\theta}$.

Therefore $1 - e^{-\frac{1}{T_n}}$ is a consistent estimator of $1 - e^{-\frac{1}{(1/\theta)}} = P_\theta(X_1 \leq 1)$

72. Explanation: (b), (c)

$X_1, \ldots, X_n$ $(n \geq 2)$ be a random sample from a $U(-\theta, 2\theta)$ distribution, where $\theta > 0$.

Let $\overline{X} = \sum_{i=1}^n X_i, X_{(1)} = min\{X_1, \ldots, X_n\}$ and $X_{(n)} = max(X_1, \ldots, X_n)$.

The p.d.f. of X is

$f(x; \theta) = \frac{1}{3\theta} I\{-\theta \leq x \leq 2\theta\}$

The likelihood is given by

$$f(x_i;\theta)$$

$$L(\theta,\underline{x}) = \prod_{i=1}^{n} = \prod_{i=1}^{n} \frac{1}{3\theta} I\{-\theta \le x \le 2\theta\} = \frac{1}{3^n} \times \frac{1}{\theta^n} \times I \left\{max\left(-x_{(1)}, \frac{x_{(n)}}{2}\right) \le \theta\right\}$$

Thus the above likelihood becomes maximum when θ take the minimum possible value given a random sample of size n which is nothing but an m.l.e. of θ given as

$$\hat{\theta} = max\left(-X_{(1)}, \frac{X_{(n)}}{2}\right)$$

The expected value of X is

$$E(X) = \frac{\theta}{2}$$

The method of moment estimator is obtained when we equate the above first population raw moment $(E(X))$ with the first sample raw moment $(\overline{X})$.

$$E(X) = \frac{\theta}{2} = \overline{X} \Rightarrow \hat{\theta} = 2\overline{X}$$

73. Explanation: (a), (b), (c)

$X_1, \ldots, X_n$ be independent and identically distributed $U(0,\theta), \theta > 0$ random variables.

Define $X(n) = \max(X_1, \ldots, X_n)$ *and* $X_{(1)} = min\{X_1, \ldots, X_n\}$.

The p.d.f. of X is

$$f_X(x) = \frac{1}{\theta}\ ; 0 \le x \le \theta$$

The c.d.f. of X is

$$F_X(x) = \frac{x}{\theta}\ ; 0 \le x \le \theta$$

The joint density of $X_{(1)}$ & $X_{(n)}$ is

$$f_{1,n}(x,y) = n(n-1)f(x)f(y)[F(y)-F(x)]^{n-2}$$

$$= n(n-1).\frac{1}{\theta^2}\left(\frac{y-x}{\theta}\right)^{n-2} = \frac{n(n-1)}{\theta^n}(y-x)^{n-2}\ ; 0 < x < y < \theta$$

Once we get the joint distribution of the $X_{(1)}$ & $X_{(n)}$ then it becomes easy to compute the options.

So only option (d) is not true. All other options are true.

74. Explanation: (c)

The probability density function (PDF) of the Uniform$(\theta, 1-\theta)$ distribution is:

$$f(x;\theta) = \begin{cases} \frac{1}{1-2\theta} & \text{if } \theta \le x \le 1-\theta, \\ 0 & \text{otherwise.} \end{cases}$$

For a random sample $X_1, X_2, \ldots, X_n$, the likelihood function is:

$$L(\theta) = \prod_{i=1}^{n} f(x_i;\theta)$$

$$= \begin{cases} \left(\frac{1}{1-2\theta}\right)^n & \text{if } \theta \le x_i \le 1-\theta \text{ for all } i, \\ 0 & \text{otherwise.} \end{cases}$$

The likelihood function $L(\theta)$ is maximized when $\frac{1}{1-2\theta}$ is maximized, which occurs when θ is as small as possible. However, θ must satisfy the constraints:

$\theta \le \min\{X_1, X_2, \ldots, X_n\}$, and $1-\theta \ge \max\{X_1, X_2, \ldots, X_n\}$.

$\theta \le \min\{X_1, X_2, \ldots, X_n\}$, and $\theta \le 1 - \max\{X_1, X_2, \ldots, X_n\}$.

$\theta \le \min\{\min\{X_1, X_2, \ldots, X_n\}, 1 - \max\{X_1, X_2, \ldots, X_n\}\}$.

To maximize $L(\theta)$, we choose the largest possible θ that satisfies this constraint. Therefore, the MLE of θ is:

$$\hat{\theta} = \min\{\min\{X_1, X_2, \ldots, X_n\}, 1 - \max\{X_1, X_2, \ldots, X_n\}\}.$$

75. Explanation: (d)

The variance of p in a simple random sample (without replacement) is:

$$\text{Var}(p) = \frac{P(1-P)}{n} \cdot \frac{N-n}{N-1}$$

To find an unbiased estimator of $P(1-P)$, we use the relationship between $\text{Var}(p)$ and $P(1-P)$. Rearrange the variance formula:

$$P(1-P) = \text{Var}(p) \cdot \frac{n(N-1)}{N-n}$$

$$\hat{\text{Var}}(p) = \frac{p(1-p)}{n-1} \frac{N-n}{N}$$

Thus, an unbiased estimator of $P(1-P)$ is:

$$P(1\hat{-}P) = \hat{\text{Var}}(p) \cdot \frac{n(N-1)}{N-n}$$

$$= \frac{p(1-p)}{n-1} \cdot \frac{N-n}{N} \cdot \frac{n(N-1)}{N-n}$$

$$P(1\hat{-}P) = \frac{p(1-p)}{n-1} \cdot \frac{n(N-1)}{N} = \frac{n(N-1)}{N(n-1)} p(1-p)$$

This matches option (d).

76. Explanation: (b), (c)

We have $X_1, X_2, \ldots, X_{13}$ as i.i.d. Poisson(θ) random variables.

Statement (a): $(\sum_{i=1}^{8} X_i)(\sum_{i=8}^{13} X_i)$ is an unbiased estimator of $48\theta^2$.

Since $X_i \sim$ Poisson(θ), we have:

$E(X_i) = \theta$.

$\sum_{i=1}^{8} X_i \sim$ Poisson(8θ).

$\sum_{i=8}^{13} X_i \sim$ Poisson(5θ).

The two sums are independent because the Poisson distribution is additive for independent variables.

- **Expected value of the product:**

$$E\left(\sum_{i=1}^{8} X_i \sum_{i=8}^{13} X_i\right) = E\left(\sum_{i=1}^{8} X_i\right) E\left(\sum_{i=8}^{13} X_i\right)$$

$$= (8\theta)(5\theta) = 40\theta^2$$

- Since $40\theta^2 \ne 48\theta^2$, this is not an unbiased estimator of $48\theta^2$.

Statement (a) is incorrect.

Statement (b)): $\frac{1}{13}\sum_{i=1}^{13} X_i$ is the method of moments (MoM) estimator of θ.

- The method of moments estimator equates the sample mean to the population mean.
- Since $E(X_i) = \theta$, we take the sample mean: $\theta_{\text{MoM}} = \frac{1}{13}\sum_{i=1}^{13} X_i$.
- This is exactly the sample mean, which is the MoM estimator.

Statement (b)) is correct.

Statement (c): There does not exist any unbiased estimator of $e^{-7\theta}$.

The Lehmann-Scheffé theorem states that if a complete sufficient statistic exists, then any unbiased estimator of a function of θ must be a function of this sufficient statistic.

- For Poisson(θ), the sufficient statistic is $T = \sum_{i=1}^{13} X_i$, which follows Poisson(13θ).
- We check whether an unbiased estimator for $e^{-7\theta}$ can exist:

If such an estimator $\delta(X_1, \dots, X_{13})$ were unbiased, we would need:$E[\delta(T)] = e^{-7\theta}$.

Since $e^{-7\theta}$ is a non-polynomial function, there does not exist an unbiased estimator in the Poisson family.

Statement (c) is correct.

Statement (d): $(e^{X_7}, \sum_{i=1}^{6} X_i, \sum_{i=8}^{13} X_i)$ is a sufficient statistic for θ.

- By the Factorization theorem, a statistic $S(X)$ is sufficient for θ if the joint density (or probability mass function for discrete distributions) can be factorized as:$P(X_1, \dots, X_{13}|\theta) = g(S(X), \theta)h(X)$.
- The minimal sufficient statistic for θ in a Poisson setting is $\sum_{i=1}^{13} X_i$, because the Poisson distribution is from the exponential family.
- However, the given statistic includes an extra term e^{X_7}, which is not necessary to capture all the information about θ.

Statement (d) is incorrect.

Thus, options (b) and (c) are correct.

77. Explanation: (b) and (c)

The cumulative distribution function (CDF) of a single X_i is:

$$F(x) = P(X_i \le x) = 1 - e^{-(x-\theta)}, x \ge \theta$$

Since $X_{(1)}$ is the minimum of n independent X_i's, its CDF is:

$$F_{X_{(1)}}(x) = 1 - (1 - F(x))^n = 1 - e^{-n(x-\theta)}$$

Differentiating gives the probability density function (PDF) of $X_{(1)}$:

$$f_{X_{(1)}}(x) = ne^{-n(x-\theta)}, x \ge \theta$$

A confidence interval for θ is derived from the cumulative probability equation:

$$P(a \le X_{(1)} - \theta \le b) = \gamma$$

Using $X_{(1)}$, we determine:

$$P(X_{(1)} - \theta \ge t) = P(X_{(1)} \ge \theta + t) = e^{-nt}$$

Thus, $P(X_{(1)} - \theta \le t) = 1 - e^{-nt}$

Setting $1 - e^{-nt} = \gamma$, we solve for t: $t = -\frac{1}{n}\ln(1-\gamma)$

Thus, the lower confidence bound for θ is:

$$\theta \in \left(X_{(1)} - \frac{1}{n}\ln(1-\gamma), X_{(1)}\right)$$

Checking the interval $\left(X_{(1)} - \frac{2}{n}\ln 5, X_{(1)}\right)$

Comparing with the formula:

$$\frac{1}{n}\ln(1-\gamma) = \frac{2}{n}\ln 5$$

Solving for γ:

$1 - \gamma = 5^{-2}$,

$$\gamma = 1 - 5^{-2} = 1 - \frac{1}{25} = 0.96$$

So, this is a 96% confidence interval

$\therefore$ Statement (b) is true and (a) is false.

Checking the interval $\left(X_{(1)} - \frac{1}{n}\ln 20, X_{(1)}\right)$

Comparing with the formula:

$$\frac{1}{n}\ln(1-\gamma) = \frac{1}{n}\ln 20$$

Solving for γ:

$$1 - \gamma = 20^{-1} = \frac{1}{20}$$

$$\gamma = 1 - \frac{1}{20} = 0.95$$

So, this is a 95% confidence interval

$\therefore$ Statement (c) is true and (d) is false.

78. Explanation: (b), (c)

An estimator T_n is unbiased for θ if $E_\theta(T_n) = \theta$

From the properties of order statistics for a uniform distribution: $E_\theta(T_n) = \theta + \frac{1}{n+1}$

Since $E_\theta(T_n) \ne \theta$, it is not an unbiased estimator.

Statement (a) is false.

From the expectation result:

$$\lim_{n\to\infty} E_\theta(T_n) = \lim_{n\to\infty}\left(\theta + \frac{1}{n+1}\right) = \theta.$$

Thus, $E_\theta(T_n)$ converges to θ, meaning:

Statement (b)) is true.

An estimator T_n is consistent for θ if:

$$T_n \to \theta \text{ in probability as } n \to \infty.$$

Since $T_n = \min(X_1, X_2, \dots, X_n)$, its variance decreases as $n \to \infty$:

$$\text{Var}_\theta(T_n) = \frac{1}{(n+1)^2}$$

which tends to 0 as $n \to \infty$, meaning T_n converges in probability to θ, proving consistency.

Statement (c) is true.

For the maximum order statistic:

$$E_\theta(\max(X_1, X_2, \dots, X_n)) = \theta + \frac{n}{n+1}$$

which tends to $\theta + 1$ instead of θ. Since it does not converge to θ, it is not a consistent estimator.

Statement (d) is false.

79. Explanation: (c)

Let counts be $n_0 = 20, n_1 = 60, n_2 = 10\ total 90$.

Log-likelihood:

$\ell(\theta) = 20\ln\frac{\theta}{3} + 60\ln!\,(1 - \frac{\theta}{2}) + 10\ln\frac{\theta}{6} = 30\ln\theta + 60\ln!\,(1 - \frac{\theta}{2}) + \text{const}.$

Differentiate and set to zero:

$\ell'(\theta) = \frac{30}{\theta} - \frac{30}{1-\theta/2} = 0 \Rightarrow \frac{1}{\theta} = \frac{1}{1-\theta/2} \Rightarrow \theta = 1 - \frac{\theta}{2}$

$\Rightarrow \theta = \frac{2}{3}$.

Second derivative is negative, so this is the MLE.

Correct Answer: c.

80. Explanation: (b)

In stratified SRSWOR, an unbiased estimator of the population mean is the stratum-weighted mean:

$\hat{Y} = \sum_{h=1}^{2} \frac{N_h}{N}, \bar{y}_h$

with $N_1 = 34$ (Statisticians), $N_2 = 51$ (Biologists), $N = 85$. Thus

$\hat{Y} = \frac{34}{85}, \hat{y}_S + \frac{51}{85}, \hat{y}_B = 0.4, \hat{y}_S + 0.6, \hat{y}_B = \frac{2\hat{y}_S + 3\hat{y}_B}{5}$.

Correct Answer: b.

81. Explanation: (b)

Let $T = \frac{X}{\theta}$. Then for $0 < x < \theta$,

$f_X(x|\theta) = \frac{3}{\theta^3}(\theta - x)^2 = \frac{1}{\theta}, 3!\left(1 - \frac{x}{\theta}\right)^2$

so $(T \sim)$ with pdf $(g(t) = 3(1-t)^2, \backslash 0 < t < 1)$. Its CDF is

$G(t) = \int_0^t 3(1-u)^2, du = 3t - 3t^2 + t^3$.

The CI $\left(\frac{X}{1-\lambda_1}, \frac{X}{1-\lambda_2}\right)$ for θ has confidence level

$\mathbb{P}!\left(\frac{X}{1-\lambda_1} < \theta < \frac{X}{1-\lambda_2}\right) = \mathbb{P}!\left(1 - \lambda_2 < T < 1 - \lambda_1\right) = G(1-\lambda_1) - G(1-\lambda_2)$.

Compute $G(1-\lambda) = 1 - \lambda^3$. Hence the confidence coefficient is

$[1 - \lambda_1^3] - [1 - \lambda_2^3] = \lambda_2^3 - \lambda_1^3 = 1 - \alpha$.

Correct Answer: 2. $\lambda_2^3 - \lambda_1^3 = 1 - \alpha$

82. Explanation: (c), (d)

Identify distribution of X_i

$X_i = \theta + Z_i, Z_i \sim \text{Exp}(1)$, PDF $f(z) = e^{-z}, z \geq 0$.

Distribution of $Y = \min(X_1, \ldots, X_n)$

$Y = \theta + M, M \sim \text{Exp}(n)$, CDF $P(Y \leq y) = 1 - e^{-n(y-\theta)}$, $y \geq \theta$.

Pivot

$W = n(Y - \theta) \sim \text{Exp}(1)$.

Two-sided $1-\alpha$ CI for θ

Find a, b such that $P(a \leq W \leq b) = 1 - \alpha$.

Choose $a = -\ln(1 - \alpha/2), b = -\ln(\alpha/2)$.

Then

$$a \leq n(Y - \theta) \leq b$$

$\Rightarrow Y - \frac{b}{n} \leq \theta \leq Y - \frac{a}{n}$.

Substitute a, b:

$\theta \in \left(Y + \frac{1}{n}\ln(\alpha/2), Y + \frac{1}{n}\ln(1 - \alpha/2)\right)$

This matches **Option d.**

Check Option c

CI: $\left(Y + \frac{2}{n}\ln(\alpha/2), Y + \frac{2}{n}\ln(1 - \alpha/2)\right)$

Let $t_1 = -2\ln(1 - \alpha/2), t_2 = -2\ln(\alpha/2)$.

$P(t_1 < W < t_2) = e^{-t_1} - e^{-t_2} = (1 - \alpha/2)^2 - (\alpha/2)^2 = 1 - \alpha$.

So coverage $1 - \alpha \rightarrow$ **True.**

Options a and b

Option 1: Lower bound makes coverage 0.

Option 2: Coverage = $\sqrt{\alpha} \neq 1 - \alpha$ in general.

Final answer: c, d

83. Explanation: (a), (c), (d)

Let the interval be $[a, b] = [\theta_1 - \theta_2, ; \theta_1 + \theta_2]$ so $b - a = 2\theta_2$.

1. $\bar{X}$ is unbiased for the center of a symmetric distribution, so $E(\bar{X}) = \theta_1$. Hence (a) true.

2. Use the known expectations for uniform order statistics. For $X_{(1)}$ (the minimum),

$$E[X_{(1)}] = a + \frac{b-a}{,n+1,} = \theta_1 - \theta_2 + \frac{2\theta_2}{n+1}.$$

So

$$E[\bar{X} - X_{(1)}] = \theta_1 - (\theta_1 - \theta_2 + \frac{2\theta_2}{n+1}) = \theta_2(1 - \frac{2}{n+1})$$

$$= \theta_2 \frac{n-1}{n+1} \neq \theta_2,$$

so $\bar{X} - X_{(1)}$ is biased for θ_2. (b) false.

3. The mid-range $\frac{X_{(1)} + X_{(n)}}{2}$ satisfies

$$E(\frac{X_{(1)} + X_{(n)}}{2}) = \frac{a+b}{2} = \theta_1,$$

and it is a function of the complete sufficient statistic $(X_{(1)}, X_{(n)})$; hence by Lehmann–Scheffé it is the UMVUE of θ_1. So (c) true.

4. For the range $R = X_{(n)} - X_{(1)}$ we have

$$E[R] = \frac{n-1}{n+1}, (b-a) = \frac{n-1}{n+1}, 2\theta_2.$$

Thus the unbiased estimator for (θ_2) is

$$\hat{\theta}_2 = \frac{n+1}{2(n-1)}(X_{(n)} - X_{(1)}),$$

which is a function of the complete sufficient statistic and hence the UMVUE. So (d) true.

84. Explanation: (a), (c)

If $X \sim \text{Laplace}(\mu = \theta, b = \theta)$ then $E[X] = \theta, \text{Var}(X) = 2\theta^2$ and $E[X^2] = 3\theta^2$. Hence $U_n = \bar{X}$ is unbiased for θ (so (a) true).

Also $E[V_n] = 3\theta^2$, so $\frac{1}{3}V_n$ is unbiased for θ^2 and by the law of large numbers $\frac{1}{3}V_n \xrightarrow{p} \theta^2$ (so (c) true).

S_n^2 is an unbiased estimator of $\text{Var}(X) = 2\theta^2$, not of θ^2 (so (b) false).

Finally (U_n, V_n) is not complete: for example

$$g(U_n, V_n) = 3U_n^2 - (1 + 2/n)V_n$$

is not a.s. zero but $E[g(U_n, V_n)] = 3(1 + 2/n)\theta^2 - (1 + 2/n)3\theta^2 = 0$ for every θ, so (d) is false.

85. Explanation: (b)

Given

$$X \sim \text{Binomial}(n, p)$$

Possible values:

$$n \in \{5,6\}, p \in \left\{\frac{1}{4}, \frac{3}{4}\right\}$$

Observed value: $X = 3$

We find the Maximum Likelihood Estimate (MLE) by choosing the pair (n, p) that gives the largest probability $P(X = 3)$.

Binomial probability

$$P(X = 3) = \binom{n}{3} p^3 (1-p)^{n-3}$$

Compute likelihood for each pair

1. $\left(5, \frac{1}{4}\right)$

$$\binom{5}{3}\left(\frac{1}{4}\right)^3\left(\frac{3}{4}\right)^2 = 10 \cdot \frac{1}{64} \cdot \frac{9}{16} = \frac{90}{1024} \approx 0.088$$

2. $\left(5, \frac{3}{4}\right)$

$$\binom{5}{3}\left(\frac{3}{4}\right)^3\left(\frac{1}{4}\right)^2 = 10\cdot\frac{27}{64}\cdot\frac{1}{16} = \frac{270}{1024} \approx 0.264$$

3. $\left(6,\frac{3}{4}\right)$

$$\binom{6}{3}\left(\frac{3}{4}\right)^3\left(\frac{1}{4}\right)^3 = 20\cdot\frac{27}{64}\cdot\frac{1}{64} \approx 0.132$$

4. $\left(6,\frac{1}{4}\right)$

$$\binom{6}{3}\left(\frac{1}{4}\right)^3\left(\frac{3}{4}\right)^3 = 20\cdot\frac{1}{64}\cdot\frac{27}{64} \approx 0.132$$

Choose maximum likelihood

Largest probability: 0.264 corresponding to $\left(5,\frac{3}{4}\right)$.

86. Explanation: (a)

PDF:

$$f(x \mid \theta) = \begin{cases} \frac{2}{\theta^2}(\theta - x), & 0 < x < \theta \\ 0, & \text{otherwise} \end{cases}$$

Since $0 < x < \theta$, we always have $\theta > X$.

So any confidence interval for θ must start at X.

Step 1: Find the distribution of $\frac{X}{\theta}$

Let $Y = \frac{X}{\theta}$

Then $0 < Y < 1$.

CDF of X:

$$F_X(x) = \int_0^x \frac{2}{\theta^2}(\theta - t)\,dt = \frac{2}{\theta^2}\left[\theta t - \frac{t^2}{2}\right]_0^x = \frac{2\theta x - x^2}{\theta^2}$$

Thus $P(X \le x) = \frac{2x}{\theta} - \left(\frac{x}{\theta}\right)^2$

Hence $P\left(\frac{X}{\theta} \le y\right) = 2y - y^2$

Step 2: Find c such that

$$P\left(\frac{X}{\theta} \ge c\right) = 0.95$$

$$P\left(\frac{X}{\theta} \le c\right) = 0.05$$

So

$$2c - c^2 = 0.05$$
$$c^2 - 2c + 0.05 = 0$$
$$c = 1 - \sqrt{0.95}$$

Step 3: Convert to a confidence interval

$$P\left(\frac{X}{\theta} \ge 1 - \sqrt{0.95}\right) = 0.95$$

$$P\left(\theta \le \frac{X}{1 - \sqrt{0.95}}\right) = 0.95$$

Since $\theta > X$,

$$P\left(X < \theta < \frac{X}{1 - \sqrt{0.95}}\right) = 0.95$$

Therefore the 95% confidence interval is

$$\left(X, \frac{X}{1 - \sqrt{0.95}}\right)$$

Final answer: Option 1.

87. Explanation: (a), (b), (c)

Consistent Estimation of $\theta = \frac{\sigma}{\mu}$:

Distribution Properties:

For the shifted exponential $f(x|\mu,\sigma)$, with $x > \mu$:

Key moments: $E[X] = \mu + \sigma$, $\mathrm{Var}(X) = \sigma^2$

Order statistic $X_{1:n}$: $E[X_{1:n}] = \mu + \frac{\sigma}{n} \to \mu$ as $n \to \infty$

By LLN and consistency results:

$\bar{X}_n \xrightarrow{p} \mu + \sigma$

$S_n^2 \xrightarrow{p} \sigma^2 \Rightarrow S_n \xrightarrow{p} \sigma$

$X_{1:n} \xrightarrow{p} \mu$

Evaluate Each Estimator

Statement 1: $S_n(X_{1:n})^{-1}$

$\frac{S_n}{X_{1:n}} \xrightarrow{p} \frac{\sigma}{\mu} = \theta$

TRUE — provided $\mu > 0$ (given), so $X_{1:n} \xrightarrow{p} \mu \ne 0$

Statement 2: $(\bar{X}_n - X_{1:n})(X_{1:n})^{-1}$

$\bar{X}_n - X_{1:n} \xrightarrow{p} (\mu + \sigma) - \mu = \sigma$

$\frac{\bar{X}_n - X_{1:n}}{X_{1:n}} \xrightarrow{p} \frac{\sigma}{\mu} = \theta$

TRUE

Statement 3: $(\bar{X}_n - X_{1:n})(\bar{X}_n - S_n)^{-1}$

Numerator: $\bar{X}_n - X_{1:n} \xrightarrow{p} \sigma$

Denominator: $\bar{X}_n - S_n \xrightarrow{p} (\mu + \sigma) - \sigma = \mu$

$\frac{\bar{X}_n - X_{1:n}}{\bar{X}_n - S_n} \xrightarrow{p} \frac{\sigma}{\mu} = \theta$

TRUE — provided $\mu \ne 0$ (given $\mu > 0$)

Statement 4: $S_n(\bar{X}_n)^{-1}$

$\frac{S_n}{\bar{X}_n} \xrightarrow{p} \frac{\sigma}{\mu+\sigma} \ne \frac{\sigma}{\mu} = \theta$

FALSE — converges to $\frac{\sigma}{\mu+\sigma}$, not θ

Correct answer: Statements 1, 2, and 3 are true.

88. Explanation: (a), (d)

Estimation for Uniform$\left[-\frac{3\theta}{2}, \frac{\theta}{2}\right]$

Distribution Properties

For $X \sim$ Uniform $\left[-\frac{3\theta}{2}, \frac{\theta}{2}\right]$:

$$E[X] = \frac{-\frac{3\theta}{2} + \frac{\theta}{2}}{2} = \frac{-\theta}{2}$$

Length $= \frac{\theta}{2} - \left(-\frac{3\theta}{2}\right) = 2\theta$

Method of Moments (Statements 1 & 2)

Set $E[X] = \bar{X}: -\frac{\theta}{2} = \bar{X} \Rightarrow \theta = -2\bar{X}$

Since $\theta > 0$ and $E[X] = -\frac{\theta}{2} < 0$, we have $\bar{X} < 0$, so $-2\bar{X} > 0$

Statement 1 is TRUE, Statement 2 is FALSE

Maximum Likelihood Estimator (Statements 3 & 4)

The likelihood function is: $L(\theta) = \frac{1}{(2\theta)^n}$ provided $-\frac{3\theta}{2} \le x_{(1)}$ and $x_{(n)} \le \frac{\theta}{2}$

Since $L(\theta) = \frac{1}{(2\theta)^n}$ is decreasing in θ, we maximize by choosing θ as small as possible.

Constraints on θ:

From upper bound $x_{(n)} \le \frac{\theta}{2}$: $\theta \ge 2x_{(n)}$

From lower bound $-\frac{3\theta}{2} \le x_{(1)}$: $\theta \ge -\frac{2x_{(1)}}{3}$

Both must hold simultaneously: $\theta \ge \max\left\{-\frac{2x_{(1)}}{3}, 2x_{(n)}\right\}$

To maximize likelihood, choose smallest valid θ:

$$\hat{\theta}_{MLE} = \max\left\{-\frac{2X_{(1)}}{3}, 2X_{(n)}\right\}$$

Statement 4 is TRUE, Statement 3 is FALSE

Correct answer: 1 and 4 .

89. Explanation: (a), (d)

Sufficient and Ancillary Statistics:

Model $X_t = a + a^2 t + \varepsilon_t, \varepsilon_t \overset{iid}{\sim} N(0, \sigma^2), t = 1, \ldots, n$

Statement 1 → TRUE

The entire sample $(X_1, \ldots, X_n)$ is always trivially sufficient for any parameter — by Factorization theorem, the joint density factors through the full data.

Statement 2 → FALSE

Expanding $\sum (X_t - a - a^2 t)^2$, the natural sufficient statistic from the exponential family is:

$(\sum X_t, \sum tX_t, \sum X_t^2)$

The given statistic contains $\sum t^2 X_t^2$ instead of $\sum X_t^2$ — incorrect.

Statement 3 → FALSE

$E[X_4 - X_3 - X_2 + X_1] = (a + 4a^2) - (a + 3a^2) - (a + 2a^2) + (a + a^2) = 0$

$\text{Var} = 4\sigma^2$

Distribution is $N(0, 4\sigma^2)$ — free of a but depends on σ.

Not ancillary for full parameter (a, σ).

Statement 4 → TRUE

Numerator: $X_4 + X_1 - X_2 - X_3 \sim N(0, 4\sigma^2)$

Denominator: $X_5 + X_2 - X_3 - X_4 \sim N(0, 4\sigma^2)$

Both have mean 0 (free of a). Their ratio:

$\frac{N(0,4\sigma^2)}{N(0,4\sigma^2)} \sim \text{Cauchy}(0,1)$

The σ^2 cancels — distribution is free of both a and σ.

Correct Answer: Statements 1 and 4 are true.

90. Explanation: (b)

We have the model

$Y_i = \beta x_i + \varepsilon_i, i = 1, 2, \ldots, n$ with $\beta > 0$ and $\sum x_i^2 > 0$.

Two estimators are given:

$\hat{\beta}_1 = \sum a_i Y_i$ where a_i are chosen to minimize $E(\sum a_i Y_i - \beta)^2$

$\hat{\beta}_2$ = ordinary least squares (OLS) estimator

For regression through origin: $\hat{\beta}_2 = \frac{\sum x_i Y_i}{\sum x_i^2}$

The OLS estimator minimizes mean squared error (MSE) among all linear unbiased estimators (Gauss–Markov idea).

Here, $MSE(\hat{\beta}) = Var(\hat{\beta}) + Bias(\hat{\beta})^2$

The estimator $\hat{\beta}_1$ is defined exactly by minimizing $E(\hat{\beta} - \beta)^2$, which is the MSE.

Therefore, $E(\hat{\beta}_1 - \beta)^2 < E(\hat{\beta}_2 - \beta)^2$

Variance comparison:

Since $\hat{\beta}_1$ is allowed to be biased, it can reduce MSE by reducing variance.

Thus typically: $Var(\hat{\beta}_1) < Var(\hat{\beta}_2)$

But $Bias(\hat{\beta}_1) \neq 0$

while OLS is unbiased.

Therefore:

$Var(\hat{\beta}_1) < Var(\hat{\beta}_2)$ and $E(\hat{\beta}_1 - \beta)^2 < E(\hat{\beta}_2 - \beta)^2$

Correct answer: Option (2)

CHAPTER 6

TESTING OF HYPOTHESIS

(DEC. 2012)

1. Suppose person A and person B draw random samples of sizes 15 and 20 respectively from $N(\mu, \sigma^2), \sigma^2 > 0$ for testing $H_0: \mu = 2$ against $H_1: \mu > 2$. In both the cases, the observed sample means and sample standard deviations are same with values $\bar{x}_1 = \bar{x}_2 = 1.8, s_1 = s_2 = s$. Both of them use the usual t-test & state the p-values p_A and p_B respectively. Then which of the following is correct?
(a) $p_A > p_B$
(b) $p_A = p_B$
(c) $p_A < p_B$
(d) Relation between p_A and p_B depends on the value of s

(DEC. 2012)

2. Let X be a discrete random variable with probability mass function $p(x), x \in \{-1, 0, 1, 2, 3\}$. The hypotheses to be tested are $H_0 : p(x) = p_0(x)$ versus $H_1 : p(x) = p_1(x)$, where $p_0(x)$ and $p_1(x)$ are as given below.

x	-1	0	1	2	3
$p_0(x)$	0.01	0.02	0.05	0.32	0.60
$p_1(x)$	0.04	0.08	0.25	0.03	0.60

Then
(a) $\{1\}$ is the cirtical region of an MP test at level $\alpha = 0.05$
(b) $\{-1, 0\}$ is the cirtical region of an MP test at level $\alpha = 0.03$
(c) $\{-1, 1\}$ is the cirtical region of an MP test at level $\alpha = 0.06$
(d) $\{-1, 0, 1\}$ is the cirtical region of an MP test at level $\alpha = 0.08$

(JUNE 2013)

3. Let X be a random variable with density function $f(x) = \begin{cases} \frac{2\theta x+1}{\theta+1}, & 0 \le x \le 1, \theta > -1 \\ 0, & \text{otherwise} \end{cases}$. Consider the problem of testing $H_0 : \theta \le 1$ against $H_1 : \theta > 1$. Let ϕ be the test given by $\phi(x) = \begin{cases} 1 & \text{if } x \ge \frac{\sqrt{9-8\alpha}-1}{2} \\ 0 & \text{if } x < \frac{\sqrt{9-8\alpha}-1}{2} \end{cases}$. Then which of the following statements are true?
(a) ϕ is a UMP size α test
(b) ϕ is not a UMP size α test
(c) For all θ > 1, the power of the test ϕ at θ is at least α
(d) For some θ > 1, the power of the test ϕ at θ can be less than α

(DEC. 2013)

4. Let $X_1, X_2, \dots, X_n$ be a random sample from uniform $\left(\theta - \frac{1}{2}, \theta + \frac{1}{2}\right)$. Consider the problem of testing $H_0: \theta = -\frac{1}{2}$ against $H_1: \theta = \frac{1}{2}$ Define $X_{(1)} = \min\{X_1, X_2, .., X_n\}$ Consider the following test : Reject H_0 if $X_{(1)} > 0$ accept otherwise Which of the following is true?
(a) power of the test =0 size of the test =0
(b) power of the test =0, size of the test =1
(c) power of the test =1, size of the test =0
(d) power of the test=1, size of the test =1

(JUNE 2014)

5. Let $X_1, X_2, \dots, X_n$ be iid with common density $f_\theta(x) = \begin{cases} \theta e^{-\theta}, & x > 0, \text{where } \theta > 0 \\ 0, & x \le 0 \end{cases}$.
For testing $H_0 : \theta = 1$ versus $H_1 : \theta = 2$, let r_n be the power of the most powerful test of size $\alpha = 0.05$ with sample size n. Then
(a) r_n increases to 1-α
(b) r_n may not converge
(c) r_n increase to 1
(d) r_n may not be an increasing sequence

(JUNE 2014)

6. Let T be a statistic whose distribution under the null hypothesis H_0 is uniform (0, 1). Let the distribution of T under an alternative hypothesis H_1 be triangular distribution with density
$g(x) = \begin{cases} x,: & 0 \le x \le 1, \\ 2 - x: & 0 \le x \le 2, \end{cases}$
Then the power β of the most powerful test for testing H_0 against the alternative H_1 based on the statistic T with size 0.1 satisfies
(a) $0 < \beta \le 0.5$ (b) $0.5 < \beta \le 0.55$
(c) $0.55 < \beta \le 0.7$ (d) $0.7 < \beta \le 1$

(JUNE 2014)

7. Let $X_1, X_2, \dots X_n$ be a random sample from $f_\theta(x) = \begin{cases} \theta e^{-\theta x} & x > 0 \\ 0 & otherwise \end{cases}$.
Consider the problem of testing $H_0 : \theta = 1$ *against* $H_1 : \theta > 1$. Define
$\varphi_1 = \begin{cases} 1 & if\ \sum_{i=1}^n x_i > c_1 \\ 0 & if\ \sum_{i=1}^n x_i \le c_1 \end{cases}$ and
$\varphi_2 = \begin{cases} 1 & if\ \sum_{i=1}^n x_i < c_2 \\ 0 & if\ \sum_{i=1}^n x_i \ge c_2 \end{cases}$
Where c_1 and c_2 are such that φ_1 and φ_2 are of size α. Which of the following statements are true?
(a) φ_1 is more powerful than φ_2
(b) P-value of the uniformly most powerful test for testing H_0 against H_1 is given by $P_{\theta_0}[\sum_{i=1}^n X_i > observed\ \sum_{i=1}^n x_i]$

(c) Power function of φ_2 is monotonically increasing
(d) φ_1 is unbiased

(DEC. 2014)

8. Let $X_1, X_2, \dots, X_n$ be independent and identically distributed observations from the distributed with density $f(x|\mu) = e^{-(x-\mu)}, x > \mu$ where $-\infty < \mu < \infty$ and μ is unknown.
Let $T_1 = 2\sum_{i=1}^{n} X_i$ and $T_2 = 2X_{(1)}$ where $X_{(1)}$ is the smallest order statistic.
To test $H_0: \mu = 0$ vesus $H_1: \mu > 0$ at level α, where $0 < \alpha < 1$,
Consider the two tests A and B given below.
A: Reject H_0 if $T_1 > C_1$ where C_1 is such that $P(Y_1 > C_1) = \alpha$ with $Y_1 \sim \chi^2_{2n}$
B: Reject H_0 if $T_2 > C_2$ where C_2 is such that $P(Y_2 > C_2) = \alpha$ with $Y_2 \sim \chi^2_2$
Then which of the following statements are valid?
(a) Both A and B are level α tests
(b) A is the uniformly most powerful level α test
(c) B is the uniformly most powerful level α test
(d) B is more powerful than A at an $\mu > 0$

(JUNE 2015)

9. Let $X_1, X_2, \dots X_7$ be a random sample from $N(\mu, \sigma^2)$ where μ and σ^2 are unknown. Consider the problem of testing $H_0: \mu = 2$ against $H_1: \mu > 2$. Suppose the observed values of $x_1, x_2, \dots x_7$ are 1.2,1.3,1.7,1.8,2.1,2.3,2.7. If we use the Uniformly Most Powerful test, which of the following is true?
(a) H_0 is accepted both at 5% and 1% levels of significance.
(b) H_0 is rejected both at 5% and 1% levels of significance.
(c) H_0 is rejected at 5% level of significance, but accepted at 1% level of significance.
(d) H_0 is rejected at 1% level of significance, but accepted at 5% level of significance.

(JUNE 2015)

10. Suppose X has density $f(x|0)$ where θ is 0 or 1. Also
$f(x|0) = 1\ if\ 0 < x < 1$ and 0 otherwise
$f(x|0) = \frac{1}{2\sqrt{x}} if\ 0 < x < 1$ and 0 otherwise
To test $H_0: \theta = 0$ versus $H_0: \theta = 1$ at level $a, 0 < a < 1$, the most Powerful test
(a) Rejects H_0 if $X > 1 - a$
(b) Rejects H_0 if $X < a$
(c) Rejects H_0 if $X < \sqrt{a}$
(d) His power $\sqrt{a}$

(DEC. 2015)

11. Consider the problem of testing $H_0 : X \sim$ Normal with mean 0 and variance $\frac{1}{2}$ against $H_1 : X \sim$ Cauchy $(0, 1)$. Then for testing H_0 against H_1, the most powerful size α test
(a) does not exist
(b) rejects H_0 if and only if $|x| > c_2$ where c_2 is such that the test is of size α
(c) rejects H_0 if and only if $|x| < c_3$ where c_3 is such that the test is of size α
(d) rejects H_0 if and only if $|x| > c_4$ or $|x| > c_5, c_4 < c_5$ where c_4 and c_5 are such that the test is of size α

(DEC. 2015)

12. Let $X_1, X_2 \dots, X_n$ denote a random sample from a distribution having a probability density function $f(x;\theta) = \theta x^{\theta-1}, 0 < x < 1$, zero elsewhere; $\theta > 0$. The set $\{(x_1, x_2, \dots, x_n) : \sum_1^n \log(x_i) \geq c\}$, where c is a suitably chosen real number, is a uniformly most powerful region for testing H_0 against H_1 when
(a) $H_0 : \theta = 1$ against $H_1 : \theta > 1$
(b) $H_0 : \theta = 1$ against $H_1 : \theta \geq 4$
(c) $H_0 : \theta = 4$ against $H_1 : \theta \leq 1$
(d) $H_0 : \theta = 4$ against $H_1 : \theta \neq 1$

(DEC. 2015)

13. $X_1, X_2 \dots, X_n$ are independently and identically distributed random variables, which follow $\text{Bin}(1, p)$. To test $H_0 : p = \frac{1}{2}$ vs $H_A : p = \frac{3}{4}$, with size $\alpha = 0.01$, consider the test
$$\phi = \begin{cases} 1 & \text{if } \sum_{i=1}^{n} X_i > c_n \\ 0 & \text{otherwise} \end{cases}$$
then, which of the following statements are true?
(a) As $n \to \infty$ power of the test converges to $\frac{1}{4}$
(b) As $n \to \infty$ power of the test converges to $\frac{1}{2}$
(c) As $n \to \infty$ power of the test converges to $\frac{3}{4}$
(d) As $n \to \infty$ power of the test converges to 1

(JUNE 2016)

14. In the context of testing of statistical hypotheses, which one of the following statements is true?
(a) When testing a simple hypothesis H_0 against an alternative simple hypothesis H_1, the likelihood ratio principle leads to the most powerful test.
(b) When testing a simple hypothesis H_0 against an alternative simple hypothesisH_1, $P[\text{rejecting } H_0 | H_0 \text{ is true}] + P[\text{accepting } H_0 | H_1 \text{ is true}] = 1$
(c) For testing a simple hypothesis H_0 against an alternative simple hypothesis H_1 , randomized test is used to achieve the desired level of the power of the test.
(d) UMP tests for testing a simple hypothesis H_0 against an alternative composite H_1 , always exist.

(JUNE 2016)

15. Let $X_1, .., X_n$ be a random sample from $f(x;\lambda) = \begin{cases} 2\lambda x e^{-\lambda x^2}; x > 0 \\ 0,\ otherwise \end{cases}$
Here $\lambda > 0$ is an unknown parameter. It is desired to test the following hypothesis at level > 0 . We want to test $H_0: \lambda \leq 1$ vs$H_1: \lambda > 1$.
Then which of the following are true?
(a) UMP test is of the form $\sum_{i=1}^{n} x_i < c_n$ with $c_n < c_{n+1}$ for all n
(b) UMP test is of the form $\sum_{i=1}^{n} x_i^2 < d_n$ with $d_n < d_{n+1}$ for all n
(c) UMP test is of the form $\sum_{i=1}^{n} x_i < c_n$ with $c_{n+1} < c_n$ for all n
(d) UMP test is of the form $\sum_{i=1}^{n} x_i^2 < d_n$ with $d_{n+1} < d_n$ for all n

(JUNE 2016)

16. Let$X_1,..,X_n$ be i.i.d. $N(\mu, 1)$. It is proposed to test $H_0: \mu = 0$ versus $H_1: \mu > 0$Let $p_n(\mu, \alpha)$ denote the power of the UMP test at of size based on sample size n. Then which of the following statements are correct?
(a) $lim_{n\to\infty} p_n(\mu, \alpha) = 1 \forall \mu > 0, \forall \alpha > 0.$
(b) $lim_{\mu\to 0} p_n(\mu, \alpha) = \alpha \; \forall n \geq 1, \forall \alpha > 0$
(c) $lim_{\alpha\to 0} p_n(\mu, \alpha) = 0 \forall n \geq 1, \forall \alpha > 0$
(d) $lim_{\alpha\to 1} p_n(\mu, \alpha) = 0 \forall n \geq 1, \forall \alpha > 0$

(DEC. 2016)

17. For a random variable X, with $E(X) > 0$, the coefficient of variation ρ is defined as $\rho = \frac{\sigma X}{E(X)}$ where $\sigma_x^2$is the variance of X. Suppose $X_1, X_2, \ldots, X_n$ are independent samples from a normal population with mean 2 and unknown coefficient of variation ρ . It is desired to test
$H_0: \rho \leq 5$ against $H_1: \rho > 5$.
The likelihood ratio test is of the form Reject H_0 if
(a) $\Sigma(X_i - 2)^2 > C.$ (b) $\Sigma(X_i - 2)^2 < C.$
(c) $\frac{\Sigma(X_i-\bar{X})^2}{\bar{X}-2} > C.$ (d) $\frac{\Sigma(X_i-\bar{X})^2}{\bar{X}-2} > C.$

(DEC. 2016)

18. Suppose the probability mass function of a random variable X under the parameter $\theta = \theta_0$ and $\theta = \theta_1(\neq \theta_0)$ are given by

x	0	1	2	3
$p_{\theta_0}(x)$	0.01	0.04	0.5	0.45
$p_{\theta_1}(x)$	0.02	0.08	0.4	0.5

Define a test ϕ such that
$\phi(x) = 1 \; if \; x = 0,1$
$= 0 \; if \; x = 2,3$
For testing $H_0: \theta = \theta_0$ against $H_1: \theta = \theta_0$, the test ϕ is
(a) a most powerful test at level 0.05
(b) a likelihood ratio test at level 0.05
(c) an unbiased test
(d) test of size 0.05

(DEC. 2016)

19. A data set gave a 95% confidence interval (2.5, 3.6), for the mean μ of a normal population with known variance. Let $\mu_0 < 2.5$ be a fixed number. If we use the same data to test $H_0: \mu = \mu_0 \; vs \; H_1: \mu \neq \mu_0$
(a) H_0 would be necessarily rejected at $\alpha = .1$
(b) H_0would be necessarily rejected at $\alpha = .025$
(c) For$\alpha = 1$ the information is not enough to draw a conclusion
(d) For $\alpha = 0.25$, the information is not enough to draw a conclusion

(JUNE 2017)

20. Consider the problem of testing $H_0 : \theta = 1$ vs $H_1 : \theta = \frac{1}{2}$ where θ is the mean of a Poisson random variable. Let X and Y be a random sample from Poisson (θ) distribution. Consider the following test procedure: Reject H_0 if either $X = 0$ or ($X = 1$ and $X + Y \leq 2$); otherwise accept H_0. Which of the following are true?
(a) P[type I error] $= e^{-1} + 2e^{-2}$
(b) P[type II error] $= 1 - \frac{1}{2}e^{-1} - e^{-\frac{1}{2}}$
(c) Size of the test is $e^{-1} + e^{-2}$
(d) Power of the test is $\frac{3}{4}e^{-1} + e^{-\frac{1}{2}}$

(JUNE 2017)

21. Suppose $\{X_1, \ldots, X_n\}$ is a random sample from the distribution with probability density function $f(x)$. Consider the following testing problem using likelihood ratio test (LRT).
$$H_0 : f(x) = \frac{1}{\sqrt{2\pi}} e^{-\frac{x^2}{2}} \text{ vs } H_1 : f(x) = \frac{1}{2}e^{-|x|}.$$
Which of the following statements are correct?
(a) There does not exist any LRT.
(b) The rejection region is a function of $|X_1|, \ldots, |X_n|$.
(c) The rejection region is a function of $X_1^2, \ldots, X_n^2$
(d) The rejection region is of the form $\{\sum_{i=1}^{n}(X_i - 1)^2 \geq c\}$

(JUNE 2017)

22. In a football league, the goals scored by home teams over 380 matches have the following frequency distribution.

Number of goals	0	1	2	3	4	5
Frequency	92	121	91	50	19	7

The average goals scored by home teams is 1.49. We want to test H_0 : Goal distribution is Poisson. Based on observations the value of the χ^2- statistic for goodness of fir is 1.27. Given $\chi^2_{0.05,6} = 1.64$, $\chi^2_{0.05,5} = 1.15$, $\chi^2_{0.95,6} = 12.59$ and $\chi^2_{0.95,5} = 11.07$, which of the following are true?
(a) H_0 is not rejected at 5% level of significance.
(b) χ^2- statistic has 5 degrees of freedom
(c) Under H_0, the maximum likelihood estimate (MLE) of the rate parameter of Poisson is 1.19
(d) Under H_0, in a game, the MLE of the probability that home team will score at most goal is 2.49 $e^{-1.49}$

(DEC. 2017)

23. Let X be a random sample of size 1 from a Cauchy distribution with probability density function
$f_\theta(x) = \frac{1}{\pi}\left(\frac{1}{1+(x-\theta)^2}\right), -\infty < x < \infty$ where$\theta \in (-\infty, \infty)$.
For testing$H_0: \theta = -1$ against, the following test is suggested. Reject H_0 if, $\frac{x}{\sqrt{1+x^2}} > C$ otherwise do not reject H_0 . What is the value of C so that the power of the test is 0.5?
(a) $\frac{\pi}{4}$
(b) 0
(c) $\tan^{-1}\left(\frac{1}{2}\right)$
(d) a solution of $tan^{-1}\sqrt{\frac{C}{1-C}} = \frac{\pi}{3}$

(JUNE 2018)

24. Suppose X and Y are two independent exponential random variables with means θ and 2θ respectively, where θ is unknown. Which of the following statements are true?
(a) $X + 2Y$ is sufficient for θ
(b) Right-tailed test based on $X + 2Y$ is UMP for testing $H_0 : \theta = 1$ against $H_1 : \theta < 1$
(c) Left-tailed test based on $2X + Y$ is UMP for testing $H_0 : \theta = 1$ against $H_1 : \theta < 1$

(d) UMP test does not exist for testing $H_0: \theta = 1$ against $H_2: \theta \neq 1$

(DEC. 2018)

25. To test the hypothesis H_0 against H_1 using the test statistic T, the proposed test procedure is not to support H_0 if T is large. Based on a given sample, the p-value of the test statistic is computed to be 0.05 assuming that the distribution of T is $N(0,1)$ under H_0. If the distribution of T under H_0 is the t-distribution with 10 degrees of freedom instead, the p-value will be

(a) 0.05 (b) $< 0.05 - \frac{1}{100}$

(c) $0.05 - \frac{1}{100}$ (d) > 0.05

(DEC. 2018)

26. X is a discrete random variable on $\{-2,-1,1,2\}$ with probability mass function $P_\theta[X = x], \theta \in \{\theta_0 \theta_1\}$ given below,.

X	-2	-1	1	2
$\theta = \theta_0$	0.05	0.6	0.3	0.05
$\theta = \theta_1$	0.2	0.4	0.2	0.2

The aim is to test $H_0: \theta = \theta_0$ against $H_1: \theta = \theta_1$. Which of the following statements are correct?

(a) The test procedure with critical region $\{x = 2\}$ is a most powerful test of size 0.05

(b) The test procedure with critical region $\{x = -2\}$ is a most powerful test of size 0.05

(c) The test procedure with critical region $\{x = -1\}$ is a most powerful test of size

(d) The test procedure with critical region $\{x = 1\}$ is a most powerful test of size

(JUNE 2019)

27. Let X_1, X_2 be $i.i.d.$ random variables with p.d.f.

$$f_\theta(x) = \begin{cases} \frac{2(\theta - x)}{\theta^2}, & 0 \leq x \leq \theta \\ 0, & otherwise \end{cases}$$

For testing $H_0: \theta = 2$ against $H_1: \theta = 3$, the following tests are suggested.

Test 1: Reject H_0 if and only if max $\{X_1, X_2\} \leq 1$

Test 2: Reject H_0 if and only if max $\{X_1, X_2\} \geq 1$

Let a_i denote the probability of Type I error for Test $i = 1,2$. Which of the following are true?

(a) Test 1 is a level 0.05 test

(b) $\alpha_1 + \alpha_2 = 1$

(c) Test 2 is unbiased

(d) Test 1 is unbiased

(DEC. 2019)

28. Let X be a discrete random variable with sample space $X = \{1,2,\ldots,10\}$ and probability mass function $p(x), x \in X$. Consider testing the hypothesis $Ho: p(x) = \frac{1}{10}; x\epsilon X$ against $H_1: p(x) \propto x; \quad x \in X$ based on a single observation X. Then which of the following statements are correct?

(a) The test with critical region $\{X \geq 2\}$ is most powerful of its size

(b) The test with critical region $\{X < 2\}$ is unbiased at level $\alpha = 0.1$

(c) If $X = 7$ the p-value of the most powerful test is 0.6

(d) There exists a nonrandomized test of size 0.05

(DEC. 2019)

29. Let $\{X_n: n \geq 1\}$ be i.i.d, with common unknown continuous distribution function $F(x - \theta)$, where θ is the unique median of F. Define

$$Y_i = \begin{cases} 1 & if X_i > 1 \\ 0 & if X_i \leq 1 \end{cases} \text{ and } S_n = \sum_{i=1}^n Y_i$$

For testing $H_0: \theta = 1$ against $H_1: \theta > 1$, which of the following statements are correct?

(a) $S_n \sim$ Binomial $\left(n, \frac{1}{2}\right)$ under H_0

(b) Test based on S_n is distribution-free under H_1

(c) Right – tailed test based on S_n is unbiased

(d) The sequence of right – tailed tests based on $S_n, n \geq 1$, is consistent

(NOV. 2020)

30. Consider the pdf given by $f(\theta) = \frac{e^{(x-\theta)}}{[1+e^{(x-\theta)}]^2} - \infty < x < \infty, -\infty < \theta < \infty$ Based on one observation X with the above pdf, a UMP test of size α for testing $H_0: \theta \leq \theta_0$ versus $H_1: \theta \leq \theta_0$ is

(a) $X > k$ for k such that $\alpha = P_{\theta_0}[X > k]$

(b) $X < k$ for k such that $\alpha = P_{\theta_0}[X > k]$

(c) $X > k$ for k such that $\alpha = P_{\theta_0}[X < k]$

(d) $X < k$ for k such that $\alpha = P_{\theta_0}[X < k]$

(JUNE 2021)

31. Let $X_1, X_2, \ldots, X_{16}$ be a random sample from normal distribution with unknown mean μ variance 4. Suppose $Z \sim N(0,1)$. For the most powerful test for testing $H_0: \mu = 3$ VS $H_1: \mu = 0$, which one of the following is the p-value where the observed sample mean is 2.5?

(a) $P(Z > 1)$ (b) $P(Z > -1)$

(c) $P(Z > 0.5)$ (d) $P(Z > -0.5)$

(JUNE 2021)

32. Suppose $X_1, X_2, , \ldots, X_n$, are i.i.d. random variables which are uniformly distributed on the Interval $(0, \theta)$ where $\theta > 0$. Let $X_{(1)} < X_{(2)} \leq \cdots \leq X_n$ be the corresponding order statistics. Consider testing the hypotheses $H_0: \theta = 1$ versus $H_1: \theta > 1$. Which of the following tests have significance level α for $0 < \alpha < 0.5$?

(a) Reject H_0 when $X_1 > 1 - \alpha$

(b) Reject H_0 when $X_{(n)} > (1 - \alpha)^{1/n}$

(c) Reject H_0 when $X_{(n)} < (1 - \alpha)^{1/n}$

(d) Reject H_0 when $X_{(1)} > 1 - \alpha^{1/n}$

(SEP. 2022)

33. Let $X_1, \ldots, X_{10}$ be a random sample of size 10 from a continuous distribution with probability density function

$$f_\theta(x) = \begin{cases} e^{\theta - x}, x \geq \theta \\ 0, otherwise \end{cases}$$

$\theta \in \mathcal{R}$ is unknown.

Consider the problem of testing the null hypothesis $H_0: \theta \leq 3$ against the alternate hypothesis $H_1: \theta > 3$,

based on $X_1, \dots, X_{10}$. Let $L(\theta)$ denote the likelihood function and $x_{(1)} = \min(x_1, \dots, x_{10})$.
Which of the following statements are correct?
(a) $\sup_{\theta \le 3} L(\theta) = e^{10x_{(1)}} e^{-\sum_{i=1}^{10} x_i}$, if $x_{(1)} \le 3$
(b) $\sup_{\theta \le 3} L(\theta) = e^{10x_{(1)}} e^{-\sum_{i=1}^{10} x_i}$, if $x_{(1)} > 3$
(c) The critical region of the likelihood ratio test of size $\alpha (0 < \alpha < 1)$, for testing H_0 against H_1 is given by $\left\{(x_1, \dots, x_{10}) \in \mathcal{R}^{10}; x_{(1)} \ge \frac{1}{3} - 10\log_e(\alpha)\right\}$
(d) The critical region of the likelihood ratio test of size $\alpha (0 < \alpha < 1)$, for testing H_0 against H_1 is given by $\left\{(x_1, \dots, x_{10}) \in \mathcal{R}^{10}; x_{(1)} \ge 3 - \frac{1}{10}\log_e(\alpha)\right\}$

(SEP. 2022)

34. Let X be a random variable with probability density function $f(\cdot)$. Then based on a single observation X, the most powerful test of size 0.2 for testing
$H_0: f(x) = \begin{cases} 4x^3, & if\ 0 < x < 1, \\ 0, & otherwise \end{cases}$ against
$H_1: f(x) = \begin{cases} 8x^7, & if\ 0 < x < 1, \\ 0, & otherwise, \end{cases}$
has power
(a) 0.81 (b) 0.89
(c) 0.64 (d) 0.36

(SEP. 2022)

35. Let X be a random variable whose probability mass functions under H_0 and H_1 are given by the following

x	1	2	3	4	5	6	7
$f_{H_0}(x)$	0.01	0.01	0.01	0.01	0.01	0.01	0.94
$f_{H_1}(x)$	0.06	0.05	0.04	0.03	0.02	0.01	0.79

where, $f(x) = PH,(X = x)$ and $f_{H_1}(x) = P_{H_1}(X = x)$.
Which of the following statements are correct?
(a) The critical region of most powerful test of size $\alpha = 0.04$ testing H_0 against H_1, is given by $\{x: x \le 4\}$
(b) The critical region of most powerful test of size $\alpha = 0.04$, for testing H_0 against H_1, is given by $\{x: 3 \le x \le 6\}$
(c) The power of the most powerful test of size $\alpha = 0.04$, for H_0 against H_1, is 0.18
(d) Most powerful test of size $\alpha = 0.04$, for testing H_0 against H_1, does not exist.

(JUNE 2023)

36. Let $X_1, \dots, X_7$ and $Y_1, \dots, Y_9$ be two random samples drawn independently from two populations with continuous $CDFs$ F and G respectively. Consider the Wald-Wolfowitz run test in the context of the following two sample testing problems:
$H_0: F(x) = G(x)\ \forall\ x$ vs. $H_1: F(x) \ne G(x)$ for some x. If the random variable R denotes the total number of runs in the combined ordered arrangement of the two given samples, then which of the following is true?
(a) $P_{H_0}(R = 6) = \frac{28}{286}, P_{H_0}(R = 9) = \frac{28}{143}$.
(b) $P_{H_0}(R = 6) = \frac{21}{286}, P_{H_0}(R = 9) = \frac{15}{286}$.
(c) $P_{H_0}(R = 6) = \frac{21}{286}, P_{H_0}(R = 9) = \frac{28}{143}$.
(d) $P_{H_0}(R = 6) = \frac{21}{286}, P_{H_0}(R = 9) = \frac{15}{286}$.

(JUNE 2023)

37. Which of the following statements are true?
(a) Maximum likelihood estimator may not be unique.
(b) A complete statistic is always sufficient.
(c) A sufficient statistic may not be complete.
(d) Any function of a sufficient statistic is always sufficient.

(JUNE 2023)

38. Suppose under the null hypothesis $H, X \sim p$, where $p(x) = P(X = x) = 1/20,\ x \in (1,2,\dots 20\}$ and under the alternative hypothesis $K, X \sim q$ where $q(x) = P(X = x) = \frac{x}{210}\ x \in (1,2,\dots 20)$. Define two test functions ϕ and ψ for testing H against K such that,
$\phi(x) = \begin{cases} 1 & if\ x \le 2 \\ 0 & otherwise \end{cases}$
And
$\psi(x) = \begin{cases} 1 & if\ x \le 19 \\ 0 & otherwise \end{cases}$
Which of the following statements are true?
(a) Size of the test ϕ is 0.1.
(b) Size of the test ψ is 0.05.
(c) (Power of the test ψ) > 0.05
(d) (Power of the test ψ) > (Power of the test ϕ).

(JULY-2024)

39. Let X_1, X_2 be a random sample from a population having probability density function $f \epsilon \{f_0, f_1\}$ where
$f_0(x) = \begin{cases} \frac{1}{2} if\ 0 \le x \le 2 \\ 0 \quad otherwise, \end{cases}$ and $f_1(x) = \begin{cases} \frac{1}{4} if\ 0 \le x \le 4 \\ 0 \quad otherwise, \end{cases}$
For testing the null hypothesis $H_0: f = f_0$. against the alternate hypothesis H_1: f = f_1, the power of a most powerful test of size a = 0.05 is equal to
(a) 0.4625 (b) 0.5425
(c) 0.7625 (d) 0.6225

(JULY 2024)

40. Consider a six faced die whose i-th face is marked with dots, $i = 1,2,\dots,6$. In a single random throw of the die, let p_i, denote the probability that the obtained upper face has i dots, $i = 1,2,\dots,6$. The die is rolled 240 times independently and the following result is obtained

Face observed	1	2	3	4	5	6
Frequency	40	55	40	25	35	45

Suppose we want to test $H_0 : p_i = \frac{1}{6}$ $for\ i = 1,2,\dots,6$; against $H_1: p_i \ne \frac{1}{6}$ for at least one i; $i = 1,2,\dots,6$. It is given that $\chi^2_{5;0.05} = 11.07, \chi^2_{6;0.05} = 15.59, \chi^2_{5;0.01} = 15.09, \chi^2_{6;0.01} = 16.81$. Based on the asymptotic goodness of fit χ^2 test for testing H, against H_1, which of the following statements are true?
(a) H_0 is rejected at 5% level of significance
(b) H_0 is rejected at 1% level of significance
(c) H_0 is not rejected at 5% level of significance
(d) Observed value of the test statistic is 12.5

(FEB. 2025)

41. Let $X_1, X_2, \dots, X_n (n \ge 2)$ be a random sample from a gamma distribution with shape parameter $\alpha > 0$ and

scale parameter $\beta = 1$. For a suitable constant C, the rejection region of the most powerful test for testing $H_0: \alpha = 1$ against $H_1: \alpha = 2$ is of the form

(a) $\prod_{i=1}^{n} X_i > C$ (b) $\sum_{i=1}^{n} X_i > C$

(c) $\prod_{i=1}^{n} X_i < C$ (d) $\sum_{i=1}^{n} X_i < C$

(FEB. 2025)

42. Suppose ϕ is a most powerful test of size 0.05 for testing a simple null hypothesis H_0 against a simple alternative hypothesis H_1. If the power of the test is 0.4, then which of the following is true?

(a) $(1 - \phi)$ is a most powerful test at level 0.6 for testing H_1 against H_0.

(b) $(1 - \phi)$ is a most powerful test at level 0.4 for testing H_1 against H_0.

(c) $(1 - \phi)$ is a most powerful test at level 0.05 for testing H_1 against H_0.

(d) $(1 - \phi)$ is NOT a most powerful test for testing H_1 against H_0 at any level.

(FEB. 2025)

43. Let X_1, X_2, X_3 be a random sample from Uniform $[0, \theta]$ distribution, $\theta > 0$. Consider the likelihood ratio test of size 0.001 for testing $H_0: \theta = 3$ against $H_1: \theta \neq 3$. Then, which of the following statements are true?

(a) If $\max\{X_1, X_2, X_3\}$ is 3.1, then H_0 is rejected.

(b) If $\max\{X_1, X_2, X_3\}$ is 1.3, then H_0 is rejected.

(c) If $\max\{X_1, X_2, X_3\}$ is 0.1, then H_0 is rejected.

(d) The power of the test at $\theta = 0.3$ is 1.

(FEB. 2025)

44. Let $\{(X_k, Y_k)\}_{k=1}^{\infty}$ be a sequence of independent and identically distributed (i.i.d.) random vectors with common joint probability density function

$$f(x, y) = \begin{cases} e^{-y}, & \text{if } 0 < x < y < \infty \\ 0, & \text{otherwise.} \end{cases}$$

For $n = 1, 2, 3, \ldots$, let N_n be a random variable denoting the number of elements in the set $\{k: k = 1, 2, \ldots, n; Y_k \geq 2\}$.

Then, which of the following statements are true?

(a) $\frac{N_n}{3n}$ converges to e^{-2} with probability one.

(b) N_n converges to e^{-2} in probability.

(c) $\frac{N_n}{n}$ converges to $3e^{-2}$ in distribution.

(d) $\frac{N_n - 3ne^{-2}}{\sqrt{3n}}$ converges in distribution to a normal random variable with mean zero and variance $e^{-2}(1 - 3e^{-2})$.

(JUNE 2025)

45. Let $X_1, X_2, \ldots, X_n$ be a random sample from a continuous distribution with the common probability density function

$$f(x|\theta) = \begin{cases} \frac{2^{\theta}\theta}{x^{\theta+1}}, & \text{if } x > 2, \\ 0, & \text{otherwise,} \end{cases}$$

where $\theta (> 0)$ is an unknown parameter. Suppose $P(Y > X^2_{m,\beta}) = \beta$, where $Y \sim X^2_m$. For testing $H_0: \theta = 1$ against $H_1: \theta > 1$, a uniformly most powerful test of size $\alpha, 0 < \alpha <$, will reject H_0 if

(a) $\sum_{i=1}^{n} In\, X_i > \frac{1}{2} X^2_{2n,\alpha} + n\, ln2$

(b) $\sum_{i=1}^{n} In\, X_i < \frac{1}{2} X^2_{2n,1-\alpha} + n\, ln2$

(c) $\sum_{i=1}^{n} In\, X_i > X^2_{n,\alpha} + n\, ln2$

(d) $\sum_{i=1}^{n} In\, X_i < X^2_{n,1-\alpha} + n\, ln2$

(JUNE 2025)

46. Let X be a random sample of size one from the probability density function

$$f(x|\theta) = \begin{cases} \theta r^{-\theta((x-1)} & \text{if } x > 1, \\ o. & \text{otherwise,} \end{cases}$$

where $\theta (> 0)$ is the unknown parameter. Suppose we want to test the null hypothesis

$H_o: \theta = 1$ against the alternative hypothesis $H_1: \theta \neq 1$, based on the observed value x of X. Then, which of the following statements are true?

(a) The likelihood function is maximized at $\theta = \frac{1}{x-1}$

(b) The maximum value of the likelihood function is $\frac{e^{-1}}{x-1}$

(c) The likelihood ratio test for testing H_o against H_1 rejects H_o if $(x-1)e^{-x} < k$, for some $k > 0$

(d) The likelihood ratio test for testing H_o against H_1 rejects H_o if $x > c$, for some $c > 1$

(JUNE 2025)

47. Let $(X_1, X_2, \ldots, X_7)$ and $(Y_1, Y_2, \ldots, Y_9)$ be two independent random samples from the continuous distribution functions $F(x - \mu)$ and $F(x - \theta)$, respectively, where F, μ and θ are all unknown. Further, let μ be the unique median of $F(x - \mu)$ and θ be the unique median of $F(x - \theta)$. Let R_i be the rank of Y_i in the combined sample, $i = 1, 2, \ldots, 9$. For testing $H_0: \mu = \theta$ against $H_1:: \mu > \theta$, the test statistic $T = \sum_{i=1}^{9} R_i$ is proposed. Then, which of the following statements are true?

(a) The maximum possible value of T is 115

(b) Right-tailed test based on T is appropriate for testing H_0 against H_1

(c) Under $H_0. E(T) = 76$

(d) Under $H_0, P(R_1 = 1, R_2 = 16) = \frac{1}{240}$

(Dec 2025)

48. Let X_1 and X_2 be a random sample from Uniform $[0, \theta]$ distribution, where $\theta > 0$. For testing the hypothesis $H_0: \theta = 1$ against $H_1: \theta = 2$,

consider a test which rejects H_0 if $X_1 + X_2 > \frac{4}{5}$. Then, the probability of type-I error is

(a) $\frac{8}{25}$ (b) $\frac{13}{25}$

(c) $\frac{17}{25}$ (d) $\frac{22}{25}$

(Dec 2025)

49. Let $X_1, X_2, \ldots, X_{15}$ be a random sample from an Exponential distribution with the probability density function

$$f(x|\sigma) = \begin{cases} \frac{1}{\sigma}\exp\left(-\frac{x}{\sigma}\right), & \text{if } x > 0, \\ 0 & \text{elsewhere,} \end{cases}$$

where the unknown parameter σ is positive. Let $\bar{X} = \frac{1}{15}\sum_{i=1}^{15} X_i$. Suppose that φ denotes the likelihood ratio test for testing $H_0: \sigma \leq 1$ against $H_1: \sigma > 1$ at level $\alpha = 0.1$. It is given that $\chi^2_{15,0.1} = 22.307, \chi^2_{15,0.9} = 8.547, \chi^2_{30,0.1} = 40.256, \chi^2_{30,0.9} = 20.599$, where $P(W > \chi^2_{n,\alpha}) = \alpha$ and $W \sim \chi^2_n$. Then which of the following statements are true?

(a) If the observed value of $\bar{X}$ is 0.6, then φ does not reject H_0

(b) If the observed value of $\bar{X}$ is 1.6, then φ rejects H_0

(c) If the observed value of $\bar{X}$ is 1.3, then φ rejects H_0

(d) If the observed value of $\bar{X}$ is 1.2, then φ does not reject H_0

Answer Key

1	**2**	**3**	**4**	**5**
c	a, c, d	a, c	c	c
6	**7**	**8**	**9**	**10**
c	c	a, c, d	a	b, d
11	**12**	**13**	**14**	**15**
b	a, b	d	a	b
16	**17**	**18**	**19**	**20**
a, b, c	a	a, b, c, d	a, d	a, d
21	**22**	**23**	**24**	**25**
b, c, d	a, b, c, d	b	c, d	d
26	**27**	**28**	**29**	**30**
a, b, c, d	b, c	a, d	a, c, d	a
31	**32**	**33**	**34**	**35**
a	a, b, d	a, d	d	a, c
36	**37**	**38**	**39**	**40**
c	a, c	a, c, d	c	a, d
41	**42**	**43**	**44**	**45**
a	a	a,c,d	a,c,d	B
46	**47**	**48**	**49**	
a,b,c	d	c	a,b,d	

:: Explanations ::

1. Explanation: (c)

For person A

$n = 15$

$\bar{x}_1 = 1.8$

$S_1 = S$

for person B

$n = 20$

$\bar{x}_2 = 1.8\,, s_2 = s$

Test statistics, $t = \frac{\bar{x}-\mu}{s/\sqrt{n}}$

Under $H_0 : \mu = 2$

$p_A = \frac{18-2}{5/\sqrt{15}} = \frac{-0.2\sqrt{15}}{5}$

$p_B = \frac{1.8-2}{5/\sqrt{18}} = \frac{0.2\sqrt{18}}{5}$

$p_A < p_B$

So, option (c) is correct

2. Explanation: (a) (c), (d)

X be a discrete r.v. with pmf

$p(x) : x \in \{-1, 0, 1, 2, 3\}$

$H_0 : p(x) = p_0(x)$ against $H_1 : p(x) = p_1(x)$

x	:	-1	0	1	2	3
$p_0(x)$	:	0.01	0.02	0.05	0.32	0.60
$p_1(x)$	:	0.04	0.08	0.25	0.03	0.60
$\frac{p_1(x)}{p_0(x)}$	:	4	4	5	0.09	1

$\alpha = P(x \in W|H_0) = p(X = 1)|H_0) = 0.05$

$X = 1$ is critical region of size 0.05

$P_0(x \in -1, 1) = P(X = -1) + P(X = 1) = 0.01 + 0.05 = 0.06$

$x \in (-1, 1)$ is mp test of size 0.06

$P_0(x \in -1, 0, 1) = p(X = -1) + p(X = 0) + p(X = 1) = 0.01 + 0.02 + 0.05 = 0.08$

$\{-1, 0, 1\}$ is mp test of size 0.08

3. Explanation: (a), (c)

X be a random variable with density function

$f(x) = \frac{2\theta x+1}{\theta+1}; 0 \le x \le 1, \theta > -1$

To test $H_0 : \theta \le 1$ against $H_1 : \theta > 1$

Using LRT, $\frac{\max_{\theta\in\theta_0} L_0}{\max_{\theta\in\theta_1} L_1} < K$

$\Rightarrow \frac{f_{\theta_0}(x)}{f_{\theta_1}(x)} < K$

$\frac{\frac{2x+1}{2}}{\frac{2\theta_1 x+1}{\theta_1+1}} < K$

$\frac{2x+1}{2\theta_1 x+1} \cdot \frac{(\theta_1+1)}{2} < K$

$2x\theta_1 + 2x + \theta_1 + 1 < 4\theta_1 xk + 2k$

$2x\theta_1 + 2x + 4x\theta_1 k < 2k - 1 - \theta_1$

$x[2\theta_1 + 2 + 4\theta_1 k] < 2k - 1 - \theta$

$x > c$ if $\theta_1 > 1$

Test function UMP

$\phi(x) = 1\,; x > c$

$\phi(x) = 0; x < c$

Size of test is α

$P[X > c \mid H_0 : \theta = 1] = \alpha$

$\int_c^1 \frac{2x+1}{2} dx = \alpha$

$\frac{1}{2}[x^2 + x]_c^1 = \alpha$

$\Rightarrow c = \frac{-1\pm\sqrt{9-8\alpha}}{2}$

UMP of size α is:

$\phi(x) = 1$ if $x > \frac{\sqrt{9-8\alpha}-1}{2}$

$\phi(x) = 0$ if $x < \frac{\sqrt{9-8\alpha}-1}{2}$

ϕ is UMP test of size α

For $\theta > 1$ power of test $\ge \alpha$

So, option (a) and (c) are correct

4. Explanation: (c)

$X_1, X_2, X_3 \ldots X_n$ be a random sample from $U\left(\theta - \frac{1}{2}, \theta + \frac{1}{2}\right)$

To test $H_0 : \theta = \frac{-1}{2}$ against $H_1 : \theta = \frac{1}{2}$

Reject $H_0 : X_{(1)} > 0$

The pdf of $X_{(1)}$ is

$f(x_{(1)}) = n[1 - F(x)]^{n-1} f(x)$

$f(x) = 1$ and $F(x) = \int_{\theta-\frac{1}{2}}^{x} 1dx = x - \theta + \frac{1}{2}$

$f(x_{(1)}) = n\left[1 - x + \theta - \frac{1}{2}\right]^{n-1} = n\left[\theta - x + \frac{1}{2}\right]^{n-1}$

Size of test $= P(x \in w \mid H_0 : \theta = \frac{-1}{2})$

$= \int_0^{\theta+\frac{1}{2}} n\left[\theta - x + \frac{1}{2}\right]^{n-1} dx$

Size of test = 0

Power of test $= P(x \in w \mid H_1 : \theta = \frac{1}{2})$

$= \int_0^{\theta+\frac{1}{2}} n\left[\theta - x + \frac{1}{2}\right]^{n-1} dx \mid H_1 : \theta = \frac{1}{2}$

$= \int_0^1 n\,(1-x)^{n-1}dx = \left[\frac{n(1-x)^n}{n}\right]_0^1$

$= 0 + 1 = 1$

Power of test = 1

So, option (c) is correct

5. **Explanation: (c)**

6. **Explanation: (c)**

$H_0 : f(x) = 1 : 0 < x < 1$

$H_1 : f(x) = \begin{cases} x & if \quad 0 < x < 1 \\ 2-x & if \quad 1 \le x < 2 \end{cases}$

$\frac{f_1(x)}{f_0(x)} = \begin{cases} x & if \quad 0 < x < 1 \\ \infty & if \quad 1 \le x < 2 \end{cases}$

The test function ϕ is $\phi(x) = \begin{cases} 1 & if \quad x \ge c \\ 0 & if \quad x < c \end{cases}$

$\alpha = E(\phi(x)|H_0) = \int_c^1 dx = 1 - c$

$c = 1 - \alpha = 1 - 0.1 = 0.9$

$\phi(x) = \begin{cases} 1 & if \quad x \ge 0.9 \\ 0 & if \quad x < 0.9 \end{cases}$

Power $\beta = E[\phi(x)|H_1] = \int_{0.9}^2 f(x)dx|H_1$

$= \int_{0.9}^1 x\,dx + \int_1^2 (2-x)\,dx = 0.595$

$\beta = 0.595$

So, option (c) is correct

7. **Explanation: (c)**

$f(x) = \theta \cdot e^{-\theta x}; x > 0$

To test $H_0 : \theta = 1$ againt $H_1 : \theta > 1$

$\theta_1 = \begin{cases} 1 & \sum_{i=1}^n x_i > c_1 \\ 0 & \sum_{i=1}^n x_i \le c_1 \end{cases}$

Size $= \alpha = E[\phi_1(x)|H_0 : \theta = 1]$

$= P[\sum_{i=1}^n x_i > c_1 | H_0 : \theta = 1]$

$\alpha = P[2\theta \sum_{i=1}^n x_i > 2\theta c_1 | H_0 : \theta = 1]$

$X_i \sim Exp\ \theta$ and $2\theta \sum_{i=1}^n X_i \sim \chi^2_{(2n)\ d.f}$

Under $H_0 : \theta = 1$, $2\sum_{i=1}^n X_i \sim \chi^2_{(2n)}$

$\alpha = P[2\sum_{i=1}^n X_i > 2c_1] = P[\chi^2 > \chi^2_{2n,\alpha}]$

$\therefore 2c_1 = \chi^2_{2n,\alpha}$

$c_1 = \frac{1}{2}\chi^2_{2n,\alpha}$

$\phi_1 = \begin{cases} 1 & \sum_{i=1}^n x_i > \frac{1}{2}\chi^2_{2n,\alpha} \\ 0 & \sum_{i=1}^n x_i \le \frac{1}{2}\chi^2_{2n,\alpha} \end{cases}$

$\beta_1 = Power = E[\phi_1(x)|H_1 : \theta > 1]$

$\beta_1 = P\left[\sum_{i=1}^n x_i > \frac{1}{2}\chi^2_{2n,\alpha} \middle| H : \theta > 1\right]$

$\phi_2 = \begin{cases} 1 & if \quad \sum_{i=1}^n x_i < C_2 \\ 0 & if \quad \sum_{i=1}^n x_i \ge C_2 \end{cases}$

$\alpha = E[\phi_2(x)|H_0 : \theta = 1]$

$= P[2\sum_{i=1}^n x_i < 2C_2 | H_0 : \theta = 1] = P[\chi^2 < \chi^2_{2n,1-\alpha}]$

$\therefore c_2 = \frac{\chi^2_{2n,1-\alpha}}{2}$

$\phi_2 = \begin{cases} 1 & if \quad \sum_{i=1}^n x_i < \frac{1}{2}\chi^2_{2n,1-\alpha} \\ 0 & if \quad \sum_{i=1}^n x_i \ge \frac{1}{2}\chi^2_{2n,1-\alpha} \end{cases}$

$\beta_2 = Power = E[\phi_2(x)|H_1 : \phi > 1]$

$\beta_2 = P[\sum_{i=1}^n x_i < \chi^2_{2n,1-\alpha} | H : \theta > 1]$

$\beta_2 > \beta_1$

$\therefore \phi_2$ is more powerful than ϕ_1

β_2 is monotonically increasing

$\alpha > \beta_1$

ϕ_1 is not unboned

So, option (c) is correct

8. **Explanation: (a), (c), (d)**

$X_i's$ are iid from the distribution with density $f(x|\mu) = e^{-(x-\mu)}; x > \mu$

$T_1 = 2\sum_{i=1}^n X_i$ and $T_2 = 2X_{(1)}$

$H_0 : \mu = 0$ versus $H_1 : \mu > 0$ at level α

Test A: Reject H_0 if $T_1 > C_1$

Under H_0 :

$X_i \sim Exp\ (1)$ which implies $\sum_{i=1}^n X_i \sim \gamma(1, n)$

$2\sum_{i=1}^n X_i \sim \chi^2_{(2n)\ df}$

$P[2\sum_{i=1}^n X_i > C_1] = \alpha \Rightarrow P[T_1 > C_1] = \alpha$

$C_1 = \chi^2_{2n,\alpha} = upper - point\ of\ chi - square\ with\ level\ \alpha\ at\ 2n\ d.f$

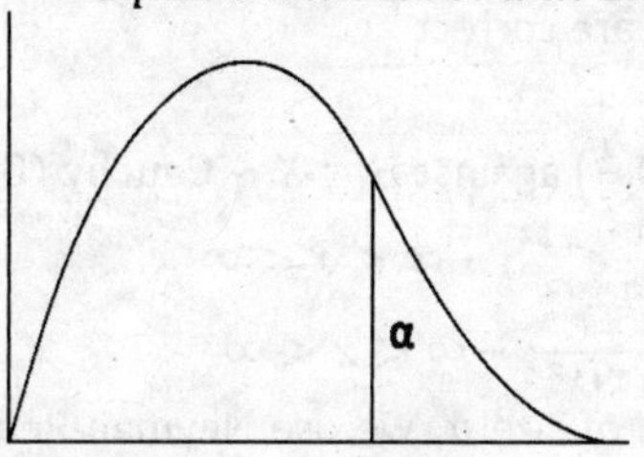

Under $H_1 : \mu > 0 = 1$

$X_i - 1 \sim Exp\ (1)$

$\sum_{i=1}^n (X_i - 1) \sim \gamma(1, n)$

$2[\sum_{i=1}^n (X_i - 1)] \sim \chi^2_{(2n)}\ d.f$

Power $= P[T_1 > C_1 | H_1 : \mu = 1]$

Power $= P[2\sum_{i=1}^n X_i > C_1] = P[2\sum_{i=1}^n (X_i - 1) > C_1 - 2n] = P[\chi^2 > \chi^2_{2n,\alpha} - 2n]$

Test B: Reject H_0 : if $T_2 > C_2$

Under $H_0 : X_i \sim Exp\ (1)$ and $X_{(1)} \sim Exp\ (n)$

$2X_{(1)} \sim \chi^2_{(2)\ d.f}$

$P[T_2 > C_2] = P[2X_{(1)} > C_2] = P[Y_2 > C_1] = \alpha$

Where $C_2 = \chi^2_{2,\alpha}$

Test B is of size α

Under $H_1 : X_i \sim Exp\ (1)$

$2(X_{(1)} - 1) \sim Exp\ (n)$

$2(X_{(1)} - 1) \sim \chi^2_{(2)\ d.f}$

Power $= P[T_2 > C_2 | H_1 : \mu = 1] = P[2X_{(1)} > C_2 | H : \mu = 1]$

$= P[2(X_{(1)} - 1) > C_2 - 2] = P[\chi^2 > \chi^2_{2n} - 2]$

So, power of test B is more than power of test A, Then B is uniformly MP test of size α

9. **Explanation: (a)**

10. **Explanation: (b), (d)**

Suppose X has density $f(x|\theta)$ where $\theta = 0\ or\ 1$

If $\theta = 0$ then

$f(x|0) = 1$ if $0 < x < 1$

If $\theta = 1$, then

$f(x|1) = \frac{1}{2\sqrt{x}}$; if $0 < x < 1$

To test $H_0 : \theta = 0$ vs $H_1 : \theta = 1$ at level α

By Neymann pearson Lemma

$\frac{L_1}{L_0} > k \Rightarrow \frac{f_1}{f_0} > k$

$\Rightarrow \frac{f(x|1)}{f(x|0)} > k \Rightarrow \frac{1}{2\sqrt{x}} > k$

$\Rightarrow 2\sqrt{x} < k$

$x < k^2/2 = c$

The critical region of size α is

$X < c$

$\alpha = P[X < C|H_0 : \theta = 0]$

$= \int_0^c f(x|0)\,dx = c$

$\Rightarrow c = \alpha$

The MP test of size α is $X < \alpha$

The power of test is $1 - \beta = P[X < \alpha|H_1 : \theta = 1]$

Power $= \int_0^\alpha f(x|1)\,dx = \int_0^\alpha \frac{1}{2\sqrt{x}}dx = \frac{1}{2}\left[2\sqrt{x}\right]_0^\alpha = \sqrt{\alpha}$

Its power is $\sqrt{\alpha}$

So, option (b) and (d) are correct

11. Explanation: (b)

To test $H_o : X \sim N\left(0, \frac{1}{2}\right)$ against $H_1 : X \sim$ Cauchy (0, 1)

Under $H_0 : f_0(x) = \frac{1}{\sqrt{\pi}} e^{-x^2}; -\infty < x < \infty$

Under $H_1 : f_1(x) = \frac{1}{\pi}\frac{1}{1+x^2}; -\infty < x < \infty$

To find critical region of size α, we use Neyman-Pearson Lemma

$\frac{f_1}{f_0} > k$

$\Rightarrow \frac{\frac{1}{\pi}\frac{1}{1+x^2}}{\frac{1}{\sqrt{\pi}}e^{-x^2}} > k \Rightarrow \frac{e^{-x^2}}{1+x^2} > k$

$\Rightarrow e^{x^2} < k(1 + x^2)$

$x^2 > \log k + \log(1 + x^2)$

$\Rightarrow x^2 > c$

$\Rightarrow |x| > c_2$

Reject H_0 if and only if $|x| > c_2$

c_2 is such that the test is of size α

So, option (b) is correct

12. Explanation: (a), (b)

$X_i's$ $(i = 1, 2, \dots n)$ be a random sample from distribution with pdf

$$f(x_i) = \theta\, x^{\theta-1}; 0 < x < 1; \theta > 0$$

$\{(x_1, x_2, \dots x_n) : \sum_{i=1}^n \log(x_i) \ge c\}$ is UMP region for testing H_0 against H_1

For $\theta = 1, X_i \sim U(0, 1)$

$\frac{L_1}{L_0} > k \Rightarrow \frac{\theta_1(\prod_{i=1}^n x_i)^{\theta_1-1}}{\theta_0(\prod_{i=1}^n x_i)^{\theta_0-1}} > k$

$\Rightarrow \frac{(\prod_{i=1}^n x_i)^{\theta_1-1}}{(\prod_{i=1}^n x_i)^{\theta_0-1}} > k\frac{\theta_0}{\theta_1}$

Taking log both sides

$(\theta_1 - 1)\sum_{i=1}^n \log(x_i) - (\theta_0 - 1)\sum_{i=1}^n \log(x_i) > c$

$(\theta_0 - X - \theta_1 + X)\ \sum_{i=1}^n \log(x_i) \ge c$

$(\theta_1 - \theta_0)\ \sum_{i=1}^n \log(x_i) \ge c$

If $\theta_1 > \theta_0$ then UMP region is

$\sum_{i=1}^n \log(x_i) \ge c$

$H_0 : \theta = 1$ against $H_1 : \theta > 1$

$H_0 : \theta = 1$ against $H_1 : \theta \ge 4$

So, option (a), (b) is correct

13. Explanation: (d)

$X_1, X_2, \dots, X_n$ are independent and identically random variables

$X_i \sim B(1, p)$

To test $H_0 : p = \frac{1}{2}\ vs\ H_1 : p = \frac{3}{4}$

Size $\alpha = 0.01$

$\phi = 1$ if $\sum_{i=1}^n x_i > c_n$

$= 0$ otherwise

Power of test $= E(\phi \mid H_1)$

$= P(\sum_{i=1}^n x_i > c_n)H_1 : p = \frac{3}{4}$

$X_i \sim B(1, p)$ and $S = \sum_{i=1}^n X_i \sim B(n, p)$

Power $= P[\sum X_i > c_n \mid H_1]$

$= \sum_{i=C_n}^n {}^nC_{C_n}\left(\frac{3}{4}\right)^{C_n}\left(\frac{1}{9}\right)^{n-C_n}$

As $n \to \infty$

Power – 1

So, option (d) is correct

14. Explanation: (a)

Option (a)

When we test simple hypothesis H_0 against simple hypothesis H_1

The Neymann Peason Lemma or Likelihood ratio test leads to the MP test so, option (a) is correct

15. Explanation: (b)

$X_1, X_2, \dots, X_n$ be a random sample form

$f(x; \lambda) = 2\lambda x . e^{-\lambda x^2}; x > 0, \lambda > 0$

λ is an unknown parameter

To test $H_0 : \lambda \le 1\ vs\ H_1 : \lambda > 1$

$L = \prod_{i=1}^n f(x_i) = (2\lambda)^n\, e^{-\lambda\sum_{i=1}^n x_i^2} \prod_{i=1}^n x_i$

$H_0 : \lambda = \lambda_0$

$L_0 = (2\lambda_0)^n\, e^{-\lambda_0\sum_{i=1}^n x_i^2} \prod_{i=1}^n x_i$

$H_1 : \lambda = \lambda_1$

$L_1 = (2\lambda_1)^n\, e^{-\lambda_1\sum_{i=1}^n x_i^2} \prod_{i=1}^n x_i$

By Neymann Pearson Lemma

$\frac{L_1}{L_0} > k$

$\Rightarrow \frac{(2L_1)^n e^{-\lambda_1\sum_{i=1}^n x_i^2}\prod_{i=1}^n x_i}{(2L_0)^n e^{-\lambda_0\sum_{i=1}^n x_i^2}\prod_{i=1}^n x_i} > k$

$\Rightarrow \left(\frac{L_1}{L_0}\right)^n\ e^{-(\lambda_1-\lambda_0)\sum_{i=1}^n x_i^2} > k$

Taking log both sides

$-(\lambda_1 - \lambda_0)\sum_{i=1}^n x_i^2 > \log k\left(\frac{\lambda_1}{\lambda_0}\right)^n$

$\therefore (\lambda_1 - \lambda_0); \sum_{i=1}^n x_i^2 < \log\left(\frac{\lambda_1}{\lambda_0}\right)^n \frac{1}{k}$

$\sum_{i=1}^n x_i^2 < \frac{1}{\lambda_1-\lambda_0}\log\left(\frac{\lambda_1}{\lambda_0}\right)^n \frac{1}{k}$

$\lambda_0 \le 1$ and $\lambda_1 > 1$

$\lambda_1 > \lambda_0\ ;\ \sum_{i=1}^n x_i^2 < d_n$

Where $d_n = \frac{1}{\lambda_1-\lambda_0}\log\left(\frac{\lambda_1}{\lambda_0}\right)^n \frac{1}{k}$

$d_n < d_{n+1}$ all n

Option (b) is correct

16. Explanation: (a), (b), (c)

$X_1, X_2, \dots X_n$ be iid $N(\mu, 1)$

To test $H_0 : \mu = 0$ against $H_1 : \mu > 0$

$L = \prod_{i=1}^{n} f(x_i) = \prod_{i=1}^{n} \frac{1}{\sqrt{2\pi}} e^{\frac{-1}{2}(x_i-\mu)^2}; \ -\infty < x_0 < \infty$

$= \frac{1}{(2\pi)^{n/2}} e^{\frac{-1}{2}\sum_{i=1}^{n}(x_i-\mu)^2}$

By Neymann Pearson Lemma

$\frac{L_1}{L_0} > k$

$\Rightarrow \frac{\frac{1}{(2\pi)^{n/2}} e^{\frac{-1}{2}\sum_{i=1}^{n}(x_i-\mu)^2}}{\frac{1}{(2\pi)^{n/2}} e^{\frac{-1}{2}\sum_{i=1}^{n} x_i^2}} > k$

On solving $\sum_{i=1}^{n} X_i \propto \log\frac{1}{k} + \frac{n\mu}{2}$

$\sum_{i=1}^{n} X_i < C'$

Critical region $W : \bar{X} < C$

Where $C = \frac{1}{n}\left[\log\frac{1}{k} + \frac{n\mu}{2}\right]$

$\alpha = p(x \in w \mid H_0 : \mu = 0) = P(\bar{X} < C \mid H_0 : \mu = 0)$

$= P\left[\frac{\bar{X}-0}{1/\sqrt{n}} < \frac{C-0}{1/\sqrt{n}}\right] = P[Z < C\sqrt{n}]$

$\alpha = \phi(C\sqrt{n})$

Power of test, $P_n(\mu, \alpha) = P(x \in w \mid H_1 : \mu > 0)$

$= P(\bar{X} < C \mid H_1 : \mu > 0)$

$= P[Z < (C-\mu)\sqrt{n}]$

$= \phi\left(\sqrt{n}(c-\mu)\right)$

$\lim_{n\to\infty} P_n(\mu, \alpha) = \lim_{n\to\infty} \phi\left(\sqrt{n}(c-\mu)\right) = \phi(\infty) = 1$

$\lim_{\mu\to 0} P_n(\mu, \alpha) = \lim_{\mu\to\infty} \phi\left(\sqrt{n}(c-\mu)\right) = \phi(\sqrt{n}\,C) = \alpha$

$\lim_{\alpha\to 0} P_n(\mu, \alpha) = \lim_{\alpha\to 0} \phi\left(\sqrt{n}(c-\mu)\right) = 0$

$\lim_{\alpha\to 1} P_n(\mu, \alpha) = \lim_{\alpha\to 1} \phi\left(\sqrt{n}(c-\mu)\right) = \phi(\infty) = 1$

So, option (a), (b) and (c) are correct

17. Explanation: (a)

$\rho = \frac{\sigma_x}{E(X)}$

To Test $H_0 : \rho \le 5$ againt $H_1 : \rho > 5$

$H_0 : \frac{\sigma_x}{E(X)} \le 5$ againt $H_1 : \frac{\sigma_x}{E(X)} > 5$

$H_0 : \sigma_x \le 10$ against $H_1 : \sigma_x > 10$

LRT : is given by

$\frac{\underset{\sigma\in\sigma_0}{Sup}\{L_0\}}{\underset{\sigma\in\sigma_1}{Sup}\{L_1\}} < k$

We know that ml.e of $\sigma^2 = \frac{1}{n}\sum_{i=1}^{n}(X_i - \bar{X})^2$

$\sigma^2 = \frac{1}{n}\sum_{i=1}^{n}(X_i - 2)^2$

Under H_o

$\underset{\sigma\in\sigma_0}{Sup}\{L_o\} = \frac{1}{10\sqrt{2\pi}}\exp\left\{-\frac{1}{200} \ ; \sum_{i=1}^{n}(X_i - 2)^2\right\}$

UnderH_1

$\underset{\sigma\in\sigma_1}{\overset{H_0}{Sup}}\{L_1\} = \frac{1}{\hat{\sigma}^2\sqrt{2n}}\exp\left\{-\frac{n}{2} \ ; \frac{\sum_{i=1}^{n}(X_i-2)^2}{\sum_{i=1}^{n}(X_i-2)^2}\right\}$

$= \frac{1}{\hat{\sigma}^2\sqrt{2n}}\exp\left\{-\frac{n}{2}\right\}$

$\therefore \frac{Sup\, L_0}{Sup\, L_1} < k$

$\frac{\exp\left\{\frac{-1}{200}\sum(X_i-2)^2\right\}}{\exp\left\{\frac{-n}{2}\right\}} < k$

Taking log both sides :-

$-\sum_{i=1}^{n}(X_i - 2)^2 < K$

$\Rightarrow \sum_{i=1}^{n}(X_i - 2)^2 > C$

LRT is of form : Reject H_0 if

$\sum_{i=1}^{n}(X_i - 2)^2 > C$

Option (a) is correct

18. Explanation: (a), (b), (c), (d)

x	0	1	2	3
$P_{\theta\,o}(x)$	0.01	0.04	0.5	0.45
$P_{\theta},(x)$	0.02	0.08	0.4	0.5

Define a test ϕ such that

$\phi(x) = 1$ if $X = 0, 1$

$= 0$ if $x = 2, 3$

For testing $H_0 : \theta = \theta_0\ against\ H_1 : \theta = \theta_1$

Size of test $= \alpha = E(\phi(x)|H_0)$

$= 1 \times P_{\theta_0}(0) + 1 \times P_{\theta_0}(1) + 0 \times P_{\theta_0}(2) + 0 \times P_{\theta_0}(3)$

$= 0.01 + 0.04$

$= 0.05$

The test ϕ is most powerful test of size 0.05

It is also likelihood ratio test of at level 0.05

Power of test $= E[\phi(x)|\, H_1]$

$= 1 \times P_{\theta_1}(0) + 1 \times P_{\theta_1}(1) + 0x\, P_{\theta_1}(2) + 0 \times P_{\theta_1}(3)$

$= 0.02 + 0.08 \ = 0.1$

Power > Size ⇒ test is an unbiased test

Option (a), (b), (c), (d) are correct

19. Explanation: (a), (d)

95% Confidence Interval for μ is (2.5, 3.6)

$\mu_0 < 2.5$ be fixed number

$H_0 : \mu = \mu_0$ against $H_1 : \mu \ne \mu_0$

At $\alpha = 5\% = 0.05$ H_0 would reject

$\Rightarrow \alpha = 10\% = 0.1, H_0$ would reject

At $\alpha = \frac{5}{2}\% = 0.025$, the information is not enough to draw conclusion.

Option (a) & (d) are correct

20. Explanation: (a), (d)

To that $H_0 : \theta = 1$ vs $H_1 : \theta = \frac{1}{2}$

X and Y be a random sample from Poisson (θ)

$X \sim P(\theta)$ and $Y \sim P(\theta)$

$\Rightarrow X + Y \sim P(2\theta)$

Reject H_0 : If either $X = 0$ or $(X = 1\ and\ X + Y \le 2)$

P [Type I Error] $= P[x \in W \mid H_0]$

$= P[X = 0\ or\ (X = 1\ and\ X + Y \le 2)] \mid H_0 : \theta = 1$

$= P[X = 0] + P[X = 1] \cdot P[Y = 1] + P[X = 1] \cdot [Y = 0]$

$= e^{-1} + e^{-1} \cdot e^{-1} + e^{-1} \cdot e^{-1}$

P [Type I error] $= e^{-1} + 2e^{-2}$

P [Type II error] $= P(x \in \overline{W} \mid H_1)$

$= 1 - P(x \in w \mid H_1)$

$= 1 - \{P[X = 0] + P[X = 1]\, P[Y = 1] + P[X = 1]\, P[Y = 0]\} \mid H_1$

$= 1 - \left[e^{\frac{-1}{2}} + e^{\frac{-1}{2}}\frac{-1}{2} \cdot e^{\frac{-1}{2}}\frac{1}{2} + e^{\frac{-1}{2}}\frac{1}{2}e^{\frac{-1}{2}}\right]$

$= 1 - \left[e^{\frac{-1}{2}} + \frac{3}{4}\, e^{-1}\right]$

Power of that $= 1 - \beta = 1 - P$ [Type II error]

$= \frac{3}{4}\, e^{-1} + e^{-1/2}$

So, option (a) & (d) are correct

21. Explanation: (b), (c), (d)

To test $H_0 : f(x) = \frac{1}{\sqrt{2\pi}}\, e^{-\frac{x^2}{2}}$ vs $H_1 : f(x) = \frac{1}{2}\, e^{-|x|}$

Likelihood Ratio Test: $\frac{\sup_{\theta\in\theta_0}\{L_0\}}{\sup_{\theta\in\theta_1}\{L_1\}} < k$

The likelihood function under H_0

$L_0 = \left(\frac{1}{\sqrt{2\pi}}\right)^n e^{-\frac{1}{2}\sum_{i=1}^n x_i^2}$

The likelihood function under H_1

$L_1 = \frac{1}{2^n}\, e^{-\sum_{i=1}^n |x_i|}$

LRT: is

$\frac{\left(\frac{1}{\sqrt{2\pi}}\right)^n e^{-\frac{1}{2}\sum_{i=1}^n x_i^2}}{\frac{1}{2^n} e^{-\sum_{i=1}^n |x_i|}} < k$

$e^{-\frac{1}{2}\sum_{i=1}^n x_i^2 + \sum_{i=1}^n |x_i|} < k'$

$\frac{-1}{2}\sum_{i=1}^n \{|X_i|^2 - 2|X_i| + 1 - 1\} < k'$

$\sum_{i=1}^n \{|X_i| - 1\}^2 \geq c$

which is rejection region

It is function $|X_1|, |X_2|, \dots, |X_n|$ and $X_1^2, \dots X_n^2$

So, option (b), (c), (d) are correct

22. Explanation: (a), (b), (c), (d)

H_0 : Goal distribution is Poisson

Calculated value of $\chi^2 = 1.27$

Tabulated value of χ^2 for 5 d.f. at 5% = 11.07

Calculated $\leq$ Tabulated value

Then H_0 may accepted

d.f. = 6 – 1 = 5

m.l.e. of Poisson is mean of the distribution

= 1.49

Under H_0 :

$P(Goal \leq 1) = P(X = 0) + P(X = 1)$

$= \frac{e^{-1.49}(1.49)^0}{0!} + \frac{e^{-1.49}(1.49)^1}{1!}$

$= 2.49\, e^{-1.49}$

So, option (a), (b), (c) & (d) are correct

23. Explanation: (b)

Let X be a random sample of size from a Cauchy distribution with pdf

$f(x) = \frac{1}{\pi}\left[\frac{1}{1+(x-\theta)^2}\right]; -\infty < x < \infty$

For testing $H_0: \theta = -1$ against $H_1: \theta = 0$

Reject H_0 if $\frac{X}{\sqrt{1+X^2}} > C$

Power of test $= 1 - \beta = 0.5$

$P[x \in w | H_1 : \theta = 0] = 0.5$; W is the critical region

$P\left[\frac{X}{\sqrt{1+X^2}} > C^2 | H_1: \theta = 0\right] = 0.5$

$P\left[\frac{X^2}{1+X^2} > C^2 | H_1: \theta = 0\right] = 0.5$

$p\left[\frac{1+X^2}{X^2} < C^2 | H_1: \theta = 0\right] = 0.5$

$p\left[X > \frac{C}{\sqrt{1-C^2}} | H_1: \theta = 0\right] = 0.5$

$\int_{\frac{c}{\sqrt{1-c^2}}}^{\infty} f(x)\, dx | H_1 = 0.5$

$\int_{\frac{c}{\sqrt{1-c^2}}}^{\infty} \frac{1}{\pi}\left[\frac{1}{1+x^2}\right] dx = 0.5$

$\Rightarrow \frac{1}{\pi}[tan^{-1}x]_{\frac{c}{\sqrt{1-c^2}}}^{\infty} = 0.5$

$\frac{1}{\pi}\left[tan^{-1}\infty - tan^{-1}\frac{c}{\sqrt{1-c^2}}\right] = 0.5$

$\frac{1}{\pi}\left[\frac{\pi}{2} - tan^{-1}\frac{c}{\sqrt{1-c^2}} = \frac{\pi}{2}\right]$

$tan^{-1}\frac{c}{\sqrt{1-c^2}} = 0$

$\frac{c}{\sqrt{1-c^2}} = \tan 0$

$\frac{c}{\sqrt{1-c^2}} = 0$

$c = 0$

Option (b) is correct

24. Explanation: (c), (d)

X and Y are two independent variates

$X \sim Exp$ with mean θ

$Y \sim Exp$ with mean 2θ

$f(x) = \frac{1}{\theta}e^{-x/\theta}; x > 0$

$g(y) = \frac{1}{2\theta}.e^{-y/2\theta}; y > 0$

The likelihood function is

$L = f(x,y) = f(x).g(y)$

$= \frac{1}{\theta}.e^{-x/\theta}\frac{1}{2\theta}.e^{-\frac{y}{2\theta}}$

$= \frac{1}{2\theta^2}.e^{-\frac{1}{2\theta}(2x+y)}.1$

$= g(2x+y,\theta).h(x)$

By factorization theorem,

$2X + Y$ is sufficient for θ

$X + 2Y$ is not sufficient

Left tail test based an $2X + Y$ is UMP for testing $H_0: \theta = 1$ againt $H_0: \theta < 1$ but UMP does not exist for testing $H_0: \theta = 1$, against $H_1: \theta \neq 1$

So, option (c) & (d) are correct

25. Explanation: (d)

For $n > 2, \mu_2 > 1$ i.e., the variance of t-distribution is greater than that of standard normal distribution.

For $n > 4$ and t distribution is more flat on the top than the normal curve, for small n

$P((t) \geq t_0) \geq P[|Z| \geq t_0], Z \sim N(0,1)$

P value for 10 degree of freedom ≥ 0.05

Option (d) is correct

26. Explanation: (a), (b) (c), (d)

X is discrete random variable

$X = \{-2, -1, 1, 2\}$ with pmf $P_\theta(X = x)$

X	:	–2	–1	1	2
$\theta = \theta_0$	:	0.05	0.6	0.3	0.05
$\theta = \theta_1$	:	0.2	0.4	0.2	0.2

To test $H_0 : \theta = \theta_0$ against $H_1 : \theta = \theta_1$

$\frac{\theta_1}{\theta_0} > 1$ on $\theta_1(x) > \theta_0(x)$ then we reject H_0 : at $X = x$

$\{X = x\}$ is critical region

X	:	–2	–1	1	2
$\theta = \theta_0$	:	0.05	0.6	0.3	0.05
$\theta = \theta_1$	:	0.2	0.4	0.2	0.2
$\frac{\theta_1}{\theta_0}$	:	4	$\frac{2}{3}$	$\frac{2}{3}$	4

At $X = -2, 2$; $\frac{\theta_1}{\theta_0} > 1$

At $X = -1, 1$; $\frac{\theta_1}{\theta_0} < 1$

$X = -1, 1$ never be the most powerful critical region

$\Rightarrow \{X = -2\}$ or $\{X = 2\}$ be most powerful critical region.

So, option (a), (b) (c) & (d) are correct

27. Explanation: (b), (c)

$f(x) = \frac{2(\theta - x)}{\theta^2} \quad : \; 0 \le x \le \theta$

For testing $H_o: \; \theta = 2$ against $H_1: \theta = 3$

Test 1: max $[X_1 \; X_2] \le 1$

Test 2: max $[X_1 \; X_2] \ge 1$

α_i denote the probability of Type I error for Test I .

We have to Find the pdf of $Y = \max[X_1 \; X_2]$

$F(x) = \int_0^x f(y)dy$

$= \frac{2}{\theta^2}\int_0^x (\theta - y)\; dy$

$= \frac{2}{\theta^2}\left[\theta y - \frac{y^2}{2}\right]_0^x$

$F(x) = \frac{2}{\theta^2} x\left(\theta - \frac{x}{2}\right)$

$g(y) = n\, f(y)\{F(y)\}^{n-1}$

$= 2\,.\, f(y).\, F(y)$

$= 2.\frac{2(\theta - y)}{\theta^2}.\left[\frac{2}{\theta^2} y\left(\theta - \frac{y}{2}\right)\right]$

$g(y) = \frac{8}{\theta^4}(\theta - y)\left(\theta - \frac{y}{2}\right).y$

$\alpha_1 = P[\,x \in W |\, H_0\,]$

$= P[\max(x_1\, x_2) \le 1 | H_0]$

$= \int_0^1 \frac{8}{\theta^4}(\theta - y)\left(\theta - \frac{y}{2}\right).y\; dy \mid H_0 : \theta = 2$

$\alpha_1 = \frac{9}{14} = 0.5625$

$\alpha_2 = P\,(x \in w|H_0)$

$= P[\max(x_1 x_2) \ge 1 |\, H_0]$

$= 1 - P\,[\max(x_1 x_2) \le 1 \mid H_0]$

$= 1 - \; 0.5625$

$\alpha_2 = 0.4375$

$\alpha_1 + \alpha_2 = 1$

Power of Test 1:

$1 - \beta_1 = P(x \in w \mid H_0 |)$

$= P[\max(x_1 x_2) \le 1 \mid H_1 : \theta = 3]$

$= \int_0^1 g(y)dy \mid H_1 : \theta = 3$

$= \int_0^1 \frac{8}{\theta^4}(\theta - y)\left(\theta - \frac{y}{2}\right) - y\; dy \mid H_1 : \theta = 3$

$= \frac{4}{81}.\frac{25}{4} = \frac{25}{81}$

$1 - \beta_1 = 0\,.3086$

$\therefore$ Power if Test 2:

$1 - \beta_2 = P\,(\,x \in w|H_1)$

$= P\,(\max(x_1, x_2) \ge \; 1 \mid H_1)$

$= 1 - P(\max(x_1 x_2) \le 1 \mid H_1)$

$= 1 - 0.3086$

$= 0.6913$

$\alpha_1 = 0.5625$ $\qquad \alpha_2 = 0.4375$

$1 - \beta_1 = 0.3086$ $\qquad 1 - \beta_2 = 0.6913$

$1 - \beta_1 < \alpha_1$ $\qquad 1 - \beta_2 > \alpha_2$

$\therefore$ *Test* 2 is unbiased

Option (b) & (c) correct

28. Explanation: (a), (d)

X be a discrete random variate with sample space

$X = \{1, 2, \ldots 10\}$

$H_0 : p(x) = \frac{1}{10}$

$H_1 : p(x) \propto x \;\; x \in X$

$p(x) = k\, x$

$\sum_{x=1}^{10} p(x) = 1$

$\sum_{x=1}^{10} kx = 1$

$k\sum_{x=1}^{10} x = 1$

$55k = 1$

$k = \frac{1}{55}$

$H_1 \;: p(x) = \frac{x}{55} \;:\; x = 1, 2, \ldots 10$

x	1	2	3	.4
P_0(x)	$\frac{1}{10}$	$\frac{1}{10}$	$\frac{1}{10}$	$\frac{1}{10}$
$P_1(x)$	$\frac{1}{55}$	$\frac{2}{55}$	$\frac{3}{55}$	$\frac{4}{55}$
$\lambda(x) = \frac{P_1(x)}{P_0(x)}$	$\frac{10}{55}$	$\frac{20}{55}$	$\frac{30}{55}$	$\frac{40}{55}$

Non – Randomised test

$\lambda(x) = \begin{cases} 1 & x \ge c \\ 0 & x < c \end{cases}$

For option (a)

Critical Region : $X \ge 2$

$\alpha = P\,(X \ge 2\,|H_0] \; = 0.9$

As we see in the table there is no other critical Region of same size 0.9

So, $X \ge 2$ is mp test if size 0.9

So, option (a) is correct

For option (b)

Unbiased test

$if\; (1 - \beta) > \propto$

$C\,R : [X < 2]$

$\alpha \; = P\,[X < 2 \mid H_0] = \; 0.1$

$1 - \beta = p[X < 2 \mid H_1] = \frac{1}{55}$

$\propto\; < 1 - \beta$

$\{X < 2\}$ is not unbiased test

For option (3)

$P - value = P[X > test\; statistic\; |H_0]$

$= P\,[X > 7 \mid H_0]$

$= P[X = 8] + P\,(X = 9) + P\,(X = 10]|\; H_0$

$= 0.1 + 0.1 + 0.1$

$= 0.3 \; \ne 0\;.6$

For option (d)

There does not exist non- randomised test of size 0.05 because Minimum size is 0.1

So, option a and d are correct

29. Explanation: (a), (c) and (d)

30. Explanation: (a)

$f(x|\theta) = \frac{e^{(x-\theta)}}{(1+e^{(x-\theta)})^2}\;; -\infty < x < \infty\,;\; -\infty < \theta < \infty$

$H_0 : \theta \le \theta_0$ V/s $H_1 : \theta > \theta_0$

Using Neymann- Peason Lemma

$\frac{L_1}{L_0} > k$

$\Rightarrow \frac{\frac{e^{(x-\theta_1)}}{\left[1+e^{(x-\theta_1)}\right]^2}}{\frac{e^{(x-\theta_0)}}{\left[1+e^{(x-\theta_0)}\right]^2}} > k$

$\Rightarrow \frac{1+e^{(x-\theta_0)}}{1+e^{(x-\theta_1)}} > \sqrt{ke^{(\theta_1 - \theta_0)}}$

$X > C$

$\alpha = P_{\theta_0}[X > C]$

Option (a) is correct

31. Explanation: (a)

$X_1, X_2, \ldots, X_{16}$ be a random sample from normal distribution with unknown mean μ and variance 4.

$Z \sim N(0,1)$

To test, $H_0 : \mu = 3$ vs $H_1 : \mu = 0$

Observed sample mean, $\bar{x} = 2.5$

Under $H_0 : \bar{x} < \mu$

P-value $P = P[Z \le t|H_0]$ for a one-sided left tail test

$Z = \frac{\bar{x}-\mu}{\sigma\sqrt{n}} \sim N(0,1)$

$P = P\left[Z \le \frac{2.5-3}{2/\sqrt{16}}\right] = P[Z \le -1] = P[Z > 1]$

So, option (a) is correct

32. Explanation: (a), (b), (d)

$X_1, X_2, \ldots, X_n$ are iid random variable which are uniformly distributed on $(0, \theta)$ i.e., $X_i \sim U(0,\theta)$; $i = 1, 2, \ldots, n$

$X_{(1)} \le X_{(2)} \le \cdots \le X_{(n)}$ be the ordered statistic

To test $H_0 : \theta = 1$ vs $H_1 : \theta > 1$

For option (a):

The pdf of X_1 is

$f(x_1) = \frac{1}{\theta} : 0 < x_1 < \theta$

Reject H_0 when $X_1 > 1 - \alpha$

$P[X_1 > 1-\alpha] = \int_{1-\alpha}^{\theta} f(x_1)\,dx_1 = \frac{1}{\theta}[\theta - 1 + x]$

Under H_0 :

$P[X_1 > 1-\alpha \mid H_0 : \theta = 1] = \int_{1-\alpha}^{1} f(x_1)\,dx = \alpha$

So, option (a) is correct

For option (b): Reject $H_0 : X_{(n)} > (1-\alpha)^{1/n}$

$f(x_{(n)}) = n[f(x)]^{n-1} f(x) = n.\frac{x^{n-1}}{\theta^{n-1}}.\frac{1}{\vartheta}$

$f(x_{(n)}) = \frac{n}{\theta^n}.x_{(n)}^{n-1}; 0 \le x_{(n)} \le \theta$

$P\left[X_{(n)} > (1-\alpha)^{\frac{1}{n}}\right] = \int_{(1-\alpha)^{\frac{1}{n}}}^{\theta} f(x_{(n)})\,dx_{(n)}$

Under $H_0 : \theta = 1$

$P[X_{(n)} > (1-\alpha)^{1/n} | H_0 : \theta = 1] =$

$\int_{(1-\alpha)^{1/n}}^{1} x_{(n)}^{n-1}\,dx_{(n)} = \alpha$

So, option (b) is correct and (c) is incorrect

For option (d): Reject H_0 when $X_{(1)} > 1 - \alpha^{1/n}$

The pdf of $X_{(1)}$ is

$f(X_{(1)}) = n[1 - F(x)]^{n-1}.f(x)$

$= n\left[1 - \frac{x}{\theta}\right]^{n-1}.\frac{1}{\theta} = \frac{n}{\theta}\left[1 - \frac{x}{\theta}\right]^{n-1}$

$P\left[X_{(n)} > (1-\alpha)^{\frac{1}{n}} H_0 : \theta = 1\right]$

$= \int_{(1-\alpha)^{1/n}}^{1} n[1-x]^{n-1}\,dx$

$= \left\{\frac{(1-x)^n}{-1}\right\}_{1-\alpha^{1/n}}^{1} = 0 + \left(1 - 1 + \alpha^{1/n}\right)^n = +\alpha$

So, option (d) is correct

Then option (a), (b) & (d) are correct

33. Explanation: (a), (d).

Let $x_1, \ldots, x_{10}$ be a random sample from a continuous random variable with p.d.f.

$f_\theta(x) = \begin{cases} e^{\theta - x}, x \ge \theta \\ 0, otherwise \end{cases}$ $\theta \in \mathbb{R}$ is unknown.

$H_0 : \theta \le 3$ Against $H_1 : \theta > 3$

Let $X_{(1)}, \ldots, X_{(10)}$ be the order statistics corresponding to given sample. Where $x_{(1)} = \text{Min}(x_1 \ldots x_n)$.

Let

$L(\theta, \underline{x}) = \prod_{i=1}^{n} e^{\theta - x_i}$

$= \prod_{i=1}^{n} e^{\theta} \cdot e^{-x_i}$

$= \prod_{i=1}^{n} e^{\theta} \prod_{i=1}^{n} e^{-x_i}$

$= e^{n\theta} \cdot e^{-\sum_{i=1}^{n} x_i}$

Taking log on both sides

$$\log L(\theta, \underline{x}) = n\theta - \sum_{i=1}^{n} x_i$$

Differentiating on both sides w.r.t. θ. & equating to 0.

$$\frac{\partial \ln L}{\partial \theta} = n \ne 0$$

Thus calculus method does not help us to find out supremum of $L(\theta, \underline{x})$.

As the range of x involves θ, order statistics will be handy in this case.

Thus

$$\theta \leqslant x_{(1)} \leqslant x_{(2)} \leqslant \cdots \leqslant x_{(n)1)} \leqslant x_{(n)}$$

Consider

$$L(\theta), \underline{x}) = e^{n\theta} e^{-\sum_{i=1}^{n} x_i}$$

$= e^{10\theta} e^{-\sum_{i=1}^{n} x_i}$ $\because$ n = 10

Note that $L(\theta, \underline{x})$ involves the function e^x which is a continuous non-decreasing function of x. Thus $L(\theta)$ will attain its maximum value whenever θ attains its maximum.

For a given sample $x_1 \ldots, x_n, \theta$ can attain its maximum if it takes value $x_{(1)}$.

$\therefore$ M.L.E. of θ is $\hat{\theta} = X_{(1)}$.

Under $H_0; \theta \le 3$. So its MLE $\hat{\theta} = X_{(1)} \le 3$.

Because if $X_{(1)} > 3$, there $\exists\ \theta \in \mathbb{R}$ such that $3 < \theta < X_{(1)}$ which is contradictory to the given null hypothesis.

$\therefore$ Likelihood function $L(\theta, \underline{x})$ attains its maximum under null hypothesis at $X_{(1)}$ if $X_{(1)} \leqslant 3$.

$\sup_{\theta \le 3} L(\theta) = e^{10x_{(1)}} e^{-\sum_{i=1}^{10} x_i}$, if $x_{(1)} \le 3$

Therefore **option (a)** is correct & option (b) is incorrect.

We have $L(\theta, \underline{x}) = e^{10\theta} e^{-\sum_{i=1}^{n} x_i}$

$$\sup_{\theta} L_{H_0}(\theta, \underline{x}) = e^{10x_{(1)}} e^{-\sum_{i=1}^{n} x_i}$$

$$\sup_{\theta} L_H(\theta, \underline{x}) = e^{10.3} e^{-\sum_{i=1}^{n} x_i}$$

The critical region C of the likelihood ratio test of size $\alpha (0 < \alpha < 1)$ is given by

Reject H_0 if $\frac{\sup_\theta L_{H_0}(\theta, \underline{x})}{\sup_\theta L_H(\theta, \underline{x})} \ge \text{k}$ $\forall \underline{x} \in C$

$\Rightarrow \frac{e^{10 \cdot x_{(1)}} e^{-\sum_{i=1}^{n} x_i}}{e^{10 \cdot 3} e^{-\sum_{i=1}^{n} x_i}} \ge k', \forall x \in C \subseteq \mathbb{R}^{10}$

$\Rightarrow e^{10(x_{(1)} - 3)} \ge k'$

$\Rightarrow 10(x_{(1)} - 3) \ge \log k'$

$$\Rightarrow x_{(1)} \geq \frac{\log k'}{10} + 3 = k$$

To decide the value of k, we will use α.

Find k such that $P[X_{(1)} \geq k|H_0] = \alpha$

$= 1 - P[X_{(1)} < k \mid H_0]$

$= 1 - F_{X_{(1)}}(k) \mid H_0$

Note that $F_{X_{(1)}}(x)|\text{H}_0 = \int_3^x f(u)du = 1 - e^{-(x-3)\cdot n}$

Consider

$$P[X_{(1)} \geq k|H_0] = \alpha$$

$\Rightarrow 1 - [1 - e^{-10(k-3)}] = \alpha$

$(\because n = 10)$

$\Rightarrow e^{-10(k-3)} = \alpha$

$\Rightarrow -10(k-3) = \log \alpha$

$\Rightarrow k = 3 - \frac{1}{10}\log_e(\alpha)$

Thus, the critical region of L.R.T. is given by $\{(x_1, \ldots, x_{10}) \in \mathbb{R}^{10}; x_{(1)} \geq 3 - \frac{1}{10}\log_e(\alpha)\}$

Thus, **option (d)** is correct and option (c) is incorrect.

34. Explanation: (d)

Given $f_X(x) = \begin{cases} \theta x^{\theta-1} & ;\text{if } 0 < x < 1 \\ 0 & ;o.w. \end{cases}$

$H_0 : \theta = 4$ against $H_1 : \theta = 8$

size of test $= \alpha = 0.2$

$\therefore \quad f_X(x)|_{H_0} = 4x^3; 0 < x < 1$

$\quad f_X(x)|_{H_1} = 8x^7; 0 < x < 1$

According to Neyman – Pearson Lemma the most powerful test for two simple hypotheses is given by Likelihood Ratio Test (L.R.T.).

To find the critical region for L.R.T. consider the ratio of the likelihood functions under H_1 and H_0 such that $\exists$ a critical region C of given size α and a non-negative constant k such that

$$\frac{L(\underline{x}; \theta_1)}{L(\underline{x}, \theta_0)} \geqslant k \quad \forall \underline{x} \in C$$

Note that the given sample size is 1. Therefore

$$L(\underline{x}, \theta) \equiv f_X(x, \theta)$$

$\therefore \frac{f_X(x, \theta_1)}{f_X(x, \theta_0)} \geqslant k'$

$\Rightarrow \frac{8x^7}{4x^3} \geqslant k'$

$\Rightarrow 2x^4 \geqslant k'$

Taking log on both sides.

$\Rightarrow \log 2 + 4\log x \geqslant \ln k'$

$\Rightarrow \log x \geqslant \frac{\log k' - \log 2}{4}$

Taking antilog on both sides.

$\Rightarrow x \geqslant e^{\left[\frac{\log k' - \log 2}{4}\right]} = k$

Thus critical region C is given by

Reject H_0 if $x \geqslant k$

We will find the value of k such that

$$P[x \geqslant k \mid H_0] = \alpha = 0.2$$

$\Rightarrow P[x \geqslant k \mid \theta_0 = 4] = 0.2$

$\Rightarrow \int_k^1 4x^3 dx = 0.2 \Rightarrow x^4|_k^1 = 0.2$

$\Rightarrow 1 - k^4 = 0.2 \Rightarrow k^4 = 0.8$

$\Rightarrow k = (0.8)^{\left(\frac{1}{4}\right)}$

$\Rightarrow k = 0.94574160900317$

Now the power of the test $= 1 - \beta$

$= P$ [Rejecting H_0 when H_0 is false]

$= P$ [Rejecting H_0 when H_1 is true]

$= p[x \geqslant k \mid H_1]$

$= P[x \geqslant k \mid \theta_1 = 8]$

$= \int_k^1 8x^7 dx = x^8|_k^1 = 1 - k^8$

Using $k = 0.94574160900317$ we get,

$$1 - \beta = 0.36$$

Thus answer is **option (d)**.

35. Explanation: (a) & (c).

X be a discrete random variable. Its probability mass function, under H_0 & H_1 is given in the table below. We have also computed the ratio of the p.m.f.s under H_1 & H_0. .

X	1	2	3	4	5	6	7
$f_{H_0(x)}$	0.01	0.01	0.01	0.01	0.01	0.01	0.94
$f_{H_1(x)}$	0.06	0.05	0.04	0.03	0.02	0.01	0.79
$\frac{f_{H_1}(x)}{f_{H_0}(x)}$	6	5	4	3	2	1	0.84

We have to find the critical region C and a non-negative constant k such that

$$\frac{f_{H_1}(x)}{f_{H_0}(x)} \geqslant k \quad \forall x \in C$$

We have to find k such that

$$P[x \in C \mid H_0] = \alpha = 0.04$$

Now observe, under H_0 there exist more than one critical regions for which size of the test will come out to be 0.04. We want to find the best critical region corresponding to the most powerful test.

Now we will list down each critical region with its power.

Note that, power of test $= 1 - \beta = P[x \in C|H_1]$

All the below listed critical regions have size $\alpha = 0.04$

Critical Region	Power of the test $1 - \beta$
$\{x: 3 \leq x \leq 6\}$	0.1
$\{x: 2 \leq x \leq 5\}$	0.14
$\{x: x \leq 4\}$	0.18

Thus, among the above critical regions $\{x; x \leq 4\}$ this critical region has maximum power which is 0.18. Therefore, this is the best critical region corresponding to the most powerful test (M.P.T.) of size $\alpha = 0.04$ for testing H_0 against H_1. The power of this M.P.T. is 0.18.

Thus, **options (a) & (c)** are correct and options (b) & (d) are incorrect.

36. Explanation: (c)

$X_1, \ldots, X_7$ and $Y_1, \ldots, Y_9$ be two random samples drawn independently from two populations with continuous CDFs F and G respectively.

$$H_0: F(x) = G(x), \forall x \quad \text{against} \quad H_1: F(x) \neq G(x) \text{ for some } x.$$

To test this hypothesis we use Wald-Wolfowitz run test whose test statistics is based on the random variable which counts the total number of runs in the combined ordered arrangement of the given two samples and is denoted by 'R'.Its probability model is given as follows.

$$P_{H_0}(R = 2k) = \frac{2\binom{n_1-1}{k-1}\binom{n_2-1}{k-1}}{\binom{n_1+n_2}{n_1}} \quad \text{if R is even}$$

Also

$P_{H_0}(R = 2k+1)$

$$= \frac{\binom{n_1-1}{k}\binom{n_2-1}{k-1} + \binom{n_2-1}{k}\binom{n_1-1}{k-1}}{\binom{n_1+n_2}{n_1}}$$

if R is odd

Where, n_1, n_2 are the sample sizes from two populations.

Here $n_1 = 7, n_2 = 9$.

1) $\boldsymbol{R = 6 = 2 \cdot 3 \Rightarrow k = 3}$

$$\therefore P_{H_0}(R = 6) = \frac{2\binom{7-1}{3-1}\binom{9-1}{3-1}}{\binom{16}{7}}$$

$$= \frac{2 \cdot \frac{6\times5}{2} \cdot \frac{8\times7}{2}}{11440} = \frac{840}{11440} = \frac{21}{286}$$

2) $\boldsymbol{R = 9 = 2\cdot 4 + 1 \Rightarrow k = 4}$

$$\therefore P_{H_0}(R = 9) = \frac{\binom{7-1}{4}\binom{9-1}{4-1} + \binom{9-1}{4}\binom{7-1}{4-1}}{\binom{16}{7}}$$

$$= \frac{\binom{6}{4}\binom{8}{3} + \binom{8}{4}\binom{6}{3}}{\binom{16}{7}}$$

$$= \frac{6\times5}{2} \cdot \frac{8\times7\times6}{3\times2} + \frac{8\times7\times6\times5}{4\times3\times2} \cdot \frac{6\times5\times4}{3\times2}$$

$$= \frac{15\cdot 56 + 70\cdot 20}{11440}$$

$$= \frac{2240}{11440}$$

$$= \frac{28}{143}$$

Therefore, **option (c)** is correct and options (a), (b), (d) are incorrect.

37. Explanation: (a), (c)

For (1)

e.g. if $x \sim U(\theta, \theta+1)$

$f(x) = \frac{1}{\theta+1-\theta} = \frac{1}{1} = 1$

M.L.E = order statistic need not to unique

Correct option

For (2)

Complete ⇒ sufficient

$e.g. x_i \sim N(\theta, \sigma^2)$

$T(x) = \frac{x_1+x_2}{2}$

$T(x)$ is statistic.

By using CRB it will not be sufficient

option is incorrect.

For (3)

Sufficient ⇏ complete

e.g. $x \sim N(\theta, \theta)$

$\theta = \sum \frac{x_i}{n}$

Sufficient statistic but not complete

option is incorrect

For (4)

Let $T \xrightarrow{sufficient} \theta$

$g(t) \xrightarrow{sufficient} g(\theta)$ only g is 1 to 1 function

Option is incorrect

∴ option (a) & (c) correct

38. Explanation: (a), (c), (d)

Here $p(x) = p(X = x) = \frac{1}{20}$; $x = \{1, 2, \ldots, 20\}$

$q(x) = p(X = x) = \frac{x}{210}$; $x = \{1, 2, \ldots. 20\}$

Let $H_0 : p = \frac{1}{20} = \phi$

$H_1 : p = \frac{x}{210} = \Psi$

Size of test = Type 1 error

$\alpha = p(w|H_0) = p(\text{Critical Region})\, |\mu_0)$

$\phi = p(x \le 2 \mid H_0) \quad = p(x = 1|H_0) + p(x = 2 \mid H_0) \quad =$

$\frac{1}{20} + \frac{1}{20} = \frac{1}{10}$

$\{\phi(x) = 1 \ ,x \ge 2$

$= 0 \ ,o.w\}$

$\phi = 0.1$

$\Psi = P(x \ge 19|H_0) + p(x = 20 \mid H_0) = \frac{1}{20} + \frac{1}{20} = \frac{1}{10}$

$\Psi = 0.1$

Power of the test

$\Psi = P(Critical\ region|(H_1)) = P(w|H_1)$

$= P(x \ge 19|H_1)$

$= P(x = 19|H_1) + p(x = 20|H_1)$

$= \frac{19}{210} + \frac{20}{210}$

$= \frac{39}{210}$

$= \frac{13}{70}$

$= 0.185$

$\phi = P(critical\ region)\, |H_1)$

$= P(w|\mu_1)$

$= P(x \le 2|H_1)$

$= P(x = 1|H_1) + P(x = 2|H_1)$

$= \frac{1}{210} + \frac{2}{210}$

$= \frac{3}{210}$

$\phi = \frac{1}{70} = 0.014$

Option (a), (c) & (d) correct.

39. Explanation: (c)

X_1, X_2 be a random sample from a population having probability density function $f \epsilon \{f_0, f_1\}$ where

$$f_0(x) = \begin{cases} \frac{1}{2} if 0 \le x \le 2 \\ 0 \quad otherwise, \end{cases} \Rightarrow X \sim Uniform(0,2)$$

$$f_1(x) = \begin{cases} \frac{1}{4} if 0 \le x \le 4 \\ 0 \quad otherwise, \end{cases} \sim Uniform(0,4)$$

$H_0: f = f_0$ against $H_1: f = f_1$

The above null hypothesis can be rewritten as $X \sim Uniform(0, \theta)$

$$\theta_0 = 2\ against\ \theta_1 = 4$$

Thus by Neyman-Pearson Lemma there exists a critical region C and a non-negative constant k such that

$$\frac{L(\theta_1, \underline{x})}{L(\theta_0, \underline{x})} \geq k \; \forall \; \underline{x} \in C$$

$$\frac{(1/16) \times I(0 < X_1 < 4) \times I(0 < X_2 < 4)}{(1/4) \times I(0 < X_1 < 2) \times I(0 < X_2 < 2)}$$

$$= \frac{1}{4}\frac{I\{0 < max(X_1, X_2) < 4\}}{I\{0 < max(X_1, X_2) < 2\}} \geq k' \; \forall \; \underline{x} \in C$$

$$\Rightarrow \frac{I\{0 < max(X_1, X_2) < 4\}}{I\{0 < max(X_1, X_2) < 2\}} \geq 4k' = k \; \forall \; \underline{x} \in C$$

$$\Rightarrow I(0 < max(X_1, X_2) < 2) \geq k \; \forall \; \underline{x} \in C$$

The c.d.f. of $Y = max(X_1, X_2)$ is

$$F_2(y) = \left(\frac{y}{\theta}\right)^2 = \frac{y^2}{\theta^2}$$

$$\alpha = 0.05 = P(Reject\ H_0 \mid H_0) = P(Y \geq k \mid \theta_0 = 2)$$

$$= 1 - \frac{k^2}{4} \Rightarrow \frac{k^2}{4} = 0.95$$

$$\Rightarrow k^2 = 0.95 \times 4 = 3.8 \Rightarrow k \cong 1.9493$$

$$1 - \beta = P(Reject\ H_0 \mid H_1) = P(Y \geq 1.9493 \mid \theta_1 = 4)$$

$$= 1 - \frac{1.9493^2}{4^2} = 1 - 0.2375 = 0.7625$$

∴ **Answer is option (c).**

40. Explanation: (a), (d)

A six faced die whose i-th face is marked with dots, $i = 1,2,\ldots,6$.

In a single random throw of the die, let p_i, denote the probability that the obtained upper face has i dots, $i = 1,2,\ldots,6$.

The die is rolled 240 times independently and the following result is obtained

Face observed	1	2	3	4	5	6
Frequency	40	55	40	25	35	45

$H_0 : p_i = \frac{1}{6}$ $for\ i = 1,2,\ldots,6$; against $H_1 : p_i \neq \frac{1}{6}$ for at least one i; $i = 1,2,\ldots,6$

Under the null hypothesis the expected frequency is as follows

Face observed	1	2	3	4	5	6
Observed Frequency (O_i)	40	55	40	25	35	45
Expected Frequency (E_i)	40	40	40	40	40	40

The test statistic for the χ^2 goodness of fit is given by

$$W = \sum_{i=1}^{n} \frac{(O_i - E_i)^2}{E_i}$$

Note that under $H_0, W \sim \chi^2_{(5)}$

$$\therefore W_0 = \frac{(40-40)^2}{40} + \frac{(55-40)^2}{40} + \frac{(40-40)^2}{40} + \frac{(25-40)^2}{40} + \frac{(35-40)^2}{40} + \frac{(45-40)^2}{40}$$

$$= 0 + \frac{(15)^2}{40} + 0 + \frac{(-15)^2}{40} + \frac{(-5)^2}{40} + \frac{(5)^2}{40}$$

$$= \frac{225 + 225 + 25 + 25}{40} = \frac{500}{40} = \frac{25}{2} = 12.5$$

The critical region at α level of significance is given by Reject H_0 $if\ W_0 > \chi^2_{5;\alpha}$

$\because W_0 = 12.5 > \chi^2_{5;0.05} = 11.07$ thus the test rejects H_0 at 5% level of significance.

$\because W_0 = 12.5 < \chi^2_{5;0.01} = 15.09$ thus the test fails to reject H_0 at 1% level of significance.

41. Explanation: (a)

The probability density function (PDF) of a Gamma $(\alpha, 1)$ distribution is:

$$f(x;\alpha) = \frac{x^{\alpha-1}e^{-x}}{\Gamma(\alpha)}, x > 0.$$

For the sample, the likelihood function under H_0 and H_1 is:

$$L(1) = \prod_{i=1}^{n} \frac{X_i^0 e^{-X_i}}{\Gamma(1)} = e^{-\sum X_i}.$$

$$L(2) = \prod_{i=1}^{n} \frac{X_i e^{-X_i}}{\Gamma(2)} = \prod_{i=1}^{n} X_i e^{-X_i}.$$

The likelihood ratio is:

$$\Lambda = \frac{L(1)}{L(2)} = \frac{e^{-\sum X_i}}{\prod_{i=1}^{n} X_i e^{-\sum X_i}} = \frac{1}{\prod_{i=1}^{n} X_i}.$$

To construct the **most powerful test**, we compare Λ to a threshold k, leading to:

$$\frac{1}{\prod_{i=1}^{n} X_i} \leq k.$$

Rearranging, we get:

$$\prod_{i=1}^{n} X_i \geq C,$$

where $C = 1/k$ is an appropriate constant. This means the rejection region is:

$$\prod_{i=1}^{n} X_i > C.$$

Thus, the correct answer is **option (a):** $\prod_{i=1}^{n} X_i > C$.

42. Explanation: (a)

Analysis of $1 - \phi$:

- The test $1 - \phi$ represents the complement of the original test. This means:
  If ϕ rejects H_0, then $1 - \phi$ accepts it.
  If ϕ accepts H_0, then $1 - \phi$ rejects it.

Size and Power for $1 - \phi$:

- Size of $1 - \phi$: The size when testing H_1 against H_0 is:Size$(1 - \phi) = 1 -$ Power$(\phi) = 1 - 0.4 = 0.6$.
- Power of $1 - \phi$: The power when testing H_1 against H_0 is:Power$(1 - \phi) =$ Size$(\phi) = 0.05$.

Evaluation of Statements:

1. Statement (a): $(1 - \phi)$ is a most powerful test at level 0.6 for testing H_1 against H_0.
   True: This statement is correct based on our analysis.
2. Statement (b): $(1 - \phi)$ is a most powerful test at level 0.4 for testing H_1 against H_0.
   False: The level is actually 0.6.
3. Statement (c): $(1 - \phi)$ is a most powerful test at level 0.05 for testing H_1 against H_0.
   False: The level is again incorrect; it is not at level 0.05.
4. Statement (d): $(1 - \phi)$ is NOT a most powerful test for testing H_1 against H_0 at any level.

False: This statement is incorrect because we established that it is indeed a most powerful test at level 0.6.

Thus, option (a) is correct.

43. Explanation: (a), (c), (d)

The likelihood function for a Uniform$(0, \theta)$ distribution is:

$$L(\theta) = \prod_{i=1}^{3} \frac{1}{\theta} 1_{\{0 \le X_i \le \theta\}}$$

Since the sample is independent, we rewrite:

$$L(\theta) = \theta^{-3} 1_{\{\max(X_1, X_2, X_3) \le \theta\}}$$

The maximum likelihood estimator (MLE) of θ is:

$\hat{\theta} = \max(X_1, X_2, X_3)$.

The likelihood ratio test (LRT) is based on:

$$\lambda = \frac{L(3)}{\sup_{\theta} L(\theta)}$$

From the likelihood function, we maximize $L(\theta)$ by setting $\theta = \hat{\theta}$, so:

$$\lambda = \frac{3^{-3} 1_{\{\max(X_1, X_2, X_3) \le 3\}}}{\hat{\theta}^{-3} 1_{\{\max(X_1, X_2, X_3) \le \hat{\theta}\}}}$$

$$\lambda = \left(\frac{3}{\hat{\theta}}\right)^3 1_{\{\hat{\theta} \le 3\}}$$

The rejection region is determined by the significance level 0.001.

For a Uniform[0, θ] sample, the distribution of $\max(X_1, X_2, X_3)$ is:

$$P(\max(X_1, X_2, X_3) \le x) = \left(\frac{x}{\theta}\right)^3, 0 \le x \le \theta$$

Thus, under $H_0: \theta = 3$, the test statistic follows:

$$P(\max(X_1, X_2, X_3) \ge c | H_0) = 1 - \left(\frac{c}{3}\right)^3.$$

For size $\alpha = 0.001$, we solve:

$$1 - \left(\frac{c}{3}\right)^3 = 0.001$$

$$\left(\frac{c}{3}\right)^3 = 0.999$$

$$c = 3 \times 0.999^{1/3} \approx 2.997$$

Thus, we reject H_0 if:

$\max(X_1, X_2, X_3) > 2.997$ or $\max(X_1, X_2, X_3) < d$

By symmetry, for the lower bound d, we solve:

$$\left(\frac{d}{3}\right)^3 = 0.001$$

$$d = 3 \times 0.001^{1/3} \approx 0.3$$

Thus, we reject H_0 if:

$\max(X_1, X_2, X_3) > 2.997$ or $\max(X_1, X_2, X_3) < 0.3$

Evaluating the Statements

1. If $\max(X_1, X_2, X_3) = 3.1$, then H_0 is rejected.
   Since $3.1 > 2.997$, we reject H_0.
   True.
2. If $\max(X_1, X_2, X_3) = 1.3$, then H_0 is rejected.
   Since $1.3 > 0.3$ and $1.3 < 2.997$, we do not reject H_0.
   False.
3. If $\max(X_1, X_2, X_3) = 0.1$, then H_0 is rejected.
   Since $0.1 < 0.3$, we reject H_0.
   True.
4. The power of the test at $\theta = 0.3$ is 1.
   The power is:
   $P(\text{Reject } H_0 | \theta = 0.3)$.

- At $\theta = 0.3$, the probability that $\max(X_1, X_2, X_3) \le 0.3$ is:

$$P(\max(X_1, X_2, X_3) \le 0.3 | \theta = 0.3) = \left(\frac{0.3}{0.3}\right)^3 = 1$$

- Since $\max(X_1, X_2, X_3)$ cannot exceed 0.3 when $\theta = 0.3$, we always reject H_0, meaning the power is 1. True.

Thus, options (a), (c) and (d) are correct.

44. Explanation: (a), (c), (d)

The given joint probability density function (PDF) is:

$$f(x, y) = \begin{cases} e^{-y}, & 0 < x < y < \infty \\ 0, & \text{otherwise.} \end{cases}$$

To find the marginal density of Y_k, we integrate out x:

$$f_Y(y) = \int_0^y e^{-y} dx = y e^{-y}, y > 0.$$

Thus, Y_k follows a Gamma(2,1) distribution, i.e., $Y_k \sim$ Gamma(2,1), which has the density:

$$f_Y(y) = y e^{-y}, y > 0.$$

Now, we analyze N_n, which counts the number of Y_k's that satisfy $Y_k \ge 2$. The probability of this event is:

$$P(Y_k \ge 2) = \int_2^{\infty} y e^{-y} dy.$$

Using integration by parts, we evaluate:

$$P(Y_k \ge 2) = \int_2^{\infty} y e^{-y} dy.$$

Let $u = y$, so that $du = dy$, and let $dv = e^{-y} dy$, so that $v = -e^{-y}$. Using integration by parts, $\int y e^{-y} dy = -y e^{-y} + \int e^{-y} dy = -y e^{-y} - e^{-y} = -(y+1)e^{-y}$.

Evaluating from 2 to ∞,

$$P(Y_k \ge 2) = -[(y+1)e^{-y}]_2^{\infty}.$$

Since the term vanishes at infinity, we obtain:

$$P(Y_k \ge 2) = (2+1)e^{-2} = 3e^{-2}.$$

Thus, N_n follows a Binomial(n, $3e^{-2}$) distribution.

We analyze each statement using probability limit theorems.

Statement (a): $\frac{N_n}{3n}$ converges to e^{-2} almost surely.

Using the Strong Law of Large Numbers (SLLN) for Bernoulli trials, $\frac{N_n}{n} \to 3e^{-2}$ almost surely.

Thus,

$$\frac{N_n}{3n} = \frac{N_n}{n} \cdot \frac{1}{3} \to \frac{3e^{-2}}{3} = e^{-2} \text{ almost surely.}$$

Statement (a) is true.

Statement (b): N_n converges to e^{-2} in probability.

Since $N_n \sim$ Binomial$(n, 3e^{-2})$, we divide by n and apply the Weak Law of Large Numbers (WLLN):

$\frac{N_n}{n} \to 3e^{-2}$ in probability.

Since N_n itself grows linearly with n, it does not converge to a constant e^{-2}. Hence, Statement 2 is false.

Statement (c): $\frac{N_n}{n}$ converges to $3e^{-2}$ in distribution.

From the WLLN, we already established:

$\frac{N_n}{n} \to 3e^{-2}$ in probability.

Since convergence in probability implies convergence in distribution,

Statement (c) is true.

Statement (d): Central Limit Theorem (CLT) Analysis

Applying the Central Limit Theorem (CLT) for $N_n \sim$ Binomial (n, p):

$\frac{N_n - np}{\sqrt{np(1-p)}} \to \mathcal{N}(0,1)$.

Substituting $p = 3e^{-2}$,

$\frac{N_n - 3ne^{-2}}{\sqrt{3ne^{-2}(1-3e^{-2})}} \to \mathcal{N}(0,1)$.

Thus, the given formulation matches the CLT form.

Statement (d) is true.

45. Explanation: (b)

Let $Z_i = \ln X_i$. From the pdf $f(x \mid \theta) = 2^\theta \theta x^{-(\theta+1)}, x > 2$, we have

$Z_i - \ln 2 \sim$ Exp(rate $= \theta$), so ; $S := \sum_{i=1}^{n} Z_i - n\ln 2 \sim$ Gamma(n,rate $= \theta$).

Hence, under (θ),

$2\theta S \sim \chi^2_{2n}$.

For testing $H_0: \theta = 1$ vs $H_1: \theta > 1$, the likelihood ratio is decreasing in $\sum \ln X_i$, so the UMP test rejects for small $\sum \ln X_i$.

Under H_0 ($\theta = 1$),

$2(\sum_{i=1}^{n} \ln X_i - n\ln 2) \sim \chi^2_{2n}$.

A size-α lower-tail rejection region is

$2(\sum_{i=1}^{n} \ln X_i - n\ln 2) < \chi^2_{2n,,1-\alpha}$,

i.e. $\sum_{i=1}^{n} \ln X_i ;<; \frac{1}{2}, \chi^2_{2n,,1-\alpha} + n\ln 2$,

which is exactly option (b).

Correct Answer: b.

46. Explanation: (a), (b), (c)

The model is the shifted exponential

$f(x \mid \theta) = \theta e^{-\theta(x-1)}, x > 1, \theta > 0$

Likelihood for a single observation (x>1) is $L(\theta) = \theta e^{-\theta(x-1)}$

(a) $\hat{\theta} = \arg\max_{\theta>0} \ln L(\theta)). (\ln L(\theta) = \ln\theta - \theta(x-1)), so (d/d\theta(\ln L) = 1/\theta - (x-1) = 0) gives (\hat{\theta} = 1/(x-1)$

(b) The maximum likelihood value is $L(\hat{\theta}) = \frac{1}{x-1}, e^{-(1/(x-1))(x-1)} = \frac{e^{-1}}{x-1}$

So (2) is true.

(c) The likelihood ratio statistic (usual form $\lambda = L(1)/\sup_\theta L(\theta)$) equals

$$\lambda = \frac{L(1)}{L(\hat{\theta})} = \frac{1 \cdot e^{-1(x-1)}}{(e^{-1}/(x-1))} = (x-1)e^{2-x}$$

Reject for small (\lambda), i.e. $(x-1)e^{2-x} < k$. Multiplying both sides by e^{-2} gives an equivalent form $(x-1)e^{-x} < k'$ for some (k'>0). Thus (c) is true.

(d) Examine $\lambda(x) = (x-1)e^{2-x}$. Its derivative sign changes: $\lambda'(x)/\lambda(x) = \frac{1}{x-1} - 1 = \frac{2-x}{x-1}$ So λ increases on ((1,2)) and decreases on $(2, \infty)$; it attains its maximum (1) at (x=2) and tends to (0) as $x \downarrow 1$ or $x \to \infty$. Thus the LR critical region $\lambda <$ const is generally a union of a left interval near (1) and a right tail, not a single one-sided region ({x>c}). Hence (d) is false.

Final: (a), (b), (c) true; (d) false.

47. Explanation: (d)

(a) Max (T) occurs when the 9 (Y)-observations occupy the largest 9 ranks 8,9, ... ,16.

$T_{\max} = \sum_{r=8}^{16} r = \frac{(8+16)\cdot 9}{2} = 108$, not (115). So (a) false.

(b) If $\mu > \theta$ then the (X)-sample is stochastically larger than the (Y)-sample, so the (Y)-ranks tend to be **small**. Thus evidence for $\mu > \theta$ corresponds to **small** values of (T) (left tail), not large values. So a right-tailed test is inappropriate. (b) false.

(c) Under H_0 the 9 (Y)-observations get a random 9-subset of the ranks 1, ... ,16, so

$$E(T) = 9 \cdot \frac{1 + 2 + \cdots + 16}{16} = 9 \cdot \frac{16+1}{2} = 9 \cdot \frac{17}{2} = \frac{153}{2} = 76.5,$$

not (76). So (c) false.

(d) Under (H_0) all rank assignments are equally likely. $P(R_1 = 1) = 1/16$; given that, $P(R_2 = 16 \mid R_1 = 1) = 1/15$. Hence $P(R_1 = 1, R_2 = 16) = 1/(16 \cdot 15) = 1/240$. So (d) true.

48. Explanation: (c)

We need the probability of Type-I error (α), which is the probability of rejecting H_0 when H_0 is true.

Type-I Error Definition

$$\alpha = P(\text{Reject } H_0 \mid H_0 \text{ is true})$$

The rejection rule is $X_1 + X_2 > \frac{4}{5}$

Hence, $\alpha = P\left(X_1 + X_2 > \frac{4}{5} \mid \theta = 1\right)$

Distribution under H_0

Under $H_0: \theta = 1$

$$X_1, X_2 \sim U(0,1)$$

The PDF is

$$f(x_i \mid \theta = 1) = \begin{cases} 1, & 0 \le x_i \le 1 \\ 0, & \text{otherwise} \end{cases}$$

Since X_1 and X_2 are independent,

$$f(x_1, x_2) = f(x_1)f(x_2) = 1$$

for

$$0 \le x_1 \le 1, 0 \le x_2 \le 1$$

Thus the joint distribution is uniform over the unit square.

We need $P\left(X_1 + X_2 > \frac{4}{5}\right)$

It is easier to first compute $P\left(X_1 + X_2 \le \frac{4}{5}\right)$

The line $x_1 + x_2 = \frac{4}{5}$ intersects the axes at $\left(\frac{4}{5}, 0\right), \left(0, \frac{4}{5}\right)$ inside the unit square, this forms a right-angled triangle.

Area of this triangle: Area $= \frac{1}{2} \times \frac{4}{5} \times \frac{4}{5} = \frac{1}{2} \times \frac{16}{25} = \frac{8}{25}$

Thus, $P\left(X_1 + X_2 \le \frac{4}{5}\right) = \frac{8}{25}$

Type-I Error:

$\alpha = P\left(X_1 + X_2 > \frac{4}{5}\right) = 1 - \frac{8}{25} = \frac{17}{25}$

49. Explanation: (a), (b), (d)

Likelihood Ratio Test for Exponential Distribution

$X_1, \dots, X_{15} \overset{iid}{\sim}$ Exp(σ), testing:

$H_0: \sigma \le 1$ vs $H_1: \sigma > 1$ at level $\alpha = 0.1$

Deriving the LRT

Likelihood Function:

$L(\sigma) = \prod_{i=1}^{15} \frac{1}{\sigma} e^{-x_i/\sigma} = \sigma^{-15} \exp\left(-\frac{\sum x_i}{\sigma}\right)$

MLE: $\hat{\sigma}_{MLE} = \bar{X} = \frac{1}{15}\sum_{i=1}^{15} X_i$

LRT Statistic: $\lambda = \frac{\sup_{\sigma \le 1} L(\sigma)}{\sup_{\sigma > 0} L(\sigma)}$

Denominator: $L(\hat{\sigma}) = \bar{X}^{-15}e^{-15}$

Numerator:

If $\bar{X} \le 1$: **MLE falls in** H_0 **region, so sup is** $L(\bar{X}) \to \lambda = 1$

If $\bar{X} > 1$: **sup over** $\sigma \le 1$ **is at** $\sigma = 1$, **so** $L(1) = e^{-15\bar{X}}$

When $\bar{X} > 1$: $\lambda = \frac{e^{-15\bar{X}}}{\bar{X}^{-15}e^{-15}} = \bar{X}^{15}e^{-15(\bar{X}-1)}$

Reject H_0 **when** λ **is small, i.e.,** $\bar{X}$ **is large.**

The test statistic: since $X_i \sim \text{Exp}(\sigma)$:

$\frac{2}{\sigma}\sum_{i=1}^{15} X_i = \frac{2 \cdot 15\bar{X}}{\sigma} = \frac{30\bar{X}}{\sigma} \sim \chi^2_{30}$

Under H_0 **boundary** ($\sigma = 1$): $30\bar{X} \sim \chi^2_{30}$

Reject H_0 **when** $\bar{X}$ **is large, i.e., when** $30\bar{X} > \chi^2_{30,0.1}$

$\chi^2_{30,0.1} = 40.256$ **(given:** $P(W > 40.256) = 0.1$**)**

Critical Region: $30\bar{X} > 40.256 \implies \bar{X} > \frac{40.256}{30} = 1.3419$

Decision Rule: Reject $H_0 \iff \bar{X} > 1.3419$

Evaluating Each Statement

Statement	$\bar{X}$	$30\bar{X}$	vs 40.256	Decision
1	0.6	18.0	< 40.256	Do NOT reject
2	1.6	48.0	> 40.256	Reject
3	1.3	39.0	< 40.256	Do NOT reject
4	1.2	36.0	< 40.256	Do NOT reject

Correct answer: statements: 1, 2 and 4

NON-PARAMETRIC

CHAPTER 7

(JUNE 2012)

1. Suppose that we have i.i.d. observations $X_1, X_2 \ldots X_n$ with a normal distribution. Suppose further that we have an independent set of observations $Y_1, Y_2 \ldots Y_n$ which are also lid, with the same normal distribution. Let R_X = the sum of the ranks of the X's when they are ranked in the combined set of X and Y values, and R_y = the sum of the ranks of the Y's in the combined set. Then
(a) P $(R_X - R_Y > 0) > \frac{1}{2}$ (b) P $(R_Y - R_X > 0) > \frac{1}{2}$
(c) E (R_X) = E (R_Y) (d) $P(R_Y - R_X) = 1$

(JUNE 2012)

2. Let $X_1, X_2, \ldots, X_n$ be i.i.d. observations from a distribution with continuous probability density function f which is symmetric around θ i.e. $f(x-\theta) = f(\theta - x)$ for all real x. Consider the test $H_0: \theta = 0$ vs $H_A: \theta > 0$ and the sign test statistic

$$S_n = \sum_{i=1}^{n} sign(X_i) \text{ where sign } (x) = \begin{cases} 1, if\ x > 0 \\ 0, if\ x = 0. \\ -1, if\ x < 0 \end{cases}$$

Let z_a be the upper 100 (1-a)th percentile of the standard normal distribution where $0 < a < 1$. Which of the following is/are correct?
(a) If $\theta = 0$, then $\lim_{n\to\infty} P\{S_n > \sqrt{n} z_a\} = 1$
(b) If $\theta = 0$, then $\lim_{n\to\infty} P\{S_n > \sqrt{n} z_a\} = \alpha$
(c) If $\theta > 0$, then $\lim_{n\to\infty} P\{S_n > \sqrt{n} z_a\} = 1$
(d) If $\theta > 0$, then $\lim_{n\to\infty} P\{S_n > \sqrt{n} z_a\} = \alpha$

(DEC. 2013)

3. Let $X_1, X_2, \ldots, X_m$ and $Y_1, Y_2, \ldots, Y_n$ be two independent random samples from two continuous distribution F_1 and F_2 respectively. Define $R_i = Rank(X_i), i = 1,2,\ldots, m$ and $S_j = Rank(Y_j), j = 1,2,\ldots, n$ in the combined sample $(X_1, X_2, \ldots, X_m, Y_1, Y_2, \ldots, Y_n)$. Also define $I(U > V) = \begin{cases} 1\ if\ U > V \\ 0\ if\ U \le V. \end{cases}$
Which of the following test statistic is/are distribution free under $H_0: F_1(x) = F_2(x)$ for all x?
(a) $\sum_{i=1}^{m} R_i$, (b) $\sum_{j=1}^{n} S_j$,
(c) $\sum_{i=1}^{m}\sum_{j=1}^{n} I(X_i > Y_j)$, (d) $\sum_{i=1}^{m}\sum_{j=1}^{n} I(S_j > R_i)$,

(JUNE 2014)

4. Let $X_1, X_2, \ldots X_n$ be independent and identically distributed random variables with common continuous distribution function F, which is symmetric about the median μ. Consider the problem of testing $H_0: \mu = 0$ against $H_1: \mu > 0$. Define
R_i^+ = rank of $|X_i|$ among $|X_1|, |X_2|, \ldots, |X_n|, i = 1, 2, \ldots, n$
L = sum of the $R_i^+ s$, for which $X_i < 0, i = 1, 2, \ldots, n$
G = sum of the $R_i^+ s$, for which $X_i > 0, i = 1, 2, \ldots, n$
Which of the following statements are true?
(a) Left tailed test based on L is appropriate for testing H_0 against H_1
(b) Right tailed test based on G is appropriate for testing H_0 against H_1
(c) Maximum possible value of L is $n(n+1)$
(d) $E_{H_1}(L+G) = \frac{n(n+1)}{2}$

(DEC. 2014)

5. A and B are two methods to determine the levels of mercury in fish. In a study to compare A and B, amount of mercury was measured using both methods on $n = 12$ fish. Let $(X_1, Y_1), \ldots, (X_n, Y_n)$ be those measurements, with $X_i's$ standing for method A and $Y_i's$ for method B. It should · be noted that the size of error in measurement can depend on the amount of mercury, so the observations $(X_1, Y_1), \ldots, (X_n, Y_n)$ may not be identically distributed. To test H_0: There is no difference between methods A and B
Versus
H_1: Method B typically gives a larger reading than method A, which of the following test statistics are appropriate?
(a) Number of pairs $(X_j > X_i)$, with $(Y_j > X_i), 1 \le i \le n; 1 \le j \le n$
(b) Sum of the ranks of the Y observations in the combined sample
(c) Number of the pairs (X_i, Y_i) with $(Y_j > X_i)$, $1 \le i \le n$
(d) $\overline{Y} - \overline{X}$

(JUNE 2015)

6. To check whether a premium version of petrol gives better fuel efficiency a random sample of 10 cars of a single model were tested with both premium and standard petrol. Let the mileages obtained be denoted by $(X_1, X_1) \ldots, (X_{10}, X_{10})$ where X_i denotes the mileage from standard and Y_i from the premium for the ith car. We want to test H_0: There is no difference in fuel efficiency between the two version of petrol
Versus
H_0: Premium petrol gives better fuel efficiency Let $D_i = Y_i - X_i, \overline{D} = \overline{X} - \overline{Y}, S_i$ = Rank of D_i when $|D_i|$ are ordered. It is felt that fuel efficieny measurement are not normally distributed and hence a non-parametric test is to be proposed. Then which of the following can be considered suitable for this purpose?
(a) $\hat{Y} - \hat{X}$

(b) Numbers of positive $D_i's$
(c) Sum of S_i corresponding to positive D_i
(d) $\frac{\bar{D}}{\sqrt{\Sigma(D_i-D)^2}}$

(DEC. 2016)

7. Suppose $X_1, X_2, \dots, X_m$ are independent and identically distributed with common continuous distribution function $F(x)$ and $Y_1, Y_2, \dots, Y_n$ are independent and identically distributed with common continuous distribution function $(x-\theta)$. Also suppose X_i and Y_j are independent for all $, j$. Consider the problem of testing $H_0: \theta = 0$ against $H_1: \theta > 0$.
Let $R_\alpha = Rank\ (X_\alpha), \alpha = 1,2,\dots,m$ and $R_{m+\beta} = Rank\ (Y_\beta), \beta = 1,2,\dots,n$ among $.X_1, X_2, \dots, X_m, Y_1, Y_2, \dots, Y_n$
Define $U = \sum_{\alpha=1}^{m}\sum_{\beta=1}^{n}\psi(X_\alpha, X_\beta)$ where,
$\psi(a,b) = 1$ if $a < b$
$= 0$ if $a \geq b$
Which of the following are true?
(a) $P[R_1 = n+m, R_2 = n+m-1, R_3 = n+m-2, \dots, R_{m+n} = 1] = \frac{1}{(m+n)!}$ under H_0
(b) U and $\sum_{a=1}^{m} R_a$ are linearly related.
(c) $E(U) = \frac{mn}{2}$ under H_0 .
(d) Right tailed test based on U is appropriate for testing H_0 against H_1 .

(JUNE 2018)

8. Consider a two-sample location problem with 6 and 8 observations from the first and second populations, respectively. Suppose that the distribution of the ith population is $F(x;\theta_i) = F(x-\theta_i); i = 1,2,$ where F is a continuous distribution function with the median at 0. Define T as the sum of the ranks of the second sample in the combined sample. For the problem of testing $H_0: \theta_1 = \theta_2$ against $H_1: \theta_1 > \theta_2$, which of the following statements are true when all observations are independent?
(a) T is distribution free under H_1
(b) It is appropriate to reject H_0 when T is small
(c) Observed value of T cannot be 85
(d) $E(T) = 60$ under H_0

(NOV. 2020)

9. Consider 35 i.i.d observations $X_1, X_2, \dots, X_{15}$ and $Y_1, Y_2, \dots, Y_{20}$ Let R be the Wilcoxon's rank sum statistic based on the ranks of the $X's$ in the combined sample. Then the expected value of R is
(a) 270 (b) 300
(c) 360.5 (d) 330.5

(JUNE 2021)

10. A newly developed algorithm for random number generation needs to be tested. The first step is to check whether the sequence of numbers generated can be considered a random sample from the uniform distribution on the interval (0, 1). Which of the following is an appropriate nonparametric test?
(a) Wilcoxon signed rank test
(b) Sign test
(c) Paired t test
(d) Kolmogorov-Smirnov test

(JULY 2024)

11. Observations on the shear strength of concrete from 5 randomly selected structures are given below:

Structure	1	2	3	4	5
Shear strength	1718.4	1787.4	2562.3	2356.9	2153.2

The null hypothesis H_0 that the median shear strength is 2000 units is tested against the alternative hypothesis H_1 that the median shear strength is greater than 2000 units at 5% level of significance. Which of the following statements are true?
(a) p-value of the sign test is 0.04
(b) H_0 is NOT rejected at 5% level of significance by the sign test
(c) The observed value of Wilcoxon signed rank test statistic W^+ is equal to 10
(d) If $P_{H_0}(W^+ \geq 14) = 0.06$, then H_0 is rejected at 5% level of significance by the Wilcoxon signed rank test

(FEB. 2025)

12. Let $X_1, X_2, \dots, X_5$ be a random sample of size 5 from an absolutely continuous distribution having median M. Let S denote the number of $X_i's$ greater than 0. For testing $H_0: M = 0$ against $H_1: M > 0$, let
$$\phi(\underline{X}) = \begin{cases} 1, & if\ S > c \\ v, & if\ S = c \\ 0, & if\ S < c \end{cases}$$
be a test of size $\alpha = 0.05$, where $v \in [0,1]$ and $c \in \{-1,0,\dots,5\}$ are fixed constants. Then $c + v$ equals
(a) $\frac{11}{25}$ (b) $\frac{49}{6}$
(c) $\frac{103}{25}$ (d) $\frac{53}{6}$

(FEB. 2025)

13. Let X_1, X_2, X_3 be a random sample of size 3 from an absolutely continuous distribution that is symmetric about 0. For $i = 1,2,3$, let R_i denote the rank of $|X_i|$ among $|X_1|, |X_2|$ and $|X_3|$. If $T^+ = \sum_{i=1,X_i>0}^{3} R_i$ is the Wilcoxon signed-rank statistic, then which of the following statements are true?
(a) $P(T^+ = 3) = \frac{1}{4}$ (b) $Var(T^+) = \frac{7}{2}$
(c) $P(T^+ > 3) = \frac{5}{8}$ (d) $P(T^+ > 4) = \frac{1}{8}$

(Dec 2025)

14. Let $X_1, X_2, \dots, X_7$ be a random sample drawn from a continuous distribution with unknown unique median M. The null hypothesis $H_0: M = 2$ is tested against the alternative $H_1: M > 2$ at level of significance 0.05 using the right-tailed test based on the Sign test statistic K, which is the number of observations in the sample greater than 2. If the observed sample is -3, -6, 1, 9, 4, 10, 12, which of the following statements are true?
(a) H_0 is rejected
(b) The p-value of the test is greater than 0.01
(c) Under $H_0, E(K) = 3.5$

(d) If $X_{(i)}$ denotes the i-th smallest observation of the sample, then $[X_{(2)}, X_{(6)}]$ is a confidence interval for M with confidence coefficient at least 0.95.

Answer Key						
1	2	3	4	5	6	7
c	b,c	a,b,c,d	a,b,d	c	b,c	a,b,c,d
8	9	11	12	13	14	
*	a	b	c	a,b	b,c	

:: Explanations ::

1. **Explanation: (c)**
Expected value of the sum of rank of X is equal to the expected value of sum of rank of Y's
i.e., $E(R_x) = E(R_y)$
So, option (c) is correct

2. **Explanation: (b), (c)**
$X_1, X_2, .., X_n$ be iid observations from a distribution with continuous pdf f which is symmetric around θ
i.e., $f(x-\theta) = f(\theta - x)\ \forall x \in \mathbb{R}$
Test: $H_\theta: \theta = 0$ against $H_1: \theta > 0$
$S_n = \sum_{i=1}^{n} sign\,(X_i)$
Where, $Sign\,(x) = \begin{cases} 1 & x > 0 \\ 0 & x = 0 \\ -1 & x < 0 \end{cases}$
For $\theta = 0$, $E(X_i) = 0 \Rightarrow E(S_n) = 0$
$Var(X_i) = 1 \Rightarrow Var(S_n) = n$
For $\theta = 0$, $\lim_{n\to\infty} P\left[S_n > \sqrt{n}\,Z_\alpha\right] = \lim_{n\to\infty} P\left[\frac{S_n - 0}{\sqrt{n}} > \frac{\sqrt{n}Z_\alpha}{\sqrt{n}}\right]$
$= P(Z > Z_\alpha) = \alpha$
For $\theta > 0$ $E(X_i) = \theta \Rightarrow E(S_n) = n\theta$
$Var(X_i) \Rightarrow Var\,(S_n) = n$
For $\theta > 0$, $\lim_{n\to\infty} P\left[S_n > \sqrt{n}\,Z_\alpha\right] = \lim_{n\to\infty} P\left[\frac{S_n - n\theta}{\sqrt{n}} > \frac{\sqrt{n}Z_\alpha - n\theta}{\sqrt{n}}\right] = P(Z > -\infty) = 1$
So, option (b) and (c) are correct.

3. **Explanation: (a), (b), (c), (d)**

4. **Explanation: (a), (b) (d)**

5. **Explanation: (c)**
$n = 12$ fish
H_0 : There is no difference between methods A and B
Versus
H_1 : Method B typically given a larger reading than method A
The appropriate test statistic is
$Y_i > X_i$ $\quad i = 1, 2, \dots, n$
So, option (c) is correct

6. **Explanation: (b), (c)**

7. **Explanation: (a), (b), (c) and (d)**
Here U *is* U- Statistics and $\sum_{\alpha=1}^{m} R_\alpha$ is Sum of Ranks of X observations
They are linearly related
Also, $E(U) = \frac{mn}{2}$ Under H_0
Here, $\theta > 0$; So test is right tailed based on U

8. **Explanation: (*)**

9. **Explanation: (a)**
Let N iid observations $X_1, X_2 \dots X_n$ and $Y_1, Y_2 \dots Y_m$. Let R be Wilcoxon rank sum statistic based on the ranks of the X`s in the combined sample. Then
$E(R) = \frac{n(n+m+1)}{2}\ Van\,(R) = \frac{nm\,(n+m+1)}{12}$
When $N = n + m$ and given that $N = 35, n = 15, m = 20$
$E(R) = \frac{n(n+m+1)}{2} = \frac{15(15+20+1)}{2} = 270$
$V(R) = \frac{mn(n+m+1)}{12} = \frac{15\times20(15+20+1)}{12} = 900$
Option (a) is correct

10. **Explanation: (d)**
Kolmogorov-Smirov Test is used to decide if a sample comes from a population with a specific distribution.
So, option (d) is correct

11. **Explanation: (b)**
Observations on the shear strength of concrete from 5 randomly selected structures are given below:

Structure	1	2	3	4	5
Shear strength	1718.4	1787.4	2562.3	2356.9	2153.2

The null hypothesis H_0 that the median shear strength is 2000 units is tested against the alternative hypothesis H_1 that the median shear strength is greater than 2000 units at 5% level of significance.
The rank given to above data is as follows. While giving the signs to following ranks the observations less than the median given under the null hypothesis are given negative sign while the observations which are greater than the median given in the null hypothesis are given positive sign.

Structure	1	2	3	4	5
Shear strength	1718.4	1787.4	2562.3	2356.9	2153.2
Ranks	1	2	5	4	3
Signed Rank	-1	-2	+5	+4	+3

The test statistic is given by
$$W^+ = \sum_{i=1}^{5} (positive\ rank) = 5 + 4 + 3 = 12$$
$$E(W^+) = \frac{n(n+1)}{4} = \frac{5\times6}{4} = 7.5 \quad ; \quad Var(W^+) = \frac{n(n+1)(2n+1)}{24} = \frac{5\times6\times11}{24} = 13.75$$
$$Z^+ = \frac{(W^+ - E(W^+))}{\sqrt{Var(W^+)}} \sim N(0,1)$$
The critical value at α level of significance is given by $Z_{0.05} = 1.64485$
$$W^+ = 12 \Rightarrow Z^+ = \frac{(12-7.5)}{\sqrt{13.75}} = 1.21356 < 1.64485 = Z_{0.05}$$
Thus we fail to reject H_0 at 5% level of significance.
The p-value of the test is given by
$$p = P(Z > Z^+) = P(Z > 1.21356) = 0.11246$$
Here in option (4) we have given a p-value as

$P_{H_0}(W^+ > 14) = 0.06 > 0.05 = \alpha$

$\Rightarrow$ the test fails to reject H_0.

12. Explanation: (c)

Under $H_0: M = 0$, each X_i has a probability of 0.5 of being greater than 0. Thus, S follows a binomial distribution with parameters $n = 5$ and $p = 0.5$:

$$S \sim \text{Binomial}(5,0.5)$$

The probability mass function of S is:

$$P(S = k) = \binom{5}{k}(0.5)^5, k = 0,1,\ldots,5.$$

The size of the test is $\alpha = 0.05$. This means:

$$P(\text{Reject } H_0 \mid H_0) = P(S > c) + v \cdot P(S = c) = 0.05.$$

We need to find c and v such that this equation holds.

Start by computing the cumulative probabilities for S:

$$P(S = 0) = \binom{5}{0}(0.5)^5 = \frac{1}{32},$$

$$P(S = 1) = \binom{5}{1}(0.5)^5 = \frac{5}{32},$$

$$P(S = 2) = \binom{5}{2}(0.5)^5 = \frac{10}{32},$$

$$P(S = 3) = \binom{5}{3}(0.5)^5 = \frac{10}{32},$$

$$P(S = 4) = \binom{5}{4}(0.5)^5 = \frac{5}{32},$$

$$P(S = 5) = \binom{5}{5}(0.5)^5 = \frac{1}{32}.$$

Now compute the cumulative probabilities:

$$P(S \geq 5) = P(S = 5) = \frac{1}{32} \approx 0.03125,$$

$$P(S \geq 4) = P(S = 4) + P(S = 5) = \frac{5}{32} + \frac{1}{32} = \frac{6}{32} \approx 0.1875,$$

$$P(S \geq 3) = P(S = 3) + P(S = 4) + P(S = 5) = \frac{10}{32} + \frac{5}{32} + \frac{1}{32} = \frac{16}{32} = 0.5.$$

To achieve $\alpha = 0.05$, we choose $c = 4$ because:

$$P(S \geq 5) = \frac{1}{32} \approx 0.03125 < 0.05,$$

$$P(S \geq 4) = \frac{6}{32} \approx 0.1875 > 0.05.$$

Thus, we set $c = 4$ and solve for v such that:

$$P(S > 4) + v \cdot P(S = 4) = 0.05.$$

$$\frac{1}{32} + v \cdot \frac{5}{32} = 0.05.$$

$$1 + 5v = 1.6.$$

$$5v = 0.6 \Rightarrow v = \frac{0.6}{5} = \frac{3}{25}.$$

We have $c = 4$ and $v = \frac{3}{25}$. Thus:

$$c + v = 4 + \frac{3}{25} = \frac{100}{25} + \frac{3}{25} = \frac{103}{25}$$

13. Explanation: (a), (b) For a given sample X_1, X_2, X_3, define:

- $|X_i|$ for $i = 1,2,3$, and assign ranks R_i (which take values in $\{1,2,3\}$).
- The Wilcoxon signed-rank statistic is:

$$T^+ = \sum_{i=1, X_i>0}^{3} R_i.$$

Since the distribution is symmetric, each X_i has an equal probability of being positive or negative.

Possible values of T^+ and their probabilities:

$$P(T^+ = 0) = \frac{1}{8}, P(T^+ = 1) = \frac{1}{8}, P(T^+ = 2) = \frac{1}{8}, P(T^+ = 3) = \frac{1}{4},$$

$$P(T^+ = 4) = \frac{1}{8}, P(T^+ = 5) = \frac{1}{8}, P(T^+ = 6) = \frac{1}{8}.$$

$P(T^+ = 3) = 1/4$ and so option (a) is correct.

Expected Value Calculation:

$$E(T^+) = \sum tP(T^+ = t)$$

$$= 0 \times \frac{1}{8} + 1 \times \frac{1}{8} + 2 \times \frac{1}{8} + 3 \times \frac{2}{8} + 4 \times \frac{1}{8} + 5 \times \frac{1}{8} + 6 \times \frac{1}{8} = 3$$

Expected Value of T^{+2}:

$$E(T^{+2}) = 0^2 \times \frac{1}{8} + 1^2 \times \frac{1}{8} + 2^2 \times \frac{1}{8} + 3^2 \times \frac{2}{8} + 4^2 \times \frac{1}{8} + 5^2 \times \frac{1}{8} + 6^2 \times \frac{1}{8} = \frac{25}{2}$$

Variance Calculation:

$\text{Var}(T^+) = E(T^{+2}) - (E(T^+))^2 = \frac{25}{2} - 3^2 = \frac{7}{2}$ and option (b) is correct.

Now, $P(T^+ > 3) = P(T^+ = 4) + P(T^+ = 5) + P(T^+ = 6) = \frac{1}{8} + \frac{1}{8} + \frac{1}{8} = \frac{3}{8}$.

So, option (c) is false.

Now, $P(T^+ > 4) = P(T^+ = 5) + P(T^+ = 6) = \frac{1}{8} + \frac{1}{8} = \frac{2}{8} = \frac{1}{4}$.

So, option (d) is false.

14. Explanation: (b), (c)

Sample: -3, -6, 1, 9, 4, 10, 12

Test statistic K = number of observations > 2

Values > 2 → 9, 4, 10, 12

So, $K = 4, n = 7$

Under H_0:

K ~ Binomial(n, 0.5)

Check rejection

Right-tailed test, $\alpha = 0.05$

Critical region for $n = 7$: K ≥ 6

Observed K = 4

So do not reject H_0

Statement 1 false

p-value

$$p = P(K \geq 4) = \frac{35 + 21 + 7 + 1}{128} = \frac{64}{128} = 0.5$$

Since 0.5 > 0.01

Statement 2 true

Expected value

E(X)=np

$E(K) = 7 \times 0.5 = 3.5$

Statement 3 true

Confidence interval

Ordered sample: $-6, -3, 1, 4, 9, 10, 12$

$[X_{(2)}, X_{(6)}] = [-3, 10]$

Coverage probability = 0.875 < 0.95

Statement 4 false

Correct answer: (2) and (3).

CHAPTER 8

BAYESIAN INFERENCE

(JUNE 2012)

1. Suppose $X_1, X_2, \dots\dots, X_{10}$ is a random sample from $N(\theta, \sigma^2), \sigma^2 = 10$. Consider the prior for $\theta, \theta \sim N(0, \tau^2), \tau^2 = 20$. Let $\bar{X} = \frac{1}{10}\sum_{i=1}^{10} X_i$. Then the mode $\hat{\theta}$ of the posterior distribution for θ satisfies:
(a) $\hat{\theta} = \bar{X}$
(b) $\hat{\theta} = \frac{20\bar{X}}{21}$
(c) $\hat{\theta} \leq \bar{X}$ if $\bar{X} \geq 0$
(d) $\hat{\theta} \geq \bar{X}$ if $\bar{X} \leq 0$

(DEC. 2012)

2. Let $X \sim$ Poisson (θ), the prior distribution of θ be exponential with median $\log_e 2$ and the loss function be squared error. Then which of the following are necessarily true?
(a) The posterior distribution is Gamma
(b) The prior is a conjugate prior
(c) The posterior mean is $\frac{(x+1)\log_e 2}{1+\log_e 2}$
(d) The Bayes estimator of θ is $\frac{X+1}{2}$

(JUNE 2013)

3. Let $X_1, X_2, \dots X_8$ be a random sample from the normal distribution with mean θ and variance 1, and let the prior distribution of θ be normal with mean 2 and variance 2. Define $\bar{X} = \frac{1}{8}\sum_{i=1}^{8} X_i$. Then which of the following statements are true?
(a) The prior is a conjugate prior
(b) Posterior mean of θ given $\bar{X}$ is $\frac{16\bar{X}+2}{17}$
(c) For absolute error loss, the Bayes estimator is $\frac{16\bar{X}+2}{17}$
(d) For squared error loss, the Bayes estimator is $\frac{16\bar{X}+2}{17}$

(DEC. 2014)

4. Suppose $X \sim$ Poisson $(\lambda), \lambda > 0$. Let the prior distribution of λ be $U(0, 1)$. if $X = 0$ is observed, then the posterior probability of the set $0 < \lambda \leq \frac{1}{2}$ is
(a) 0.5
(b) 1
(c) $\frac{e-\sqrt{e}}{e-1}$
(d) $\frac{1}{e}$

(DEC. 2014)

5. Let $X_1, X_2, \dots, X_n$ be independent and identically distributed Bernoulli (θ), where $0 < \theta < 1$ and $n > 1$. Let the prior density of θ be proportional to $\frac{1}{\sqrt{\theta(1-\theta)}}, 0 < \theta < 1$. Define $S = \sum_{i=1}^{n} X_i$. Then valid statements among the following are:
(a) The posterior mean of θ does not exist;
(b) The posterior mean of θ exists;
(c) The posterior mean of θ exists and it is larger than the maximum likelihood estimator for all values of S;
(d) The posterior mean of θ exists and it is larger than the maximum likelihood estimator for some values of S.

(DEC. 2014)

6. Let $X_1, X_2, \dots, X_n$ be a random sample from $N(\theta, \sigma^2)$ where $\sigma^2 > 0$ is known. Suppose θ has the Cauchy prior with density $\frac{1}{\pi}\left(1+\left(\frac{\theta-\mu}{\tau}\right)^2\right)^{-1}$, $-\infty < \theta < \infty$ with μ and τ known. Then with reference to the posterior distribution of θ
(a) the posterior mean does not exist and the posterior variance is ∞
(b) the posterior mean exists but the posterior variance is ∞
(c) the posterior variance is finite but the posterior mean does not exist
(d) the posterior mean exists but the posterior variance is finite

(DEC. 2015)

7. Let X_1, X_2, X_3 and X_4 be independent and identically distributed random variables with common distribution normal with mean μ and variance 2. If the prior distribution of μ is normal with mean 0 and variance $\frac{1}{2}$, then which of the following is true?
(a) The prior distribution is not a conjugate prior
(b) Posterior mode of μ given X_1, X_2, X_3 and X_4 is $\frac{\sum_{i=1}^{4} x_i}{8}$
(c) Posterior median of μ given X_1, X_2, X_3 and X_4 is $\frac{\sum_{i=1}^{4} x_i}{4}$
(d) Posterior variance of μ given X_1, X_2, X_3 and X_4 is $\left(\frac{\sum_{i=1}^{4} x_i}{4}\right)^2$

(JUNE 2016)

8. Let X be a random sample from a Poisson distribution with parameter λ. The parameter λ has a prior distribution $f(z)$; where
$$f(z) = \begin{cases} e^{-z}; z > 0 \\ 0, otherwise \end{cases}$$
Under the squared error loss function, which of the following statements are correct?
(a) The Bayes' estimator of e^{λ} is 2^{X+1}.
(b) The posterior mean of λ is $\frac{X+1}{2}$.
(c) The posterior distribution of λ is gamma.
(d) The Bayes' estimator of $e^{2\lambda}$ is $2^{2(X+1)}$

(DEC. 2016)

9. θ is the probability of obtaining a head in the toss of a coin. The coin is tossed three times and we record
$Y = 1$ if all the three tosses result in heads
$Y = 2$ if all the three tosses result in tails

$Y = 3$ otherwise

If the prior density θ of is Beta(α,β) , and $\hat{\theta}_i$ is the posterior mean of θ given $= i$, for $i = 1,2$, then

(a) $\hat{\theta}_1 > \hat{\theta}_2$

(b) $\hat{\theta}_1 < \hat{\theta}_2$

(c) The posterior density of θ given $Y = 3$ is a Beta density

(d) The posterior density ofθ given $Y = 3$ is not a Beta density

(JUNE 2017)

10. Let X be a random random sample from an exponential distribution with mean $1/\lambda$. If λ has a prior distribution with probability density function

$$g(\lambda) = \begin{cases} \lambda e^{-\lambda x} & ; \lambda > 0 \\ 0 & ; \lambda \le 0 \end{cases}$$

then the Bayes estimator of $1/\lambda$ with respect to the squared error loss function is

(a) $\frac{2}{X+1}$ (b) $\frac{1}{X}$

(c) X (d) $\frac{X+1}{2}$

(DEC. 2017)

11. Suppose we have a random sample of size$n(n \ge 1)$ from the density

$$f_\lambda(x) = \begin{cases} 2\lambda x e^{-\lambda x^2} & If x > 0 \\ 0, & Otherwise \end{cases}$$

If the prior of λ is an exponential distribution with mean 1, then which of the following statements are correct?

(a) the posterior distribution of λ is an exponential distribution

(b) the Bayes estimator of λ w.r.t. the squared error loss function exists and is unique

(c) the Bayes estimator of λ w.r.t. the absolute error loss function exists and is unique

(d) the Bayes estimator of $e^{-\lambda}$ of does not exist

(JUNE 2018)

12. Consider the problem of estimation of a parameter θ on the basis of X, where $X \sim N(\theta,1)$ and $-\infty < \theta < \infty$. Under squared error loss, X has uniformly smaller risk than that of kX, for

(a) $k < 0$ (b) $0 < k < 1$

(c) $k > 1$ (d) no value of k

(JUNE 2018)

13. We observe $X \sim$ Binomial (n,p), where $0 < p < 1$ is known but $n \in \{0,1,2,...\}$ is an unknown parameter. Note that when $n = 0, X$ is degenerate at 0. Suppose that n has a prior distribution which is Poisson with a known mean $\lambda > 0$. Which of the following statements are correct?

(a) The posterior distribution of n is also Poisson but with a mean different from λ

(b) If $X = 0$, the posterior distribution of n is Poisson with mean $\lambda(1-p)$

(c) The Bayes estimate of n has bias $(\lambda - n)/2$ when $p = 1/2$

(d) The Bayes estimate of n has larger variance than the variance of the unbiased estimate X/p

(JUNE 2018)

14. Consider a two-class classification problem, where the densities of the two competing classes are given by $f_1(x) = \begin{cases} 1 & \text{if } 0 \le x \le 1 \\ 0 & \text{otherwise} \end{cases}$ and $f_2(x) = \begin{cases} 2x & \text{if } 0 \le x \le 1 \\ 0 & \text{otherwise} \end{cases}$. Let π_1 and π_2 be the prior probabilities of these two classes. Now consider a classifier δ, which classifies an observation x to class 1 if $x < 1/2$ and to class 2 if $x \ge 1/2$.

(a) If $\pi_1 = \pi_2$, then δ is the Bayes classifier

(b) If $\pi_1 > \pi_2$, then δ is the Bayes classifier

(c) If $\pi_1 < \pi_2$, then δ is the Bayes classifier

(d) If $\pi_1 = \pi_2$, then the average probability of misclassification for δ is 3/8.

(DEC. 2018)

15. Suppose $Y|\theta - Possion\ (\theta), \theta > 0$ and prior density τ of 0 is given by $\tau(\theta) \propto e^{-\alpha 0}\theta^{\beta-1}$, where $a > 0$ and $\beta > 0$ are parameters. Which of the following are true?

(a) marginal distribution of Y is hypergeometric

(b) Posterior distribution of θ given $Y = y$ is Gamma

(c) τ is a conjugate prior

(d) Bayes estimate of θ for squared error loss function is $\frac{\beta+y}{\alpha+1}$

(JUNE 2019)

16. Consider a classification problem between two classes having densities $f_1(x) = 1; 0 \le x \le 1$ and $f_2(x) = 1 + \cos(2\pi x); 0 \le x \le 1$, respectively. Assume that the prior probabilities of the two classes are equal. Which of the following are true?

(a) The Bayes classifier classifies an observation to class-I if $x \in \left(\frac{1}{4},\frac{3}{4}\right)$

(b) A randomly chosen observation from class-I is misclassified with probability $\frac{1}{2}$

(c) A randomly chosen observation from class-2 is misclassified with probability $\frac{\pi-2}{2\pi}$

(d) The average misclassification probability of the Bayes Classifier is $\frac{\pi-1}{2\pi}$

(DEC. 2019)

17. Suppose the conditional p.d.f of a random variable X is given θ is $f(x|\theta) = \begin{cases} \frac{2x}{\theta^2} & 0<x<\theta \\ 0, & otherwise \end{cases}$

Where the prior distribution of θ is uniform (0,1). Based on a single observation x from X, which of the following statements are correct?

(a) The Bayes estimate for θ under squared error loss function is $-x\ log_e x$

(b) The Bayes estimate for θ under squared error loss function is $-\frac{x\ log_e x}{1-x}$

(c) The Bayes estimate for θ under absolute error loss function is x

(d) The Bayes estimate for θ under absolute error loss function is $\frac{2x}{1+x}$

(NOV. 2020)

18. X has binomial distribution with parameters n and p. supposes that n is given and the unknown parameter p has prior distribution, which is uniform on the interval [0, 1]. Consider the squared error loss function and the observation $X = n$. Identify the correct statement.
(a) The Bayes estimate of p is $\left(\frac{n+1}{n+2}\right)$
(b) The Bayes estimate of p is $2^{-1/(n+1)}$
(c) The median of the posterior distribution of p is $2^{-1/(n+1)}$
(d) The median of the posterior distribution of p is $\left(\frac{n+1}{n+2}\right)$

(NOV. 2020)

19. Let X_1, X_2, X_3 be a random sample from the uniform distribution on the interval (0, θ). Suppose the prior distribution of θ is uniform on the interval (0, 1). Let $X_{(3)} = max\{X_1, X_2, X_3\}$. Consider the squared error loss function. Which of the following statements are necessarily true?
(a) Bayes estimator of θ is unique
(b) $\frac{1}{X_{(3)}}$ Is a Bayes estimator of θ
(c) $X_{(3)}$ Is a Bayes estimator of θ
(d) $\frac{1-X_{(3)}}{X_{(3)}}$ Is a Bayes estimator of θ

(JUNE 2021)

20. Suppose Poisson $X|\lambda \sim Poisson(\lambda)$ where $\lambda > 0$. Consider the exponential distribution with mean 1/4 for the prior on λ. If the observed value of X is 0, then which among the following is the 95% Bayesian credible (confidence) interval for λ of smallest length?
(a) $(0, c)$ where $c = 0.95$
(b) $(0, c)$ where $c = \frac{\log(20)}{5}$
(c) $(c, \exp(c))$ where $c = \frac{\log(20)}{5}$
(d) $(0.2 - c, 0.2 + c)$ where $c = \frac{\log(20)}{5}$

(JUNE 2021)

21. Consider a small clinical trial to study the effectiveness of a treatment for a particular illness. 10 patients are enrolled in this experiment. Let θ denote the probability that a randomly chosen patient in the population recovers from this illness due to this treatment. For a standard Bayesian analysis, consider the Beta (0.5, 0.5) prior on θ (with density proportional to $(\theta(1-\theta))^{-1/2}$). Suppose exactly 6 out of the 10 patients recover. Which of the following are Bayes estimates of θ under the squared error loss function?
(a) $\frac{13}{22}$
(b) $\frac{11}{20}$
(c) $\frac{1}{2}$
(d) $E(\theta | 6\ out\ of\ 10\ patients\ recovered)$

(JULY 2024)

22. Let $Y_1, \ldots, Y_n$ $(n \geq 2)$ be independent observations; $Y_i \sim N(\beta x_i, \sigma^2), i = 1, \ldots, n$; where, x_1 and σ^2 (> 0) are known constants and $\beta \in \mathbb{R}$ is an unknown parameter. Consider $N(\beta_0, \mathcal{T}^2)$ prior for the parameter β, where β_0 and $\mathcal{T}^2 (> 0)$ are known constants, and $N(\mu, \lambda^2)$ denotes a normal distribution with mean μ and variance λ^2. Suppose $\overline{y} = \frac{1}{n}\sum_{i=1}^{n} y_i$ and $\overline{x} = \frac{1}{n}\sum_{i=1}^{n} x_i$ are observed sample means. Under squared error loss function, and which of the following statements are true?
(a) Bayes estimate of β tends to β_0 as $\mathcal{T}^2 \to 0$
(b) Bayes estimate of β tends to $\frac{\overline{y}}{\overline{x}}$ as $\mathcal{T}^2 \to 0$
(c) Bayes estimate of β tends to the BLUE of β as $\mathcal{T}^2 \to \infty$
(d) Bayes estimate of β tends to the MLE of β as $\mathcal{T}^2 \to \infty$

(JULY-2024)

23. Let $X_1 \ldots X_{10}$ be a random sample from a distribution with the probability density function
$$f(x|\theta) = \begin{cases} \theta x^{\theta-1}, & if\ 0 > x < 1, \\ 0, & otherwise. \end{cases}$$
where $\theta > 0$ is an unknown parameter. The prior distribution of θ is given by
$$\pi(\theta) = \begin{cases} \theta e^{-\theta}, & if\ \theta > 0, \\ 0, & otherwise. \end{cases}$$
The Bayes estimator of θ under squared error loss is
(a) $\frac{12}{1-\sum_{i=1}^{10} ln\, X_i}$ (b) $\frac{11}{2-\sum_{i=1}^{10} ln\, X_i}$
(c) $\frac{3+\sum_{i=1}^{10} ln\, X_i}{13}$ (d) $\frac{2+\sum_{i=1}^{10} ln\, X_i}{11}$

(FEB. 2025)

24. Let $X_1, X_2, \ldots, X_n$ be a random sample from $N(\theta, 1)$ distribution, where $\theta \in \mathbb{R}$ is unknown. Let δ_n be the Bayes estimator of θ, under the squared error loss function $L(\theta, a) = (a - \theta)^2, a, \theta \in \mathbb{R}$ and the prior distribution $N(1,2)$. If $\frac{1}{\sqrt{n}}[(2n+1)\delta_n - 1 - 2n\theta]$ converges in distribution to a random variable Z, as $n \to \infty$, then which of the following statements are true?
(a) $\delta_n \xrightarrow{P} \theta$, as $n \to \infty$, for all $\theta \in \mathbb{R}$
(b) Z follows normal distribution.
(c) $E(Z^4) = 48$
(d) $E(Z^2) = 1$

(JUNE 2025)

25. Suppose the distribution of X given θ is normal with mean θ and variance 15. Further, let the prior (improper) distribution of θ be proportional to 1, $-\infty < \theta < \infty$. If the observed value of X is 13, then which of the following statements is true?
(a) Posterior mean = Maximum likelihood estimate of θ, Posterior variance $= Var(X|\theta)$
(b) Posterior mean = Maximum likelihood estimate of θ, Posterior variance $< Var(X|\theta)$
(c) Posterior mean > Maximum likelihood estimate of θ, Posterior variance $= Var(X|\theta)$
(d) Posterior mean > Maximum likelihood estimate of θ, Posterior variance $< Var(X|\theta)$

(JUNE 2025)

26. Let $X_1, X_2, \ldots \ldots X_n$ be a random sample from $N(\theta, 1)\theta \in \mathbb{R}$, If A is the Bayes estimator of θ with respect to some prior $\pi(\theta)$ and loss function $L(\theta, d)$. Then, which of the following statements are true?
(a) $\ddot{\theta} = \frac{\sum_{i=1}^{n} x_i}{n+r^2}$, if the prior is $N\left(0, \frac{1}{r^2}\right), r^2$ known and $L(\theta, d) = (\theta - d)^2$
(b) $\ddot{\theta} = \frac{\sum_{i=1}^{n} x_i}{n+r^2}$ if the prior is $N(0, r^2), r^2$ known and $L(\theta, d) = |\theta - d|$
(c) $\ddot{\theta} = \frac{\sum_{i=1}^{n} x_i}{n+\frac{1}{r^2}}$, if the prior is $N\left(0, \frac{1}{r^2}\right), r^2$ known and $L(\theta, d) = |\theta - d|$
(d) $\ddot{\theta} = \frac{\sum_{i=1}^{n} x_i}{n}$, if the prior is the Jeffreys prior and $L(\theta, d) = (\theta - d)^2$

(Dec 2025)

27. Let $X|\theta \sim \text{Uniform}[0, \theta]$ and θ has an Exponential distribution with mean λ, where $\lambda > 3$ is known. If the realized value of X is 2025, then the posterior mode equals
(a) 0 (b) 2025
(c) $\frac{2025}{\lambda}$ (d) 2025λ

(Dec 2025)

28. Suppose $X|\theta \sim \text{Binomial}(7, \theta), 0 < \theta < 1$, and the prior distribution of θ is Beta(a, β) where $a > 0$ and $\beta > 0$ are known. Then which of the following statements MAY NOT be true?
(a) Posterior mean of θ given $X = 2$ is less than the prior mean
(b) Posterior mean of θ given $X = 3$ is greater than the prior mean
(c) Posterior mean of θ given $X = 4$ is not equal to the prior mean
(d) Posterior mean of θ given $X = 5$ is equal to the prior mean

Answer Key

1	2	3	4	5	6
b,c,d	a,b,d	a,b,c,d	c	b,d	c
7	8	9	10	11	12
B	a,b,c	a, c	d	b,c	C
13	14	15	16	17	18
b,c	a,d	b,c,d	a,b,c,d	b,d	a, c
19	20	21	22	23	24
a	b	a, d	a,c,d	a	a,b,c
25	26	27	28		
a	a,d	b	a,b,c,d		

:: Explanations ::

1. **Explanation: (b), (c), (d)**

$X_1, X_2, \ldots, X_{10}$ is a random sample from $N(\theta, \sigma^2), \sigma^2 = 10$

$f(x_i) = \frac{1}{\sigma\sqrt{2\pi}} e^{-\frac{1}{2}\left(\frac{x_i - \theta}{\sigma}\right)^2}$; $-\infty < x_i < \infty$

The likelihood function is

$L(x) = \frac{1}{(2\pi\sigma^2)^{n/2}} e^{\frac{-1}{2\sigma^2}\sum_{i=1}^{10}(x_i - \theta)^2}$

$L(z) = \frac{1}{(20\pi)^5} - e^{-\frac{1}{20}\sum_{i=1}^{10}(x_i - \theta)^2}$

The prior distribution of θ is

$\theta \sim N(0, \zeta^2), \zeta^2 = 20$

$g(\theta) = \frac{1}{\sqrt{40\,\pi}} e^{-\frac{1}{40}\theta^2}$; $-\infty < \theta < \infty$

The posterior distribution of θ is

$\pi(\theta(x)) \propto g(\theta). f(x)$

$\propto e^{-\frac{\theta^2}{40}\sum_{i=1}^{10}(x_i - \theta)^2}$

$\propto \exp\left\{\frac{-1}{2}\frac{\left(\theta - \frac{20}{21}\bar{x}\right)^2}{20/21}\right\}$

Which is pdf of Normal distribution with mean $\frac{20\bar{x}}{21}$ and variance $\frac{20}{21}$

In normal, mean = mode

Mode of posterior distribution, $\hat{\theta} = \frac{20\bar{x}}{21}$

If $\bar{x} \geq 0 \Rightarrow \hat{\theta} \leq \bar{x}$

And $\bar{x} \leq 0 \Rightarrow \theta \geq \bar{x}$

So, option (b), (c) & (d) are correct.

2. **Explanation: (a), (b), (d)** $X \sim$ Poisson (θ)

The prior distribution of θ with median $\log_e 2$

So parameter = 1

$g(\theta) = e^{-\theta}$; $\theta > 0$

$f(x) = \frac{e^{-\theta}\theta^x}{x!}$; $x = 0, 1, 2, \ldots$

The posterior distribution of θ

$\pi(\theta|x) \propto g(\theta)\, f(x) = e^{-\theta} \cdot e^{-\theta}\theta^x$

$= e^{-2\theta} \cdot \theta^x$

$= \frac{e^{-2\theta} \cdot \theta^{x+1-1}\, 2^{x+1}}{\lfloor x+1}$

$\pi(\theta|x) = \frac{1}{\lfloor x+1} 2^{x+1} . e^{-2\theta}\, \theta^{x+1-1}$

Which is pdf of Gamma distribution with parameter 2 and $x + 1$

Prior and posterior are of same family so prior is conjugate prior.

Under SELF, Baye's estimate is posterior mean

Baye's estimator $= \frac{X+1}{2}$

So, option (a), (b) and (d) are correct

3. **Explanation: (a), (b), (c), (d)**

$X_i \sim N(\theta, 1)\ i = 1, 2, \ldots, 8$

$f(x_i) = \frac{1}{\sqrt{2\pi}} e^{-\frac{1}{2}(x_i - \theta)^2}$; $-\infty < x_i < \infty$

$L = \prod_{i=1}^{n} f(x_i) = \frac{1}{(2\pi)^4} e^{-\frac{1}{2}\sum_{i=1}^{\infty}(x_i - \theta)^2}$

The prior distribution of θ is normal with mean 2 and variance 2

$g(\theta) = \frac{1}{\sqrt{4\pi}} e^{-\frac{1}{2}\frac{(\theta-2)^2}{2}}$

The posterior distribution of θ is

$\pi(\theta|\tilde{x}) \propto g(\theta) \cdot L(\tilde{x})$

$\propto \exp\left\{\frac{-1}{4}(\theta - 2)^2 - \frac{1}{2}; \sum_{i=1}^{\infty}(x_i - \theta)^2\right\}$

$\propto \exp\left\{\frac{-1}{2}\left(\frac{\theta^2}{2} + 2 - 2\theta\right) + \sum x_i^2 + 8\theta^2 - 160\,\bar{x}\right\}$

$$\propto \exp\left\{\frac{-1}{2}\frac{\left(\theta-\frac{16\bar{X}+2}{17}\right)^2}{2/17}\right\}$$

Which is normal distribution with mean $\frac{16\bar{X}+2}{17}$ and variance $\frac{2}{17}$

Posterior mean $= \frac{16\bar{X}+2}{17}$

Under absolute error loss, bayes estimator is the median of posterior distribution

Under squared error loss, bayes estimator is the mean of posterior distribution

In normal distribution, mean = median

Bayer estimator $= \frac{16\bar{X}+2}{17}$ [for absolute error loss as well as squared error loss]

Prior and posterior distribution is of same family i.e., normal distribution, the prior is conjugate prior

So, option a, b, c and d are correct

4. Explanation: (c)

$X \sim P(\lambda), \lambda > 0$

The prior distribution of λ is $U(0,1)$

$g(\lambda) = 1 \quad ; \qquad 0 < \lambda < 1$

$f(x) = \frac{e^{-\lambda}.\lambda^x}{x!}; \qquad x = 0, 1, 2 \ldots$

The posterior distribution of λ is

$\pi(\lambda|x) \propto g(\lambda)\, f(x) = e^{-\lambda}.\lambda^x$

$\pi(\lambda|x) \propto e^{-\lambda}.\lambda^x$

If $x = 0$ is observed, the posterior distribution

$\pi(\lambda|0) \propto e^{-\lambda}$

posterior prob $\left[0 < \lambda \le {}^1\!/_2 \,|\, 0 < \lambda < 1\right] = \frac{P[0<\lambda\le 1/2]}{P[0<\lambda<1]} =$

$\frac{\int_0^{1/2} e^{-\lambda} d\lambda}{\int_0^1 e^{-\lambda} d\lambda} = \frac{e-\sqrt{e}}{e-1}$

So, option (c) is correct

5. Explanation: (b), (d)

$X_i \sim Bernoulli(\theta)\,; 0 < \theta < 1, n > 1$

$f(x_i) = \theta^{x_i}(1-\theta)^{1-x_i}$

$L\left(\underset{\sim}{x}\right) = \theta^{\sum x_i}(1-\theta)^{n-\sum x_i} = \theta^s.(1-\theta)^{n-s}$

The prior distribution of θ is

$g(\theta) \propto \frac{1}{\sqrt{\theta(1-\theta)}}$

The posterior distribution of θ is

$$\pi\left(\theta\middle|\underset{\sim}{x}\right) \propto L\left(\underset{\sim}{x}\right) g(\theta) = \theta^s(1-\theta)^{n-s}\,\theta^{-\frac{1}{2}}(1-\theta)^{-\frac{1}{2}}$$

$$= \theta^{s-\frac{1}{2}}(1-\theta)^{n-s-\frac{1}{2}}$$

$$= \theta^{s+\frac{1}{2}-1}(1-\theta)^{n-s+\frac{1}{2}-1}$$

Which is pdf of beta distribution of first kind.

Posterior mean exists and is equal to

$E\left[\theta\middle|\underset{\sim}{x}\right] = \frac{s+\frac{1}{2}}{n-s+\frac{1}{2}}$ when $s = \sum_{i=1}^n X_i$

Maximum likelihood estimator of θ is sample mean

$= \frac{\sum_{i=1}^n X_i}{n} = \frac{s}{n}$

for some value of s, posterior mean is larger than Maximum likelihood estimator

So, option (b) and (d) are correct

6. Explanation: (c)

7. Explanation: (b)

X_1, X_2, X_3 and X_4 be independent and identically distributed normal with mean μ and variance 2

$$f(x_i) = \frac{1}{2\sqrt{\pi}}\, e^{-\frac{1}{4}(x_i-\mu)^2};\ -\infty < x < \infty$$

The likelihood function is

$L(\tilde{x}|\mu) = \frac{1}{16\,\pi^2} e^{-\frac{1}{4}\sum_{i=1}^n (x_i-\mu)^2}$

The prior distribution of μ is

$g(\mu) = \frac{1}{\sqrt{\pi}} e^{-\mu^2}$

The posterior distribution of μ is

$\pi(\mu|\tilde{x}) \propto L(\tilde{x}|\mu)\, g(\mu)$

$\propto e^{-\mu^2} e^{-\frac{1}{4}\sum_{i=1}^n (x_i-\mu)^2} = e^{-\frac{1}{4}[\sum x_i^2+4\mu^2-2\mu\sum x_i]-\mu^2}$

$= e^{-\frac{1}{4}[\sum x_i^2+8\mu^2-2\mu\sum x_i]}$

$= e^{-\frac{1}{4}[8\mu^2-2\mu\sum x_i]} e^{-\frac{1}{4}\sum x_i^2}$

$\propto e^{-\frac{8}{4}[\mu^2-\frac{\mu}{4}\sum x_i]}$

$= e^{-2\left[\mu^2-\bar{x}\mu+\frac{\bar{x}^2}{4}-\frac{\bar{x}^2}{4}\right]} = e^{-2\left[\mu-\frac{\bar{x}}{2}\right]^2} = e^{-\frac{1}{2}\frac{\left[\mu-\frac{\bar{x}}{2}\right]^2}{1/4}}$

$\mu|\tilde{x} \sim N\left(\frac{\bar{x}}{2}, \frac{1}{4}\right)$

Prior distribution and posterior distribution is of same family i.e. normal

Prior distribution is a conjugate prior

In normal distribution, mean = median = mode

Posterior mean $= \frac{\bar{x}}{2} = \frac{\sum_{i=1}^4 X_i}{8}$

So, Posterior median = Posterior mode $= \frac{\sum_{i=1}^4 X_i}{8}$

Posterior variance $= \frac{1}{4}$

So, option (b) is correct

8. Explanation: (a), (b), (c)

X be a random sample from Poisson λ

$g(x|\lambda) = \frac{e^{-\lambda}\lambda^x}{x!}; x = 0, 1, 2, \ldots$

The prior density function of λ is given by

$f(\lambda) = e^{-\lambda};\ \lambda > 0$

The posterior density of λ is

$$\pi(\lambda|x) = \frac{g(x|\lambda)\cdot f(\lambda)}{\int_\lambda g(x|\lambda)\cdot f(\lambda) d\lambda} = \frac{\frac{e^{-\lambda}\lambda^x e^{-\lambda}}{x!}}{\frac{1}{x!}\int_0^\infty e^{-2\lambda}.\lambda^x d\lambda} = \frac{e^{-2\lambda}\lambda^x}{\frac{\Gamma(x+1)}{2^{x+1}}}$$

$$= \frac{2^{x+1}e^{-2\lambda}\lambda^x}{\Gamma(x+1)}$$

$\lambda|x \sim$ Gamma $(2, x+1)$

Mean of Posterior distribution

$E(\lambda|x) = \frac{x+1}{2}$

Baye's estimator w.r.t. squared error loos function is mean of posterior distribution

Baye's estimator of λ is $\frac{X+1}{2}$

Baye's estimator of e^λ is

$E[e^\lambda] = \int_0^\infty e^\lambda\, \pi(\lambda|x)\partial\lambda$

$E[e^\lambda] = 2^{X+1}$

So, option (a), (b), (c) are correct

9. Explanation: (a), (c)

Y	1	2	3
$P(Y=4)$	θ^3	$(1-\theta)^3$	$1-\theta^3-(1-\theta)^3$

Prior distribution of θ is

$\theta \sim \beta\, eta\,(\alpha,\beta)$

Posteriors distribution of θ,

$\pi(\theta|Y) \propto \sum_{y=1}^{3} P(y=y)\, f(\theta)$

$= \sum_{y=1}^{3} P(Y=y) \frac{1}{\beta(\alpha,\beta)}\, \theta^{\alpha-1}(1-\theta)^{\beta-1}$

$\pi(\theta|y) = \frac{\theta^3\theta^{\alpha-1}.(1-\theta)^{\beta-1}}{\beta(\alpha,\beta)} + \frac{(1-\theta)^3\theta^{\alpha-1}(1-\theta)^{\beta-1}}{\beta(\alpha,\beta)} + \frac{\{1-\theta^3-(1-\theta)^3\}\theta^{\alpha-1}.(1-\theta)^{\beta-1}}{\beta(\alpha,\beta)}$

$\hat{\theta}_1 = E[\theta|\, Y=1] = \frac{\alpha+3}{\alpha+3+\beta}$

$\hat{\theta}_2 = E[\theta|Y=2] = \frac{\alpha}{\alpha+\beta+3}$

$\therefore\ \hat{\theta}_1 > \hat{\theta}_2$

Also, when $Y=3$, Posterior density of θ is Beta distribution

Option (a) & (c) are correct

10. Explanation: (d)

X be a random sample from an exponential distribution with mean $\frac{1}{\lambda}$

$f(x) = \lambda\cdot e^{-\lambda x}\,; x>0$

Prior distribution of λ is

$g(\lambda) = \lambda.e^{-\lambda}\,;\ \lambda>0$

Posterior distribution of λ is

$\pi(\lambda|x) \propto g(\lambda) - f(x)$

$\propto \lambda\cdot e^{-\lambda x}\,\lambda\cdot e^{-\lambda}$

$\propto \lambda^2 e^{-\lambda(x+1)} = \frac{1}{\Gamma(3)}\, e^{-\lambda(x+1)}.\lambda^{3-1}.(x+1)^3$

Which is the pdf of gamma with parameter $(x+1)$ and 3

Baye`s estimator of $1/\lambda$ with respect to the squared error loss function is $E\left(\frac{1}{\lambda}|x\right)$

$E\left(\frac{1}{\lambda}|x\right) = \int_0^\infty \frac{1}{\lambda}.\pi(\lambda|x)d\lambda = \int_0^\infty \frac{1}{\lambda}.\frac{1}{\Gamma(3)}.e^{-\lambda(x+1)}\,\lambda^2\,(x+1)^3$

$= \frac{(x+1)^3}{\Gamma(3)}\int_0^\infty e^{\lambda(x+1)}\,\lambda^{2-1}d\lambda$

$= \frac{(x+1)^3}{\Gamma(3)}.\frac{\Gamma(2)}{(x+1)^2}$

$E\left(\frac{1}{\lambda}|x\right) = \frac{(x+1)}{2}$

Bayes estimates of $1/\lambda$ w.r.t. SELF $= \frac{(x+1)}{2}$

So, option (d) is correct

11. Explanation: (b), (c)

$f_\lambda(x) = 2\lambda\, e^{-\lambda x^2}; x>0$

Prior distribution of λ is exponential distribution with mean 1.

$\zeta(\lambda) = e^{-\lambda}\,;\ \lambda>0$

The posterior distribution of λ is

$\pi\,(\lambda|x) \propto L(x).\zeta(\lambda)$

$\propto (2\lambda)^n e^{-\lambda\sum_{i=1}^{n} x_i^2}\, e^{-\lambda}$

$\propto \lambda^n.e^{-\lambda(y+1)}$

Where $Y = \sum X_i^2$

Which is not pdf of exponential

The posterior distribution of λ is not an exponential distribution

$\Rightarrow$ Bayes estimator with respect to squared error los function is the posterior mean

Posterior mean is exist & unique

So, Bayes estimates w.r.t SELF exist & unique

$\Rightarrow$ Bayes estimates with respect to absolute error loss function is the median of posterior distribution and Median of posterior distribution is exist & unique

So, Baye's estimator of λ w.r.t absolute error loss function exists & unique

So, option (b) & (c) are correct.

12. Explanation: (c)

13. Explanation: (b), (c)

14. Explanation: (a), (d)

15. Explanation: (b), (c), (d)

$Y|\theta \sim P(\theta);\ \theta>0$

$f(y|\theta) = \frac{e^{-\theta}\,\theta^y}{y!}; y = 0,1,2,\ldots$

Prior density τ of θ is given by

$\tau(\theta)\ \alpha\ e^{-\alpha\theta}\,\theta^{\beta-1}\ \because \alpha>0, \beta>0$

$\tau(\theta) = \frac{\alpha^\beta}{\sqrt{\beta}}\, e^{-\alpha\theta}\theta^{\beta-1}$

Which is pdf of gamma distribution

Posterior distribution

$\pi(\theta|y)\ \alpha\ f(y|\theta\cdot\tau(\theta)$

$\pi(\theta|y)\ \alpha\ \frac{e^{-\theta}\,\theta^y}{y!}\, e^{-\alpha\theta}\,\theta^{\beta-1}$

$\alpha\ e^{-(1+\alpha)\theta}\,\theta^{y+\beta-1}$

Which is the density function of gamma.

So, option (2) is correct

Distribution of prior & posterior are the same family of gamma distribution

So, τ is a conjugate prior

Mean of Posterior distribution $= \frac{\beta+y}{\alpha+1}$

So, option (3) & (4) are correct

Marginal distribution of y is

$h(y) = \int_0^\infty f(y|\theta)\,\tau(\theta)\,d\theta$

$= \int_0^\infty \frac{e^{-\theta}\,\theta^y}{y!}\frac{\alpha^\beta}{\sqrt{\beta}}\, e^{-\alpha\theta}\,\theta^{\beta-1}\,d\theta$

On solving which is not pmf of hypergeometric distribution

So, option (a) is incorrect

Option (b), (c) and (d) are correct

16. Explanation: (a), (b), (c), (d)

17. Explanation: (b), (d)

$X_1, X_2 \ldots. X_n$ be random sample

$f(x|\theta) \rightarrow$ Sample distribution

$g(\theta) \rightarrow$ Prior distribution

$\prod(\theta|x) \rightarrow$ Posterior distribution

$\prod(\theta|x) = \frac{f(x|\theta).g(\theta)}{\int_\theta f(x|\theta).g\,(\theta)d\,(\theta)}$

$f(x|\theta) = \frac{2x}{\theta^2}\ ;0<x<\theta$

$g\,(\theta) = 1\ \ ;0<\theta<1\ \ ;x<\theta<1$

$\prod(\theta|x) = \frac{\frac{2x}{\theta^2}}{\int_x^1 \frac{2x}{\theta^2}\,d\theta} = \frac{1}{\theta^2}\frac{1}{\left(\frac{-1}{\theta}\right)_x^1}$

$= \frac{1}{\theta^2}\frac{1}{\left(-1+\frac{1}{x}\right)}$

$\prod(\theta|\underline{x}) = \frac{x}{\theta^2(1-x)}$; $x < \theta < 1$

Baye's estimate w.r.t squared error loss function is mean of posterior distribution.

$E(\theta|\underline{x}) = \int_x^1 \theta.\prod(\theta|\underline{x})\, d\theta$

$= \int_x^1 \theta.\frac{x}{\theta^2(1-x)}\, d\theta = \frac{x}{1-x}(\log\theta)_x^1$

$= \frac{-x\log x}{1-x}$

Baye's estimate w.r.t absolute error loss function is median of posterior distribution

Let M be the median

$\int_x^M \prod(\theta|x)\, d\theta = \frac{1}{2}$

$\Rightarrow \int_x^M \frac{x}{\theta^2(1-x)}\, d\theta = \frac{1}{2} \Rightarrow \frac{x}{1-x}\left[\frac{-1}{\theta}\right]_x^M = 1$

$\Rightarrow M = \frac{2x}{1+x}$

So option (b) & (d) is correct

18. Explanation: (a), (c)

$X \sim B(n,p) \Rightarrow f(x;n,p) = \binom{n}{x} p^x(1-p)^{n-x}$

$p \sim U(0,1) \Rightarrow h(p) = 1; 0 < p < 1$

$L(X,p) = f(x;n,p)\, h(p) = \binom{n}{x} p^x(1-p)^{n-x}$

$L(X=n,p) = f(x=n;n,p)\, h(p) = \binom{n}{n} p^n(1-p)^{n-n} = p^n$

$g(x=n) = \int_0^1 p^n\, dp = \frac{1}{n+1}$

Posterior probability

$\Pi(p|X=n) = \frac{L(X=n,p)}{g(x=n)} = (n+1)p^n; 0 < p < 1$

Bayes estimate of p under squared error loss function is

$\hat{p}_B = E(p|X=n) = \int_0^1 (n+1)\, p^n = \frac{n+1}{n+2}$

Thus, Bayes estimate of p is $\left(\frac{n+1}{n+2}\right)$

$\int_0^{M_d} k(p|X=n)\, dp = \frac{1}{2} \Rightarrow M_d = \left(\frac{1}{2}\right)^{\frac{1}{n+1}} = 2^{-1/n+1}$

Thus, median of the posterior distribution of p is $2^{-1/(n+1)}$

Hence option (a) and (c) are correct.

19. Explanation: (a)

$X_i \sim U(0,\theta) \Rightarrow f(x) = \frac{1}{\theta}; 0 < x < \theta \Rightarrow F(x) = \int_0^x f(x)\, dx = \frac{x}{\theta}$

$\theta \sim U(0,1) \Rightarrow h(\theta) = 1; 0 < \theta < 1$

Let $Y = X_{(3)} = \max[X_1, X_2, X_3]$

$f(y) = n[F(x)]^{n-1} f(x) = \frac{3y^2}{\theta^3}; 0 < y < \theta$

$L(y,\theta) = f(y|\theta)h(\theta) = \frac{3y^2}{\theta^3}; 0 < y < \theta < 1$

$g(y) = \int_y^1 \frac{3y^2}{\theta^3}\, d\theta = \frac{3}{2}(1-y^2)$

Posterior probability

$\Pi(\theta|y) = \frac{L(y,\theta)}{g(y)} = \frac{2y^2}{\theta^3(1-y^2)}; y < \theta < 1$

Under the squared error loss function Bayes estimate

$$\hat{\theta}_B(y) = E(\theta|y) = \int_y^1 \theta\, k(\theta|y) d\theta = \frac{2y}{1+y} = \frac{2X_{(3)}}{1+X_{(3)}}$$

20. Explanation: (b)

$X|\lambda \sim P(\lambda); \lambda > 0$

$f(x|\lambda) = \frac{e^{-\lambda}.\lambda^x}{x!}; \lambda > 0$

The prior distribution of λ is

$g(\lambda) = 4.e^{-4\lambda}$

The posterior distribution of λ is

$\pi(\lambda|x) \propto f(x|\lambda).g(\lambda) = \frac{e^{-\lambda}.\lambda^x}{x!}.e^{-4\lambda}$

$\pi(\lambda|x) \propto \lambda^x.e^{-5\lambda}$

The observed value of X is 0,

$\pi(\lambda|0) \propto e^{-5\lambda}$

The posterior distribution of λ when observed value of X is 0 is exponential distribution with mean 1/5 i.e.,

$\pi(\lambda|0) = 5.e^{-5\lambda}$

95% Bayesian credible confidence interval for λ is

$0.95 = P[0 < \lambda < c]$

$0.95 = \int_0^c 5.e^{-5\lambda}\, d\lambda = 5\left[\frac{e^{-5\lambda}}{-5}\right]_0^c$

$0.95 = 1 - e^{-5c}$

$0.05 = +e^{-5c}$

$\log 0.05 = -5\,c$

$c = \frac{-1}{5}\log 0.05 = \frac{-1}{5}\log\frac{5}{100} = \frac{-1}{5}\log\frac{1}{20}$

$c = \frac{1}{5}\log 20$

So, option (b) is correct

21. Explanation: (a), (d)

θ be the probability that a randomly chosen patient in the population recovers from this illness due to treatment

X = no. of patients recover

$X \sim B(10,\theta)$

$f(x|\theta) = \binom{10}{x}\theta^x(1-\theta)^{10-x}$; x= 0,1,2,...,10

The prior distribution of θ *is*

$g(\theta) = \frac{1}{\beta\left(\frac{1}{2},\frac{1}{2}\right)}\theta^{-\frac{1}{2}}(1-\theta)^{-\frac{1}{2}}$

The posterior distribution of θ is

$\Pi(\theta|x) \propto \binom{10}{x}\theta^x(1-\theta)^{10-x}\theta^{-\frac{1}{2}}(1-\theta)^{-\frac{1}{2}}$

Suppose exactly 6 out of 10 patients recover

$\Pi(\theta|6) \propto \theta^6(1-\theta)^4\theta^{-\frac{1}{2}}(1-\theta)^{-\frac{1}{2}} = \theta^{\frac{11}{2}}(1-\theta)^{\frac{7}{2}}$

$\Pi(\theta|6) = \theta^{\frac{13}{2}-1}(1-\theta)^{\frac{9}{2}-1}; 0 < \theta < 1$

Under SELF, the bayes estimator of θ is the mean of the posterior distribution i.e.,

Bayes estimator of θ = E $(\theta|6) = \frac{\frac{13}{2}}{\frac{13}{2}+\frac{9}{2}} = \frac{13}{22}$

So, option (a), and (d) are correct.

22. Explanation: (a), (c), (d)

This is a theory question.

The options (1),(3),(4) are the direct result of the application of Bayesian approach to regression analysis. While option (2) is not true.

23. Explanation: (a)

$X_1.....X_{10}$ be a random sample from a distribution with the probability density function

$$f(x|\theta) = \begin{cases}\theta x^{\theta-1}, & if\ 0 > x < 1, \quad \theta > 0\\ 0, & otherwise.\end{cases}$$

The prior distribution of θ is given by

$$\pi(\theta) = \begin{cases}\theta e^{-\theta}, & if\ \theta > 0,\\ 0, & otherwise.\end{cases}$$

The above p.d.f. can be rewritten as

$$f(x \mid \theta) = \frac{\theta x^{\theta}}{x} \Rightarrow f(x \mid \theta) \propto \theta x^{\theta}$$

$$L(\theta, \underline{x}) \propto \theta^{10} \left(\prod_{i=1}^{10} x_i \right)^{\theta}$$

The posterior likelihood is given as

$$L(\theta, \underline{x}) \propto \theta^{11} e^{-\theta} \left(\prod_{i=1}^{10} x_i \right)^{\theta}$$

Let $H = \prod_{i=1}^{10} x_i$

$$L(\theta, \underline{x}) \propto \theta^{11} e^{-\theta} \left(\prod_{i=1}^{10} x_i \right)^{\theta} = \theta^{11} e^{-\theta} H^{\theta}$$

$$= \theta^{11} e^{-\theta} e^{\ln H^{\theta}} = \theta^{11} e^{-\theta} e^{\theta \ln H} = \theta^{11} e^{-\theta(1-\ln H)}$$

Thus the posterior distribution of θ is $Gamma(scale = 1 - \ln H, shape = 12)$

The Bayes estimator of θ under squared error loss is

$$E(\theta) = \frac{shape}{scale} = \frac{12}{1 - \ln H} = \frac{12}{1 - \ln \prod_{i=1}^{10} X_i}$$

$$= \frac{12}{1 - \sum_{i=1}^{10} \ln X_i}$$

24. Explanation: (a), (b), (c)

We are given that $X_1, X_2, \ldots, X_n$ is a random sample from $N(\theta, 1)$, where θ is unknown, and we are given a prior $N(1,2)$. We want to analyze the behavior of the Bayes estimator δ_n and the limiting distribution of the given expression.

The likelihood function for a normal sample with known variance is:

$$f(X_1, \ldots, X_n | \theta) \propto \exp\left(-\frac{1}{2} \sum_{i=1}^{n} (X_i - \theta)^2 \right)$$

The prior is $N(1,2)$, meaning $\theta \sim N(1,2)$ with mean 1 and variance 2.

Using the standard formula for the posterior mean when combining a normal prior with a normal likelihood:

$$\theta | X_1, \ldots, X_n \sim N\left(\frac{n\bar{X} + \frac{1}{2}}{n + \frac{1}{2}}, \frac{1}{n + \frac{1}{2}} \right)$$

The Bayes estimator under squared error loss is the posterior mean:

$$\delta_n = \frac{n\bar{X} + 1}{n + 2}$$

Asymptotic Behavior of δ_n

Consistency of δ_n:

Since $\bar{X} \to \theta$ in probability as $n \to \infty$, it follows that:

$$\delta_n = \frac{n\bar{X} + 1}{n + 2} \to \theta, \text{ for all } \theta \in \mathbb{R}$$

Hence, Statement (a) is true.

Limiting Distribution of Given Expression:

First, express δ_n in terms of $\bar{X}$:

$$\delta_n = \frac{n\bar{X} + 1}{n + 2}$$

Multiply both sides by $2n + 1$:

$$(2n + 1)\delta_n = \frac{(2n + 1)(n\bar{X} + 1)}{n + 2}$$

Consider the given transformation:

$$Z_n = \frac{1}{\sqrt{n}} [(2n + 1)\delta_n - 1 - 2n\theta].$$

Substituting δ_n:

$$Z_n = \frac{1}{\sqrt{n}} \left[\frac{(2n + 1)(n\bar{X} + 1)}{n + 2} - 1 - 2n\theta \right].$$

Since $\sqrt{n}(\bar{X} - \theta) \sim N(0,1)$, and the leading term in the numerator is approximately $2n(\bar{X} - \theta)$, we get:

$$Z_n \approx \frac{2n(\bar{X} - \theta)}{\sqrt{n}} = 2\sqrt{n}(\bar{X} - \theta).$$

Since $\sqrt{n}(\bar{X} - \theta) \sim N(0,1)$, it follows that Z_n converges in distribution to $N(0,4)$, which implies $Z \sim N(0,4)$.

Hence, Statement (b) is true.

Checking Moments of Z:

Since $Z \sim N(0,4)$, its variance is:

$E[Z^2] = 4.$

So, Statement (d) is false.

For the fourth moment, using the property $E[Z^4] = 3(E[Z^2])^2$:

$E[Z^4] = 3 \times 4^2 = 48.$

Hence, Statement (c) is true.

25. Explanation: (a)

With known variance $\sigma^2 = 15$ and improper flat prior $\pi(\theta) \propto 1$, the posterior is

$\theta \mid x \sim \mathcal{N}!(x, \sigma^2) = \mathcal{N}(13,15).$

Thus:

- Posterior mean $= x = 13$ equals the MLE of θ.
- Posterior variance $= \sigma^2 = 15 = \text{Var}(X \mid \theta).$

So option a is true; the others are false.

Correct Answer: a.

26. Explanation: (a), (d)

- With known variance (1), likelihood precision is n.

  Prior $N(0, \tau^2)$ has precision $1/\tau^2$. Posterior is normal with precision $n + 1/\tau^2$ and mean$\mu_{\text{post}} = \frac{n,\bar{x}}{,n+1/\tau^2,} = \frac{\sum x_i}{,n+1/\tau^2,}$.
- Squared loss: Bayes estimator = posterior mean.
- Absolute loss: Bayes estimator = posterior median; for a normal posterior, mean = median, so it's the same value.

  Apply:

1. Prior $N(0,1/r^2) \Rightarrow 1/\tau^2 = r^2$. Estimator $= \frac{\sum x_i}{n+r^2}$. True.
2. Prior $N(0, r^2) \Rightarrow 1/\tau^2 = 1/r^2$. Estimator should be $\frac{\sum x_i}{n+1/r^2}$, not $n + r^2$. False.
3. Prior $N(0,1/r^2)$ with absolute loss still gives $\frac{\sum x_i}{n+r^2}$, not $n + 1/r^2$. False.
4. Jeffreys prior (flat) $\Rightarrow$ posterior mean $\bar{x} = (\sum\ x_i)/n$. True.

Correct Answer : True: a and d

False: b and c

27. Explanation: (b)

Likelihood of $X \mid \theta$

Given: $X \mid \theta \sim \text{Uniform}(0, \theta)$

So the density is

$$f(x \mid \theta) = \begin{cases} \frac{1}{\theta}, & 0 \le x \le \theta \\ 0, & \text{otherwise} \end{cases}$$

Since the observed value is $x = 2025$,

$$f(2025 \mid \theta) = \frac{1}{\theta}, \theta \ge 2025$$

Prior distribution of θ

θ has Exponential distribution with mean λ.

For exponential:

$$f(\theta) = \frac{1}{\lambda} e^{-\theta/\lambda}, \theta > 0$$

Posterior distribution

Using Bayes theorem

Posterior ∝ Likelihood × Prior

$$f(\theta \mid x) \propto \frac{1}{\theta} \times \frac{1}{\lambda} e^{-\theta/\lambda}$$

Ignoring constants,

$$f(\theta \mid x) \propto \frac{e^{-\theta/\lambda}}{\theta}, \theta \ge 2025$$

Posterior mode = value of θ where posterior density is maximum.

Look at the function

$$g(\theta) = \frac{e^{-\theta/\lambda}}{\theta}$$

For $\theta \ge 2025$:

- $e^{-\theta/\lambda}$ decreases as θ increases
- $\frac{1}{\theta}$ also decreases

Therefore the whole expression decreases as θ increases.

So the maximum occurs at the smallest allowed value of θ.

From the likelihood constraint:

$$\theta \ge 2025$$

Hence the posterior is maximized at

$$\theta = 2025$$

⟹ Posterior mode = 2025

28. Explanation: (a), (b), (c), (d)

Bayesian Analysis: Binomial-Beta Model

Setup $X|\theta \sim \text{Binomial}(7, \theta), \theta \sim \text{Beta}(\alpha, \beta)$

Posterior Distribution By conjugacy of Beta-Binomial:

$\theta|X = x \sim \text{Beta}(\alpha + x, \beta + 7 - x)$

Formulas: Prior mean $= \frac{\alpha}{\alpha+\beta}$

Posterior mean given $X = x = \frac{\alpha+x}{\alpha+\beta+7}$

General Comparison:

Posterior mean > Prior mean when: $\frac{\alpha+x}{\alpha+\beta+7} > \frac{\alpha}{\alpha+\beta}$

$$(\alpha + x)(\alpha + \beta) > \alpha(\alpha + \beta + 7)$$
$$\alpha(\alpha + \beta) + x(\alpha + \beta) > \alpha(\alpha + \beta) + 7\alpha$$
$$x(\alpha + \beta) > 7\alpha$$
$$x > \frac{7\alpha}{\alpha+\beta} = 7 \times \text{Prior mean}$$

So:

Posterior mean > Prior mean ⟺ $x > 7 \times$ Prior mean

Posterior mean < Prior mean ⟺ $x < 7 \times$ Prior mean

Posterior mean = Prior mean ⟺ $x = 7 \times$ Prior mean

Now, Analyzing Each Statement

Statement 1: Posterior mean < Prior mean when $X = 2$

Requires: $2 < 7 \times \frac{\alpha}{\alpha+\beta} \Rightarrow \frac{\alpha}{\alpha+\beta} > \frac{2}{7}$

This is NOT always true. If prior mean $\le \frac{2}{7}$, posterior mean $\ge$ prior mean.

Example where it fails: $\alpha = 1, \beta = 4 \rightarrow$ Prior mean $= \frac{1}{5} = 0.2 < \frac{2}{7}$

Posterior mean $= \frac{1+2}{1+4+7} = \frac{3}{12} = 0.25 > 0.2 =$ Prior mean

Statement 1 MAY NOT be true

Statement 2: Posterior mean > Prior mean when $X = 3$

Requires: $3 > 7 \times \frac{\alpha}{\alpha+\beta}$

$\frac{\alpha}{\alpha+\beta} < \frac{3}{7}$

This is NOT always true. If prior mean $\ge \frac{3}{7}$, posterior mean $\le$ prior mean.

Example where it fails: $\alpha = 3, \beta = 2 \rightarrow$ Prior mean $= \frac{3}{5} = 0.6 > \frac{3}{7}$

Posterior mean $= \frac{3+3}{3+2+7} = \frac{6}{12} = 0.5 < 0.6 =$ Prior mean

Statement 2 MAY NOT be true

Statement 3: Posterior mean ≠ Prior mean when $X = 4$

Posterior mean = Prior mean requires:

$$\frac{\alpha+4}{\alpha+\beta+7} = \frac{\alpha}{\alpha+\beta}$$
$$\Rightarrow 4(\alpha + \beta) = 7\alpha \Rightarrow 4\beta = 3\alpha \Rightarrow \frac{\alpha}{\alpha+\beta} = \frac{4}{7}$$

This CAN happen Choose $\alpha = 4, \beta = 3$:

Prior mean $= \frac{4}{7}$, Posterior mean $= \frac{4+4}{4+3+7} = \frac{8}{14} = \frac{4}{7}$

So, when $\frac{\alpha}{\alpha+\beta} = \frac{4}{7}$, posterior mean equals prior mean, making Statement 3 false.

Statement 3 MAY NOT be true

Statement 4: Posterior mean = Prior mean when $X = 5$

Posterior mean = Prior mean requires:

$$\frac{\alpha+5}{\alpha+\beta+7} = \frac{\alpha}{\alpha+\beta}$$
$$5(\alpha + \beta) = 7\alpha \Rightarrow 5\beta = 2\alpha \Rightarrow \frac{\alpha}{\alpha+\beta} = \frac{5}{7}$$

This CAN happen Choose $\alpha = 5, \beta = 2$:

Prior mean $= \frac{5}{7}$, Posterior mean $= \frac{5+5}{5+2+7} = \frac{10}{14} = \frac{5}{7}$

But if prior mean $\ne \frac{5}{7}$, posterior mean ≠ prior mean.

So, Statement 4 is sometimes true, sometimes false → MAY NOT be true

Correct Answer: All four statements are MAY NOT be true

CORRELATION & REGRESSION ANALYSIS

CHAPTER 9

(JUNE 2012)

1. Consider a simple linear regression model
$Y = \beta X + \varepsilon$
Let $\hat{Y}_0$ be the least squares predictor of Y at $X = x_0$ based on n observations
$(Y_i, X_i), i = 1, \dots n$ and $\bar{X} = \frac{1}{n}\sum_{i=1}^{n} X_i$.
Then the standard error of the predictor $\hat{Y}_0$
(a) decreases as x_0 moves away from $\bar{X}$
(b) increases as x_0 moves away from $\bar{X}$
(c) increases as x_0 moves closer to 0
(d) decreases as x_0 moves closer to 0

(JUNE 2012)

2. Consider the following five observations on (X, Y) : (0, 1), (1, 2), (2, 3), (3, 2), (4, 1). Then
(a) The least – square linear regression of Y on X is Y = $\frac{9}{5}$
(b) The least – square linear regression of X and Y is X = 2
(c) The correlation coefficient between X and Y is 0.
(d) The correlation coefficient between X and Y is +1.

(DEC. 2012)

3. In logistic regression model involving a binary response Y and two explanatory variables X_1 and X_2, the coefficient of X_2 is
(a) $\frac{P(Y=1|X_1,X_2+1)}{P(Y=1|X_1,X_2)}$
(b) $\log\left\{\frac{P(Y=1|X_1,X_2+1)}{P(Y=1|X_1,X_2)}\right\}$
(c) $\frac{P(Y=1|X_1,X_2+1)}{P(Y=0|X_1,X_2+1)} \times \frac{P(Y=0|X_1,X_2)}{P(Y=1|X_1,X_2)}$
(d) $\log\left\{\frac{P(Y=1|X_1,X_2+1)}{P(Y=0|X_1,X_2+1)} \times \frac{P(Y=0|X_1,X_2)}{P(Y=1|X_1,X_2)}\right\}$

(DEC. 2012)

4. Consider the linear model
$y_1 = \theta_1 + 2\theta_2 - 2\theta_3 + \varepsilon_1$
$y_2 = \theta_1 + 3\theta_2 - \theta_3 + \varepsilon_2$
$y_3 = \theta_2 + \theta_3 + \varepsilon_3$
Where y_i are observations, θ_i are parameters and ε_i are uncorrelated random variables with mean zero and constant variance for $i = 1, 2, 3$. Then which of the following is true?
(a) $2y_1 - y_2 - y_3$ is an unbiased estimator of $\theta_1 - 4\,\theta_3$
(b) $2y_1 - y_2 - y_3$ is the BLUE of $\theta_1 - 4\,\theta_3$
(c) $y_2 - 3y_3$ is the BLUE of $\theta_1 - 4\,\theta_3$
(d) $y_1 - 4y_3$ is an unbiased estimator of $\theta_1 - 4\,\theta_3$

(DEC. 2012)

5. In the linear regression fit involving independent and identically distributed pairs of observations of a response variable (Y) and an explanatory variable (X), indicate which of the following statements are necessarily correct?
(a) The residuals of the regression of Y on X have the same variance.
(b) The multiple R^2 computed from the regression fit of Y on X and X^2 cannot be smaller than that computed from the regression fit of Y on X alone.
(c) The adjusted R^2 computed from the regression fit of Y on X and X^2 cannot be smaller than that computed from the regression fit of Y on X alone.
(d) The variance of the estimated regression coefficient of X computed from the regression of Y on X and X^2 is larger than that computed from the regression of Y on X alone.

(DEC. 2012)

6. Consider a linear model $E(\tilde{Y}) = X\tilde{\beta}$ where $\tilde{Y}$ is the vector of n observations and $\tilde{\beta}$ is the vector of n parameters. The $(i,j)^{th}$ element of the design matrix X is of the form: $1 + ij + i^2 j^2, 1 \le i, j \le n$. Then $\tilde{\beta}$ is estimable for
(a) $n = 20$ (b) $n = 3$
(c) $n = 10$ (d) $n = 50$

(JUNE 2013)

7. Suppose observations on the pair (X, Y) are

X	1	7	5	9	11	3
Y	20	68	58	70	181	37

Let r_p and r_s respectively denote the Pearson's and Spearman's rank correlation coefficient between X and Y based on the above data. Then which of the following is true?
(a) $r_p = 1, r_s = 1$
(b) $0 < r_p < 1, r_s = 1$
(c) $r_p = 1, 0 < r_s < 1$
(d) $0 < r_p < 1,\ 0 < r_s < 1$

(JUNE 2013)

8. Consider the following linear model
$Y_i = a + (-1)^i b + e_i\ ; i = 1, \dots, n,\ n \ge 3,$
where e_i' are independent distributed random variables following normal distribution with mean zero and variance σ^2. Which of the following statements is correct?
(a) The maximum likelihood estimators of a and b always exist
(b) The maximum likelihood estimators of a and b always exist, but they may not be unique
(c) The maximum likelihood estimators of σ^2 does not exist
(d) The maximum likelihood estimators of a and b are not consistent

(JUNE 2013)

9. Consider the model $Y_{ijk} = \mu + \alpha_i + \beta_{ij} + \varepsilon_{ijk}\,; i,j,k = 1,2,\dots,5$ where ε_{ijk} are independent and identically distributed random variables each following normal distributions with mean 0 and variance $\sigma^2 > 0$, and $\mu, \alpha_i, \beta_{ij},\ i,j = 1,2,\dots,5$ are fixed parameters.
Then which of the following statements are true?
(a) μ is estimable
(b) All linear functions of $\alpha_i, i = 1,2,\dots,5$ are estimable
(c) $\mu + \alpha_1 + \beta_{12}$ is estimable
(d) $\beta_{21} - \beta_{22}$ is estimable

(JUNE 2013)

10. For a bivariate data set $(x_i, y_i), i = 1,2,\dots,n$, suppose the least squares regression lines are:
Equation 1: $5x - 8y + 14 = 0$
Equation 2: $2x - 5y + 11 = 0$
Then which of the following statements are true?
(a) The value of the correlation coefficient is -0.80
(b) The value of the correlation coefficient is 0.80
(c) The standard deviation of y is less than the standard deviation of x
(d) $(\bar{x}, \bar{y}) = (2,3)$, where $\bar{x} = \frac{1}{n}\sum_{i=1}^{n} x_i$ and $\bar{y} = \frac{1}{n}\sum_{i=1}^{n} y_i$

(DEC. 2013)

11. Let $X_0, \epsilon_1, \epsilon_2, \epsilon_3$ and ϵ_4 be independent and identically distribution normal random variables with mean 0 and variance $\sigma^2 > 0$ Define $X_{i+1} = \rho X_i + (\sqrt{1-\rho^2})\epsilon_{i+1}$ where $0 < p < 1$ for $i = 0,1,2,3$ Let $\rho_{ij.k}$ *denotes the partial* correlation between X_i and X_j gives X_k
Then $\rho_{14.2} =$
(a) ρ^3 (b) ρ^2
(c) ρ (d) 0

(DEC. 2013)

12. Let $Y_1, Y_2, \dots\dots, Y_n$ be random variables such that $E(Y_i) = i\theta, Var(Y_i) = i^2\sigma^2$ and $Cov(Y_i, Y_j) = 0$ for all $1 \le i,j \le n, i \ne j$, where θ and σ^2 are unknown parameters. Consider the following two estimators of θ:
$$T_1 = \frac{1}{n}\sum_{i=1}^{n}\frac{Y_i}{i},$$
$$T_2 = \frac{6}{n(n+1)(2n+1)}\sum_{i=1}^{n} iY_i,$$
Which of the following statement(s) is (are) true?
(a) T_1 is the best linear unbiased estimator of θ.
(b) T_2 is the ordinary least squares estimator of θ.
(c) $Var(T_1) = \frac{\sigma^2}{n}$
(d) An unbiased estimator of $\sigma^2$is $\frac{1}{n-1}\left[\sum_{i=1}^{n}\frac{Y_i^2}{i^2} - \frac{1}{n}\left(\sum_{i=1}^{n}\frac{Y_i}{i}\right)^2\right]$.

(JUNE 2014)

13. Let Y_1, Y_2, Y_3 be uncorrelated random variables with common unknown variance σ^2 and expectations given by $E(Y_1) = \beta_0 + \beta_1\ E(Y_2) = \beta_0 + \beta_2\ E(Y_3) = \beta_0 + \beta_3$.
Where $\beta_0, \beta_1, \beta_2, \beta_3$ are unknown parameters. Which of the following statements is true?
(a) The degrees of freedom associated with the error sum of squares is 1
(b) An unbiased estimator of σ^2 is $\frac{1}{6}[(Y_1 - Y_2)^2 + (Y_1 - Y_3)^2 + (Y_2 - Y_3)^2]$
(c) $\beta_0, \beta_1, \beta_2$ and β_3 are each individually estimable
(d) $\beta_1 - 2\beta_2 + \beta_3$ is estimable

(JUNE 2014)

14. For any set of data which of the following statements are NOT possible? (Notations have their usual significance)
(a) $r_{1.234} = 0.47, r_{1.23} = 0.52$
(b) $r_{1.23} = 0.32, r_{12.3} = -0.23$
(c) $r_{12} = 0.3, r_{13} = 0.2,\ r_{12.3} = -0.23$
(d) $r_{1.234} = 0.47, r_{12} = 0.73$

(JUNE 2014)

15. Aerial observation Y_1, Y_2, Y_3 *and* Y_4 are made on angles $\theta_1, \theta_2, \theta_3$ *and* θ_4 respectively, of a quadrilateral on the ground. If the observation $\{Y_i, i = 1,2,3,4\}$ are subject to normal errors with mean 0 and variance σ^2, then which of the following statements are true?
(a) The bests linear unbiased estimator of θ_i is $\hat{\theta}_i = Y_i - \bar{Y} + \frac{\pi}{2}, i = 1,2,3,4$ where $\bar{Y} = \frac{1}{4}\sum_{i=1}^{4} Y_i$
(b) The best linear unbiased estimator of θ_i is $\hat{\theta}_i = Y_i, i = 1,2,3,4$
(c) The error sum of squares is $4\left(\bar{Y} - \frac{\pi}{2}\right)^2$
(d) The error sum of squares is $\sum_{i=1}^{4}\left(Y_i - \frac{\pi}{2}\right)^2$

(DEC. 2014)

16. Suppose $X \sim N(0,1)$ and the conditional distribution of Y given $X = x$ is $N(\alpha x, 1)$, for $0 < \alpha < 1$. When we regress Y on X. The coefficient of determination R^2 is
(a) α^2 (b) α
(c) $\frac{\alpha}{\sqrt{1+\alpha^2}}$ (d) $\frac{\alpha^2}{1+\alpha^2}$

(DEC. 2014)

17. Consider the linear model $E(Y) = X\beta, Cov(Y) = \sigma^2 I$ where X is a matrix of size $n \times p$ having rank $r \le p$. Then which of the following statements are necessarily true?
(a) The set of estimable linear functions from a vector space of dimension r.
(b) If $E(c'Y) = 0$ for some nonzero vector c, then there is a function $l'\beta$ which is not estimable.
(c) If all linear functions $l'\beta$ are estimable, then $r = p$.
(d) The set of functions $c'Y$ with $E(c'Y) = 0$ form a vector space of dimension r.

(DEC. 2014)

18. Consider the linear model
$y_1 = 2\theta + \beta + \epsilon_1$
$y_2 = \beta + 2\gamma + \epsilon_2$
$y_3 = \theta + \beta + \gamma + \epsilon_3$
where θ, β, γ are unknown parameters and e $\epsilon_1, \epsilon_2, \epsilon_3$ are uncorrelated random errors with mean 0 and constant variance. Then which of the following statements are true?

(a) θ, β and γ are estimable (b) $\theta - \gamma$ is estimable
(c) $2\gamma - 2\theta$ is estimable (d) $\theta + \gamma$ is estimable

(JUNE 2015)

19. Consider the model $Y_i = i\beta + \epsilon_i, i = 1,2,3$ where $\epsilon_1, \epsilon_2, \epsilon_3$ are independent with mean 0 and variance $\sigma^2, 2\sigma^2, 3\sigma^2$ respectively. Which of the following is the best unbiased estimate of β?
(a) $\frac{y_1+2y_2+3y_3}{6}$ (b) $\frac{6}{11}\left(y_1 + \frac{y_2}{2} + \frac{y_3}{3}\right)$
(c) $\frac{y_1+y_2+y_3}{6}$ (d) $\frac{3y_1+2y_2+y_3}{10}$

(JUNE 2015)

20. Consider the linear model $Y \sim N_n(X\beta, \sigma^2 I)$, where X is a n X (k + 1) matrix of rank $k+1 < n$. Let $\hat{\beta}$ *and* $\widehat{\sigma^2}$ be the maximum likelihood estimators of β and σ^2 respectively. Then which of the following statements are true?
(a) $cov(\beta) = \sigma^2 X'X$
(b) $\hat{\beta}$ and $\hat{\sigma}^2$ are independently distributed
(c) $\hat{\sigma}^2$ is sufficient for σ^2
(d) $\hat{\sigma}^2 = Y'AY$ where A is a suitable matrix of rank $(n - k - 1)$

(JUNE 2015)

21. Consider the linear model
$Y_1 = \mu_1 - \mu_2 + \epsilon_1$
$Y_2 = \mu_2 - \mu_3 + \epsilon_3$
.
.
$Y_{n-1} = \mu_{n-1} - \mu_n + \epsilon_{n-1}$
$Y_n = \mu_n - \mu_1 + \epsilon_n$
Where $\mu_1, \ldots, \mu_n$ are unknown parameter and $\epsilon_1, \ldots . \epsilon_n$ are uncorrelated with mean 0 and common variance. Let Y be the column vector $(Y_1, Y_2, \ldots, Y_n)'$ and $\bar{Y} = \frac{1}{n}\sum_{i=1}^{n} Y_i$.
Which of the following are correct?
(a) If $E(c'Y) = 0$, then all elements of c' are equal
(b) The best linear unbiased estimator of $\mu_1 - \mu_3$ is $Y_1 + Y_2$
(c) The best linear unbiased estimator of $\mu_2 - \mu_3$ is $Y_2 - \bar{Y}$
(d) All linear function $d_1\mu_1 + \cdots + d_n\mu_n$

(JUNE 2015)

22. Let Y_1, Y_2, Y_3 be uncorrelated observation with common variance σ^2 and expressions given by $E(Y_1) = \theta_0 + \theta_1, E(Y_2) = \theta_0 + \theta_2, E(Y_3) = \theta_0 + \theta_3$, where $\theta_i's$ are unknown parameters. In the framework of the linear model which of the following statement (s) is (are) true?
(a) Each of $\theta_0, \theta_1, \theta_2$ and θ_3 is individually estimable.
(b) $\sum_{i=0}^{3}\theta_i$ is estimable
(c) $\theta_1 - \theta_2, \theta_1 - \theta_3$ and $\theta_2 - \theta_3$ are each estimable
(d) The error sum of squares is zero

(DEC. 2015)

23. Let Y_1, Y_2, Y_3 and Y_4 be uncorrelated observations with common unknown variance σ^2 and expectations given by $E(Y_1) = \beta_1 + \beta_2 + \beta_3 = E(Y_2)$, $E(Y_3) = \beta_1 - \beta_2 = E(Y_4)$, where β_1, β_2 and β_3 are unknown parameters. Define $e_1 = \frac{1}{\sqrt{2}}(Y_1 - Y_2)$ and $e_2 = \frac{1}{\sqrt{2}}(Y_3 - Y_4)$. An unbiased estimator of σ^2 is
(a) $\frac{1}{2}(e_1^2 - e_2^2)$ (b) $\frac{1}{2}(e_1^2 + e_2^2)$
(c) $\frac{1}{4}(e_1^2 + e_2^2)$ (d) $e_1^2 + e_2^2$

(JUNE 2016)

24. Let Y_1, Y_2, Y_3 be uncorrelated observations with common variance σ^2 and expectations given by $\mathbb{E}(Y_1) = \beta_1, \mathbb{E}(Y_2) = \beta_2$ and $\mathbb{E}(Y_3) = \beta_1 + \beta_2$, where β_1, β_2 are unknown parameters. The best linear unbiased estimator of $\beta_1 + \beta_2$ is
(a) Y_1 (b) $Y_1 + Y_2$
(c) $\frac{1}{3}(Y_1 + Y_2 + 2Y_3)$ (d) $\frac{1}{2}(Y_1 + Y_2 + Y_3)$

(JUNE 2016)

25. Let Y_1, Y_2, Y_3, Y_4 be uncorrelated observations such that $\mathbb{E}(Y_1) = \beta_1 + \beta_2 + \beta_3 = \mathbb{E}(Y_2), \mathbb{E}(Y_3) = \beta_1 - \beta_2 = \mathbb{E}(Y_4)$ and $Var(Y_i) = \sigma^2 for\ i = 1,2,3,4$. Then, which of the following statements are true?
(a) $p_1\beta_1 + p_2\beta_2 + p_3\beta_3$ is estimable if and only if $p_1 + p_2 = 2p_3$.
(b) An unbiased estimator of σ^2 is $[(Y_1 - Y_2)^2 + (Y_3 - Y_4)^2]/4$
(c) The best linear unbiased estimator of $\beta_1 - \beta_2$ is $\frac{1}{2}(Y_3 + Y_4)$
(d) The variance of the best linear unbiased estimator of $\beta_1 + \beta_2 + \beta_3$ is σ^2 .

(JUNE 2016)

26. Consider a linear regression model $\underline{Y} = X\underline{\beta} + \underline{\varepsilon}$, where X is an $n \times p$ matrix, rank$(X) = p, \mathbb{E}(\underline{\varepsilon}) = \underline{0}, \mathbb{D}(\underline{\varepsilon}) = \sigma^2 I, \mathbb{E}(.)$, stands for expectation, $\mathbb{D}(.)$ denotes the variance covariance matrix and I is the n-th order identity matrix. Define the $n \times n$ matrix $H = ((h_{ij})) = X(X'X)^{-1}X'$. Then, which of the following are correct?
(a) 1. $0 \le h_{ii} \le 1,\ 1 \le i \le n$
(b) 2. If $h_{ii} = 0$ or 1 for some, then $h_{ij} = 0$ for all $\neq i$.
(c) 3. The variance-covariance matrix of the vector of the predicted values $\hat{\underline{Y}}$ (of Y) is $\sigma^2 H$. .
(d) For $1 \le i \le n$, if e_i is the residual corresponding to $Y_i i.i., e_i = Y_i - \hat{Y}_i, \hat{Y}_i$ being the predicted value of Y_i, , then the variance of e_i equals $\sigma^2(1 - h_{ii})$. (Here, Y_i is the i-th component of $\underline{Y}$).

(DEC. 2016)

27. $(x_1, y_1), (x_2, y_2), \ldots, (x_n, y_n)$ are data on X –cultivable land in a district and Y –the area actually under cultivation, both measured in square feet. Let $\hat{a}, \hat{\beta}$ be the least squares estimates of a, β in the model $Y = a + \beta x + \epsilon$, where ϵ is the random error. If the data are converted to square meters, then
(a) $\hat{a}$ may change but $\hat{\beta}$ will not.
(b) $\hat{\beta}$ may change but $\hat{a}$ will not.
(c) both $\hat{a}$ and $\hat{\beta}$ may change.
(d) Neither $\hat{a}$ nor $\hat{\beta}$ will change

(DEC. 2016)

28. For a data set $(x_1, y_1), (x_2, y_2), \ldots, (x_n, y_n)$ the following two models were fitted using least square method.
Model 1: $y_i = \beta_0 + \beta_1 x_i \quad i = 1,2, \ldots n$
Model 2: $y_i = \beta_0 + \beta_1 x_i + \beta_2 x_i^2 \quad i = 1,2, \ldots n$

Let $\hat{\beta}_0, \hat{\beta}_1$ be least square estimates of β_0, β_1 from model 1 and $\beta_0^*, \beta_1^*, \beta_2^*$ be the least square estimates from model 2.

Let $A = \sum_1^n \left(Y_i - (\hat{\beta}_0 + \hat{\beta}_1 x_i)\right)^2$

$B = \sum_1^n \left(Y_i - (\beta_0^* + \beta_1^* X_i + \beta_2^* x_i^2)\right)^2$

Then

(a) $A \geq B$

(b) $A \leq B$

(c) It can happen that $A = 0$ but $B > 0$

(d) It can happen that $B = 0$ but $A > 0$

29. Consider a logistic regression model with a single regressor x, where the log odds ratio has intercept β_0 and slope β_1. Let T_1 be the ratio of the odds of success when $x = 0$ to that when $x = -1$. Similarly, let T_2 be the ratio of the odds of success when $x = 1$ to that when $x = 0$. Which of the following are true?

(a) $T_1 = T_2$ (b) $T_1 T_2 = 1$

(c) $T_1 T_2 = e^{\beta_0}$ (d) $T_1 T_2 = e^{2\beta_1}$

(JUNE 2017)

30. Consider the linear statistical model $y_{ij} = \mu + \tau_i + \varepsilon_{ij}$; $i = 1,2,\ldots,a; j = 1,2,\ldots,n$

where μ is unknown, τ_i are independently and identically distributed as $N(0, \sigma_\tau^2)$, ε_{ij} are independently and identically distributed as $N(0, \sigma^2)$; τ_i and ε_{ij} are independent for all i and j. Note that τ_i is the ith treatment effect. Suppose $SS_{total}, SS_{treatment}, SS_{error}$ are total sum of squares, total treatment sum of squares and error sum of squares, respectively.

To test: $H_0: \sigma_\tau^2 = 0$ vs $H_A: \sigma_\tau^2 > 0$ which of the following statements is not true?

(a) The sum of squares identity is

$SS_{total} = SS_{treatment} + SS_{error}$

(b) $SS_{error} \sim \sigma^2 \chi^2_{n(a-1)}$

(c) Under H_0, $\dfrac{\frac{SS_{treatment}}{a-1}}{\frac{SS_{error}}{n(a-1)}} \sim F_{a-1, n(a-1)}$

(d) $E(SS_{error}) = n(a-1)(\sigma^2 + \sigma_\tau^2)$

(JUNE 2017)

31. Consider the model $Y = X\beta + \epsilon$, where $Y = \begin{bmatrix} y_1 \\ y_2 \\ \vdots \\ y_n \end{bmatrix}$, $X = ((x_{ij}))_{n \times p}$ and $\beta = \begin{bmatrix} \beta_1 \\ \vdots \\ \beta_p \end{bmatrix}$, $\epsilon = \begin{bmatrix} \epsilon_1 \\ \epsilon_2 \\ \vdots \\ \epsilon_n \end{bmatrix}$. $E(\epsilon) = 0$ and $D(\epsilon) = \sigma^2 I_n, p < n$. Let $\hat{\beta}$ be the solution of

$X^T X \beta = X^T Y$.

Which of the following are true?

(a) If $C^T \beta$ is estimable then $C^T \hat{\beta}$ is the best linear unbiased estimator (BLUE) of $C^T \beta$

(b) All linear parametric functions are estimable if and only if Rank $(X) > p$.

(c) If Rank $(X) < p$ then some linear parametric functions are not estimable.

(d) $(Y - X\hat{\beta})^T (Y - X\hat{\beta})/(n-p)$ is an unbiased estimator of σ^2.

(DEC. 2017)

32. Consider the following regression problem $Y_i = \alpha + \beta_i + \epsilon_i; i = 1, \ldots, n$

Here $\epsilon_i; i = 1,2,\ldots,n$ are i.i.d $N(0,1)$ random variables. It is assumed that $\alpha \neq 0$ and β is known. If $\hat{a}_n$ is the MLE of , which of the following statements is true?

(a) $lim_{n \to \infty} E(\hat{a}_n) \neq \alpha$

(b) $lim_{n \to \infty} E(\hat{a}_n) = 0$

(c) $lim_{n \to \infty} Var(\hat{a}_n) = \infty$

(d) $lim_{n \to \infty} Var(\hat{a}_n) = 0$

(DEC. 2018)

33. Consider a linear model $Y_i = \theta_1 + \theta_2 + \epsilon_i \; for \; i = 1,2$ and $Y_i = \theta_1 - \theta_3 + \epsilon_i \; for \; i = 3,4$, where ϵ_i are independent with $E(\epsilon_i) = 0$, $Var(\epsilon_i) = \sigma^2 > 0$ for $i = 1, \ldots 4$, and $\theta_1, \ldots \theta_3 \in \mathbb{R}$. Which of the following parametric function is estimable?

(a) $\theta_1 + \theta_3$ (b) $\theta_2 - \theta_3$

(c) $\theta_2 + \theta_3$ (d) $\theta_2 + \theta_2 + \theta_3$

(DEC. 2018)

34. Consider a linear model $Y_{4\times1} = X_{4\times4}\beta_{4\times1} + \varepsilon_{4\times1}$ where $Disp(\varepsilon) = \sigma^{2/4}$ for some $\sigma^2 > 0$. One need to choose the design matrix X such that its elements take values in the set {-1,0,1}. Now, consider the following three choice of X

$X_1 = \begin{bmatrix} 1 & 0 & 0 & 0 \\ 0 & 1 & 0 & 0 \\ 0 & 0 & 1 & 0 \\ 0 & 0 & 0 & 1 \end{bmatrix}, X_2 = \begin{bmatrix} 1 & -1 & 0 & 0 \\ 1 & 1 & 0 & 0 \\ 0 & 0 & 1 & -1 \\ 0 & 0 & 1 & 1 \end{bmatrix}$ and

$X_3 = \begin{bmatrix} 1 & 1 & 1 & 1 \\ 1 & 1 & -1 & -1 \\ 1 & -1 & -1 & 1 \\ 1 & -1 & 1 & -1 \end{bmatrix}$

Which of the following statement are true?

(a) For all three choices of X, $\beta = (\beta_1, \beta_2, \beta_3, \beta_4)$ is estimable

(b) For all three choices of X, $\hat{\beta}_i$ *and* $\hat{\beta}_j$, the least squared estimates of β_i and β_j are uncorrelated for all $i = j$

(c) X_2 is better choice than X_1

(d) X_2 is better choice than X_3

(JUNE 2019)

35. Suppose $r_{1.23}$ *and* $r_{1.234}$ are sample multiple correlation coefficient of X_1 on X_2, X_3 and X_1 on X_2, X_3, X_4 respectively. Which of the following is possible?

(a) $r_{1.23} = -0.3, r_{1.234} = 0.7$

(b) $r_{1.23} = -0.7, r_{1.234} = 0.3$

(c) $r_{1.23} = -0.3, r_{1.234} = 0.7$

(d) $r_{1.23} = -0.7, r_{1.234} = -0.3$

(NOV. 2020)

36. Let I, J>5. Consider two-way ANOVA where the observation satisfy the linear model

$$y_{ij} = \alpha + \beta_i + \gamma_j + \varepsilon_{ij}, 1 \leq i \leq I, 1 \leq j \leq J$$

$$E(\varepsilon_{ij}) = 0, Var(\varepsilon_{ij}) = \sigma^2, \sum_{i=1}^{I} \beta_i = \sum_{j=1}^{J} \gamma_j = 0$$

In this set-up

(a) β_1 is estimable
(b) γ_1 is estimable
(c) $\beta_1 - \beta_2$ is estimable
(d) $\beta_1 + \gamma_2$ is estimable

(NOV. 2020)

37. Consider the Gauss-Markov model $Y_{n\times 1} = X_{n\times p}\beta_{p\times 1} + \varepsilon_{n\times 1}$, where $E(\varepsilon) = 0$ and Dispersion$(\varepsilon) = \sigma^2 I_{n\times n}$. Suppose that $p < n$. Which of the following are correct?
(a) Least-squares estimate of β is unique
(b) Least-squares estimate of an estimable linear function of β is unique
(c) Least-squares estimate Xβ is unique
(d) Determinant $(X^T X) > 0$

(NOV. 2020)

38. Let $p > 1$ and $1 > \rho \geq 0$. Consider a multiple linear regression problem with p independent variables $X_1, X_2, \dots, X_p$ and a dependent variable Y. Suppose that the correlation between Y and X_i is ρ and the correlation between X_i and X_j is also ρ for all $1 \leq i \leq j \leq p$. Which of the following are correct?
(a) The multiple correlation between Y and $(X_1, \dots, X_p)$ is larger than or equal to ρ
(b) The multiple correlation between Y and $(X_1, \dots, X_p)$ will be ρ if $\rho = 0$
(c) The multiple correlation between Y and $(X_1, \dots, X_p)$ will be ρ if only if $\rho = 0$
(d) The multiple correlation between Y and $(X_1, \dots, X_p)$ tends to 1 as $p \to \infty$

(JUNE 2021)

39. Suppose $(x_1, y_1), (x_2, y_2), \dots, (x_n, y_n)$ are bivariate measurements where $n > 2$. Assume that all the x_i are distinct and all the y_i are distinct too. Let r_p denote the ordinary (Pearson) correlation coefficient and r_s denote the (Spearman) rank correlation coefficient. Suppose $r_p = 1$. Which of the following is true?
(a) $0.5 < r_s < 1$
(b) $r_s = 0.5$
(c) $r_s = 1$
(d) $r_s = -1$

(SEP 2022)

40. Consider the multiple linear regression model $Y_i = \beta_1 x_{i1} + \cdots + \beta_p x_{ip} + \epsilon_i$, with $E(\epsilon_i) = 0$, $Cov(\epsilon_i, \epsilon_k) = 0$, if $i \neq k$ and $Var(\epsilon_i) = \sigma^2$, for $i, k = 1, \dots, n$.
If $\hat{y}_1$, is the least squares fit of y_i, and $\hat{\epsilon}_i$, is the corresponding estimated residual for $i = 1, \dots, n$, then which of the following statements are always correct?
Options:
(a) $\sum_i \hat{\epsilon}_i = 0$ and $\sum_i \hat{y}_i \hat{\epsilon}_i = 0$
(b) $\sum_i x_{ij} \hat{\epsilon}_i = 0$; for all $j = 1, \dots, p$
(c) $\sum_i \hat{\epsilon}_i = 0$ and $\sum_i x_{ij} \hat{\epsilon}_i = 0$; for all $j = 1, \dots, p$
(d) $\sum_i \hat{y}_i \hat{\epsilon}_i = 0$

(SEP 2022)

41. Let $\begin{pmatrix} X \\ Y \\ Z \end{pmatrix} \sim N_3\left(\begin{pmatrix} 0 \\ 0 \\ 0 \end{pmatrix}, \begin{pmatrix} 1 & \rho & 0 \\ \rho & 1 & 0 \\ 0 & 0 & 1 \end{pmatrix}\right)$, where $|\rho| < 1$. Which of the following is TRUE?
(a) $Cor(X^2, Y^2) = \rho^2$
(b) $Cor(X^2, Y) = 0$
(c) $Cor(X^2, Z^2) = 0$
(d) $Cor(X^2, Y^2 + Z^2) = \rho^2$

(SEP 2022)

42. Consider the simple linear model $Y_i = \beta X_i + \varepsilon_i$, for $i = 1, \dots, n$ where $\varepsilon_i's$ are i.i.d $N(0, \sigma^2)$ random variables and $X_i's$ are non-random, positive and distinct. Consider two estimates of β given below

$$\hat{\beta} = \frac{\sum_{i=1}^n (Y_i - \bar{Y})(X_i - \bar{X})}{\sum_{i=1}^n (X_i - \bar{X})^2}$$

$$\hat{\beta}_2 = \frac{\sum_{i=1}^n Y_i X_i}{\sum_{i=1}^n X_i^2}$$

(a) Both $\hat{\beta}_1$ and $\hat{\beta}_2$ are unbiased estimates for β.
(b) $\hat{\beta}_1$ has larger variance than $\hat{\beta}_2$.
(c) $\hat{\beta}_2$ has larger variance than $\hat{\beta}_1$.
(d) $\hat{\beta}_1$ has the same variance as that of $\hat{\beta}_2$.

(JUNE 2023)

43. Let a continuous random variable X follow Uniform $(-1,1)$. Define $Y = x^2$. Which of the following are NOT true for X and Y?
(a) They are independent and uncorrelated.
(b) They are independent but correlated.
(c) They are not independent but correlated.
(d) They are neither independent nor correlated.

(JUNE 2023)

44. Consider the linear model $E(Y_1) = 2\beta_1 - \beta_2 - \beta_3, E(Y_2) = \beta_2 - \beta_4, E(Y_3) = \beta_2 + \beta_3 - 2\beta_4$ with uncorrelated and homoscedastic random error. Which of the following linear parametric functions are estimable?
(a) $16\beta_1 - 9\beta_2 - 7\beta_3$
(b) $\beta_3 - \beta_4$
(c) $57\beta_1 - 18\beta_2 - 13\beta_3 - 26\beta_4$
(d) $23\beta_1 - 9\beta_2 - 10\beta_3 + 4\beta_4$

(JULY-2024)

45. An analyst considers standardized values of observations on three variables, consumption (C), saving (S) and total income (TI) so that they have zero means and unit variances. She further considers disposable income (DI) where DI=C+S. In the simple linear regressions of DI on TI, DI on C and S on TI, the regression coefficients are 0.8, 0.5 and 0.4, respectively. There are 21 sample observations. Sample covariance's and variances are calculated with divisor 20. Then, the value of sum of squared residuals in the regression of DI on s is
(a) 5
(b) 10
(c) 15
(d) 20

(JULY 2024)

46. In a standard linear regression model, let R^2 and $\overline{R}^2$ respectively, denote the coefficient of determination and adjusted coefficient of determination. Which of the following statements are true?
(a) $\overline{R}^2 < R^2$

(b) R^2 increases as the number of independent variables increase

(c) $\overline{R}^2$ decreases as the number of independent variables increase

(d) $\overline{R}^2 > 0$

(FEB. 2025)

47. Consider a multiple linear regression model $Y_i = \beta_0 + \beta_1 x_{i1} + \cdots + \beta_p x_{ip} + \epsilon_i,\ 1 \le i \le n, n > (p+1)$, where the errors ϵ_i's are uncorrelated with zero mean and finite variance $\sigma^2 > 0$. Here, Y_i is the i-th response. Let $\widehat{Y_i}$ be the i-th predicted response by the least squares estimation method, and let $\widehat{\epsilon_i} = Y_i - \widehat{Y}_i, 1 \le i \le n$. Then, which of the following statements is true?

(a) $Var(\hat{\epsilon}_i) \le Var(\epsilon_i), 1 \le i \le n$

(b) $Cov(\hat{\epsilon}_i, \hat{\epsilon}_k) = Cov(\epsilon_i, \epsilon_k)$, for all $i \ne k = 1,2,\ldots,n$

(c) $Var(\widehat{Y}_i) = Var(Y_i), 1 \le i \le n$

(d) $E(\widehat{Y}_i) < E(Y_i), 1 \le i \le n$

(FEB. 2025)

48. Consider a linear regression model $Y = X\beta + \epsilon$, with r regressors and an intercept. Random error $\epsilon \sim N_n(0, \sigma^2 I_n)$ and X has full column rank. Here I_n denotes the identity matrix of order n. Regression coefficients are estimated by the least squares estimation method. Let $\widehat{\sigma}^2$ and $\widehat{\sigma}^2{}_{MLE}$, respectively, be the mean squares residuals and the maximum likelihood estimator of σ^2. Then, which of the following statements are true?

(a) $MSE(\widehat{\sigma}^2{}_{MLE}) < MSE(\widehat{\sigma}^2)$ if $r = 2, n = 12$

(b) $Var(\widehat{\sigma}^2{}_{MLE}) > Var(\widehat{\sigma}^2)$ if $2 \le r \le n-2, n \ge 12$

(c) $Var(\widehat{\sigma}^2{}_{MLE}) < Var(\widehat{\sigma}^2)$ if $1 \le r \le n-2, n \ge 3$

(d) $MSE(\widehat{\sigma}^2{}_{MLE}) > MSE(\widehat{\sigma}^2)$ if $r = 7, n = 12$

(FEB. 2025)

49. Consider a linear model $Y_i = \beta_1 + \beta_2 + \cdots + \beta_i + \epsilon_i, 1 \le i \le n$, where errors ϵ_i's are uncorrelated with zero mean and finite variance $\sigma^2 > 0$. Let $\widehat{\beta}_i$ be the best linear unbiased estimator (BLUE) of $\beta_i, i = 1,2,\ldots,n$. Then, which of the following statements are true?

(a) The sum of squares residuals is strictly positive with probability 1.

(b) For every $\beta_{i,} 1 \le i \le n, 1 \le i \le n$, there are infinitely many linear unbiased estimators.

(c) $Var(\widehat{\beta}_1) = \sigma^2$

(d) $Y_3 - Y_2$ is the BLUE of β_3.

(JUNE 2025)

50. Suppose $\begin{pmatrix} X_1 \\ X_2 \\ X_3 \end{pmatrix} \sim N_3\left(\begin{pmatrix} 0 \\ 0 \\ 0 \end{pmatrix}, \begin{pmatrix} 1 & 0 & 0 \\ 0 & 1 & 0 \\ 0 & 0 & 1 \end{pmatrix}\right)$ and $\begin{pmatrix} X \\ Y \\ Z \end{pmatrix} = \begin{pmatrix} 3 & 0 & 0 \\ 2 & 2 & 0 \\ 4 & 0 & 4 \end{pmatrix}\begin{pmatrix} X_1 \\ X_2 \\ X_3 \end{pmatrix}$.

Then the partial correlation coefficient $pyz.x$ is

(a) $\frac{1}{2}$ (b) $\frac{2}{3}$

(c) $\frac{3}{4}$ (d) 0

(JUNE 2025)

51. Consider a paired data (x, y); $i = 1, 2, 3, 4, 5$, where $(x_1, x_2, x_3, x_4, x_5) = (-2, -1, 0, 1, 2)$ and $y_i = x_i^2$ for all i = 1, 2, 3, 4, 5. On this data, a simple linear regression model with an intercept term and a simple linear regression model without an intercept term are fitted using the method of least squares. Which of the following statements are true?

(a) The two fitted lines have the same slope

(b) The two fitted models have the same intercept

(c) The model with intercept passes through at least one of the observed data points

(d) The model without intercept passes through at lesast one of the observed data points

(JUNE 2025)

52. An analyst fits a multiple linear regression model $Y_1 = \beta_0 + \beta_0 X_{1i} + +\beta_4 X_{4i} + \epsilon_i, i = 1,2,\ldots,n,$ using the method of least squares. However, his coordinator insists that the intercept and two regressors $Z_1 - X_1 + X_3$, and $Z_2 - X_2 - X_4$, are enough to represent the model. Suppose the coordinator's claim can be tested in the form of a general linear hypothesis, viz., $H_0: L^T\beta = 0$ against $H_A: H_0$ is not true, where $\beta^T = (\beta_0, \beta_1, \ldots, \beta_n)$. Suppose we have n observations on the response Y and each regressor. Further, assume that the errors with or without restrictions are independent $N(0, \sigma^2)$ variables. Then, which of the following statements are true?

(a) A possible choice of L is $\begin{pmatrix} 0 & 0 \\ 1 & 0 \\ 0 & 1 \\ -1 & 0 \\ 0 & 1 \end{pmatrix}$

(b) The test statistic for testing H_0 against H_A follows an F-distribution with $(2, n-4)$ degrees of freedom under H_0

(c) Sum of squares residuals under the restrictions $L^T\beta = 0$ follows $\sigma^2 x_{n-1}^2$ distribution

(d) Sum of squares residuals without the restrictions $L^T\beta = 0$ follows a non-central $\sigma^2 x_{n-1}^2$ distribution

Answer Key									
1	**2**	**3**	**4**	**5**	**6**	**7**	**8**	**9**	**10**
d	a,b,c	d	a	b,d	b	b	a	c,d	b,c,d
11	**12**	**13**	**14**	**15**	**16**	**17**	**18**	**19**	**20**
d	a,b,c,d	d	a,b,c,d	a,c	d	a,b,c	b,c	c	b,d
21	**22**	**23**	**24**	**25**	**26**	**27**	**28**	**29**	**30**
a,c	c,d	b	c	a,b,c	a,b,c,d	a	a,d	a,d	b,c,d
31	**32**	**33**	**34**	**35**	**36**	**37**	**38**	**39**	**40**
a,c,d	d	c	a,b,c	c	c	b	a	c	b, d
41	**42**	**43**	**44**	**45**	**46**	**47**	**48**	**49**	**50**
a, b, c	a, b	a,b,c	a,b,c	c	a,b	a	a,c	c,d	d
51	**52**								
a,d	a,c								

:: Explanations ::

1. Explanation: (d)

$Y = \beta X + \in$

$\hat{Y}_0$ be the least square prediction of Y at $X = x_0$

The standard error of $\hat{Y}_0 = \sigma\sqrt{1 + x_0(X'X)^{-1}x_0'}$ is decrease when x_0 closed to zero

So, option (d) is correct.

2. Explanation: (a), (b), (c)

$(X\ Y): (0,1)(1,2)\ (2,3)\ (3,2)\ (4,1)$

The least square linear regression of Y on X is $\overline{Y}$

The least square linear regression of X on Y is $\overline{X}$

$\overline{X} = \frac{0+1+2+3+4}{5} = 2$

$\overline{Y} = \frac{1+2+3+2+1}{5} = \frac{9}{5}$

Correction $\rho = \frac{(0(x,y))}{\sqrt{Var\ (X)\ Var\ (Y)}}$

$Cov(X,Y) = \frac{1}{n}\left[\sum_{i=1}^{n} x_i\, y_i - n\bar{x}\bar{y}\right]$

$\sum_{i=1}^{5} X_i\, Y_i = 0 + 2 + 6 + 6 + 4 = 18$

$Cov\ (x, y) = \frac{1}{5}\left[18 - 5 \times 2 \times \frac{9}{5}\right] = 0$

$\therefore$ correlation $= 0$

So, option (a), (b) and (c) are correct.

3. Explanation: (d)

4. Explanation: (a)

5. Explanation: (b), (d)

$R^2 = 1 - \frac{SS_{Res}}{SS_{Total}}$

Where SS_{Res} represents sum of square due to regression Y on X and SS_{Total} be the total sum of square

$Var(\boldsymbol{\beta}) = \sigma^2(X'X)^{-1}$

Option (b) and (d) are correct

6. Explanation: (b)

7. Explanation: (b)

If the relationship is that one variable increases when the other increases, but the amount is not consistent the Pearson correlation coefficient is positive but less then $+1$.The spearman coefficient still equals $+1$ in this case. This implies, $0 < r_p < 1$ and $r_s = 1$

So, option (b) is correct

8. Explanation: (a)

The model

$Y_i = a + (-1)^i b + e_i\ ; i = 1, 2, \ldots n\ ; n \geq 3$

$e_i^1\ s$ are iid $N(0, \sigma^2)$

The mle of a & b are same as least square estimator of a & b

For given model least square are always exists, which implies mle of a and b are exists

So, option (a) is correct

9. Explanation: (c), (d)

10. Explanation: (b), (c), (d)

Equation (1): $5x - 8y + 14 = 0$

$x = \frac{8y}{5} - \frac{14}{5}$ Which is regression line of x on y

$b_{xy} = 8/5$

Equation (2): $2x + 5y + 11 = 0$

$y = \frac{2}{5}x + \frac{11}{5}$ Which is regression line of y on x

$b_{yx} = \frac{2}{5}$

The correlation coefficient is the geometric mean of the regression coefficients i.e.

$r = \sqrt{b_{yx} \cdot b_{xy}} = \sqrt{\frac{2}{5} \times \frac{8}{5}} = \pm\frac{4}{5} = \pm 0.8$

Regression coefficients are positive so, correlation coefficient is also positive

$r = +0.8$

$\therefore b_{yx} = \frac{r\,\sigma_y}{\sigma_x}$

$\frac{2}{5} = \frac{4}{5}\frac{\sigma_y}{\sigma_x}$

$\Rightarrow \sigma_x = 2\,\sigma_y$

σ_y is less than σ_x

$5x - 8y + 14 = 0$

$2x - 5y + 11 = 0$

On solving these equation simultaneously, we get $x = 2$ and $y = 3$

$\therefore (\bar{x}, \bar{y}) = (2, 3)$

So, option (b), (c) and (d) are correct

11. Explanation: (d)

$X_0, \varepsilon_1, \varepsilon_2, \varepsilon_3, \varepsilon_4$ are iid $N(0, \sigma^2)$

Define $X_{i+1} = \rho\, X_i + \left(\sqrt{1 - \rho^2}\right) \varepsilon_{i+1}$

where $o < \rho < 1\ i = 0, 1, 2, 3$

$\rho_{14.2} = \frac{\rho_{14} - \rho_{12}\,\rho_{24}}{\sqrt{(1-\rho_{12}^2)(1-\rho_{24}^2)}}$

$i = 3$

$X_4 = \rho\, X_3 + \left(\sqrt{1 - \rho^2}\right) \varepsilon_4$

$= \rho\left[P\, X_2 + \sqrt{1 - \rho^2}\ \varepsilon_3\right] + \left(\sqrt{1 - \rho^2}\right) \varepsilon_4$

$X_4 = \rho^2\, X_2 + \rho\,\sqrt{1 - \rho^2}\ \varepsilon_3 + \left(\sqrt{1 - \rho^2}\right) \varepsilon_4$

$= \rho^2\left[\rho\, X_1 + \left(\sqrt{1 - \rho^2}\right) \varepsilon_2\right] + \rho\,\sqrt{1 - \rho^2}\ \varepsilon_3 + \sqrt{1 - \rho^2}\ \varepsilon_4$

$= \rho^3\, X_1 + \rho^2\sqrt{1 - \rho^2}\ \varepsilon_2 + \rho\sqrt{1 - \rho^2}\ \varepsilon_3 + \sqrt{1 - \rho^2}\ \varepsilon_4$

$X_4 = \rho^4\, X_0 + \rho^3\sqrt{1 - \rho^2}\ \varepsilon_1 + \rho^2\sqrt{1 - \rho^2}\ \varepsilon_2 + \rho\,\sqrt{1 - \rho^2}\ \varepsilon_3 + \sqrt{1 - \rho^2}\ \varepsilon_4$

$X_1 = \rho\, X_0 + \sqrt{1 - \rho^2}\ \varepsilon_1$

$X_2 = \rho^2\, X_0 + \rho\sqrt{1 - \rho^2}\ \varepsilon_1 + \sqrt{1 - \rho^2}\ \varepsilon_2$

$Cov\ (X_1, X_2) = \rho^3 Var(X_0) + \rho(1 - \rho^2)Var(\varepsilon_1)$

$= \rho^3\,\sigma^2 + \rho\,(1 - \rho^2)\sigma^2$

$= \sigma^2[\rho^3 + \rho - \rho^3] = \rho\,\sigma^2$

$Cov\ (X_1, X_4) = \rho^5\, Var(X_0) + \rho^3\,(1 - \rho^2)\, Var(\varepsilon_1)$

$= \sigma^2\,[\rho^5 + \rho^3 - \rho^5] = \rho^3\,\sigma^2$

$Var\ (X_1) = \rho^2\sigma^2 + (1 - \rho^2)\,\sigma^2 = \sigma^2$

$Var(X_2) = \rho^4\sigma^2 + \rho^2(1 - \rho^2)\sigma^2 + (1 - \rho^2)\sigma^2$

$= \sigma^2[\rho^4 + \rho^2 - \rho^4 + 1 - \rho^2] = \sigma^2$

$Var(X_4) = \rho^8\sigma^2 + \rho^6(1 - \rho^2)\sigma^2 + \rho^4(1 - \rho^2)\sigma^2 + \rho^2(1 - \rho^2)\sigma^2 + (1 - \rho^2)\sigma^2$

$= \sigma^2$

$Cov(X_2\ X_4) = \rho^6\sigma^2 + \rho^4(1 - \rho^2)\sigma^2 + \rho^2(1 - \rho^2)\sigma^2 = \rho^2\sigma^2$

$\rho_{12} = \frac{Cov\ (X_1\ X_2)}{\sqrt{Var(X_1)Var(X_2)}} = \frac{\rho\,\sigma^2}{\sqrt{\sigma^2\,\sigma^2}} = \rho$

$\rho_{24} = \frac{Cov\ (X_1\ X_2)}{\sqrt{Var(X_2)Var(X_4)}} = \rho^2$

$\rho_{14} = \frac{Cov\ (X_1\ X_4)}{\sqrt{Var(X_1)Var(X_2)}} = \rho^3$

$\rho_{14.2} = \frac{\rho^3 - \rho\,\rho^2}{\sqrt{(1-\rho^2)(1-\rho^4)}} = 0$

$\rho_{14.2} = 0$

So, option (d) is correct

12. Explanation: (a), (b), (c), (d)

13. Explanation: (d)

Y_1, Y_2, Y_3 be uncorrected random variable with unknown variance σ^2 and

$E(Y_1) = \beta_0 + \beta_1$ ________ (1)

$E(Y_2) = \beta_0 + \beta_2$ ________ (2)

$E(Y_3) = \beta_0 + \beta_3$ ________ (3)

Subtract (2) from (1) & (2) from (3)

$E(Y_1 - Y_2) = \beta_1 - \beta_2$ & $E(Y_3 - Y_2) - \beta_3 - \beta_2$ ____ (5)

Add equation (4) & (5)

$E[Y_1 - Y_2 + Y_3 - Y_2] = \beta_2 - 2\beta_2 + \beta_3$

$E[Y_1 - 2Y_2 + Y_3] = \beta_1 - 2\beta_2 + \beta_3$

So, $\beta_1 - 2\beta_2 + \beta_3$ is estimable

So, option (d) is correct

14. Explanation: (a), (b), (c), (d)

15. Explanation: (a), (c)

16. Explanation: (d)

$X \sim N(0,1)$ and $Y|X = x \sim N(\alpha x, 1)\ 0 < \alpha < 1$

When regress Y on X, the coefficient of determination,

$R^2 = 1 - \frac{SS_{Reg}}{SS_{Total}}$

$SS_{total} = Var(Y)$ and $SS_{Reg} = Var[Y|X = x]$

$Var(Y) = Var\,(E(Y|X = x) + E[Var\,(Y|X = x)]$

$= Var(\alpha x) + E[1]$

$SS_{Total} = \alpha^2 + 1$

$Var[Y|X = x] = 1$

$SS_{Reg} = 1$

$R^2 = 1 - \frac{1}{1+\alpha^2} = \frac{1+\alpha^2-1}{1+\alpha^2} = \frac{\alpha^2}{1+\alpha^2}$

So, option (d) is correct

17. Explanation: (a), (b), (c)

18. Explanation: (b), (c)

$y_1 = 2\theta + \beta + \varepsilon_1$ _____ (1)

$y_2 = \beta + 2\gamma + \varepsilon_2$ _____ (2)

$y_3 = \theta + \beta + \gamma + \varepsilon_3$ _____ (3)

θ is not estimable because there is no linear combination of $y_i's$ which is equal to θ.

Subtract equation (3) from (1)

$y_1 - y_3 = \theta - \gamma + \varepsilon_1 - \varepsilon_3$

taking expectation

$E(y_1 - y_3) = \theta - \gamma$

$\theta - \gamma$ is estimable

Similarly, $E[2y_3 - 2y_1] = 2\gamma - 2\theta$

$2\gamma - 2\theta$ is estimable

So, option (b) and (c) are correct

19. Explanation: (c)

$Y_i = i\beta + \varepsilon_i\ i = 1, 2, 3$

Where $\varepsilon_1, \varepsilon_2, \varepsilon_3$ are independent with mean 0 and variance $\sigma^2, 2\sigma^2, 3\sigma^2$ respectively

Let $T_1 = \frac{Y_1 + 2Y_2 + Y_3}{6}$

$E(T_1) = \frac{1}{6}[E(Y_1) + 2E(Y_2) + 3E(Y_3)]$

$= \frac{1}{6}[\beta + 2.2\beta + 3.3\beta] = \frac{1}{6}[14\beta] = \frac{7}{3}\beta$

T_1 is not an unbiased for β

$T_2 = \frac{6}{11}\left(Y_1 + \frac{Y_2}{2} + \frac{Y_3}{3}\right)$

$E(T_2) = \frac{6}{11}\left[E(Y_1) + \frac{E(Y_2)}{2} + \frac{E(Y_3)}{3}\right] = \frac{6}{11}\left[\beta + \frac{2\beta}{2} + \frac{3\beta}{3}\right]$

$= \frac{6}{11}.3\beta = \frac{18}{11}\beta$

T_2 is not an unbiased estimator for β

$T_3 = \frac{Y_1 + Y_2 + Y_3}{6}$

$E(T_3) = \beta$

T_3 is an unbiased for β

$T_4 = \frac{3Y_1 + 2Y_2 + Y_3}{10}$

$E(T_4) = \frac{3E(Y_1) + 2E(Y_2) + E(Y_3)}{10} = \frac{3\beta + 4\beta + 3\beta}{10}$

$E(T_4) = \beta$

T_4 is also an unbiased estimator for β

Now, check the variance T_3 and T_4 which is minimum

$Var(T_3) = \frac{1}{36}[Var(Y_1) + Var(Y_2) + Var(Y_3)]$

$= \frac{1}{36}[\sigma^2 + 2\sigma^2 + 3\sigma^2] = \frac{6\sigma^2}{36} = \frac{\sigma^2}{6}$

$Var(T_4) = \frac{1}{100}[9Var(Y_1) + 4Var(Y_2) + Var(Y_3)]$

$= \frac{1}{100}[9\sigma^2 + 8\sigma^2 + 3\sigma^2] = \frac{20\sigma^2}{100} = \frac{\sigma^2}{5}$

$\therefore Var(T_3) < Var(T_4)$

$T_3 = \frac{Y_1 + Y_2 + Y_3}{6}$ is BLUE for β

So, option (c) is correct

20. Explanation: (b), (d)

21. Explanation: (a), (c)

Consider the model

$Y_1 = \mu_1 - \mu_2 + \varepsilon_1$

$Y_2 = \mu_2 - \mu_3 + \varepsilon_3$

$Y_{n-1} = \mu_{n-1} - \mu_n + \varepsilon_{n-1}$

$Y_n = \mu_n - \mu_1 + \varepsilon_n$

Let $c' = (c_1\ c_2 \ldots c_n)'$

When $c_1 = c_2 = \cdots c_n$

$E(C'Y) = E[CY_1 + CY_2 + \cdots CY_n]$

$= C(E(Y_1) + E(Y_2) + \cdots + E(Y_n))$

$= C[\mu_1 - \mu_2 + \mu_2 - \mu_3 + \cdots + \mu_{n-1} - \mu_n + \mu_n - \mu_1] = 0$

If all elements of c' are equal then $E(C'Y) = 0$

$E(Y_1) = \mu_1 - \mu_2$ $E(Y_1 + Y_2) = \mu_1 - \mu_3$

$E(Y_2) = \mu_2 - \mu_3$ $E(Y_1 + Y_3 + \bar{Y}) = \mu_1 - \mu_3$

$\therefore E(Y_1 + Y_2) = \mu_1 - \mu_3$

$Var(Y_1 + Y_2 + \bar{Y}) \leq Var(Y_1 + Y_3)$

So $Y_1 + Y_2$ is not BLUE

$E(Y_2 - \bar{Y}) = E(Y_2) - E(\bar{Y}) = E(Y_2) = \mu_2 - \mu_3$

$Y_2 - \bar{Y}$ is BLUE for $\mu_2 - \mu_3$

All linear function $d_1\mu_1 + \cdots + d_n\mu_n$ are not estimator

For ex.: $d_1 = 1, d_2 = 1, d_3 = d_4 = 0$

$\mu_1 + \mu_2$ is not a estimable

So, option (a) and (c) are correct

22. Explanation: (c), (d)

Y_1, Y_2, Y_3 be uncorrelated observations with common variance σ^2

$E(Y_1) = \theta_0 + \theta_1$ ………… (1)

$E(Y_2) = \theta_0 + \theta_2$ .... (2)

$E(Y_3) = \theta_0 + \theta_3$ .... (3)

θ_i's are unknown parameter

θ_0 cannot be estimable because there is no linear combination of Y_i which is equal to θ_0

Similarly, $\theta_1 + \theta_2 + \theta_3 = \sum_{i=1}^{3} \theta_i$ is not estimable

So, option (a), (b) are incorrect

Equation (1) – equation (2)

$E(Y_1 - Y_2) = \theta_1 - \theta_2$

And equation (1) – equation (3), equation (2) – equation (3)

$E(Y_1 - Y_3) = \theta_1 - \theta_3$ and $E(Y_2 - Y_3) = \theta_2 - \theta_3$

Error sum of square $= \sum_{i=1}^{n} \varepsilon_i^2 = \varepsilon'\varepsilon$

$= (Y - X\underline{\theta})'(\underline{Y} - 1X\theta)$

$= X'X\theta - X'\underline{Y} = 0$

So, option (c) and (d) are correct

23. Explanation: (b)

Y_1, Y_2, Y_3 and Y_4 be uncorrelated observation with common variance σ^2 and

$E[Y_1] = \beta_1 + \beta_2 + \beta_3 = E(Y_2)$

$E[Y_3] = \beta_1 - \beta_2 = E(Y_4)$

Define $e_1 = \frac{1}{\sqrt{2}}(Y_1 - Y_2)$ and $e_2 = \frac{1}{\sqrt{2}}(Y_3 - Y_4)$

$E[e_1^2] = E\left[\frac{1}{2}(Y_1 - Y_2)^2\right] = \frac{1}{2}[E(Y_1^2) + E(Y_2^2) - 2E(Y_1)E(Y_2)]$

$= \frac{1}{2}\{2E(Y_1^2) - 2[E(Y_1)]^2\}$

24. Explanation: (c)

Y_1, Y_2, Y_3 be uncorrelated observations with common variance σ^2, $E(Y_1) = \beta_1, E(Y_2) = \beta_2$ and $E(Y_3) = \beta_1 + \beta_2$

We need to find the Bert linear unbiased estimator for $\beta_1 + \beta_2$

$E(Y_3) = \beta_1 + \beta_2$

Y_3 is an unbiased estimator for $\beta_1 + \beta_2$

$E(Y_1 + Y_2) = \beta_1 + \beta_2$

$\therefore Y_1 + Y_2$ is also unbiased estimator for $\beta_1 + \beta_2$

$E\left[\frac{1}{3}(Y_1 + Y_2 + 2Y_3)\right] = \frac{1}{3}[\beta_1 + \beta_2 + 2(\beta_1 + \beta_2)] = \beta_1 + \beta_2$

$\therefore \frac{1}{3}(Y_1 + Y_2 + 2Y_3)$ is also an unbiased for $\beta_1 + \beta_2$

$E\left[\frac{1}{2}(Y_1 + Y_2 + Y_3)\right] = \frac{1}{2}[\beta_1 + \beta_2 + (\beta_1 + \beta_2)] = \beta_1 + \beta_2$

$\therefore \frac{1}{2}(Y_1 + Y_2 + Y_3)$ is also an unbiased for $\beta_1 + \beta_2$

$Var(Y_3) = \sigma^2$

$Var(Y_1 + Y_2) = Var(Y_1) + Var(Y_2) = 2\sigma^2$

$Var\left[\frac{1}{2}(Y_1 + Y_2 + Y_3)\right] = \frac{1}{4}[\sigma^2 + \sigma^2 + \sigma^2] = \frac{3}{4}\sigma^2$

$\therefore Var\left[\frac{1}{3}(Y_1 + Y_2 + Y_3)\right]$ is minimum among the four unbiased estimator for $\beta_1 + \beta_2$

So $\frac{1}{3}(Y_1 + Y_2 + 2Y_3)$ is BLUE for $\beta_1 + \beta_2$

Then option (c) is correct

25. Explanation: (a), (b), (c)

26. Explanation: (a), (b), (c), (d)

The model $Y = X\beta + \varepsilon$

The fitted values are $\hat{Y} = X(X'X)^{-1}X'Y = HY$

H is hat matrix

$e = Y - \hat{Y}$

$e = (I - H)Y$

The elements of hat matrix have their values between 0 and 1 always and their sum is p i.e., $0 \le h_{ii} \le 1$ and $\sum_{i=1}^{n} h_{ii} = p$ and if $h_{ii} = 0$ or 1 then $h_{ij} = 0 \ \forall \ i \neq j$

p is number of regression parameter with intercept term

$\hat{Y} = HY$

$Var - Cov(Y) = \sigma^2 I$

$Var - Cov(\hat{Y}) = \sigma^2 H$

$Var(e) = E[e - E(e_i)][e - E(e_i)]'$

$= (I - H)E(\varepsilon\,\varepsilon')\,(I - H)'$

$= (I - H)\sigma^2 I(I - H)' = (I - H)\,(I - H)^1\sigma^2$

$= (I - H)\sigma^2$

$Var(e_i)$ is the i-th diagonal element $(1 - h_{ii})$

$Var(e_i) = (1 - h_{ii})\sigma^2$

So, option (a), (b), (c), (d) are correct

$= E(Y_1^2) - [E(Y_1)]^2 = Var(Y_1)$

$E[e_1^2] = \sigma^2$

Similarly, $E[e_2^2] = \sigma^2$

$E\left[\frac{e_1^2 + e_2^2}{2}\right] = \sigma^2$

$\therefore \frac{1}{2}[e_1^2 + e_2^2]$ is an unbiased estimator of σ^2

So, option (b) is correct

27. Explanation: (a) 1 Square Feet $= 0.0929$ Square metre

$Y = \alpha + \beta x + \varepsilon$

α is the intercept parameter and β is the slope parameter

On changing the unit of X_i & Y_i, slope of the line will remain Same but intercept will change acc. to unit.

So, α Charges but $\hat{\beta}$ will not

So, option (a) is correct

28. Explanation: (a), (d)

$A = \sum_{i=1}^{n}\left(Y_i - (\hat{\beta}_0 + \hat{\beta}_1 x_i)\right)^2$ is the Error Sum of Square of Model 1.

B is Error Sum of Square of Model 2

In Model 2, One variable is more than Model 1

$\Rightarrow B \le A$

Also, it can happen that $B = 0$ but $A > 0$

($\because$ More variable in Model, less Error Sum of Square)

29. Explanation: (a), (d)

30. Explanation: (b), (c), (d)

$y_{ij} = \mu + \tau_i + \varepsilon_{ij}$; $i = 1, 2, \dots a$; $j = 1, 2, \dots n$

$\tau_i \sim N(0, \sigma_\tau^2)$

$\varepsilon_{ij} \sim N(0, \sigma^2)$

To test: $H_0 : \sigma_\tau^2 = 0$ v/s $H_A : \sigma_\tau^2 > 0$

Total sum of square = SS due to treatment + SS due to error

$\sum_i \sum_j (y_{ij} - \bar{y}_{..})^2 = n\sum_i (\bar{y}_{i.} - \bar{y}_{..})^2 + \sum_i \sum_j (y_{ij} - \bar{y}_{i.})^2$

$\frac{SS_{error}}{\sigma^2} \sim X^2_{a(n-1)}$

F ratio $= \frac{\text{Mean sum of square due to treatement}}{\text{Mean sum of square due to error}} \sim F_{a-1, a(n-1)}$

$\frac{\frac{SS_{Treat}}{a-1}}{\frac{SS_{Error}}{a(n-1)}} \sim F_{a-1, a(n-1)}$

$E(SS_{Error}) = a(n-1)\,(\sigma^2 + n\,\sigma_\tau^2)$

So, option (b), (c) & (d) are correct

31. Explanation: (a), (c), (d)

$Y = X\beta + \varepsilon$

Let $\hat{\beta}$ be the solution of $X^TX\beta = X^TY$

$\hat{\beta} = (X^TX)^{-1} X^TY$

By Gauss-Markov Theorem,

$C^T\beta$ is estimable then $C^T\hat{\beta}$ is the BLUE of $C^T\beta$

All linear parametric functions are estimable if

Rank $(X) = p$

If Rank $(X) < p$, some linear function may not be estimable because in this case we need to calculate Generalized inverse of X^TX which is not unique

$E\left[\frac{(Y-X\hat{\beta})^T(Y-X\hat{\beta})}{n-p}\right] = \sigma^2$

$\Rightarrow \frac{(Y-X\hat{\beta})^T(Y-X\hat{\beta})}{n-p}$ is an unbiased estimate for σ^2

Option (a), (c), (d) are correct

32. Explanation: (d)

$Y_i = \propto + \beta_i + \varepsilon_i\, ; i = 1, 2, .. n$

ε_i are iid N(0,1) ; $i = 1,2,..,n$ $\propto \neq 0$ & β is known

If $\hat{\alpha}_n$ is the maximum likelihood estimate of α

We know that maximum likelihood estimate is consistent estimates so

$\lim_{n\to\infty} E(\hat{\alpha}_n) = \alpha$ and

$\lim_{n\to\infty} Var(\hat{\alpha}_n) = 0$

Option (d) is correct.

33. Explanation: (c)

$Y_i = \theta_1 + \theta_2 + \varepsilon_i$ for $i = 1, 2$

$Y_i = \theta_1 - \theta_3 + \varepsilon_i$ for $i = 3, 4$

$E(\varepsilon_i) = 0\, ; \varepsilon_i$`s are independent

For $i = 1$

$Y_1 = \theta_1 + \theta_2 + \varepsilon_1$ .... (1)

For $i = 3$

$Y_3 = \theta_1 - \theta_2 + \varepsilon_3$ .... (2)

(1) – (2)

$Y_1 = \theta_1 + \theta_2 + \varepsilon_1$

$Y_3 = \theta_1 - \theta_2 + \varepsilon_3$

$Y_1 - Y_3 = \theta_2 + \theta_3 + \varepsilon_1 - \varepsilon_3$

Taking expectation

$E(Y_1 - Y_3) = \theta_2 + \theta_3 + E(\varepsilon_1) - E(\varepsilon_3)$

$E(Y_1 - Y_3) = \theta_2 + \theta_3$

$\theta_2 + \theta_3$ is estimable

So, option (c) is correct

34. Explanation: (a), (b), (c)

$Y_{4\times1} = X_{4\times4}\, \beta_{4\times1} + \varepsilon_{4\times1}$

Disp. $(\varepsilon) = \sigma^{2/4}$ for some $\sigma^2 > 0$

$\beta = (\beta_1, \beta_2, \beta_3, \beta_4)'$

$Y = (Y_1, Y_2, Y_3, Y_4)'$

Estimate of β,

$\hat{\beta} = (X'X)^{-1}X'Y$

$Cov(\hat{\beta}) = \sigma^2\,(X'X)^{-1}$

$Cov(\varepsilon) = \sigma^2 I = Cov(Y)$

$\Rightarrow Y_i\, \&\, Y_j$ are uncorrelated if $i \neq j$

$\Rightarrow Cov(Y_i, Y_j) = 0$

Case 1: $X = X_1$ (Given in question)

$\hat{\beta} = (Y_1, Y_2, Y_3, Y_4)$ & $Cov(\hat{\beta}) = \sigma^2 I$

Case 2: $X = X_2$ (Given in question)

$\hat{\beta} = \left(\frac{Y_1-Y_2}{2}, \frac{Y_1+Y_2}{2}, \frac{Y_3-Y_4}{2}, \frac{Y_3+Y_4}{2}\right)$ & $Cov(\hat{\beta}) = \frac{\sigma^2}{2}I$

Case 3: $X = X_3$

$\hat{\beta} = \left(\frac{Y_1+Y_2+Y_3+Y_4}{4}, \frac{Y_1+Y_2-Y_3-Y_4}{4}, \frac{Y_1-Y_2-Y_3+Y_4}{4}, \frac{Y_1-Y_2+Y_3-Y_4}{4}\right)$ &

$Cov(\hat{\beta}) = \frac{\sigma^2}{4}I$

$\left(Cov\,(\hat{\beta})\right)_{X_3} < \left(Cov\,(\hat{\beta})\right)_{X_2} < \left(Cov\,(\hat{\beta})\right)_{X_1}$

$\therefore X_2$ is better than X_1

X_2 is not better choice than X_3

Option (c) is correct & (d) is incorrect

Covariance between $\beta_1, \beta_2, \beta_3, \beta_4$ are zero

So, option (b) is correct

Finally, (a), (b), (c) are correct

35. Explanation: (c)

Multiple correlation coefficient is lies between 0 to 1 $r_{1.23}$ represent the multiple correlation coefficient of if X_1 *on* X_2, X_3 and $r_{1.234}$ represent the multiple correlation coefficient of if X_1 *on* $X_2, X_3\, \&\, X_4$ *So* $r_{1.234} > r_{1.23}$

$\therefore$ *Acc.* to option it may be possible

$r_{1.23} = 0.3$ *and* $r_{1.234} = 0.7$

Option (c) is correct

36. Explanation: (c)

Given two – way ANOVA model

$y_{ij} = \propto + \beta_i + \gamma_j + \varepsilon_{ij}$ ----- (i) ; $1 \le i \le I, 1 \le j \le]$; $I, J > 5$

With following assumption

$E(\varepsilon_{ij}) = 0\; Var(\varepsilon_{ij}) = \sigma^2$

$\sum_{i=1}^{I} \beta_i = \sum_{j=1}^{J} \gamma_j = 0$

From the given model, put $i = 1$ and sum over j

$\sum_{j=1}^{J} y_{1j} = J \propto + J\beta_1 + \sum_{j=1}^{J}\gamma_j + \sum_{j=1}^{J}\varepsilon_{1j}$ ------ (ii)

And now again put $i = 2$, and sum over j

$\sum_{j=1}^{J} y_{2j} = J \propto + J\beta_2 + \sum_{j=1}^{J}\gamma_j + \sum_{j=1}^{J}\varepsilon_{2j}$ ------ (iii)

Subtracting equation (iii) from (ii)

$\sum_{j=1}^{J} y_{1j} - \sum_{j=1}^{J} y_{2j} = J(\beta_1 - \beta_2) + \left[\sum_{j=1}^{J}\varepsilon_{1j} - \sum_{j=1}^{J}\varepsilon_{2j}\right]$

Take expectation both sides-

$E\left[\sum_{j=1}^{J} y_{1j} - \sum_{j=1}^{J} y_{2j}\right] = J(\beta_1 - \beta_2) + E\left[\sum_{j=1}^{J}\varepsilon_{1j} - \sum_{j=1}^{J}\varepsilon_{2j}\right]$

$\Rightarrow \beta_1 - \beta_2 = E\left[\frac{1}{J}.\sum_{j=1}^{J}\gamma_{1j} - \frac{1}{J}.\sum_{j=1}^{J} y_{2J}\right]$

$\therefore (\beta_1 - \beta_2)$ is estimable

Option (c) is correct

37. Explanation: (b)

Gauss-Markov model $Y_{n\times1} = X_{n\times p}\beta_{p\times1} + \varepsilon_{n\times1}$, where $E(\varepsilon) = 0$ and Dispersion $(\varepsilon) = \sigma^2\, I_{n\times n}$.

Suppose that $p < n$

If Rank $(X) = p < n$ then

$\hat{\beta} = (X'X)^{-1}X'Y$

But Rank $(X_{n\times p})$ is not mention, then least-square estimate of $\beta_{p\times1}$ is not unique.

If $\beta_{p\times 1}$ estimable then their least-square estimate is unique.

$$|X^T X| \neq 0$$

Option (b) is correct

38. Explanation: (a)

$Corr\ (Y, X_i) = \rho\ \forall\ i$ and $Corr\ (X_i, X_j) = \rho\ ; i \neq j$

$$R^2_{y.1,2,\dots p} = 1 - \frac{w}{w_{11}}\ ; w = \begin{vmatrix} 1 & \rho & \cdots & \rho \\ \rho & 1 & \cdots & \rho \\ \vdots & \vdots & \ddots & \vdots \\ \rho & \rho & \cdots & 1 \end{vmatrix}_{(p+1)\times(p+1)} \text{ and}$$

$w_{11} = \begin{vmatrix} 1 & \rho \\ \rho & 1 \end{vmatrix}$, $R_{Y.1,2,\dots p}$ is the multiple correlation between Y and $(X_1, \dots, X_p)$

If we take $\rho = 0$ then $R_{Y.1,2,\dots p} = 1$

Since $R_{Y.1,2,\dots p} \geq Corr\ (Y, X_i)\ or\ Corr\ (X_i, X_j)$

$$R_{Y.1,2,\dots p} \geq \rho$$

Hence option (a) is correct.

39. Explanation: (c)

$(x_1\ y_1), (x_2\ y_2), \dots, (x_n\ y_n)$ are bivariate measurements where $n > 2$

r_p denote the ordinary (Pearson) correlation coefficient

r_s denote the rank (Spearman) correlation coefficient

⇒ The pearson correlation can evaluate ONLY a linear relationship between two continuous variables

It has a value between $+1$ and -1

If $r_p = +1$ then it represents perfect linear correlation i.e., if x_i increases then y_i increases with constant value

⇒ The spearman correlation can evaluate a monotonic relationship between two variable (continuous or ordinal)

A monotonic relationship is a relationship that as the value of one variable increases, the other variable value decreases.

So, $r_p = +1 \Rightarrow r_s = +1$

So, option (c) is correct

40. Explanation: (b), (d)

$$Y_i = \beta_1 x_{i1} + \cdots + \beta_p x_{ip} + \varepsilon_i$$

$E(\varepsilon_i) = 0 \qquad \text{Var}(\varepsilon_i) = \sigma^2 \qquad \text{Cov}(\varepsilon_i, \varepsilon_k) = 0\ , \quad i \neq k \quad i, k = 1, 2, \dots, n.$

The least square equations for this model are,

$S = \sum_{i=1}^n \varepsilon_i^2$

$= \sum_{i=1}^n \left(y_i - \beta_1 x_{i1} - \cdots \beta_r x_{ir} - \cdots \beta_p x_{ip}\right)^2$

Now

$$\frac{\partial S}{\partial \beta_r} = -2 \sum_{i=1}^n \left(y_i - \beta_1 x_{i1} - \cdots \beta_r x_{ir} - \cdots \beta_p x_{ip}\right) x_{ir}$$

Equating it to zero & simplifying.

$\sum_i \left(y_i - \beta_1 x_i - \cdots .. - \beta_r x_{ir} - \cdots - \beta_p x_{ip}\right) x_{ir} = 0 \qquad r = 1, 2, \dots, p \qquad (1)$

Solving these p equations simultaneously, we get $\hat{\beta}_r$, $r = 1, 2 \dots p$. as 'p' least square estimators. Thus $\hat{\beta}_r, r = 1, \dots p$ will satisfy these equations.

$$\sum_i \left(y_i - \hat{\beta}_1 x_{i1} \dots . \hat{\beta}_r x_{ir} \dots . . \hat{\beta}_p x_{ip}\right) x_{ir} = 0$$

$$\Rightarrow \sum_i (y_i - \hat{y}_i) x_{ir} = 0$$

$$\Rightarrow \sum_i \hat{\varepsilon}_i x_{ir} = 0 \quad r$$

$= 1, \dots p. \qquad (2)$

Now consider

$$\sum_{i=1}^n \hat{y}_i \hat{\varepsilon}_i$$

$$= \sum_i \left(\hat{\beta}_1 x_{i1} + \cdots + \hat{\beta}_2 x_{ir} + \cdots + \hat{\beta}_p \hat{x}_{ip}\right) \hat{\varepsilon}_i$$

$= \hat{\beta}_1 \sum_{i=1}^n \hat{\varepsilon}_i x_{i1} + \cdots + \hat{\beta}_p \sum_{i=1}^n \hat{\varepsilon}_i x_{ip}$

Using equation (2) for $r = 1, \dots, p$.

$= \hat{\beta}_1 \cdot 0 + \cdots \hat{\beta}_r \cdot 0 + \cdots + \hat{\beta}_p \cdot 0 = 0$

Let us assume that

$$\sum_{i=1}^n \hat{\varepsilon}_i = 0.$$

$$\Rightarrow \sum_i (y_i - \hat{y}_i) = 0$$

$$\sum_i \left(y_i - \hat{\beta}_1 x_{i1} \dots . \hat{\beta}_r x_{ir} \dots . . \hat{\beta}_p x_{ip}\right) = 0$$

Note that $\hat{\beta}_i s$ are solutions of this equations. But this is not true as we estimate $\beta_1, \dots, \beta_p$ using p equations which have different form as written in equation (1).

Thus there is contradiction.This is because we assumed incorrect assumption that $\sum_{i=1}^n \hat{\varepsilon}_i = 0$.

Therefore $\sum_{i=1}^n \hat{\varepsilon}_i \neq 0$.

Therefore **option (b) & (d)** are correct while option (a) & (c) are incorrect.

41. Explanation: (a), (b) & (c)

$$\begin{pmatrix} X \\ Y \\ Z \end{pmatrix} \sim N_3 \left[\begin{pmatrix} 0 \\ 0 \\ 0 \end{pmatrix}, \begin{pmatrix} 1 & \rho & 0 \\ \rho & 1 & 0 \\ 0 & 0 & 1 \end{pmatrix}\right], \text{ where } |\rho| < 1$$

Option 1 :

$$\text{Cov}(X^2, Y^2) = E[X^2 \cdot Y^2] - E[X^2] \cdot E[Y^2]$$

Note that here marginally $X \sim N_1(0,1) \qquad Y \sim N_2(0,1)$

Further $\begin{pmatrix} X \\ Y \end{pmatrix} \sim N_2 \left[\begin{pmatrix} 0 \\ 0 \end{pmatrix}, \begin{pmatrix} 1 & \rho \\ \rho & 1 \end{pmatrix}\right]$

$\Rightarrow X^2 \sim \chi_1^2\ \&\ Y^2 \sim \chi_1^2$

$\Rightarrow E(X^2) = 1 \quad E(Y^2) = 1$

$$\text{Var}(X^2) = 2 \quad \text{Var}\ (Y^2) = 2$$

$$S.D.(X^2) = \sqrt{2} \quad S.D.(Y^2) = \sqrt{2}$$

Now to find $E[X^2 Y^2]$, we will use the moment generating function M of the bivariate normal distribution. $N_2(\mu_1, \mu_2, \sigma_1^2, \sigma_2^2, \rho)$ of (X, Y).

$$M(t_1, t_2) = \exp\left(\underline{\mu}'\underline{t} + \frac{1}{2}\underline{t}'\Sigma\underline{t}\right)$$

for $\underline{t} = [t_1, t_2]'$, $\underline{\mu} = [\mu_1, \mu_2]'$, $\Sigma = \begin{bmatrix} \sigma_1^2 & \rho\sigma_1\sigma_2 \\ \rho\sigma_1\sigma_2 & \rho_2^2 \end{bmatrix}$

$$\therefore E(X^2 Y^2) = \frac{\partial^4}{\partial^2 t_1\, \partial^2 t_2} M(t_1, t_2)\Bigg|_{t_1 = t_2 = 0}$$

$= 4\mu_1\mu_2\rho\sigma_1\sigma_2 + (\mu_1^2 + \sigma_1^2)(\mu_2^2 + \sigma_2^2) + 2\rho^2\sigma_1^2, \sigma_2^2$

Here $\mu_1 = \mu_2 = 0 \qquad \sigma_1^2 = \sigma_2^2 = 1 \qquad \rho = 1$

$\therefore E[X^2 Y^2] = 1 + 2\rho^2$

$\therefore \text{Cov}(X^2, Y^2) = E[X^2 Y^2] - E(X^2)E(Y^2)$

$= 1 + 2\rho^2 - 1 \cdot 1 = 2\rho^2$

$$\therefore \text{Corr}(X^2, Y^2) = \frac{\text{Cov}(X^2, Y^2)}{SD(X^2)\, SD(Y^2)}$$

$$= \frac{2\rho^2}{\sqrt{2} \cdot \sqrt{2}} = \rho^2$$

Option 3:

Now here $\binom{X}{Z} \sim N_2\left[\binom{0}{0}, \begin{pmatrix}1 & 0\\ 0 & 1\end{pmatrix}\right]$

$X^2 \sim \chi_1^2$ $\quad Z^2 \sim \chi_1^2$

$E(X^2) = 1$ $\quad E(Z^2) = 1$

$\text{Var}(X^2) = 2$ $\quad \text{Var}(Z^2) = 2$

$\text{SD}(X^2) = \sqrt{2}$ $\quad \text{SD}(Z^2) = \sqrt{2}$

Same as in option 1, by using M.G.F. for Bivariate Normal random vector we get

$$E(X^2Z^2) = 4\mu_1\mu_2\rho\sigma_1\sigma_2 + (\mu_1^2+\sigma_1^2)(\mu_2^2+\sigma_2^2) + 2\rho^2\sigma_1^2\sigma_2^2$$

here $\mu_1 = \mu_2 = 0 \quad \sigma_1^2 = \sigma_2^2 = 1 \quad \rho = 0$

$\therefore E[X^2Z^2] = 0 + 1\cdot 1 + 0 = 1$

$\therefore \text{Cov}(X^2, Z^2) = E(X^2Z^2) - E(X^2)\cdot E(Z^2)$

$= 1 - 1\cdot 1 = 0$

$$\text{Corr}(X^2, Z^2) = \frac{\text{Cov}(X^2, Z^2)}{\text{SD}(X^2)\cdot \text{SD}(Z^2)} = 0$$

Option 4:

$$\text{Corr}(X^2, Y^2 + Z^2) = \frac{\text{Cov}(X^2, Y^2+Z^2)}{\sqrt{\text{Var}(X^2)\cdot \text{Var}(Y^2+Z^2)}}$$

Now using a property of covariance we get,

$$\text{Cov}(X^2, Y^2+Z^2) = \text{Cov}(X^2, Y^2) + \text{Cov}(X^2, Z^2)$$
$$= 2\rho^2 + 0 = 2\rho^2$$
$$\text{var}(X^2) = 2$$
$$\text{Var}(Y^2+Z^2) = \text{Var}(Y^2) + \text{Var}(Z^2) + 2\cdot \text{Cov}(Y^2, Z^2)$$

Here

$$\binom{Y}{Z} \sim N_2\left[\binom{0}{0}, \begin{pmatrix}1 & 0\\ 0 & 1\end{pmatrix}\right]$$

$\therefore$ By using similar procedure as used for proving option 3, we get $\text{Cov}(Y^2, Z^2) = 0$.

$\therefore \text{Var}(Y^2+Z^2) = \text{Var}(X^2) + \text{Var}(Z^2) = 2 + 2 = 4$

$$\therefore \text{Corr}(X^2, Y^2+Z^2) = \frac{2\rho^2}{\sqrt{2.4}} = \frac{2\rho^2}{2\sqrt{2}} = \frac{\rho^2}{\sqrt{2}}$$
$$\neq \rho^2 \ (Given)$$

$\therefore$ **Options (a) & (c)** are correct but option (d) is incorrect.

Option 2:

$$Corr(X^2, Y) = \frac{Cov(X^2, Y)}{\sqrt{Var(X^2).Var(Y)}}$$
$$= \frac{E(X^2Y) - E(X^2)\,E(Y)}{\sqrt{Var(X^2).Var\ (Y)}}$$

$\because \binom{X}{Y} \sim N_2\left[\binom{0}{0}, \begin{pmatrix}1 & \rho\\ \rho & 1\end{pmatrix}\right]$

M.G.F. of $\binom{X}{Y}$ is

$$M(t_1, t_2) = \exp\left(\underline{\mu}'\underline{t} + \frac{1}{2}\underline{t}'\Sigma\underline{t}\right)$$

Here $\underline{\mu} = \binom{0}{0}$ & $\underline{\Sigma} = \begin{pmatrix}1 & \rho\\ \rho & 1\end{pmatrix}$

$$\therefore M(t_1, t_2) = \exp\left(\frac{1}{2}\underline{t}'\Sigma\underline{t}\right)$$
$$= \exp\left(\frac{1}{2}[t_1 + t_2]\begin{bmatrix}1 & \rho\\ \rho & 1\end{bmatrix}\begin{bmatrix}t_1\\ t_2\end{bmatrix}\right)$$
$$= \exp\left(\frac{1}{2}[t_1 + \rho t_2 \quad \rho t_1 + t_2]\begin{bmatrix}t_1\\ t_2\end{bmatrix}\right)$$
$$= \exp\left(\frac{1}{2}[t_1^2 + \rho t_1 t_2 + \rho t_1 t_2 + t_2^2]\right)$$
$$= \exp\left(\frac{1}{2}[t_1^2 + t_2^2 + 2\rho t_1 t_2]\right)$$

Differentiating on both sides, 2 times w.r.t. t_1 & 1 time w.r.t. t_2 and evaluating its value at $t_1 = 0, t_2 = 0$, we get, $E(X^2Y)$.

$$\therefore E(X^2Y) = \left.\frac{\partial^2 M(t_1, t_2)}{\partial t_1^2\,\partial t_2}\right|_{\substack{t_1=0\\ t_2=0}} = 0$$

$\therefore \text{Cov}(X^2, Y) = E(X^2Y) - E(X^2)E(Y)$

$= 0 - 1\cdot 0 = 0$

$\because Y \sim N(0,1) \quad \& \quad X^2 \sim \chi_1^2$

$\therefore \text{Corr}(X^2, Y) = 0$

$\therefore$ **Option (b)** is correct.

42. Explanation: (a) & (b)

Let

$$Y_i = \beta X_i + \varepsilon_i, i = 1, \dots, n$$

is a simple linear model where ε_i's are i.i.d. $N(0, \sigma^2)$ random variables.

Let

$$\hat{\beta}_1 = \frac{\sum_{i=1}^n (y_i - \bar{y})(x_i - \bar{x})}{\sum_{i=1}^n (x_i - \bar{x})^2}$$
$$\hat{\beta}_2 = \frac{\sum_{i=1}^n y_i x_i}{\sum_{i=1}^n x_i^2}$$

Note that here x_i's are non-random, positive and distinct.

Option 1:

Consider $\hat{\beta}_1$

Take numerator

$$\sum_{i=1}^n (y_i - \bar{y})(x_i - \bar{x})$$
$$= \sum_{i=1}^n x_i(y_i - \bar{y}) - \bar{x}\sum_{i=1}^n (y_i - \bar{y})$$
$$= \sum_{i=1}^n x_i y_i - \bar{y}\sum_{i=1}^n x_i - \bar{x}\sum_{i=1}^n y_i + n\bar{x}\bar{y}$$
$$= \sum_{i=1}^n x_i y_i - n\bar{x}\bar{y} - n\bar{x}\bar{y} + n\bar{x}\bar{y}$$
$$= \sum_{i=1}^n x_i y_i - n\bar{x}\bar{y}$$

Take denominator

$$\sum_{i=1}^n (x_i - \bar{x})^2$$
$$= \sum_{i=1}^n (x_i^2 + \bar{x}^2 - 2x_i\bar{x})$$
$$= \sum_{i=1}^n x_i^2 + n\bar{x}^2 - 2\bar{x}\sum_{i=1}^n x_i$$
$$= \sum_{i=1}^n x_i^2 + n\bar{x}^2 - 2n\bar{x}^2$$
$$= \sum_{i=1}^n x_i^2 - n\bar{x}^2$$

To check whether $\hat{\beta}_1$ is an unbiased estimator of β.

Let us examine whether $E(\hat{\beta}_1) = \beta$.

$$E(\hat{\beta}_1) = \frac{1}{\sum x_i^2 - n\bar{x}^2} E\left[\sum x_i y_i - n\bar{x}\bar{y}\right]$$

$\because x_i$'s are non–random.
$\because Y_i = \beta X_i + \varepsilon_i$ where ε_i's are i.i.d.
Normal $(0, \sigma^2)$ and β & X_i are non-random.
Also note that $E(\varepsilon_i) = 0$ & $Var(\varepsilon_i) = \sigma^2$
$\therefore E(Y_i) = \beta X_i + E(\varepsilon_i) = \beta X_i$
$Var(Y_i) = V(\varepsilon_i) = \sigma^2$.
Consider,

$$\frac{1}{n}\sum y_i = \beta\frac{\sum x_i}{n} + \frac{\sum \varepsilon_i}{n}$$
$$\bar{y} = \beta\bar{x} + \bar{\varepsilon}$$

Where

$$E(\bar{\varepsilon}) = \frac{1}{n}E\left(\sum \epsilon_i\right) = \frac{1}{n}\sum E(\varepsilon_i) = 0$$

and

$$\text{Var}(\bar{\varepsilon}) = \frac{1}{n^2}\text{Var}\left(\sum \varepsilon_i\right) = \frac{1}{n^2}\sum_{i=1}^{n}\text{Var}(\varepsilon_i) = \frac{n\sigma^2}{n^2}$$
$$= \frac{\sigma^2}{n} \quad \because \text{cov}(\varepsilon_i, \varepsilon_k) = 0 \text{ for } i \neq k$$

$\therefore E(\bar{y}) = E(\beta\bar{x} + \bar{\varepsilon}) = \beta\bar{x} + E(\bar{\varepsilon})$

$= \beta\bar{x}$ & $\text{Var}(\bar{y}) = \text{Var}(\bar{\varepsilon}) = \dfrac{\sigma^2}{n}$

$$\therefore E(\hat{\beta}_1) = \frac{1}{\sum x_i^2 - n\bar{x}^2}\left[E\left(\sum x_i y_i\right) - n\bar{x}\cdot E(\bar{y})\right]$$
$$= \frac{1}{\sum x_i^2 - n\bar{x}^2}\left[\sum x_i E(y_i) - n\bar{x}E(\bar{y})\right]$$
$$= \frac{1}{\sum x_i^2 - n\bar{x}^2}\left[\sum x_i\beta x_i - n\bar{x}\cdot\beta\bar{x}\right]$$
$$= \beta\frac{1}{\sum x_i^2 - n\bar{x}^2}[\Sigma x_i^2 - n\bar{x}^2]$$
$$= \beta.$$

Thus $\hat{\beta}_1$ is an unbiased estimator of β.

Now consider $\hat{\beta}_2 = \frac{\Sigma y_i x_i}{\Sigma x_i^2}$

$$E(\hat{\beta}_2) = \frac{1}{\sum x_i^2}E\left(\sum y_i x_i\right)$$

$\because x_i$'s are non-random

$$= \frac{1}{\sum x_i^2}\sum x_i E(y_i)$$
$$= \frac{1}{\sum x_i^2}\sum x_i\beta x_i$$
$$= \beta\frac{1}{\sum x_i^2}\Sigma x_i^2 = \beta$$

Thus, $\hat{\beta}_2$ is also an unbiased estimator of β.
$\therefore$ **Option (a)** is correct.
Options 2, 3, 4 :
To compare variances

$$\text{Var}(\hat{\beta}_1) = \text{Var}\left[\frac{\Sigma(y_i - \bar{y})(x_i - \bar{x})}{\Sigma(x_i - \bar{x})^2}\right]$$
$$= \frac{1}{[\sum x_i^2 - n\bar{x}^2]^2}\text{Var}\left[\sum x_i y_i - n\bar{x}\bar{y}\right]$$

$\because x_i$'s are non-random

$\text{Var}[\sum x_i y_i - n\bar{x}\bar{y}]$
$= \text{Var}(\sum x_i y_i) + \text{Var}(n\bar{x}\bar{y}) - 2.\text{Cov}(\sum x_i y_i, n\bar{x}\bar{y})$
$= \sum x_i^2\text{Var}(y_i) + n^2\bar{x}^2\text{Var}(\bar{y}) - 2n\bar{x}\sum x_i.\text{Cov}(y_i, \bar{y})$

$$= \sigma^2\sum x_i^2 + n^2\cdot\bar{x}^2.\frac{\sigma^2}{n} - 2n\bar{x}\sum x_i\,\text{Cov}(y_i, \bar{y})$$
$$= \sigma^2\sum x_i^2 + n\bar{x}^2\sigma^2 - 2n\bar{x}\sum x_i\cdot\frac{\sigma^2}{n}$$

$\left(\because \text{Cov}(y_i, \bar{y}) = \frac{\sigma^2}{n}\right)$

$$= \sigma^2\sum x_i^2 + n\bar{x}^2\sigma^2 - 2n\bar{x}^2\sigma^2$$
$$= \sigma^2[\Sigma x_i^2 + n\bar{x}^2 - 2n\bar{x}^2]$$
$$= \sigma^2[\Sigma x_i^2 - n\bar{x}^2]$$

Now

$$\text{Var}(\hat{\beta}_1) = \frac{\sigma^2}{[\Sigma x_i^2 - n\bar{x}^2]^2}[\Sigma x_i^2 - n\,\bar{x}^2]$$
$$= \frac{\sigma^2}{\Sigma x_i^2 - nx^2}$$

Now

$$\text{Var}(\hat{\beta}_2) = \text{Var}\left[\frac{\Sigma y_i x_i}{\Sigma x_i^2}\right]$$
$$= \frac{1}{[\Sigma x_i^2]^2}\text{Var}[\Sigma y_i x_i]$$

As $y_i's$ are functions independent $\varepsilon_i's$ thus $y_i's$ are also independent. Therefore $\text{Cov}(y_i, y_k) = 0,\ i \neq k$.

$$\therefore \text{Var}(\hat{\beta}_2) = \frac{1}{[\Sigma x_i^2]^2}\Sigma x_i^2\,\text{Var}(y_i)$$
$$= \frac{\sigma^2}{[\Sigma x_i^2]^2}\Sigma x_i^2$$
$$= \frac{\sigma^2}{\Sigma x_i^2}$$

Now compare

$\text{Var}(\hat{\beta}_1) = \frac{\sigma^2}{\Sigma x_i^2 - n\bar{x}^2}$ and $\text{Var}(\hat{\beta}_2) = \frac{\sigma^2}{\Sigma x_i^2}$

Observe the denominator of both variances. $\text{Var}(\hat{\beta}_2)$ has larger term in its denominator compared to Var $(\widehat{\beta_1})$.
Thus $\text{Var}(\hat{\beta}_2)$ is smaller than the $\text{Var}(\widehat{\beta_1})$.
$\therefore$ **Option (b)** is correct and options (c) and (d) are incorrect.

43. Explanation: (a), (b), (c)

$X \sim U(-1, 1)$
$f(x) = \frac{1}{1-(-1)} = \frac{1}{2}$
$E(x) = \frac{a+b}{2} = 0$
$v(x) = \frac{(b-a)^2}{12} = \frac{1}{3}$
$y = x^2$
i.e. y is dependent
i.e. 1st & 2nd false statement
$cov\ (x, y) = 0$ Then $(x$ & $y)$ are uncorrected
$cov(x, y) = E(x, y) - E(x).E(y)$
$= E(x, x^2) - 0$
$= E(x^3)$
$= \int_{-1}^{1} x^3\frac{1}{2}dx = \frac{x^4}{2}\frac{1}{2}\Big|_{-1}^{1}$
$= \frac{1}{4}[1 - 1] = 0$
$cov\ (x, y) = 0$
$\therefore x$ & y are uncorrected
$\therefore$ 3rd also false statement
$\therefore$ Option (a) (b) & (c) are correct

44. Explanation: (a), (b), (c)

$E(y_1) = 2\beta_1 - \beta_2 - \beta_3$
$E(y_2) = \beta_2 - \beta_4$
$E(y_3) = \beta_2 + \beta_3 - 2\beta_4$

In matrix from

$$\begin{bmatrix} 2 & -1 & -1 & 0 \\ 0 & 1 & 0 & -1 \\ 0 & 1 & 1 & -2 \end{bmatrix}_{3\times4} \begin{bmatrix} \beta_1 \\ \beta_2 \\ \beta_3 \\ \beta_4 \end{bmatrix}_{4\times1}$$

Result

$E(1) = \sum b_i\beta_i$

Such that, rank (A) is full rank then $\phi(\beta_i)$ is estimable if $\sum b_i = 0$

$$A = \begin{bmatrix} 2 & -1 & -1 & 0 \\ 0 & 1 & 0 & -1 \\ 0 & 1 & 1 & -2 \end{bmatrix}_{3\times4}$$

For option

(1) $15 - 9 - 7 = 0$
(2) $1 - 1 = 0$
(3) $57 - 18 - 13 - 26 = 0$
(4) $23 - 9 - 10 + 4 \neq 0$

∴ option (a), (b), & (c) are estimable
∴ (a), (b), (c) are correct.

45. Explanation: (c)

Given

$E(C) = E(S) = E(TI) = 0 \;\; ; \;\; Var(C) = Var(S) = Var(DI) = 1$

$DI = C + S$

$n = 21$

Given regression coefficients are

$b_{DT} = 0.8\,; b_{DC} = 0.5\,; b_{ST} = 0.4$

Consider

$DI = C + S \Rightarrow b_{DS} = 1$

$Total\ variance = Var(DI) = 1$

$Mean\ regression\ sum\ of\ squares = b_{DC}^2 \times Var(C) = 0.5^2 \times 1 = 0.5^2 = 0.25$

$Mean\ residual\ sum\ of\ squares = 1 - 0.25 = 0.75$

$Residual\ sum\ of\ squares = 0.75 \times 20 = 15$

46. Explanation: (a), (b)

This is a theoretical question. Here

$$R^2 = \frac{Regression\ Sum\ of\ Square}{Total\ Sum\ of\ Square} \ \& \ Adj.R^2 = \overline{R}^2 = 1 - \left[\frac{(1-R^2)(n-1)}{(n-k-1)}\right]$$

Note that as the number of independent variables increases the more part of the total variation is explained by the regression sum of square. Thus numerator in the above formula of R^2 increases. Hence R^2 increases.

Increase in the R^2 results in the increase in the $\overline{R}^2$.

There is no any restriction on the $\overline{R}^2$ as stated in the option (4).

$$\overline{R}^2 = 1 - \left[\frac{(1-R^2)(n-1)}{(n-k-1)}\right] \Rightarrow 1 - \overline{R}^2 = \left[\frac{(1-R^2)(n-1)}{(n-k-1)}\right]$$

Note that here the term $\frac{(n-1)}{(n-k-1)} > 1$

$\Rightarrow 1 - \overline{R}^2 > 1 - R^2 \Rightarrow \overline{R}^2 < R^2$

47. Explanation: (a)

Statement (a):

$$\text{Var}(\hat{\epsilon}_i) \le \text{Var}(\epsilon_i), 1 \le i \le n$$

True.

The residual variance is given by:

$$\text{Var}(\hat{\epsilon}_i) = \sigma^2(1 - h_{ii}),$$

where h_{ii} is the leverage (diagonal of the hat matrix **H**).

Since $0 \le h_{ii} \le 1$, we have $\text{Var}(\hat{\epsilon}_i) \le \sigma^2 = \text{Var}(\epsilon_i)$.

Statement (b):

$$\text{Cov}(\hat{\epsilon}_i, \hat{\epsilon}_k) = \text{Cov}(\epsilon_i, \epsilon_k), \forall i \neq k$$

False.

- Original errors ϵ_i are uncorrelated: $\text{Cov}(\epsilon_i, \epsilon_k) = 0$.
- Residuals $\hat{\epsilon}_i$ have covariance: $\text{Cov}(\hat{\epsilon}_i, \hat{\epsilon}_k) = -\sigma^2 h_{ik}, i \neq k$, where h_{ik} is the off-diagonal element of **H**. This does not generally equal $\text{Cov}(\epsilon_i, \epsilon_k) = 0$.

Statement (c):

$$\text{Var}(\hat{Y}_i) = \text{Var}(Y_i), 1 \le i \le n$$

False.

$$\text{Var}(Y_i) = \sigma^2.$$

- $\text{Var}(\hat{Y}_i) = \sigma^2 h_{ii}$. Since $h_{ii} \le 1$, we have $\text{Var}(\hat{Y}_i) \le \sigma^2$, with equality only if $h_{ii} = 1$, which is impossible here ($n > p + 1$).

Statement (d):

$$E(\hat{Y}_i) < E(Y_i), 1 \le i \le n$$

False.

OLS is unbiased: $E(\hat{Y}_i) = E(Y_i)$. There is no systematic underestimation or overestimation.

48. Explanation: (a), (c)

We are given a linear regression model:

$$Y = X\beta + \epsilon$$

where $\epsilon \sim N_n(0, \sigma^2 I_n)$, and the least squares estimator (LSE) of β is used. The residual variance estimators we are comparing are:

- MLE of σ^2: $\hat{\sigma}^2_{\text{MLE}} = \frac{RSS}{n}$
- Unbiased estimator (Mean Squares Residual, MSE): $\hat{\sigma}^2 = \frac{RSS}{n-r}$

where $RSS = (Y - X\hat{\beta})^T(Y - X\hat{\beta})$.

Key Properties of These Estimators

1. Expectation:
   $E(\hat{\sigma}^2_{\text{MLE}}) = \frac{(n-r)}{n}\sigma^2$ (biased)
   $E(\hat{\sigma}^2) = \sigma^2$ (unbiased)
2. Variance:
   $\text{Var}(\hat{\sigma}^2_{\text{MLE}}) = \frac{2(n-r)}{n^2}\sigma^4$
   $\text{Var}(\hat{\sigma}^2) = \frac{2(n-r)^2}{n(n-r)^2}\sigma^4 = \frac{2\sigma^4}{n-r}$
3. Mean Squared Error (MSE):
   $\text{MSE}(\hat{\sigma}^2_{\text{MLE}}) = \text{Var}(\hat{\sigma}^2_{\text{MLE}}) + \text{Bias}^2$
   $\text{MSE}(\hat{\sigma}^2) = \text{Var}(\hat{\sigma}^2)$ (since it is unbiased)

Let's check options one by one:

(a) $\text{MSE}(\hat{\sigma}^2_{\text{MLE}}) < \text{MSE}(\hat{\sigma}^2)$ if $r = 2, n = 12$.

For $r = 2, n = 12$, we have

$\text{MSE}(\hat{\sigma}^2_{\text{MLE}}) = \frac{1}{6}\sigma^4$ and $\text{MSE}(\hat{\sigma}^2) = \frac{1}{5}\sigma^4$

Since $\frac{1}{6} < \frac{1}{5}$, we conclude $\text{MSE}(\hat{\sigma}^2_{\text{MLE}}) < \text{MSE}(\hat{\sigma}^2)$

Thus, Statement (a) is correct.

(b) $\text{Var}(\hat{\sigma}^2_{\text{MLE}}) > \text{Var}(\hat{\sigma}^2)$ if $2 \le r \le n-2, n \ge 12$

Since $\text{Var}(\hat{\sigma}^2) = \frac{2\sigma^4}{n-r}$ and $\text{Var}(\hat{\sigma}^2_{\text{MLE}}) = \frac{2(n-r)}{n^2}\sigma^4$, their ratio is: $\frac{\text{Var}(\hat{\sigma}^2_{\text{MLE}})}{\text{Var}(\hat{\sigma}^2)} = \frac{(n-r)^2}{n^2} < 1.$

So, MLE variance is actually lower, contradicting the claim.

So, this statement is incorrect.

(c) $\text{Var}(\hat{\sigma}^2_{\text{MLE}}) < \text{Var}(\hat{\sigma}^2)$ if $1 \le r \le n-2, n \ge 3$

As shown above, $\text{Var}(\hat{\sigma}^2_{\text{MLE}}) < \text{Var}(\hat{\sigma}^2)$ always holds.

So, this statement is correct.

(d) $\text{MSE}(\hat{\sigma}^2_{\text{MLE}}) > \text{MSE}(\hat{\sigma}^2)$ if $r = 7, n = 12$

For $r = 7, n = 12$, we have

$\text{MSE}(\hat{\sigma}^2_{\text{MLE}}) = \frac{59}{144}\sigma^4$ and $\text{MSE}(\hat{\sigma}^2) = \frac{2}{5}\sigma^4$

Comparing,

$$\frac{59}{144} \approx 0.41, \frac{2}{5} = 0.4$$

Since $\frac{59}{144} \approx 0.41$ is slightly larger than 0.4, MSE of $\hat{\sigma}^2_{\text{MLE}}$ is NOT strictly greater than MSE of $\hat{\sigma}^2$, making Statement (d) incorrect.

Thus, options (a) and (c) are correct.

49. Explanation: (c), (d)

Statement (a): The sum of squares residuals is strictly positive with probability 1.

- The sum of squared residuals (RSS) measures the discrepancy between observed and fitted values.
- If the number of observations n is equal to the number of unknowns, the model can perfectly fit the data, resulting in zero residuals.
- In such cases, the sum of squares of residuals is not strictly positive, contradicting the given statement.

Statement (a) is incorrect.

Statement (b): For every β_i, there are infinitely many linear unbiased estimators.

- In a standard linear model with full column rank, the best linear unbiased estimator (BLUE) is unique.
- While multiple unbiased estimators may exist, the claim that there are infinitely many is not necessarily true.
- The structure of this model suggests a unique BLUE for each β_i.

Statement (b) is incorrect.

Statement (c): $\text{Var}(\hat{\beta}_1) = \sigma^2$.

- From the given model equation for Y_1:$Y_1 = \beta_1 + \epsilon_1$

The natural unbiased estimator for β_1 is:$\hat{\beta}_1 = Y_1$

Its variance is:$\text{Var}(\hat{\beta}_1) = \text{Var}(Y_1) = \text{Var}(\epsilon_1) = \sigma^2$

Statement (c) is correct.

Statement (d): $Y_3 - Y_2$ is the BLUE of β_3.

- Consider the equations:$Y_3 = \beta_1 + \beta_2 + \beta_3 + \epsilon_3 Y_2 = \beta_1 + \beta_2 + \epsilon_2$
- Subtracting these:$Y_3 - Y_2 = (\beta_1 + \beta_2 + \beta_3 + \epsilon_3) - (\beta_1 + \beta_2 + \epsilon_2) = \beta_3 + (\epsilon_3 - \epsilon_2)$
- Expectation:$E(Y_3 - Y_2) = \beta_3$
- Variance: $\text{Var}(Y_3 - Y_2) = \text{Var}(\epsilon_3 - \epsilon_2) = \sigma^2 + \sigma^2 = 2\sigma^2$
- Since $Y_3 - Y_2$ is a linear unbiased estimator of β_3 and follows the structure of the model optimally, it is the BLUE of β_3.

Statement (d) is correct.

Thus, options (c) and (d) are correct.

50. Explanation: (d)

Since $X = 3X_1,; Y = 2X_1 + 2X_2,; Z = 4X_1 + 4X_3$ with independent $X_i \sim N(0,1)$,

$\rho_{XY} = \rho_{XZ} = \frac{1}{\sqrt{2}}, \rho_{YZ} = \frac{1}{2}$.

Thus , $\rho_{YZ\cdot X} = \frac{\rho_{YZ} - \rho_{YX}\rho_{ZX}}{\sqrt{(1-\rho^2_{YX})(1-\rho^2_{ZX})}} = \frac{\frac{1}{2} - \frac{1}{2}}{\sqrt{(1-\frac{1}{2})(1-\frac{1}{2})}} = 0.$

(Equivalently: conditioning on (X) removes the shared X_1 component, leaving independent residuals $2X_2$ and $4X_3$.)

Correct Answer: d. 0

51. Explanation: (a), (d)

Data: $(-2,4),,(-1,1),,(0,0),,(1,1),,(2,4)$.

- With intercept: fit $y = a + bx$. Since $\bar{x} = 0$, $b = \frac{\sum(x-\bar{x})(y-\bar{y})}{\sum(x-\bar{x})^2} = \frac{\sum x(y-\bar{y})}{\sum x^2} = 0$.

And $\bar{y} = 2 \Rightarrow a = \bar{y} - b\bar{x} = 2$. So the fitted line is $y = 2$.

- Without intercept: fit $y = \beta x$. The least-squares slope is $\beta = \frac{\sum xy}{\sum x^2} = 0$. So the fitted line is $y = 0$.

Hence:

1. Both slopes $= 0 \Rightarrow$ true.
2. Intercepts: 2 vs $0 \Rightarrow$ false.
3. Line $y = 2$ doesn't hit any observed point (y-values are $4,1,0,1,4) \Rightarrow$ false.
4. Line $y = 0$ passes through $(0,0) \Rightarrow$ true.

Correct answer : True: a and b

False: b and c

52. Explanation: (a), (c)

DESIGN OF EXPERIMENT

CHAPTER 10

(JUNE 2012)

1. Consider the following block design involving 5 treatments, labelled 1, 2, ……., 5 and two blocks:
Block I: {1, 2, 3}; Block II: {1, 4, 5}.
Which of the following statements is/are true?
(a) The design is connected.
(b) The variance of the best linear unbiased estimator of an elementary treatment contrast is either $2\sigma^2$ or $4\sigma^2$, where σ^2 is the variance of an observation.
(c) There is no non-trivial linear function of observations collected through the design whose expectation is identically equal to zero.
(d) The degree of freedom associated with the error is zero.

(DEC. 2012)

2. Consider a 2^3 factorial design laid out in 2 blocks, each of size 4, as follows
Block 1: 1 a b c
Block 2: ab ac bc abc
Here the treatment combinations are written in Yates' notation. Then which of the following are always true?
(a) Main effect A is confounded
(b) Main effect B is unconfounded
(c) Interactions AB, BC, AC are all unconfounded
(d) Interactions ABC is confounded

(DEC. 2012)

3. Consider the following design with 6 treatments 1, 2, …., 6 and 4 blocks as follows: {1,2,2}, {2,3,3}, {3,4,4} and {5,6,6}. Which of the following is true?
(a) The design is orthogonal and all treatment contrasts are estimable
(b) The design is non-orthogonal and all treatment contrasts are estimable
(c) The design is orthogonal and not all treatment contrasts are estimable
(d) The design is non-orthogonal and not all treatment contrasts are estimable.

(DEC. 2012)

4. For which of the following set of values will a Balanced Incomplete Block design with parameters v, b, r, k, λ not exist?
(a) $v = 11, b = 22, r = 6, k = 3, \lambda = 1$
(b) $v = 21, b = 4, r = 4, k = 21, \lambda = 4$
(c) $v = 7, b = 7, r = 4, k = 4, \lambda = 2$
(d) $v = 7, b = 7, r = 3, k = 3, \lambda = 1$

(JUNE 2013)

5. Consider a 2^5 factorial experiment laid out as a block design with 4 blocks of size 8 each. Suppose the principal block of this design consists of the treatment combinations (1), ab, de and five others. Which of the following interaction effects can e confounded in this design?
(a) ABC, CDE, ABDE (b) ABC, CDE, ABCDE
(c) AB, BC, AC (d) AB, CDE, ABCDE

(JUNE 2013)

6. Consider a design with 4 treatments labelled 1, 2, 3, 4 and with 5 blocks given by
1, 2 | 1, 3 | 1, 2, 4 | 1, 2, 3 | 1, 2, 3, 4
Which of the following statements are true?
(a) The design is connected but not orthogonal
(b) The design is connected and orthogonal
(c) All treatment contrasts are estimable
(d) Only some pairwise treatment contrasts are estimable

(DEC. 2013)

7. A factorial experiments involving 4 factor F_1, F_2, F_3 and F_4 each at 2 levels, 0 and 1 is planned in 4 blocks each of size 4 One of these blocks has the following contents:

F_1	F_2	F_3	F_4
0	0	0	0
0	1	0	1
1	0	1	1
1	1	1	0

The confounded factorial effects are
(a) F_1F_2, F_1F_3, F_2F_3 (b) $F_1F_3, F_1F_2F_3, F_2F_3F_4$
(c) $F_3F_4, F_1F_2F_3, F_1F_2F_4$ (d) $F_1F_4, F_2F_3F_1, F_2F_3F_4$

(DEC. 2013)

8. An incomplete block design involving 5 treatments, labelled 1,2,….,5 and two blocks has the following block contents:
Block I: (1,2,3);
Block II: (1,4,5).
For $i = 1,2, \dots ,5$ let t_i be the effect of the ith treatment. Which of the following statement(s) is (are) true?
(a) The design is disconnected.
(b) All contrast $t_i - t_j (i, j = 1,2, \dots ,5, i \neq j)$ are estimable
(c) The variances of the best linear unbiased estimators of all contrasts $t_i - t_j$ are the same, assuming that all observations have the same variance.
(d) The variance of the best linear unbiased estimators of $t_i - t_j$ is either $2\sigma^2$ or $4\sigma^2$, where σ^2 is the variance of an observation.

(JUNE 2014)

9. Consider an experiment using a balanced incomplete block design with $v = 4$ treatments, $b = 6$ block size $k = 2$. Let $t_i(i = 1, 2, 3,4)$ be the effect of the i-th treatment and σ^2 be the variance of an observation. Which of the following statements are true?
(a) The variance of the best linear unbiased estimator (BLUE) of $\sum_{i=1}^{4} p_i t_i$ where $\sum_{i=1}^{4} p_i = 0$ and $\sum_{i=1}^{4} p_i^2 = 1$ is $\sigma^2/2$
(b) The covariance between the BLUEs of the contrasts $\sum_{i=1}^{4} p_i t_i$ and $\sum_{i=1}^{4} q_i t_i$ where $\sum_{i=1}^{4} p_i q_i = 0$ is zero
(c) The degrees of freedom associated with the error sum of squares is 3
(d) The efficiency factor of the design relative to a randomized block design with 3 replicates is 2/3

(DEC. 2014)

10. For testing the effectiveness of four teaching techniques, five teachers of a college were involved. A class of 120 students was divided into 5 groups of 24 each at random; one group was assigned to each of the five teachers. Each teacher further divided his/her group into four equal subgroups at random, and used one technique per subgroup. All of them used the same course material. After all the classes were over, a common examination was conducted and the marks were noted. Suppose we want to test whether all the four teaching techniques are equally effective. What is the degrees of freedom associated with the residual sum of squares?
(a) 60 (b) 100
(c) 119 (d) 460

(JUNE 2015)

11. Consider a Balanced Incomplete Block Design (BIBD) with parameters (b, k, v, r, λ). Which of the following cannot possible be the parameters of a BIBD?
(a) $(b-1, k-\lambda, b-k, k, \lambda)$
(b) $(b, v-k, v, b-r, b-2r+\lambda)$
(c) $\left(\frac{v(v-1)}{2}, 2, v, v-1, 1\right)$
(d) $(k, b, r, v, \lambda - 1)$

(DEC. 2015)

12. Consider a randomized block design involving 3 treatments and 3 replicates and let t_i denote the effect of the ith treatment $(i = 1, 2, 3)$. If σ^2 denotes the variance of an observation, which of the following statements is true?
(a) The variance of the best linear unbiased estimators (BLUE) of $(t_1 - t_2)/\sqrt{2}$ and $(t_1 - 2t_2 + t_3)/\sqrt{6}$ are equal
(b) The covariance between the BLUE of $t_1 - t_3$ and the BLUE of $t_1 - 2t_2 + t_3$ is $2\sigma^2/3$.
(c) The variance of the BLUE of $t_i - t_j$, $(i \neq j, i.j = 1, 2, 3)$ is $\sigma^2/3$
(d) The variance of the BLUE of $t_1 - 2t_2 + t_3$ is $\sigma^2/6$

(DEC. 2015)

13. A 2^4 experiment involving factors F_1, F_2, F_3 and F_4, each at two levels, coded 0 and 1 is conducted in blocks of size 4 each. The block contents are as below:

Block I

F_1	F_2	F_3	F_4
0	0	0	0
0	1	1	0
1	0	1	1
1	1	0	1

Block II

F_1	F_2	F_3	F_4
0	0	0	1
0	1	1	1
1	0	1	1
1	1	0	0

Block III

F_1	F_2	F_3	F_4
0	0	1	0
0	1	0	0
1	0	0	1
1	1	1	1

Block IV

F_1	F_2	F_3	F_4
0	0	1	1
0	1	0	1
1	0	0	0
1	1	1	0

Then, which of the following statements are true?
(a) The confounded effects are $F_1 F_2 F_3, F_1F_2 F_4, F_3F_4$
(b) The confounded effects are $F_1 F_2 F_3, F_2F_3 F_4, F_1F_4$
(c) The design is connected
(d) The design is disconnected

(JUNE 2016)

14. Consider a balanced incomplete block design d with v treatments, b blocks, replication$r$, block size k and pairwise concurrence parameterλ. Assume the standard fixed effects model for the data obtained through. Which of the following statement is (are) true?
(a) The design is connected if$k \geq 2$.
(b) The inequality holds for$b \geq v$.
(c) The variance of the best linear unbiased estimator (BLUE) of a normalized treatment contrast is a constant.
(d) The covariance between the BLUEs of two orthogonal treatment contrasts is zero.

(DEC. 2016)

15. Suppose in a one-way analysis of variance model, the sum of squares of all the group means is 0 (Assume that all the observations are not same). Then the value of the usual $F-$ test statistic for testing the equality of means
(a) cannot be determined from the above information.
(b) is undefined.
(c) is 0.
(d) is 1.

(DEC. 2016)

16. (v, b, r, k, λ) are the standard parameters of a balanced incomplete block design $(BIBD)$. Which of the following can be parameters of a $BIBD$?
(a) $(v, b, r, k, \lambda) = (44,33,9,12,3)$
(b) $(v, b, r, k, \lambda) = (17,45,8,3,1)$
(c) $(v, b, r, k, \lambda) = (35,35,17,17,9)$
(d) $(v, b, r, k, \lambda) = (16,24,9,6,3)$

17. We are given some balanced incomplete block designs (BIBDs) with parameters (v, b, r, k, λ) such that $\lambda = 1$ and

k = 1 (are fixed). With which of the following values of v can one construct such a BIBD?

(a) v= 15 (b) v= 23
(c) v = 25 (d) v= 28

(JUNE 2017)

18. If we interchange two columns of a Latin square design (LSD), then the new design is
(a) an LSD
(b) a completely randomised design (CRD) but not an LSD
(c) a randomised block design (RBD) but not an LSD
(d) a balanced incomplete block design (BIBD) but not an LSD

(DEC. 2017)

19. Consider a BIBD (v, b, r, k, λ) with $k = 5$.
Let $N = \left((n_{ij})\right)$ be the incidence matrix, where $n_{ij} =$ number of times i-th treatment appears in jth block, $1 \leq i \leq v, 1 \leq j \leq b$. Let $C = rI - \frac{1}{k}NN^t$. Which of the following are true?
(a) C has a characteristic root 0
(b) rank of N is v
(c) the above BIBD is connected
(d) trace of the C is $4b$

(JUNE 2018)

20. In a Latin Square Design, the "error degrees of freedom" is 30. The "treatment degrees of freedom" for any treatment is
(a) 4 (b) 5
(c) 6 (d) 7

(DEC. 2018)

21. In a 2^4 experiment with two blocks and factors A,B,C and D, one block contains the following treatment combinations a, b, c, ad, bd, cd, abc, abcd. Which of the following effects is confounded?
(a) ABC (b) ABD
(c) BCD (d) ABCD

(DEC. 2018)

22. Consider a block design with three blocks and four treatments A, B, C and D where only A and B are allotted to block -1, only A, B and D are allotted to block-2 and only C is allotted to block-3. Then the resulting block design is
(a) incomplete and not connected
(b) incomplete and not balanced
(c) balanced and connected
(d) neither balanced nor connected

(JUNE 2019)

23. In a design with four treatments and three blocks of 2 plots each, treatments A and B are allotted to blocks 1 and 3 and treatments C and D are allotted to block 2. Hence the resulting design
(a) is incomplete
(b) is connected
(c) is non-orthogonal
(d) has all elementary treatment contrasts estimable

(DEC. 2019)

24. In a 2^3 - factorial design, the treatment combinations of three treatments A, B and C are allotted to 2 blocks of 4 plots each. Suppose the key block is as follows.
Key block: (1), a, bc, abc
Then the confounded treatment combination is
(a) AB (b) AC
(c) BC (d) ABC

(DEC. 2019)

25. Suppose that $M_{pXp} \sim Wishart_p(1.m)$ and $z \sim N_p(0, \Sigma)$ are independent where Σ is positive definite matrix. Let $a \in \mathbb{R}^p$ be a fixed $p - vector$ such that $a \neq 0$ and define $d = Z/||Z||$. Then which of the following random variables has a χ^2 distribution, possible after being scaled by a constant factor?
(a) $d'M^{-1}d$ (b) $(d'M^{-1}d)^{-1}$
(c) $a'Ma$ (d) $(a'M^{-1}a)^{-1}$

(DEC. 2019)

26. Consider a Balance Incomplete Block Design (v, b, r, k, λ) of v treatments and b block of k plots each. Let N be the vXb incidence matrix of the design. Then which of the following statements are correct?
(a) $\lambda(K - 1) = r(v - 1)$ (b) $b \geq v$
(c) rank $(NN') = v$ (d) trace $(NN') = bk$

(DEC. 2019)

27. To test the equality of effects of 10 schools against all alternatives, we take a random sample of 5 students from each school and note their marks in a common examination. "Between sum of squares" and "total sum of squares" are found to be 180 and 500 respectively. What is the p-value for the standard F-test?
(a) $P[F_{4.45} \geq 1.5]$ (b) $P[F_{9.40} \geq 1.6]$
(c) $P[F_{4.45} \geq 3.6]$ (d) $P[F_{9.40} \geq 2.5]$

(NOV. 2020)

28. Consider a Randomized Block Design with b blocks and k treatments.
Let the observation corresponding to the ith treatment and the jth block be $y_{ij}, 1 \leq i \leq k, 1 \leq j \leq b$, which satisfies the usual linear model. Which of the following is true?
(a) The estimated of any two treatment contrasts are uncorrelated
(b) The error sum of square ha bk-1 degrees of freedom
(c) The estimate of any treatment contrast is uncorrelated with estimated of any block contrast
(d) The correlation between the estimated of two treatment contrasts is always negative

(NOV. 2020)

29. In a Randomized Block Design with one observation per cell, and date satisfying the standard linear model, which of the following are correct?
(a) Mean treatment effects are estimable
(b) Mean block effects are estimable
(c) Treatment-Block interactions are NOT estimable

(d) Treatment and block effects as well as treatment-block interactions are estimable

(JUNE 2021)

30. Consider a BIBD (Balanced Incomplete Block Design) with v treatments in b blocks, each of which has k plots. Let r denote the number of blocks in which each treatment occurs. Let λ be the number of blocks in which each pair of treatment occurs. Which of the following statements is necessarily true?
(a) $vb = rk$
(b) $vr = bk$
(c) $r(b-1) = \lambda(k-1)$
(d) $r(v-1) = \lambda(b-1)$

(JULY 2024)

31. Consider the two-way ANOVA model $Y_{ij} = \mu + \alpha_i + \beta_j + \epsilon_{ij},\ i = 1,2;\ j = 1,2,$ where μ is the overall mean effect, α_i is the effect of the i-th level of factor A, β_j is the effect of j-th level of factor B, Y_{ij} is the response of the (i,j)-th experimental unit and ϵ_{ij} is the corresponding error with $E(\epsilon_{ij}) = 0$ for $i = 1,2;\ j = 1,2$. Which of the following are estimable linear parametric functions?
(a) $\mu + \alpha_2 + \beta_2$
(b) $\alpha_1 - \beta_1$
(c) $\alpha_2 - \beta_2$
(d) $\mu - \alpha_1 - \beta_1$

(JULY 2024)

32. Consider the following ANOVA table for a randomized block design:

Source of variation	Sum of squares	Degrees of freedom	Mean squares	F calculated
Treatments	48	4	12	β
Blocks	72	3	24	12
Error	α	m	γ	
Total	144	19		

Which of the following statements are true?
(a) $\alpha = 20$
(b) $\beta = 6$
(c) $m = 10$
(d) $\gamma = 2$

(FEB. 2025)

33. Consider the following design where the columns represent blocks and the letters represent treatments:

A C A B A B E
B D C D D C F
E E F F G G G

Then, which of the following statements are true?
(a) The design is a balanced incomplete block design.
(b) The design is not connected.
(c) The design is binary.
(d) The design is symmetric.

(JUNE 2025)

34. Consider the multiple linear regression model $y_i = \beta_0 + \beta_1 x_1 + \cdots + \beta_8 x_{8i} + \epsilon_i, i = 1, 2, \ldots, 29,$ where $\epsilon_1, \epsilon_2, \ldots, \epsilon_{29}$ are independent and identically normal distributed with mean 0 and variance σ^2. Suppose the model is fitted using the method of least squares. If the calculated value of the F-statistic for testing the significance of regression is 2.50, then the possible values of R^2 and Adjusted R^2 are respectively
(a) 0.30 and 0.10
(b) 0.50 and 0.30
(c) 0.50 and 0.16
(d) 0.30 and -0.10

(JUNE 2025)

35. If the incidence matrix of a block design is given by $N = \begin{bmatrix} 1 & 1 & 1 & 0 \\ 1 & 1 & 0 & 1 \\ 1 & 0 & 1 & 1 \\ 0 & 1 & 1 & 1 \end{bmatrix}$, then which of the following statements are true?
(a) The design is incomplete
(b) The design is connected
(c) The design is balanced
(d) The design is orthogonal

(Dec 2025)

36. Consider the linear model

$$Y_1 = \beta_1 + \beta_2 + \epsilon_1$$
$$Y_2 = \beta_1 + 2\beta_2 + \epsilon_2$$
$$Y_3 = \beta_1 + c\beta_2 + \epsilon_3,$$

where $\beta_1 + \beta_2 \in \mathbb{R}$ are unknown parameters, and the uncorrelated errors $\epsilon_i, i = 1,2,3$ have zero mean and finite variance $\sigma^2 (> 0)$. The constant c is such that $\hat{\beta}_1$ and $\hat{\beta}_2$ are uncorrelated, where $\hat{\beta}_1$ and $\hat{\beta}_2$ are the best linear unbiased estimators of β_1 and β_2, respectively.
Which of the following statements is the correct option for $\left(Var(\hat{\beta}_1), Var(\hat{\beta}_2)\right)$?
(a) $\left(\frac{\sigma^2}{3}, \frac{\sigma^2}{14}\right)$
(b) $(3\sigma^2, 14\sigma^2)$
(c) $\left(\frac{\sigma^2}{14}, \frac{\sigma^2}{3}\right)$
(d) $(14\sigma^2, 3\sigma^2)$

(Dec 2025)

37. Let $Y = X\beta + \epsilon$ be a multiple linear regression model with p regressors and an intercept, where $\beta = (\beta_0, \beta_1, \ldots, \beta_p)^T$ and the random error $\epsilon \sim N_n(0, \sigma^2 I), \sigma > 0$ and $n > p + 1$. Here, the least squares estimation method provides unique estimator of β, say $\hat{\beta}$. Let the total sum of squares (corrected), sum of squares due to regression/model and sum of squares due to error/residual, based on $\hat{\beta}$, be denoted by $Y^T AY, Y^T BY$ and $Y^T CY$, respectively, so that $Y^T AY = Y^T BY + Y^T CY$. Which of the following statements are always true?
(a) $\frac{Y^T AY}{\sigma^2}$ follows a central χ^2 distribution with $(n-1)$ degrees of freedom.
(b) $\frac{Y^T BY}{\sigma^2}$ follows a central χ^2 distribution with p degrees of freedom if $\beta_1 = \beta_2 = \cdots = \beta_p = 0$.
(c) $\frac{Y^T BY}{Y^T CY}$ follows a central F distribution with $(p, n-p)$ degrees of freedom.
(d) $Y^T BY$ and $Y^T CY$ are independently distributed if and only if $\beta_1 = \beta_2 = \cdots = \beta_p = 0$.

(Dec 2025)

38. Consider the following 2^5-factorial design with 8 blocks.

Block	Treatment combinations
1	(1), acd, bce, abde
2	e, acde, bc, abd
3	a, cd, abce, bde
4	ab, bcd, ace, de
5	b, abcd, ce, ade

6	ac, d, abe, bcde
7	abc, bd, ae, cde
8	c, ad, be, abcde

Which of the following statements are true?
(a) ABC is confounded with blocks
(b) BCD is confounded with blocks
(c) CDE is confounded with blocks
(d) ABDE is confounded with blocks

Answer Key

1	2	3	4	5	6	7	8	9	10
a,b,c,d	a,c,d	d	a,b	(*)	a,c	b	b,d	a,b,c,d	b
11	12	13	14	15	16	17	18	19	20
d	a	b,d	a,b,c,d	c	d	a,c	a	a,b,c,d	b
21	22	23	24	25	26	27	28	29	30
a	a,b,d	a,c	c	b,c,d	b,c,d	b	c	a,b,c	B
31	32	33	34	35	36	37	38		
a	b,d	a,c,d	b	a,b,c	a	b	a,b,c,d		

:: Explanations ::

1. **Explanation: (a), (b), (c) and (d)**
2. **Explanation: (a), (c) and (d)**
3. **Explanation: (d)**
4. **Explanation: (a), (b)**
Condition for existence of BIBD
(i) $vr = bk$
(ii) $\lambda(v-1) = r(k-1)$
(iii) $b \geq v$ (fisher's inequality)
Option (a) & (b) satisfies the above condition
So, option (a) & (b) are correct
5. **Explanation: (*)**
6. **Explanation: (a), (c)**
7. **Explanation: (b)**
8. **Explanation: (b), (d)**
9. **Explanation: (a), (b), (c), (d)**
10. **Explanation: (b)**
For testing the effectiveness of four teaching techniques factor A represents five groups of 24 student each i.e., $p = 5$
Factor B represent four subgroups of 6 students each i.e., $q = 4$
Each subgroup has 6 level (students) i.e., $m = 6$
Using technique of ANOVA of two way with m observation per cell.
H_0 : four teaching technique are equally effective
Degree of freedom of Residual $SS = pq(m-1)$
$= 5 \times 4(6-1) = 100$
So, option (b) is correct
11. **Explanation: (d)**
Consider a BIBD with parameters (b, k, v, r, λ)
The necessary condition for the existence of BIBD are
(i) $vr = bk$
(ii) $\lambda(v-1) = r(k-1)$
(iii) $b \geq v$
If there condition are not satisfied by any one of the given option that will be not be the parameters of BIBD
Option (d) is correct
12. **Explanation: (a)**
13. **Explanation: (b), (d)**
14. **Explanation: (a), (b), (c), (d)**
15. **Explanation: (c)**
Given Sum of Square of Group mean (SST) = 0
To test $H_0 : \mu_1 = \mu_2 \dots . \mu_k$ Vs $H_1 : \mu_i \neq \mu_j \ \forall (i \neq j)$
$$\text{F – Test statistic} = \frac{\frac{SST}{K-1}}{MSE} = 0$$
Option (c) is correct
16. **Explanation: (d)**
The necessary condition for the existence of a B I B D
(i) $vr = bk$
(ii) $\lambda(v-1) = r(k-1)$
(iii) $b \geq v$
For option (d)
$24 \geq 16 \Rightarrow b \geq v$

$vr = bk$	$\lambda(v-1) = r(k-1)$
$16 \times 9 = 24 \times 6$	$3(16-1) = 9(6-1)$
$144 = 144$	$45 = 45$

$(v, b\ r, k, \lambda) = (16, 24, 9, 6, 3)$ satisfied the conditions of B I B D
So, option (d) is correct
17. **Explanation: (a), (c)**
18. **Explanation: (a)**
If we interchange the two column of LSD a new design is also LSD.
Option (a) is correct
19. **Explanation: (a), (b), (c), (d)**
BIBD (v, b, r, k, λ) with $k = 5$
$N = (n_{ij})$ be the incident matrix
Where n_{ij} = number of times with i-th treatment appear in j^{th} block.
$1 \leq i \leq v$ and $1 \leq j < b$
$$C = rI - \frac{1}{k}NN'$$
$$NN' = \begin{bmatrix} r & \lambda & \lambda & \cdots & \lambda \\ \lambda & r & \lambda & \cdots & \lambda \\ \vdots & \vdots & \vdots & & \vdots \\ \lambda & \lambda & \lambda & \cdots & r \end{bmatrix}_{v \times v}$$
$$C = \begin{bmatrix} r & 0 & 0 & \cdots & 0 \\ 0 & r & 0 & \cdots & 0 \\ & & & \cdots & \\ 0 & 0 & & & r \end{bmatrix} - \begin{bmatrix} \frac{r}{k} & \frac{\lambda}{k} & \cdots & \lambda\backslash k \\ \frac{\lambda}{k} & \frac{r}{k} & \cdots & \\ \frac{\lambda}{k} & & & \frac{r}{k} \end{bmatrix}$$
$$= \begin{bmatrix} \frac{4r}{5} & -\frac{\lambda}{5} & \cdots & -\frac{\lambda}{5} \\ \frac{-\lambda}{5} & \frac{4r}{5} & \cdots & \frac{-\lambda}{5} \\ \frac{-\lambda}{5} & \frac{-\lambda}{5} & \cdots & \frac{4r}{5} \end{bmatrix} = \frac{1}{5}\begin{bmatrix} 4r & -\lambda & \cdots & -\lambda \\ -\lambda & 4r & \cdots & -\lambda \\ -\lambda & -\lambda & \cdots & 4r \end{bmatrix}$$
Every row sum of matrix C is $4r - \lambda(v-1)$
Every column sum of matrix C is $4r - \lambda(v-1)$
One characteristic root of matrix $= 4r - \lambda(v-1)$

Condition of $BIBD$ is
$\lambda(v-1) = r(k-1)$
$4r - \lambda(v-1) = 4r - r(k-1)$
$= 4r - r(5-1)$
$= 4r - 5r$
$= 0$
Characteristic root of matrix $C = 0$
We know that Rank $(NN') = Rank(N)$
$\therefore Rank\ (NN') = v$
$\therefore Rank(N) = v$
Trace of matrix $C = \frac{4r}{5} \times v$
$= \frac{4r}{5} v$
$= \frac{4}{5} bk\ \ [rv = bk]$
$= \frac{4}{5} b \times 5\ = 4b$
So, option (a), (b), (c) & (d) are correct.

20. Explanation: (b)
Error d.f in LSD $= (m-1)(m-2) = 30$
$(m-1)(m-2) = 30$
On solving, $m = 7$
d.f for treatment $= m - 1 = 7 - 1 = 6$
Option (b) is correct

21. Explanation: (a)
Block I: {a, b, c, ad, bd, cd, abc, abcd}
ABC treatment have odd number of letter common in separate Block I so, ABC is confounded

22. Explanation: (a), (b), (d)
A block design with three blocks and four treatment A, B, C and D

Block 1	:	A	B	
Block 2	:	A	B	D
Block 3	:	C		

We can easily see that every block does not receive all the treatment so the design is incomplete
So, the block design is known as incomplete block design
Treatments A & B is repeated in 2 times but treatment C & D is repeated only 1 times so, every treatment does not repeat same no. of times
So, the incomplete block design in not balanced
The block of this design can be represented graphical as follows

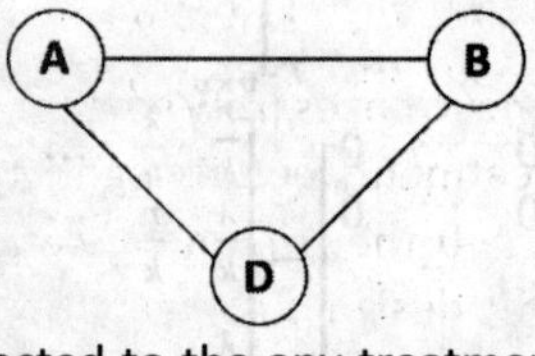

C is not connected to the any treatment so the design is not connected
So, option (a), (b) & (d) is correct

23. Explanation: (a), (c)

24. Explanation: (c)
Key Block: (1) a bc abc
If we get even/odd number of letter in the Key block not both, then the given treatment combination is confounded
BC treatment combination get even no. of letter common in key block, So, BC is confounded
Option (c) is correct

25. Explanation: (b), (c), (d)

26. Explanation: (b), (c), (d)
For any design to be BIBD, if following conditions are hold:
(1) $bk = vr$
(2) $\lambda\ (v-1) = r(k-1)$
(3) $b \geq v$
So, option (a) is incorrect and (b) is correct
Now, N is incidence matrix of $v \times b$
$N = (n_{ij}) =$
$$\begin{cases} n_{ij} = 1 & if i - th\ treament\ belongs\ to\ j - th\ block \\ \quad\ \ = 0 & otherwise \end{cases}$$
$$NN^t = \begin{bmatrix} r & \lambda & \lambda & \cdots & \lambda \\ \lambda & r & \cdots & \cdots & \lambda \\ \vdots & \vdots & & & \vdots \\ \lambda & \lambda & \cdots & \cdots & r \end{bmatrix}_{v\times v} \neq 0$$
Rank $(NN^t) = v\ \&\ trace\ (NN^t) = rv = bk$
Option (b), (c) & (d) are correct

27. Explanation: (b)
Between sum of square $= 180$
Total sum of square $= 500$
Error sum of square $= 500 - 180 = 320$
$P - value = P\left[F_{10-1,50-10} \geq \frac{320/9}{500/40}\right] = P[F_{9,40} \geq 2.8]$
So, option (d) is correct

28. Explanation: (c)
RBD with one observation per cell.
The linear model
$y_{ij} = \mu + \zeta_i + \beta_j + \varepsilon_{ij}$
$i\ = 1, 2 \ldots.k$
$j = 1, 2, \ldots., b$
Where $\varepsilon_{ij} \sim N(0, \sigma_e^2)$
$y_{ij} \sim N(\mu + \zeta_i + \beta_j, \sigma_e^2)$
$\mu \rightarrow$ general mean effect
$\zeta_i \rightarrow$ mean treatment effect
$\beta_j \rightarrow$ mean block effect
The estimate of the parameters, ζ_i, β_j, μ are
(1) $\hat{\mu} = \overline{y}.. \Rightarrow E(\hat{\mu}) = \mu$
(2) $\hat{\zeta}_i = \overline{y}_{i.} - \overline{y}_{..} \Rightarrow E(\hat{\zeta}_i) = \zeta_i$
(3) $\hat{\beta}_j = \overline{y}_{ij} - \overline{y}.. \Rightarrow E(\hat{\beta}_j) = \beta_j$
Treatment contrast: $\hat{\zeta}_i - \hat{\zeta}_{i'} = \overline{y}_{i.} - \overline{y}_{i'.}\ \ ; i \neq j$
Block contrast: $\hat{\beta}_j - \hat{\beta}_{j'} = \overline{y}_{.j} - \overline{y}_{.j'}\ ; i \neq j$
$Cov\ (\hat{\zeta}_i - \hat{\zeta}_{i'}, \hat{\beta}_j - \hat{\beta}_{j'}) = Cov\left(\overline{y}_{i.} - \overline{y}_{i'.}, \overline{y}_{.j} - \overline{y}_{.j'}\right) =$
0
$\Rightarrow$ The estimate of any treatment contrast is uncorrelated with the estimate of any block contrast
So, option (c) is correct.

29. Explanation: (a), (b), (c)
Randomized Block Design with one observation per cell, and data satisfying the standard linear model
$y_{ij} = \mu + \tau_i + \beta_j + \varepsilon_{ij}\ ; i = 1, 2, \ldots, p, j = 1, 2, \ldots, q$
Where, $\varepsilon_{ij} \sim N(0, \sigma_\varepsilon^2)$ and $y_{ij} \sim N(\mu + \tau_i + \beta_j, \sigma_\varepsilon^2)$
$\mu =$ General Mean effect

τ_i = Mean treatment effect

β_j = Mean block effect

The estimate of the parameters, τ_i and β_j are

$\hat{\mu} = \bar{y}_{..} \Rightarrow E(\hat{\mu}) = \mu$

$\hat{\tau}_i = \bar{y}_{i.} - \bar{y}_{..} \Rightarrow E(\hat{\tau}_i) = \tau_i$

$\hat{\beta}_j = \bar{y}_{.j} - \bar{y}_{..} \Rightarrow E(\hat{\beta}_j) = \beta_j$

There is not treatment-block an interaction exists in R. B. D, then it will not be hold estimability criteria.

Hence option (a), (b) and (c) are correct.

30. Explanation: (b)

In BIBD (balanced Incomplete Block Design) with v treatments in b block, each of which has k plots and r denote the no. of blocks in which each treatment occurs and λ be the number of blocks in which each pair of treatment occur.

The following parametric relation serve as a necessary condition for the existence of a B.I.B.D.

(i) $vr = bk$

(ii) $\lambda(v-1) = r(k-1)$

(iii) $b \geq v$ (fisher's inequality)

So, option (b) is correct.

31. Explanation: (a)

This is a theory question. Here only the quantity given in option (a) is estimable parametric function.

32. Explanation: (b), (d)

ANOVA table for a randomized block design:

Source of variation	Sum of squares	Degrees of freedom	Mean squares	F calculated
Treatments	48	4	12	β
Blocks	72	3	24	12
Error	α	m	γ	
Total	144	19		

(a) $\alpha = SSError = SSTotal - SSTreatments - SSBlocks = 144 - 48 - 72 = 24 \neq 20$

(c) $m = dfError = dfTotal - dfTreatments - dfBlocks = 19 - 4 - 3 = 12 \neq 10$

(d) $\gamma = MSError = \frac{SSError}{dfError} = \frac{24}{12} = 2$

(b) $\beta = FTreatments = \frac{MSTreatments}{MSError} = \frac{12}{2} = 6.$

33. Explanation: (a), (c), (d)

Understanding the Given Design

The columns represent blocks.

The letters represent treatments.

The blocks are:

a. $\{A, B, E\}$, b. $\{C, D, E\}$, c. $\{A, C, F\}$, d. $\{B, D, F\}$, e. $\{A, D, G\}$, f. $\{B, C, G\}$, g. $\{E, F, G\}$

Let:

- v = number of treatments.
- b = number of blocks.
- k = block size (number of treatments per block).
- r = number of times each treatment appears.
- λ = number of times each pair of treatments appears together.

Checking if it is a Balanced Incomplete Block Design (BIBD)

A Balanced Incomplete Block Design (BIBD) satisfies:

1. Each treatment appears in exactly r blocks.
2. Each block contains exactly k treatments.
3. Each pair of treatments appears together in exactly λ blocks.

From the blocks:

- The total number of treatments used: A, B, C, D, E, F, G (i.e., $v = 7$).
- Number of blocks: $b = 7$.
- Each block contains exactly 3 treatments (i.e., $k = 3$).
- Each treatment appears in exactly 3 blocks (i.e., $r = 3$).
- Each pair of treatments appears together exactly 1 time (i.e., $\lambda = 1$).

Since all conditions of BIBD are met, the design is a BIBD.

So, Statement (a) is true.

A design is connected if there exists a path between any two treatments through a series of common blocks.

Observing the blocks, each treatment appears in multiple blocks, and there are overlapping elements across the blocks. Hence, every treatment is linked to another through shared blocks.

Since the design is connected, Statement (b) is false.

A design is binary if each treatment appears at most once in any block.

In this design, each treatment appears only once per block.

So, Statement (c) is true.

A design is symmetric if $b = v$.

Here, $b = 7$ and $v = 7$, so the design is symmetric.

So, Statement (d) is true.

34. Explanation: (b)

Quick check:

- With $n = 29$ and $k = 8$, $df_1 = 8$, $df_2 = 20$.
- $F = \frac{(R^2/k)}{(1-R^2)/(n-k-1)} \Rightarrow R^2 = \frac{kF}{kF+(n-k-1)} = \frac{8 \cdot 2.5}{8 \cdot 2.5+20} = 0.50.$
- Adjusted $R^2 = 1 - (1-R^2)\frac{n-1}{n-k-1} = 1 - (1-0.5)\frac{28}{20} = 0.30.$

Correct Option (b): 0.50 *and* 0.30

35. Explanation: (a), (b), (c)

- Row-sums $r_i = 3$ and column-sums $k_j = 3$ while $v = 4$. Since block size $k = 3 < v = 4$ the design is **incomplete**. (a) true.
- The pairwise concurrences (row inner products) are all (2): every pair of treatments occurs together in exactly $\lambda = 2$ blocks. Since $\lambda > 0$ the treatment–concurrence graph is connected, so the design is **connected**. (b) true.
- Because $r = 3, ; k = 3, ; \lambda = 2$ and the concurrence λ is constant for every pair, the design is a balanced incomplete block design (BIBD). So it is **balanced**. (c) true.
- "Orthogonal" would require orthogonality of block (or treatment) indicator vectors (e.g. $N^T N$ diagonal). Here inner products of distinct columns (and distinct rows) are $2 \neq 0$, so the incidence vectors are not orthogonal. (d) false.

36. Explanation: (a)

Given model

$$Y_1 = \beta_1 + \beta_2 + \varepsilon_1, Y_2 = \beta_1 + 2\beta_2 + \varepsilon_2, Y_3 = \beta_1 + c\beta_2 + \varepsilon_3$$

The model in matrix form

$$Y = X\beta + \varepsilon$$

where

$$X = \begin{pmatrix} 1 & 1 \\ 1 & 2 \\ 1 & c \end{pmatrix}, \beta = \begin{pmatrix} \beta_1 \\ \beta_2 \end{pmatrix}$$

For the BLUE estimator

$$\hat{\beta} = (X'X)^{-1}X'Y$$

and

$$\mathrm{Var}(\hat{\beta}) = \sigma^2(X'X)^{-1}$$

X'X:

$$X'X = \begin{pmatrix} 1 & 1 & 1 \\ 1 & 2 & c \end{pmatrix}\begin{pmatrix} 1 & 1 \\ 1 & 2 \\ 1 & c \end{pmatrix} = \begin{pmatrix} 3 & 3+c \\ 3+c & 5+c^2 \end{pmatrix}$$

Inverse of X'X:

$$(X'X)^{-1} = \frac{1}{3(5+c^2) - (3+c)^2}\begin{pmatrix} 5+c^2 & -(3+c) \\ -(3+c) & 3 \end{pmatrix}$$

Condition for uncorrelated estimators: $\mathrm{Cov}(\beta_1, \beta_2)$ is the off-diagonal element of $\mathrm{Var}(\hat{\beta})$.

For uncorrelated estimators,

$$-(3+c) = 0$$

$$\Rightarrow c = -3$$

Substitute $c = -3$

$$X'X = \begin{pmatrix} 3 & 0 \\ 0 & 14 \end{pmatrix}$$

$$\Rightarrow (X'X)^{-1} = \begin{pmatrix} 1/3 & 0 \\ 0 & 1/14 \end{pmatrix}$$

Variance

$$\mathrm{Var}(\hat{\beta}) = \sigma^2(X'X)^{-1}$$

$$\mathrm{Var}(\hat{\beta}_1) = \frac{\sigma^2}{3}, \mathrm{Var}(\hat{\beta}_2) = \frac{\sigma^2}{14}$$

So, the correct option is (1).

37. Explanation: (b)

Multiple Linear Regression: Analysis of Sum of Squares Distributions

Model Setup $Y = X\beta + \varepsilon, \varepsilon \sim N(0, \sigma^2 I_n)$

With p regressors + intercept, so parameter vector β has $(p+1)$ components, design matrix X is $n \times (p+1)$ with full column rank $(p+1)$.

Partition: $SS_T = SS_R + SS_E$

Key Results from Distribution Theory

Let $H = X(X'X)^{-1}X'$ be the hat matrix (projection onto column space of X).

Quantity	Quadratic Form	Rank of Matrix
SS_E	$Y'(I-H)Y$	$n-(p+1)$
SS_R	$Y'(H-\frac{1}{n}J)Y$	p
SS_T	$Y'(I-\frac{1}{n}J)Y$	$n-1$

where $J = 11'$ is the $n \times n$ matrix of ones.

Statement 2: $\frac{SS_R}{\sigma^2} \sim \chi^2(p)$ if $\beta_1 = \beta_2 = \cdots = \beta_p = 0$ →TRUE

$$\frac{SS_R}{\sigma^2} = \frac{Y'\left(H - \frac{1}{n}J\right)Y}{\sigma^2}$$

The projection matrix $\left(H - \frac{1}{n}J\right)$ has rank p.

Non-centrality parameter: $\lambda = \frac{1}{\sigma^2}\beta'X'\left(H - \frac{1}{n}J\right)X\beta$

When $\beta_1 = \cdots = \beta_p = 0$ (only intercept $\beta_0 \neq 0$):

$X\beta = \beta_0 1$, which lies in column space of 1

$\left(H - \frac{1}{n}J\right)1 = H1 - 1 = 1 - 1 = 0$

So $\lambda = 0$ and: $\frac{SS_R}{\sigma^2} \sim \chi^2(p)$ centrally

Correct answer: Only Statement 2 is always true.

38. Explanation: (a), (b), (c), (d)

In a 2^5 factorial with 8 blocks, each block contains $2^{5-3} = 4$ runs.

Hence 3 independent effects are confounded with blocks (block generators).

The remaining confounded effects are obtained by multiplying these generators.

Look at Block 1:

(1) acd, bce, abde

Write the letters in each treatment:

$$(1) = \emptyset$$
$$acd = ACD$$
$$bce = BCE$$
$$abde = ABDE$$

Notice

$$ACD \times BCE = ABDE$$

Thus, the block is generated by the defining contrast

$$I = ACD = BCE = ABDE$$

Now multiply effects to see what aliases appear.

1. ABC

   Multiply with ACD:

   $$ABC \times ACD = BCD$$

   So ABC and BCD are aliased with the same block effect, hence confounded.

   Statement 1 true.

2. BCD

   Since

   $$BCD = ABC \times ACD$$

   it belongs to the same alias chain generated by the block generators.

   Statement 2 true.

3. CDE

   Multiply with generator BCE:

   $$CDE \times BCE = BD$$

   Thus CDE is also aliased with the block defining relation.

   Statement 3 true.

4. $ABDE$

   This already appears directly in the block defining contrast

   $$I = ACD = BCE = ABDE$$

   So, it is explicitly confounded with blocks.

   Statement 4 true.

All statements are correct.

CHAPTER 11

SAMPLING

(JUNE 2012)

1. A box contains N tickets which are numbered 1, 2, ...N. The value of N is however, unknown. A simple random sample of n tickets is drawn without replacement from the box. Let $X_1, X_2 \ldots X_n$ be numbers on the tickets obtained in the 1st, 2nd,...nth draws respectively. Which of the following is an unbiased estimator of N?
(a) $2\bar{X}-1$ where $\bar{X}=\frac{1}{N}(X_1+\ldots+X_n)$
(b) $2\bar{X}+1$
(c) $2\bar{X}+\frac{1}{2}$
(d) $2\bar{X}-\frac{1}{2}$

(JUNE 2012)

2. In a clinical trial n randomly chosen persons were enrolled to examine whether two different skin creams, A and B, have different effects on the human body. Cream A was applied to one of the randomly chosen arms of each person, cream B to the other arm. Which statistical test is to be used to examine the difference? Assume that the response measured is a continuous variable.
(a) Two-sample t-test if normality can be assumed.
(b) Paired t-test if normality can be assumed.
(c) Two-sample Kolmogorov-Sminov test.
(d) Test for randomness,

(JUNE 2012)

3. In a survey to estimate the proportion p of votes that a party will poll in an election, statisticians A and B follow different sampling strategies as follows:
Statistician A: Selects a simple random sample without replacement (SRSWOR) of 200 voters, finds that x of them will vote for the party and estimates p by $p_1=\frac{x}{200}$
Statistician B: Divides the voters' list into Male and Female lists, selects 100 from each list by SRSWOR, find that x_1, x_2 respectively will vote for the party and estimates p by $p_2=\frac{x_1+x_2}{200}$.
The number of voters in the two lists are the same. Then
(a) p_1 is an unbiased estimate but p_2 is not.
(b) p_1 and p_2 are both unbiased estimates.
(c) p_1 and p_2 are both unbiased estimates, but p_2 has a smaller variance than p_1, or the same variance as p_1.
(d) Variances of p_1, p_2 are the same only if the proportions of male and female voters who vote for the party are the same.

(DEC. 2012)

4. Consider a population of 50 units {1,2,...,50} and suppose that 50 possible samples are listed as: {1}, {1,2}, {1,2,3}, {1,2,3,4}, ..., {1,2,3,...,50}. One of these samples is chosen at random. Let π_i be the probability that unit i is in the selected sample. Then which of the following is necessarily true?
(a) The expected sample size is 25
(b) The expected sample size is 25.5
(c) $\sum_{i=1}^{50}\pi_i=1$
(d) $\sum_{i=1}^{50}\pi_i=25$

(JUNE 2013)

5. A simple random sample of size n is drawn with replacement (SRSWR) from a population of N units. The expected number of distinct units in the sample is
(a) $n\left[1-\left(\frac{N-1}{N}\right)^n\right]$ (b) $n\left[1-\left(\frac{N-2}{N}\right)^n\right]$
(c) $N\left[1-\left(\frac{N-1}{N}\right)^n\right]$ (d) $N\left[1-\frac{n(N-1)}{N}\right]^2$

(JUNE 2013)

6. A simple random sample of size n is to be drawn from a large population to estimate the population proportion θ. Let p be the sample proportioin. Using the normal approximation, determine which of the following sample size values will ensure $|\rho-\theta|\leq 0.02$ with probability at least 0.95, irrespective of the true value of θ? [You may assume $\Phi(1.96)=0.975, \Phi(1.64)=0.95$, where Φ denotes the cumulative distribution function of the standard normal distribution.]
(a) $n=1000$ (b) $n=1500$
(c) $n=2500$ (d) $n=3000$

(DEC. 2013)

7. A population contains three units u_1, u_2 and u_3. For $i=1,2,3$ let Y_i be the value of a study variable for u_i. A simple random sample of size two is drawn from the population without replacement. Let T_1 denote the usual sample mean and let T_2 and T_3 be two other estimators, defined as follows:

$$T_2=\begin{cases}\frac{1}{2}(Y_1+Y_2)\, if\; u_1,u_2\; are\; in\; the\; sample\\ \frac{1}{2}\left(Y_1+\frac{2}{3}Y_3\right)\; if\; u_1,u_3\; are\; in\; the\; sample\\ \frac{1}{2}Y_2+\frac{1}{3}Y_3\; if\; u_2,u_3\; are\; in\; the\; sample\end{cases}$$

$$T_3=\begin{cases}\frac{1}{2}(Y_1+Y_2)\, if\; u_1,u_2\; are\; in\; the\; sample\\ Y_1+\frac{1}{2}Y_3\; if\; u_1,u_3\; are\; in\; the\; sample\\ \frac{1}{2}Y_2+\frac{1}{2}Y_3\; if\; u_2,u_3\; are\; in\; the\; sample\end{cases}$$

If $\bar{Y}$ is the population mean then which of the following statements is true?

(a) All the three estimators T_1, T_2, T_3 are unbiased $\vec{Y}$

(b) T_2 and T_3 are biased estimator of $\vec{Y}$ but T_1 is not

(c) T_1 and T_2 are unbiased for $\vec{Y}$ but T_3 is not

(d) T_1 and T_2 are unbiased for $\vec{Y}$ but T_2 is not

(DEC. 2013)

8. A sample of size $n(n \geq 2)$ is drawn from a finite population of N units by probability proportional to size sampling with selection probability p_i $(1 \leq i \leq N, 0 < p_i < 1, \sum_{i=1}^{N} p_i = 1)$. Let $T = \frac{1}{n}\sum \frac{yi}{pi}$ where y_i is the value of a study variable for the ith unit and the sum extends over the units included in the sample. Which of the following statement(s) is(are) true?

(a) $T$is an unbiased estimator of the population total $\sum_{i=1}^{N} y_i$

(b) $nT$is an unbiased estimator of the population total $\sum_{i=1}^{N} y_i$

(c) The variance of T reduces to 0 if $p_i = 1/N$ for all $i, 1 \leq i \leq N$.

(d) The variance of T reduces to 0 if y_i is proportional to $p_i$for all $i, 1 \leq i \leq N$.

(JUNE 2014)

9. A finite population has 8 units, labeled $\mu_1, \mu_2, \ldots, \mu_8$ and the value of a study variable for the unit μ_1 is $Y_i (i = 1, 2, \ldots 8)$. Let $\bar{Y} = \left(\frac{1}{8}\right)\sum_{i=1}^{8} Y_i$. A sample of size 4 units is drawn from this population in the following manner: a simple random sample (SRS) of size 2 is drawn from the units $\mu_1, \mu_2, \ldots, \mu_7$ and the sample so selected is augmented by the units μ_1 and μ_8 to get a sample of size 4. Let $\bar{Y}$ be the sample mean based on the SRS of size two and let $T = (Y_1 + 6\bar{y} + Y_8)/8$. Which of the following statements is true?

(a) T is a biased estimator of $\bar{Y}$

(b) T is a unbiased for $\left(\frac{1}{6}\right)\sum_{i=2}^{7} Y_i$

(c) T is unbiased for $\bar{Y}$ and $V(T) = 3V(\bar{y})/4$

(d) T is unbiased for $\bar{Y}$ and $V(T) = 9V(\bar{y})/16$

(JUNE 2014)

10. Consider a finite population containing $N = nk$ units $n \geq 2, k \geq 2$ being integers and let these units be numbered 1 to N in some order. In order to select a sample of n units, a unit is selected at random from the first k units and every k-th unit thereafter. Under the scheme, let π_i be the probability that the i-th unit is included in the sample and π_{ij} be the probability that both i-th and j-th units are included in the sample. Also, let $\bar{y}$ denote the sample mean of a study variable, say y. Which of the following statements are true?

(a) $\pi_i = \frac{n}{N}, \pi_{ij} = \frac{n(n-1)}{N(N-1)}$ for all $i, j = 1, 2, \ldots, N, i \neq j$

(b) $\pi_i = \frac{n}{N}$, for all $i = 1, 2, \ldots, N$ and $\pi_{ij} = 0$ for at least one pair $(i, j), i, j = 1, 2, \ldots, N, i \neq j$

(c) $\pi_i = \frac{1}{N}$, for all $i = 1, 2, \ldots, N$ and $\pi_{ij} > 0$ for all $i \neq j, i, j = 1, 2, \ldots, N$

(d) $N\bar{y}$ is an unbiased estimator of the population total.

(DEC. 2014)

11. How many distinct samples of size n can be drawn with replacement from the population $\{u_1, u_2, \ldots, u_n\}$ of n units?

(a) n^n

(b) $\binom{2n-1}{n}$

(c) $\binom{2n-1}{n+1}$

(d) 1

(DEC. 2014)

12. Suppose a sample of size n is drawn using simple random sampling without replacement from a finite population of N units where $N > n$ and denote the sample mean of the study variables corresponding to the selected units by $\bar{y}$. Now suppose we know one variate value y_1 corresponding to one unit and draw a simple random sample of size n without replacement from the remaining $(N - 1)$ units and denote the sample mean of the study variables corresponding to the selected units by $\bar{y}_o$. Define $t_1 = N\bar{y}, t_2 = (N - 1)\bar{y}_o + y_1, V_1 = Var(t_1)$ and $V_2 = Var(t_2)$. Which of the following are necessarily true?

(a) t_1 is unbiased for population total

(b) t_2 is unbiased for population total

(c) $V_1 = N^2 \frac{\sigma^2}{n}\frac{N-n}{N-1}$ where σ^2population variance

(d) $V_2 \leq V_1$ for all n, N

(JUNE 2015)

13. Suppose there are k strata of $N = kM$ units each with size M. Draw a sample of size n_i with replacement from the ith stratum and denote by $\bar{y}_i$ the sample mean of the study variable selected in the ith stratum, $i = 1, 2, \ldots, k$. Define

$$\bar{y}_s = \frac{1}{k}\sum_{i=1}^{k} \bar{y}_i \text{ and } \bar{y}_w = \frac{\sum_{i=1}^{k} n_i \bar{y}_i}{n}$$

Which of the following is necessarily true?

(a) $\bar{y}_s$ is unbiased but $\bar{y}_w$ is not unbiased for the population mean.

(b) $\bar{y}_s$ is not unbiased but $\bar{y}_w$ is unbiased for the population mean.

(c) Both $\bar{y}_s$ and $\bar{y}_w$ are unbiased for the population mean.

(d) Neither $\bar{y}_s$ nor $\bar{y}_w$ is unbiased for the population mean.

(DEC. 2015)

14. A finite population has N units, labelled $U_1, U_2 \ldots, U_N$ and the value of a study variable on unit U_i is $Y_i (i = 1, 2, \ldots, N)$. Let $Y = \sum_{i=1}^{N} Y_i$ and $\bar{Y} = \frac{1}{2}\sum_{i=1}^{N} Y_i$. A sample of size $n > 1$ is drawn from the population with probability proportional to size with replacement, with selection probabilities $p_1, p_2 \ldots, p_n; 0 < p_i < 1, i = 1, 2, \ldots, N$ and $\sum_{i=1}^{N} p_i = 1$. Define $T = \frac{1}{n}\sum_{i \in s} Y_i/p_i$, where the sum extends over the units in the sample. Then, which of the following statements are true?

(a) T is an unbiased estimator of $\bar{Y}$

(b) T is an unbiased estimator of Y

(c) The variance of T is zero if Y_i is proportional to p_i for all $i, i = 1, 2, \ldots, N$.

(d) An unbiased estimator of variance of T is $\frac{1}{n(n-1)}\sum_{i\in s}\left(\frac{Y_i}{p_i}-T\right)^2$

(JUNE 2016)

15. A sample of size $n(\geq 2)$ is drawn without replacement from a finite population of size N, using an arbitrary sampling scheme. Let π_i denote the inclusion probability of the $i-th$ unit and π_{ij} , the joint inclusion probability of units i and $j, 1\leq i<j\leq N$. This of the following statements is always true?
(a) $\sum_{i=1}^{N}\pi_i = n$
(b) $\sum_{j=1, j\neq i}^{N}\pi_{ij} = n\pi_i, 1\leq i\leq N$
(c) $\pi_{ij} > 0$ for all $i,j, 1\leq i<j\leq N$
(d) $\pi_i\pi_j - \pi_{ij} > 0\ for\ all\ i,j, 1\leq i<j\leq N$

(JUNE 2016)

16. A sample of size two is drawn from a population of 4 units using probability proportional to size, sampling with replacement. The selection probabilities are $p_1 = 0.2, p_2 = 0.3, p_3 = 0.1$ and $p_4 = 0.4$ and for units 1,2,3and4 in the population, respectively. Let the value of a study variable for the *i*-th unit be $y_i, i = 1,2,3,4$, Let π_i denote the inclusion probability of the *i*-th unit and π_{ij} the joint inclusion probability of units i and j ,$i<j, i,j = 1,2,3,4$. . Then, which of the following statements are correct?
(a) $T = \left(\frac{1}{2}\right)\sum\frac{y_i}{p_i}$ is an unbiased estimator of the population total, where the sum is over the units in the sample
(b) $\pi_1 = 0.36, \pi_2 = 0.51$
(c) $\pi_{12} = 0.12$
(d) $\pi_1+\pi_2+\pi_3+\pi_4 = 2$

(DEC. 2016)

17. A simple random sample (without replacement) of size n is drawn from a finite population of size $N(\geq 7)$. What is the probability that the 4th population unit is included in the sample but the 6th population unit is not included in the sample?
(a) $\frac{n(n-1)}{N(N-1)}$
(b) $\frac{n(N-n)}{N(N-1)}$
(c) $\frac{(n-1)(N-n+1)}{N(N-1)}$
(d) $\frac{n}{N}$

(DEC. 2016)

18. Suppose $\overline{Y}$ is the sample mean of the study variables corresponding to a sample of size n using simple random sampling with replacement scheme and $\overline{Y}_{st}$ is the sample mean of the study variables corresponding to a sample of size n using stratified random sampling with replacement scheme under proportional allocation. Which of the following is/are sufficient condition/conditions for $(\overline{Y}) = Var(\overline{Y}_{st})$?
(a) All the stratum sizes are equal
(b) All the stratum totals are equal
(c) All the stratum means are equal
(d) All the stratum variances are equal

(DEC. 2017)

19. Suppose we draw a random sample of size from a population of size, where $1<n<N$ using simple random sampling without replacement scheme. Let P be the population proportion of units possessing a particular attribute and p be the corresponding sample proportion. Which of the following is an unbiased estimator for $P(1-P)$?
(a) $p(1-p)$
(b) $\frac{N-n}{N-1}p(1-p)$
(c) $\frac{n(n-1)}{N(N-1)}p(1-p)$
(d) $\frac{N(N-1)}{n(n-1)}p(1-p)$

(DEC. 2017)

20. Suppose there are k groups each consisting of N boys. We want to estimate the mean age μ of these kN boys. Fix $1<n<N$ and consider the following two sampling schemes.
I. Draw a simple random sample without replacement of size kn out of all kN boys.
II. From each of the k groups draw a simple random sample with replacement of size n. Let $\overline{Y}$ and $\overline{Y}_G$ be the respective sample mean ages for the two schemes. Which of the following are true?
(a) $E(\overline{Y}) = \mu$
(b) $E(\overline{Y}_G) = \mu$
(c) Var $(\overline{Y})$ may be less than Var $(\overline{Y}_G)$ in some cases
(d) Var $(\overline{Y})$=Var $(\overline{Y}_G)$ if all the group means are same

(JUNE 2018)

21. A simple random sample of size n will be drawn from a class of 125 students, and the mean mathematics score of the sample will be computed. If the standard error of the sample mean for "with replacement sampling" is twice as much as the standard error of the sample mean for "without replacement" sampling, the value of n is
(a) 32
(b) 63
(c) 79
(d) 94

(JUNE 2018)

22. A statistician has drawn a simple random sample of size 2 with replacement from 4 boys with distinct heights. Let $\bar{x}_1$ be the sample mean of their heights. Then, another statistician has drawn a simple random sample of size 2 without replacement from those 4 boys. Let $\bar{x}_2$ be the sample mean of their heights. Which of the following statements are correct?
(a) $(\bar{x}_1+\bar{x}_2)/2$ has larger variance than that of $(2\bar{x}_1+3\bar{x}_2)/5$
(b) $(\bar{x}_1+2\bar{x}_2)/3$ has larger variance than that of $(2\bar{x}_1+3\bar{x}_2)/5$
(c) $(\bar{x}_1+\bar{x}_2)/2$ has smaller variance than that of $(2\bar{x}_1+3\bar{x}_2)/5$
(d) $(\bar{x}_1+2\bar{x}_2)/3$ has smaller variance than that of $(2\bar{x}_1+3\bar{x}_2)/5$

(JUNE 2019)

23. A sample of size n = 2 is drawn from a population of size N = 4 using probability proportional to size without replacement sampling scheme, where the probabilities proportional to size are

i: 1 2 3 4

Pi: 0.4 0.2 0.2 0.2

The probability of inclusion of unit 1 in the sample is

(a) 0.4 (b) 0.6

(c) 0.7 (d) 0.75

(JUNE 2019)

24. Let $Y_1, Y_2, \ldots\ldots, Y_N \sim i.i.d.\, N(\mu, \sigma^2)$, where μ and σ^2 are unknown. Consider a SRSWR $\{u_1, u_2, \ldots, u_n\}$ of size n from $Y_1, Y_2, \ldots\ldots, Y_N$, as well as a SRSWOR $\{v_1, v_2, \ldots, v_n\}$ of size n from $Y_1, Y_2, \ldots\ldots, Y_N$. To estimate $Y = \sum_{i=1}^{N} Y_i = N\bar{Y}$, define $\hat{Y}_{WR} = \frac{N}{n}\sum_{i=1}^{n} u_i$ and $\hat{Y}_{WOR} = \frac{N}{n}\sum_{i=1}^{n} v_i$. Then which of the following are true?

(a) The conditional variance of $\hat{Y}_{WR}$ given $Y_1, Y_2, \ldots\ldots, Y_N$ is $\frac{N(N-n)}{n(N-1)}\sum_{i=1}^{n}(Y_i - \bar{Y})^2$

(b) The conditional variance of $\hat{Y}_{WOR}$ given $Y_1, Y_2, \ldots\ldots, Y_N$ is $\frac{N(N-n)}{n(N-1)}\sum_{i=1}^{n}(Y_i - \bar{Y})^2$

(c) The unconditional variance of $\hat{Y}_{WR}$ is $\frac{N(N-1)}{n}\sigma^2$

(d) The unconditional variance of $\hat{Y}_{WOR}$ is $\frac{N^2}{n}\sigma^2$

(DEC. 2019)

25. To draw a sample of size n(≥5) using a without replacement scheme from a finite population $\{U_1, U_2, \ldots, U_N\}$ of size N, the first unit is chosen using PPS$(p_1, p_2, \ldots, p_N)$ scheme and the remaining (n – 1) units are drawn using SRSWOR. Then the probability that U_2 is included in the sample is

(a) $\frac{N-n}{N-1}p_2 + \frac{1}{N-1}$ (b) $\frac{N-n}{N-1}p_2 + \frac{n-2}{N-1}$

(c) $\frac{N-n}{N-1}p_2 + \frac{N-n}{N-1}$ (d) $\frac{N-n}{N-1}p_2 + \frac{n-1}{N-1}$

(DEC. 2019)

26. To estimate the population total $Y = \sum_{i=1}^{N} y_i$ where $y_1, y_2, \ldots, y_n$ are study variables and N is the size of the finite population, a sample of size n is drawn using PPSWR $(p_1, p_2, \ldots p_N)$ scheme. If $\hat{Y}_{HH}$ is the Hansen-Hurwitz estimator for Y then which of the following are correct?

(a) $\hat{Y}_{HH}$ is unbiased for Y

(b) $var(\hat{Y}_{HH}) = \frac{1}{n}\left\{\sum_{i=1}^{N}\frac{y_i^2}{p_i} - Y^2\right\}$

(c) $var(\widehat{Y_{HH}}) = \frac{1}{n}\sum_{i=1}^{n}\left\{\frac{y_i}{p_i} - E(\hat{Y}_{HH})\right\}^2 p_i p_j$

(d) $var(\hat{Y}_{HH}) = \frac{1}{n(n-1)}\sum_{i-1}^{N}\sum_{j=1 j\neq i}^{N}\left(\frac{y_i}{p_i} - \frac{y_j}{p_j}\right)^2 p_i p_j$

(NOV. 2020)

27. 10 units are chosen by simple random sampling without replacement from a population of size 100. Consider the sample variance $\frac{1}{10}\sum_{i=1}^{10}(y_i - \bar{y})^2 = s^2$. An unbiased estimated of population variance $\sigma^2 = \frac{1}{100}\sum_{i=1}^{100}(Y_i - \bar{Y})^2$ is

(a) s^2 (b) $\frac{11}{10}s^2$

(c) $\frac{100}{99}s^2$ (d) $\frac{100}{111}s^2$

(NOV. 2020)

28. For circular systematic sampling, which of the following are correct?

(a) Sample mean is an unbiased estimate for population mean but sample variance is not an unbiased estimate for population variance

(b) Sample mean and sample variance are unbiased estimates for population mean and population variance respectively

(c) Sample mean is not an unbiased estimate for population mean but sample variance is an unbiased estimate for population variance

(d) Neither sample mean nor sample variance is an unbiased estimate for their population counterparts

(JUNE 2021)

29. A population of size N is divided into L strata of sizes $N_1, N_2, \ldots, N_L$, respectively. A stratified random sample of size n is drawn from the population where $n_1, n_2, \ldots, n_L$ denote the sample size in each of the L strata. Note that within each stratum units are chosen using simple random sampling.

Suppose the sample mean of the j-th stratum is denoted by $\bar{y}_j$ and let

$\bar{y}_{st} = \sum_{i=1}^{L}\frac{N_j\bar{y}_j}{N}$ But $\sigma_{st}^2 = V(\bar{y}_{st})$.

Consider a simple random sample of size n drawn from the population, independently of the first sample. Let $\bar{y}$ and σ^2 denote the sample mean and the variance of the sample mean for this sample. Which of the following statements are correct?

(a) $\bar{y}_{st}$ is an unbiased estimator of the population mean

(b) $\bar{y}$ is an unbiased estimator of the population mean

(c) $\sigma_{st}^2 \leq \sigma^2$

(d) If $\frac{n_i}{N_i} = \frac{n}{N}$ for all j, then $\sigma_{st}^2 = \sigma^2$

(JULY-2024)

30. The expected number of distinct units in a simple random sample of 3 units drawn with replacement from a population of 100 units is

(a) $3 - \left(\frac{99}{100}\right)^3$ (b) $100 - \frac{99^3}{100^2}$

(c) $2 + \frac{99^2}{100^3}$ (d) $3 - \left(\frac{99}{100}\right)^2$

(Dec 2025)

31. Consider a finite population of size $N = 100$. Let T_1 be the sample mean of a study variable based on a sample of size $n(1 < n < N)$ under simple random sampling with replacement scheme. Let T_2 be the sample mean of the same study variable based on a sample of size n under simple random sampling without replacement scheme. If $Var(T_1) = 9Var(T_2)$, then the sample size n equals

(a) 33 (b) 69

(c) 89 (d) 93

Answer Key									
1	2	3	4	5	6	7	8	9	10
a	b	b,c	B	A	c,d	b	a,d	d	d
11	12	13	14	15	16	17	18	19	20
b	a,b,c,d	a	b,c,d	A	a,b,c	b	c	c	a,b,c
21	22	23	24	25	26	27	28	29	30
d	a,b	c	b,d	d	a,b,c	a	a	c,d	b
31									
c									

:: Explanations ::

1. **Explanation: (a)**
In SRSWOR, probability of selecting specified unit at any draw is $\frac{1}{N}$
$E(X_i) = \sum_{x=1}^{N} x \cdot \frac{1}{N} = \frac{1}{N}\frac{N(N+1)}{2} = \frac{N+1}{2}$
$E(\overline{X}) = \frac{1}{N}\sum_{i=1}^{N} E(X_i) = \frac{1}{N} N\frac{(N+1)}{2}$
$E(2\overline{X}) = N + 1$
$E(2\overline{X} - 1) = N$
$2\overline{X} - 1$ is an unbiased estimator of N
So, option (a) is correct.
2. **Explanation: (b)**
3. **Explanation: (b), (c)**
4. **Explanation: (b)**
π_i be the prob. Of unit i is in the selected sample
$\pi_i = \frac{i}{50}$; $i = 1, 2, \dots, 50$
Expected no. of sample size $= \sum_{i=1}^{50}\pi_i = \sum_{i=1}^{50}\frac{i}{50}$
$= \frac{1}{50}\frac{50\times 51}{2} = 25.5$
So, option (b) is correct
5. **Explanation: (a)**
The expected no. of distinct units in sample (SRSWR) is $n\left[1 - \left(\frac{N-1}{N}\right)^n\right]$
Option (a) is correct
6. **Explanation: (c), (d)**
7. **Explanation: (b)**
The sample space = $\{Y_1\ Y_2\ Y_3\}$
In SRSWOR, sample mean (T_1) is an unbiased estimator of population mean
$E(T_2) = \frac{1}{^3C_2}\left[\frac{Y_1+Y_2}{2} + \frac{1}{2}\left(Y_1 + \frac{2}{3}Y_3\right) + \frac{Y_2}{2} + \frac{Y_3}{3}\right]$
$= \frac{1}{3}\left[\frac{Y_1}{2} + \frac{Y_2}{2} + \frac{Y_1}{2} + \frac{1}{3}Y_3 + \frac{Y_2}{2} + \frac{Y_3}{3}\right]$
$= \frac{1}{3}\left[Y_1 + Y_2 + \frac{2Y_3}{3}\right]$
$\neq \overline{Y}$
T_2 is not an unbiased estimator of $\overline{Y}$
$E(T_3) = \frac{1}{^3C_2}\left[\frac{Y_1+Y_2}{2} + Y_1 + \frac{Y_3}{2} + \frac{Y_2}{2} + \frac{Y_3}{3}\right]$
$= \frac{1}{3}\left[\frac{3Y_1}{2} + Y_2 + \frac{5}{6}Y_3\right] \neq \overline{Y}$
T_3 is not an unbiased estimator of $\overline{Y}$
T_2 and T_3 are biased and T_1 is unbiased for $\overline{Y}$
So, option (b) is correct
8. **Explanation: (a), (d)**
9. **Explanation: (d)**
A finite population has 8 units $\mu_1, \mu_2, \dots, \mu_8$
Value of study variable for unit is Y_i $(i = 1, 2, \dots, 8)$
$\overline{Y} = \frac{1}{8}\sum_{i=1}^{8} y_i$
A simple random sample of size 2 is drawn form $\mu_2, \mu_3, \dots, \mu_7$ of size 6. Let $\overline{y}$ be sample mean of size two
$E(\overline{y}) = \overline{y}_6$
Where $\overline{Y}_6 = \frac{y_2+y_3+\dots+y_7}{6}$
$T = \frac{y_1+6\overline{y}+y_8}{8}$
$E(T) = \frac{y_1+6E(\overline{y})+y_8}{8} = \frac{y_1+6\overline{Y}_6+y_8}{8} = \frac{\sum_{i=1}^{8} Y_i}{8} = \overline{Y}$
T is an unbiased for $\overline{Y}$
$Var(T) = Var\left(\frac{y_1+6\overline{y}+y_8}{8}\right) = \frac{1}{64}\cdot 36\, Var(\overline{y}) = \frac{9}{16}\, Var(\overline{y})$
So, option (d) is correct
10. **Explanation: (d)**
$N = nK$ units, $x \geq 2, k \geq 2$
Using systematic random sampling draw a sample of size n.
π_i = prob. Of i-th unit is included in the sample $= \frac{1}{k}$
$\pi_i = \frac{1}{k} = \frac{1}{N/n} = \frac{n}{N}$ $i = 1, 2, \dots, N$
π_{ij} = prob of i-th unit & j-th unit is included in the sample
$\pi_{ij} = 0$ if i-th or j-th unit is not included in the sample
So, $\pi_{ij} = 0$ for at least one pair (i, j)
In systematic sampling, sample mean is an unbiased estimate of population mean i.e.
$E(\overline{y}) = \overline{Y}$
$E(\overline{y}) = \frac{\sum_{i=1}^{N} Y_i}{N}$
$E(N\,\overline{y}) = \sum_{i=1}^{N} Y_i$
$\therefore N\overline{y}$ is an unbiased estimate of population total
So, option (b) & (d) are correct
11. **Explanation: (b)**
The no. of district samples of size n can be drawn with replacement from the population of n units is $^{2n-1}C_n$
So, option (b) is correct
12. **Explanation: (a), (b), (c), (d)**
Draw a random sample of size n from the population of size N using SRSWOR
Sample mean = $\overline{y}$ is an unbiased estimator of population mean $\overline{Y}_n$
$t_1 = N\overline{y}$
$E(t_1) = NE(\overline{y}) = N\overline{Y_N} = Y = Population\ total$
t_1 is an unbiased estimator of population total y
Now, y_1 is the value of variate corresponding to one unit and then draw a sample of size n from $(N-1)$ units using SRSWOR
Sample mean $= \overline{y}_0$ is an unbiased estimation of population mean $\overline{Y_{N-1}}$
$t_2 = (N-1)\overline{y}_0 + y_1$
$E(t_2) = (N-1)E(\overline{y}_0) + y_1 = (N-1)\overline{Y_{N-1}} + \overline{y_1}$
$= Y_{N-1} + y_1$
$= Y$ = Total population

t_2 is an unbiased estimator of population total

$V_1 = Var\ (t_1) = Var(N\ \overline{y}) = N^2\ Var(\overline{y})$

$= N^2 \cdot \frac{N-n}{Nn} \frac{N}{N-1} \sigma^2$

$Var(t_1) = N^2 \frac{\sigma^2}{n} \cdot \frac{N-n}{N-1}$

Where σ^2 population variance

$V_2 = Var(t_2) = Var\ [(N-1)\overline{y}_0 + y_1]$

$= (N-1)^2 Var(\overline{y}_0) + Var\ (y_1) + 2(1-1)Ca(\overline{y}_0, y_1)$

$= (N-1)^2 \left(\frac{1}{N-1} - \frac{1}{n}\right) \frac{N-1}{N-2}\ \sigma^2 + \sigma^2 + 2(N-1)\ Cov(y_0, y_1)$

$\therefore V_2 \le V_1$

So, option (a), (b), (c) & (d) are correct

13. Explanation: (a)

There are k strata of N = KM units each with size M. Draw a sample of size n_i with replacement from i-th stratum

$\overline{y}_i \rightarrow$ sample mean of i –th stratum $i = 1, 2, \ldots k$

$\Rightarrow E(\overline{y}_i) = \overline{Y}_i$

Sample mean is an unbiased estimator of population mean

$\overline{y}_s = \frac{1}{K} \sum_{i=1}^{k} \overline{y}_i$

$E(\overline{y}_s) = \frac{1}{K} \sum_{i=1}^{k} E(\overline{y}_i) = \frac{1}{K} \sum_{i=1}^{k} \overline{Y}_i = \overline{Y}_N$

$\therefore \overline{y}_s$ is an unbiased for the population mean $\overline{Y}_N$

$\overline{y}_w = \frac{\sum_{i=1}^{k} n_i \overline{y}_i}{n}$

$E(\overline{y}_w) = \frac{\sum_{i=1}^{k} n_i E(\overline{y}_i)}{n} = \frac{\sum_{i=1}^{k} n_i \overline{Y}_i}{n} \ne \overline{Y}_N$

So, option (a) is correct

14. Explanation: (b), (c), (d)

Let $Y = \sum_{i=1}^{N} Y_i$ and $\overline{Y} = \frac{1}{N} \sum_{i=1}^{N} Y_i$

A sample of size $n > 1$ is drawn from PPS with replacement with selection probabilities $p_1, p_2, \ldots, p_N; 0 < p < 1\ ; i = 1, 2, \ldots N$ and $\sum_{i=1}^{N} P_i = 1$

Define $T = \frac{1}{n} \sum_{\in S} \frac{Y_i}{P_i}$

Taking expectation

$E(T) = \frac{1}{n} \sum_{r=1}^{n} \left[\frac{Y_1}{p_1} p_1 + \frac{Y_2}{p_2} p_2 + \cdots + \frac{Y_N}{p_N} p_N\right]$

$= \frac{1}{n} \sum_{r=1}^{n} [\sum_{i=1}^{N} Y_i] = \frac{1}{n} \sum_{r=1}^{n} Y$

$E(T) = Y$

T is an unbiased estimator of Y

We know that

$Var(T) = \frac{1}{n}\left[\sum_{i=1}^{N} \frac{Y_i^2}{p_i} - Y^2\right]$

$Y_i \propto P_i$

$Y_i = c\ P_i$

$Var(T) = \frac{1}{n}\left[\sum_{i=1}^{N} \frac{c^2 p_i^2}{p_i} - Y^2\right]$

$= \frac{1}{n}[c^2 \sum_{i=1}^{N} P_i - Y^2]$

$Var(T) = 0$

An unbiased estimator of the $Var(T)$ is

$Var(T) = \frac{1}{n(n-1)} \sum_{i \in S} \left(\frac{Y_i}{p_i} - T\right)^2$

So, option (b), (c) and (d) are correct

15. Explanation: (a)

Let N be a population size and Y_i is the value of study variable for i-th unit of the population;

$i = 1, 2, \ldots N$

Define a random variable $\alpha_i (i = 1, 2, \ldots N)$ as

$\alpha_i = \begin{cases} 1 & \text{If } Y_i \text{ is included in the sample of size } n \\ 0 & \text{otherwise} \end{cases}$

$E(\alpha_i) = 1. P(Y_i \in S) + 0. P(Y_i \notin S)$ where S is sample $= \pi_i$ is the prob. Of including the unit i in the sample

Since, there are exactly n values of α_i which are 1 and $(N-n)$ values which are zero, so

$\sum_{i=1}^{N} \alpha_i = n$

$\sum_{i=1}^{N} E(\alpha_i) = n$

$\sum_{i=1}^{N} \pi_i = n$

Option (a) is correct

16. Explanation: (a), (b), (c)

17. Explanation: (b)

In SRS WOR,

The probability that a specified unit is included in the sample $= \frac{n}{N}$

Where n is sample size & N is population Size

Probability that 4th population Unit is included in the sample $= \frac{n}{N}$

Now, One unit is included in the samples, we have (N- 1) population unit left

The prob. That 6th population unit is not included in the sample $= \frac{N-n}{N-1}$

$\therefore$The prob. That 4th unit is included in the sample but 6th population unit is not included

In the sample $= \frac{n}{N} \times \frac{N-n}{N-1} = \frac{n(N-n)}{N(N-1)}$

So, option (b) is correct

18. Explanation: (C)

This condition $Var(\overline{Y}) = Var\ (\overline{Y_{ST}})$ if all the stratum means are equal

19. Explanation: (c)

In Simple Random sampling without replacement

p→ Sample proportion

P → population proportion

As, we know, sample proportion is an unbiased estimate of population proportion i.e.

$E(p) = P$

We need to find an unbiased estimate of $P(1-P)$

In SRS WOR, $Var\ (p) = \frac{N-n}{(N-1)n} P(1-P)$

$E(p(p-1)] = E(p^2) - E(p)$

$= \frac{N-n}{(N-1)n} P(1-P) + P^2 - P$

$= \frac{N-n}{(N-1)n} P(1-P) - P(1-P)$

$= P(1-P)\left[\frac{N-n}{(N-1)n} - 1\right]$

$= P(1-P) \frac{N-n-Nn+n}{(N-1)n}$

$= P(1-P) \frac{N(n-1)}{(N-1)n}$

$E\left[\frac{(N-1)n}{N(n-1)} p(p-1)\right] = P(1-P)$

Option (c) is correct.

20. Explanation: (a), (b), (c)

Suppose there are k groups each consisting of N boys

Scheme 1: Draw a sample without replacement of size kn out of all kN boys

This case of simple random sampling without replacement.

In SRSWOR, same mean is an unbiased estimator of population mean i.e.

$E(\overline{Y}) = \mu$ (population mean)

$Var(\overline{Y}) = \frac{N-n}{Nn} S^2$

Where S^2 in the population mean squares

Scheme 2: Draw a sample from each of k groups with replacement of size n

This case is of stratified Random sampling with replacement, sample mean is unbiased estimate of population mean i.e.

$E(\overline{y}_G) = \mu$

$Var(\overline{y}_G) = \sum_{i=1}^{k} \left(\frac{N_i - 1}{N_i n_i}\right) p_i^2 S_i^2$

Variance $(\overline{Y}) \le Var(\overline{Y}_G)$

So, option (a), (b), (c) are correct.

21. Explanation: (d)

Standard error for with replacement = $\sqrt{\frac{N-1}{Nn} S^2}$

Standard error for without replacement = $\sqrt{\frac{N-n}{Nn} S^2}$

$\therefore \sqrt{\frac{N-1}{Nn} S^2} = 2\sqrt{\frac{N-n}{Nn} . S^2}$

$N = 125$

$\frac{N-1}{Nn} = 4 . \frac{N-n}{Nn}$

$125 - 1 = 4(125 - n)$

$\frac{124}{4} = 125 - n$

$n = 125 - 31$

$n = 94$

Option (d) is correct

22. Explanation: (a), (b)

$N = 4$ (population size)

$n = 2$ (sample size)

$\overline{x}_1$ be the sample mean of height of boys drawn with replacement from population

$\overline{x}_2$ be the sample mean of height of boy drawn without replacement from population

$Var(\overline{x}_1) = \frac{N-1}{Nn} S^2 = \frac{4-1}{4 \times 2} S^2 = \frac{3}{8} S^2$

$Var(\overline{x}_2) = \frac{N-n}{Nn} S^2 = \frac{4-2}{4 \times 2} S^2 = \frac{1}{4} S^2$

$\therefore Var\left(\frac{\overline{x}_1 + \overline{x}_2}{2}\right) = \frac{1}{4}[Var(\overline{x}_1) + Var(\overline{x}_2)]$

$= \frac{1}{4}\left[\frac{3}{8} S^2 + \frac{1}{4} S^2\right]$

$= \frac{1}{4} \frac{3S^2 + 2S^2}{8} = \frac{5}{32} S^2 = 0.15626 S^2$

$Var\left(\frac{2\overline{x}_1 + 3\overline{x}_2}{5}\right) = \frac{1}{25}[4Var(\overline{x}_1) + 9Var(\overline{x}_2)]$

$= \frac{1}{25}\left[4 \times \frac{3}{2} S^2 + 9 \times \frac{1}{4} S^2\right]$

$= \frac{1}{25}\left[\frac{6S^2 + 9S^2}{4}\right]$

$= \frac{15}{25 \times 4} S^2 = \frac{3}{20} S^2 = 0.15\, S^2$

$\therefore Var\left(\frac{\overline{x}_1 + \overline{x}_2}{2}\right) \ge Var\left(\frac{2\overline{x}_1 + 3\overline{x}_2}{5}\right)$

Similarly, $Var\left(\frac{\overline{x}_1 + 2\overline{x}_2}{3}\right) = \frac{1}{9}[Var(\overline{x}_1) + 4Var(\overline{x}_2)]$

$= \frac{1}{9}\left[\frac{3}{8} S^2 + 4 \times \frac{1}{4} S^2\right]$

$= \frac{1}{9}\left[\frac{3S^2 + 8S^2}{8}\right]$

$= \frac{11}{72} S^2 = 0.1527\, S^2$

$Var\left(\frac{2\overline{x}_1 + 3\overline{x}_2}{5}\right) = \frac{3}{20} S^2 = 0.15$

$Var\left(\frac{\overline{x}_1 + 2\overline{x}_2}{3}\right) > Var\left(\frac{2\overline{x}_1 + 3\overline{x}_2}{5}\right)$

Option (a), (b) are correct

23. Explanation: (c)

$n = 2$ (2 draws) and $N = 4$

$\prod_1 = P[unit\ 1\ is\ included\ in\ 1^{st}\ draw]$ + P [unit is selected in 2nd draw]

$\prod_1 = p_1 + p_2$

$p_1 = 0.4\ (Given)$

$P_2 = \sum_{j=2}^{4} P\ [j\ unit\ is\ selected\ in\ 1^{st}\ draw] \times$ $P[\,1^{st}\ unit\ is\ seleted\ in\ 2^{nd}\ draw\ |$ j-th unit is not selected in 2nd draw] $j \neq 1$

$P_2 =$

$\sum_{j=2}^{4} p_j \frac{P[1^{st}\ unit\ is\ selected\ in\ 2^{nd}\ draw\ ; j-th\ is\ not\ selected\ at\ 2^{nd}\ draw]}{P\ [\ j-th\ is\ not\ selected\ in\ 2^{nd}\ draw]}$

$= \sum_{j=2}^{4} p_j \frac{p_i}{1-p_j} = 0.4 \sum_{j=2}^{4} \frac{p_j}{1-p_j}$

$= 0.4\left[\frac{p_2}{1-p_2} + \frac{p_3}{1-p_3} + \frac{p_4}{1-p_4}\right]$

$= 0.4\left[\frac{0.2}{0.8} + \frac{0.2}{0.8} + \frac{0.2}{0.8}\right]$

$P_2 = 0.3$

$\prod_1 = p_1 + p_2$

$= 0.4 + 0.3$

$= 0.7$

Option (c) is correct.

24. Explanation: (b), (d)

25. Explanation: (d)

26. Explanation: (a), (b), (c)

27. Explanation: (a)

In simple Random sampling without replacement,

N = population size = 100

n = Sample size = 10

$\sigma^2 = \frac{1}{N} \sum_{i=1}^{N} (Y_i - \overline{Y})^2$ and $S^2 = \frac{1}{N-1} (Y_i - \overline{Y})^2$

$\Rightarrow N\sigma^2 = (N-1)S^2$ and $\frac{N}{(N-1)} \sigma^2 = S^2$

$\therefore s^2 = \frac{1}{n-1} \sum_{i=1}^{n} (y_i - \overline{y})^2$

$\therefore s^2$, sample mean square is an unbiased estimate of Population mean square S^2

$E(s^2) = S^2$

$E(s^2) = \frac{N}{(N-1)} \sigma^2$

$E\left[\frac{N-1}{N} s^2\right] = \sigma^2$

$\Rightarrow E\left[\frac{100-1}{100} s^2\right] = \sigma^2$

Here, it is given that

$s^2 = \frac{1}{10} \sum_{i=1}^{10} (y_i - \overline{y})^2$ is sample variance

$s^2 = \frac{1}{9} \sum_{i=1}^{10} (y_i - \overline{y})^2$ is sample mean square

$\Rightarrow 10\, S^2 = 9\, s^2$

$\Rightarrow s^2 = \frac{10\,s^2}{9}$

$E\left[\frac{99}{100} \times \frac{10}{9} s^2\right] = \sigma^2$

$E\left[\frac{11\,s^2}{10}\right] = \sigma^2$

$\Rightarrow \frac{11\,s^2}{10}$ is unbiased estimate of σ^2

28. Explanation: (a)

$E(\bar{y}) = \frac{1}{N}\sum_{i=1}^{N}\left(\frac{1}{n}\sum_{i=1}^{n} y_i\right)_r = \frac{1}{Nn}\sum_{i=1}^{N}\left(\frac{1}{n}\sum_{i=1}^{n} y_i\right)_r = Y$

Where r stands for the sample selected with the random start r

$Var(\bar{y}) = \frac{1}{N}\sum_{r=1}^{N}(\bar{y}_r - \bar{Y})^2$

$E\left(Var(\bar{y})\right) = E\left(\frac{1}{N}\sum_{r=1}^{N}(\bar{y}_r - \bar{Y})^2\right) \neq \sigma^2$

Sample mean is an unbiased estimate for population mean but sample variance is not an unbiased estimate for population variance.

Hence option (a) is correct.

29. Explanation: (c), (d)

A population of size N is divided into L strata of sizes $N_1, N_2, \ldots, N_L$ respectively.

A stratified random sample of size n is drawn from the population where $n_1, n_2, \ldots, n_L$ denote the sample size in each L strata

$\bar{y}_{st} = \sum_{j=1}^{L}\frac{N_j}{N}\bar{y}_j, \qquad \sigma_{st}^2 = Var(\bar{y}_{st})$

$E(\bar{y}_{st}) = \frac{1}{N},\sum_{j=1}^{L} N_j\, E(\bar{y}_j)$

$= \frac{1}{N}\sum_{y=1}^{L} N_j\,\bar{Y}_j = \bar{Y}_N$

$\Rightarrow \bar{y}_{st}$ is an unbiased estimator of population mean $\bar{Y}_N$

In simple random sampling, sample mean $\bar{y}$ is an unbiased estimator of population mean $\bar{Y}$

So, option (a) & (b) are correct

If $\frac{n_i}{N_i} = \frac{n}{N}$ or $n_i \propto N_i S_i$ then $\sigma_{st}^2 \leq \sigma^2$ but it is not given so, option (c) & (d) is in correct

30. Explanation: (b)

Here the sample of size 100 is drawn using the method of SRSWR. Thus the underlying distribution is binomial. Note that the each unit out of 100 from the population is selected at least once and at most three times as the sample size is itself three. Define a random variable as

$X_i = \begin{cases} 1, & \text{if } i^{th} \text{ unit is selected at least once in the sample of size three} \\ 0, & else \end{cases} \; ; \; i = 1,2,\ldots,100$

Here

$X_i \sim Binomial(n = 100, p)\,;\; i = 1,2,\ldots,100$

Where

p=P(i^{th} unit is selected at least once in the sample of size three)

$= 1 - P(i^{th}$ unit is not selected in the sample of size three)

$= 1 - \left(\frac{99}{100}\right)^3$

$\therefore E(X_i) = np = 100 \times \left\{1 - \left(\frac{99}{100}\right)^3\right\} = 100 - \frac{99^3}{100^2}$

31. Explanation: (c)

Given: Population size $N = 100$

T_1: sample mean under SRS with replacement (SRSWR)

T_2: sample mean under SRS without replacement (SRSWOR)

$$Var(T_1) = 9\,Var(T_2)$$

Variance formulas:

For SRSWR

$$Var(T_1) = \frac{\sigma^2}{n}$$

For SRSWOR

$$Var(T_2) = \frac{\sigma^2}{n}\left(\frac{N-n}{N-1}\right)$$

The term $\frac{N-n}{N-1}$ is the finite population correction (FPC).

Given condition: $Var(T_1) = 9Var(T_2)$

Substitute formulas:

$$\frac{\sigma^2}{n} = 9\left[\frac{\sigma^2}{n}\left(\frac{N-n}{N-1}\right)\right]$$

Cancel $\frac{\sigma^2}{n}$:

$$1 = 9\left(\frac{N-n}{N-1}\right)$$

Substitute $N = 100$

$$1 = 9\left(\frac{100-n}{99}\right)$$

$$\Rightarrow \frac{100-n}{99} = \frac{1}{9}$$

$$\Rightarrow 100 - n = 11$$

$\Rightarrow n = 89$

CHAPTER 12

MULTIVARIATE ANALYSIS

(DEC. 2012)

1. Suppose that $\begin{pmatrix} X_1 \\ X_2 \end{pmatrix}$ has normal $(\mu_{2\times1}, \sum_{2\times2})$ distribution, where $\sum_{2\times2}$ is nonsingular. Let $X_3 = -2X_2$. Then which of the following has a singular normal distribution?
(a) $\begin{pmatrix} X_1 - 2X_2 \\ X_2 - 2X_3 \end{pmatrix}$ (b) $\begin{pmatrix} X_1 - X_2 - X_3 \\ 2X_1 + 2X_2 \end{pmatrix}$
(c) $\begin{pmatrix} X_1 + X_2 \\ 2X_1 + 2X_3 \end{pmatrix}$ (d) $\begin{pmatrix} X_1 + X_2 + X_1 \\ X_1 + X_2 \end{pmatrix}$

(DEC. 2012)

2. Let $N(\tilde{\mu}, \sum)$ denote the multivariate normal distribution with mean vector $\tilde{\mu}$ and dispersion matrix $\sum$. Which of the following are correct?
(a) The Bayes classifier between $N(\tilde{\mu}_1, \sum_1)$ and $N(\tilde{\mu}_2, \sum_2)$ consists of comparing a linear function of the classifiable vector with a threshold
(b) The misclassification probability of the Bayes classifier between the populations $N(\tilde{\mu}_1, \sum)$ and $N(\tilde{\mu}_2, \sum)$ is more than that of the Bayes classifier between the populations $N(2\tilde{\mu}_1, 2\sum)$ and $N(2\tilde{\mu}_2, 2\sum)$
(c) When $\tilde{\mu}_1$ and $\tilde{\mu}_2$ are unknown, the maximum likelihood classifier between $N(\tilde{\mu}_1, \mathrm{I})$ and $N(\tilde{\mu}_2, \mathrm{I})$, based on sampled data from the two populations, depends on the data only through the respective sample means.
(d) The Bayes classifier between $N(1, 0)$ and $N(10, 4)$ would classify the data point 2 as belonging to the first population.

(JUNE 2013)

3. (X, Y) follows the bivariate normal distribution $N_2(0, 0, 1, 1, \rho), -1 < \rho < 1$. Then,
(a) $X + Y$ and $X - Y$ are uncorrelated only if $\rho = 0$
(b) $X + Y$ and $X - Y$ are uncorrelated only if $\rho < 0$
(c) $X + Y$ and $X - Y$ are uncorrelated only if $\rho > 0$
(d) $X + Y$ and $X - Y$ are uncorrelated for all values of ρ

(DEC. 2013)

4. Let $X \sim N_p(\mu, I)$ and $B_{p\times p}$ be any real symmetric matrix of rank $k \le p$ such that $B\mu = 0$ and $B^2 = B$. Then the probability distribution of $X'BX$ is
(a) Wishart
(b) χ^2_{k-1}
(c) χ^2_k
(d) The same as that of $\sum_{i=1}^k Z_i^2$ where Z_i are independent $N(0,1)$.

(DEC. 2013)

5. Let $U_1, U_2, \ldots, U_n$ be i.i.d. random vectors with common distribution $N_P(0, \sum), \sum = \left(\left(\sigma_{ij}\right)\right)$. Define $S = \sum_{i=1}^n U_i U'_j, S = \left(\left(s_{ij}\right)\right)$. Which of the following is/are true?
(a) $\sum_i \sum_j s_{ij} \sim \text{constant} \cdot \chi^2_n$.
(b) $s_{11} - 2s_{12} - s_{22} \sim \text{constant} \cdot \chi^2_n$.
(c) $s_{11} \sim \text{constant} \cdot \chi^2_n$
(d) $s_{11} + s_{12} - 2s_{12} \sim \text{constant} \cdot \chi^2_n$.

(DEC. 2014)

6. Let $X_1, \ldots, X_n$ be a random sample of size n from a $p-$variate Normal distribution with mean μ and positive definite covariance matrix $\sum$. Choose the correct statement
(a) $(X_1 - \mu)'\Sigma^{-1}(X_1 - \mu)$ has chi-square distribution with 1d.f.
(b) $\overline{X}\,\overline{X}'$ has Wishart distribution with pd. f.
(c) $\sum_{i=1}^n (X_i - \mu)(X_i - \mu)'$ has Wishart distribution with nd. f.
(d) $X_1 + X_2$ and $X_1 - X_2$ are independently distributed.

(DEC. 2014)

7. Let Y follow multivariate normal distribution $N_n(0, I)$ and let A and B be $n \times n$ symmetric, idempotent matrices. Then which of the following statements are true?
(a) If $AB = 0$, then $Y'AY$ and $Y'BY$ are independently distributed.
(b) If $Y'(A + B)Y$ has chi-square distribution then $Y'AY$ and $Y'BY$ are independently distributed.
(c) $Y'(A - B)Y$ has chi-square distribution.
(d) $Y'AY$ and $Y'BY$ have chi-square distribution

(DEC. 2014)

8. Consider a 3-vaiate population with covariance matrix $\begin{pmatrix} \sigma^2 & \sigma^2\rho & 0 \\ \sigma^2\rho & \sigma^2 & \sigma^2\rho \\ 0 & \sigma^2\rho & \sigma^2 \end{pmatrix}$ where $\sigma^2 > 0, \rho > 0$. Then which of the following statements are true?
(a) $\rho < \frac{1}{\sqrt{2}}$
(b) The proportion of the total population variance explained by the first principal $\frac{1+2\rho}{3}$ component
(c) The second principal component is uncorrelated with the first and the third principal component.
(d) The proportion of the total population variance explained by the first two principal components is $\frac{\sqrt{2}}{3}(\rho + \sqrt{2})$

(JUNE 2014)

9. Let X be a $p \times 1$ random vector such that $X \sim N_p(0, \sum)$ where rank $(\sum) = p$. Which of the following is true?

(a) $E(X'\Sigma^{-1}X) = 2p, V(X'\Sigma^{-1}X) = 2p$
(b) $E(X'\Sigma^{-1}X) = 2p, V(X'\Sigma^{-1}X) = p$
(c) $E(X'\Sigma^{-1}X) = p, V(X'\Sigma^{-1}X) = p$
(d) $E(X'\Sigma^{-1}X) = p, V(X'\Sigma^{-1}X) = 2p$

(JUNE 2015)

10. Let $Y = (Y_1, \ldots, Y_n)'$ have the multivariate normal distribution $N_n(0, I)$. Which of the following is the covariance matrix of the conditional distribution of Y given $\sum_{i=1}^n Y_i$?
(1 denotes the $n \times 1$ vector with all elements 1.)
(a) I (b) $I + \frac{11'}{n}$
(c) $I - \frac{11'}{n}$ (d) $\frac{11'}{n}$

(JUNE 2015)

11. Let Y_1, Y_2, Y_3, Y_4 ne i.i.d standard normal variables. Which of the following has Wishart distribution with 2.d.f?
(a) $\begin{bmatrix} Y_1^2 + Y_2^2 & Y_2^2 + Y_3^2 \\ Y_2^2 + Y_3^2 & Y_3^2 + Y_4^2 \end{bmatrix}$
(b) $\begin{bmatrix} Y_1^2 & Y_2^2 \\ Y_3^2 & Y_4^2 \end{bmatrix}$
(c) $\begin{bmatrix} Y_1^2 + Y_2^2 & 0 \\ 0 & Y_3^2 + Y_4^2 \end{bmatrix}$
(d) $\begin{bmatrix} Y_1^2 + Y_2^2 & Y_1Y_3 + Y_2Y_4 \\ Y_1Y_3 + Y_2Y_4 & Y_3^2 + Y_4^2 \end{bmatrix}$

(JUNE 2015)

12. Let $\Sigma = ((\sigma_{ij}))$ be an n x n symmetric and positive definite matrix such that $\sigma_{ij} \neq 0$ for all $i.j$. Which of the following matrixes will always be the covariance matrix of a multivariate normal random vector?
(a) Σ
(b) The matrix with the (ij) the elementσ_{ij}^2 for the each $i.j$
(c) The matrix with $(i.j)$ the element $\frac{1}{\sigma_{ij}}$ for each $i.j$
(d) Σ^{-1}

(JUNE 2015)

13. Consider a random sample $(X_1, Y_1) \ldots, (X_n, Y_n)$ from the bivariate normal distribution with $E(X_i) = \mu = EY_i, Var(X_i) = \sigma^2 = Var(Y_i)$ and $Cov(X_i, Y_i) = \rho\sigma^2$ for all i. Let $\hat{\mu}, \hat{\sigma}^2$ and $\hat{\rho}$ denote the maximum likelihood estimator of μ, σ^2 and ρ respectively. Also,
$$S_X^2 = \sum_{i=1}^n (X_i - \bar{X})^2, S_Y^2 = \sum_{i=1}^n (Y_i - \bar{Y})^2$$
And
$$S_{XY} = \sum_{i=1}^n (X_i - \bar{X})^2, (Y_i - \bar{Y})$$
Then
(a) $X_1 - Y_1$ and $X_1 + Y_1$ are independent
(b) $\hat{\mu} = \frac{1}{2}(\bar{X} + \bar{Y}), \hat{\sigma}^2 = \frac{1}{2n}(S_X^2 + S_Y^2), \hat{\rho} = \frac{2S_{XY}}{S_X^2 + S_Y^2}$
(c) $\hat{\sigma}^2(1 + \hat{\rho}) = \frac{1}{2n}(S_X^2 + S_Y^2 + 2S_{XY})$
(d) $\hat{\sigma}^2(1 - \hat{\rho}) = \frac{1}{2n}(S_X^2 + S_Y^2 - 2S_{XY})$

(DEC. 2015)

14. Let the $n \times 1$ vector $\underline{x}$ follow an n-variate normal distribution with mean vector $\underline{\mu}(\neq \underline{0})$ and variance – covariance matrix $V(\neq I_n$, the nth order identity matrix). Also, let A be a symmetric matrix of order n. Which of the following statements is true?
(a) $\underline{x}'A\underline{x}$ follows a central chi-square distribution if and only if $(AV)^2 = AV$
(b) $\underline{x}'A\underline{x}$ follows a central chi-square distribution if and only if $A^2 = A$
(c) The mean of $\underline{x}'A\underline{x}$ is $\underline{\mu}'A\underline{\mu} + tr(AV)$, where $tr(\cdot)$ denotes the trace of a square matrix.
(d) $\underline{x}'A\underline{x}$ always has a central chi-square distribution with n degrees of freedom.

(DEC. 2015)

15. Suppose that (X, Y) has a joint distribution with the marginal distribution of X being $N(0,1)$ and $E(Y|X = x) = x^3$ for all $x \in \mathbb{R}$. Then, which of the following statements are true?
(a) Corr $(X, Y) = 0$
(b) Corr $(X, Y) > 0$
(c) Corr $(X, Y) < 0$
(d) X and Y are independent

(DEC. 2015)

16. Suppose $\begin{pmatrix} X \\ Y \end{pmatrix}$ is a random vector such that the marginal distribution of X and the marginal distribution of Y are the same and each is normally distributed with mean 0 and variance 1. Then, which of the following conditions imply independence of X and Y?
(a) Cov $(X, Y) = 0$
(b) $aX + bY$ is normally distributed with mean 0 and variance $a^2 + b^2$ for all real a and b
(c) $P(X \leq 0, Y \leq 0) = {}^1/_4$
(d) $E[e^{itX + isY}] = E[e^{itX}]E[e^{isY}]$ for all ral s and t

(DEC. 2015)

17. Let $X = (X_1, X_2, X_3, X_4)'$ be 4×1 random vector such that $X \sim N_4(0, \Sigma)$ where $\Sigma = \begin{pmatrix} 1 & \rho & \rho & \rho \\ \rho & 1 & \rho & \rho \\ \rho & \rho & 1 & \rho \\ \rho & \rho & \rho & 1 \end{pmatrix}$ is positive definite. Then, which of the following statements are true?
(a) X_1, X_2, X_2, X_3 and X_3, X_4 have identical distribution
(b) $\frac{(X_1 - X_2)^2}{(X_1 - X_3)^2} \sim F_{1,1}$
(c) $\{(X_1 - X_3)^2 + (X_2 - X_4)^2\}.\frac{1}{2(1-\rho)} \sim \chi_2^2$
(d) $\frac{(X_1 - X_2)^2}{(X_3 - X_4)^2} \sim F_{1,1}$

(DEC. 2015)

18. Let X be a 4×1 random vector with Multivariate normal distribution with mean μ and dispersion matrix Σ. Suppose, the eigenvalues of Σ are $\lambda_1 = 6, \lambda_2 = 3, \lambda_3 = 2, \lambda_4 = 1$. Let Y_1, Y_2, Y_3, Y_4 be the four principal components. Which of the following statements are correct?
(a) The percentage of variation explained by the first two components is $\leq 95\%$
(b) The percentage of variation explained by the first three components is $\geq 95\%$

(c) Y_1, Y_2, Y_3, Y_4 are independent
(d) Y_1, Y_2, Y_3, Y_4 have identical distribution.

(DEC. 2015)

19. Let $Y_1, Y_2 \dots, Y_n$ be random variables with common unknown mean θ. The variance-covariance matrix V of the vector $(Y_1, Y_2 \dots, Y_n)$, is such that the inverse of V has all its diagonal elements equal to c and all its off-diagonal elements equal to d. Let T_1 be the best unbiased estimator of θ and T_2 be the ordinary least squares estimator of θ. Which of the following statements are true?
(a) $T_1 = \frac{1}{n}\sum_{i=1}^{n} Y_i = T_2$
(b) $T_2 = nY$ and $T_1 = \sum_{i=1}^{n} Y_i = \bar{Y}$ where $\bar{Y}$ is the mean of the Y_i's.
(c) There are exactly $(n-1)$ linearly independent linear functions of $Y_1, Y_2 \dots, Y_n$ each with zero expectation
(d) There are exactly $(n-2)$ linearly independent linear functions of $Y_1, Y_2 \dots, Y_n$ each with zero expectation

(JUNE 2016)

20. Let $\underline{X} \sim N_3\left(\underline{\mu}, \Sigma\right)$ where $\underline{\mu} = (1,1,1)$ and $\Sigma = \begin{pmatrix} 1 & 1 & 1 \\ 1 & 3 & c \\ 1 & c & 2 \end{pmatrix}$.
The value of c such that X_2 *and* $-X_1 + X_2 - X_3$ are independent is
(a) -2 (b) 0
(c) 2 (d) 1

(JUNE 2016)

21. Let (X, Y) follow a bivariate normal distribution with mean vector(0,0) , and dispersion matrix $\Sigma = \begin{bmatrix} 1 & p \\ p & 1 \end{bmatrix}, p \neq 0$. Suppose $Z = \frac{X-Y}{X+Y}\sqrt{\frac{1+p}{1-p}}$. Then which of the following statements are correct?
(a) $\sqrt{\frac{1+p}{1-p}} \times \frac{X-Y}{\sqrt{X^2+Y^2+2XY}}$ has a student-t distribution.
(b) $\sqrt{\frac{1-p}{1+p}} \times \frac{X-Y}{\sqrt{X^2+Y^2+2XY}}$ has a student-t distribution.
(c) Z is symmetric about 0.
(d) $\mathbb{E}(Z)$ exists and equals zero.

(DEC. 2016)

22. $X_1, X_2, \dots, X_p$ be a random vector with mean μ and a positive definite dispersion matrix Σ. Then the coefficient vector $(l_1, l_2, \dots, l_2)$ of the first principal component $\sum_{i=1}^{p} l_1 X_i$ is
(a) the vector of all the eigenvalues of Σ.
(b) the eigenvector corresponding to the smallest eigenvalue of Σ.
(c) the eigenvector corresponding to the largest eigenvalue of Σ.
(d) the vector of all the eigenvalues of Σ^{-1}.

(DEC. 2016)

23. Suppose $X_1, X_2, \dots, X_k$ are independent and identically distributed standard normal random variables, and $\underline{X} = (X_1, X_2, \dots, X_k)^T$. If A is an idempotent $k \times k$ matrix, then which of the following statements are true?
(a) $\underline{X}^T A \underline{X}$ and $\underline{X}^T (I - A)\underline{X}$ are independent.
(b) $\underline{X}^T A \underline{X}$ and $\underline{X}^T (I - A)\underline{X}$ are identically distributed if k is even and trace$(A) = \frac{k}{2}$.
(c) $\frac{1}{2}\underline{X}^T A \underline{X}$ follows a gamma distribution if $A \neq 0$.
(d) $\underline{X}^T (I - A)\underline{X}$ follows a chi-squared distribution if $A \neq I$

(DEC. 2016)

24. Let $\phi(x, y; p)$ be the density of bivariate normal distribution with mean vector $\begin{pmatrix} 0 \\ 0 \end{pmatrix}$ and Variance-Covariance matrix$\begin{pmatrix} 1 & p \\ p & 1 \end{pmatrix}$. Consider a random vector$\begin{pmatrix} X \\ Y \end{pmatrix}$ having density $\frac{1}{2}\left(\phi\left(\left(x, y; \frac{1}{2}\right) + \phi\left(\left(x, y; -\frac{1}{2}\right)\right)\right)\right)$. Then
(a) Marginal distribution of both X and Y is standard normal.
(b) $Covariance(X, Y) = 0$
(c) X and Y are independent.
(d) (X, Y) has a bivariate normal distribution.

(JUNE 2017)

25. Suppose (X_1, X_2) follows a bivariate normal distribution with $E(X_1) = E(X_2) = 0$, $V(X_1) = V(X_2) = 2$ and $Cov(X_1, X_2) = -1$. If $\Phi(x) = \frac{1}{\sqrt{2\pi}}\int_{-\infty}^{x} e^{-y^2/2} dy$, then $P[X_1 - X_2 > 6]$ is equal to
(a) $\Phi(-1)$ (b) $\Phi(-3)$
(c) $\Phi(\sqrt{6})$ (d) $\Phi(-\sqrt{6})$

(JUNE 2017)

26. Let X_1 and X_2 be independent random variables each having $N(\mu, \sigma^2)$ distribution, where $\mu \in \mathbb{R}, \sigma^2 > 0$. Let $0 \leq \theta < 2\pi$ and $A = \begin{pmatrix} \cos\theta & \sin\theta \\ -\sin\theta & \cos\theta \end{pmatrix}$. Put $\underline{Y} = (Y_1, Y_2)^t = A\underline{X}$ with $\underline{X} = (X_1, X_2)^t$. Which of the following statements are connecting?
(a) $\underline{Y} = \underline{X}$ in distribution if and only if $\mu = 0$
(b) $\underline{Y} = \underline{X}$ in distribution if and only if $\mu = 0, \theta = 0$
(c) Y_1 and Y_2 are Gaussian
(d) Y_1 and Y_2 may be correlated.

(JUNE 2017)

27. Let X_1 and X_2 be two i.i.d. $N_p(0, \Sigma)$ random variables with rank $(\Sigma) = p$. Suppose A is a $p \times p$ symmetric matrix of rank r, and $A^2 = A$. Which of the following statements are correct?
(a) $X_1^T A X_1 \sim \chi_r^2$
(b) $X_1^T A X_1 + X_2^T A X_2 \sim 2\chi_r^2$
(c) $X_1^T A X_2 + X_2^T A X_1 \sim 2\chi_r^2$
(d) $X_1^T A X_1 + X_2^T A X_2 \sim \chi_{2r}^2$

(DEC. 2017)

28. Suppose $X_1 \sim N_{p_1}(0, \Sigma_1), X_2 \sim N_{p_2}(0, \Sigma_2)$, where$X_1$ and $X_2$are independently distributed. If $p_1 > p_2$ and Σ_1, Σ_2 are positive definite then which of the following statements is necessarily true?
(a) $X_1^T \Sigma_1 X_1 + X_2^T \Sigma_2 X_2 \sim \chi_{p_1+p_2}^2$
(b) $X_1^T \Sigma_1^{-1} X_1 + X_2^T \Sigma_2^{-1} X_2 \sim \chi_{p_1+p_2}^2$
(c) $X_1^T \Sigma_1^{-1} X_1 - X_2^T \Sigma_2^{-1} X_2 \sim \chi_{p_1+p_2}^2$
(d) $\frac{p_1 X_1^T \Sigma_1^{-1} X_1}{p_2 X_2^T \Sigma_2^{-1} X_2} \sim F_{p_1, p_2}$

(JUNE 2018)

29. The covariance matrix of a four-dimensional random vector X is of the form $\begin{bmatrix} 1 & \rho & \rho & \rho \\ \rho & 1 & \rho & \rho \\ \rho & \rho & 1 & \rho \\ \rho & \rho & \rho & 1 \end{bmatrix}$, where $\rho < 0$. If v is the variance of the first principal component, then
(a) v cannot exceed 5/4
(b) v can exceed 5/4, but cannot exceed 4/3
(c) v can exceed 4/3, but cannot exceed 3/2
(d) v can exceed 3/2

(DEC. 2018)

30. If $X - N_p(0,1)$ and $A_{p\times p}$ is an idempotent matrix with rank $(A) = k < p$, then which of the following statements is correct?
(a) $\frac{X'AX}{X'X} - \frac{k}{p}F_{k.p}$
(b) $\frac{X'AX}{X'X} - \frac{k}{p-k}F_{k.p-k}$
(c) $\frac{X'AX}{X'X} - Beta\left(\frac{k}{2},\frac{p}{2}\right)$
(d) $\frac{X'AX}{X'X} - Beta\left(\frac{k}{2},\frac{p-k}{2}\right)$

(JUNE 2019)

31. Suppose (X,Y) follows bivariate normal distribution with mean μ_1,μ_2 standard deviation σ_1,σ_2 and correlation coefficient ρ where all the parameters are unknown Then testing $H_0:\sigma_1 = \sigma_2$ is equivalent to testing the independence of
(a) $X\ and\ Y$
(b) $X\ and\ X - Y$
(c) $X + Y\ and\ Y$
(d) $X + Y\ and\ X - Y$

(JUNE 2019)

32. Suppose that $\binom{X}{Y}$ has a bivariate density $f = \frac{1}{2}f_1 + \frac{1}{2}f_2$, Where f_1 and f_1 are respectively, the densities of bivariate normal distributions $N(\mu_1,\Sigma)$ and $N(\mu_2,\Sigma)$ with $\mu_1 = \binom{1}{1}$, $\mu_2 = \binom{-1}{-1}$ and $\Sigma = I_2$, the 2 x 2 identity matrix. The which of the following is correct?
(a) $X\ and\ Y$ are positively correlated
(b) $X\ and\ Y$ are negatively correlated
(c) $X\ and\ Y$ are correlated but they are not independent
(d) $X\ and\ Y$ are independent

(JUNE 2019)

33. Let S_θ be the square region with four vertices $(\theta,0),(0,\theta),(-\theta,0)$ and $(0,\theta)$, where $\theta > 0$ is unknown. Suppose that $\binom{X}{Y}$ follows the uniform distribution on S_θ. Which of the following statements are true?
(a) X and Y are uncorrelated
(b) X and Y are independent
(c) $|X| + |Y|$ cannot exceed θ
(d) If $\binom{x_1}{y_1}$ and $\binom{x_2}{y_2}$ are two observations drawn independently, then the maximum likelihood estimate of θ is $max\{|x_1| + |y_1|, |x_2| + |y_2|\}$

(JUNE 2019)

34. $\boldsymbol{X}$ follows a p –variate $(p > 2)$ distribution with $E(X) = \mu$ and $Var(X) = \Sigma$. Which of the following are true?
(a) $E(\boldsymbol{XX'}) = \Sigma + \mu\mu'$
(b) $E(\boldsymbol{X'X}) = \mu'\mu + trace\ (\Sigma\ )$
(c) $E\left((\boldsymbol{X} - \mu)'\Sigma^{-1}(\boldsymbol{X} - \mu)\right) = p$
(d) $P[(\boldsymbol{X} - \mu)'\Sigma^{-1}(\boldsymbol{X} - \mu) \geq t^2] \leq \frac{p}{t^2}$, for $t \neq 0$

(DEC. 2019)

35. Let $(X_1,Y_1), (X_2, Y_2) \ldots (X_n, Y_n)$, $n \geq 25$, be a random sample from a Bivariate Normal $(\mu_1, \mu_2, \sigma_1, \sigma_2, p)$ distribution with all parameters unknown. For testing H_0: p = 0 against H_1:P $\neq$ 0 if you use the usual t-test and your observed sample correlation coefficient is 0, then what is the p-value?
(a) 0
(b) 0.05
(c) 0.5
(d) 1

(NOV. 2020)

36. Let X_1 and X_2 be two i.i.d p x 1 multivariate normal random vectors with mean μ and positive definite dispersion matrix Σ. then which of the following ran dom variables always has a central chi-square distribution
(a) $\frac{1}{2}(X_1 - X_2)^T (X_1 - X_2)$
(b) $2(X_1 - X_2)^T (X_1 - X_2)$
(c) $2\ (X_1 - X_2)^T \Sigma^{-1} (X_1 - X_2)$
(d) $\frac{1}{2}(X_1 - X_2)^T \Sigma^{-1} (X_1 - X_2)$

(NOV. 2020)

37. Let $n > 2$ and $0 < \theta < \frac{\pi}{2}$ be fixed. Let $X_1, \ldots. X_n$ be i.i.d. normal random variables with mean zero and variance $\sigma^2 > 0$. For $i = 1, \ldots., n$ define $Y_{2i-1} = X_i\ cos\ \theta$ and $Y_{2i} = X_i\ sin\ \theta$. Further, let $Z^T = (Y_1, Y_2, \ldots Y_{2n})$, and $V^T = (X_1, Y_1, Y_2, X_2, Y_3, Y_4, \ldots, X_n, Y_{2n-1}, Y_{2n})$
Which of the following statements are correct?
(a) Z^T has a multivariate normal distribution
(b) There exists a constant C, such that CZ^TZ has a chi-square distribution
(c) V^T has a multivariate normal distribution
(d) $E\left(\frac{1}{V^TV}\right) < \infty$

[SEP 2022]

38. Consider the hierarchical single linkage agglomerative clustering algorithm for three points X=(1,0), Y=(0,2), Z=(3,3), and the squared Euclidean distance matrix. The clustering algorithm starts with three clusters. Then which of the following statements are correct.
(a) At the first step, after combining two nearest clusters, the single linkage distance between the two newly formed clusters is 10
(b) At the first step, X and Y are merged to form a new cluster
(c) At the first step, after combining two nearest clusters, the single linkage distance between the two newly formed clusters is 13
(d) At the first step, X and Z are merged to form a new cluster

[SEP 2022]

39. For a given bivariate data $(y_i, x_i), i = 1, \ldots, n$, Analyst A fits Y on X, i.e., $\widehat{Y}_i = \widehat{\alpha_0} + \widehat{\alpha_1}x$, while Analyst B fits X on Y, i.e., $\widehat{X}_i = \widehat{\beta_0} + \widehat{\beta_1}y_i$, using the ordinary least squares estimation method. Which of the following pairs is a possible value for $(\hat{\alpha}_1, \hat{\beta}_1)$?
(a) (-0.5, 3.5)
(b) (0.5, 3.5
(c) (-3.0, 0.4)
(d) (-3.0, -0.4)

(JUNE 2023)

40. Suppose that cars arrive at a petrol pump following a Poisson distribution at the rate of 10 per hour. The time to perform the refilling is exponentially distributed and the single available staff takes an average of 4 minutes to refill each car. Further assume that the cars leave immediately after refilling. Let α denote the probability of finding 3 or more cars waiting to refill and let β denote the mean number of cars in the queue. Which of the following statements are correct?

(a) $\alpha = \frac{8}{27}$ (b) $\beta = 1$

(c) $\beta - \alpha = \frac{46}{27}$ (d) $\alpha\beta = 3$

(JUNE 2023)

41. Let $X = (X_1, X_2)^T$ follow a bivariate normal distribution with mean vector $(0,0)^T$ and covariance matrix $\sum$ such that

$\Sigma = \begin{bmatrix} 5 & -3 \\ -3 & 10 \end{bmatrix}$

The mean vector and covariance matrix of $Y = (X_1, 5 - 2X_2)^T$ are

(a) $\begin{pmatrix} 0 \\ 5 \end{pmatrix}, \begin{bmatrix} 5 & -3 \\ -3 & 40 \end{bmatrix}$. (b) $\begin{pmatrix} 0 \\ 5 \end{pmatrix}, \begin{bmatrix} 5 & -6 \\ -6 & 20 \end{bmatrix}$.

(c) $\begin{pmatrix} 0 \\ 5 \end{pmatrix}, \begin{bmatrix} 5 & 3 \\ 3 & 20 \end{bmatrix}$. (d) $\begin{pmatrix} 0 \\ 5 \end{pmatrix}, \begin{bmatrix} 5 & 6 \\ 6 & 40 \end{bmatrix}$.

[JULY-2024]

42. Let $X_0, X_1, \dots X_p (p \geq 2)$ be independent and identically distributed random variables with mean 0 and variance 1. Suppose $Y_i = X_0 + X_i, i = 1, \dots. p$. The first principal component based on the covariance matrix of $Y = (Y_1, \dots, Y_p)^T$ is

(a) $\frac{1}{\sqrt{p}} \sum_{i=1}^{p} Y_i$ (b) $\frac{1}{p} \sum_{i=1}^{p} Y_i$

(c) $\sqrt{p} \sum_{i=1}^{p} Y_i$ (d) $\sum_{i=1}^{p} Y_i$

[JULY-2024]

43. Let $\begin{pmatrix} X_1 \\ X_2 \end{pmatrix}$ be a bivariate random vector with covariance matrix

$$\Sigma = \begin{pmatrix} 1 & \sqrt{2} \\ \sqrt{2} & 2 \end{pmatrix}$$

Which of the following statements are true?

(a) The first principal component based on Σ explains exactly 90% of the total variability

(b) The second principal component based on explains exactly 10% of the total variability

(c) $sup\{\underline{a}^T \Sigma \underline{a} \in \mathbb{R}^2 \; and \; \underline{a}^T \underline{a} = 1\} = 3$

(d) The first principal component based on Σ is $\frac{1}{\sqrt{3}}(X_1 + \sqrt{2}X_2)$

(FEB. 2025)

44. Let X, Y and Z be random variables such that $S = \begin{pmatrix} X & Y \\ Y & Z \end{pmatrix} \sim W_2(10, \Sigma)$, where W_2 denotes the Wishart distribution and $\Sigma = \begin{pmatrix} 1 & \frac{1}{2} \\ \frac{1}{2} & 1 \end{pmatrix}$. Define $T = Z - \frac{Y^2}{X}$. Then, $\text{Var}(T)$ equals

(a) $\frac{77}{6}$ (b) $\frac{81}{8}$

(c) $\frac{83}{9}$ (d) $\frac{79}{7}$

(FEB. 2025)

45. Let (X_1, X_2) be a bivariate normal random vector with $E(X_1) = 1, E(X_2) = 0, Var(X_1) = 1, Var(X_2) = 1,$ and correlation coefficient $\frac{1}{2}$. Let U be a $U(0,1)$ random variable, which is independent of (X_1, X_2). If $Z = \frac{UX_1 + X_2 - U}{\sqrt{U^2 + U + 1}}$, then which of the following statements are true?

(a) The distribution of Z is symmetric about 0.

(b) $E(Z^2) = 2$

(c) $Var(Z^2) = 1$

(d) Z and U are independent random variables.

(FEB. 2025)

46. Suppose that a sequence of random variables $\{X_n\}_{n \geq 1}$ and the random variable X are defined on the same probability space. Then which of the following statements are true?

(a) X_n converges to X almost surely as $n \to \infty$ implies that X_n converges to X in probability as $n \to \infty$.

(b) X_n converges to X in probability as $n \to \infty$ implies that X_n converges to X almost surely as $n \to \infty$.

(c) If $\sum_{n=1}^{\infty} \mathbb{P}[|X_n - X| > \delta] < \infty$ for all $\delta > 0$, then X_n converges to X almost surely as $n \to \infty$.

(d) If X_n converges to X in distribution as $n \to \infty$, and X is a constant with probability 1, then X_n converges to X in probability as $n \to \infty$.

(JUNE 2025)

47. Let the random vector $\begin{pmatrix} X_1 \\ X_2 \\ X_3 \end{pmatrix}$ have the positive definite dispersion matrix $\begin{pmatrix} 1 & \rho & \rho \\ \rho & 1 & \rho \\ \rho & \rho & 1 \end{pmatrix}$. Then, which of the following statements are true?

(a) ρ may be 0.47

(b) The first principal component can only explain 32% of the total variation for some ρ

(c) The second principal component can explain more than 32% of the total variation for any ρ

(d) The variance of the first principal component is 1+ 2ρ for any ρ

(Dec 2025)

48. Let $X = (X_1, X_2, X_3)^T$ be a 3×1 random vector with $E(X) = (3,2,1)^T$ and $Cov(X) = \Sigma = \begin{pmatrix} 3 & -2 & 0 \\ -2 & 3 & -2 \\ 0 & -2 & 3 \end{pmatrix}$.

Suppose that $Y = (Y_1, Y_2, Y_3)^T = \frac{1}{\sqrt{3}} X$. Then the value of the multiple correlation coefficient between Y_1 and (Y_2, Y_3) equals

(a) $\frac{2}{\sqrt{5}}$ (b) $\sqrt{\frac{2}{5}}$

(c) $\frac{2}{\sqrt{3}}$ (d) $\frac{1}{\sqrt{3}}$

(Dec 2025)

49. Let $X_1, X_2, \dots, X_{20}$ be a random sample from $N_{12}(\mu, \Sigma)$, where $\mu \in \mathbb{R}^{12}$ and Σ is positive definite matrix. Suppose $\bar{X} = \frac{1}{20}\sum_{i=1}^{20} X_i$ and $S = \frac{1}{19}\sum_{i=1}^{20}(X_i - \bar{X})(X_i - \bar{X})^T$. Then which of the following statements are true?

(a) $19(\bar{X}^T S \bar{X})(\bar{X}^T \Sigma \bar{X})^{-1} \sim \chi^2_{19}$

(b) $E(S^{-1}) = \frac{19}{6}\Sigma^{-1}$

(c) $S \sim W_{12}(19, 19\Sigma)$

(d) $\text{trace}(19\Sigma^{-1}S) \sim \chi^2_{228}$

Answer Key

1	2	3	4	5	6	7	8	9	10
b	b,c	d	c,d	a,c,d	c	*	a,c,d	d	c,
11	**12**	**13**	**14**	**15**	**16**	**17**	**18**	**19**	**20**
d	a,b,d	a,b,c,d	a,d	b	b,d	a,c,d	a,c	a,c	c
21	**22**	**23**	**24**	**25**	**26**	**27**	**28**	**29**	**30**
a,c	c	a,b,c,d	a,b	d	a,c	a,d	b	b	d
31	**32**	**33**	**34**	**35**	**36**	**37**	**38**	**39**	**40**
d	a,b,c,d	d	d	*	*	d	a, b	d	a,c
41	**42**	**43**	**44**	**45**	**46**	**47**	**48**	**49**	
d	a	c,d	b	a,d	a,c,d	a	a	a,b,d	

:: Explanations ::

1. **Explanation: (b)**

$\begin{pmatrix} X_1 \\ X_2 \end{pmatrix} \sim N(\mu_{2x1}, \Sigma_{2\times2})$ and $X_3 = 2X_2$ (given)

Option (a)

$\begin{pmatrix} X_1 - 2X_2 \\ X_2 - 2X_3 \end{pmatrix} = \begin{pmatrix} X_1 - 2X_2 \\ 5X_2 \end{pmatrix}$

$\Rightarrow \begin{pmatrix} X_1 - 2X_2 \\ 5X_2 \end{pmatrix} = \begin{pmatrix} 1 & -2 \\ 0 & 5 \end{pmatrix}\begin{pmatrix} X_1 \\ X_2 \end{pmatrix}$

$\begin{pmatrix} 1 & -2 \\ 0 & 5 \end{pmatrix}$ is non-singular matrix

Option (b)

$\begin{pmatrix} X_1 - X_2 - X_3 \\ 2X_1 + 2X_2 \end{pmatrix} = \begin{pmatrix} X_1 + X_2 \\ 2X_1 + 2X_2 \end{pmatrix} = \begin{pmatrix} 1 & 1 \\ 2 & 2 \end{pmatrix}\begin{pmatrix} \alpha_1 \\ X_2 \end{pmatrix}$

$\begin{pmatrix} 1 & 1 \\ 2 & 2 \end{pmatrix}$ is singular matrix so

$\begin{pmatrix} X_1 - X_2 - X_3 \\ 2X_1 + 2X_2 \end{pmatrix}$ is a singular normal distribution

So, option (b) is correct

2. **Explanation: (b), (c)**
3. **Explanation: (d)**

$(X, Y) \sim BVN(0, 0, 1, 1, \rho);\ -1 < \rho < 1$

$Corr\ (X, Y) = \rho$

$\Rightarrow Cov\ (X, Y) = \rho$

$Cov(X + Y, X - Y) = Cov(X, X) - Cov(Y, Y) +$
$Cov\ (X, Y) - Var(Y) = 1 - 1 = 0$

$Corr[X + Y, X - Y] = 0$ for all value of ρ

So, option (d) is correct

4. **Explanation: (c), (d)**
5. **Explanation: (a), (c), (d)**
6. **Explanation: (c)**

$X_1, \dots, X_n$ be a random sample of size n from a p-variate normal distribution with mean μ and positive definite covariance matrix Σ

Quadric form, $(X_1 - \mu)^{-}\Sigma^{-1}(X_1 - \mu) \sim \chi^2_{(p)d.f}$

Wishart distribution is the generalization of chi-square distribution

Then, $\sum_{i=1}^{n}(X_i - \mu)(X_i - \mu)$ has wishart distribution with n d.f

$Cov\ (X_1 + X_2, X_1 - X_2) \neq 0$

So, $X_1 + X_2$ and $X_1 - X_2$ are not independently distributed.

So, option (c) is correct

7. **Explanation: (*)**
8. **Explanation: (a), (c), (d)**

3-variate population with covariance matrix

$$A = \begin{pmatrix} \sigma^2 & \sigma^2\rho & 0 \\ \sigma^2\rho & \sigma^2 & \sigma^2\rho \\ 0 & \sigma^2\rho & \sigma^2 \end{pmatrix}$$

Where, $\sigma^2 > 0$ and $\rho > 0$

Covariance matrix is positive definite matrix so

$|A| > 0$

$\sigma^2[1 - 2\rho^2] > 0$

$1 - 2\rho^2 > 0$

$\Rightarrow \rho > \frac{1}{\sqrt{2}}$

The characteristic polynomial of A

$|A - \lambda I| = 0$

$\sigma^2[(1 - \lambda)^3 - 2p^2(1 - \lambda)] = 0$

$(1 - \lambda)[1 - \lambda + \sqrt{2}p][1 - \lambda - \sqrt{2}p] = 0$

$\lambda = 1, 1 - \sqrt{2}p, 1 + \sqrt{2}p$

The eigen value

$\lambda_1 = 1 + \rho\sqrt{2}\ , \lambda_2 = 1$ and $\lambda_3 = 1 - \rho\sqrt{2}$

Proportion of total pop^n variance explained by First principal $= \frac{\lambda_1}{\lambda_1 + \lambda_2 + \lambda_3} = \frac{1 + \sqrt{2}\rho}{3}$

Proportion of total pop^n variance explained by first and second principal component $= \frac{\lambda_1 + \lambda_2}{\lambda_1 + \lambda_2 + \lambda_3}$

$= \frac{1 + \sqrt{2}\rho + 1}{3} = \frac{2 + \sqrt{2}\rho}{3} = \frac{\sqrt{2}}{3}(\sqrt{2} + \rho)$

The principal components are uncorrelated and orthogonal to each other.

So, option (a), (c) and (d) are correct

9. **Explanation: (d)**
$\underset{\sim}{\mathbf{X}}$ be a $p \times 1$ random vector
$\underset{\sim}{\mathbf{X}} \sim N_p(0, \Sigma), rank(\Sigma) = p$
$\Rightarrow \underset{\sim}{\mathbf{X}}'\Sigma^{-1}\underset{\sim}{\mathbf{X}} \sim \chi^2_{(p)d.f}$
$E\left(\underset{\sim}{\mathbf{X}}'\Sigma^{-1}\underset{\sim}{\mathbf{X}}\right) = p$ and $Var\left(\underset{\sim}{\mathbf{X}}'\Sigma^{-1}\underset{\sim}{\mathbf{X}}\right) = 2p$
So, option (d) is correct
10. **Explanation: (c)**
11. **Explanation: (d)**
Y_1, Y_2, Y_3, Y_4 are iid standard normal variate and Wishart matrix is defined as the $p \times p$ symmetric matrix of sum of square and cross-product of sample observation from a p-variate non-singular normal distribution
$A = \begin{bmatrix} Y_1^2 + Y_2^2 & Y_1Y_3 + Y_2Y_4 \\ Y_1Y_3 + Y_2Y_4 & Y_3^2 + Y_4^2 \end{bmatrix}$ is the 2×2 symmetric matrix of sum of square and cross-product of Y_1, Y_2, Y_3, Y_4 from the standard normal distribution
So, A has wishart distribution with 2 d.f.
Then, option (d) is correct
12. **Explanation: (a) (b), (d)**
13. **Explanation: (a), (b), (c) (d)**
14. **Explanation: (a), (d)**
15. **Explanation: (b)**
$X \sim N(0,1)$ and $E(Y|X = x) = x^3$ for $x \in \mathbb{R}$
$Corr\,(X,Y) = \frac{Cov\,(X,Y)}{\sqrt{Var(X).Var(Y)}}$
$Cov\,(X,Y) = E(XY) - E(X).E(Y) \quad = E(XY) - 0.E(Y)$
$= E(XY)$
$= E[E(XY\,X = x)] = E[X\,E(Y|X = x)]$
$= E[X\,X^3] = E(X^4)$
$= 1.3.5.7.\sigma^{2\times 4} = 105$
$Corr\,(X,Y) > 0$, So, X and Y are not independent
16. **Explanation: (b), (d)**
$\binom{X}{Y}$ is a random vector such that the
Marginal distribution of X is normal (0, 1)
Marginal distribution of Y is normal (0, 1)
If X and Y are independent then
$Cov(X,Y) = 0$ but converse not true
Linear combination of X and Y is normal i.e.
$aX + bY \sim N(0, a^2 + b^2)$
Converse is true
$E[e^{itX+isY}] = E[e^{itX} \cdot e^{isY}] = E[e^{itX}] \cdot E[e^{isY}]$
[X and Y are independent $\Rightarrow g\,(X)\,\&\,g(Y)$ are also independent]
$P(X \le 0, Y \le 0) = \frac{1}{4}$ it does not imply X & Y are independent
So, option (b) and (d) are correct
17. **Explanation: (a), (c) (d)**
$\mathbf{X} = (X_1, X_2, X_3, X_4)'$ be 4×1 random vector such that $\mathbf{X} \sim N_4(0, \Sigma)$
Where $\Sigma \begin{pmatrix} 1 & p & p & p \\ p & 1 & p & p \\ p & p & 1 & p \\ p & p & p & 1 \end{pmatrix}$ is positive definite
$E(X) = \mathbf{0} = (0,0,0,0)'$
$E(X_1) = E(X_2) = E(X_3) = E(X_4) = 0$
$Var(X_1) = Var(X_2) = Var(X_3) = Var(X_4) = 1$
$X_i \sim N(0,1)\ i = 1,2,3,4$
X_1, X_2, X_3, X_4 are identically distributed
$X_i's$ are not independent because $Cov(X_1, X_2) = \rho$
$\Rightarrow \frac{(X_1-X_2)^2}{(X_1-X_3)^2}$ does not follow F-distribution
$Var(X_1 - X_3) = Var(X_1) + Var(X_3) - 2\,Cov(X_1, X_3)$
$= 1 + 1 - 2\rho = 2(1-\rho)$
$Var(X_2 - X_4) = 2(1-\rho)$
$\frac{(X_1-X_2)^2}{2(1-\rho)} \sim X_1^2\ d.f.$ and $\frac{(X_2-X_4)^2}{2(1-\rho)} \sim X_1^2\ d.f.$
$\Rightarrow \frac{(X_1-X_2)^2 + (X_1-X_4)^2}{2(1-\rho)} \sim X_1^2\ d.f.$
The ratio of two chi-square divided by its d.f. is f-distribution
$\frac{(X_1-X_2)^2}{(X_3-X_4)^2} \sim F_{1,1}$
So, option (a), (c), (d) are correct
18. **Explanation: (a), (c)**
The eigen values of Σ are
$\lambda_1 = 6, \lambda_2 = 3, \lambda_3 = 2, \lambda_4 = 1$
Percentage of variation explained by first two component$= \frac{\lambda_1+\lambda_2}{\lambda_1+\lambda_2+\lambda_3+\lambda_4} \times 100 = \frac{9}{12} \times 100$
$= 75\% < 95\%$
Percentage of variation explained by first three component$= \frac{\lambda_1+\lambda_2+\lambda_3}{\lambda_1+\lambda_2+\lambda_3+\lambda_4} \times 100 = \frac{11}{12} \times 100 = 91\%$
The principal components are uncorrelated and orthogonal. Then Y_1, Y_2, Y_3, Y_4 are independent
So, option (a) and (c) are correct
19. **Explanation: (a), (c)**
20. **Explanation: (c)**
$X \sim N_3(\boldsymbol{\mu}, \Sigma)$ where $\boldsymbol{\mu} = (1,1,1)$ and $\Sigma = \begin{pmatrix} 1 & 1 & 1 \\ 1 & 3 & c \\ 1 & c & 2 \end{pmatrix}$
$Cov\,(X_1\,X_2) = 1$
$Cov\,(X_2\,X_3) = c$
X_2 and $-X_1 + X_2 - X_3$ are independent then
$Cov(X_2, -X_1 + X_2 - X_3) = -Cov(X_2, X_1) + Var(X_2) - Cov(X_2, X_3)$
$0 = -1 + 3 - c$
$c = 2$
Option (c) is correct
21. **Explanation: (a), (c)**
(X,Y) follows a bivariate normal distribution with mean vector (0, 0) and dispersion matrix
$\Sigma = \begin{pmatrix} 1 & \rho \\ \rho & 1 \end{pmatrix}; \rho \neq 0$
Suppose $Z = \frac{X-Y}{X+Y} \cdot \sqrt{\frac{1-\rho}{1+\rho}}$
$X \sim N(0,1)$ and $Y \sim N(0,1)$
$E(X - Y) = 0, Var(X - Y) = Var(X) + Var(Y) - 2Cov(X,Y) = 1 + 1 - 2\rho$
$Var(X - Y) = 2(1-\rho)$
Similarly,
$E(X + Y) = 0\ \&\ Var(X + Y) = 2(1+\rho)$

$$\frac{\frac{X-Y}{\sqrt{2(1-\rho)}}}{\frac{X+Y}{\sqrt{2(1+\rho)}}} \sim \text{Standard Cauchy}\ /t_{(1)}df$$

$Z = \frac{X-Y}{X+Y}\sqrt{\frac{1-\rho}{1+\rho}}$ is the ratio of the standard normal variate

$E(Z)$ does not exist (become mean of standard Cauchy variate does not exist)

$Z \sim t_{(1)} df$

t-distribution is symmetric about 0

So Z is symmetric about 0

$$\frac{(X-Y)/\sqrt{2(1-\rho)}}{\sqrt{\frac{(X+Y)^2}{(2(1+\rho)^2}}} \sim \text{standard t} - \text{distribution}$$

$$\sqrt{\frac{1+\rho}{1-\rho}}\frac{X-Y}{\sqrt{X^2+Y^2+2XY}} \sim \text{student's t} - \text{distribution}$$

So, option (a), (c) are correct

22. Explanation: (c)

The first principal component if $\sum_{i=1}^{p} l_i X_i$ is always the eigen vector corresponding to the largest eigen value of Σ.

23. Explanation: (a), (b), (c), (d)

Since $A(I-A) = A - A^2 = A - A = 0 \qquad [A^2 = A]$

$\Rightarrow \underline{X}^T A \underline{X}$ and $\underline{X}^T(I-A)\underline{X}$ are independent

$(I-A)^2 = (1-A)$

tr $(I-A) = \frac{k}{2} = tr\ (A)$

$\Rightarrow \underline{X}^t A\underline{X}$ and $\underline{X}^t(I-A)\underline{X}$ are identically distributed

Result: $X \sim \chi^2_{(n)}$ then $\frac{1}{2}X \sim \gamma\left(\frac{n}{2}\right)$

$\underline{X}^T A\underline{X} \sim \chi^2$ if $A \neq 0$

$\frac{1}{2}\underline{X}^T A\underline{X} \sim$ gamma distribution

Since $(I-A)^2 = I - A$

$\Rightarrow \underline{X}^t(I-A)\underline{X}$ follows a chi-squared distribution if $A \neq I$

Option (a), (b), (c), (d) are correct.

24. Explanation: (a), (b)

$\phi(x, y : \rho)$ be the density of bivariate normal distribution with mean vector $\binom{0}{0}$ and variance − covariace matrix $\begin{pmatrix} 1 & \rho \\ \rho & 1 \end{pmatrix}$.

$$\phi(x,y;\rho) = \frac{1}{2\pi\sqrt{1-\rho^2}}\exp\left\{\frac{-1}{2(1-\rho^2)}(x^2 - 2\rho xy + y^2)\right\}$$

$$\phi\left(x,y;\frac{1}{2}\right) = \frac{1}{2\pi\sqrt{\frac{3}{4}}}\exp\left\{\frac{-1}{2\times\frac{3}{4}}(x^2 - xy + y^2)\right\}$$

$$\phi\left(x,y;\frac{-1}{2}\right) = \frac{1}{2\pi\sqrt{\frac{3}{4}}}\exp\left\{\frac{-1}{2\times\frac{3}{4}}(x^2 + xy + y^2)\right\}$$

A random Vector (x, y) have density

$$f(x,y) = \frac{1}{2}\left[\phi\left(x,y,\frac{1}{2}\right) + \left(x,y,\frac{-1}{2}\right)\right]$$

$f(x,y)$ is not the pdf of bivariate normal distribution

The marginal distribution of X is given by

$$f(x) = \frac{1}{2}\left[\int_{-\infty}^{\infty}\phi(x,y,\tfrac{1}{2})dy + \int_{-\infty}^{\infty}\phi(x,y),\tfrac{-1}{2})\,dy\right]$$

$$= \frac{1}{2}\left[\frac{1}{\sqrt{2\pi}}e^{-x^2/2} + \frac{1}{\sqrt{2\pi}}e^{-x^2/2}\right]$$

$$f(x) = \frac{1}{\sqrt{2\pi}}e^{-x^2/2}$$

$X \sim N(0,1)$

Similarly, $Y \sim N\,(0,1)$

Marginal distribution of both X and Y are standard normal distribution

$Cov(X,Y) = \frac{1}{2}\times\frac{1}{2} + \frac{1}{2}\times\frac{-1}{2} = 0$

$\rho \neq 0$

$\Rightarrow X$ & Y are not independent

So, Option (a), (b) are correct

25. Explanation: (d)

(X_1, X_2) follow bivariate normal

$E(X_1) = 0\ E(X_2) = 0$ and $Var(X_1) = Var(X_2) = 2$

$Cov(X_1\ X_2) = -1$

If $\phi(x) = \frac{1}{\sqrt{2\pi}}\int_{-\infty}^{x} e^{-y^2/2}\,dy$

$X_1 \sim N(0,2)$ & $X_2 \sim N(0,2)$

$$\begin{aligned} Var(X_1 - X_2) &= Var(X_1) + Var(X_2) - 2\,Cov\,(X_1\,X_2) \\ &= 2 + 2 - 2\times -1 \\ &= 4 + 2 = 6 \end{aligned}$$

$E(X_1 - X_2) = 0$

$X_1 - X_2 \sim N(0,6)$

$$P[X_1 - X_2 > 6) = P\left[\frac{X_1 - X_2 - E(X_1 - X_2)}{\sqrt{Var(X_1 - X_2)}} > \frac{6-0}{\sqrt{6}}\right]$$

$= P[Z > \sqrt{6}]$

$= 1 - P[Z \leq \sqrt{6}]$

$= 1 - \phi(\sqrt{6})$

$= \phi(-\sqrt{6})$

Option (d) is correct

26. Explanation: (a), (c)

X_1, X_2 be independent r.v. each having $N(\mu, \sigma^2)$

$A = \begin{pmatrix} \cos\theta & \sin\theta \\ -\sin\theta & \cos\theta \end{pmatrix}$

$\tilde{Y} = (Y_1\ Y_2)^t = A\tilde{X}$

Where $\tilde{X} = (X_1\ X_2)^t \sim N_2(\mu, \sigma^2)$

Result: If $\tilde{X} \sim N_p(\mu, \Sigma)$ & $\tilde{Y} = C\tilde{X}$ where C is non-singular matrix

Then $\tilde{Y} = C\tilde{X} \sim N_p(C\tilde{\mu}, C\Sigma_x C^t)$

$|A| = \cos^2\theta + \sin^2\theta = 1$

A is non-singular matrix & $\tilde{X} \sim N_2(\tilde{\mu}, \Sigma)$ where

$\Sigma = \begin{pmatrix} \sigma^2 & 0 \\ 0 & \sigma^2 \end{pmatrix}$

$\tilde{Y} = A\tilde{X} = N_2(A\tilde{\mu}, A\Sigma A')$

$$A\tilde{\mu} = \begin{bmatrix} \cos\theta & \sin\theta \\ -\sin\theta & \cos\theta \end{bmatrix}\begin{bmatrix} \mu \\ \mu \end{bmatrix} = \begin{bmatrix} \mu\cos\theta + \sin\theta \\ \mu\cos\theta - \sin\theta \end{bmatrix}$$

$$A\Sigma A' = \begin{bmatrix} \cos\theta & \sin\theta \\ -\sin\theta & \cos\theta \end{bmatrix}\begin{bmatrix} \sigma^2 & 0 \\ 0 & \sigma^2 \end{bmatrix}\begin{bmatrix} \cos\theta & -\sin\theta \\ \sin\theta & \cos\theta \end{bmatrix}$$

$$= \begin{bmatrix} \sigma^2\cos\theta & \sigma^2\sin\theta \\ -\sigma^2\sin\theta & \sigma^2\cos\theta \end{bmatrix}\begin{bmatrix} \cos\theta & -\sin\theta \\ \sin\theta & \cos\theta \end{bmatrix}$$

$$= \begin{bmatrix} \sigma^2 & 0 \\ 0 & \sigma^2 \end{bmatrix} = \Sigma$$

If $\mu = 0$

$A\tilde{\mu} = \begin{bmatrix} 0 \\ 0 \end{bmatrix}$

$A\Sigma A' = \begin{bmatrix} \sigma^2 & 0 \\ 0 & \sigma^2 \end{bmatrix}$

$\tilde{Y} \sim N_2(\tilde{0}, \Sigma)$ If $\tilde{X} \sim N_2(\tilde{0}, \Sigma)$

If $\mu = 0$ then $\tilde{X}$ & $\tilde{Y}$ has same distribution

$\Rightarrow Y_1$ & Y_2 are Gaussian

$Corr(Y_1\ Y_2) = 0$

Y_1 & Y_2 are uncorrelated

So, option (a) & (c) are correct

27. Explanation: (a), (d)

X_1 & X_2 are iid $N_p(\tilde{0}, \Sigma)$ with rank $(\Sigma) = p$

Suppose A is a $p \times p$ symmetric matrix of rank r, and $A^2 = A \Rightarrow A$ is an idempotent matrix

Result: $\tilde{X}_{p\times1} \sim N_p(\tilde{\mu}, \Sigma)$ and A is real symmetric & idempotent matrix then

$X^T A X \sim \chi_r^2$ If rank $(A) = r$

$X_1 \sim N_p(\tilde{0}, \Sigma)$ rank $(A) = r$ $\quad X_2 \sim N_p(\tilde{0}, \Sigma)$

$X_1^T A X_1 \sim \chi^2_{r.d.f.}$ $\quad X_2^T A X_2 \sim \chi^2_{r.d.f.}$

Using additive property of chi-square

$X_1^T A X_1 + X_2^T A X_2 \sim \chi^2_{(2r)d.f.}$

So, option (a) & (d) are correct

28. Explanation: (b)

$X_1 \sim N_{p1}(0, \Sigma_1)$ and $X_2 \sim N_{p_2}(0, \Sigma_2)$.

Where X_1 & X_2 are independent

Result: If $X \sim N_p(\mu, \Sigma)$ then

$(X-\mu)^T \Sigma^{-1} (X-\mu) \sim \chi^2_{p\,d.f}$

So, $X_1 \sim N_{p_1}(0, \Sigma_1)$

Then $X_1^T \Sigma_1^{-1} X_1 \sim \chi^2_{p1\,d.f}$

Then $X_2^T \Sigma_2^{-1} X_2 \sim \chi^2_{p_2\,d.f}$

Using Additive property of Chi square distribution,

$X_1^T \Sigma_1^{-1} X_1 + X_2^T \Sigma_2^{-1} X_2 \sim \chi^2_{(p_1+p_2)\,d.f}$

Option (b) is correct

29. Explanation: (b)

The covariance matrix is $\begin{bmatrix} 1 & \rho & \rho & \rho \\ \rho & 1 & \rho & \rho \\ \rho & \rho & 1 & \rho \\ \rho & \rho & \rho & 1 \end{bmatrix}, \rho < 0$

Two of the eigenvalues of the matrix are $1 + 3\rho$ *and* $1 + 3\rho$ because each row and each column sum is $1 + 3\rho$

v is the variance of the first principal component which is equal to

$v = \frac{value\ of\ greatest\ eigenvalue}{4}$

$v > \frac{5}{4}$ *and* $v \ngtr \frac{4}{3}$

So, option b is correct

30. Explanation: (d)

$X \sim N_p(0, 1)$

$A_{p\times p}$ is an idempotent matrix

Rank (A) $= k < p$

$\Rightarrow X'AX \sim \chi^2_{(k)d.f}$

$X'X \sim \chi^2_{p\,d.f}$

We know that

$X \sim \chi^2_{(n)d.f}$ then $\frac{1}{2}X \sim \gamma\left(\frac{1}{2}n\right)$

$\Rightarrow X'AX \sim \chi^2_{k.d.f.}$ *then* $\frac{1}{2}(X'AX) \sim \gamma\left(\frac{k}{2}\right)$

$\Rightarrow X'X \sim \chi^2_{p.d.f.}$ then $\frac{1}{2}(X'X) \sim \gamma\left(\frac{p}{2}\right)$

$\Rightarrow X'X - X'AX \sim \chi^2_{(p-k)d.f.}$

$\Rightarrow \frac{1}{2}(X'X - X'AX) \sim \gamma\left(\frac{p-k}{2}\right)$

Result: $X \sim \gamma(m)$ and $y \sim \gamma(n)$

$\frac{X}{X+Y} \sim \beta_1(m, n)$

$\therefore \frac{1}{2}(X'AX) \sim \gamma\left(\frac{k}{2}\right)$ & $\frac{1}{2}(X'X - X'AX) \sim \gamma\left(\frac{p-k}{2}\right)$

$\therefore \frac{\frac{1}{2}(X'AX)}{\frac{1}{2}(X'AX) + \frac{1}{2}(X'X - X'AX)} \sim \beta_1\left(\frac{k}{2}, \frac{p-k}{2}\right)$

$\Rightarrow \frac{X'AX}{X'X} \sim \beta_1\left(\frac{k}{2}, \frac{p-k}{2}\right)$

31. Explanation: (d)

Testing $H_0: \sigma_1 = \sigma_2$ is equivalent to testing the independence of

$X + Y$ & $X - Y$ because

$Cov\,(X+Y, X-Y) = Var\,(X) - Var\,(Y)$

Covariance between $X + Y$ & $X - Y$ represent the difference the variance of X *and* Y.

Option (d) is Correct

32. Explanation: (d) It is given that

$f(x,y) = \frac{1}{2}f_1(x,y) + \frac{1}{2}f_2(x,y)$

Correlation $(X,Y) = \frac{cov(X,Y)}{\sqrt{Var\,(X).Var\,(Y)}}$

$cov\,(X,Y) = E\,(XY) - E\,(X)E(Y)$

$E(X) = \int_y \int_x x f(x,y)dx\,dy$

$= \iint x\left[\frac{1}{2}\{f_1(x,y) + f_2(x,y)\}dx\,dy\right]$

$= \frac{1}{2}\int_x x\left[\int_y f_1(x,y)dy\right]dx +$

$\frac{1}{2}\int_x x\left[\int_y f_2(x,y)dy\,)0)\,dx\right]$

$= \frac{1}{2}\int_x x f_1(x)dx + \frac{1}{2}\int_x x f_2(x)dx$

$E(X) = \frac{1}{2}E_1(X) + \frac{1}{2}E_2(X)$

$= \frac{1}{2} \times 1 + \frac{1}{2}. -1$

$E(X) = 0$

Similarly, $E(Y) = 0$

$E\,(XY) = \int_x \int_y xy\,f(x,y)\,dx\,dy$

$= \frac{1}{2}\int_x \int_y xy\,f_1(x,y)dx\,dy + \frac{1}{2}\int_x \int_y xy\,f_1(x,y)dx +$

$\frac{1}{2}\int_x \int_y xy\,f_2(x,y)dx\,dy$

$= \frac{1}{2}E_1(XY) + \frac{1}{2}E_2(XY)$

$\Sigma = \begin{matrix} X \\ Y \end{matrix}\begin{bmatrix} 1 & 0 \\ 0 & 1 \end{bmatrix}$ *for* f_1

$cov_1\,(X,Y) = 0$

$E_1\,(XY) - E_1(X).E_2(Y) = 0$

$E_1(XY) - 1 \times 1 = 0$

$E_1\,(XY) = 1$

Similarly for f_2-

$E_2\,(XY) = 1$

$E(XY) = \frac{1}{2}E_1(XY) + \frac{1}{2}E_2(XY)$

$= \frac{1}{2} + \frac{1}{2}$

$E(X\,Y) = 1$

Cov(X, Y) = 1

$cov\,(X,Y)$ is positive

So, correlation is positive

$\Rightarrow X$ & Y are positively correlated

Option (d) is correct.

33. Explanation: (*)

34. Explanation: (*)

35. Explanation: (d)

For the sample correlation coefficient is 0 then the p value is equal to 1

So, option (d) is correct

36. Explanation: (d)

Result:- $\underline{X} \sim N_p\left(\underline{\mu}, \Sigma\right)$

Then $\left(\underline{X}-\underline{\mu}\right)^T \Sigma^{-1}\left(\underline{X}-\underline{\mu}\right) \sim \chi_p^2$

$E(X_1 - X_2) = \mu - \mu = 0$ and

$Var\,(X_1 - X_2) = Var\,(X_1) + Var(X_2) - 2Cov(X_1, X_2)$

$= \Sigma + \Sigma - 0$

$[X_1\ \&\ X_2\ are\ independent]$

$= 2\,\Sigma$

$[(X_1 - X_2) - 0]^T (2\Sigma\,)^{-1} (X_1 - X_2) - 0] \sim \chi^2{}_p$

$\frac{1}{2}(X_1 - X_2)^T \Sigma^{-1} (X_1 - X_2) \sim \chi_p^2$

Option (d) is correct.

37. Explanation: (a), (b), (c), (d)

$X_i \sim i.i.d\ N(0, \sigma^2)$

$Y_{2i-1} = X_i \cos\theta \sim i.i.d\ N\,(0, \sigma^2\, cos^2\theta)$;

$Y_{2i} = X_i \sin\theta \sim i.i.d\ N\,(0, \sigma^2\, sin^2\theta)$

$cov\,(X_i \cos\theta, X_i \sin\theta) = \sin\theta\cos\theta\ cov\,(X_i, X_j) = \sigma^2 \sin\theta\cos\theta\,;\,i = j$

$Z^T = (Y_1, Y_2, \ldots, Y_{2n}), \Sigma_Z =$

$$\sigma^2 \begin{bmatrix} \sin\theta\cos\theta & 0 & \cdots & 0 \\ 0 & \sin\theta\cos\theta & \ddots & \vdots \\ \vdots & \vdots & \sin\theta\cos\theta & 0 \\ & 0 \quad 0 & & \end{bmatrix}$$

Since Σ_Z symmetric and positive definite matrix.

Z^T has multivariate normal distribution.

There exists a constant c;

$CZ^TZ = C\{Y_1^2 + Y_2^2 + \cdots + Y_{2n}^2\} \sim \chi_{2n}^2$

The value of C is depend on θ if we take $\theta = \frac{\pi}{4}$ then it will hold the condition.

$V^T = [X, Z]\,;\ \Sigma_V = \begin{bmatrix} \Sigma_X & \Sigma_{XZ} \\ \Sigma_{XZ} & \Sigma_Z \end{bmatrix}$

Therefore V^T has multivariate Normal distribution.

$E\left(\frac{1}{V^TV}\right) < \frac{1}{E(V^TV)} < \infty\,; E(V^TV) > 0$

Option (a), (b), (c) and (d) are correct.

38. Explanation: (a), (b).

Single Linkage Hierarchical Agglomerative Clustering.

Given distance - Squared Euclidean distance.

If $(x_1, y_1)\ \&\ (x_2, y_2)$ are 2 points then Squared Euclidean distance between them is given by

$d = (x_2 - x_1)^2 + (y_2 - y_1)^2$.

Single Linkage method suggests that Minimum Distance among all the possible distances between each possible pair from 2 clusters is regarded as the distance between those 2 clusters.

Hierarchical Agglomerative Clustering suggests the use of bottom-up approach. That is start with considering every single data point as a separate cluster and then go on combining the clusters based on their nearness using given linkage method & given distance function until we get a single cluster containing all the given data points in it.

Given 3 points are $x = (1,0), y = (0,2)\ \&\ z = (3,3)$

Let C_1, C_2, C_3 be 3 clusters containing each data point $x, y\ \&\ z$ respectively.

The Squared Eudidean distance matrix between them is given by

$$\begin{array}{c c} & \begin{array}{ccc} x & y & z \end{array} \\ \begin{array}{c} x \\ y \\ z \end{array} & \begin{bmatrix} 0 & 5 & 13 \\ 5 & 0 & 10 \\ 13 & 10 & 0 \end{bmatrix} \end{array}$$

Where a_{ij} = Squared Euclidean distance between point $i\ and\ j.\, i, j = 1,2,3$

Note that according to single linkage method,

Distance $(C_1, C_2) = 5$

Distance $(C_1, C_3) = 13$

Distance $(C_2, C_3) = 10$

Now the minimum distance is 5 and that shows that clusters $C_1\ \&\ C_2$ containing $x\ \&\ y$ respectively are more closer to each other compared to any other pair of clusters.

Thus we will combine C_1 and C_2 into a single cluster. Thus now there will be only 2 clusters.

C_1	C_2
$x = (1,0)$	$z = (3,3)$
$y = (0,2)$	

So at first stage points $x\ \&\ y$ merged into a single cluster.

∴ **Option (b)** is correct and Option (d) is incorrect.

Now again using single linkage method.

Distance

$$(C_1, C_2) = Min[distance\ (x,z), distance\ (y,z)]$$
$$= Min\ [13,10] = 10.$$

∴ **Option (a)** is correct and option (c) is incorrect.

39. Explanation: (d)

The bivariate data is $(y_i, x_i)\,;\, i = 1, 2, \ldots .\, n$

Analyst A fit y on x_i,

$\widehat{y_i} = \widehat{\alpha_0} + \widehat{\alpha_1} x_i$

Analyst B fit X on Y

$\widehat{x_i} = \widehat{\beta_0} + \widehat{\beta_1}\, y_i$

The regressor coefficient are

$b_{xy} = \widehat{\beta_1}\ \&\ b_{yx} = \widehat{\alpha}_1$

bxy & byx should be same in sign

∴ option (1) & (3) incorrect

Let we know that

$r = \sqrt{b_{yx} \cdot b_{xy}}$

For option (2)

$r = \sqrt{0.5 \times 2.5}$

$r = \sqrt{1.25} > 1$

But r lie between $-1\ to\ 1$

∴ 2nd option also incorrect

For last option

$r = \sqrt{(-2.0)(-0.4)}$

$= \sqrt{40.16}$

$r = 0.4$

$-1 < r = 0.4 < 1$

∴ option (d) is correct

40. Explanation: (a), (c)

$Car \sim Poisson\ (10) \leftarrow$ Discrete Distribution

Time refill $\sim Exp\ (4\ min.each)$ ← Continuous Distribution

1st case is discrete & 2nd is continuous so it's follow queuing model m|m|1

Arrived rate $\lambda = 10$

Service rate $\mu = \frac{60}{4} = 15\ min$

$\alpha = p(x \geq 3)$

$= 1 - p(x \leq 2)$

$= 1 - [p(x = 0) + p(x = 1) + p(x = 2)]$

$\{\ p(x = x)\left(1 - \frac{\lambda}{\mu}\right)\left(\frac{\lambda}{\mu}\right)^x$,

$p(x = 1) = \left(1 - \frac{2}{3}\right)\left(\frac{2}{3}\right)^1 = \frac{1}{3}\left(\frac{2}{3}\right) = \frac{2}{9}$,

$p(x = 2) = \left(1 - \frac{2}{3}\right)\left(\frac{2}{3}\right)^2 = \frac{1}{3}\left(\frac{4}{9}\right) = \frac{4}{27}$,

$p(x = 0) = \left(1 - \frac{2}{3}\right)\left(\frac{2}{3}\right)^0 = \frac{1}{3}\ \}$

$\therefore \alpha = 1 - \left[\frac{1}{3} + \frac{2}{9} + \frac{4}{27}\right]$

$= 1 - \frac{1}{3}\left[1 + \frac{2}{3} + \frac{4}{9}\right]$

$= 1 - \frac{1}{3}\left[\frac{9+6+4}{9}\right]$

$= 1 - \frac{1}{3}\left[\frac{19}{9}\right] = \frac{27-19}{27} = \frac{08}{27}$

$\alpha = \frac{8}{27}$

Now

$\beta = E(Car)$

$= \frac{\lambda}{\mu - \lambda}$

$= \frac{10}{15-10}$

$= \frac{10}{5}$

$\beta = 2$

$\beta - \alpha = 2 - \frac{8}{27} = \frac{54-8}{27} = \frac{46}{27}$

$\beta.\alpha = 2\left(\frac{8}{27}\right)$

$\alpha\beta = \frac{16}{27}$

$\therefore$ The option (a) & (c) correct

41. Explanation: (d)

$x = (x_1, x_2)^T \sim BN\begin{bmatrix} 3 & -3 \\ -3 & 10 \end{bmatrix}$

Consider

$y_1 = x_1$

$y_2 = 5 - 2x_2$

Let $E(y_1)$ & $E(y_2)$ are the mean Of y_1& y_2 respectively

$\therefore \begin{bmatrix} E(y_1) \\ E(y_2) \end{bmatrix} = \begin{bmatrix} 0 \\ 5 \end{bmatrix}$ from given .... (1)

The covariance matrix is

$\begin{bmatrix} var(y_1) & cov(y_1, y_2) \\ cov(y_2, y_1) & var(y_2) \end{bmatrix}$

$V(y_1) = V(x_1) = 5$

$V(y_2) = V(5 - 2x_2)$

$= 0 + 4var\ (x_2)$

$= 4(10)$

$V(y_2) = 40$

$cov\ (y_1, y_2) = cov\ (y_2, y_1)$

$\therefore cov\ (y_1, y_2) = E(y_1, y_2) - E(y_1), E(y_2)$

$= E(5x_1 - 2x_1x_2) - 0$

$= 5E(x_1) - 2E(x_1x_2)$

$= 0 - 2(-3)$ from given

$= 6$

$\therefore covariance\ matrix\ is\ \begin{bmatrix} 5 & 6 \\ 6 & 40 \end{bmatrix}$ .... (2)

From (1) and (2)

Option (d) is correct.

42. Explanation: (a)

$X_0, X_1, \ldots X_p (p \geq 2)$ be independent and identically distributed random variables with mean 0 and variance 1.

Suppose $Y_i = X_0 + X_i, i = 1, \ldots. p.$

Let us find it for $p = 2$.

$$Y_1 = X_0 + X_1\ \&\ Y_2 = X_0 + X_2$$
$$Var(Y_1) = Var(X_0) + Var(X_1) = 1 + 1 = 2$$
$$Var(Y_2) = Var(X_0) + Var(X_2) = 1 + 1 = 2$$
$$Cov(Y_1, Y_2) = Var(X_0) + Cov(X_0, X_2) + Cov(X_1, X_0) + Cov(X_1, X_2) = Var(X_0) = 1$$

Thus the covariance matrix is

$$\Sigma = \begin{bmatrix} 2 & 1 \\ 1 & 2 \end{bmatrix}$$

Note that as the row sum of all the rows of Σ is constant that is 3. Thus one of the eigenvalues is 3. The trace of Σ is 4 therefore the other eigenvalue is 1. Thus 3 is the highest eigenvalue of Σ.

The eigenvector corresponding to the eigenvalue 3 is

$$(\Sigma - \lambda I)X = 0 \Rightarrow \begin{bmatrix} 2-3 & 1 \\ 1 & 2-3 \end{bmatrix} X = 0$$
$$\Rightarrow \begin{bmatrix} -1 & 1 \\ 1 & -1 \end{bmatrix}\begin{bmatrix} Y_1 \\ Y_2 \end{bmatrix} = \begin{bmatrix} -Y_1 + Y_2 \\ Y_1 - Y_2 \end{bmatrix} = \begin{bmatrix} 0 \\ 0 \end{bmatrix}$$
$$\Rightarrow Y_1 = Y_2$$

Thus the eigenvector related to the highest eigenvalue 3 is $\begin{bmatrix} 1 \\ 1 \end{bmatrix}$

Therefore the first principal component is

$$\frac{1}{\sqrt{2}}[1\quad 1]\begin{bmatrix} Y_1 \\ Y_2 \end{bmatrix} = \frac{1}{\sqrt{2}}(Y_1 + Y_2) = \frac{1}{\sqrt{2}}\sum_{i=1}^{2} Y_i$$

Therefore in general for p the first principal component is given by

$$\frac{1}{\sqrt{p}}\sum_{i=1}^{p} Y_i$$

43. Explanation: (c),(d)

$X = \begin{pmatrix} X_1 \\ X_2 \end{pmatrix}$ be a bivariate random vector with covariance matrix

$$\Sigma = \begin{pmatrix} 1 & \sqrt{2} \\ \sqrt{2} & 2 \end{pmatrix}$$

To find the eigenvalues the equation is given by

$$|\Sigma - \lambda I| = 0$$

$$\left|\begin{pmatrix} 1-\lambda & \sqrt{2} \\ \sqrt{2} & 2-\lambda \end{pmatrix}\right| = 0 \Rightarrow (1-\lambda)(2-\lambda) - \sqrt{2}\sqrt{2}$$
$$= \lambda^2 - 3\lambda = 0 \Rightarrow \lambda = 0\ \&\ 3$$

(a) The percentage variation explained by the first principle component is $\frac{3}{0+3} \times 100 = 100\%$.

(b) The percentage variation explained by the second principle component is $\frac{0}{0+3} \times 100 = 0\%$.

(d) The first principle component is obtained by finding the eigenvector related to the highest eigenvalue. Solving the equation

$$\Sigma X = \lambda X$$

$$\begin{pmatrix} 1 & \sqrt{2} \\ \sqrt{2} & 2 \end{pmatrix}\begin{pmatrix} X_1 \\ X_2 \end{pmatrix} = 3\begin{pmatrix} X_1 \\ X_2 \end{pmatrix} \Rightarrow \begin{pmatrix} X_1 + \sqrt{2}X_2 \\ \sqrt{2}X_1 + 2X_2 \end{pmatrix} = \begin{pmatrix} 3X_1 \\ 3X_2 \end{pmatrix}$$

$$\Rightarrow X_2 = \sqrt{2}X_1$$

Thus

$P = k\begin{pmatrix} 1 \\ \sqrt{2} \end{pmatrix}, k \in \mathbb{R}$ is the eigenvector related to the highest eigenvalue 3.

The principal component related to the above eigenvector is given by

$$P'X = k(X_1 + \sqrt{2}X_2), k \in \mathbb{R}$$

Thus

$\frac{1}{\sqrt{3}}(X_1 + \sqrt{2}X_2)$ is a first principal component based on Σ.

(c) To obtain $sup\{ \underline{a}^T \Sigma \underline{a} \in \mathbb{R}^2 \text{ and } \underline{a}^T \underline{a} = 1\}$

Note that $\underline{a} = \begin{pmatrix} a_1 \\ a_2 \end{pmatrix}, a_1, a_2 \in \mathbb{R}$; $\underline{a}^T \underline{a} = 1 \Rightarrow a_1^2 + a_2^2 = 1 \Rightarrow -1 < a_1, a_2 < 1$

The given quadratic form is $\underline{a}^T \Sigma \underline{a}$. As now we have the eigenvalues of Σ with us, we can write an equivalent quadratic form of the given quadratic form as follows

$$\underline{a}^T \Sigma \underline{a} \text{ is equivalent to } \underline{a}^T E \underline{a} \text{ where } E = \begin{pmatrix} 0 & 0 \\ 0 & 3 \end{pmatrix}$$

$$\underline{a}^T \Sigma \underline{a} = \underline{a}^T E \underline{a} = (a_1 \quad a_2)\begin{pmatrix} 0 & 0 \\ 0 & 3 \end{pmatrix}\begin{pmatrix} a_1 \\ a_2 \end{pmatrix} = 3a_2^2$$

$$\therefore sup\{ \underline{a}^T \Sigma \underline{a} \in \mathbb{R}^2 \text{ and } \underline{a}^T \underline{a} = 1\}$$

$$= sup\{ 3a_2^2, a_2 \in \mathbb{R} \text{ and } -1 < a_2 < 1\} = 3$$

44. Explanation: (b)

For a Wishart matrix $S \sim W_p(n, \Sigma)$, the Schur complement $Z - \frac{Y^2}{X}$ follows a scaled chi-squared distribution:

$$T \sim (\Sigma_{22} - \Sigma_{21}\Sigma_{11}^{-1}\Sigma_{12}) \cdot \chi^2(n-1)$$

Here, $\Sigma_{22} - \Sigma_{21}\Sigma_{11}^{-1}\Sigma_{12} = 1 - \frac{1}{4} = \frac{3}{4}$, and $T \sim \frac{3}{4} \cdot \chi^2(9)$.

Variance Calculation:

$\text{Var}(T) = \left(\frac{3}{4}\right)^2 \cdot \text{Var}(\chi^2(9)) = \frac{9}{16} \times 2 \times 9 = \frac{9}{16} \times 18 = \frac{162}{16} = \frac{81}{8}$.

$$[\text{Var}(\chi^2(n)) = 2n]$$

45. Explanation: (a), (d) Given $U = u$, $Z = \frac{uX_1 + X_2 - u}{\sqrt{u^2+u+1}}$.

$uX_1 + X_2$ is a linear combination of jointly normal random variables, so it is also normally distributed.

$E(uX_1 + X_2) = uE(X_1) + E(X_2) = u(1) + 0 = u$.

$Var(uX_1 + X_2) = u^2 Var(X_1) + Var(X_2) + 2uCov(X_1, X_2)$.

$Cov(X_1, X_2) = Corr(X_1, X_2) \cdot \sqrt{Var(X_1) \cdot Var(X_2)} = \frac{1}{2} \cdot \sqrt{1 \cdot 1} = \frac{1}{2}$.

$Var(uX_1 + X_2) = u^2(1) + 1 + 2u(\frac{1}{2}) = u^2 + u + 1$.

$Z|U = u \sim N(\frac{u-u}{\sqrt{u^2+u+1}}, \frac{u^2+u+1}{u^2+u+1}) = N(0,1)$.

Since $Z|U = u \sim N(0,1)$ for any u, the unconditional distribution of Z is also $N(0,1)$.

The normal distribution with mean 0 is symmetric about 0.

Therefore, the distribution of Z is symmetric about 0.

Since $Z \sim N(0,1)$, $E(Z^2) = Var(Z) + (E(Z))^2 = 1 + 0^2 = 1$.

$Var(Z^2) = E(Z^4) - (E(Z^2))^2$.

For a standard normal distribution, $E(Z^4) = 3$.

$Var(Z^2) = 3 - 1^2 = 2$.

The conditional distribution of Z given $U = u$ is $N(0,1)$, which does not depend on u.

Therefore, Z and U are independent.

Thus, options (a) and (d) are correct.

46. Explanation: (a), (c), (d)

Statement (a): Almost Sure Convergence ⇒ Convergence in Probability

Almost sure (a.s.) convergence means:

$$P\left(\lim_{n\to\infty} X_n = X\right) = 1$$

This implies that for every $\epsilon > 0$,

$P(|X_n - X| \geq \epsilon \text{ infinitely often}) = 0$.

This, in turn, implies that for large n, $P(|X_n - X| \geq \epsilon)$ becomes arbitrarily small, which is the definition of convergence in probability:

$$X_n \xrightarrow{a.s.} X \Rightarrow X_n \xrightarrow{P} X.$$

Thus, Statement (a) is true.

Statement (b): Convergence in Probability ⇒ Almost Sure Convergence

Convergence in probability means that for every $\epsilon > 0$,

$$P(|X_n - X| \geq \epsilon) \to 0 \text{ as } n \to \infty.$$

However, this does not necessarily imply almost sure convergence. A counterexample is when X_n oscillates infinitely often around X in such a way that it does not satisfy the almost sure convergence criterion.

For almost sure convergence, we need a stronger condition, such as the Borel-Cantelli lemma, which is not necessarily guaranteed by convergence in probability.

Thus, Statement (b) is false.

Statement (c): If $\sum_{n=1}^{\infty} P(|X_n - X| \geq \delta) < \infty$ for all $\delta > 0$, then $X_n \to X$ almost surely

This follows from the Borel-Cantelli Lemma:

- If $\sum_{n=1}^{\infty} P(|X_n - X| \geq \delta) < \infty$, then by the second Borel-Cantelli lemma, we conclude that: $P(|X_n - X| \geq \delta \text{ infinitely often}) = 0$.
- This implies that $X_n \to X$ almost surely.

Thus, Statement (c) is true.

Statement (d): Convergence in Distribution to a Constant ⇒ Convergence in Probability

If $X_n \to X$ in distribution and X is a constant (say c), then:

$$X_n \xrightarrow{d} c$$

which means that for any continuous bounded function g,

$$E[g(X_n)] \to E[g(c)] = g(c).$$

However, convergence in distribution does not necessarily imply convergence in probability in general. But if X is a constant, then convergence in distribution implies convergence in probability because for any $\epsilon > 0$,

$$P(|X_n - c| \geq \epsilon) \to 0.$$

This follows from Portmanteau's Theorem.

Thus, Statement (d) is true.

47. Explanation: (a) For the equicorrelation matrix

$$\Sigma = \begin{pmatrix} 1 & \rho & \rho \\ \rho & 1 & \rho \\ \rho & \rho & 1 \end{pmatrix}$$

the eigenvalues are

$\lambda_1 = 1 + 2\rho$ (mult. 1), $\lambda_2 = \lambda_3 = 1 - \rho$ (mult. 2).

Positive definiteness requires $1 - \rho > 0$ and $1 + 2\rho > 0$, i.e. $\rho \in (-\frac{1}{2}, 1)$.

(a) $\rho = 0.47$ lies in $(-1/2, 1)$, so Σ is positive definite for $\rho = 0.47$. — **True.**

(b) The proportion of total variance explained by the first PC is $\lambda_{\max}/3$. There is no $\rho \in (-\frac{1}{2}, 1)$ that gives $\lambda_{\max}/3 = 0.32$ $solve(\lambda_{\max} = 0.96$ and check both eigenvalue formulas — no admissible ρ satisfies it). — **False.**

(c) The second PC variance is $\lambda_2 = 1 - \rho$, so its fraction of total variance is $(1 - \rho)/3$. This exceeds (0.32) only when $\rho < 0.04$; it is not true for every admissible ρ. — **False.**

(d) The first PC variance equals $1 + 2\rho$ only when that is the largest eigenvalue (i.e. when $\rho \geq 0$). For negative ρ the largest eigenvalue is $1 - \rho$. So the statement "for any ρ" is false. — **False.**

48. Explanation: (a)

Given: $Y = \frac{1}{\sqrt{3}} X$

Property:

$$\text{Cov}(aX) = a^2 \text{Cov}(X)$$

Thus

$$\text{Cov}(Y) = \frac{1}{3}\text{Cov}(X) = \frac{1}{3}\Sigma$$

So

$$\text{Cov}(Y) = \begin{pmatrix} 1 & -\frac{2}{3} & 0 \\ -\frac{2}{3} & 1 & -\frac{2}{3} \\ 0 & -\frac{2}{3} & 1 \end{pmatrix}$$

Since diagonal entries are 1, this matrix is also the correlation matrix.

From the matrix:

$$r_{12} = -\frac{2}{3}, r_{13} = 0, r_{23} = -\frac{2}{3}$$

Multiple correlation formula

$$R^2_{1(23)} = \frac{r^2_{12} + r^2_{13} - 2r_{12}r_{13}r_{23}}{1 - r^2_{23}}$$

Substitute values:

$$R^2_{1(23)} = \frac{\left(\frac{4}{9}\right) + 0 - 0}{1 - \frac{4}{9}} = \frac{\frac{4}{9}}{\frac{5}{9}} = \frac{4}{5}$$

$$\Rightarrow R_{1(23)} = \sqrt{\frac{4}{5}} = \frac{2}{\sqrt{5}}$$

49. Explanation: (a), (b), (d)

Statement 1: $19(\hat{X}^T S \hat{X})(\hat{X}^T \Sigma \hat{X})^{-1} \sim \chi^2_{19}$

Since $\hat{X}$ and S are independent, condition on $\hat{X} = x$ (treat it as fixed vector).

Define the fixed unit-like vector:

$$u = \frac{x}{\|x\|} \in \mathbb{R}^{12}$$

Analyze $x^T S x$: $x^T S x = x^T \left(\frac{19S}{19}\right) x$

Since $19S \sim W_{12}(19, \Sigma)$, use the Wishart quadratic form property:

$$\frac{x^T(19S)x}{x^T \Sigma x} \sim \chi^2_{19}$$

This is because for $A \sim W_p(v, \Sigma)$ and fixed vector c:

$$\frac{c^T A c}{c^T \Sigma c} \sim \chi^2_v$$

Statement 1: $19 \cdot \frac{\hat{X}^T S \hat{X}}{\hat{X}^T \Sigma \hat{X}} = \frac{\hat{X}^T (19S) \hat{X}}{\hat{X}^T \Sigma \hat{X}}$

Apply the property

For fixed $\hat{X} = x$, since $19S \sim W_{12}(19, \Sigma)$:

$$\frac{x^T(19S)x}{x^T \Sigma x} \sim \chi^2_{19}$$

This distribution does not depend on x – it is χ^2_{19} regardless of the value of x.

Since the conditional distribution given $\hat{X} = x$ is χ^2_{19} for every value of x:

$$19 \frac{\hat{X}^T S \hat{X}}{\hat{X}^T \Sigma \hat{X}} \sim \chi^2_{19} \text{ unconditionally} \rightarrow \text{TRUE}$$

Statement 2: TRUE

$$19S \sim W_{12}(19, \Sigma), E(A^{-1}) = \frac{\Sigma^{-1}}{v - p - 1}$$

$$E((19S)^{-1}) = \frac{\Sigma^{-1}}{19 - 12 - 1} = \frac{\Sigma^{-1}}{6} \Rightarrow E(S^{-1}) = \frac{19}{6}\Sigma^{-1}$$

Statement 3: FALSE

$$19S \sim W_{12}(19, \Sigma) \neq W_{12}(19, 19\Sigma)$$

Statement 4: TRUE

$$\text{trace}(\Sigma^{-1} \cdot 19S) \sim \chi^2_{pv} = \chi^2_{12 \times 19} = \chi^2_{228}$$

Correct answer: Statements 1, 2 and 4 are true.

CHAPTER 13

MARKOV CHAIN

(JUNE 2012)

1. Let $\{X_n: n \geq 0\}$ be a Markov chain on a finite state space S with stationary transition probability matix. Suppose that the chain is not irreducible. Then the Markov chain
(a) admits many stationary distributions.
(b) admits a unique stationary distribution.
(c) may not admit any stationary distribution
(d) cannot admit exactly two stationary distributions

(JUNE 2012)

2. Consider a Markov chain with state space S = {1,2,3,4,5} and stationary transition probability matrix P given by

$$P = \begin{pmatrix} 0.1 & 0 & 0.2 & 0.7 & 0 \\ 0 & 1 & 0 & 0 & 0 \\ 0.7 & 0 & 0.1 & 0.2 & 0 \\ 0.2 & 0 & 0.1 & 0.1 & 0 \\ 0 & 0.5 & 0 & 0 & 0.5 \end{pmatrix}$$

Let $p_{ij}^{(n)}$ be the (i, j) th element of P^n. Then
(a) $\sum_{i=1}^{5} \lim_{n\to\infty} p_{ij}^{(n)} = 1$
(b) $(0.25, 0.25, 0.25, 0.25, 0)$ is a stationary distribution for the Markov chain.
(c) $\sum_{n=1}^{\infty} p_{33}^{(n)} < \infty$
(d) $\lim_{n\to\infty} p_{14}^{(n)} = 1/3$

(DEC. 2012)

3. Let $\{p_n, n \geq 0\}$ be a sequence of numbers, such that for all $n \geq 0, p_n > 0, \sum_{n=0}^{\infty} p_n = 1$ and $\sum_{n=0}^{\infty} np_n < \infty$. Consider a Markov chain on the state space $\{0, 1, 2, \ldots\}$ with transition probability matrix

$$\begin{pmatrix} p_0 & p_1 & p_2 & \cdots \\ 1 & 0 & 0 & \cdots \\ 0 & 1 & 0 & \cdots \\ 0 & 0 & 1 & \cdots \\ \vdots & \vdots & \vdots & \ddots \end{pmatrix}$$

Then
(a) the chain is not irreducible
(b) the chain is irreducible and transient
(c) the chain is irreducible and null recurrent
(d) the chain is irreducible and positive recurrent

(DEC. 2012)

4. One chooses letters with replacement from the set $\{a, b, c, d\}$ as follows:
After one letter is observed at step n, in $(n+1)^{th}$ step another letter will be chosen from the other three with equal probability 1/3. Let Xn denote the letter chosen at the n-th step. Which of the following are necessarily true for the Markov chain X_n?
(a) $P[X_n = a]$ converges to 1/3
(b) $P[X_n = b]$ converges to 1/4
(c) The average proportion of time c is observed converges to $\frac{1}{4}$
(d) The chain is not irreducible

(DEC. 2012)

5. Consider a Markov chain $\{X_n : n \geq 0\}$ on the state space $\{0, 1\}$ with transition probability matrix P. Which of the following statements are necessarily true?
(a) When $P = \begin{pmatrix} 1 & 0 \\ 0 & 1 \end{pmatrix}$, $\lim_{n\to\infty} P_v[X_n = i]$ converges for $i = 0, 1$, but the limits depend on the initial distribution v
(b) When $P = \begin{pmatrix} 0 & 1 \\ 1 & 0 \end{pmatrix}$, $\lim_{n\to\infty} P_v[X_n = 1]$ exists and is positive for all choices of the initial distribution v
(c) When $P = \begin{pmatrix} 1/2 & 1/2 \\ 0 & 1 \end{pmatrix}$, $\lim_{n\to\infty} P_v[X_n = 0]$ does not exist for any choice of the initial distribution v
(d) When $P = \begin{pmatrix} 1/2 & 1/2 \\ 0 & 1 \end{pmatrix}$, $\lim_{n\to\infty} P_v[X_n = 0]$ always exist but may be 0 for some choice of the initial distribution v

(JUNE 2013)

6. Consider a Markov chain on the state space {1, 2, 3, 4, 5} with transition probability matrix

$$\begin{pmatrix} 1/2 & 1/4 & 0 & 1/4 & 0 \\ 1/3 & 0 & 0 & 2/3 & 0 \\ 0 & 0 & 1 & 0 & 0 \\ 2/5 & 1/5 & 0 & 2/5 & 0 \\ 1/5 & 1/5 & 1/5 & 1/5 & 1/5 \end{pmatrix}.$$

Then which of the following statements are true?
(a) Sates 1, 2, 4 are recurrent and states 3, 5 are transient
(b) States 1, 2, 3, 4 are recurrent and state 5 is transient
(c) The chain has a unique stationary distribution
(d) The chain has more than one stationary distributions

(DEC. 2013)

7. Let $X_1, X_2, \ldots$ be a Markov chain with state space {1,2,3,4} Let the transition probability matrix P be given by

$$P \begin{pmatrix} \frac{1}{3} & 0 & 0 & \frac{2}{3} \\ \frac{1}{4} & \frac{1}{.4} & \frac{1}{4} & \frac{1}{4} \\ 0 & 0 & 1 & 0 \\ \frac{2}{3} & 0 & 0 & \frac{1}{3} \end{pmatrix}$$

Which of the following is a stationary distribution for the Markov chain?

(a) (1/4 1/4 1/4 1/4) (b) (1/3 0 0 2/3)
(c) (0 1/4 1/2 1/4) (d) (1/3 0 1/3 1/3)

(DEC. 2013)

8. Let $X_1, X_2, \ldots \ldots$ be a Markov chain. For $n \geq 1$ and for any two states$k$ and l, let
$$p_{kl}^n = P(X_{m+n} = l | X_m = k) \text{ for all } m \geq 1.$$
Suppose $p_{ij}^n > 0$ and $p_{ji}^m > 0$ for some states i and j and for some $n, m \geq 1$. Identify the correct statements.
(a) If i is transient then j is transient.
(b) $d(i) = d(j)$where for any state $l, d(l)$ denotes the period of state l
(c) If the Markov chain is aperiodic then $\lim_{n\to\infty} p_{ii}^n = \lim_{n\to\infty} p_{jj}^n$.
(d) If the period of state j is 1, then $\lim_{n\to\infty} p_{ij}^n = \lim_{n\to\infty} p_{jj}^n$

(JUNE 2014)

9. Let $(X_n)_{n\geq 0}$ be a Markov chain on the state space $S = \{0, 1\}$. Then
(a) The chain has a unique stationary distribution
(b) $P = (X_n = 0 | X_0 = 0)$ converges as $n \to \infty$
(c) The chain may have one recurrent and one transient state
(d) The chain is always irreducible

(JUNE 2014)

10. Let $(X_n)_{n\geq 0}$ be a Markov chain on state space $S = \{-N, -N+1, \ldots, -1, 0, 1, \ldots N-1, N\}$ with the transition probabilities given by $p_{i,i+1} = p_{i,i-1} = \frac{1}{2}$ for all $-N+1 \leq i \leq N-1$ $\quad p_{N,N-1} = p_{-N,-N+1} = p_{N,N} = p_{-N,-N} = \frac{1}{2}$.
Then
(a) $(X_n)_{n\geq 0}$ has a unique stationary distribution
(b) $(X_n)_{n\geq 0}$ is irreducible
(c) $\lim_{n\to\infty} P(X_n = N | X_0 = 0) = \lim_{n\to\infty} P(X_n = -N | X_0 = 0)$
(d) $(X_n)_{n\geq 0}$ is recurrent

(DEC. 2014)

11. Consider a Markov chain with state space {1, 2, ... ,100}. Suppose states $2i$ and $2j$ communicate with each other and states $2i-1$ and $2j-1$ communicate with each other for every $i, j = 1, 2, \ldots, 50$. Further suppose that $p_{3,3}^{(2)} > 0, p_{4,4}^{(3)} > 0$ and $p_{2,5}^{(7)} > 0$. Then
(a) The Markov chain is irreducible.
(b) The Markov chain is aperiodic.
(c) State 8 is recurrent.
(d) State 9 is recurrent.

(DEC. 2014)

12. For a Markov chain with finite state space, the number of stationary distributions can be
(a) 0 (b) 1
(c) 2 (d) ∞

(JUNE 2015)

13. $\{N(t): t \geq 0\}$ is a Poisson process with rate $\lambda > 0$. Let $X_n = N(n), n = 0,1,2,\ldots$ Which of the following is correct?
(a) $\{X_n\}$ is a transient Markov chain.
(b) $\{X_n\}$ is a recurrent Markov chain, but has no stationary distribution.
(c) $\{X_n\}$ has a stationary distribution.
(d) $\{X_n\}$ is an irreducible Markov chain

(JUNE 2015)

14. Consider a Markov chain with state space S = {0, 1, 2, 3} and with transition probability matrix P given by
$$P = \begin{pmatrix} \frac{2}{3} & 0 & \frac{1}{3} & 0 \\ 1 & 0 & 0 & 0 \\ \frac{1}{2} & 0 & \frac{1}{2} & 0 \\ \frac{1}{4} & \frac{1}{4} & \frac{1}{4} & \frac{1}{4} \end{pmatrix}$$
Then
(a) 1 is a recurrent state (b) 0 is a recurrent state
(c) 3 is a recurrent state (d) 2 is a recurrent state

(DEC. 2015)

15. Let $(X_n)_{n\geq 0}$ be a Markov chain on the state space $S = \{1, 2, \ldots, 23\}$ with transition probability given by $p_{i,i+1} = p_{i,i-1} = \frac{1}{2}\ \forall\, 2 \leq i \leq 22\ p_{1,2} = p_{1,23} = \frac{1}{2}, p_{23,1} = p_{23,22} = \frac{1}{2}$. Then, which of the following statement are true?
(a) $(X_n)_{n\geq 0}$ has a unique stationary distribution
(b) $(X_n)_{n\geq 0}$ is irreducible
(c) $\mathbb{P}(X_n = 1) \to \frac{1}{23}$
(d) $(X_n)_{n\geq 0}$ is recurrent

(JUNE 2016)

16. Let X_n be the result of the n-th roll of a fair die$n \geq 1$. Let $S_n = \sum_{i=1}^{n} X_i$ *and* Y_n be the last digit of S_n, for$n \geq 1$ and $Y_0 = 0$. Then, which of the following statements are correct?
(a) $\{Y_n: n \geq 0\}$ is an irreducible Markov chain.
(b) $\{Y_n: n \geq 0\}$ is an aperiodic Markov chain.
(c) $P(Y_n = 0) \to \frac{1}{6}$as $n \to \infty$.
(d) $P(Y_n = 5) \to \frac{1}{10}$ as $n \to \infty$.

(DEC. 2016)

17. Consider the Markov Chain with state space $S = \{1, 2, \ldots, n\}$ where > 10. Suppose that the transition probability matrix $P = ((p_{ij}))$ satisfies
$p_{ij} > 0$ if$|i-j|$ is even
$p_{ij} = 0$ if$|i-j|$ is odd.
Then
(a) The Markov chain is irreducible.
(b) There exists a state which is transient.
(c) There exists a state with period $(i) = 1$.
(d) There are infinitely many stationary distributions.

(JUNE 2017)

18. Let $\{X_n\}$ be a Markov chain on {0,1,2,...} with $P_{00} = \frac{2}{3}, P_{01} = \frac{1}{3}, P_{i,i+1} = \frac{2}{3}, P_{i,i-1} = \frac{1}{3}, i \geq 1, P_{ij} = 0$ otherwise.
Which of the following statements are correct?
(a) $\{X_n\}$ is recurrent (b) $\{X_n\}$ is transient
(c) $P\left(\lim_{n\to\infty} X_n = 0\right) > 0$ (d) $P\left(\lim_{n\to\infty} X_n = +\infty\right) > 0$

(DEC. 2017)

19. Consider a Markov chain$\{X_n | n \geq 0\}$ with state space {1,2,3} and transition matrix

$$P = \begin{pmatrix} 0 & \frac{1}{2} & \frac{1}{2} \\ \frac{1}{2} & 0 & \frac{1}{2} \\ \frac{1}{2} & \frac{1}{2} & 0 \end{pmatrix}$$ then $P(X_3 = 1 | X_0 = 1)$ equals

(a) 0 (b) $\frac{1}{4}$

(c) $\frac{1}{2}$ (d) $\frac{1}{8}$

(DEC. 2017)

20. Consider a Markov chain with five states {1, 2, 3, 4, 5} and transition matrix $P = \begin{pmatrix} \frac{1}{2} & 0 & 0 & \frac{1}{2} & 0 \\ 0 & \frac{1}{7} & 0 & 0 & \frac{6}{7} \\ \frac{1}{5} & \frac{1}{5} & \frac{1}{5} & \frac{1}{5} & \frac{1}{5} \\ \frac{1}{3} & 0 & 0 & \frac{2}{3} & 0 \\ 0 & \frac{5}{8} & 0 & 0 & \frac{3}{8} \end{pmatrix}$ which of the following are true?

(a) 3 and 1 are in the same communicating class

(b) 1 and 4 are in the same communicating class

(c) 4 and 2 are in the same communicating class

(d) 2 and 5 are in the same communicating class

(JUNE 2018)

21. Consider a Markov chain having state space $S = \{1, 2, 3, 4\}$ with transition probability matrix $P = (p_{i,j})$ given by

	1	2	3	4
1	1/2	0	1/2	0
2	1/4	1/4	1/4	1/4
3	1/3	0	1/3	1/3
4	1/2	0	1/2	0

Then

(a) $\lim_{n\to\infty} p_{2,2}^{(n)} = 0, \sum_{n=0}^{\infty} p_{2,2}^{(n)} = \infty$

(b) $\lim_{n\to\infty} p_{2,2}^{(n)} = 0, \sum_{n=0}^{\infty} p_{2,2}^{(n)} < \infty$

(c) $\lim_{n\to\infty} p_{2,2}^{(n)} = 1, \sum_{n=0}^{\infty} p_{2,2}^{(n)} = \infty$

(d) $\lim_{n\to\infty} p_{2,2}^{(n)} = 1, \sum_{n=0}^{\infty} p_{2,2}^{(n)} < \infty$

(JUNE 2018)

22. Consider a Markov chain on state space $S = \{1, 2, 3\}$ with transition probability matrix P given by $P = \begin{pmatrix} 0 & 1/2 & 1/2 \\ 1/2 & 0 & 1/2 \\ 1/2 & 1/2 & 0 \end{pmatrix}$. Let $\pi = (\pi_1, \pi_2, \pi_3)$ be a stationary distribution of the Markov chain and $d(1)$ denote the period of state 1. Which of the following statements are correct?

(a) $d(1) = 1$ (b) $d(1) = 2$

(c) $\pi_1 = 1/2$ (d) $\pi_1 = 1/3$

(DEC. 2018)

23. Suppose $\{X_n\}$ is, a Markov Chain with 3 states and transition probability matrix $\begin{pmatrix} \frac{1}{3} & \frac{1}{3} & \frac{1}{3} \\ \frac{1}{2} & \frac{1}{2} & 0 \\ 0 & 0 & 1 \end{pmatrix}$. Then which of the following statement is true?

(a) $\{X_n\}$ is irreducible

(b) $\{X_n\}$ is recurrent

(c) $\{X_n\}$ does not admit a stationary probability distribution

(d) $\{X_n\}$ has an absorbing state

(DEC. 2018)

24. Let $\{X_n\}$ be a Markov chain with state space S. For any $i, j \in S$, let $P_{ij}^{(n)}$ denote the n-step transition probability of going from i to j. Let d (i) denote the period of state $i (i \in S)$. Which of the following statements are correct?

(a) If $d(i) = d(j)$ then $\lim_{n\to\infty} P_{ij}^{(n)} > 0$

(b) If $d(i) = d(j)$ then $\lim_{n\to\infty} P_{ij}^{(n)} > 0$ and $P_{ij}^{(n)} > 0$ for some $n, m \geq 1$

(c) If $P_{ij}^{(n)} > 0$ and $P_{ij}^{(n)} > 0$ for some $n, m \geq 1$ $d(i) = d(j)$

(d) $\lim_{n\to\infty} P_{ij}^{(n)} > 0$ implies $d(i) = d(j)$

(DEC. 2018)

25. Consider a markov chain with transition probability matrix P given by

$$P = \begin{pmatrix} 1/2 & 1/2 & 0 \\ 0 & 1/2 & 1/2 \\ 1/3 & 1/3 & 1/3 \end{pmatrix}$$

for any two states i and j. Let $P_{ij}^{(n)}$ denote the $n - step$ transition probability of going from i and j. Identify correct statements.

(a) $\lim_{n\to\infty} P_{11}^{(n)} = 2/9$. (b) $\lim_{n\to\infty} P_{21}^{(n)} > 0$

(c) $\lim_{n\to\infty} P_{32}^{(n)} = 1/3$. (d) $\lim_{n\to\infty} P_{13}^{(n)} = 1/3$

(JUNE 2019)

26. Consider a Markov Chain with state space {0, 1, 2, 3, 4} the transition matrix

$$P = \begin{pmatrix} 1 & 0 & 0 & 0 & 0 \\ \frac{1}{3} & \frac{1}{3} & \frac{1}{3} & 0 & 0 \\ 0 & \frac{1}{3} & \frac{1}{3} & \frac{1}{3} & 0 \\ 0 & 0 & \frac{1}{3} & \frac{1}{3} & \frac{1}{3} \\ 0 & 0 & 0 & 0 & 1 \end{pmatrix}$$

Then $\lim_{n\to\infty} P_{23}^{(n)}$ equals

(a) $\frac{1}{3}$ (b) $\frac{1}{2}$

(c) 0 (d) 1

(JUNE 2019)

27. Consider a Markov Chain with state space {0,1,2} and transition matrix

$$P = \begin{matrix} & \begin{matrix} 0 & 1 & 2 \end{matrix} \\ \begin{matrix} 0 \\ 1 \\ 2 \end{matrix} & \begin{pmatrix} \frac{1}{4} & \frac{5}{8} & \frac{1}{8} \\ \frac{1}{4} & 0 & \frac{3}{4} \\ \frac{1}{2} & \frac{3}{8} & \frac{1}{8} \end{pmatrix} \end{matrix}$$. Then which of the following are true?

(a) $\lim_{n\to\infty} p_{12}^{(n)} = 0$ (b) $\lim_{n\to\infty} p_{12}^{(n)} = \lim_{n\to\infty} p_{21}^{(n)}$

(c) $\lim_{n\to\infty} p_{22}^{(n)} = \frac{1}{8}$ (d) $\lim_{n\to\infty} p_{21}^{(n)} = \frac{1}{3}$

(DEC. 2019)

28. Let $\{X_n: n \geq 0\}$ be a two state Markov chain with state space S = {0,1} and transition matrix $P = \begin{bmatrix} \frac{1}{2} & \frac{1}{2} \\ \frac{1}{3} & \frac{2}{3} \end{bmatrix}$

Assuming, $X_0 = 0$, the expected return time to O is

(a) $\frac{5}{2}$ (b) $\frac{9}{4}$

(c) $\frac{3}{2}$ (d) 3

(DEC. 2019)

29. Let $\{X_n : n \geq 0\}$ be a Markov chain with state space $N \cup \{0\}$ such that the transition probabilities are given by

$$P_{ij} = \begin{cases} q & for\ j = 0 \\ 1-q & for\ j = i+1 \\ 0 & otherwise \end{cases}$$

for i = 0,1,2,..., where 0<q<1. Then which of the following statements are correct?

(a) The Markov chain is irreducible

(b) The Markov chain is aperiodic

(c) $P_{00}^{(n)} = q\ for\ all\ n \geq 1$

(d) The Markov chain is positive recurrent

(DEC. 2019)

30. Consider a Markov chain with state space S. Let d(k) denote the period of state $k \in S$. Which of the following statements are correct?

(a) for $i, j \in S, if\ \exists n, m > 0$ such that $P_{ij}^{(n)} > 0$ and $P_{ji}^{(m)} > 0$ and i is recurrent, then j is recurrent

(b) for $i, k \in S, if \exists n, m > 0$ such that $p_{ij}^{(n)} > 0\ and\ p_{ij}^{(m)} > 0, then\ d(i) = d(j)$

(c) for $i, j \in s, if\ \exists r > 0$ such that $p_{ij}^{(r)} > 0$ then j cannot be transient

(d) For $i, j \in S, if\ \exists r > 0$ such that $p_{ij}^{(r)} > 0$ and I is null recurrent then j is positive recurrent

31. Let $S = \{1,2,3,4,5\}$. Consider a Markov chain on the state space s with transition probability matrix

$$\begin{pmatrix} 0 & 0.3 & 0.7 & 0 & 0 \\ 0 & 0 & 0.3 & 0.7 & 0 \\ 0 & 0 & 0 & 0.3 & 0.7 \\ 0.7 & 0 & 0 & 0 & 0.3 \\ 0.3 & 0.7 & 0 & 0 & 0 \end{pmatrix}.$$

Then which of the following is always true?

(a) State 1 has period 2

(b) State 2 is recurrent

(c) State 3 is transient

(d) The chain admits at least two stationary distributions

32. Consider a Markov chain with state space $S = \{0,1,2,\dots,\}$ and transition probabilities given as follows:

$p_{0,j} = 1/(j!\,e)$ for $j \geq 0$

$p_{i,i-1} = 1$ for $i > 0$ and i odd; $p_{i,i+1} = 1$ for $i > 0$ and i given

Which of the following are true?

(a) The chain is irreducible

(b) The chain has period 2

(c) There are infinitely many recurrent classes

(d) Zero is a transient state

(NOV. 2020)

33. Consider a Markov chain $X_0, X_1, X_2, \dots$ with state space S. suppose I, $j \in S$ are two states? Which communicate with each other? Which of the Following statements is NOT correct?

(a) Period of $i = period\ of\ j$

(b) i is recurrent if and only if j is recurrent

(c) $\lim_{n\to\infty} P(X_n = i|X_0 = k) = \lim_{n\to\infty} P(X_n = j|X_0 = k)$ for all $k \in S$

(d) $\lim_{n\to\infty} P[X_n = j \mid X_0 = i] = \lim_{n\to\infty} P[X_n = j \mid X_0 = j]$

(NOV. 2020)

34. Consider a Markov chain with transition probability matrix

$$P = \begin{pmatrix} 0 & 0 & \frac{1}{2} & 0 & \frac{1}{2} \\ 0 & \frac{1}{2} & 0 & \frac{1}{2} & 0 \\ \frac{1}{2} & 0 & 0 & 0 & \frac{1}{2} \\ 0 & \frac{1}{2} & 0 & \frac{1}{2} & 0 \\ \frac{1}{2} & 0 & \frac{1}{2} & 0 & 0 \end{pmatrix}$$

Let $\pi = \left(\frac{1}{5}, \frac{1}{5}, \frac{1}{5}, \frac{1}{5}, \frac{1}{5}\right)$.

(a) π is a stationary distribution

(b) If η is a stationary distribution, then $\eta = \pi$

(c) The Markov chain is periodic

(d) The Markov chain is irreducible

[SEP 2022]

35. Let

$$P = \begin{bmatrix} \frac{1}{2} & \frac{1}{2} & 0 & 0 & 0 \\ \frac{1}{2} & \frac{1}{2} & 0 & 0 & 0 \\ \frac{1}{5} & \frac{1}{5} & \frac{1}{5} & \frac{1}{5} & \frac{1}{5} \\ \frac{1}{4} & \frac{1}{4} & \frac{1}{4} & \frac{1}{4} & 0 \\ 0 & 0 & 0 & 0 & 1 \end{bmatrix}$$

be the one step transition probability matrix of a stationary Markov Chain. Which of the following statements are true?

(a) All the states have same periods

(b) All the states are transient

(c) Some states are transient

(d) All the states are recurrent

[SEP 2022]

36. Let $P = \begin{bmatrix} 0 & 1 & 0 & 0 \\ 1 & 0 & 0 & 0 \\ 0 & 0 & 0 & 1 \\ 0 & 0 & 1 & 0 \end{bmatrix}$ be the one step transition probability matrix of a homogeneous Markov chain. Which of the following statements are true?

(a) It is an irreducible Markov Chain.

(b) All the states are recurrent.

(c) $\lim_{n\to\infty} P^n$ exists

(d) All the states have same period.

(JUNE 2023)

37. Let $n \geq 2$ be a positive integer. Consider a Markov chain on the state space $\{1,2,\dots,n\}$ with a given transition probability matrix P. Let I, denote the identity matrix of order n. Which of the following statements are necessarily true?

(a) At least one state is recurrent.

(b) At least one state is transient.

(c) $-\frac{1}{3}I_n + \frac{4}{3}P$ is also a transition probability matrix of some Markov chain.

(d) 5 is an eigenvalue of $I_n + 3P + P^2$

[JULY-2024]

38. Let $\{X_n | n \geq 0\}$ be a homogeneous Markov chain with state space $S = \{0,1,2,3,4\}$ and transition probability matrix

$$P = \begin{matrix} 0 \\ 1 \\ 2 \\ 3 \\ 4 \end{matrix} \begin{pmatrix} 1/4 & 0 & 0 & 3/4 & 0 \\ 0 & 1 & 0 & 0 & 0 \\ 1/3 & 2/3 & 0 & 0 & 0 \\ 3/4 & 0 & 0 & 1/4 & 0 \\ 1/8 & 1/8 & 1/2 & 1/8 & 1/8 \end{pmatrix}$$

Let a denote the probability that starting with state 4 the chain will eventually get absorbed in closed class {0,3}. Then the value of a is

(a) $\frac{6}{21}$ (b) $\frac{11}{21}$

(c) $\frac{8}{21}$ (d) $\frac{10}{21}$

[JULY 2024]

39. Transition probability matrix of a homogeneous Markov chain with states 0,1,2,3 is

$$p = \begin{matrix} \\ 0 \\ 1 \\ 2 \\ 3 \end{matrix} \begin{pmatrix} 0 & 1 & 2 & 3 \\ 1/4 & 3/4 & 0 & 0 \\ 1 & 0 & 0 & 0 \\ 2/3 & 0 & 1/3 & 0 \\ 0 & 0 & 2/5 & 3/5 \end{pmatrix}$$

Which of the following statements are true?

(a) state 0 is positive recurrent

(b) state 3 is transient

(c) state 1 is aperiodic and positive recurrent

(d) state 2 is aperiodic and null-recurrent

(FEB. 2025)

40. In an examination question paper, all questions are 'True' or 'False' type. These are arranged in such a way that three-fourth of times a question with answer 'True' is followed by a question with answer 'True'. Also, two-third of times a question with answer 'False' is followed by a question with answer 'False'. If the question paper has 100 questions, the approximate probability that the correct answer of the 100-th question is 'True', is

(a) $\frac{3}{7}$ (b) $\frac{4}{7}$

(c) $\frac{3}{4}$ (d) $\frac{5}{6}$

(FEB. 2025)

41. Consider the Markov chain with state space {0, 1, 2} and the transition probability matrix P given by $P = \begin{pmatrix} 0 & \frac{1}{2} & \frac{1}{2} \\ \frac{3}{4} & 0 & \frac{1}{4} \\ \frac{3}{4} & \frac{1}{4} & 0 \end{pmatrix}$. Let $P^{(n)} = \left(\left(P_{ij}^{(n)}\right)\right)$ denote the n-step transition probability matrix. Then, which of the following statements are true?

(a) $P_{00}^{(2)} = \frac{3}{4}$

(b) $P_{10}^{(3)} = \frac{39}{64}$

(c) The stationary probability that the chain is in state 2 is $\frac{2}{7}$.

(d) State 1 is transient.

(JUNE 2025)

42. Consider a Markov chain $\{X_n : n \geq 1\}$ on state space {1,2,3,4,5} with the transition probability matrix

$$P = \begin{pmatrix} 0 & 1/2 & 1/2 & 0 & 0 \\ 0 & 0 & 1 & 0 & 0 \\ 0 & 1/3 & 0 & 1/3 & 1/3 \\ 1 & 0 & 0 & 0 & 0 \\ 0 & 0 & 0 & 0 & 1 \end{pmatrix}$$

Then, which of the following statements are true?

(a) Stationary distribution is (0,0,0,0,1).

(b) State 5 is absorbing and recurrent.

(c) All states are aperiodic.

(d) $\lim_{n\to\infty} P_{55}^{(n)} = 1$

(Dec 2025)

43. Let $\{X_n : n \geq 0\}$ be any homogeneous Markov Chain on the state space $S = \{1,2,3,4\}$ having the transition probability matrix $P = (p_{ij})_{i,j\in S}$ given by

$$P = \begin{pmatrix} \frac{1}{4} & 0 & \frac{2}{3} & \frac{1}{12} \\ 0 & 1 & 0 & 0 \\ \frac{1}{12} & 0 & \frac{1}{4} & \frac{2}{3} \\ \frac{2}{3} & 0 & \frac{1}{12} & \frac{1}{4} \end{pmatrix}$$

Which of the following statements about stationary distributions of any such Markov Chain is true?

(a) There is no stationary distribution

(b) Stationary distribution exists and is unique

(c) There are exactly two stationary distributions

(d) There are infinitely many stationary distributions

(Dec 2025)

44. Suppose that the transition probability matrix of a homogeneous Markov chain with state space {1, 2, 3, 4} is given by

$$P = \begin{pmatrix} \frac{1}{4} & \frac{3}{4} & 0 & 0 \\ 1 & 0 & 0 & 0 \\ \frac{1}{8} & 0 & \frac{7}{8} & 0 \\ 0 & 0 & \frac{1}{9} & \frac{8}{9} \end{pmatrix}$$

Which of the following statements are true?

(a) State 2 is a positive recurrent state

(b) Mean recurrence time of state 1 is $\frac{7}{4}$

(c) State 4 is a transient state

(d) State 3 is aperiodic and ergodic

Answer Key

1	2	3	4	5	6	7	8	9	10
d	b,d	d	b,c	A	b,d	d	a,b,d	c	a,b,c,d
11	12	13	14	15	16	17	18	19	20
d	d	a	b,d	a,b,c,d	*	c,d	c,d	b	b,d
21	22	23	24	25	26	27	28	29	30
b	c,d	d	d	a,b	c	b,d	d	a,b,c,d	a,b

31	32	33	34	35	36	37	38	39	40
b	c,d	c	a	a,c	b,d	a,d	d	a,b,c	b
41	42	43	44						
a,b,c	a,b,c,d	d	a,b,c						

:: Explanations ::

1. Explanation: (d)

$\{X_n ; n \geq 0\}$ be a markov chain on finite state space S. The chain is not irreducible which implies, the chain may admit unique or infinitely many or no stationary distribution but cannot exactly two stationary distribution.

So, option (d) is correct.

2. Explanation: (b), (d)

$S = \{1,2,3,4,5\}$ with tpm

$$P = \begin{pmatrix} 0.1 & 0 & 0.2 & 0.7 & 0 \\ 0 & 1 & 0 & 0 & 0 \\ 0.7 & 0 & 0.1 & 0.2 & 0 \\ 0.2 & 0 & 0.7 & 0.1 & 0 \\ 0 & 0.5 & 0 & 0 & 0.5 \end{pmatrix}$$

Let $p_{(ij)}^{(n)}$ be the (i,j) th element of P^n

Transition graph.

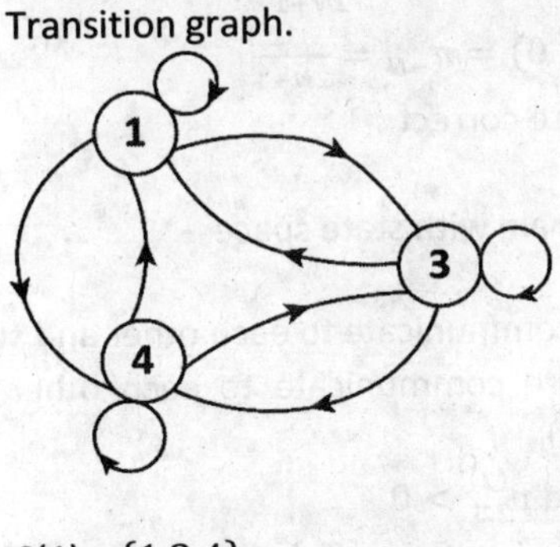

C(1) = {1,3,4}

State 1, 3, 4 are closed chain

Chain using state 1, 3, 4 are irreducible, positive recurrent

And aperiodic then

$\lim_{n\to\infty} p_{14}^{(n)} = \pi_4 = \frac{1}{n} = \frac{1}{3}$

$\lim_{n\to\infty} p_{(ij)}^{(n)}$ in independent of initial state i

$\sum_{i=1}^{5} \lim_{n\to\infty} p_{(ij)}^{(n)} = 5 \lim_{n\to\infty} p_{(ij)}^{(n)} \neq 1$

$\pi = (\pi_1, \pi_2, \pi_3, \pi_4, \pi_5)$ is a stationary distribution if satisfy $\pi = \pi P$

(0.25, 0.25, 0.25, 0.25, 0) satisfied $\pi = \pi P$

So, it is stationary distribution

$\sum_{n=1}^{\infty} p_{33} < \infty$

$\Rightarrow$ State 3 is transient

But state 3 is recurrent

So, option (b) & (d) are correct

3. Explanation: (d)

$\{p_n, n \geq 0\}$ be a sequence of number $\sum_{n=0}^{\infty} p_n = 1$ and $\sum_{n=0}^{\infty} p_n < \infty$

State space $S = \{0, 1, 2, ...\}$

T_{pm}

$$P = \begin{pmatrix} p_0 & p_1 & p_2 & \cdots \\ 1 & 0 & 0 & \cdots \\ 0 & 1 & 0 & \cdots \\ 0 & 0 & 1 & \cdots \\ \vdots & \vdots & \vdots & \cdots \end{pmatrix}$$

Transition Graph

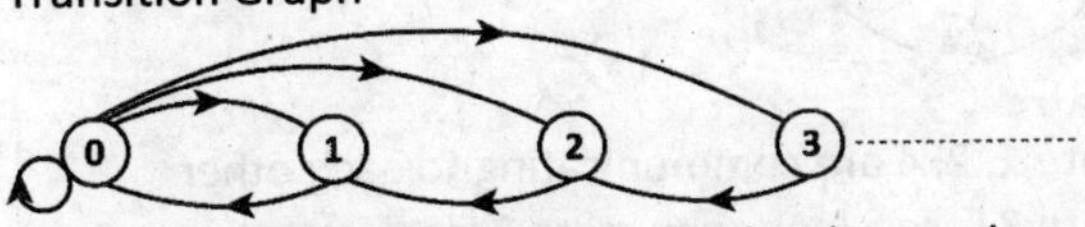

All state are communicating to each other so there is only communicating class which is equal to state space then the chain is irreducible

We are given, $\sum_{n=0}^{\infty} np_n < \infty$, the chain is positive recurrent

So, option (d) is correct

4. Explanation: (b), (c)

5. Explanation: (a)

$\{X_n : n \geq 0\}$ be a Markov chain with state space $S = \{0, 1\}$

Option (a) $P = \begin{pmatrix} 1 & 0 \\ 0 & 1 \end{pmatrix}$

The chain is positive recurrent, aperiodic and reducible so $\lim_{n\to\infty} P(X_n = i) = v_i \; for \; i = 0, 1$

Option (a) is correct

Option (b) $P = \begin{pmatrix} 0 & 1 \\ 1 & 0 \end{pmatrix}$

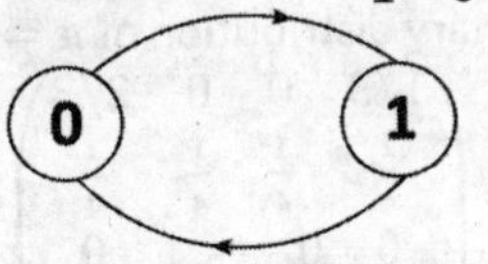

The chain is irreducible and period 2

$\lim_{n\to\infty} P(X_n = 1) = 2v$

Option (b) is incorrect

Option (c) $P = \begin{pmatrix} 1/2 & 1/2 \\ 0 & 1 \end{pmatrix}$

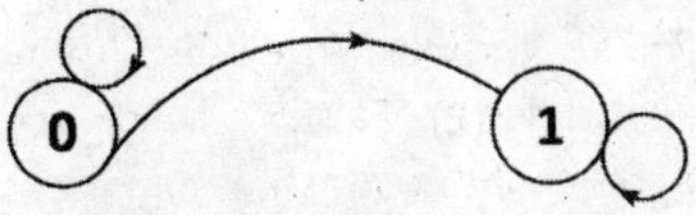

State 0 is transient so

$\lim_{n\to\infty} P(X_n = 0) = 0$

Option (d) $P = \begin{pmatrix} 1/2 & 1/2 \\ 1 & 0 \end{pmatrix}$

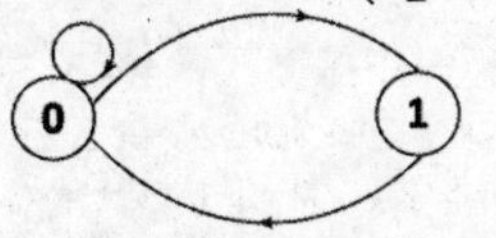

The chain irreducible, aperiodic and positive recurrent so

$\lim_{n\to\infty} P(X_n = 0) = \pi_0 \neq 0$

So, option (d) is incorrect

6. Explanation: (b), (d)

Markov chain with state space $S = \{1, 2, 3, 4, 5\}$ with tpm

$$P = \begin{pmatrix} 1/2 & 1/4 & 0 & 1/4 & 0 \\ 1/3 & 0 & 0 & 2/3 & 0 \\ 0 & 0 & 1 & 0 & 0 \\ 2/5 & 1/5 & 0 & 2/5 & 0 \\ 1/5 & 1/5 & 1/5 & 1/5 & 1/5 \end{pmatrix}$$

Transition Graph

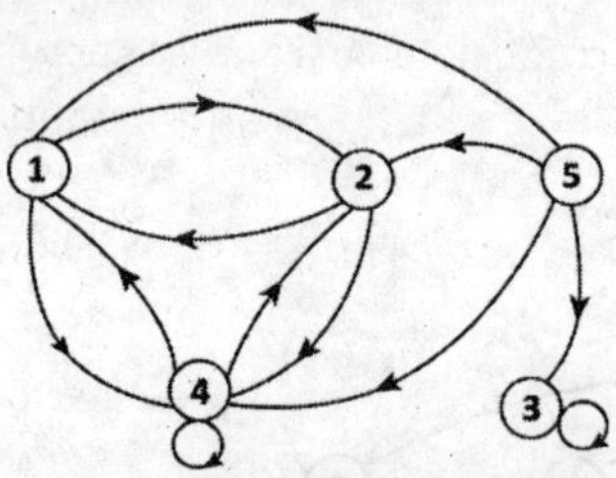

State 1, 2, 4 are communicating to each other
State 3 is self-loop then state 3 is recurrent
State 1 is recurrent because every path leaving from state 1 will come back to state 1 in any step.
State 1, 2, 4 are in same communicating class
So, state 1, 2, 4 are also recurrent
State 5 is transient
The chain has more than one communicating class, so the chain is reducible which implies
Chain has more than one stationary distribution
So, option (b) and (d) are correct

7. Explanation: (d)

TPM is given by

$$P = \begin{pmatrix} 1/3 & 0 & 0 & 2/3 \\ \frac{1}{4} & \frac{1}{4} & \frac{1}{4} & \frac{1}{4} \\ 0 & 0 & 1 & 0 \\ \frac{2}{3} & 0 & 0 & \frac{1}{3} \end{pmatrix}$$

$\pi = (\pi_1\ \pi_2\ \pi_3\ \pi_4)$ is the stationary distribution of $\pi = \pi P$

$$(\pi_1\ \pi_2\ \pi_3\ \pi_4) = (\pi_1\ \pi_2\ \pi_3\ \pi_4)\begin{pmatrix} 1/3 & 0 & 0 & 2/3 \\ \frac{1}{4} & \frac{1}{4} & \frac{1}{4} & \frac{1}{4} \\ 0 & 0 & 1 & 0 \\ \frac{2}{3} & 0 & 0 & \frac{1}{3} \end{pmatrix}$$

$\pi_1 = \frac{\pi_1}{3} + \frac{\pi_2}{4} + \frac{2\pi_4}{3}$

$\frac{2}{3}\pi_1 = \frac{3\pi_2 + 8\pi_4}{12}$

$8\pi_1 = 3\pi_2 + 8\pi_4$ (1)

$\pi_3 = \frac{\pi_2}{4} + \pi_3$ and $\pi_2 =$

$\Rightarrow \pi_2 = 0$ (2)

$\pi_4 = \frac{2\pi_1}{3} + \frac{\pi_2}{4} + \frac{\pi_4}{3}$

$\pi_1 = \pi_4$

$\pi_1 + \pi_2 + \pi_3 + \pi_4 = 1$

$2\pi_1 + \pi_3 = 1$

$\pi_1 = \frac{1}{3}, \pi_2 = 0, \pi_3 = \pi_4 = \frac{1}{3}$

So, option (d) is correct

8. Explanation: (a), (b), (d)

$\{X_n\}$ be a Markov chain

$P_{ij}^{(n)} > 0$ and $P_{ji}^{(n)} > 0$

$\Rightarrow i$ and j are communicating to each other

Transient has class property so i is transient then j is also transient

Period of state has also class property

$d(i) = d(j)$

Limiting probability does not depend on initial state

$\lim_{n\to\infty} P_{ij}^{(n)} = \lim_{n\to\infty} P_{jj}^{(n)}$

So, option a, b and d are correct

9. Explanation: (c)

$\{X_n : n \geq 0\}$ be a markov chain with state speace $S = \{0, 1\}$

In finite markov chain there should at least one recurrent state

Then the chain may have one recurrent and one transient state

So, option (c) is correct

10. Explanation: (a), (b), (c), (d)

$\{X_n : n \geq 0\}$ be a markov chain on $S = \{-N, -N+1, \dots -1, 0, 1, \dots H, N\}$

$p_{1,i+1} = p_{i,i-1} = \frac{1}{2}\ \forall -N+1 \leq i \leq N-1$

$p_{N.N+1} = p_{-N,-N+1} = p_{N,N} = p_{-N,-N} = \frac{1}{2}$

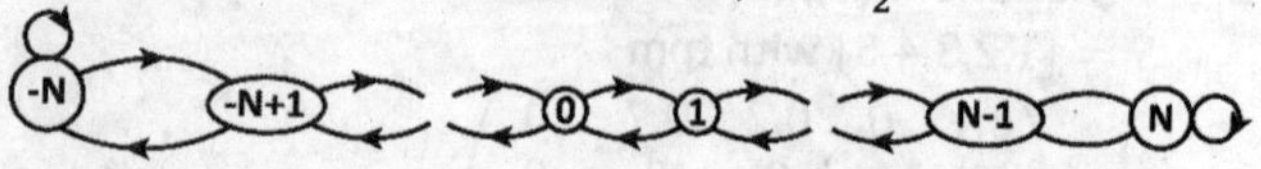

The chain is irreducible, positive recurrent, aperiodic this implies chain has a unique stationary distribution

$\lim_{n\to\infty} p_{ij}^{(n)} = \pi_j = \frac{1}{2N+1}$

$\lim_{n\to\infty} P(X_n = N|X_0 = 0) = \pi_N = \frac{1}{2N+1}$

$\lim_{n\to\infty} P(X_n = N|X_0 = 0) = \pi_{-N} = \frac{1}{2N+1}$

So, option a, b, c, d are correct

11. Explanation: (d)

Consider a Markov chain with state space

$S = \{1, 2, \dots, 100\}$

States $2i$ and $2j$ are communicate to each other and state $2i-1$ and $2j-1$ are communicate to each other far every $i, j = 1, 2, \dots, 50$

$p_{3,3}^{(2)} > 0, p_{4,4}^{(3)} > 0$ and $p_{2,5}^{(7)} > 0$

There are two classes i.e. $C_1 = \{2, 4, 6, \dots, 98\}$ and $C_2 = \{1, 3, 5, \dots, 99\}$ so the chain is reducible. Every states are not self loop so the markov chain is periodic.

Here, $p_{2,5}^{(7)} > 0$

We can go from state 2 to state 5 in 7-step $\Rightarrow$ state 2 in even and even state may or may not recurrent

State 9 (i.e., odd) they are communicate to each other,

So state 9 is recurrent

So, option (d) is correct

12. Explanation: (d)

For finite markov chain, the stationary distribution can be unique or infinitely many

So, option (b) and (d) are correct

13. Explanation: (a)

14. Explanation: (b), (d)

State space $S = \{0, 1, 2, 3\}$

TPM

$$P = \begin{pmatrix} \frac{2}{3} & 0 & \frac{1}{3} & 0 \\ 1 & 0 & 0 & 0 \\ \frac{1}{2} & 0 & \frac{1}{2} & 0 \\ \frac{1}{4} & \frac{1}{4} & \frac{1}{4} & \frac{1}{4} \end{pmatrix}$$

If state i is recurrent then every path which is coming from state i will return to state i

Transition Graph

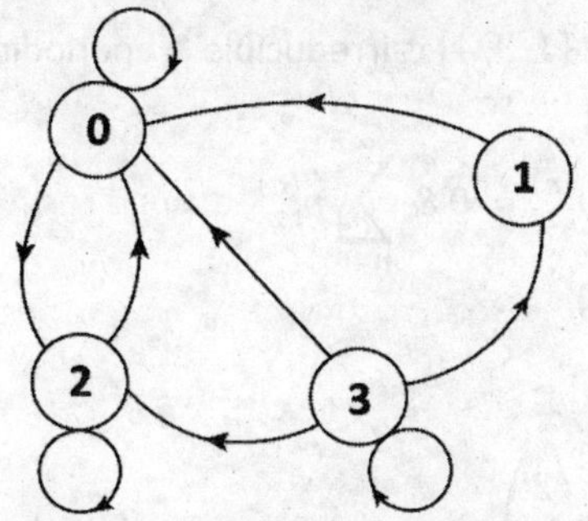

State 0 is self-loop that means state 0 is recurrent

State 2 is recurrent because state 2 and State 0 are communicating to each other.

So, option (b) and (d) are correct

15. Explanation: (a), (b), (c), (d)

$\{X_n\}_{n\geq 0}$ be a Markov chain on state space $S = \{1, 2, \dots, 2, 3\}$

$p_{i,i+1} = p_{i,i-1} = \frac{1}{2}\ \forall z \leq i \leq 22$ and $p_{1,2} = p_{1,23} = \frac{1}{2}$ and

$p_{23,1} = p_{23,22} = \frac{1}{2}$

Transition Graph

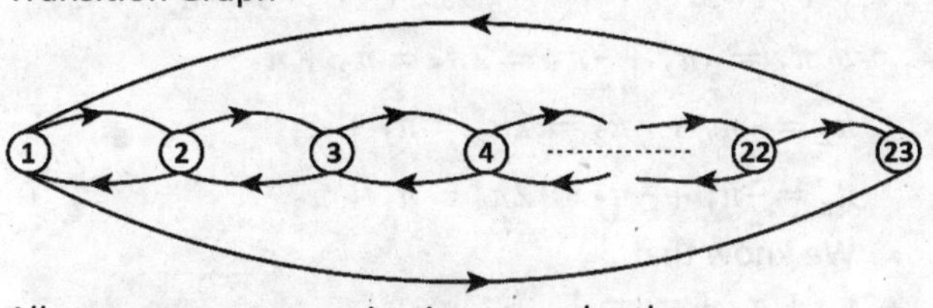

All states are communicating to each other

Finite Markov chain, so the chain irreducible, positive recurrent

So, It has unique stationary distribution

$\lim_{n\to\infty} P(X_n = 1 \mid X_0 = i) = \pi_i = \frac{1}{n} = \frac{1}{23}$

$P(X_n = 1) \to \frac{1}{23}$

So, option (a), (b), (c) & (d) are correct

16. Explanation: (*)

17. Explanation: (c), (d)

Markov chain with state space $S = \{1,2, \dots . n\}\,; n > 10$

$P = (p_{ij}) \to$ transition prob. Matrix

Satisfies $\begin{cases} P_{ij} > 0, If\ |i-j|\ is\ even \\ P_{ij} = 0, if\ |i-j|\ is\ odd \end{cases}$

If $n = 11 > 10$ then $S = \{1,2,3,4,5,6,7,8,9,10,11\}$

$P_{11} > 0\,, P_{12} = 0, P_{13} > 0, P_{14} = 0\ P_{15} > 0$

$P_{21} = 0\ P_{22} > 0\ P_{23} = 0\ P_{24} > 0, \dots$

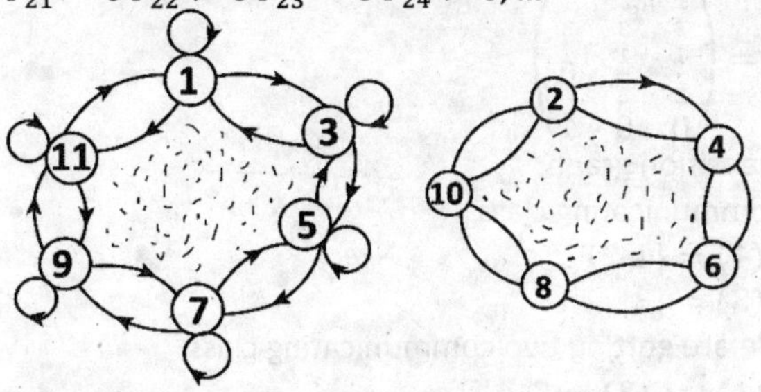

State 1 & 2 are not communicate to each other.

Similarly, (1) & (4), (1) & (5), ... etc are not communicate to each other

⇒ Markov chain is not irreducible & we may know that reducible markov chain admits many stationary distribution

We can easily see that does not exists any state i which is transient

Now, d(i) = g cd $\left\{n \geq 1 \mid P_{ij}^{(n)} > 0\right\}$ is called period of state i

$d(1) = gc\,d\,\{1,2,3, \dots .\} = 1$

$d(2) = gc\,d\,\{1,2,3, \dots .\} = 1$

$d\,(i) = 1$

Option (c), (d) are correct

18. Explanation: (c), (d)

$\{X_n\}$ be a Markov Chain state space $S = \{0, 1, 2, \dots\}$ with $P_{00} = \frac{2}{3}, P_{01} = \frac{1}{3}, P_{i,i+1} = \frac{2}{3}, P_{i,i-1} = \frac{1}{3}, i \geq 1, P_{ij} = 0$ otherwise

Suppose $S = \{0, 1, 2\}$

$\left\{P_{00} = \frac{2}{3}, P_{01} = \frac{1}{3}, P_{i,i+1} = \frac{2}{3}, P_{i,i-1} = \frac{1}{3}, i \geq 1, P_{ij} = 0\right\}$

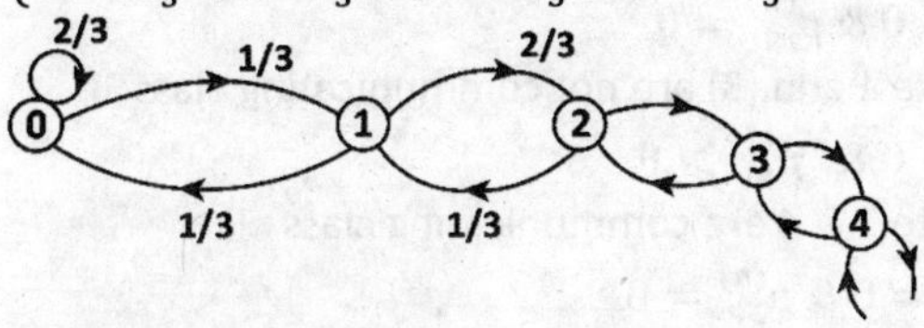

This chain is not closed

⇒ Every states are transient

⇒ Chain is transient

Option (a) is incorrect & (b) is correct

Acc. to chain

$P\left(\lim_{n\to\infty} X_n = 0\right) = 0$

$P\left(\lim_{n\to\infty} X_n = +\infty\right) \neq 0$

Option (c) & (d) are correct

19. Explanation: (b)

$\{X_n : n \geq 0\}$ with state space $S = \{1,2,3\}$ and tpm

$$P = \begin{pmatrix} 0 & \frac{1}{2} & \frac{1}{2} \\ \frac{1}{2} & 0 & \frac{1}{2} \\ \frac{1}{2} & \frac{1}{2} & 0 \end{pmatrix}$$

Then $P(X_3 = 1|X_0 = 1) = p_{11}^{(3)}$

Using transition Graph

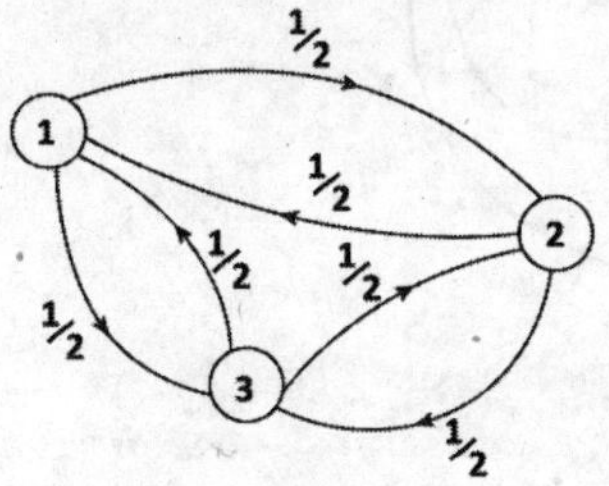

$p_{11}^{(3)} = p_{12}p_{23}p_{31} + p_{13}p_{32}p_{21}$

$= \frac{1}{2} \times \frac{1}{2} \times \frac{1}{2} + \frac{1}{2} \times \frac{1}{2} \times \frac{1}{2}$

$= \frac{1}{8} + \frac{1}{8} = \frac{1}{4}$

Option (b) is correct

20. Explanation: (b), (d)

State space $S = \{1,2,3,4,5\}$

$$P = \begin{pmatrix} \frac{1}{2} & 0 & 0 & \frac{1}{2} & 0 \\ 0 & \frac{1}{7} & 0 & 0 & \frac{6}{7} \\ \frac{1}{5} & \frac{1}{5} & \frac{1}{5} & \frac{1}{5} & \frac{1}{5} \\ \frac{1}{3} & 0 & 0 & \frac{2}{3} & 0 \\ 0 & \frac{5}{8} & 0 & 0 & \frac{3}{8} \end{pmatrix}$$

Transition Graph

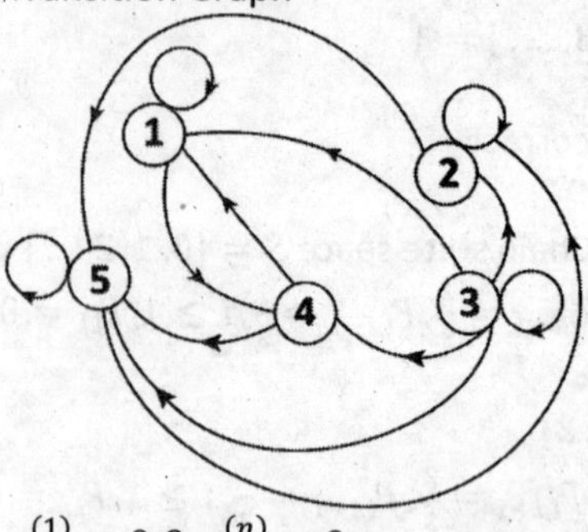

$p_{31}^{(1)} > 0$ & $p_{13}^{(n)} = 0$

⇒ State 1 and (3) are not communicating class

$p_{14}^{(1)} > 0$ & $p_{41}^{(1)} > 0$

⇒ State 1 & 4 are communicating class

$p_{42}^{(n)} 0 = 0$ & $p_{24}^{(n)} = 0$

⇒ State 2 & 4 are not communicating class

$p_{25}^{(1)=} 0$ & $p_{52}^{(1)} > 0$

⇒ State 2 and 5 are communicating class

So, option (2) and (4) are correct.

21. Explanation: (b)

State Space $S = \{1, 2, 3, 4\}$

TPM

$$P = \begin{bmatrix} 1/2 & 0 & 1/2 & 0 \\ 1/4 & 1/4 & 1/4 & 1/4 \\ 1/3 & 0 & 1/3 & 1/3 \\ 1/2 & 0 & 1/2 & 0 \end{bmatrix}$$

Transition graph

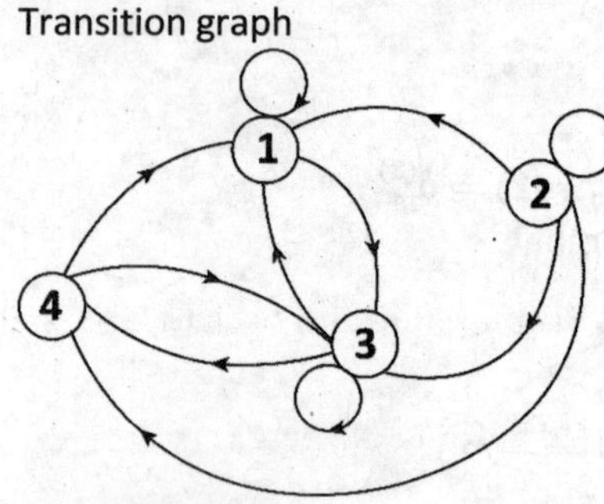

Communicating class

$C(1) = (1, 3, 4)$

$C(2) = \{2\}$

We are getting two communicating class

So, the chain in reducible

$\{1, 3, 4\}$ closed

$$P` = \begin{matrix} & 1 & 3 & 4 \\ 1 & 1/2 & 1/2 & 0 \\ 3 & 1/3 & 1/3 & 1/3 \\ 4 & 1/2 & 1/2 & 0 \end{matrix}$$

X_n with state space $\{1, 3, 4\}$ is irreducible & aperiodic

Far state 2 is transient, so

$$\lim_{n\to\infty} p_{22}^{(n)} = 0 \ \& \ \sum_{n=0}^{\infty} p_{22}^{(n)} < \infty$$

22. Explanation: (c), (d)

$S = \{1, 2, 3\}$

Tpm

$$P = \begin{pmatrix} 0 & 1/2 & 1/2 \\ 1/2 & 0 & 1/2 \\ 1/2 & 1/2 & 0 \end{pmatrix}$$

$\pi = (\pi, \pi_2, \pi_3)$ be a stationary distribution

We know that

$\pi = \pi P$

$$(\pi_1\ \pi_2\ \pi_3) = (\pi_1\ \pi_2\ \pi_3) \begin{pmatrix} 0 & 1/2 & 1/2 \\ 1/2 & 0 & 1/2 \\ 1/2 & 1/2 & 0 \end{pmatrix}$$

$$(\pi_1\ \pi_2\ \pi_3) = \left(\tfrac{1}{2}\pi_2 + \tfrac{1}{2}\pi_3 \tfrac{1}{2}\pi_1 + \tfrac{1}{2}\pi_3 \tfrac{1}{2}\pi_1 + \tfrac{1}{2}\pi_2\right)$$

$\therefore\ \pi_1 = \frac{1}{2}\pi_2 + \frac{1}{2}\pi_3 \Rightarrow 2\pi_1 = \pi_2 + \pi_3$

$\pi_2 = \frac{1}{2}\pi_1 + \frac{1}{2}\pi_3 \Rightarrow 2\pi_2 = \pi_1 + \pi_3$

$\pi_3 = \frac{1}{2}\pi_1 + \frac{1}{2}\pi_2 \Rightarrow 2\pi_3 = \pi_1 + \pi_2$

We know that

$\pi_1 + \pi_2 + \pi_3 = 1$

$\pi_1 + 2\pi_1 = 1$

$\pi_1 = \frac{1}{3}$

Transition graph

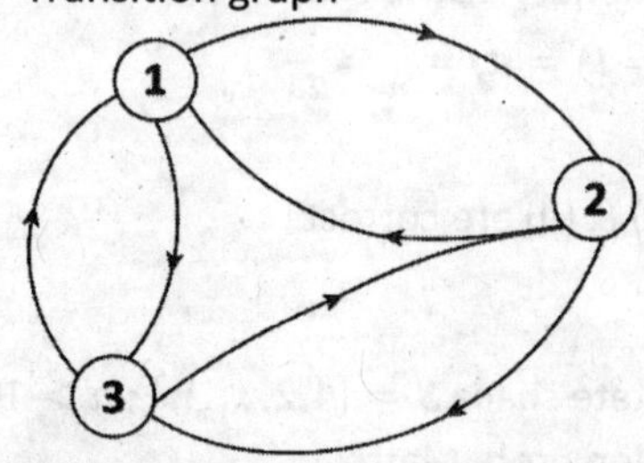

$d(1) = \gcd\{n; n \geq 1\} = \gcd\{2, 3, 4, 5, \dots\}$

$d(1) = 1$

So, option (c) & (d) are correct

23. Explanation: (d)

TPM

$$P = \begin{pmatrix} \frac{1}{3} & \frac{1}{3} & \frac{1}{3} \\ \frac{1}{2} & \frac{1}{2} & 0 \\ 0 & 0 & 1 \end{pmatrix}$$

Transition graph:

Communicating class

$C(1) = \{1, 2\}$

$C(3) = \{3\}$

We are getting two communicating class

$C(1) \cup C(3) = S$

So, chain is reducible

There is one path from state 1 → 3 but no return path from state 3, so state 1 is transient

So, $\{X_n\}$ is not recurrent

State 3 is self - loop with prob. 1

So, state 3 is an absorbing state

So, $\{X_n\}$ has an absorbing state

Option (d) is correct

24. Explanation: (d)

Counter Example: $S = \{1, 2, 3\}$

Transition Graph

$d(1) = 1$

$d(2) = 1$

$d(3) = 1$

$P = \begin{bmatrix} 1 & 0 & 0 \\ 0 & 1 & 0 \\ 0 & 0 & 1 \end{bmatrix}$ = 1 step transition prob. Matrix

$P^n = \begin{bmatrix} 1 & 0 & 0 \\ 0 & 1 & 0 \\ 0 & 0 & 1 \end{bmatrix}$ = n-th step transition prob. Matrix

$\lim_{n\to\infty} p_{ij}^{(n)} = 0$

So option (1), (2) are incorrect

Suppose $p_{ij}^{(n)} > 0$ and $p_{ji}^{(m)} > 0$

$\Rightarrow i \leftrightarrow j$ implies state i & j are communicating to each other

$\Rightarrow d(i) = d(j)$

So, option (3) is correct

For option (4)

Counter example:

$P = \begin{bmatrix} 0 & 1 \\ 0 & 1 \end{bmatrix}$

$P^n = \begin{bmatrix} 0 & 1 \\ 0 & 1 \end{bmatrix}$

$p_{12}^{(n)} = 1 > 0$

But $d(1) = 0$ & $d(2) = 1$

$\therefore p_{12}^{(n)} = 1 > 0$

$\Rightarrow d(1) \neq d(2)$

So, option (d) is incorrect

25. Explanation: (a), (b)

State Space $S = \{1, 2, 3\}$

$$P = \begin{pmatrix} \frac{1}{2} & \frac{1}{2} & 0 \\ 0 & \frac{1}{2} & \frac{1}{2} \\ \frac{1}{3} & \frac{1}{3} & \frac{1}{3} \end{pmatrix}$$

$p_{ij}^{(n)}$ denote the n-step transition prob. of going from i to j

Transition Graph

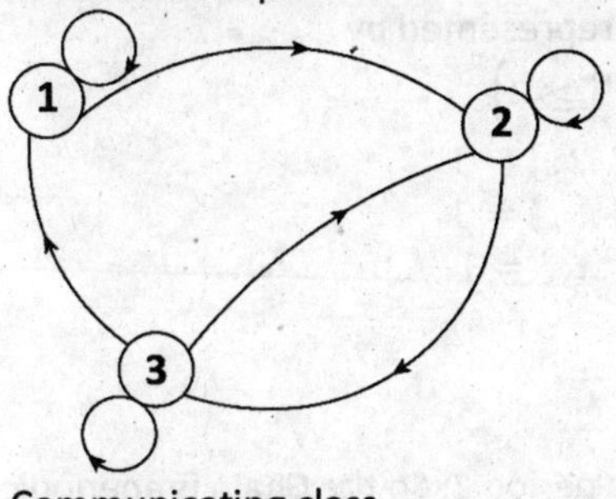

Communicating class

$C(1) = \{1, 2, 3\} = S$

We are only getting one communicating class which is equal to state space then $\{X_n\}$ is irreducible

Period of state 1

$d(1) = \gcd\{n\,; p_{11}^{(n)} > 0\}$

$= \gcd\{1, 2, 3, 4, \ldots.\}$

$d(1) = 1$

$d(1) = d(2) = d(3) = 1$

$\{X_n\}$ is irreducible & aperiodic then

$\lim_{n\infty} p_{ij}^{(n)} = \pi_j$

We know that, π is a stationary distribution

$\pi = \pi P$

$$(\pi_1\ \pi_2\ \pi_3) = (\pi_1\ \pi_2\ \pi_3) \begin{pmatrix} \frac{1}{2} & \frac{1}{2} & 0 \\ 0 & \frac{1}{2} & \frac{1}{2} \\ \frac{1}{3} & \frac{1}{3} & \frac{1}{3} \end{pmatrix}$$

$\pi_1 = \frac{1}{2}\pi_1 + \frac{1}{3}\pi_3$

$\pi_2 = \frac{1}{2}\pi_1 + \frac{1}{2}\pi_2 + \frac{1}{3}\pi_3$

$\pi_3 = \frac{1}{2}\pi_2 + \frac{1}{3}\pi_3$

On solving these equation,

$\pi_1 = \frac{2}{9}\ \pi_2 = \frac{4}{9}, \pi_3 = \frac{1}{3}$

$\lim_{n\to\infty} p_{11}^{(n)} = \pi_1 = \frac{2}{9}$ & $\lim_{n\to\infty} p_{21}^{(n)} = \frac{2}{9}$

$\lim_{n\to\infty} p_{32}^{(n)} = \pi_2 = \frac{4}{9}$ & $\lim_{n\to\infty} p_{13}^{(n)} = \pi_3 = \frac{1}{9}$

26. Explanation: (c)

We know that

$\lim_{n\to\infty} P_{ij}^{(n)} = 0$ if j is transient $\forall\ i \in S$

$T\,P\,M$:

$$P = \begin{pmatrix} 1 & 0 & 0 & 0 & 0 \\ \frac{1}{3} & \frac{1}{3} & \frac{1}{3} & 0 & 0 \\ 0 & \frac{1}{3} & \frac{1}{3} & \frac{1}{3} & 0 \\ 0 & 0 & \frac{1}{3} & \frac{1}{3} & \frac{1}{3} \\ 0 & 0 & 0 & 0 & 1 \end{pmatrix}$$

Transition Graph:

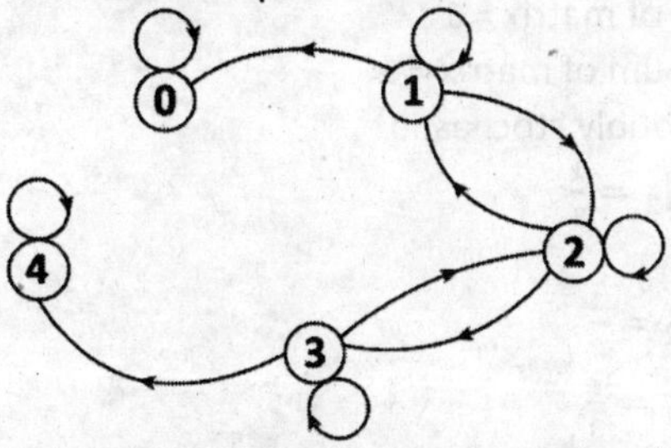

If We noticed there is one path $3 \to 4$

We go from $3 \to 4$ we cannot return back to 4 So, state 3 is transient then

$\lim_{n\to\infty} P_{23}^{(n)} = 0$ if state 3 is transient

Option (c) is correct

27. Explanation: (b), (d)

State space $S = \{0,1,2\}$

$$P = \begin{pmatrix} \frac{1}{4} & \frac{5}{8} & \frac{1}{8} \\ \frac{1}{4} & 0 & \frac{3}{4} \\ \frac{1}{2} & \frac{3}{8} & \frac{1}{8} \end{pmatrix}$$

Transition graph

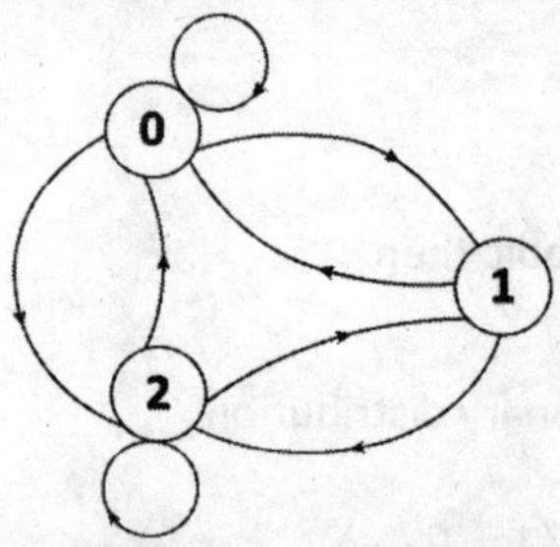

Result 1: If Markov chain is aperiodic, irreducible & recurrent then $\lim_{n\to\infty} P_{ij}^{(n)} = \prod_j$

Result 2: If Markov chain is aperiodic, irreducible & recurrent and doubly stochastic then

$\prod_0 = \frac{1}{no.\ of\ state}$

First we will check our given Markov chain aperiodic or not

Period of state i represent

$\lambda(i) = \gcd\{n\,; p_{ii}^{(n)} > 0\}$

$\lambda(0) = \gcd\{1,2,3 \ldots\ldots\} = 1$

$\lambda(1) = \gcd\{2,3,4 \ldots\ldots\} = 1$

$\lambda(2) = \gcd\{1,2,3 \ldots\ldots\} = 1$

Period of each state is 1 So the Markov chain is aperiodic

Communicating class

$c(0) = \{0,1,2\} = S$

We are getting only one Communicating class which is equal to state space, So, the chain is irreducible

If every state is a member if same Communicating class then one state is recurrent So other will be recurrent

We can easily see that in the transition graph, from every path state 0, can come back to state 0. So, State 0 is recurrent

⇒ State 1,2 are also recurrent

⇒ chain is recurrent

Every row sum of matrix = 1

Every column Sum of matrix = 1

The matrix is doubly stochastic

$\prod_0 = \prod_1 = \prod_2 = \frac{1}{3}$

Acc. To option

$\lim_{n\to\infty} p_{12}^{(n)} = \prod_2 = \frac{1}{3}$

$\lim_{n\to\infty} p_{21}^{(n)} = \prod_1 = \frac{1}{3}$

$\lim_{n\to\infty} p_{22}^{(n)} = \prod_2 = \frac{1}{3}$

So option (b), (d) are correct

28. Explanation: (d)

State space $S = \{0, 1\}$

$t\ pm$

$$P = \begin{bmatrix} \frac{1}{2} & \frac{1}{2} \\ \frac{1}{3} & \frac{2}{3} \end{bmatrix}$$

Assuming $X_0 = 0$, find the expected return time to 0 i.e.

$$\mu_{00} = \frac{1}{\prod_0}$$

We known that,

$\prod = \prod P$

Where $\prod$ is Stationary distribution

$$(\prod_0\ \prod_1) = (\prod_0\ \ \prod_1)\begin{bmatrix} \frac{1}{2} & \frac{1}{2} \\ \frac{1}{3} & \frac{2}{3} \end{bmatrix}$$

$(\prod_0\ \ \prod_1) = (\frac{1}{2}\prod_0 + \frac{1}{3}\prod_1\ \ \frac{1}{2}\prod_0 + \frac{2}{3}\prod_1)$

$\Rightarrow \prod_0 = \frac{1}{2}\prod_0 + \frac{1}{3}\prod_1$

$\frac{1}{2}\prod_0 = \frac{1}{3}\prod_1$

$3\prod_0 = 2\prod_1$

$\prod_1 = \frac{1}{2}\prod_0 + \frac{2}{3}\prod_1$

$\frac{1}{3}\prod_1 = \frac{1}{2}\prod_0$

$2\prod_1 = 3\prod_0$

$\therefore \prod_0 + \prod_1 = 1$

$\prod_0 + \frac{3}{2}\prod_0 = 1$

$\frac{5}{2}\prod_0 = 1$

$\prod_0 = \frac{2}{5}$

$\mu_{00} = \frac{1}{\prod_0} = \frac{1}{\frac{2}{5}} = \frac{5}{2}$

Option (d) is correct

29. Explanation: (a), (b), (c), (d)

$\{X_n\ ; n \geq 0\}$ be maskov chain with state space $N \cup \{0\}$

$$P_{ij} = \begin{cases} q & for\ j = 0 \\ 1-q & for\ j = 1+1 \\ 0 & otherwise \end{cases}$$

$T\ PM$ is

$$P = \begin{bmatrix} q & 1-q & 0 & 0 & \cdots \\ q & 0 & 1-q & 0 & \cdots \\ q & 0 & 0 & 1-q & \cdots \\ q & 0 & 0 & 0 & \cdots \\ \vdots & & & 0 & \cdots \end{bmatrix}$$

Transition Graph:

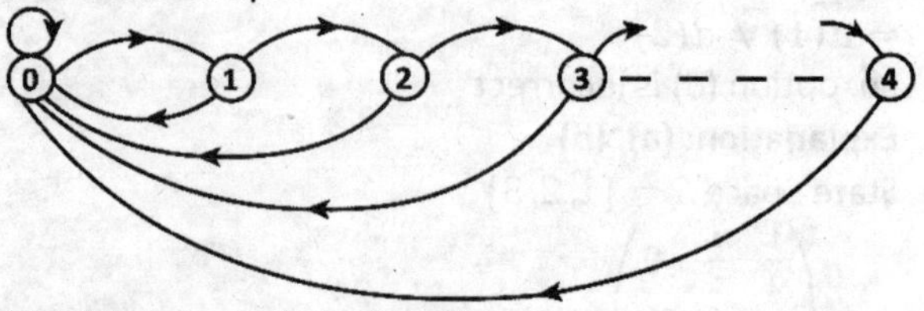

The Markov chain is closed

If every state can be reached from every state then a Markov chain is irreducible

So, Given Markov chain is irreducible

A Markov chain is aperiodic if every state has period 1

Period if state i is represented by

$\lambda(i) = gcd\{n\,; p_{ij}^{(n)} \geq 0\}$

$\lambda(0) = gcd\ \{1,2,3 \ldots.\} = 1$

$\lambda(1) = gcd\ \{2,3,4 \ldots.\} = 1$

$\lambda(2) = gcd\{2,3,4 \ldots.\} = 1$

.

.

.

So, every state has period 1, So the Chain is aperiodic

By Chapman Kolmogorov`s -

$P_{ij}^{(m+n)} = \sum_r P_{ir}^{\ (m)} P_{rj}^{\ (n)}$

$P_{oo}^{\ (n)} = P_{oo}^{\ ((n-1)+1)} = \sum_r P_{or}^{\ (n-1)} P_{ro}^{\ (1)}$

$P_{ro} \to prob$ from going state r to state 0 = q

$P_{oo}^{\ (n)} = \sum_r P_{or}^{\ (n-1)} . q = q\ \sum_r P_{or}^{\ (n-1)} = q$

$[\therefore \sum_r P_{or}^{(n-1)} = row\ sum = 1]$

In an irreducible Chain if one state is non-null recurrent (positive recurrent) then all other will be same and the Markov Chain will be called positive recurrent if state 0 is positive recurrent then

$\mu_{oo} < \infty$

$\mu_{oo} = \sum_{n=1}^{\infty} n\, f_{oo}^{(n)}$

$f_{oo}^{(1)} = q$

$f_{oo}^{(2)} = P_{01}P_{10} = (1-q).q$

$f_{oo}^{(3)} = q(1-q)^2$

$f_{oo}^{(4)} = q(1-q)^3$

$\mu_{oo} = \sum_{n=1}^{\infty} n\, f_{oo}^{(n)}$

$= 1 \times q + 2 \times q(1-q) + 3q(1-q)^2 + \cdots$

Let $S = 1 + 2(1-q) + 3\,(1-q)^2 + \cdots$

$(1-q)S = (1-q) + 2\,(1-q)^2 - 1 \ldots.$

$S[1-1+q] = 1 + (1-q) + (1-q)^2 + \cdots..$

$qS = \frac{1}{1-1+q} =$

$S = \frac{1}{q^2}$

$\mu_{oo} = q.\frac{1}{q^2} = \frac{1}{q} < \infty$

So, state 0 is positive recurrent

Option (a), (b), (c) & (d) are correct

30. Explanation: (a), (b)

For option (1)

$P_{ij}^{(n)} > 0\ and\ P_{ji}^{(m)} > 0$

$\Rightarrow i\ \&\ j$ are communicate to each other $i \leftrightarrow j$

So, the properties of state i & j are same

Then if state i is recurrent $\Rightarrow j$ is recurrent

For option (2)

$i \leftrightarrow j$

Period of $i\ \&\ j$ are same

$\therefore d\,(i) = d(j)$

For option (c)

$P_{ij}^{(r)} > 0\ \Rightarrow$ state j is accessible from state i So, state j may be recurrent or transient

For option (4)

$P_{ij}^{(r)} > 0\ \Rightarrow$ State j is accessible from State i

If i is null recurrent $\not\Rightarrow$j is positive recurrent

Option (a) & (b) are correct

31. Explanation: (b)

State space $S = \{1,2,3,4,5\}$ with transition matrix

$$P = \begin{pmatrix} 0 & 0.3 & 0.7 & 0 & 0 \\ 0 & 0 & 0.3 & 0.7 & 0 \\ 0 & 0 & 0 & 0.3 & 0.7 \\ 0.7 & 0 & 0 & 0 & 0.3 \\ 0.3 & 0.7 & 0 & 0 & 0 \end{pmatrix}$$

Transition graph

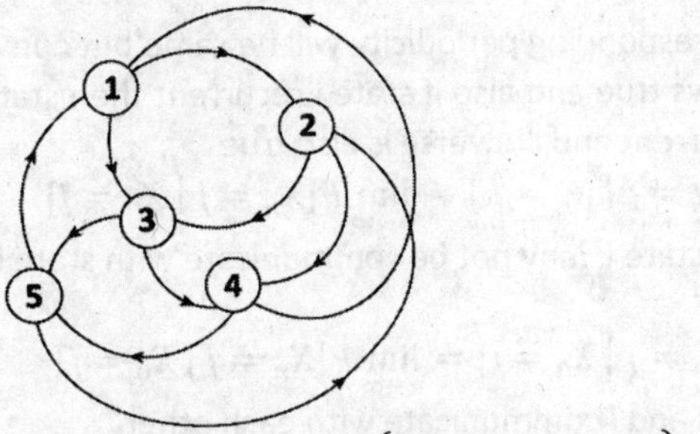

Period of state $i = \gcd\{n \geq 1\,;\ P_{ii}^{(n)} > 0\}$

Period of state $1 = \gcd\{3,6,9,\ldots\} = 3$

If state 2 is recurrent then from each and every path which comes from state 2 should return back to state 2 in any no. of steps, otherwise state 2 is transient

There is only two path state 2 is coming i.e.,

$2 \to 3 \to 5 \to 2$

$2 \to 4 \to 1 \to 2$

So, state 2 is recurrent.

If state 2 and state 3 are communicating to each other i.e., 2, 3 both are recurrent

So, option (b) is correct

32. Explanation: (c), (d)

For Markov chain with state space $S = \{0,1,2,\ldots\}$

Transition probabilities given as follows:

$P_{0,j} = \frac{1}{j!e}$ for $j \geq 0$

$P_{i,i-1} = 1$ for $i > 0$ and i is odd

$P_{i,i+1} = 1$ for $i > 0$ and i is even

TPM

	0	0	2	3	----
0	$\frac{1}{e}$	$\frac{1}{e}$	$\frac{1}{2!e}$	$\frac{1}{3!e}$	----
1	1	0	0	0	----
2	0	0	0	1	----
3	0	0	1	0	----

Transition Graph

Transition Graph

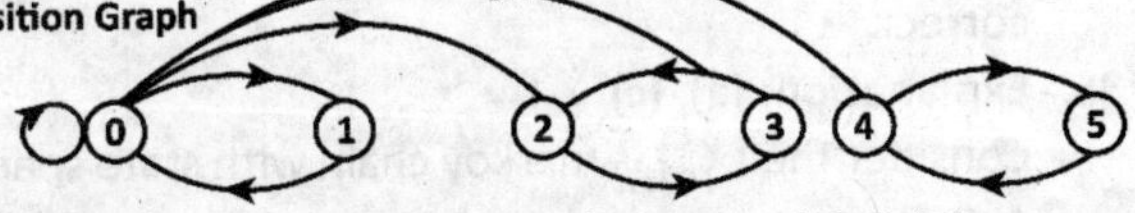

State 0 & 1 are communicating but state (1) & (2) are not communicating so, we are get more than one communicating or infinitely many communicating class

Then, there are infinitely many recurrent class

Period of state 0 = 1

Period of state 2 = 2

Then the period of chain will not be 2

If state 0 is transient state then there should one path from which state 0 never return back to state 0

State 0 → State 2

So, state 0 is transient state

Finally, option (c) and (d) are correct

33. Explanation: (c)

Given Markov Chain $X_0, X_1, X_2 \ldots$ with state space if $i, j \in S$ are two state which communicate with each other. Then their corresponding periodicity will be same but converse not always true and also if state i recurrent then state j is also recurrent and converse is also true

$$\lim_{n\to\infty} P[X_n = i \mid X_0 = k] \neq \lim_{n\to\infty} P[X_n = j \mid X_0 = j]$$

Because state k may not be communicate with state i and j

$$\lim_{n\to\infty} P[X_n = j \mid X_0 = i] = \lim_{n\to\infty} P[X_n = j \mid X_0 = j]$$

Because i and j communicate with each other

Option (c) is correct

34. Explanation: (a)

Since given Markov chain with state space S = {1,2,3,4,5} with transition probability matrix

$$P = \begin{pmatrix} 0 & 0 & \frac{1}{2} & 0 & \frac{1}{2} \\ 0 & \frac{1}{2} & 0 & \frac{1}{2} & 0 \\ \frac{1}{2} & 0 & 0 & 0 & \frac{1}{2} \\ 0 & \frac{1}{2} & 0 & \frac{1}{2} & 0 \\ \frac{1}{2} & 0 & \frac{1}{2} & 0 & 0 \end{pmatrix}$$

Communicating class : C(1) = {1,3,5} and C(2) = {2,4}

All states are not communicating to each other

So, the markov chain is reducible

d(i) represents the period of state i

d(i) = gcd {n; $p_{ii}^{(n)} > 0$ }

d(1) = gcd{2,3,4,5,.....}= 1

state 1 3, and 5 are in same communicating class member so

d(1) = d(3)= d(5) = 1

State 2 and 4 are self loop so d(2)= d(4) =1

Every state has period 1, so the Markov chain is aperiodic

We know that, a finite reducible chain has infinite many stationary distribution and one of these stationary distribution is

$\left(\frac{1}{n}, \frac{1}{n}, \frac{1}{n}, \frac{1}{n}, \frac{1}{n}\right) = \left(\frac{1}{5}, \frac{1}{5}, \frac{1}{5}, \frac{1}{5}, \frac{1}{5}\right)$ where $n = 5$

For option (2)

If $\eta = \pi$, implies that it has unique stationary distribution but the chain has infinite many stationary distribution

Option (a) is correct and option (c), (b) and (d) are not correct.

35. Explanation: (a), (c)

Consider the $\{X_n\}$ is markov chain with state space 1, 2, 3, 4, & 5

$$P = \begin{bmatrix} \begin{bmatrix} 1/2 & 1/2 \\ 1/2 & 1/2 \end{bmatrix} & \begin{matrix} 0 & 0 & 0 \\ 0 & 0 & 0 \end{matrix} \\ \begin{matrix} 1/5 & 1/5 \\ 1/4 & 1/4 \\ 0 & 0 \end{matrix} & \begin{matrix} 1/5 & 1/5 & 1/5 \\ 1/4 & 1/4 & 0 \\ 0 & 0 & [1] \end{matrix} \end{bmatrix}$$

Here

$$c_1 = \begin{bmatrix} \frac{1}{2} & \frac{1}{2} \\ \frac{1}{2} & \frac{1}{2} \end{bmatrix} \ \& \ c_2 = [1]$$

are the closed set of matrices.

∴ The matrix is reduciable.

The transition diagram is

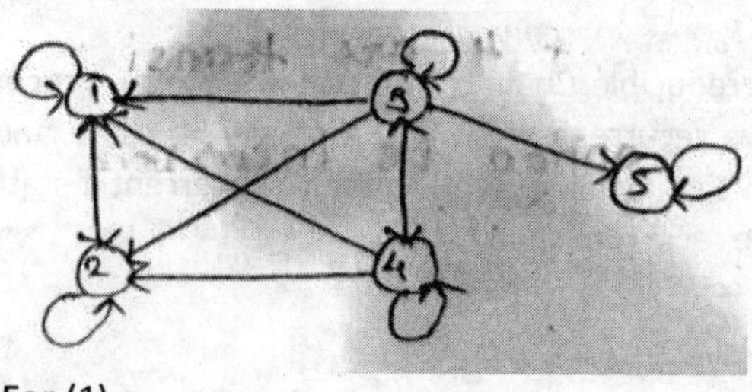

For (1)

In this stochastic matrix every state is itself loop.

⇒ The state come to its initial position at every step.

∴ period of every step is 1. i.e., All states have same period.

For (2)

C_1 & C_2 are closed set.

i.e. states within C_1& C_2 are persistent & remaining are transient implies states 3 & 4 are transient.

∴ 2nd option is incorrect.

For (3)

State 3 & 4 are transient & state 1, 2, & 5 are persisted.

For (4)

Persistent is also known as transient

⇒ state {1, 2} & {5} are recurrent states.

Option (a) & (c) are correct.

36. Explanation: (b), (d)

Let consider the state space 1, 2, 3, & 4. The transition probability matrix is

$$P = \begin{bmatrix} \begin{bmatrix} 0 & 1 \\ 1 & 0 \end{bmatrix} & \begin{matrix} 0 & 0 \\ 0 & 0 \end{matrix} \\ \begin{matrix} 0 & 0 \\ 0 & 0 \end{matrix} & \begin{bmatrix} 0 & 1 \\ 1 & 0 \end{bmatrix} \end{bmatrix}$$

$$C_1 = \begin{bmatrix} 0 & 1 \\ 1 & 0 \end{bmatrix} \ \& \ C_2 = \begin{bmatrix} 0 & 1 \\ 1 & 0 \end{bmatrix}$$

The transition diagram

Here clearly observe that the chain is reduciable

∴ 1st is correct

Matrix is reduciable & C_1& C_2 are closed set of matrix every state of closed set is persistent

∴ ⇒ All state are persistent.

$$P^n = \begin{cases} \begin{bmatrix} 0 & 1 \\ 1 & 0 \end{bmatrix} & ; n \text{ is even} \\ \begin{bmatrix} 1 & 0 \\ 0 & 1 \end{bmatrix} & ; n \text{ is odd} \end{cases}$$

$\lim_{n\to\infty} p^n$ does not exist.

i.e. steady state distribution does not exist, however station dist exist.

Period of state 1

$$d_{(1)} = GCD\{n | p_{11}^{(n)} > 0 ; \forall n > 0\}$$

$P_{11} = 0$

$P_{11}^{(2)} = 1 > 0$

$P_{11}^{(3)} = 0$

$P_{11}^{(4)} > 0$

$d_{(1)} = GCD\{2, 4, 6, 8, \dots\} = 2$

State 1 & 2 are communicating

⇒ period of state 1 & 2 is 2.
Period of state 3.

$d_{(3)} = GCD\{n|F_{33} > 0\ ;\ \forall n > 0\}$

$P_{33} = 0$

$P_{33}^{(2)} = 1 > 0$

$P_{33}^{(3)} = 0$

$P_{33}^{(4)} = 1 > 0$

$\therefore d_{(3)} = GCD\{2, 4, 6, 8, \ldots\} = 2$

∴ state 3 & 4 are communicating
⇒ Period of state 3 & 4 is 2
∴ (b) & (d) are correct.

37. Explanation: (a), (d)

$n > 2$ be positive integer
The state space of markov chain is 1, 2, …, n ; If Transition probability matrix P & If $I_n$is Identity matrix of order n.
Let consider $n = 2$

The identity matrix is $\begin{bmatrix} 1 & 0 \\ 0 & 1 \end{bmatrix}_{2\times2}$

i.e $P = \begin{bmatrix} 1 & 0 \\ 0 & 1 \end{bmatrix}$

$1 \leftrightarrow 1$

$2 \leftrightarrow 2$

i.e.

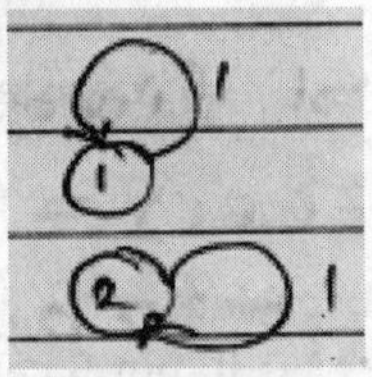

∴ state 1&2 are absorbing
⇒ absorbing state are of way recurrent
In transition probability matrix sum of row /column is 1 in Identity matrix (double stochastic matrix)
∴ The eigen value of identity matrix is one.
Now,

$I_n + 3p + p^2$

$= (1) + 3(1) + (1)^2$ in is identity matrix.

$= 1 + 3 + 1 = 5$

Let $\frac{-1}{3} I_n + \frac{4}{3} P$

$= \frac{4P - I_n}{3}$

Consider,

$P = \begin{bmatrix} 0 & 1 \\ 0 & 1 \end{bmatrix}$ & $I = \begin{bmatrix} 1 & 0 \\ 0 & 1 \end{bmatrix}$

$\frac{4p - I}{3} = \frac{1}{3}\begin{bmatrix} 0 & 4 \\ 0 & 4 \end{bmatrix} - \frac{1}{3}\begin{bmatrix} -1 & 0 \\ 0 & 1 \end{bmatrix}$

$\frac{4p - I}{3} = \frac{1}{3}\begin{bmatrix} -1 & 4 \\ 0 & 3 \end{bmatrix} = \begin{bmatrix} -1/3 & 4/3 \\ 0 & 1 \end{bmatrix}$

Its not transition probability matrix

$a_{11} = -\frac{1}{3} < 0$

∴ The option (a) & (d) are correct only.

38. Explanation: (d)

$\{X_n | n \geq 0\}$ be a homogeneous Markov chain with state space $S = \{0,1,2,3,4\}$ and transition probability matrix

$$P = \begin{matrix} 0 \\ 1 \\ 2 \\ 3 \\ 4 \end{matrix}\begin{pmatrix} 1/4 & 0 & 0 & 3/4 & 0 \\ 0 & 1 & 0 & 0 & 0 \\ 1/3 & 2/3 & 0 & 0 & 0 \\ 3/4 & 0 & 0 & 1/4 & 0 \\ 1/8 & 1/8 & 1/2 & 1/8 & 1/8 \end{pmatrix}$$

Note that here {0,3} is a closed absorbing class. Define p_i: The state i evantually reaches to the absorbing closed class {0,3}.

$$p_0 = 1\ ;\ p_1 = 0\ ;\ p_2 = \frac{1}{3}p_0\ ;\ p_3 = 1$$

$$p_4 = \frac{1}{8} + \frac{1}{2}p_2 + \frac{1}{8} + \frac{1}{8}p_4 \Rightarrow \frac{7}{8}p_4 = \frac{1}{4} + \frac{1}{6} = \frac{5}{12}$$

$$\Rightarrow p_4 = \frac{5}{12} \times \frac{8}{7} = \frac{10}{21}$$

39. Explanation: (a), (b), (c)

Transition probability matrix of a homogeneous Markov chain with states 0,1,2,3 is

$$p = \begin{matrix} \\ 0 \\ 1 \\ 2 \\ 3 \end{matrix}\begin{pmatrix} 0 & 1 & 2 & 3 \\ 1/4 & 3/4 & 0 & 0 \\ 1 & 0 & 0 & 0 \\ 2/3 & 0 & 1/3 & 0 \\ 0 & 0 & 2/5 & 3/5 \end{pmatrix}$$

Observe the state 3. Only state 2 is accessible from the state 3 but state 3 is not accessible from any other state. Thus return to state 3 starting from the state 3 itself is not certain. So state 3 is a transient state.
Observe the state 2. States 0 & 1 are accessible from the state 2 but state 2 is not accessible from states 0 & 1.Thus return to state 2 starting from the state 2 itself is not certain. So state 2 is a transient state.
Further note that states 0 & 1 communicate with each other and hence they are in the same class.
Being a finite states space there exists at least one positive recurrent state and the states in one class are also of the one type. But we know that states 2 & 3 transient. Therefore either of the states 0 or 1 are positive recurrent and as a result of being in the one class the other state is also positive recurrent. Thus states 0 & 1 both are positive recurrent.
Further compute the periods of the states. It is obvious from the above t.p.m. that

$$d(0) = d(1) = d(2) = d(3) = 1$$

Thus state 1 is aperiodic and positive recurrent.
But state 2 is aperiodic and transient.

40. Explanation: (b)

Let:

- P_n be the probability that the n-th question has answer **True.**
- $Q_n = 1 - P_n$ be the probability that the n-th question has answer **False.**

From the given data:

- If a question is **True,** then the next question is also **True** with probability 3/4, and **False** with probability 1/4.
- If a question is **False**, then the next question is also **False** with probability 2/3, and **True** with probability 1/3.

This gives the **transition probabilities:**

$$P(T_{n+1} \mid T_n) = \frac{3}{4}, P(F_{n+1} \mid T_n) = \frac{1}{4}$$
$$P(F_{n+1} \mid F_n) = \frac{2}{3}, P(T_{n+1} \mid F_n) = \frac{1}{3}$$

Let p be the steady-state probability of a question being **True**, and $q = 1 - p$ be the probability of a question being **False**.

At equilibrium, the probability flow must be balanced:

$$p = p \cdot \frac{3}{4} + q \cdot \frac{1}{3}$$

Since $q = 1 - p$, substitute:

$$p = p \cdot \frac{3}{4} + (1-p) \cdot \frac{1}{3}$$
$$p = \frac{3}{4}p + \frac{1}{3} - \frac{1}{3}p$$
$$p - \frac{3}{4}p + \frac{1}{3}p = \frac{1}{3}$$
$$p\left(1 - \frac{3}{4} + \frac{1}{3}\right) = \frac{1}{3}$$
$$p \cdot \frac{7}{12} = \frac{1}{3}$$
$$p = \frac{1}{3} \times \frac{12}{7} = \frac{4}{7}$$

41. Explanation: (a), (b), (c)

Given the Markov chain with transition probability matrix:

$$P = \begin{bmatrix} 0 & \frac{1}{2} & \frac{1}{2} \\ \frac{3}{4} & 0 & \frac{1}{4} \\ \frac{3}{4} & \frac{1}{4} & 0 \end{bmatrix}$$

(a) Compute $P_{00}^{(2)}$

The second-step transition probability is obtained from $P^2 = P \times P$.

$$P^2 = \begin{bmatrix} 0 & \frac{1}{2} & \frac{1}{2} \\ \frac{3}{4} & 0 & \frac{1}{4} \\ \frac{3}{4} & \frac{1}{4} & 0 \end{bmatrix} \times \begin{bmatrix} 0 & \frac{1}{2} & \frac{1}{2} \\ \frac{3}{4} & 0 & \frac{1}{4} \\ \frac{3}{4} & \frac{1}{4} & 0 \end{bmatrix}$$

Calculating the (0,0) entry:

$$P_{00}^{(2)} = (0 \times 0) + \left(\frac{1}{2} \times \frac{3}{4}\right) + \left(\frac{1}{2} \times \frac{3}{4}\right) = 0 + \frac{3}{8} + \frac{3}{8} = \frac{6}{8}$$
$$= \frac{3}{4}$$

(a) is correct.

(b) Compute $P_{10}^{(3)}$

We need the (1,0) entry of $P^3 = P^2 \times P$.

Using P^2 from above:

$$P^2 = \begin{bmatrix} \frac{3}{4} & \frac{1}{8} & \frac{1}{8} \\ \frac{9}{16} & \frac{1}{4} & \frac{3}{16} \\ \frac{9}{16} & \frac{3}{16} & \frac{1}{4} \end{bmatrix}$$

Now, multiplying P^2 with P:

$$P^3 = P^2 \times P$$

Calculating $P_{10}^{(3)}$:

$$P_{10}^{(3)} = \left(\frac{9}{16} \times 0\right) + \left(\frac{1}{4} \times \frac{3}{4}\right) + \left(\frac{3}{16} \times \frac{3}{4}\right) = 0 + \frac{3}{16} + \frac{9}{64}$$
$$= \frac{12}{64} + \frac{9}{64} = \frac{39}{64}$$

(b) is correct.

(c) Compute the stationary distribution

The stationary distribution $\pi = (\pi_0, \pi_1, \pi_2)$ satisfies:

$$\pi P = \pi$$

So,

$$\pi_0 = \frac{1}{2}\pi_1 + \frac{1}{2}\pi_2$$
$$\pi_1 = \frac{3}{4}\pi_0 + \frac{1}{4}\pi_2$$
$$\pi_2 = \frac{3}{4}\pi_0 + \frac{1}{4}\pi_1$$

With normalization:

$$\pi_0 + \pi_1 + \pi_2 = 1$$

Solving these equations, we get:

$$\pi_0 = \frac{3}{7}, \pi_1 = \frac{2}{7}, \pi_2 = \frac{2}{7}$$

(c) is correct.

(d) Checking if State 1 is transient

A state is **transient** if the probability of returning to it is less than 1.

From the stationary distribution:

- $\pi_1 = \frac{2}{7}$ is **nonzero**, implying that state 1 is **not transient.**

(d) is incorrect.

42. Explanation: (a), (b), (c), (d)

From state 5: $P_{55} = 1 \Rightarrow$ state 5 is **absorbing.**

States {1,2,3,4} can reach 5 (e.g., 1→3→5), but 5 cannot return to them ⇒ {1,2,3,4} are **transient**, {5} is **recurrent.**

Only recurrent class is {5}, so unique stationary distribution is (0,0,0,0,1).

Statement a: True.

State 5 properties

Absorbing ⇒ recurrent.

Statement b: True.

Periodicity

State 5: aperiodic (period 1).

States 1–4: possible return times without visiting 5 have gcd = 1 ⇒ aperiodic.

Statement c: True.

Limit of $P_{55}^{(n)}$

Since 5 is absorbing, $P_{55}^{(n)} = 1$ for all $n \Rightarrow$ limit = 1.

Statement d: True.

Final: All statements are true.

43. Explanation: (d)

Given :

The transition probability matrix is $P = \begin{pmatrix} \frac{1}{4} & 0 & \frac{2}{3} & \frac{1}{12} \\ 0 & 1 & 0 & 0 \\ \frac{1}{12} & 0 & \frac{1}{4} & \frac{2}{3} \\ \frac{2}{3} & 0 & \frac{1}{12} & \frac{1}{4} \end{pmatrix}$

Statespace: $S = \{1,2,3,4\}$

Communicating/closed classes

From row 2

$$(0,1,0,0)$$

So $P_{22} = 1$

Once the chain enters state 2, it remains there forever.

Hence $\{2\}$ is a closed (absorbing) class.

Now observe rows 1, 3, 4.

- State 1 can move to 1,3,4
- State 3 can move to 1,3,4
- State 4 can move to 1,3,4

There is no transition to state 2.

Thus $\{1,3,4\}$ forms another closed communicating class.

A closed class means that once the chain enters it, it cannot leave that set of states.

Use the stationary distribution theorem

For a finite Markov chain:

- Each closed irreducible class has a stationary distribution.
- If there are more than one closed classes, then infinitely many stationary distributions exist (convex combinations of the class distributions).

Apply to this chain

Closed classes are

$$\{2\}, \{1,3,4\}$$

Since there are two closed classes, the stationary distributions are not unique and we obtain infinitely many stationary distributions.

So, the correct option is (4).

44. Explanation: (a), (b), (c)

From the given matrix: $P = \begin{pmatrix} \frac{1}{4} & \frac{3}{4} & 0 & 0 \\ 1 & 0 & 0 & 0 \\ \frac{1}{8} & 0 & \frac{7}{8} & 0 \\ 0 & 0 & \frac{1}{9} & \frac{8}{9} \end{pmatrix}$

Communication classes:

States 1 and 2: $1 \to 2$ ($p = \frac{3}{4}$), $2 \to 1$ ($p = 1$), so $\{1,2\}$ communicate

State 3: $3 \to 1$ ($p = \frac{1}{8}$), $3 \to 3$ ($p = \frac{7}{8}$), but 3 is not accessible from $\{1,2\}$

State 4: $4 \to 3$ ($p = \frac{1}{9}$), $4 \to 4$ ($p = \frac{8}{9}$), but 3 and 4 cannot reach each other bidirectionally; $4 \to 3$ but $3 \nrightarrow 4$

Classes: $\{1,2\}, \{3\}, \{4\}$

From state 3: goes to state 1 with prob $\frac{1}{8}$ → state 3 can leave to class $\{1,2\}$, so $\{3\}$ is transient

From state 4: goes to state 3 with prob $\frac{1}{9}$ → state 4 can leave, so $\{4\}$ is transient

Class $\{1,2\}$: closed (no exit), finite → positive recurrent

Checking Each Statement

Statement 1: State 2 is positive recurrent → TRUE

States 1 and 2 form a closed communicating class in a finite chain → both are positive recurrent.

Statement 2: Mean recurrence time of state 1 is $\frac{7}{4}$ → TRUE

For the closed class $\{1,2\}$, find the stationary distribution π where $\pi P = \pi$:

$\pi_1 = \frac{1}{4}\pi_1 + 1 \cdot \pi_2$

$\pi_2 = \frac{3}{4}\pi_1$

From equation 1: $\pi_1 - \frac{1}{4}\pi_1 = \pi_2 \Rightarrow \frac{3}{4}\pi_1 = \pi_2$

Normalizing: $\pi_1 + \pi_2 = 1 \Rightarrow \pi_1 + \frac{3}{4}\pi_1 = 1 \Rightarrow \pi_1 = \frac{4}{7}$

Mean recurrence time of state 1 = $\frac{1}{\pi_1} = \frac{7}{4}$

Statement 3: State 4 is transient → TRUE

State 4 transitions to state 3 with probability $\frac{1}{9} > 0$, and state 3 transitions to state 1 with probability $\frac{1}{8} > 0$. Since state 4 can leave and never return (states 1, 2, 3 cannot reach state 4), state 4 is transient.

Statement 4: State 3 is aperiodic and ergodic →FALSE

State 3 has a self-loop: $p^{33} = \frac{7}{8} > 0$, so period = 1 (aperiodic)

But state 3 is transient (it can reach state 1 and never return), so it is NOT ergodic (ergodic requires positive recurrence)

Statement 4 is false.

Correct answer: Statements 1, 2, and 3 are true.

LINEAR PROGRAMMING PROBLEM

CHAPTER 14

(JUNE 2012)

1. Suppose that the variables $x_1 \geq 0$ and $x_2 \geq 4$ satisfy the constraints $x_1 + x_2 \geq 3$ *and* $x_1 + 2x_2 \geq 4$. Wich of the following is true?
   (a) The maximum value of $5x_1 + 7x_2$ is 21 and it does not have any finite minimum.
   (b) The minimum value of $5x_1 + 7x_2$ is 17 and it does not have any finite maximum.
   (c) The maximum value of $5x_1 + 7x_2$ is 21 and its minimum value is 17.
   (d) $5x_1 + 7x_2$ neither has a finite maximum nor a finite minimum.

(JUNE 2012)

2. Consider the variables $x_1 \geq 0$ and $x_2 \geq 0$ satisfying the constraints $x_1 + x_2 \geq 5$, $4x_1 - x_2 \leq 15$ and $4x_2 - x_1 \leq 15$. Which of the following statements is/are correct?
   (a) The maximum value of $3x_1 + 2x_2$ *is* 25
   (b) The minimum value of $3x_1 + 2x_2$ *is* 11
   (c) $3x_1 + 2x_2$ has no finite maximum
   (d) $3x_1 + 2x_2$ has no finite minimum

(DEC. 2012)

3. A linear programming problem $\max_{\tilde{x}} \tilde{c'}\,\tilde{x}$, subject to $A\tilde{x} \leq \tilde{b}$, $\tilde{x} \geq \tilde{0}$, attain the optimum value at two distinct feasible solutions. Which of the following must be true?
   (a) There must be infinitely many feasible solutions where the optimal value is attained.
   (b) All feasible solutions must be optimal solutions
   (c) The dual problem has unbounded feasible region
   (d) Rank of $\begin{pmatrix} \tilde{c'} \\ A \end{pmatrix}$ = Rank of A

(JUNE 2013)

4. Consider the following linear programming problem:
   Maximize $z = 3x_1 + 2x_2$
   Subject to
   1. $x_1 + x_2 \geq 1$
   2. $x_1 + x_2 \leq 5$
   3. $2x_1 - 3x_2 \leq 6$
   4. $-2x_1 + 3x_2 \leq 6$

   The problem has
   (a) an unbounded solution
   (b) exactly one optimal solution
   (c) more than one optimal solution
   (d) no feasible solutions

(JUNE 2013)

5. Consider the following optimization problem:
   Maximize $3x + 47 + 2z$,
   subject to $x + y + z \leq 12$,
   $x + 2y - z \leq 5$,
   $x - y + z \leq 2$,
   where $x, y, z \geq 0$. Then
   (a) the problem has more than one feasible solution
   (b) the objective function of the dual problem is to minimize $12u + 5v + 2w$
   (c) one of the constraints of the dual problem is $u - v + w \geq 2$
   (d) two of the constraints of the dual problem are $u + v + w \leq 3, u + 2v - w \leq 4$

(DEC. 2013)

6. Consider the following linear programming problem.
   Maximize $z = 2x_1 + 4x_2$
   Subject to $x_1 + 2x_2 \leq 5$
   $x_1 + x_2 \leq 3$
   $x_1, x_2 \geq 0$.
   (a) An optimum solution is (x_1, x_2) = (1,2).
   (b) An optimum solution is (x_1, x_2) = (3,1).
   (c) An optimum solution is (x_1, x_2) = (0, 2.5).
   (d) The objective function is unbounded.

(JUNE 2014)

7. Consider the following primal Linear Programming Problem
   $\max z = -3x_1 + 2x_2$
   Subject to
   $x_1 \leq 3$,
   $x_1 - x_2 \leq 0$,
   $x_1, x_2 \geq 0$
   Which of the following statements are true?
   (a) The primal problem has an optimal solution
   (b) The primal problem has an unbounded solution
   (c) The dual problem has an unbounded solution
   (d) The dual problem has no feasible solution

(DEC. 2014)

8. Consider the linear programming problem:
   Minimize: $z = -2x - 5y$ subject to $3x + 4y \geq 5, x \geq 5, x\ 0, y \geq 0$.
   Which of the following is correct?
   (a) Set of feasible solutions is empty.
   (b) Set of feasible solutions is non-empty but there- is no optimal solution.
   (c) Optimal value is attained at $\left(0, \frac{5}{4}\right)$.
   (d) Optimal value is attained at $\left(\frac{5}{3}, 0\right)$.

(DEC. 2015)

9. Consider the following Linear Programming Problem.

Max $x_1 + \frac{5}{2}x_2$
Subject to $5x_1 + 3x_2 \le 15$
$-x_1 + x_2 \le 1$
$2x_1 + 5x_2 \le 10$
$x_1, x_2 \ge 0$
The problem
(a) has no feasible solution
(b) has infinitely many optimal solution
(c) has a unique optimal solution
(d) has an unbounded solution

(JUNE 2016)

10. Maximize $3x + 4y$ subject to
$x \ge 0, y \ge 0, x \le 3$
$\frac{1}{2}x + y \le 4, x + y \le 5$
Which among the following are correct?
(a) The optimal value is 19.
(b) The optimal value is 18.
(c) (3,2) is an extreme point of the feasible region.
(d) $\left(3, \frac{5}{2}\right)$ is an extreme point of the feasible region.

(DEC. 2016)

11. Consider the linear programming problem (LPP) maximize $z = 3x + 5y$
Subject to $+5y \le 10$, $2x + 2y \le 5$, $x \ge 0, y \ge 0$
Then
(a) The LPP does not admit any feasible solutions.
(b) There exists a unique optimal solution to the LPP.
(c) There exists a unique optimal solution to the dual problem.
(d) The dual problem has an unbounded solution

(JUNE 2017)

12. Consider the problem:
Maximize $2y_1 + 3y_2 + 5y_3 + 4y_4$
Subject to $y_1 + y_2 \le 1, y_2 + y_3 \le 1, y_3 + y_4 \le 1, y_4 + y_1 \le 1$ and $y_i \ge 0$ for $i = 1,2,3,4$. Then the optimum value is
(a) equal to 8 (b) between 8 and 9
(c) greater than or equal to 7 (d) less than or equal to 7

(JUNE 2017)

13. Let (x_1, x_2, x_3, x_4) be an optimal solution to the problem of minimizing $x_1 + x_2 + x_3 + x_4$ subject to constraints $x_1 + x_2 \ge 300, x_2 + x_3 \ge 500, x_3 + x_4 \ge 400, x_4 + x_1 \ge 200, x_1 \ge 0, x_2 \ge 0, x_3 \ge 0, x_4 \ge 0$. Which of the following are not possible values for any x_i?
(a) 300 (b) 400
(c) 500 (d) 600

(JUNE 2018)

14. Suppose that $|3x| + |2y| \le 1$. Then the maximum value of $9x + 4y$ is
(a) 1 (b) 2
(c) 3 (d) 4

(DEC. 2018)

15. Suppose ABC is a triangle on the xy-plane with centroid D. Which of the following points can NEVER be a minimizer of the function $7x - 10y + 1$ as (x, y) runs over the triangle ABC?
(a) A (b) B
(c) C (d) D

(JUNE 2019)

16. The maximum value of the objective function $z = 5x + 2y$ under the linear constraints $x \ge 0, y \ge 0, x \ge y$ and $2 \le x + y \le 4$ is
(a) 14 (b) 20
(c) 25 (d) 2

(JUNE 2019)

17. You want to invest Rs. 1000 in companies I and II. If the market is good, company I will declare dividend of 50% while company II will declare 30%. If the market is bad, company I will declare dividend of 10% while company II will declare 20%. The prediction is that market will be good with probability 0.4 and bad with probability 0.6. The investment that maximizes expected dividend is
(a) Rs.1000 in company I and nil in company II
(b) Nil in company I and Rs.1000 in company II
(c) Rs.500 in each of the two companies
(d) Rs.600 in company I and Rs.400 in company II

(DEC. 2019)

18. Subject to the conditions
0 ≤ X ≤ 10, 0 ≤ y ≤ 5,
the minimum value of the function 4x-5y+10 is
(a) 10 (b) 0
(c) -25 (d) -15

19. Consider the following Linear programming Problem
Minimize $14x + 9y + 6z$ subject to
$2x + y + z > -8$
$3x + 2y + Z \ge 10$
$x \ge 0, y \ge 0, z \ge 0.$
(a) 52 (b) 48
(c) 50 (d) 56

(NOV. 2020)

20. The maximum and the minimum values of $5x + 7y$, when |x|+|y|≤1 are
(a) 5 and -5 (b) 5 and -7
(c) 7 and -5 (d) 7 and -7

(SEP 2022)

21. Consider the following maximization problem:
maximize: $x_1 + 3x_2$
subject to the constraints $x_1 \ge 0, x_2 \ge 0$ and
$x_1 + x_2 \le 6$
$2x_1 + x_2 \le 8$
$x_1 + 2x_2 \le 9$
Which of the following is the dual problem?
(a) Minimize: $6y_1 + 8y_2 + 9y_3$ subject to $y_1 \ge 0, y_2 \ge 0, y_3 \ge 0, y_1 + 2y_2 + y_3 \ge 1, y_1 + y_2 + 2y_3 \ge 3$
(b) Minimize: $6y_1 + 8y_2 + 9y_3$ subject to $y_1 \ge 0, y_2 \ge 0, y_3 \ge 0, y_1 + 2y_2 + y_3 \ge 3, y_1 + y_2 + 2y_3 \ge 1$
(c) Minimize: $9y_1 + 8y_2 + 6y_3$ subject to $y_1 \ge 0, y_2 \ge 0, y_3 \ge 0, y_1 + 2y_2 + y_3 \ge 1, y_1 + y_2 + 2y_3 \ge 3$
(d) Minimize: $6y_1 + 8y_2 + 9y_3$ subject to $y_1 \ge 0, y_2 \ge 0, y_3 \ge 0, y_1 + 2y_2 + y_3 \ge 1, y_1 + y_2 + 2y_3 \ge 3$

(JUNE 2023)

22. Consider the linear programming problem maximize $x + 3y$, subject to $A\begin{pmatrix} x \\ y \end{pmatrix} \le b$,

where $A = \begin{pmatrix} -1 & -1 \\ 0 & 1 \\ -1 & 1 \\ 1 & 2 \\ 0 & -1 \end{pmatrix}$ and $b = \begin{pmatrix} -1 \\ 5 \\ 5 \\ 14 \\ 0 \end{pmatrix}$. Which of the following statements is true?

(a) The objective function attains its maximum at $\begin{pmatrix} 0 \\ 5 \end{pmatrix}$ in the feasible region.

(b) The objective function attains its maximum at $\begin{pmatrix} -2 \\ 3 \end{pmatrix}$ in the feasible region.

(c) The objective function attains its maximum at $\begin{pmatrix} 1 \\ 0 \end{pmatrix}$ in the feasible region.

(d) The objective function does not attain its maximum at $\begin{pmatrix} 14 \\ 0 \end{pmatrix}$ in the feasible region.

[JULY 2024]

23. Consider the linear programming problem:

$$max\ \{x_1 + x_2 + x_3\}$$

subject to constraints

$$x_1 + x_2 - x_3 \le 1,$$
$$x_1 + x_3 \le 2$$
$$0 \le x_1 \le \frac{1}{2}, x_2 \ge 0$$
$$\text{and } 0 \le x_3 \le 1$$

Which of the following statements are true?

(a) The optimum value is 3

(b) The optimum value is $\frac{3}{2}$

(c) (0,2,1) is an extreme point of the feasible region

(d) $\left(\frac{1}{2}, 0, 1\right)$ is the optimal solution

(FEB. 2025)

24. Consider maximizing the objective function $P = x_1 + x_2$ subject to

$$x_1 + x_2 + 2x_3 \le 5$$
$$2x_1 - 3x_3 \ge 1$$
$$x_2 + x_3 \le 0$$
$$x_1 \ge 0, x_2 \ge 0, x_3 \ge 0.$$

Then, which of the following statements are true?

(a) The optimal solution is 4.

(b) An optimal point is (4, 1, 0).

(c) The optimal solution is 6.

(d) $\left(\frac{1}{2}, 0, 0\right)$ is a corner point.

(JUNE 2025)

25. Solve the following linear programming problem:

maximize z = x + y

subject to

$5x + 3y \le 30$

$2x + 6y \le 25$

$2x - y \le 8$

$x \ge 0, y \ge 0.$

Then the optimal value of the objective function is

(a) $\frac{45}{11}$ (b) $\frac{74}{11}$

(c) $\frac{85}{12}$ (d) $\frac{25}{6}$

(Dec 2025)

26. Consider the following linear programming problem:

Maximize $3x_1 + 4x_2$

subject to

$3x_1 + 2x_2 \le 12,$

$3x_1 + 5x_2 \le 15,$

$2x_1 - x_2 \ge 0,$

$x_2 \le 2,$

and $x_1, x_2 \ge 0.$

Which of the following values is the optimum value of the objective function in the feasible region?

(a) 11 (b) 13

(c) 14 (d) 15

Answer Key

1	2	3	4	5	6	7	8	9	10
b	a, b	a, d	b	a, b, c	a, c	b, d	b	B	b, c
11	12	13	14	15	16	17	18	19	20
b, c	c, d	c, d	c	d	b	a	d	a	c
21	22	23	24	25	26				
a	d	a,c	d	c	c				

:: Explanations ::

1. Explanation: (b)

Constraints

$x_1 + x_2 \ge 3$

$x_1 + 2x_2 \ge 4$

$x_1, x_2 \ge 0$

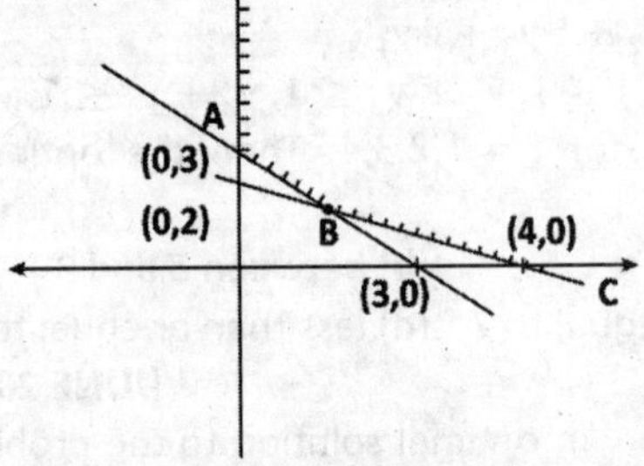

The given LPP does not have maximum value because it has unbounded feasible region

Minimum value of $Z = 5x_1 + 7x_2$ i.e. at $B(2,1)$

B is the point of intersection of line $x_1 + x_2 = 3$ and $x_1 + 2x_2 = 4$

$x_1 + x_2 = 3$ $\quad x_2 = 1$

$x_1 + 2x_2 = 4$ $\quad x_1 = 2$

$-x_2 = -1$

Min value of Z = $5x_1 + 7x_2 = 5 \times 2 + 7 \times 1 = 17$

So, option (b) is correct

2. Explanation: (a), (b)

$x_1 + x_2 \ge 5$

$4x_1 - x_2 \le 15$

$4x_2 - x_1 \le 15$

$x_1, x_2 \ge 0$

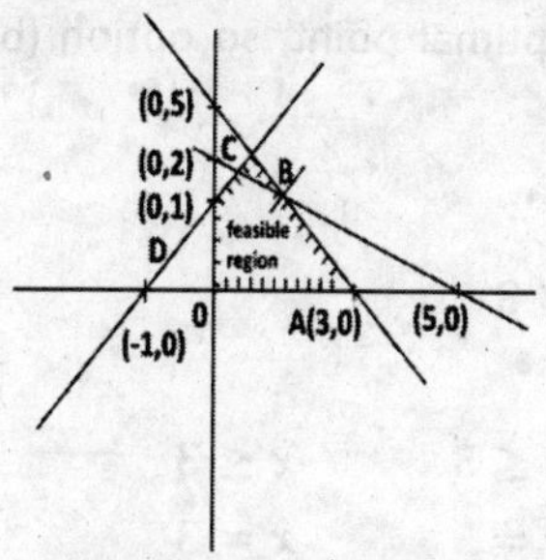

A is point of interaction of lines

$x_1 + x_2 = 5$

$4x_1 - x_2 = 15$

On solving, $x_1 = 4, x_2 = 1 \Rightarrow A(4,1)$

B is point of intersection of lines

$4x_1 - x_2 = 15$

$4x_2 - x_1 = 15$

On solving $x_1 = 5, x_1 = 5 \Rightarrow B(5,5)$

C is the point of intersection of line

$4x_2 - x_1 = 15$

$x_1 + x_1 = 5$

On solving, $x_1 = 1, x_2 = 4 \Rightarrow C(1,4)$

$Z = 3x_1 + 2x_2$

$Z_A = 13 \,, Z_B = 25 \,, Z_C = 11$

Minimum value of $Z = 3x_1 + 2x_2 = 11$

Maximum value of $Z = 3x_1 + 2x_2 = 25$

Option (a) & (b) are correct

3. **Explanation: (a), (d)**

4. **Explanation: (b)**

Max. $Z = 3x_1 + 2x_2$

Subject to

$x_1 + x_2 \geq 1$

$x_1 + x_2 \leq 5$

$2x_1 - 3x_2 \leq 6$

$-2x_1 + 3x_2 \leq 6$

Using Graphical method

Using Graphical Method

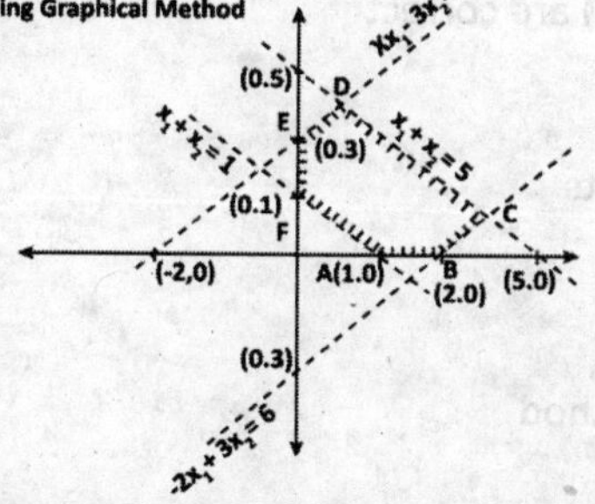

ABCDEF (shaded region) is feasible region

The optimal values of objective function lies on the any of the A, B, C, D, E & F. It has exactly one optimal solution.

So, option (b) is correct

5. **Explanation: (a), (b), (c)**

Primal Problem

Max. $Z = 3x + 4y + 2z$

$x + y + z \leq 12$

$x + 2y - z \leq 5$

$x - y + z \leq 2$

$x, y, z \geq 0$

The dual problem is

Min $U = 12u + 5v + 2w$

Subject to

$u + v + w \leq 3$

$u + 2v - w \geq 4$

$u - v + w \leq 2$

$u, v, z \leq 0$

And the problem has more than one feasible solution

So, option (a), (b) and (c) are correct

6. **Explanation: (a), (c)**

Max $Z = 2x_1 + 4x_2$

Subject

$x_1 + 2x_2 \leq 5$

$x_1 + x_3 \leq 3$

$x_1, x_2 \geq 0$

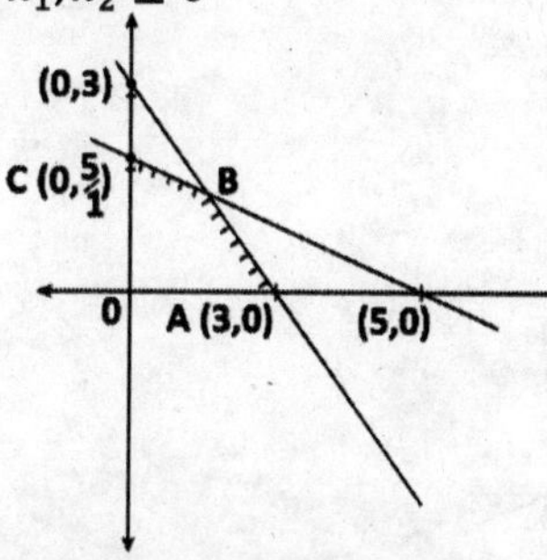

OABC is a feasible region

$Z = 2x_1 + 4x_2$

$O(0,0), Z_o = 0$

$A(3,0), Z_A = 6$

B is the point of intersection of lines $x_1 + 2x_2 = 5$ and $x_1 + x_2 = 3$

$x_2 = 2$ and $x_1 = 1$

$B(1,2), Z_B = 2 + 8 = 10$

$C\left(0, \frac{5}{2}\right), Z_C = 0 + 4 \times \frac{5}{2} = 10$

The optimum solution is (1, 2) and (0, 2.5)

So, option (a) and (c) are correct

7. **Explanation: (b), (d)**

Primal LLP

$\max Z = -3x_1 + 2x_2$

Subject to $x_1 \leq 3$

$x_1 - x_2 \leq 0$

$x_1, x_2 \geq 0$

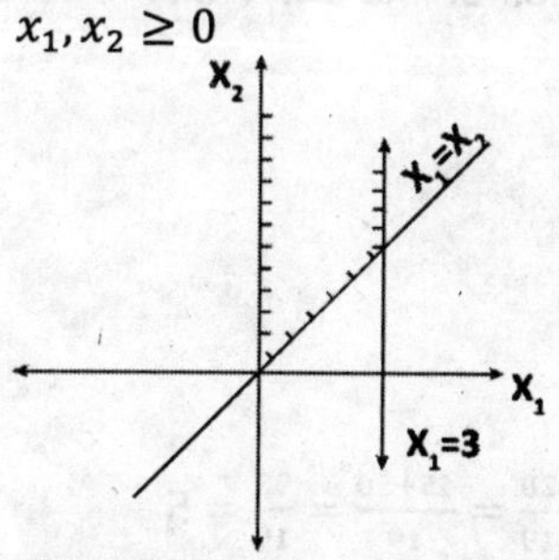

The solution has an unbounded solution implies that dual problem has no feasible solution

So, option (b) & (d) are correct

8. **Explanation: (b)**

Min. $Z = -2x - 5y$

Subject to

$3x + 4y \geq 5$

$x \geq 0, y \geq 0$

Using graphical method,

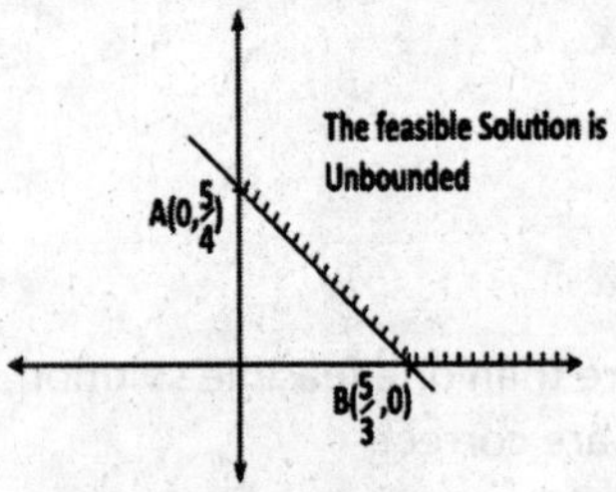

Set of feasible solution is non-empty but there is no optimal solution.

9. Explanation: (b)

$Max\ Z = x_1 + \frac{5}{6}x_2$

Subject to $5x_1 + 3x_2 \le 15$

$-x_1 + x_2 \le 1$

$2x_1 + 5x_2 \le 10$

$x_1, x_2 \ge 0$

Using Graphical method

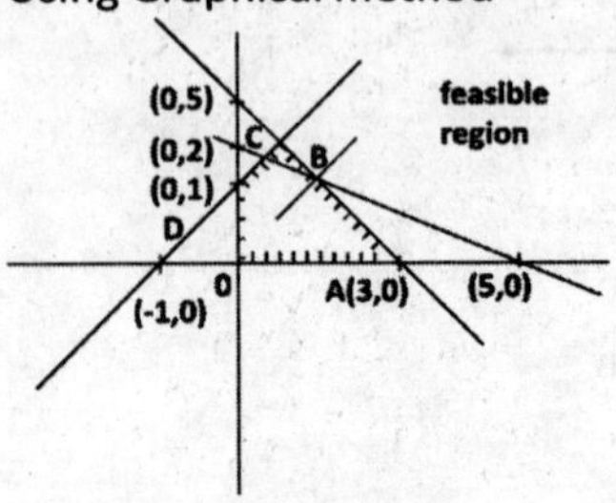

1) $5x_1 + 3x_2 = 15$
   $x_1 = 0, x_2 = 5$
   $x_2 = 0, x_1 = 3$

2) $-x_1 + x_2 = 1$
   $x_1 = 0, x_2 = 1$
   $x_2 = 0, x_1 = -1$

3) $2x_1 + 5x_2 = 10$
   $x_1 = 0, x_2 = 2$
   $x_2 = 0, x_1 = 5$

OABCD is a feasible region

$Z = X_1 + \frac{5}{2}x_2$

$O\ (0,0), Z_O = 0$

$A(3,0), Z_A = 3$

B is the point of intersection of line $2x_1 + 5x_2 = 10$ and $5x_1 + 3x_2 = 15$

$(2x_1 + 5x_2 = 10) \times 5$

$(5x_1 + 3x_2 = 15) \times 2$

$10x_1 + 25x_2 = 50$

$10x_1 + 6x_2 = 30$

$19x_2 = 20$

$\Rightarrow x_2 = \frac{20}{19}$ and $x_1 = \frac{45}{19}$

$B\left(\frac{45}{19}, \frac{20}{19}\right), Z_B = \frac{45}{19} + \frac{5}{2} \times \frac{20}{19} = \frac{45+50}{19} = \frac{95}{19} = 5$

C is the intersection of linear $2x_1 + 5x_2 = 10$ and $-x_1 + x_2 = 1$

$2x_1 + 5x_2 = 10$

$-2x_1 + 2x_2 = 2$

$7x_2 = 12$

$x_2 = \frac{12}{7}, x_1 = \frac{5}{7}$

$C\left(\frac{5}{7}, \frac{12}{7}\right), Z_C = \frac{5}{7} + \frac{5}{2} \times \frac{12}{7} = \frac{35}{7} = 5$

$D(0,1), Z_D = \frac{5}{2}$, the maximum value of $Z = 5$

We have more than one optimal point, so option (b) is correct

10. Explanation: (b), (c)

Maximize $z = 3x + 4y$

Subject to $x \ge 0, y \ge 0, x \le 3$

$\frac{1}{2}x + y \le 4, x + y \le 5$

$\frac{1}{2}x + y \le 4$	$x + y \le 5$	$x \le 3$
$x + 2y \le 8$	$x + y = 5$	$x = 3$
$\therefore x + 2y = 8$	$x = 0, y = 5$	
$x = 0, y = 4$	$y = 0, x = 5$	
$y = 0, x = 8$		

Now, plot these point in the graph and draw the feasible region of LPP

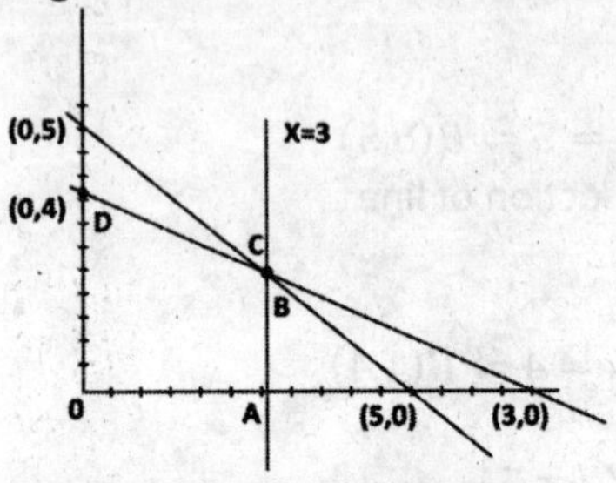

The feasible region in OABCD

The extreme points of feasible region are $O(0,0)\ A(3,0), B(3,2), C(2,3)$ and $D(0,4)$

B is the point of intersection of line $x = 3$ & $x + y = 5$

$x = 3, y = 2$

$B(3,2)$

C is the point of intersection of line $x + y = 5$ & $x = y = 8$

$y = 3$ and $x = 2$

$Z_O = 0 \qquad Z_A = 9$

$Z_B = 17 \qquad Z_C = 18$

$Z_D = 16$

The optional value of Z is 18

So, option (b) and (c) are correct

11. Explanation: (b), (c)

Max. $Z = 3x + 5y$

Subject to constraints

$x + 5y \ge 10$

$2x + 2y \le 5$

$x, y \ge 0$

Using Graphical method

$x + 5y = 10$

$x = 0, y = 2\ ; (0,2)$

$y = 0, y = 2\ ; (10,0)$

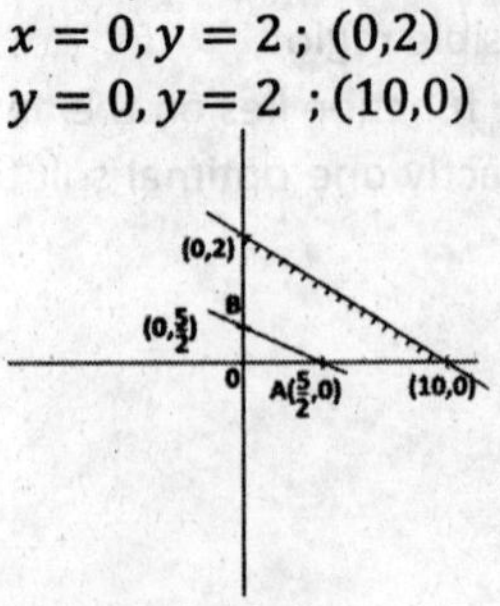

$2x + 2y = 5$

$x = 0, y = \frac{5}{2}\ \left(0, \frac{5}{2}\right)$

$y = 0, x = \frac{5}{2}\ \left(\frac{5}{2}, 0\right)$

AB be the feasible region At the corner the solution is Optimum There exist unique optimal solution to primal & dual problem.

12. Explanation: (c), (d)

Maximize $2y_1 + 3y_2 + 5y_3 + 4y_4$

Sub. To

$y_1 + y_2 \le 1, y_2 + y_3 \le 1$

$y_3 + y_4 \le 1, y_4 + y_1 \le 1$ & $y_i \ge 0$ $i = 1, 2, 3, 4$

$y_1 + y_2 = 1$

$y_2 = 1 - y_1$

$y_4 = 1 - y_1$

$Z^* = 2y_1 + 3(1 - y_1) + 5y_3 + 4(1 - y_1)$

$= 2y_1 + 3 - 3y_1 + 5y_3 + 4 - 4y_1$

$Z^* = 5y_3 - 5y_1 + 7$

Optimum value of Z^* may be greater than 7 or less then equal to 7

So, option (c) & (d) are correct

13. Explanation: (c), (d)

Minimize $Z = x_1 + x_2 + x_3 + x_4$

Subjects to

$x_1 + x_2 \ge 300, x_2 + x_3 \ge 500$

$x_3 + x_4 \ge 400, x_4 + x_1 \ge 200$

$x_1, x_2 \ge 0$

$x_3, x_4 \ge 0$

$x_2 = 300 - x_1$ & $x_4 = 200 - x_1$

Minimize $Z^* = x_1 + x_2 + x_3 + x_4$

$= x_1 + 300 - x_1 + x_3 + 200 - x_1$

$= x_3 - x_1 + 500$

Add all constraints

$2(x_1 + x_2 + x_3 + x_4) \ge 1400$

$x_1 + x_2 + x_3 + x_4 \ge 700$

$x_2 \ge 0$

$300 - x_1 \ge 0$

$x_1 \le 300$

$x_4 = 200 - x_1$

$x_4 \ge 0$

$200 > x_1$

$x_1 \le 200$

$x_1 \le 200$

$x_3 + x_4 \ge 400$

$x_3 \ge 400 - x_4$

$x_4 \le 400$

$x_3 \le 400$

$\Rightarrow x_1, x_2, x_3, x_4 < 500$

500 & 600 are not possible value of x_i

Option (c) & (d) are correct

14. Explanation: (c) $|3x| + |2y| \le 1$

Maximum value of $z = 9x + 4y$

$|3x| + |2y| \le 1$

$3x + 2y \le 1$

$-3x + 2y \le 1$

$3x - 2y \le 1$

$-3x - 2y \le 1$

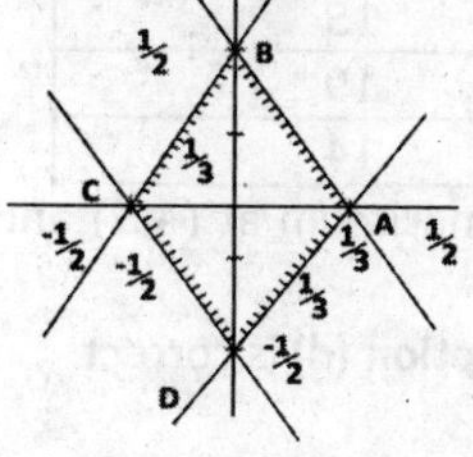

ABCD is feasible region

$A\left(\frac{1}{3}, 0\right)$ $Z_A = 3$

$B\left(0, \frac{1}{2}\right)$ $Z_B = 2$

$C\left(\frac{-1}{3}, 0\right)$ $Z_C = -3$ $\max z = 3$

$D\left(0, \frac{-1}{2}\right)$ $Z_D = -2$

15. Explanation: (d)

$Z = 7x - 10y + 1$

The minimum value of function $7x - 10y + 1$ must be on the corner point of the triangle ABC

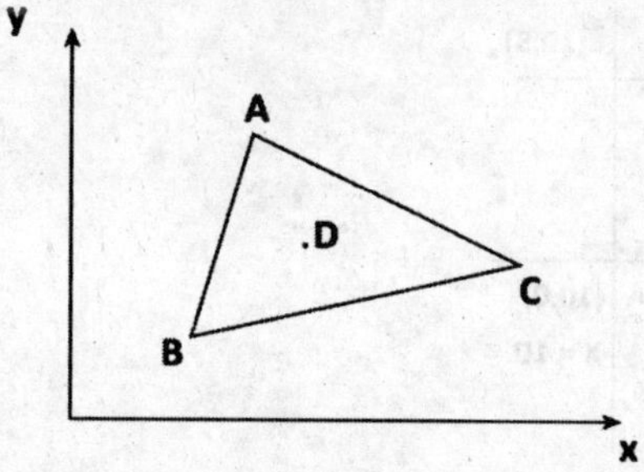

So, D cannot be minimizer of the function

So, option (d) is correct

16. Explanation: (b)

Objective function

$Z = 5x + 2y$

Subject to constraint

$x \ge 0$

$y \ge 0$

$x \ge y$

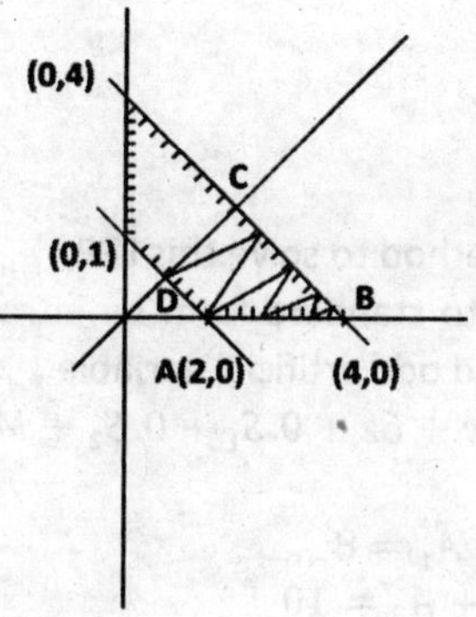

$2 \le X + Y \le 4$

$\Rightarrow X + Y \ge 2$

$X + Y \le 4$

Now plot these constraints in the graph.

A B C D is the feasible region

The maximum value is lie on the corner point of the feasible region

$A\ (2,0)$, $B\ (4,0)$

$X + Y = 4$

$X = Y$ C (2,2)

2X = 4 D (1, 1)

$Y = 2$

C (2,2)

D (1, 1)

$Z + 5x + 2y$

$Z_A = 10$

$Z_B = 20$

$Z_C = 14$
$Z_D = 7$
Max value is 20
Option (b) is correct

17. Explanation: (a)
Option (a) Is Correct

18. Explanation: (d)
$0 \le X \le 10\ \&\ 0 \le y \le 5$
Minimum value of $Z = 4x - 5y + 10$
$X \ge 0\ \&\ Y \ge 0$
$X \le 10\ Y \le 5$

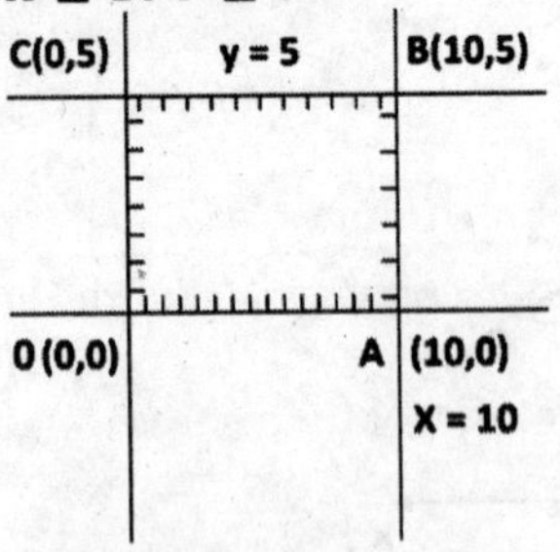

Corner points

$0(0,0)$	$Z_0 = 10$
$A(10,0)$	$Z_A = 50$
$B(10,5)$	$Z_B = 25$
$C(0,5)$	$Z_c = -15$

Minimum value =- 15
So, option (d) is correct

19. Explanation: (a)
Minimize $Z = 14x + 9y + 6z$
Subject to
$2x + y + z \le 8$
$3x + 2y + z \ge 10$
$x, y, z \ge 0$
We use simplex method to solve this LPP,
Step 1: Convert into standard farm by introducing stock surplus variable and odd artificial variable
Min. $Z = 14x + 9y + 6z + 0.S_1 + 0.S_2 + MA_1 + MA_2$
Subject to
$2x + y + z - S_1 + A_1 = 8$
$3x + 2y + z - S_2 + A_2 = 10$
$A_1, A_2, x, y, z, S_1, X_2 \ge 0$
And solve further using simplex procedure
The minimum value is 52
So, option (a) is correct

20. Explanation: (c)
$|x| + |y| \le 1$
We use graphical method to find maximum and minimum value of $5x + 7y$

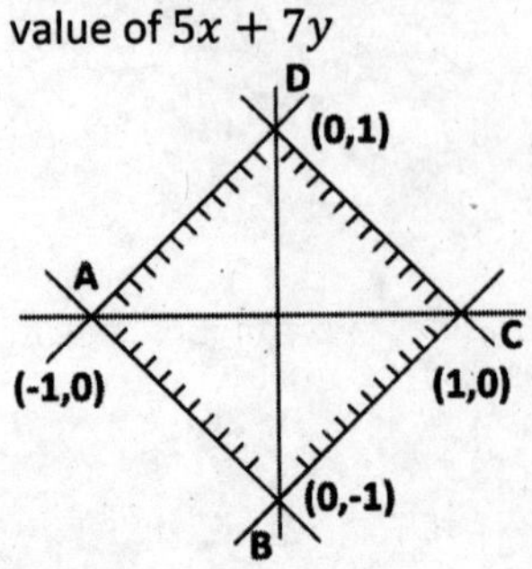

The feasible region is ABCD
We need to find the optimum value of objective function
$Z = 5x + 7y$
A $(-1,0)$, $Z = -5$
B $(0,-1)$, $Z = -7$
C $(1,0)$ $Z = 5$
D $(0,1)$ $Z = 7$
Max. value $= 7$ & Min. value $= -5$
Option (c) is correct

21. Explanation: (a)
The primal of the LPP is Maximize $Z = x_1 + 3x_2$
S.T.C. $x_1 + x_2 \le 6$
$2x_1 + x_2 \le 8$
$x_1 + 2x_2 \le 9$
Then the dual of LPP is minimize $w = 6y_1 + 8y_2 + 9y_3$
S.T.C. $y_1 + 2y_2 + y_3 \ge 1$
$y_1 + y_2 + 2y_2 \ge 3$
$y_1, y_2, y_3 \ge 0$
$\therefore$ option (a) is correct.

22. Explanation: (d)
Maximize $x + 3y$ subject to $A\begin{pmatrix} x \\ y \end{pmatrix} \le b$

$$A = \begin{pmatrix} -1 & -1 \\ 0 & 1 \\ -1 & 1 \\ 1 & 2 \\ 0 & -1 \end{pmatrix} \text{ and } b = \begin{pmatrix} -1 \\ 5 \\ 5 \\ 14 \\ 0 \end{pmatrix}$$

Expanding we get constraints as follows.
$-x - y \le -1$
$y \le 5$
$-x + y \le 5$
$x + 2y \le 14$
$-y \le 0 \Rightarrow y > 0$
So the final simplified constraints are as follows.
$x + y > 1$
$y - x \le 5$
$x + 2y \le 14$
$0 < y \le 5$
Now we will use these constraints to get the feasible region satisfying given constraints.
Using all the given constraints we got an irregular pentagon as the feasible region. Thus we got 5 optimal points in the form of 5 vertices of the pentagon.
Now we will compute the value of objective function at all of the optimal points. Here is the table of optimal points and value of the objective function at those points.

Optimal Point	Value of the objective function at the point
(1,0)	1
(−2,3)	7
(0,5)	15
(4,5)	19
(14,0)	14

Thus the objective function is maximum at (4,5) and its maximum value is 19 .
Therefore from given options **Option (d)** is correct.

23. Explanation: (a), (c)

$$max\ \{x_1 + x_2 + x_3\}$$

subject to constraints

$$x_1 + x_2 - x_3 \le 1,$$
$$x_1 + x_3 \le 2$$
$$0 \le x_1 \le \frac{1}{2}, x_2 \ge 0$$
$$\text{and } 0 \le x_3 \le 1$$

To find the optimal value convert the given inequalities into equalities and solve them simultaneously to obtain the solution.

$$x_1 + x_2 - x_3 = 1\ \&\ x_1 + x_3 = 2$$

Adding the above two equations we get

$$2x_1 + x_2 = 3 \Rightarrow x_2 = 3 - 2x_1$$

Also from the second equation $x_1 = 2 - x_3 \Rightarrow x_2 = 3 - 2x_1 = 3 - 2(2 - x_3) = 2x_3 - 1$

The given objective function is

$$x_1 + x_2 + x_3 = 2 - x_3 + 2x_3 - 1 + x_3 = 2x_3 + 1$$

Now

$$0 \le x_3 \le 1 \Rightarrow 1 \le 2x_3 + 1 \le 3$$

Thus the maximum value of the given objective function is 3.

(4) Thus any point (x_1, x_2, x_3) satisfying the above two equations becomes an optimal solution.

$$\left(\frac{1}{2}, 0, 1\right) \Rightarrow x_1 = \frac{1}{2} \ne 1 = 2 - 1 = 2 - x_3$$

Thus the point given in the option (4) is not an optimal solution.

(3) The extreme point of the feasible region of an LPP is the point which satisfies at least one given constraint.

$$(0,2,1) \Rightarrow x_1 + x_2 - x_3 = 0 + 2 - 1 = 1$$

Thus the point given in the option (4) satisfies the first constraint so it is an extreme point.

24. Explanation: (d)

From the constraint $x_2 + x_3 \le 0$, and given that $x_2, x_3 \ge 0$, we conclude: $x_2 = 0, x_3 = 0$.

Substituting $x_2 = 0, x_3 = 0$ into the first constraint:

$$x_1 + 0 + 0 \le 5 \Rightarrow x_1 \le 5.$$

The second constraint becomes:

$$2x_1 - 3(0) \ge 1 \Rightarrow 2x_1 \ge 1 \Rightarrow x_1 \ge \frac{1}{2}.$$

Thus, the feasible region is:

$$\frac{1}{2} \le x_1 \le 5, x_2 = 0, x_3 = 0.$$

Since $P = x_1 + x_2 = x_1$ (as $x_2 = 0$), we maximize x_1 in the feasible range:

$$\max P = x_1, \text{ for } \frac{1}{2} \le x_1 \le 5.$$

The maximum value is at $x_1 = 5$, giving: $P = 5$.

Checking the Given Options

1. The optimal solution is 4.
   The actual optimal solution is 5, not 4.
2. An optimal point is (4,1,0).
   $x_2 = 1$ is not feasible since we established $x_2 = 0$.
3. The optimal solution is 6.
   The maximum achievable P is 5, not 6.
4. (1/2,0,0) is a corner point.

Since $x_1 = 1/2$, $x_2 = 0$, and $x_3 = 0$ satisfy all constraints and lie at an extreme point, it is a valid corner point.

So, option (d) is correct.

25. Explanation: (c)

Feasible corner points come from intersecting binding constraints:

- $5x + 3y = 30$ with $2x + 6y = 25 \Rightarrow (x, y) = \left(\frac{35}{8}, \frac{65}{24}\right)$ gives $z = x + y = \frac{85}{12}$.
- Other feasible corners $\left(0, \frac{25}{6}\right)$, $(4,0)$, $\left(\frac{54}{11}, \frac{20}{11}\right)$ yield smaller z.

Thus the maximum is $\frac{85}{12}$.

Correct Answer: *c*.

26. Explanation: (c)

Convert the inequalities into equalities and plot the lines:

- $3x_1 + 2x_2 = 12$
- $3x_1 + 5x_2 = 15$
- $x_2 = 2x_1$
- $x_2 = 2$

together with the coordinate axes.

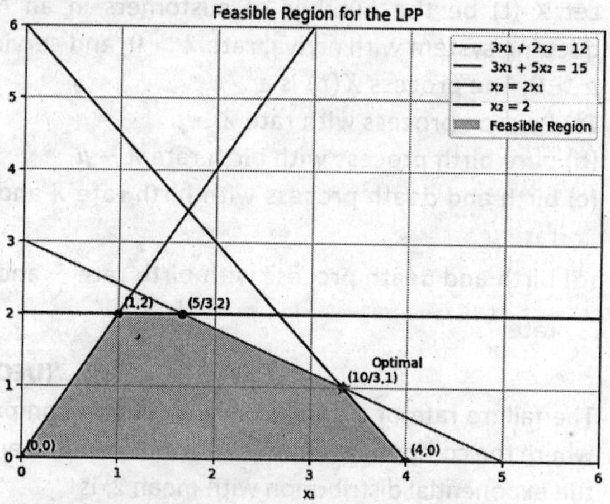

Determine the feasible region:

The region satisfying all inequalities simultaneously is the shaded region in the graph.

The intersection points (corner points) of the feasible region are:

$$(0,0), (4,0), \left(\frac{10}{3}, 1\right), \left(\frac{5}{3}, 2\right), (1,2)$$

Evaluate the objective function

$$Z = 3x_1 + 4x_2$$

Point	Z
(0, 0)	0
(4, 0)	12
$\left(\frac{10}{3}, 1\right)$	14
$\left(\frac{5}{3}, 2\right)$	13
(1, 2)	11

Optimal solution:

The maximum value of the objective function occurs at $(x_1, x_2) = \left(\frac{10}{3}, 1\right)$

Hence, $Z_{\max} = 14$.

CHAPTER 15

RELIABILITY & QUEUEING THEORY

(JUNE 2012)

1. The hazard rates of two life time variable T_1 and T_2 with respectively c.d.f.s $F_1(t)$ and $F_2(t)$ and p.d.f.s $f_1(t) and f_2(t)$ are $h_1(t) = 3t^2$ and $h_2(t) = 4t^3, t > 0$ respectively. Then
(a) $F_1(t) \geq F_2(t)$ for all t > 0
(b) $F_1(t) < F_2(t)$ for all t > 0
(c) $E(T_1) < E(T_2)$
(d) $f_1(t) < f_2(t)$ for all t > 0

(JUNE 2012)

2. Let X (t) be the number of customers in an M/M/1 queuing system with arrival rate $\lambda > 0$ and service rate $\mu > 0$. The process $X(t)$ is a
(a) Poisson process with rate $\lambda - \mu$
(b) pure birth process with birth rate $\lambda - \mu$
(c) birth and death process with birth rate λ and death rate μ
(d) birth and death process with birth rate $\frac{1}{\lambda}$ and death rate $\frac{1}{\mu}$

(DEC. 2012)

3. The failure rate of a parallel system of two components, where the component lifetimes are independent and have the exponential distribution with mean 2, is
(a) a constant
(b) a monotone and bounded function
(c) a monotone and unbounded function
(d) a non-monotone function

(DEC. 2012)

4. Men arrive in a queue according to a Poisson process with rate λ_1 and women arrive in the same queue according to another Poisson process with rate λ_2. The arrivals of men and women are independent. The probability that the first arrival in the queue is a man is
(a) $\frac{\lambda_1}{\lambda_1+\lambda_2}$ (b) $\frac{\lambda_2}{\lambda_1+\lambda_2}$
(c) $\frac{\lambda_1}{\lambda_2}$ (d) $\frac{\lambda_2}{\lambda_1}$

(DEC. 2012)

5. The lifetimes (measured in hours) of a batch of lithium batteries are independent and identically distributed with density $f(t) = \lambda^2 te^{-\lambda t}, t \geq 0, \lambda > 0$. One battery from this batch is put to test and is observed to fail after 3 hours, while another battery is observed for 2 hours with no failure. Which of the following statements are necessarily correct?
(a) The censoring involved here is of type II
(b) The likelihood for λ is proportional to $\lambda^2(1 + 3\lambda)e^{-5\lambda}$
(c) The maximum likelihood estimate of λ is 2
(d) The maximum likelihood estimate of $\frac{1}{\lambda}$ is 2

(JUNE 2013)

6. Consider a parallel system with two components. The lifetimes of the two components are independent and identically distributed random variables each following an exponential distribution with mean 1. The expected lifetime of the system is
(a) 1 (b) 1/2
(c) 3/2 (d) 2

(JUNE 2013)

7. Let X be a random variable with probability density function
$f(x) = \alpha(x - \mu)^{\alpha-1} e^{-(x-\mu)^\alpha}; -\infty < \mu < \infty, \alpha > 0, x < \mu.$
The hazard function is
(a) constant for all α
(b) an increasing function for some α
(c) independent of α
(d) independent of μ when $\alpha = 1$

(DEC. 2013)

8. Suppose the cumulative distribution function of failure time T of a component is $1 - \exp(-ct^\alpha), t > 0\ \alpha > 1, c > 0$. Then the hazard rate of $\lambda(t)$ is
(a) constant
(b) non-constant monotonically increasing in t
(c) non-constant monotonically decreasing in t.
(d) not a monotone function in t

(DEC. 2013)

9. Suppose T denotes the survival time of a component having probability density function $f(t)$. T has an exponential distribution if and only if
(a) $\frac{f(t)}{P(T>t)}$ is independent of t for all $t > 0$
(b) $P\{T > t + s\} = P\{T > t\}P\{T > s\}$ for all $t, s > 0$.
(c) $P\{T < t + s\} = P\{T < t\}P\{T < s\}$ for all $t, s > 0$.
(d) $P\{t < T < t + s\} = P\{T > t\}P\{T < s\}$ for all $t, s > 0$.

(DEC. 2013)

10. Consider a queuing model with one service counter. The arrival and service processes are Poisson with rate λ and μ respectively. For $n = 0,1,2, \ldots$ and $\mu > \lambda$, let $p_n = P$(at any point of time there are n customers in the system) $= \left(1 - \frac{\lambda}{\mu}\right)\left(\frac{\lambda}{\mu}\right)^n$.
Then the average queue length is
(a) $\frac{\lambda}{\mu-\lambda}$ (b) $\frac{\lambda}{\mu(\mu-\lambda)}$

(c) $\frac{\lambda^2}{\mu(\mu-\lambda)}$ (d) $\frac{\mu}{\mu-\lambda}$

(JUNE 2014)

11. At a doctor's clinic patients arrive at an average rate of 10 per hour. The consultancy time per patient is exponentially distributed with an average of 6 minutes per patient. The doctor does not admit any patient if at any time 10 patients are waiting. Then at the steady state of this M/M/1/R queue the expected number of patients waiting is

(a) 0 (b) 5

(c) 9 (d) 10

(JUNE 2014)

12. Suppose that system 1 has 2 components C_1 and C_2 in series while system 2 has 2 components C_3 and C_4 in parallel. The components C_1, C_2, C_3 and C_4 and have independent and identically distributed life times each being exponential with mean 1. Suppose $S_i(t)$ and $h_i(t)$ are the survival and hazard rate function. For the i-th system, $i = 1,2$. Then which of the following statements are true?

(a) $S_1(t) < S_2(t)$ for all $t > 0$

(b) $h_1(t) < h_2(t)$ for all $t > 0$

(c) The expected life time of the system 1 is 1/2

(d) The expected life time of the system 2 is 1

(DEC. 2014)

13. Let $X(t)$ = number of customers at time t in the system in an $M/M/1$ queueing model with arrival rate $\lambda > 0$ and service rate $\mu > 0$. Let $\pi_k = \lim_{t\to\infty} P(X(t) = k), k = 0,1,2 \ldots$ whenever it exists. Which of the following are true?

(a) $\{X(t)\}$ is a birth and death process with birth rates $\lambda_k = \lambda, k = 0,1,2, \ldots$ and death rates $\mu_k = \mu, k = 1,2, \ldots$

(b) $\{X(t)\}$ is a birth and death process with birth rates $\lambda_k = \frac{1}{\lambda}, k = 0,1,2, \ldots$ and death rates $\mu_k = \frac{1}{\mu}, k = 1,2, \ldots.$

(c) Limiting distribution $\{\pi_k\}$ exists if and only if $\mu > \lambda$, and is the geometric distribution with parameter$(\frac{\lambda}{\mu})$.

(d) If an arriving customer finds exactly one customer, then his total waiting time in the system has an exponential distribution with parameter (2μ).

(JUNE 2015)

14. Let $X(x)$ = number of customers in the system at time t in an M/M/C queuing model with C=3 arrival rate $\lambda > 0$ and service rate $\mu > 0$ which of the following is /are true?

(a) $\{X(t)\}$ is a birth and death death process with constant birth ad death rates

(b) If $\{X(t)\}$ has a stationary distribution, then $\lambda < 3\mu$

(c) If $\lambda < 3\mu$ then the stationary distribution with parameter $\frac{\lambda}{3\mu}$

(d) The number of customers undergoing service at time t is min $\{X(t), 3\}$

(DEC. 2015)

15. A system consists of 3 components arranged as in the figure below:

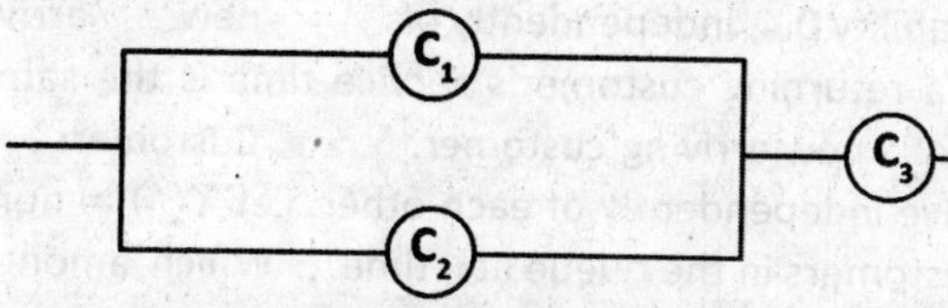

Each of the components C_1, C_2, C_3 has independent and identically distributed lifetimes whose distribution is exponential with mean 1. Then, the survival function, $S(t)$, of the system is given by

(a) $S(t) = e^{-3t}$, for $t > 0$

(b) $S(t) = (1 - e^{-t})^2 e^{-t}$, for $t > 0$

(c) $S(t) = (1 - e^{-2t})^2 e^{-t}$, for $t > 0$

(d) $S(t) = (1 - (1 - e^{-t})^2)\, e^{-t}$, for $t > 0$

(DEC. 2015)

16. Consider an M/M/1 queue with arrivals as a Poisson process at a rate of 8 per hour and a service time which is exponentially distributed at a rate of 6 minutes per customer. The waiting time of a customer in the queue

(a) has a gamma distribution with p.d.f.

$$f(x) = \begin{cases} \frac{(10)^8 x^7 e^{-10x}}{7!} & \text{for } x > 0 \\ 0 & \text{otherwise} \end{cases}$$

(b) has distribution function given by

$$f(x) = \begin{cases} 1 - (0.8)e^{-2x} & \text{for } x > 0 \\ 0 & \text{otherwise} \end{cases}$$

(c) has mean 4 minutes

(d) has mean 24 minutes.

(JUNE 2016)

17. Let $\{X_t\}$ and $\{Y_t\}$ be two independent pure birth processes with birth rates λ_1 and λ_2 respectively. Let $Z_t = X_t + Y_t$. Then

(a) $\{Z_t\}$ is not a pure birth process.

(b) $\{Z_t\}$ is a pure birth process with birth rate $\lambda_1 + \lambda_2$.

(c) $\{Z_t\}$ is a pure birth process with birth rate min (λ_1, λ_2)

(d) $\{Z_t\}$ is a pure birth process with birth rate $\lambda_1\, \lambda_2$.

(JUNE 2016)

18. Consider a series system with two independent components. Let the component lifespan have exponential distribution with density

$$f(x) = \begin{cases} \lambda e^{-\lambda x}, & \lambda > 0, x > 0 \\ 0, & \text{otherwise.} \end{cases}$$

If n observations $X_1, X_2, \ldots, X_n$ on lifespan of this components are available and

$$\overline{X} = \frac{1}{n}\sum_{1}^{n} X_i,$$

then the maximum likelihood estimator of the reliability of the system is given by

(a) $\left(1 - e^{-t/\overline{X}}\right)^2$ (b) $1 - \left(1 - e^{-t/\overline{X}}\right)^2$

(c) $e^{-2t/\overline{X}}$ (d) $1 - e^{-2t/\overline{X}}$

(JUNE 2016)

19. Customers arrive at an ice cream parlour according to a Poisson process with rate 2. Service time distribution has density function

$$f(x) = \begin{cases} 3e^{-3x}, & x > 0 \\ 0, & x \le 0 \end{cases}$$

Upon being served a customer may rejoin the queue with probability 0.4, independently of new arrivals; also a returning customer's service time is the same as that of a new arriving customer. Customers behave independently of each other. Let $X(t)$ = number of customers in the queue at time t. Which among the following is correct?

(a) $\{X(t)\}$ grows without bound with probability 1

(b) $\{X(t)\}$ has stationary distribution given by $\pi_k = \left(\frac{1}{3}\right)\left(\frac{2}{3}\right)^k, k = 0,1,2,...$

(c) $\{X(t)\}$ has stationary distribution given by $\pi_k = (0.1)(0.9)^k, k = 0,1,2,...$

(d) $\{X(t)\}$ has stationary distribution given by $\pi_k = (0.4)(0.6)^k, k = 0,1,2,...$

(JUNE 2016)

20. Suppose X is a random variable with following pdf

$$f(x) = \begin{cases} pe^{-x} + 2(1-p)e^{-2x}; x > 0 \\ 0, \ otherwise \end{cases}$$

And$0 \le p \le 1$. Then the hazard function of is a

(a) constant function for$p = 0$ and $p = 1$

(b) constant function for all $0 \le p \le 1$

(c) decreasing function for all $0 < p < 1$

(d) non-monotone function for all$0 < p < 1$

(JUNE 2016)

21. Three types of components are used in electrical circuits 1, 2, 3 as shown below

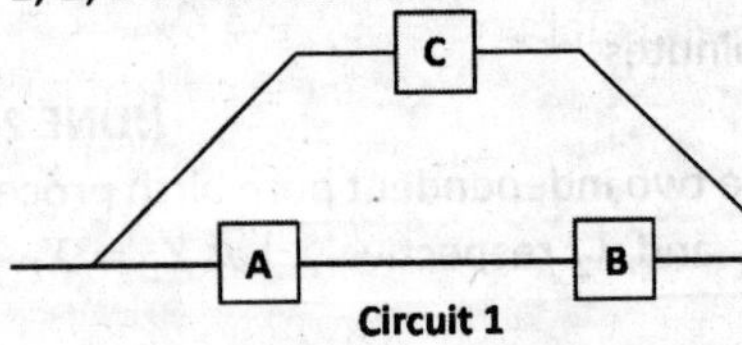

Circuit 1

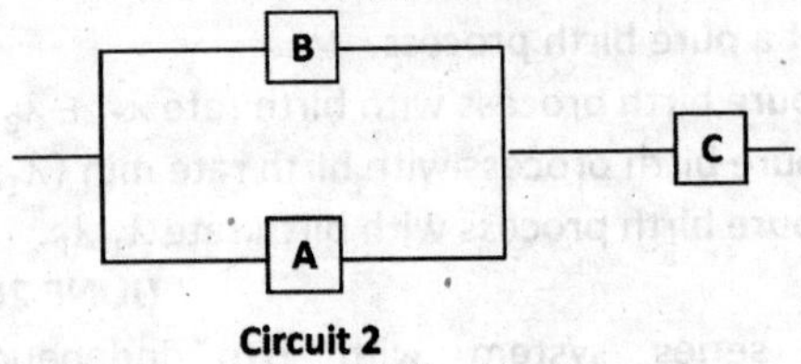

Circuit 2

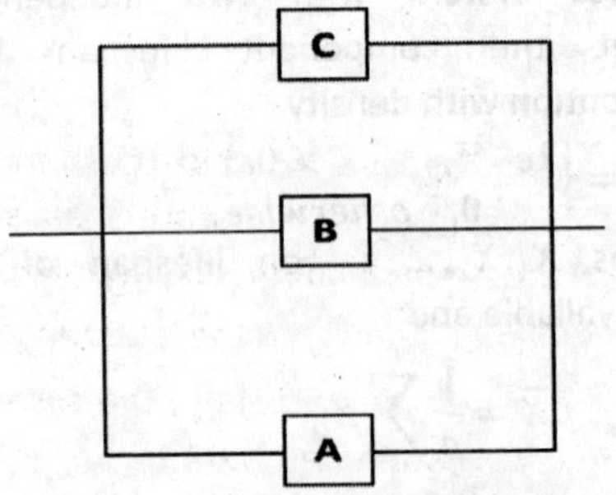

Circuit 3

Suppose that each of the three components fail with probability p and independently of each other. Let q_i = Prob (Circuit does not fail); $i = 1,2,3$. For$0 < p < 1$, we have

(a) $q_3 > q_1$ (b) $q_1 = q_2$

(c) $q_2 > q_1$ (d) $q_2 > q_3$

(DEC. 2016)

22. Suppose T follows exponential distribution with unit mean. Which of the following statement(s) are correct?

(a) The hazard function of T is a constant function.

(b) The hazard function of T^2 is a constant function.

(c) The hazard function ofT^3 is the identity function.

(d) The hazard function of $\sqrt{2T}$ is the identity function

(JUNE 2017)

23. Suppose the random variable X has the following probability density function

$$f(x) = \begin{cases} \alpha(x-\mu)^{\alpha-1}e^{-(x-\mu)^\alpha} & x > \mu \\ 0 & x \le \mu' \end{cases}$$

where $\alpha > 0, -\infty < \mu < \infty$. Which of the following statements are correct? The hazard function of X is

(a) an increasing function for all $\alpha > 0$

(b) a decreasing function for all $\alpha > 0$

(c) an increasing function for some $\alpha > 0$

(d) a decreasing function for some $\alpha > 0$

(DEC. 2018)

24. In an airport, domestic passengers and international passengers arrive independently according to Poisson processes with race 100 and 70 per hour, respectively. If it is given that the total number of passengers (domestic and international) arriving in that airport between 9:00 AM and 11:00 AM on a particular day was 520, then what is the conditional distribution of the number of domestic passengers arriving in this period?

(a) Poisson (200) (b) Poisson (100)

(c) Binomial $\left(520, \frac{10}{17}\right)$ (d) Binomial $\left(520, \frac{7}{17}\right)$

(DEC. 2018)

25. Suppose X is a positive random variable with the following probability density function

$f(x) = (\alpha x^{\alpha-1} + \beta x^{\beta-1})\, e^{-x^\alpha - x^\beta}, x > 0$ for $\alpha <$ 0 *and* $\beta > 0$.

Then the hazard function of X for some choices of α *and* β can be

(a) an increasing function

(b) a decreasing function

(c) a constant function

(d) a non-monotonic function

(JUNE 2019)

26. Consider a system with two components whose lifetimes are *i. i. d.* exponential with hazard rate λ. Let h_1 and h_2 be the hazard functions of the system if the components are put in series and parallel, respectively. Then which of the following are true?

(a) $h_2(t) < h_1(t)$ for all $t > 0$

(b) $h_2(t) < \lambda$ for all $t > 0$

(c) $h_1(t) < \lambda$ for all $t > 0$

(d) h_2 is a strictly increasing function of t.

(DEC. 2019)

27. Consider the following system with three independent components u_1, u_2 and u_3:

Support that the failure probability of each component is p and let $f(P)$ be the probability that the whole system is still functioning. Then which of the following statements are correct?

(a) $f\left(\frac{1}{2}\right) = \frac{5}{8}$ (b) $f\left(\frac{1}{2}\right) = \frac{3}{8}$

(c) $f\left(\frac{1}{3}\right) = \frac{22}{27}$ (d) $f\left(\frac{1}{4}\right) = \frac{50}{64}$

28. Consider a M/M/1 queueing system with traffic intensity $\rho < 1$. The probability of having n customers in the system at the steady state is given by

(a) ρ^n (b) $\rho(1-\rho^n)$

(c) $\rho^{n-1}(1-\rho)$ (d) $\rho^n(1-\rho)$

(NOV. 2020)

29. Suppose $\lambda(t)$ for $t \geq 0$ is a continuous hazard function of a non-negative random variable X, where $\lambda(t) \geq 1$. Which of the following statements are always true?

(a) $\frac{1}{\lambda(t)}$ is a hazard function

(b) $\lambda^2(t)$ is also a hazard function

(c) $c\lambda(t)$ for $c \geq 0$ is also a hazard function

(d) $log\ \lambda(t)$ is a hazard function

[July-2024]

30. Consider a petrol pump which has a single petrol dispensing unit. Customers arrive there in accordance with a Poisson process having rate $\lambda = 1$ minutes. An arriving customer enters the petrol pump only if there are two or less customers in the petrol pump, otherwise he/she leaves the petrol pump without taking the petrol (at any point of time a maximum of three customers are present in the petrol pump). Successive service times of the petrol dispensing unit are independent exponential random variables having mean $\frac{1}{2}$ minutes. Let X denote the average number of customers in the petrol pump in the long run. Then E(X) is equal to

(a) 7/15 (b) 3/5

(c) 11/15 (d) 13/15

[July 2024]

31. Let X_1, X_2 denote lifetimes (in years) of 2 components of an electronic system. Let $Y_1 = X_1 + X_2$ $Y_2 = max\{X_1, X_2\}$ and $Y_3 = min\{X_1, X_2\}$. Assume that X_1 and X_2 are independent, each following exponential distribution with probability density function

$$f(x) = \begin{cases} \frac{1}{2}e^{-x/2}, & if\ x > 0 \\ 0, & otherwise. \end{cases}$$

Which of the following statements are true?

(a) $P(Y_1 > 2) = 2e^{-1}$

(b) $P(Y_2 > 2) = e^{-2}$

(c) $P(Y_3 > 2) = e^{-2}$

(d) $Var\ (Y_1 + Y_2 + Y_3) = 32$

[July 2024]

32. Let X_1, X_2, X_3 be a random sample from a continuous distribution having cumulative distribution function $F(t)$, probability density function $f(t)$, and failure rate function $r(t) = \frac{f(t)}{1-F(t)}$ $t > 0$, where $F(0) = 0$. If $r(t) = 1$ for all $t > 0$ then which of the following statements are true?

(a) $P(\max(X_1, X_2\} < 1) = \frac{1}{2e}$

(b) $P(\min\{X_1, X_2\} > 1) = \frac{1}{2e}$

(c) $P(\min\{X_1, X_2\} < X_3) = \frac{2}{3}$

(d) $P(max\{X_1, X_2\} < X_3) = \frac{1}{3}$

(FEB. 2025)

33. Consider an M/G/1 queuing system with arrival rate $\lambda = 1$ and independent and identically distributed successive service times having probability density function

$$g(x) = \begin{cases} xe^{-x} & \text{if } x > 0 \\ 0 & \text{otherwise} \end{cases}$$

Define, for $i = 1,2, ...,$

$$I_i = \begin{cases} 1 & \text{if the first transition is from } i \text{ to } i-1 \\ 0 & \text{if the first transition is from } i \text{ to } i+1 \end{cases}$$

Then, $Var(I_2)$ equals

(a) $\frac{5}{32}$ (b) $\frac{5}{24}$

(c) $\frac{3}{16}$ (d) $\frac{8}{15}$

(FEB. 2025)

34. Let X_1 and X_2 be random variables having absolutely continuous distribution functions. Let $h_i(t)$ denote the hazard function of $X_i, i = 1,2$. If $h_1(t) \leq h_2(t)$ for all $t \in \mathbb{R}$, then which of the following statements are true?

(a) $P(X_1 > 1) \geq P(X_2 > 1)$

(b) $P(X_1 > 1) \leq P\left(X_2 > \frac{1}{2}\right)$

(c) $E(X_1) \geq E(X_2)$ provided both the expectations exist.

(d) $h(t) = h_1(t) + h_2(t), t \in \mathbb{R}$, is the hazard function of the random variable $Y = \min\{X_1, X_2\}$.

(JUNE 2025)

35. A system has two components C_1 and C_2 put in parallel. The components C_1 and C_2 have independent lifetimes X_1 and X_2, respectively. The probability distribution of X_j is exponential with mean $\frac{1}{j}$, j = 1,2. Suppose that R(t) and h(t) are the reliability and the hazard rate functions of the system, respectively. Then, which of the following statements are true?

(a) $R(t) = e^{-2t} + e^{t} - e^{-3t}, t > 0$

(b) The expected lifetime of the given system is 1

(c) $h(1) = \frac{2e+e^2-3}{e+e^2-1}$

(d) $h(1) = \frac{4e+e^6-5}{e^3+e^6-1}$

(JUNE 2025)

36. Consider the M/M/1 queue in which customers arrive according to a Poisson process with rate 3 and successive service times are independent exponential random variables having mean $\frac{1}{9}$. Let P_n be the long run probability that there are exactly n customers in the system. Then, which of the following statements are true?

(a) $P_0 = \frac{1}{3}$

(b) $P_1 = \frac{2}{9}$

(c) The average number of customers in the system is 1

(d) The average amount of time that a customer spends in the system is $\frac{1}{6}$

(Dec 2025)

37. Consider a series system comprising four components, having independent and identically distributed lifetimes with hazard rate $\lambda(t) = \frac{1}{1+t}, t > 0$, and survival function $S(t), t > 0$. If Y denotes the lifetime of the series system, then which of the following statements are true?
    (a) Cumulative hazard function of each component is $H(t) = 2\ln(1+t), t > 0$
    (b) $S(t) = \frac{1}{(1+t)^2}, t > 0$
    (c) $P\left(Y < \frac{1}{2}\right) = \left\{S\left(\frac{1}{2}\right)\right\}^4$
    (d) $P\left(Y < \frac{1}{2}\right) = \frac{65}{81}$

(Dec 2025)

38. Consider an $M/M/2$ queuing system with the birth rate $\lambda = 4$ per minute, the death rate $\mu = 1$ per minute, and the total capacity of 3 customers (including the ones that are being served). Let p_0 and p_3 denote the long-run probabilities that the system will be empty (i.e. without customers) and will be blocked (i.e. full), respectively. Which of the following statements are true?
    (a) $p_0 + p_3 = \frac{17}{29}$ (b) $p_0 > p_3$
    (c) $\frac{p_3}{p_0} = 2$ (d) $p_3 - p_0 = \frac{15}{29}$

Answer Key

1	**2**	**3**	**4**	**5**	**6**	**7**	**8**	**9**	**10**
b	c	b	a	d	c	b,d	b	a,b,d	c
11	**12**	**13**	**14**	**15**	**16**	**17**	**18**	**19**	**20**
b	a,c	a,c	b,c	d	b,d	b	c	*	a,c
21	**22**	**23**	**24**	**25**	**26**	**27**	**28**	**29**	**30**
a	a,d	c,d	c	a,b,c,d	a,b,d	a,c	d	b,c	c
31	**32**	**33**	**34**	**35**	**36**	**37**	**38**		
a,c,d	c,d	c	a,c	a,c	b,d	d	a,d		

:: Explanations ::

1. **Explanation: (b)**
   Lifetime variable T_1 and T_2 with cdf $F_1(t)$ and $F_2(t)$ and with pdf $f_1(t)$ and $f_2(t)$ respectively Hazard rate, $h_1(t) = \frac{f_1(t)}{1-f_1(t)}$ and $h_2(t) = \frac{f_2(t)}{1-F_2(t)}$
   We are given,
   $h_1(t) = 3t^2 ; t > 0$ and $h_2(t) = 4t^3 ; t > 0$
   $\Rightarrow F_1(t) < F_2(t) ; t > 0$
   So, option (b) is correct.
2. **Explanation: (c)**
   $X(t) =$ no. of customer in $M|M|1$ queueing system with arrival rate λ and service rate μ.
   $\Rightarrow X(t)$ is birth and birth process with rate λ and death rate μ.
   So, option (c) is correct
3. **Explanation: (b)**
   $f(t) = \frac{1}{2}e^{-\frac{t}{2}} ; t > 0$
   $F(t) = 1 - e^{-\frac{t}{2}}$
   Parallel system of component
   Reliability of the system, $R(t) = 1 - F_1(t) \cdot F_2(t)$
   Failure rate $= 1 - R(t) = F_1(t)\,F_2(t) = \left(1 - e^{-\frac{t}{2}}\right)^2$
   So, option (b) is correct
4. **Explanation: (a)**
   Mean arrival in a queue according to poisson process with rate λ_1 and woman arrival in same queue with rate λ_2
   Prob. Of first arrival is man $= \frac{\lambda_1}{\lambda_1+\lambda_2}$
   So, option (a) is correct
5. **Explanation: (d)**
6. **Explanation: (c)**
   The lifetimes of two components are iid random variable each following exponential distribution with mean 1.
   A parallel system with two component, the system will work when atleast one component work
   Case (i) if only one component work, the expected lifetime is 1
   Case (ii) if both component work the expected lifetime is $\frac{1}{2}$
   So, The expected lifetime of the system is $1 + \frac{1}{2} = \frac{3}{2}$
   So, option (c) is correct
7. **Explanation: (b), (d)**
   $f(x) = \alpha(x-\mu)^{\alpha-1}\, e^{-(x-\mu)^\alpha} : x > \mu$
   $F(x) = \alpha \int_\mu^x (x-\mu)^{\alpha-1}\, e^{-(x-\mu)^\alpha}\, dx$
   $= 1 - e^{-(x-\mu)^\alpha}$
   Hazard function $= \frac{f(t)}{1-F(t)} = \frac{\alpha(x-\mu)^{\alpha-1}\, e^{-(x-\mu)^\alpha}}{1-\{1-e^{-(x-\mu)^\alpha}\}}$
   $= \alpha(x-\mu)^{\alpha-1};\ \alpha > 0$
   Is increasing function for some α
   If $\alpha = 1$
   Hazard function $= 1$
   Which is independent of μ
   So, option (b) and (d) are correct
8. **Explanation: (b)**
   Hazard rate $= \frac{f(t)}{1-F(t)}$
   $F(t) = 1 - \exp(-ct^\alpha)$
   $f(t) = c\,\alpha\, t^{\alpha-1} \cdot e^{-ct^\alpha}$
   Hazard rate $= \frac{c\,\alpha\, t^{\alpha-1} \cdot e^{-ct^\alpha}}{1-1+e^{-ct^\alpha}} = c\,\alpha\, t^{\alpha-1}; t > 0, \alpha > 1$
   Is non-constant monotonically increasing in t
   So, option (b) is correct
9. **Explanation: (a), (b), (d)**
   T has exponential distribution with parameter θ
   $f(t) = \theta\, e^{-\theta t}; t > 0$
   $F(t) = 1 - e^{-\theta t}$
   $\frac{f(t)}{P(T>t)} = \frac{\theta\, e^{-\theta t}}{e^{-\theta t}} = \theta$ is independent of t
   Exponential distribution has memory less property
   $P[T > t + s \mid T > s] = P[T > t]$
   $\frac{P(T>t+s)}{P(T>s)} = P(T > t)$
   $\Rightarrow P(T > t + s) = P(T > t)\, P(T > s)$
   $P(T < t + s) = 1 - P(T > t + s)$
   $= 1 - P(T > t).P(T > s)$
   $= P(T < s) + P(T < t) - P(T < s)\, P(T < t)$

$P(T < t+s) = P(T < s) + P(T < t) - P(T < s)\, P(T < t)$

$P(T < t+s) - P(T < t) = P(T < s) - P(T < s)\, P(T < t)$

$\Rightarrow P(t < T < t+s) = P(T < s)\, P(T > t)$ for all $t, s, > 0$

So, option (a), (b), (d) are correct

10. Explanation: (c)

The average queue length $= \frac{\lambda^2}{\mu(\mu-\lambda)}$

So, option (c) is correct

11. Explanation: (b)

12. Explanation: (a), (c)

13. Explanation: (a), (c)

14. Explanation: (b), (c)

15. Explanation: (d)

A system consists of 3 components C_1, C_2, C_3 lifetime whose distribution is exponential with mean 1

$f(t) = e^{-t}; t > 0$

$F(t) = P.(T \le t) = 1 - e^{-t}$

Survival function for C_1 is

$S_{C_1}(t) = 1 - F(t) = e^{-t}$

Survival function for C_2 and C_3 is

$S_{C_2}(t) = 1 - F(t) = e^{-t}$

$S_{C_3}(t) = 1 - F(t) = e^{-t}$

The survival function for the system is

$S(t) = [1 - \{1 - S_{C_1}(t)\}\{1 - S_{C_2}(t)\}] S_{C_3}(t)$

$= [1 - (1 - e^{-t})^2]\, e^{-t}$

So, option (d) is correct

16. Explanation: (b), (d)

17. Explanation: (b)

18. Explanation: (c)

Consider a series with two independent components life span of each component follows exponential distribution with pdf

$$f(x) = \lambda . e^{-\lambda x}; x > 0, \lambda > 0$$

We know that the reliability of each component is $e^{-\lambda t}$

So, Reliability of the system $= e^{-\lambda t} . e^{-\lambda t}$ [both components are independent]

$$= e^{-2\lambda t}$$

$\therefore$ Mle of λ in exponential distribution is $1/\bar{X}$

Maximum likelihood estimator has an invariance property so, m.l.e of $g(\lambda) = e^{-2\lambda t}$ is given by Mle of $e^{-2\lambda t}$ is $e^{-2t/\bar{X}}$

$\therefore$ Mle of Reliability of system is $e^{-2t/\bar{X}}$

Option (c) is correct

19. Explanation: (*)

20. Explanation: (a), (c)

X is a random variable with pdf

$f(x) = pe^{-x} + 2(1-p)e^{-2x}, x > 0$

$0 \le p \le 1$

The hazard function is

$h(t) = \frac{f(t)}{1-F(t)}$

$F(t) = P(x \le t) = \int_0^t f(x)\, dx$

$F(t) = p(1 - e^{-t}) + (1-p)[1 - e^{-2t}]$

$= p(1 - e^{t}) + (1-p)(1 - e^{t})(1 + e^{-t})$

$= (1 - e^{-t})[p + (1-p)(1 + e^{-t})]$

$= (1 - e^{-t})[p + 1 + e^{-t} - p - p\, e^{-t}]$

$= (1 - e^{-t})[1 + e^{-t}(1-p)]$

$F(t) = 1.e^{-t} + e^{-t}(1.e^{-t})(1-p)$

$h(t) = \frac{p\, e^{-t} + 2(1-p)e^{-2t}}{1 + \{1 - e^{-t} + e^{-t}(1 - e^{-t})(1-p)\}}$

$= \frac{p\, e^{-t} + 2(1-p)e^{-2t}}{1 - 1 + e^{-t} - e^{-t}(1.e^{t})(1-p)}$

$= \frac{e^{-t}[p + 2(1-p)e^{-t}]}{e^{-t}[1 - (1-p)(1 - e^{-t})]}$

$h(t) = \frac{p + 2(1-p)e^{-t}}{1 - (1-p)(1 - e^{-t})}$

If $= 0$; $h(t) = \frac{2\, e^{-t}}{1 - 1 + e^{-t}} = 2$

If $= 1$; $h(t) = \frac{1}{1} = 1$

So, at $p = 0$ and 1, the hazard function is constant function

If $0 < p < 1$, the function is decreasing

Then, option (a) and (c) are correct

21. Explanation: (a)

Three types of component A, B and C are used in circuit 1, 2 and 3

A, B, C represent component work

$\bar{A}, \bar{B}, \bar{C}$ represent components does not work

P is the probability of each components fail

Circuit 1:

$q_1 = P[\text{Circuit 1 does not fail}] = 1 - P[\text{Circuit 1 fail}]$

$= 1 - [P(\bar{A} \cap \bar{B} \cap \bar{C}) + P(\bar{A} \cap B \cap \bar{C}) + P(A \cap \bar{B} \cap \bar{C})]$

$= 1 - \{p^3 + p^2(1-p) + p^2(1-p)\}$

$= 1 - 2p^2 + p^3 = p^3 - 2p^2 + 1$

Circuit 2:

$q_2 = P[\text{Circuit 2 does not fail}] = P(A \cap B \cap C) + P(A \cap \bar{B} \cap C) + P(\bar{A} \cap B \cap C)$

$= (1-p)^3 + (1-p)^2 p + (1-p)^2 p$

$= (1-p)^2\,(1 - p + 2p)$

$q_2 = (1-p)^2(1+p)$

Circuit 3:

$q_3 = P[\text{Circuit 3 does not fail}] = 1 - P[\text{Circuit 3 fail}]$

$= 1 - P(\bar{A} \cap \bar{B} \cap \bar{C})$

$q_3 = 1 - p^3$

Let us suppose $p = \frac{1}{4}$

$q_1 = \frac{57}{64}, q_2 = \frac{45}{64}, q_3 = \frac{63}{64}$

$\therefore q_3 > q_1$

So, option (a) is correct

22. Explanation: (a), (d)

$T \sim Exp(1)$

$f(T) = e^{-T}; T > 0$

Hazard function,

$h(t) = \frac{f(t)}{1-F(t)}$

where, $F(t)$ is the c d f of T

$F(t) = 1 - e^{-t}$; $t > 0$

$h(t) = \frac{e^{-t}}{1-(1-e^{-t})}$

$h\,(t) = 1$

Hazard function of T is constant function

Let $T^2 = Y$

$G(Y) = P(Y \le y) = P[T^2 \le y]$

$= P[T \le \sqrt{y}]$

$= \int_0^{\sqrt{y}} f(t)dt = \int_0^{\sqrt{y}} e^{-t}\, dt$

$= \left[\frac{e^{-t}}{-1}\right]_0^{\sqrt{y}}$

$G(y) = 1 - e^{-\sqrt{y}}$

$g(y) = \frac{1}{2\sqrt{y}}\, e^{-\sqrt{y}}$

Hazard function of $T^2 = Y$ *is*

$h(t) = \frac{g(t)}{1-G(t)} = \frac{\frac{1}{2\sqrt{t}}e^{-\sqrt{t}}}{e^{-\sqrt{t}}} = \frac{1}{2\sqrt{t}}$

which is not constant function

Let $T^3 = U$

$G(U) = P(U \le u) = P\,(T^3 \le U) = P\left[T \le U^{1/3}\right]$

$= \int_0^{u^{1/3}} f(t)\, dt$

$= \int_0^{u^{1/3}} e^{-t}\, dt$

$G(u) = 1 - e^{-u^{1/3}}$

$g(u) = \frac{1}{3\, u^{2/3}}\, e^{-u^{1/3}} \quad u > 0$

The hazard function of $T^3 = U$ is

$h(t) = \frac{g(u)}{1-G(u)} = \frac{1}{3u^{2/3}}$

which is not identity function

Let $Z = \sqrt{2T}$

$G(z) = P[Z \le z] = P\left[\sqrt{2T} \le z\right]$

$= P\left[T \le \frac{z^2}{2}\right]$

$= \int_0^{z^2/2} f(t)dt$

$G(z) = 1 - e^{-z^2/2}$

$g(z) = z\, e^{-z^2/2}$

The hazard function of $\sqrt{2T} = Z$ is

$h(t) = \frac{g(t)}{1-G(t)}$

$= \frac{t\, e^{t^2/2}}{1-\left(1-e^{-t^2/2}\right)}$

$h(t) = t$

which is identity function

So, option (a) & (d) are correct

23. Explanation: (c), (d)

$f(x) = \alpha\,(x-\mu)^{\alpha-1}\, e^{-(x-\mu)^{\alpha}}; x > r$

Where $\alpha > 0, -\infty < \mu < \infty$

Hazard function of X is

$h(x) = \frac{f(x)}{1-F(x)}$

Where $F(x)$ is the cdf of X

$F(X) = P(X \le x) = \int_\mu^x f(t)\, dt = \int_\mu^x \alpha\,(t-\mu)^{\alpha-1}\, e^{-(t-\mu)^{\alpha}} dt$

$= 1 - e^{-(x-\mu)^{\alpha}}$

$h(x) = \frac{\alpha\,(x-\mu)^{\alpha-1}\, e^{-(x-\mu)^{\alpha}}}{1-[1-e^{-(x-\mu)^{\alpha}}]}$

$h(x) = \alpha \cdot (x-\mu)^{\alpha-1}$

This function increasing for some $\alpha > 0$ & decreasing some $\alpha > 0$,

So, option (c) & (d) are correct

24. Explanation: (c)

X is number of domestic passenger arrived $\sim P$ (100 per hour)

Y is number of international passenger arrived $\sim P$ (70 per hour)

No. of domestic & international passenger arrive between 9 am and 11 am $\sim P(170)$

$X + Y = 520 \sim P(170)$

Result: $X \sim P(\lambda_1)\;\; y \sim P(\lambda_2)$

$\frac{X}{X+Y=n} \sim B\left(n, \frac{\lambda_1}{\lambda_1+\lambda_2}\right)$

∴ conditional distribution of no. of domestic passenger arriving given that no. of domestic & international passenger arrive bet. 9 am and 11 am is 520

$\frac{X}{X+Y=520} \sim B\left(520, \frac{10}{10+7}\right) = B\left(520, \frac{10}{17}\right)$

25. Explanation: (a), (b), (c), (d)

$f(x) = \left(\alpha x^{\alpha-1} + \beta x^{\beta-1}\right) e^{-x^{\alpha}-x^{\beta}} : x > 0$

The hazard function is

$h(x) = \frac{f(x)}{1-F(x)}$

where $F(x)$ is cdf

$F(x) = \int_0^x f(t)\, dt = \int_0^x \left(\alpha t^{\alpha-1} + \beta t^{\beta-1}\right)\, e^{-t^{\alpha}-t^{\beta}} dt$

$F(x) = 1 - e^{-x^{\alpha}-x^{\beta}}$

$h(x) = \frac{\left(\alpha x^{\alpha-1}+\beta x^{\beta-1}\right) e^{-x^{\alpha}-x^{\beta}}}{1-\left(1-e^{-x^{\alpha}-x^{\beta}}\right)}$

$h(x) = \alpha x^{\alpha-1} + \beta x^{\beta-1}$

Case (i) $\alpha > 1$ and $\beta > 1 \Rightarrow h(x)$ is increasing function

Case (ii) $\alpha < 1$ and $\beta < 1 \Rightarrow h(x)$ is decreasing function

Case (iii) $\alpha = 1$ and $\beta = 1 \Rightarrow h(x)$ is constant

Case (iv) $\alpha = 2$ and $\beta = \frac{1}{2} \Rightarrow h(x) = 2x + \frac{1}{2\sqrt{x}}$

$h'(x) = 2 \frac{1}{4\, x\sqrt{x}}$

For $x > 0$

$f'(x) > 0$ for some x

$f'(x) < 0$ for some x

$h(x)$ is non-monotonic

So, option (a), (b), (c), (d) are correct

26. Explanation: (a), (b), (d)

27. Explanation: (a), (c)

$W \to$ *working*

$\overline{W} \to$ *not working*

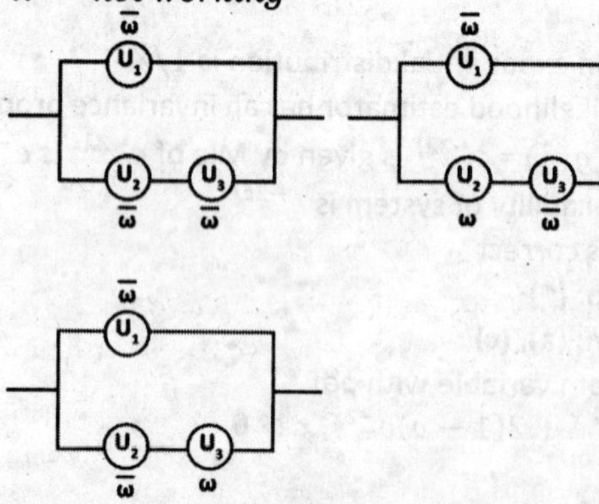

In these case system will not work

Let p be the probability of failure and (1-p) be probability of success

P(system not working) = p.p.p + p. (1-p).p+p.p(1-p)

$= p^2[p + 1 - p + 1 - p]$

$= p^2[2 - p]$

P [System is working] $= 1 - p^2(2-p)$

$f(p) = 1 - p^2(2-p)$

According to option

$f\left(\frac{1}{2}\right) = 1 - \left(\frac{1}{2}\right)^2\left(2-\frac{1}{2}\right) = \frac{5}{8}$

$f\left(\frac{1}{3}\right) = 1 - \left(\frac{1}{3}\right)^2\left(2-\frac{1}{3}\right) = \frac{22}{27}$

$f\left(\frac{1}{4}\right) = 1 - \left(\frac{1}{4}\right)^2\left(2-\frac{1}{4}\right) = \frac{48}{64}$

So, option (a) & (c) are correct

28. Explanation: (d)

In $M|M|1$ queueing system

It is the queueing model, where the arrivals follows a Poisson with parameter λ, service times are exponentially distributed with parameter μ and there is only one server.

Traffic intensity/Utilization factor. It is the ratio of average arrival where there are one server rate and average service rate,

$$\rho = \frac{\lambda}{\mu}$$

Let P_n be the probability of having n customer in the system for long run and P_i be the probability of having i customer in the system for long run $P = (P_o, P_1, P_2, \dots)$ be the stationary distribution.

$\sum_{i=1} P_i = 1$

$P\,\theta = 0$

$0 = -\lambda\, P_0 + \mu\, P_1$

$0 = \lambda\, P_{i-1} - (\lambda+\mu)\, P_i + \mu\, P_{i+1}$

$P_1 = \frac{\lambda}{\mu} P_0$ and $P_{i-1} = \frac{\lambda}{\mu} P_i$

$P_{i-1} = \frac{\lambda^{i-1}}{\mu^{i-1}} P_0\; i = 1, 2, \dots$

Take, $\rho = \frac{\lambda}{\mu}$

Then $P_0 = 1 - \rho$

$P_n = (1-\rho)\, P^n\,; \rho < 1$ (stable system)

ρ is traffic intensity

So, option (d) is correct

29. Explanation: (b) and (c)

30. Explanation: (c)

Here the customers are arriving in the petrol pump according to Poisson process with rate 1.

The successive service time is exponentially distributed with parameter 2.

Thus using the concepts of Poisson distribution this can be solved.

31. Explanation: (a), (c), (d)

X_1, X_2 denote lifetimes (in years) of 2 components of an electronic system.

Let $Y_1 = X_1 + X_2\; Y_2 = max\{X_1, X_2\}$ and $Y_3 = min\{X_1, X_2\}$.

Assume that X_1 and X_2 are independent, each following exponential distribution with probability density function

$$f(x) = \begin{cases} \frac{1}{2} e^{-x/2}, & if\; x > 0 \\ 0 & , otherwise \end{cases}$$

$$X_1, X_2 \sim Exp\left(\frac{1}{2}\right) \Rightarrow Y_1$$

$$= X_1 + X_2 \sim Gamma\left(scale = \frac{1}{2}, shape = 2\right)$$

$$\equiv Gamma\left(scale = \frac{1}{2}, shape = \frac{4}{2}\right) \equiv \chi^2_{(4)}$$

The p.d.f. of Y_1 is

$$f_{Y_1}(y) = \frac{1}{4} e^{-\frac{y}{2}} y\,; y > 0$$

$$P(Y_1 > 2) = \frac{1}{4}\int_2^\infty y e^{-\frac{y}{2}}\, dy = \frac{1}{4}\left[-2ye^{-\frac{y}{2}} - 4e^{-\frac{y}{2}}\right]_2^\infty$$

$$= e^{-1} + e^{-1} = 2e^{-1}$$

The p.d.f. of Y_2 is

$$f_{Y_2}(y) = n[F_X(y)]^{n-1} f_X(y) = 2\left(1 - e^{-\frac{y}{2}}\right).\frac{1}{2}e^{-\frac{y}{2}}$$

$$= e^{-\frac{y}{2}} - e^{-y}\,; y > 0$$

$$P(Y_2 > 2) = \int_2^\infty \left(e^{-\frac{y}{2}} - e^{-y}\right) dy = \left[-2e^{-\frac{y}{2}} + e^{-y}\right]_2^\infty$$

$$= 2e^{-1} - e^{-2} = \frac{2e-1}{e^2} \neq e^{-2}$$

The p.d.f. of Y_3 is

$$f_{Y_3}(y) = n[1 - F_X(y)]^{n-1} f_X(y) = 2\left(e^{-\frac{y}{2}}\right).\frac{1}{2}e^{-\frac{y}{2}}$$

$$= e^{-y}; y > 0$$

$$P(Y_3 > 2) = \int_2^\infty e^{-y}\, dy = [-e^{-y}]_2^\infty = e^{-2}$$

$$\because Y_1 \sim Gamma\left(scale = \frac{1}{2}, shape = 2\right) \Rightarrow Var(Y_1)$$

$$= \frac{2}{(1/2)^2} = 8$$

$$E(Y_2) = \int_0^\infty y f_{Y_2}(y)\, dy = \int_0^\infty y\left(e^{-\frac{y}{2}} - e^{-y}\right) dy$$

$$= 2\int_0^\infty \frac{y}{2} e^{-\frac{y}{2}}\, dy - \int_0^\infty y e^{-y}\, dy = 2\times 2 - 1 = 3$$

$$E(Y_2^2) = \int_0^\infty y^2 f_{Y_2}(y)\, dy = \int_0^\infty y^2\left(e^{-\frac{y}{2}} - e^{-y}\right) dy$$

$$= 2\int_0^\infty \frac{y^2}{2} e^{-\frac{y}{2}}\, dy - \int_0^\infty y^2 e^{-y}\, dy = 2\times 8 - 2 = 14$$

$$Var(Y_2) = E(Y_2^2) - [E(Y)]^2 = 14 - (3)^2 = 5$$

$\because Y_3 \sim Exp(1) \Rightarrow Var(Y_3) = 1$

We know that

$$Y_2 = \max(X_1, X_2) = \frac{1}{2}[X_1 + X_2 + |X_1 - X_2|]$$

$$Y_3 = \min(X_1, X_2) = \frac{1}{2}[X_1 + X_2 - |X_1 - X_2|]$$

$$Y_2 + Y_3 = X_1 + X_2 \Rightarrow Y_1 + Y_2 + Y_3 = X_1 + X_2 + X_1 + X_2$$

$$= 2(X_1 + X_2)$$

$$Var(Y_1 + Y_2 + Y_3) = Var(2(X_1 + X_2))$$

$$= 4Var(X_1 + X_2) = 4\times Var(Y_1) = 4\times 8 = 32$$

32. Explanation: (c), (d)

X_1, X_2, X_3 be a random sample from a continuous distribution having cumulative distribution function $F(t)$, probability density function $f(t)$.

Failure rate function $r(t) = \frac{f(t)}{1-F(t)}$ $t > 0$, where $F(0) = 0$. If $r(t) = 1$ for all $t > 0$

Given

$$r(t) = 1\ \forall\, t > 0 \Rightarrow f(t) = 1 - F(t)$$

$$\Rightarrow \frac{d}{dt}F(t) = f(t) = 1 - F(t) \Rightarrow \frac{dF(t)}{1-F(t)} = dt$$

$$-\ln|1 - F(t)| = t + C \Rightarrow 1 - F(t) = e^{-t+C} = e^{-t}e^{C}$$

$$= ke^{-t} \Rightarrow F(t) = 1 - ke^{-t}$$

At $t = 0, F(0) = 0 \Rightarrow 1 - ke^{0} = 0 \Rightarrow k = 1$

$$F(t) = 1 - e^{-t}$$

$$f(t) = e^{-t}, t > 0$$

$$\sim Exp(1)$$

Once we get the distribution of t then it becomes easy to compute the probabilities given in options.

So only options (c), (d) are true.

33. Explanation: (c)

X has PDF $g(x) = xe^{-x}$ for $x > 0$.

Thus, $P(X < A) = \int_0^\infty P(X < a) f_A(a)\, da$

Since $P(X < a) = \int_0^a xe^{-x}\, dx = -xe^{-x} + \int e^{-x}\, dx = -xe^{-x} - e^{-x} = [-(x+1)e^{-x}]_0^a$

$= 1 - (a+1)e^{-a}$,

$$P(I_2 = 1) = \int_0^\infty (1 - (a+1)e^{-a})e^{-a}\, da$$

$$= \int_0^\infty e^{-a}\, da - \int_0^\infty (a+1)e^{-2a}\, da$$

Solving these integrals:

- $\int_0^\infty e^{-a}\, da = 1$.
- $\int_0^\infty ae^{-2a}\, da = \frac{1}{4}$, and $\int_0^\infty e^{-2a}\, da = \frac{1}{2}$

$$P(I_2 = 1) = 1 - \left(\frac{1}{4} + \frac{1}{2}\right) = 1 - \frac{3}{4} = \frac{1}{4}$$

$$P(I_2 = 0) = 1 - P(I_2 = 1) = \frac{3}{4}$$

Since I_2 is a Bernoulli random variable with $P(I_2 = 1) = \frac{1}{4}$, its variance is:

$$\text{Var}(I_2) = P(I_2 = 1)(1 - P(I_2 = 1)) = \frac{1}{4} \times \frac{3}{4} = \frac{3}{16}$$

34. Explanation: (a), (c)

Statement (a): $P(X_1 > 1) \geq P(X_2 > 1)$

The survival function is $S(t) = P(X > t) = e^{-\int_0^t h(u)du}$.

Since $h_1(t) \leq h_2(t)$, then $\int_0^1 h_1(u)du \leq \int_0^1 h_2(u)du$.

Therefore, $e^{-\int_0^1 h_1(u)du} \geq e^{-\int_0^1 h_2(u)du}$.

This implies $P(X_1 > 1) \geq P(X_2 > 1)$.

Statement (a) is true.

Statement (b): $P(X_1 > 1) \leq P(X_2 > \frac{1}{2})$

This statement is not necessarily true.

Consider a case where $h_1(t)$ is very small and $h_2(t)$ is large.

It is possible that $P(X_1 > 1)$ is close to 1 and $P(X_2 > \frac{1}{2})$ is close to 0.

Statement (b) is false.

Statement (c): $E(X_1) \geq E(X_2)$

$E(X) = \int_0^\infty S(t)dt$.

Since $h_1(t) \leq h_2(t)$, then $S_1(t) \geq S_2(t)$ for all t.

Therefore, $\int_0^\infty S_1(t)dt \geq \int_0^\infty S_2(t)dt$.

This implies $E(X_1) \geq E(X_2)$.

Statement (c) is true.

Statement (d): $h(t) = h_1(t) + h_2(t)$ is the hazard function of $Y = \min\{X_1, X_2\}$

The problem does not explicitly state that X_1 and X_2 are independent.

If X_1 and X_2 are dependent, the hazard function of the minimum is not necessarily the sum of individual hazard functions.

Statement (d) is false.

Thus, options (a) and (c) are correct.

35. Explanation: (a), (c)

Rates are $\lambda_1 = 1, \lambda_2 = 2$. For the parallel system $R(t) = 1 - (1 - e^{-t})(1 - e^{-2t}) = e^{-t} + e^{-2t} - e^{-3t}$, so (a) is false

$\mathbb{E}[T] = \int_0^\infty R(t), dt = 1 + \frac{1}{2} - \frac{1}{3} = \frac{7}{6} \neq 1$, so (b) is false.

The density $f(t) = -R'(t) = e^{-t} + 2e^{-2t} - 3e^{-3t}$, hence

$$h(1) = \frac{e^{-1} + 2e^{-2} - 3e^{-3}}{e^{-1} + e^{-2} - e^{-3}} = \frac{e^2 + 2e - 3}{e^2 + e - 1}$$

$$= \frac{2e + e^2 - 3}{e + e^2 - 1},$$

so (c) is true. (d) is incorrect.

36. Explanation: (b), (d)

$\lambda = 3$, mean service $= \frac{1}{9} \Rightarrow \mu = 9, \rho = \frac{\lambda}{\mu} = \frac{1}{3}$.

$$P_n = (1-\rho)\rho^n \Rightarrow P_0 = 1 - \rho = \frac{2}{3}$$

So, (1) false, $P_1 = (1-\rho)\rho = 2/9$, so (2) true.

Average number $L = \frac{\rho}{1-\rho} = \frac{1/3}{2/3} = \frac{1}{2}$, so (3) false.

Average time $W = \frac{L}{\lambda} = \frac{\frac{1}{2}}{3} = 1/6$, so (4) true.

37. Explanation: (d)

Given hazard rate of each component:

$$\lambda(t) = \frac{1}{1+t}, t > 0$$

Cumulative hazard is the integral of the hazard rate:

$$H(t) = \int_0^t \lambda(s), ds$$

$$H(t) = \int_0^t \frac{1}{1+s} ds = \ln(1+t)$$

Statement 1 is false because it claims $H(t) = 2\ln(1+t)$.

Relationship between survival and cumulative hazard:

$S(t) = e^{\{-H(t)\}}$

So,

$$S(t) = e^{-\ln(1+t)} = \frac{1}{1+t}$$

Statement 2 is false because it says $S(t) = \frac{\{1\}}{\{(1+t)^2\}}$.

For a series system, the system fails when the first component fails.

$Y = \min(X_1, X_2, X_3, X_4)$

Thus, system survival:

$P(Y > t) = P(X_1 > t, X_2 > t, X_3 > t, X_4 > t) = S(t)^4$

Therefore,

$P(Y < 1/2) = 1 - P(Y > 1/2) = 1 - S(1/2)^4$

Statement 3 is false because it says $P(Y < 1/2) = S\left(\frac{1}{2}\right)^4$.

Calculate $P\left(Y < \frac{1}{2}\right)$

$$S(1/2) = \frac{1}{1 + 1/2} = \frac{1}{3/2} = \frac{2}{3}$$

$$S(1/2)^4 = \left(\frac{2}{3}\right)^4 = \frac{16}{81}$$

$$P(Y < 1/2) = 1 - \frac{16}{81} = \frac{65}{81}$$

Statement 4 is true.

Correct Answer: Only statement (4) is true.

38. Explanation: (a), (d)

This is a finite capacity birth–death process.

States: $0, 1, 2, 3$

Total capacity = 3 customers.

Arrival rate: $\lambda = 4$

Service rate per server: $\mu = 1$

Servers = 2

Effective service rates

For an M/M/2 system:

State	Service rate
1	(1μ =1)
2	(2μ =2)
3	(2μ =2)

Birth–death ratios

Stationary probabilities satisfy

$$p_n = p_0 \prod_{k=1}^{n} \frac{\lambda_{k-1}}{\mu_k}$$

Compute stepwise.

$$p_1 = p_0 \frac{4}{1} = 4p_0$$

$$p_2 = p_1 \frac{4}{2} = 4p_0 \times 2 = 8p_0$$

$$p_3 = p_2 \frac{4}{2} = 8p_0 \times 2 = 16p_0$$

Normalization

$$p_0 + p_1 + p_2 + p_3 = 1$$

$$p_0 + 4p_0 + 8p_0 + 16p_0 = 1$$

$$29p_0 = 1$$

$$p_0 = \frac{1}{29}$$

Compute p_3:

$$p_3 = 16p_0$$

$$p_3 = \frac{16}{29}$$

Check options:

(1) $p_0 + p_3 = \frac{17}{29}$

$$\frac{1}{29} + \frac{16}{29} = \frac{17}{29}$$

TRUE

(2) $p_0 > p_3$

$$\frac{1}{29} < \frac{16}{29}$$

FALSE

(3) $p_3/p_0 = 2$

$$\frac{16/29}{1/29} = 16$$

FALSE

(4) $p_3 - p_0 = \frac{15}{29}$

$$\frac{16}{29} - \frac{1}{29} = \frac{15}{29}$$

TRUE

Final Answer: (1) and (4)